Vol. 68 2005

Theilheimer's
Synthetic Methods
of Organic Chemistry

Editor **Alan F. Finch, Cambridge**

Assistant Editor Gillian Tozer-Hotchkiss, Thomson Scientific Ltd.
Editorial Consultant William Theilheimer, Nutley, N.J.

Basel • Freiburg
Paris • London
New York • Bangalore
Bangkok • Singapore
Tokyo • Sydney

KARGER

Deutsche Ausgaben

Vol. 1	1946	1. Auflage
	1948	2., unveränderte Auflage
	1950	3., unveränderte Auflage
Vol. 2	1948	
Vol. 3	1949	with English Index key
	1953	2., unveränderte Auflage
	1966	3., unveränderte Auflage
	1975	4., unveränderte Auflage
Vol. 4	1950	with English Index key
	1966	2., unveränderte Auflage

English Editions

Vol. 1	1948	Interscience Publishers
	1975	(Karger) Second Edition
Vol. 2	1949	Interscience Publishers
	1975	(Karger) Second Edition
Vol. 5	1951	with Reaction Titles Vol. 1-5 and Cumulative Index
	1966	Second Edition
Vol. 6	1952	
	1975	Second Edition
Vol. 7	1953	
	1975	Second Edition
Vol. 8	1954	
	1975	Second Edition
Vol. 9	1955	
Vol. 10	1956	with Reaction Titles Vol. 6-10 and Cumulative Index
	1975	Second Edition
Vol. 11	1957	
	1975	Second Edition
Vol. 12	1958	
	1975	Second Edition
Vol. 13	1959	
	1975	Second Edition
Vol. 14	1960	
	1975	Second Edition
Vol. 15	1961	with Reaction Titles Vol. 11-15 and Cumulative Index
Vol. 16	1962	
Vol. 17	1963	
Vol. 18	1964	
Vol. 19	1965	
Vol. 20	1966	with Reaction Titles Vol. 16-20 and Cumulative Index
Vol. 21	1967	
Vol. 22	1968	
Vol. 23	1969	
Vol. 24	1970	
Vol. 25	1971	with Reaction Titles Vol. 21-25 and Cumulative Index
Vol. 26	1972	
Vol. 27	1973	
Vol. 28	1974	
Vol. 29	1975	
Vol. 30	1976	with Reaction Titles Vol. 26-30 and Cumulative Index
Vol. 31	1977	
Vol. 32	1978	
Vol. 33	1979	
Vol. 34	1980	
Vol. 35	1981	with Reaction Titles Vol. 31-35 and Cumulative Index
Vol. 36	1982	
Vol. 37	1983	
Vol. 38	1984	
Vol. 39	1985	
Vol. 40	1986	with Reaction Titles Vol. 36-40 and Cumulative Index
Vol. 41	1987	
Vol. 42	1988	
Vol. 43	1989	
Vol. 44	1990	
Vol. 45	1991	with Reaction Titles Vol. 41-45 and Cumulative Index
Vol. 46	1992	
Vol. 47	1993	
Vol. 48	1994	
Vol. 49	1995	
Vol. 50	1996	with Reaction Titles Vol. 46-50
Vol. 51	1997	
Vol. 52	1997	
Vol. 53	1998	
Vol. 54	1998	
Vol. 55	1999	
Vol. 56	1999	
Vol. 57	2000	
Vol. 58	2000	
Vol. 59	2001	
Vol. 60	2001	
Vol. 61	2002	
Vol. 62	2002	
Vol. 63	2003	
Vol. 64	2003	
Vol. 65	2004	
Vol. 66	2004	
Vol. 67	2005	

Library of Congress, Cataloging-in-Publication Data

Theilheimer's synthetic methods of organic chemistry = Synthetische Methoden der organischen Chemie. – Vol. 68 (2005) - Basel; New York: Karger, © 1982 -
v.
Continues: Synthetic methods of organic chemistry.
Editor: Alan F. Finch.
1. Chemistry, Organic – yearbooks   I. Finch, Alan F.   II. Theilheimer, William, 1914–
ISBN 3-8055-7989-6

All rights reserved.
No part of this publication may be translated into other languages, reproduced or utilized in any form or by any means, electronic or mechanical, including photocopying, recording, microcopying, or by any information storage and retrieval system, without permission in writing from the publisher.

© Copyright 2005 by S. Karger AG, Basel (Switzerland), and the Thomson Corporation
Distributed by S. Karger AG, Allschwilerstrasse 10, P.O. Box, CH-4009 Basel (Switzerland)
ISBN 3-8055-7989-6

Theilheimer's
Synthetic Methods
of Organic Chemistry

Vol. 68

Contents

Preface to Volume 68	VI
Advice to the User	VII
General Remarks	VII
Method of Classification	VIII
High-Coverage Searches	X
Further Trends and Developments in Synthetic Organic Chemistry 2005	XI
Systematic Survey	XXIV
Abbreviations and Symbols	XXVI
Reactions	1
Reviews	321
Subject Index	331
Supplementary References	387

Preface

This is the second of the biannual volumes of *Theilheimer* for 2005 containing abstracts of new synthetic methods and supplementary data mainly from papers published in the literature up to March 2005.

For browsing purposes, abstracts are displayed according to the Systematic Classification (symbol notation; summary s. p. VIII) so that reactions of the same type and associated data appear together. For example, all deprotections appear in the early symbols (under HO↓↑, HN↓↑, HS↓↑); reduction of oxo compds., imines and carbon-carbon multiple bonds under the HC⇓ sections; C-defunctionalization under the HC sections; oxy-functionalization under the OC sections; aminations, nitrations, peptide coupling etc. under the NC sections; halogenation under the HalC sections; sulfurations under the SC sections; selenation, stannylation, phosphorylation, etc. under the RemC sections; syntheses involving C-C bond formation in the latter half of the book under the CC sections; and data on resolutions (Res) at the end. A list of reaction symbols and references thereto is given in the Systematic Survey (p. XXIV).

The displayed data are supported by the customary in-depth Subject Index (p. 331) and access to supplementary data can be made in the usual manner via the Supplementary Reference Index, e.g. the reader interested in updates on Suzuki coupling (Synth. Meth. *37*, 902) will note from p.387 that additional references can be found on p. 291 of this volume.

As usual, the volume contains a 'Reviews' section (p. 321), and a 'Trends' section (p. XI) incorporating key developments in synthetic chemistry up to and including September 2005.

I would like to express my gratitude to my colleagues at Thomson Scientific, especially my Assistant Editor, Gill Tozer-Hotchkiss, Lynda Parsons, Kath Davies, and those involved in the production of the *Journal of Synthetic Methods*. My appreciation also goes to Jill Entwistle, Lucy Ranner, Eliot Cartwright-Finch and Martha Burrough for assistance in the electronic processing of this volume.

October 2005   *A.F. Finch*, Editor

Advice to the User

General Remarks

New methods for the synthesis of organic compounds and improvements of known methods are being recorded continuously in this series.

Reactions are classified on a simple though purely formal basis by symbols, which can be arranged systematically. Thus searches can be performed without knowledge of the current trivial or author names (e.g. 'Oxidation' and 'Friedel-Crafts reaction').

Users accustomed to the common notations will find these in the subject index (see page 331). By consulting this index, use of the classification system may be avoided. It is thought that the volumes should be kept close at hand. The books should provide a quick survey, and obviate the immediate need for an elaborate library search. Syntheses are therefore recorded in the index by starting materials and end products, along with the systematic arrangement for the methods. This makes possible a sub-classification within the reaction symbols by reagents, a further methodical criterion. Complex compounds are indexed with cross reference under the related simpler compounds. General terms, such as synthesis, replacement, heterocyclics, may also be brought to the attention of the reader.

A brief review (*Trends* section, see page XI), stresses highlights of general interest and calls attention to key methods too recent to be included in the body of the text.

The abstracts are limited to the information needed for an appraisal of the applicability of a desired synthesis. In order to carry out a particular synthesis it is therefore advisable to have recourse to the original papers or, at least, to an abstract journal. In order to avoid repetition, selections are made on the basis of most detailed description and best yields whenever the same method is used in similar cases. Continuations of papers already included will not be abstracted, unless they contain essentially new information. They may, however, be quoted at the place corresponding to the abstracted papers. These supplementary references (see page 387) make it possible to keep abstracts of previous volumes up-to-date.

Syntheses that are divided into their various steps and recorded in different places can be followed with the help of the notations such as *startg. m. f.* (starting material for the preparation of ...).

Method of Classification

Reaction Symbols. As summarized in the Systematic Survey (page XXIV), reactions are classified firstly according to the bond formed in the synthesis, secondly according to the reaction type, and thirdly according to the bond broken or the element eliminated. This classification is summarized in the reaction symbol, e.g.

$$\text{OC} \uparrow \text{N}$$

Bond formed ↗ ↑ Reaction type ↖ Bond broken or element eliminated

The first part of the symbol refers to the chemical bond formed during the reaction, expressed as a combination of the symbols for the two elements bonded together, e.g. HN, NC, CC. The order of the elements is as follows:

H, O, N, Hal (Halogen), S, Rem (Remaining elements), and C.

Thus, for the formation of a hydrogen-nitrogen bond, the notation is HN, not NH.

If two or more bonds are formed in a reaction, the 'principle of the latest position' applies. Thus, for the reduction

$$\text{RCH=O} + \text{H}_2 \longrightarrow \text{R-CH(H)-OH}$$

in which both hydrogen-oxygen and hydrogen-carbon bonds are formed, the symbol is HC⇓OC and not HO⇓OC.

The second part of the symbol refers to the reaction type. Four types are distinguished: addition (⇓), rearrangement (∩), exchange (⇅), and elimination (⇑), e.g.

RCH=CH$_2$ + H$_2$O ⟶ R-CH(OH)-CH$_3$	OC⇓CC
(thiophene-allyl) ⟶ (rearranged)	CC∩SC
R-Cl + CN⁻ ⟶ R-CN [+ Cl⁻]	CC⇅Hal
R-CH(Br)-CH$_3$ ⟶ RCH=CH$_2$ [+ HBr]	CC⇑Hal

Monomolecular reactions are either rearrangements (∩), where the molecular weight of the starting material and product are the same, or eliminations (⇑), where an organic or inorganic fragment is lost; bimolecular and multicomponent reactions are either additions (⇓), such as intermolecular

Diels-Alder reactions, Michael addition and 1,4-addition of organometallics, or exchanges (⇅), such as substitutions and condensations, where an organic or inorganic fragment is lost.

The last part of the symbol refers to the essential bond broken or, in the case of exchange reactions and eliminations, to a characteristic fragment which is lost. While the addition symbol is normally followed by the two elements denoting the bond broken, in the case of valency expansion, where no bonds are broken, the last part of the symbol indicates the atom at which the addition occurs, e.g.

R_2S ⟶ R_2SO		OS⇅S
RONO ⟶ $RONO_2$		ON⇅N

For addition, exchanges, and eliminations, the 'principle of the latest position' again applies if more than one bond is broken. However, for rearrangements, the most descriptive bond-breakage is used instead. Thus, for the thio-Claisen rearrangement depicted above, the symbol is CC∩SC, and not CC∩CC.

Deoxygenations, quaternizations, stable radical formations, and certain rare reaction types are included as the last few methods in the yearbook. The reaction symbols for these incorporate the special symbols El (electron pair), Het (heteropolar bond), Rad (radical), Res (resolutions), and Oth (other reaction types), e.g.

$R_2S=O$ ⟶ R_2S		ElS⇅O
R_3N + R'Cl ⟶ R_3N^+R' Cl^-		Het⇅N

The following rules simplify the use of the reaction symbols:

1. The chemical bond is rigidly classified according to the structural formula without taking the reaction mechanism into consideration.

2. Double or triple bonds are treated as being equivalent to two or three single bonds, respectively.

3. Only stable organic compounds are usually considered: intermediates such as Grignard compounds and sodiomalonic esters, and inorganic reactants, such as nitric acid, are therefore not expressed in the reaction symbols.

Reagents. A further subdivision, not included in the reaction symbols, is based on the reagents used. The sequence of the reagents usually follows that of the periodic system. Reagents made up of several components are arranged according to the element significant for the reaction (e.g. $KMnO_4$ under Mn, NaClO under Cl). When a constituent of the reagent forms part of the product, the remainder of the reagent, which acts as a 'carrier' of this constituent, is the criterion for the classification; for example, phosphorus is the carrier in a chlorination with PCl_5 and sodium in a nitrosation with $NaNO_2$.

High-Coverage Searches

A search through *Synthetic Methods* provides a selection of key references from the journal literature. For greater coverage, as for bibliographies, a supplementary search through the following publications is suggested:

Derwent Reaction Service[1]. Designed for both current awareness and retrospective retrieval. Its monthly publication, the *Derwent Journal of Synthetic Methods*, covers the journal and patent literature, and provides 3,000-3,600 abstracts of recently published papers annually.

Access is available in-house via RX-JSM to over 100,000 reactions, including the data in all the abstracts in *Synthetic Methods*, while online access to data from 1980 is provided on STN as DJSMONLINE.

Science Citation Index[2]. For which *Synthetic Methods* serves as a source of starting references. This is particularly useful for accessing papers quoting details of a particular method which has been included in these volumes from a preliminary communication.

Chemical Abstracts Service[3]. References may not be included in *Synthetic Methods* (1) to reactions which are routinely performed by well known procedures; (2) to subjects which can be easily located in handbooks and indexes of abstracts journals, such as the ring system of heterocyclics or the metal in case of organometallic compounds, and (3) to inadequately described procedures, especially if yields are not indicated.

References to less accessible publications such as those in the Chinese or Japanese language are usually only included if the method in question is not described elsewhere.

[1] Thomson Scientific Ltd., 14 Great Queen Street, London WC2B 5DF, England.
[2] Thomson Scientific Inc., Philadelphia, Pa., USA.
[3] Chemical Abstracts Service, Columbus, Ohio, USA.

Further Trends and Developments in Synthetic Organic Chemistry 2005

A *golden* year is coming to a conclusion as new syntheses under Au(I)- and Au(III)-catalysis are seemingly materializing by the day, principally in the context of reactions with functionalized alkynes. Here, Lewis acid activation of the acetylenic bond by cationic gold is the preliminary to a range of diverse conversions wherein attack of the triple bond by an appended nucleophile is the central theme. This has been recently extended to a cycloisomerization of acetylenediols to bicyclic ketals with AuCl or $AuCl_3$[1], while a Au(I)-catalyzed ring expansion of 1-alkynylcycloalkanols to cyclic α-alkylideneketones is terminated by a 1,2-alkyl shift[2]. The intermediate formation of vinylgold species in such conversions may also give rise to a carbenoid manifold through back-bonding from the metal into the unsaturation. Subsequent quenching by intramolecular trapping of a carbonium ion can lead to interesting rearrangements (*à la 68, 344*), but equally notable is termination by the departure of a suitably positioned leaving group. This is nicely illustrated in a new Au(I)-catalyzed pyrrole synthesis from 3-acetyleneazides where ring closure onto the alkyne residue is followed by expulsion of nitrogen[3]. The oxophilic nature of Au(III) is a further bonus, evidenced in a new route to 3-halogenofurans from 3-halogeno-2,3-dienones where intramolecular Michael addition of halogen to the enone residue precedes ring closure[4]. Gold may also be implicated in hydrogenative and oxidative conversions: a chiral gold(I) bis(phospholane) dimer, for example, affords enantioselectivities up to 95% in the hydrogenation of olefins and azomethines[5], at the same time rivalling the corresponding iridium and platinum complexes in activity and selectivity. A gold(I)-Xantphos complex, however, is the catalyst of choice in a dehydrogenative silylation of alcohols[6], whereas gold nanoparticles deposited on nano-crystalline CeO_2 provide a highly effective system for an economical, environmentally friendly, aerobic oxidation of alcohols at atmospheric pressure[7]. Arguably more notable is the design of a gold(I) imidazol-2-ylidene complex for carbene transfer from ethyl diazoacetate [with negligible loss of the latter by dimerization!][8] Here, the emergence of yet another catalytic cyclopropanation is perhaps not remarkable, but preferential intermolecular carbene insertion into an aromatic C-H bond of styrene is without precedent. Immobilization of catalysts on thiolate monolayer-protected gold clusters is another theme, exemplified by the recent design of readily recyclable and highly active ruthenium carbene complexes for ring-closing metathesis: significantly, such supported catalysts are homogeneous in methylene chloride but can be simply recovered by precipitation in methanol[9]. Chiral rhodium di(phosphine) complexes have also been grafted onto thiolate-modified gold surfaces to provide efficient colloidal [readily removable] catalysts for the asymmetric hydrogenation of olefins, both activity and enantioselectivity being on a par with that of the homogeneous counterpart[10].

Turning to the more familiar ground of transition metal catalysis with Group VIII complexes, it will make a change to by-pass the omnipresent Pd, Ru and Rh by jumping directly to less prominent iridium, where some interesting parallels with gold are apparent: note, for example, alkyne activation with $[Ir(cod)Cl]_2$ in a new route to cyclic ketals from acetylenealcohols[11], and oxidative esterification of aldehydes with the same reagent[12]. A new solvent-free oxidative quinoline synthesis from o-aminobenzyl alcohols (with $[Ir(cod)Cl]_2$ or $IrCl_3$) has also been reported[13] along with new routes to functionalized and unfunctionalized nitriles from cyclobutanone O-benzoyloximes[14]. The more familiar territory of iridium-catalyzed allylation has also broadened in recent months, most notably with the development of a highly regio- and enantio-selective N-allylation of 2-ethylenesulfonylamines[15] as well as the first *intramolecular* asymmetric C-α-allylation[16] (in each instance with a chiral, 1,1′-bi-2-naphthol-based iridium(I) phosphoromonoamidite complex). Catalysis with neighbouring platinum, however, is relatively untried, save in the classical arena of heterogeneous hydrogenation, although more recently $PtCl_2$ has emerged as a versatile catalyst for cycloisomerization of polyunsaturated systems, such as ring-closing ene-yne metathesis[17]. This has now been extended to the novel cyclo isomerization of enynes to condensed cyclobutenes through an interesting cationic manifold[18]. A range of platinum N-heterocyclic carbene complexes is also available for hydrosilylation of olefins, these being a significant improvement on the classical chloroplatinic acid in that by-product formation is minimal. The latest offering is a series of platinum(0) benzimidazol-2-ylidene complexes, being superior in activity to the more familiar imidazol-2-ylidene analogs[19]. As an aside, new polymer-based N-heterocyclic carbene ligands have recently been designed for simplified catalyst retrieval[20], but the choicest newcomers are N-alkyl-3-spiropyrrolidin-2-ylidenes having enhanced electron-donating characteristics and being readily modifiable to adjust the steric environment around the reaction centre. Again, they outperform the more familiar imidazolylidene [3-aza] analogs, notably in facilitating the clean α-arylation of ketones and even aldehydes with aryl *chlorides* at room temperature![21]

Turning to the Pd-Ru-Rh triad, developments outside the specialized sphere of asymmetric synthesis (*q.v.*) are many and varied. Perhaps special mention might be given to the novel application of Se-ligated palladium pincer complexes for the preparation of functionalized allyl boronic acids (and K-allyl(trifluoro)borates) by nucleophilic displacement of allylic derivatives or vinylcyclopropanes[22]. Palladium-catalyzed activation of aromatic C-H bonds has also been extended in a novel *o*-arylation of anilides and aromatic aldimines[23], and in a tandem cyclization of 1-aryl- or 1-hetaryl-2-bromo-1,n-enynes to polycondensed heterocyclics[24]. Catalysis with *multifunctionalized* hydrotalcite-supported transition metals is a relatively new concept, further exemplified in an interesting reductive α-alkylation of nitriles with ketones or aldehydes[25]. Here, the basic sites on the hydrotalcite facilitate the initial Knoevenagel condensation while supported palladium nanoparticles effect hydrogenation of the intermediate in one pot. A recent palladium-catalyzed cyclopropanation of norbornene derivatives *with alkynes* is especially notable[26], reaction being facilitated by phosphinous acids as ligand and thought to involve intermediate formation of a palladium *vinylidene* species. Rhodium vinylidene species, on the other hand, are implicated in a new Rh-catalyzed cycloisomerization of enynes, proceeding, most likely, via condensed rhodacyclobutanes[27]. More remarkable still is a simple and efficient Rh-catalyzed stereospecific dimerization of 1,2,7,8-tetraenes to 18,19-norsteroids [how simple is that!?][28], while Wilkinson's catalyst and BF_3 cooperate in in an unusual α-vinylation *of alcohols* thought to involve C-H bond activation in a radical manifold[29]. Under ruthenium catalysis, an anti-Markovnikov addition of acylamines comes to mind, the choice of monodentate tri-*tert*-butylphosphine or chelating bis(dicyclo hexylphosphino)methane being critical in dictating formation of the (E)- and (Z)-product, respectively[30]. Ruthenium-catalyzed olefin metathesis is, of course, ever-present, especially in the sphere of natural product synthesis. A novel approach to phenols by ring-closing metathesis merits particular attention[31], as does the emergence of olefin metathesis *on metal surfaces* which has the potential of sustaining the growth of molecular wires and other such molecular devices[32].

Under catalysis with the Fe-Co-Ni triad of metals, a mild Ni-catalyzed route to functionalized 2-cyclopentenones from allyl halides and acetylene derivatives is now available by carbonylation[33]. Here, the addition of iron in stoichiometric amount is critical in reducing Ni(II) to Ni(I), while at the same time facilitating termination of the catalytic cycle through Ni→Fe exchange prior to aerobic oxidation. A new Ni-catalyzed carboxylative ring closure of enynes has also been reported[34], along with a mild, inexpensive synthesis of azides from unactivated olefins via regiospecific cobalt-catalyzed hydroazidation with tosyl azide[35]. Under iron(III) catalysis, note a new route to 1,1-diarylalkanes by Friedel-Crafts-type benzylation with benzyl acetates[36]. Reference is also given to a mild and simple $FeCl_3$-catalyzed cross-coupling of arylmagnesium halides with *prim-* or *sec-*alkyl halides *possessing β-hydrogens*[37], while AgOTs is the preferred catalyst for the homocoupling of alkylmagnesium halides[38]. Silver(I) triflate, however, is suitable for a highly efficient regiospecific addition of active methylene groups to styrene [reversible at elevated temperature!][39], whereas $AgSbF_6$ is to the fore in a novel conversion of acetylene derivatives to α,β-ethyleneketones, wherein the alkyne effectively serves as an (α-acylalkylidene)phosphorane equivalent[40]. The first stable silver(I) N-heterocyclic carbene complex has also materialized as catalyst in a new 1,2-diborylation of alkenes with bis(catecholato)diboron *en route* to glycols[41]. On the other hand, copper(I) is favoured in a simple and efficient Heck-type arylation of electron-deficient ethylene derivatives in the presence of *dabco as ligand*[42], while the same catalyst (CuI) is effective in the first intramolecular O-vinylation of ketones with vinyl bromides[43]. Copper(I) chloride and bromide, however, are preferred in recent 3-component syntheses of allylamines and propargylamines[44].

In the field of asymmetric synthesis, organocatalyzed routes still capture the limelight courtesy of (S)-proline et al.[45] Developing the theme, L-proline amides based on chiral 2-aminoalcohols are now available for the asymmetric aldol condensation of a broad range of aldehydes with ketones *at low catalyst loadings*[46], whereas bifunctional (S)-2-(triflyl aminomethyl)pyrrolidine is more effective for the asymmetric condensation of aliphatic α-branched aldehydes with aromatic aldehydes to secure chiral quaternary hydrocarbon groups[47]. Interestingly, simple *aliphatic* chiral α-amino acids, such as L-alanine, are also effective for asymmetric aldol condensation (with enantioselectivities exceeding 99%)[48], while (S)-homoproline generally offers higher enantio selectivities than (S)-proline in the asymmetric Michael addition of ketones to 1,1-nitroethylene derivatives[49] More remarkable still is the application of (S)-proline and related organocatalysts to asymmetric αfluorination of aldehydes[50], and due note has been made of the first organocatalyzed asymmetric hetero-Diels-Alder reaction [with preformed or *in situ*-generated imines][51] as well as an asymmetric epoxidation of enones with *tert*-butyl hydroperoxide in the presence of (S)-prolinol[52]. As an alternative, cinchonine at the 10 mol% level is favoured in asymmetric Mannich reactions with β-keto esters[53], while a range of chiral additives (organic and metallic) is available for the the asymmetric Friedel-Crafts-type alkylation of the indole nucleus[54]. In ligand design for transition metal-catalyzed asymmetric syntheses, the emphasis is still largely on securing more efficient chiral P-ligands, with economy, manageability and enhanced enantioselectivity in mind[55]. Lately, however, there has been a trend towards utilizing readily available *chiral dienes* instead, as manifested in the Rh-catalyzed asymmetric 1,4-addition of arylboronic acids to cinnamaldehydes[56] or α,β-ethylene hydroxamic acid esters[57], and in Rh-catalyzed asymmetric arylative ring closures of enynes[58]; a *hybrid* chiral 7-(diphenylphosphino)bicyclo [2.2.1]hept-2-ene, however, offers more scope for Rh-catalyzed asymmetric 1,4-addition to maleimides[59], although the old standby, (S)-BINAP, is still favoured for the asymmetric 1,6-addition of arylzinc chlorides to dienones[60]. In the ever-developing field of transition metal-catalyzed asymmetric homogeneous hydrogenation, due note has been taken of the first practical Ru-catalyzed asymmetric hydrogenation of *tert*-alkyl ketones by utilizing α-picolylamine as the diamine component of Noyori-type chiral (diamine)(dichloro)(BINAP)ruthenium(II) complexes[61]. For hydrogenation of simple ketones, however, readily prepared and modular BINOL-based *trans*-(diamine)(chloro)bis (phosphonite)ruthenium hydride complexes are highly effective[62], as also is the BINOL-based bidentate cyclic phosphoromonoamidite, (R_a, R_C)-QUINAPHOS, in the presence of a chiral or achiral diamine as co-catalyst[63]. An interesting ploy has also evolved for the rapid screening of chiral ruthenium complexes involving the *in situ*-formation of *both ligand and catalyst*[64]. A novel 'mixed ligand' approach to generating chiral rhodium complexes has also been developed following the pioneering work of Reetz et al. with a combination of chiral monodentate ligands. The new trick is to combine a chiral [BINOL-derived] phosphoro monoamidite with a simple *achiral* tertiary phosphine, the outcoming being a drastic improvement in enantioselectivity and rate for the asymmetric hydrogenation of α,β-ethylenecarboxylic acids[65]. A new class of mono dentate cyclic phosphoromonoamidites based on the chiral 4,5-diaryl-2-imidazolidone motif has also evolved for a highly enantioselective (ca. 100% e.e.!) asymmetric hydrogenation of enacylamines[66], while chiral 3,4-bis(phospholan-1-yl)thiophenes are useful alternatives to MeDuPHOS, being more easy to prepare, more active, and affording enantioselectivities approaching 99.5% for the asymmetric hydrogenation of both olefins and ketones[67]. A new class of chiral bis(Δ^2-oxazolines) possessing an anionic borato bridge [*borabox* ligands] has also emerged, notably effective in the desymmetrization of glycols by asymmetric benzoylation and in copper(I)-catalyzed asymmetric cyclo propanation[68]. Interestingly the latter conversion and asymmetric Diels-Alder reactions can also be effected with a chiral bis(Δ^2-oxazoline) immobilized on a mesocellular foam-type silica surface, wherein the environment around the catalytic site can be simply modified (notably by silylating the free silanol residues) to enhance reactivity[69]. Among other asymmetric conversions recently broadcast, particular mention might be given to: a novel Rh-catalyzed asymmetric [2+2+2]-cyclo addition to provide atropoisomeric biphenyls[70]; a catalytic [gram-scale] asymmetric cyanohydrin formation from aromatic aldehydes with an inexpensive chiral lithium-BINOLate aqua (or alcohol) complex[71]; an entirely new synthesis of enolesters by asymmetric [2+2]-cycloaddition *of aldehydes* to ketenes with Fu's chiral 4-aminopyridine base[72]; the first effective aldol condensation of aldehydes *with methyl vinyl ketone* using Trost's chiral binuclear zinc complex[73]; an asymmetric Negishi cross-coupling of alkylzinc halides with *sec*-benzyl halides[74]; and two catalytic routes for the asymmetric 1,4-addition of terminal acetylene derivatives[75].

It has taken a long while to come to terms with the fact that pure water *can* support reactivity if substrate(s) are insoluble[76]. What is more, reaction can even be faster in water than under homogeneous conditions in classical organic solvents. Note, for example, an accelerated Wittig synthesis from stabilized ylids with enhanced (E)-selectivity[77], as well as a novel Ru(IV)-catalyzed N-deallylation wherein water promotes isomerization to the enamine prior to hydrolysis[78]. A simple and practical oxidation of thioethers to sulfoxides with N-bromosuccinimide can also be effected in water under *supramolecular catalysis* with enzyme-like β-cyclodextrin, the organic substrate(s) being effectively 'taken into solution' via hydrogen bonding to hydrophobic cavities within the oligo saccharide[79]. Thermomorphic catalysis in a recyclable micellar-type system has also been adapted to facilitate reaction in water, as illustrated in a phosphotungstate-catalyzed oxidation of alcohols with H_2O_2[80]. Here, the anion is supported on an insoluble polyacrylamide supramolecular network, wherein reaction takes place at elevated temperature in an emulsion; the catalyst then separates on cooling leaving the product as an organic layer above the water. Alternatively, the catalyst can be immobilized on reversed-phase silica gel with the aid of an ionic liquid embedded within the pores of the support[81]. This is illustrated by a heterogeneous Heck arylation in pure water with remarkably high TONs and TOFs and yields averaging 95% after the 6th cycle. Another sustainable and benign *solid-phase* procedure has been developed specifically for reaction in water or other highly polar hydrophilic media[82]. In this instance, a covalently anchored substrate is attached during reaction to standard C_{18}-modified reversed-phase silica gel by *non-covalent* interaction; thereafter, filtration and washing of the support with a *non-polar* organic solvent releases the anchored product, which, after cleavage of the anchor, liberates the product; the cycle can be simply repeated by switching back to the polar medium. Such *phase-switching* may also be effected *with the same medium*! This is illustrated by converting a mixture of an alcohol and amine (dbu) to an ionic liquid by simply bubbling CO_2 through the solvent at room temperature; subsequent bubbling with an inert gas (preferably at 50°) then returns the original non-polar medium[83].

Under Lewis acid catalysis perhaps the most striking advances have been made with indium(III), particularly in the arena of asymmetric synthesis. Note, in particular, the highly enantioselective nucleophilic allylation of *ketones* with allylstannanes [in the presence of chiral indium(III) BINOL complexes][84], as well as asymmetric nucleophilic allylation of a wide range of aldehydes in friendly ionic liquids [with the same complexes][85]. These same reagents are also implicated in a highly enantioselective Diels-Alder reaction (e.g. up to 98%)[86], although an alternative strategy based on Lewis acid *template catalysis* should not be overlooked. In a recent manifestation, both reacting partners are *self-assembled* on the same chiral bimetallic BINOL template, the dienophile through Lewis acid activation with magnesium and the diene through a zinc alkoxide tether[87]. Chiral 2-chloro-1,3,2-oxazasilacyclo pentanes have also emerged as invaluable Lewis acidic organocatalysts[88], as also have chiral BINOL-based cyclic phosphoric acid diesters as mild Brønsted acids for, among others, the asymmetric synthesis of β-acylamino-α-diazocarboxylic acid esters through C-H bond activation of ethyl diazoacetate[89]. Among Lewis bases, attention is drawn to the application of N,N,N',N'-tetramethylethylenediamine (at the 20 mol% level) for the ring opening of N-tosylaziridines with Si-nucleophiles[90], while 10 mol% KOEt is favoured for the novel 1,2-addition of trialkoxysilylacetylenes to oxo compounds and imines via silicon-ate complexes[91]. A Brønsted basic ionic liquid, namely 1-butyl-3-methyl imidazolium hydroxide, has also been developed as both catalyst and medium for a generalized Michael addition of active methylene compounds[92], whereas as little as 5 mol% NaOH is effective for the crossed Claisen condensation of esters with O-silyl O-alkyl keteneacetals, notable for the generation of quaternary carbon centres[93].

Among novel radical procedures, the pick of the bunch goes to a non-toxic version of the Barton-McCombie deoxygenation of alcohols, where trimethylborane-water complex is an invaluable alternative to unfriendly tin hydrides[94]. Hydrogen atom transfer can also be effected cleanly with relatively non-toxic dimethyl phosphite, as in a new cyclopentene ring closure from alkynes[95]. Arguably more remarkable is a new, mild procedure for generating aminyl radicals from N-protected 3-aminocyclohexa-1,4-dienes under neutral conditions, the most notable consequence being the evolution of the first transition metal-free transfer-hydroamination of ethylene derivatives[96]. A mild, *metal-free*, radical approach to diaryl ethers from phenols and N,N-dialkyl-4-phenylthioanilines is also at hand through the agency of a bis(triarylmethylium) bis(perchlorate), which facilitates oxidative *ipso*-substitution via attack of aroxyl radical and liberation of phenylthiyl radical[97]. Digressing on the theme of oxidation, two new outlets for osmium(VIII) have been realized: a direct osmate-catalyzed conversion of ethylene derivatives to N-protected α-aminoketones ['ketamination'] in the presence of Chloramine-T[98], and a new stereospecific oxidative ring closure of 5-ene-1,2-diols to oxy-functionalized tetrahydrofurans with OsO_4 as catalyst[99]. A waste-free oxidative coupling of *o*-diamines with aldehydes under the sole influence of atmospheric oxygen has also surfaced in a new benzimidazole synthesis[100], along with a new selective epoxidation of alkenes with a polyoxovanadometalate and H_2O_2 *in stoichiometric* amount[101]. Equally welcome are *catalytic* oxidations with *in situ*-generated *o*-iodoxybenzoic acid in the presence of inexpensive Oxone as re-oxidant[102]. A few, more random, highlights include: a phosphine-catalyzed intramolecular Baylis-Hillman-type reaction with an allylic leaving group as the electrophilic partner *en route* to densely functionalized cyclic enones[103]; a Pd-catalyzed cross-coupling of Baylis-Hillman acetates with bis(pinacolato)diboron with subsequent stereospecific allylboration of aldehydes in one pot[104]; a mild N-decarballyloxylation with iodine in wet acetonitrile [without recourse to transition metal catalysis!][105]; a modified Bruylants synthesis of tertiary amines with 1,2,3-triazole as a safe and practical substitute for cyanide ion[106]; a new stereoselective formation of 1,2-*cis*-glycosides directed by the (S)-phenylthiomethylbenzyloxy residue attached at C_2[107]; the first hetero-Diels-Alder reaction with 2-substituted pyridines facilitated by coordination to a [hydridotris(pyrazolyl)borato]-(nitroso)tungsten phosphine complex[108]; the simultaneous incorporation of *two* adjacent carbon chains onto the benzene ring via the facile insertion of benzynes into a C-C σ-bond of β-dicarbonyl compounds[109]; and two new ketone syntheses: one directly from nitriles and alkylidenephosphoranes[110], and the other by coupling thiolic acid esters with thiophilic triorganoindium compounds[111].

In-roads to molecular diversity have widened enormously with the emergence of multistep syntheses[112], none more so than the classical Ugi condensation. This has now been effectively *multiplied* by using bifunctional building blocks (dicarboxylic acids and diisonitriles) as a route to complex macrocyclic steroidal peptide hybrids[113]. Natural product-like complexity has also been grafted in one step by multiple [4+2]-cycloaddition of maleimides onto [4]dendralene, now readily available on a large scale[114]. Tandem catalysis, highlighted in the *Trends* section of the previous volume, is an 'add-on', illustrated by a dual catalytic 4-component route to complex 4,5,6,7-tetrahydro-2*H*-isoindoles. In this, a copper(II)-catalyzed 3-component Mannich-type reaction furnishes the 4-aza-1,6-enyne system, which undergoes iridium(I)-catalyzed cycloisomerization prior to Diels-Alder reaction and aromatizing dehydrogenation *in the same pot*[115].

Self-assembly is a relatively new element of the expanding field of heterogeneous catalysis. When combined with the element of asymmetry, the trick is to design a readily recyclable catalyst which offers the same or better enantioselectivity than the homogeneous counterpart. This has been achieved recently in the Ti(IV)-catalyzed asymmetric synthesis of secondary alcohols from aldehydes and dialkylzincs. Here, *zeolite-type* homochiral metal-organic frameworks, having permanent porosity and absorption capacity, have been designed on the basis of a chiral 4,4'-bis(4-pyridyl)-1,1'-bi-2-naphthol template, which assembles uniformly through strong hydrogen bonding into a highly ordered structure in the presence of $Ti(OPr-i)_4$[116]. A similar self-assembly is at play in the design of a *thermomorphic* immobilized rhodium complex. Here, the hydrogen-bonded network is based on a 2,4,6-triamino-1,3,5-triazine molecule and a barbiturate substituted by a phosphine residue for coordination to the metal: the system is homogeneous at elevated temperature, but separates out on cooling to ease retrieval[117]. Interestingly, rhodium nanoclusters have been immobilized with greatly enhanced activity by combining with a pyrrolidone-substituted cationic co-polymer solubilized in an ionic liquid[118]. The application of supports to remove transition metal impurities has also been highlighted. In one example, mercaptopropyl-modified mesoporous silica effectively removes traces of palladium from both aqueous and organic media[119], while Teflon tape, adhered to the inside of a reaction vessel, is capable of 'fishing out' a fluorous rhodium catalyst by surface adhesion on cooling[120].

Two gems to savour in conclusion: the design of a *volatilizable* support for high-throughput synthesis[121], and the first synthesis of a stable, enantiopure [*ligand-less*] polyoxometalate[122]. And, lastly, a word on tetra cycline: omitted from the top 46 drugs of all-time (superbly overviewed in a recent Special Issue of Chem. Eng. News[123]), but still very much in the news thanks to a new total synthesis in *17* steps[124].

[1] S. Antoniotti, V. Michelet, J.-P. Genêt et al., J. Am. Chem. Soc. *127*, 9976-7 (2005); review of catalysis with gold s. *Reviews* section under *27,* 851.
[2] J.P. Markham, S.T. Staben, F.D. Toste, J. Am. Chem. Soc. *127*, 9708-9 (2005).
[3] D.J. Gorin, N.R. Davis, F.D. Toste, J. Am. Chem. Soc. *127*, 11260-1 (2005).
[4] A.W. Sromek, M. Rubina, V. Gevorgyan, J. Am. Chem. Soc. *127*, 10500-1 (2005).
[5] C. González-Arellano, A. Corma et al., Chem. Commun. *2005*, 3451-3.
[6] I. Ito, M. Sawamura et al., Org. Lett. *7*, 3001-4 (2005).
[7] A. Abad, A. Corma et al., Angew. Chem. Int. Ed. Engl. *44*, 4066-9 (2005).
[8] M.R. Fructos, S.P. Nolan, M. Mar Díaz-Requejo, P.J. Pérez et al., Angew. Chem. Int. Ed. Engl. *44*, 5284-8 (2005).
[9] B.S. Lee, S.K. Namgoong, S.-G. Lee, Tetrahedron Lett. *46*, 4501-3 (2005).
[10] T. Belser, M. Stöhr, A. Pfaltz, J. Am. Chem. Soc. *127*, 8720-31 (2005).
[11] E. Genin, V. Michelet, J.-P. Genêt et al., Angew. Chem. Int. Ed. Engl. *44*, 4949-53 (2005).
[12] S.-I. Kiyooka, M. Ueno, E. Ishii, Tetrahedron Lett. *46*, 4639-42 (2005); Au(III)-catalyzed procedure cf. *68,* 85.
[13] K. Taguchi, S. Sakaguchi, Y. Ishii, Tetrahedron Lett. *46*, 4539-42 (2005).
[14] T. Nishimura, S. Uemura et al., Org. Lett. *7*, 2425-8 (2005).
[15] R. Weihofen, G. Helmchen et al., Chem. Commun. *2005*, 3541-3; review of Pd- and Ir-catalyzed allylation s. *Reviews* section under *27,* 851.
[16] S. Streiff, G. Helmchen et al., Chem. Commun. *2005*, 2957-9.
[17] Recent applications s. *56,* 326s68
[18] A. Fürstner, P.W. Davies, T. Gress, J. Am. Chem. Soc. *127*, 8244-5 (2005).
[19] O. Buisine, I.E. Markó et al., Chem. Commun. *2005*, 3856-8; review of N-heterocylic carbene complexes s. *Reviews* section under *27,* 851.

[20] J.-H. Kim, Y.-S. Lee et al., J. Org. Chem. *70*, 6714-20 (2005).
[21] V. Lavallo, G. Bertrand et al., Angew. Chem. Int. Ed. Engl. *44*, 5705-9 (2005).
[22] S. Sebelius, V.J. Olsson, K.J. Szabó, J. Am. Chem. Soc. *127*, 10478-9 (2005).
[23] O. Daugulis, V.G. Zaitsev, Angew. Chem. Int. Ed. Engl. *44*, 4046-8 (2005).
[24] H. Ohno, T. Tanaka et al., Angew. Chem. Int. Ed. Engl. *44*, 5103-6 (2005).
[25] K. Motokura, K. Kaneda et al., Tetrahedron Lett. *46*, 5507-10 (2005).
[26] J. Bigeault, L. Giordano, G. Buono, Angew. Chem. Int. Ed. Engl. *44*, 4753-7 (2005).
[27] H. Kim, C. Lee, J. Am. Chem. Soc. *127*, 10180-1 (2005).
[28] S. Ma et al., Angew. Chem. Int. Ed. Engl. *44*, 5275-8 (2005).
[29] L. Shi, Y.-Q. Tu et al., J. Am. Chem. Soc. *127*, 10836-7 (2005).
[30] L.J. Goo²en, J.E. Rauhaus, G. Deng, Angew. Chem. Int. Ed. Engl. *44*, 4042-5 (2005).
[31] K. Yoshida, T. Imamoto, J. Am. Chem. Soc. *127*, 10470-1 (2005).
[32] P. McBreen, M. Siaj, Science *309*, 588-90 (2005); s.a. C. Nuckolls, G.S. Tulevski, M.L. Steigerwald, ibid. 591-3.
[33] M.L. Nadal, J.M. Moretó et al., J. Am. Chem. Soc. *127*, 10476-7 (2005).
[34] M. Takimoto, Y. Sato, M. Mori et al., Tetrahedron Lett. *46*, 5173-6 (2005).
[35] J. Waser, H. Nambu, E.M. Carreira, J. Am. Chem. Soc. *127*, 8294-5 (2005).
[36] I. Iovel, M. Beller et al., Angew. Chem. Int. Ed. Engl. *44*, 3913-7 (2005); alternative route from benzyl alcohols cf. F. Muhlrich, O. Schuster, T. Bach, J. Am. Chem. Soc. *127*, 9348-9 (2005).
[37] R.B. Bedford et al., Chem. Commun. *2005*, 4161-3.
[38] T. Nagano, T. Hayashi, Chem. Lett. *34*, 1152-3 (2005).
[39] X. Yao, C.-J. Li, J. Org. Chem. *70*, 5752-5 (2005).
[40] J.U. Rhee, M.J. Krische, Org. Lett. *7*, 2493-6 (2005).
[41] J. Ramírez, E. Peris, E. Fernandez et al., Chem. Commun. *2005*, 3056-8.
[42] J.-H. Li, D.-P. Wang, Y.-X. Xie, Tetrahedron Lett. *46*, 4941-4 (2005).
[43] Y. Fang, C. Li, Chem. Commun. *2005*, 3574-6.
[44] Allylamines s. M. Kozuka, T. Tsuchida, M. Mitani, Tetrahedron Lett. *46*, 4527-30 (2005); propargylamines s. N. Gommermann, P. Knochel, Chem. Commun. *2005*, 4175-7.
[45] Review of asymmetric organocatalysis s. *Reviews* section under 27, 57.
[46] Z. Tang, L.-Z. Gong et al., J. Am. Chem. Soc. *127*, 9285-9 (2005).
[47] W. Wang, H. Li, J. Wang, Tetrahedron Lett. *46*, 5077-9 (2005).
[48] A. Córdova et al., Chem. Commun. *2005*, 3586-8.
[49] D. Terako, M. Takano, T. Oriyama, Chem. Lett. *34*, 962-3 (2005).
[50] M. Marigo, K.A. Jøgensen et al., Angew. Chem. Int. Ed. Engl. *44*, 3703-6 (2005); s.a. Y. Hamashima, M. Sodeoka et al., J. Am. Chem. Soc. *127*, 10164-5 (2005).
[51] H. Sundén, A. Córdova et al., Angew. Chem. Int. Ed. Engl. *44*, 4877-80 (2005); with chiral diamines cf. K. Ishihara, K. Nakano, J. Am. Chem. Soc. *127*, 10504-5 (2005).
[52] A. Lattanzi, Org. Lett. *7*, 2579-82 (2005).
[53] S. Lou, S.E. Schaus et al., J. Am. Chem. Soc. *127*, 11256-7 (2005).
[54] H.D. King et al., Org. Lett. *7*, 3437-40 (2005); with copper(II) bis(Δ^2-oxazoline) complexes cf. M.-C. Ye, Y. Tang et al., J. Org. Chem. *70*, 6108-10 (2005).
[55] Reviews s. *Reviews* section under 27, 57.
[56] J.-F. Paquin, E.M. Carreira et al., J. Am. Chem. Soc. *127*, 10850-1 (2005).

57 R. Shintani, T. Kimura, T. Hayashi, Chem. Commun. *2005*, 3213-4.
58 R. Shintani, T. Hayashi et al., Angew. Chem. Int. Ed. Engl. *44*, 3909-12 (2005).
59 R. Shintani, T. Hayashi et al., Angew. Chem. Int. Ed. Engl. *44*, 4611-4 (2005).
60 T. Hayashi, S. Yamamoto, N. Tokunaga, Angew. Chem. Int. Ed. Engl. *44*, 4224-7 (2005).
61 T. Ohkuma, R. Noyori et al., J. Am. Chem. Soc. *127*, 8288-9 (2005).
62 R. Guo, R.H. Morris et al., Chem. Commun. *2005*, 3050-2.
63 S. Burk, G. Franció, W. Leitner, Chem. Commun. *2005*, 3460-2.
64 P. Västilä, J. Wettergren, H. Adolfsson, Chem. Commun. *2005*, 4039-41.
65 R. Hoen, A.J. Minnaard, J.G. de Vries, B.L. Feringa et al., Angew. Chem. Int. Ed. Engl. *44*, 4209-12 (2005).
66 Y. Liu, K. Ding, J. Am. Chem. Soc. *127*, 10488-9 (2005).
67 T. Benincori, F. Sannicolò et al., J. Org. Chem. *70*, 5436-41 (2005).
68 C. Mazet, V. Köhler, A. Pfaltz, Angew. Chem. Int. Ed. Engl. *44*, 4888-91 (2005).
69 T.M. Lancaster, S.S. Lee, J.Y. Ying, Chem. Commun. *2005*, 3577-9.
70 K. Tanaka et al., Org. Lett. *7*, 3119-22 (2005); review of axially chiral biaryls s. *Reviews* section under *27, 57*.
71 M. Hatano, K. Ishihara et al., J. Am. Chem. Soc. *127*, 10776-7 (2005).
72 C. Schaefer, G.C. Fu, Angew. Chem. Int. Ed. Engl. *44*, 4606-8 (2005).
73 B.M. Trost, S. Shin, J.A. Sciafani, J. Am. Chem. Soc. *127*, 8602-3 (2005).
74 F.O. Arp, G.C. Fu, J. Am. Chem. Soc. *127*, 10482-3 (2005).
75 Asymmetric 1,4-addition of copper(I) acetylides s. T.F. Knöpfel, E.M. Carreira et al., J. Am. Chem. Soc. *127*, 9682-3 (2005); with Me_2Zn and a chiral 2-aminoalcohol cf. M. Yamashita, K. Yamada, K. Tomioka, Org. Lett. *7*, 2369-72 (2005).
76 Reviews of water as medium s. *Reviews* section under *47, 48*.
77 J. Dambacher, M. Bergdahl et al., Tetrahedron Lett. *46*, 4473-7 (2005).
78 V. Cadierno, J. Gimeno et al., Chem. Commun. *2005*, 4086-8.
79 K. Surendra, K. Rama Rao et al., Tetrahedron Lett. *46*, 4581-3 (2005); nucleophilic allylation of aldehydes under the same conditions s. N.S. Krishnaveni, K. Ramo Rao et al., ibid. 4299-301.
80 H. Hamamoto, S. Ikegami et al., Angew. Chem. Int. Ed. Engl. *44*, 4536-8 (2005).
81 H. Hagiwara et al., Chem. Commun. *2005*, 2942-4.
82 A. Porzelle, W.-D. Fessner, Angew. Chem. Int. Ed. Engl. *44*, 4724-8 (2005).
83 P.G. Jessop, Nature *436*, 1102 (2005).
84 Y.-C. Teo, J.-D. Goh, T.-P. Loh, Org. Lett. *7*, 2743-6 (2005); with PyBox ligands cf. J. Lu, S.-J. Ji, T.-P. Loh et al., Chem. Commun. *2005*, 4217-8.
85 Y.-C. Teo, E.-L. Goh, T.-P. Loh, Tetrahedron Lett. *46*, 4573-5 (2005).
86 Y.-C. Teo, T.-P. Loh, Org. Lett. *7*, 2539-42 (2005).
87 D.E. Ward, M.S. Souweha, Org. Lett. *7*, 3533-6 (2005).
88 S. Shirakawa, P.J. Lombardi, J.L. Leighton, J. Am. Chem. Soc. *127,* 9974-5 (2005).
89 D. Uraguchi, K. Sorimachi, M. Terada, J. Am. Chem. Soc. *127*, 9360-1 (2005); s.a. T. Akiyama et al., Org. Lett. *7*, 2583-7 (2005).
90 S. Minakata, M. Komatsu et al., Org. Lett. *7*, 3509-12 (2005).
91 R.B. Lettan II, K.A. Scheidt, Org. Lett. *7*, 3227-30 (2005); 1,2-addition of trimethylsilyl acetonitrile to N-tosylimines with LiOAc s. Y. Kawano, H. Fujisawa, T. Mukaiyama, Chem. Lett. *34*, 1134-5 (2005).

[92] B.C. Ranu, S. Banerjee, Org. Lett. *7*, 3049-52 (2005).
[93] A. Iida, Y. Tanabe et al., Chem. Commun. *2005*, 3171-3.
[94] J.L. Wood et al., J. Am. Chem. Soc. *127*, 12513-4 (2005).
[95] F. Beaufils, F. Dénès, P. Renaud, Angew. Chem. Int. Ed. Engl. *44*, 5273-4 (2005).
[96] J. Kemper, A. Studer, Angew. Chem. Int. Ed. Engl. *44*, 4914-7 (2005).
[97] T. Saitoh, J. Ichikawa, J. Am. Chem. Soc. *127*, 9696-7 (2005).
[98] A. Villar, K. Muniz et al., Chem. Commun. *2005*, 3304-6.
[99] T.J. Donohoe, S. Butterworth, Angew. Chem. Int. Ed. Engl. *44*, 4766-8 (2005).
[100] S. Lin, L. Yang, Tetrahedron Lett. *46*, 4315-9 (2005).
[101] Y. Nakagawa, N. Mizuno et al., Angew. Chem. Int. Ed. Engl. *44*, 5136-41 (2005).
[102] A.P. Thottumkara, M.S. Bowsher, T.K. Vinod, Org. Lett. *7*, 2923-6 (2005).
[103] M.E. Krafft, T.F.N. Haxell, J. Am. Chem. Soc. *127*, 10168-9 (2005).
[104] G.W. Kabalka, B. Venkataiah, G. Dong, Tetrahedron Lett. *46*, 4209-11 (2005).
[105] R.H. Szumigala, Jr., R.A. Miller et al., Tetrahedron Lett. *46*, 4403-5 (2005).
[106] M. Prashad, Y. Liu, D. Har et al., Tetrahedron Lett. *46*, 5455-8 (2005).
[107] G.J. Boons et al., J. Am. Chem. Soc. *127*, 12090-1 (2005).
[108] P.M. Graham, W.D. Harman et al., J. Am. Chem. Soc. *127*, 10568-72 (2005).
[109] H. Yoshida, A. Kunai et al., Chem. Commun. *2005*, 3292-4; *o*-allylbiphenyls from benzynes s. T.T. Jayanth, M. Jeganmohan, C.-H. Cheng, Org. Lett. *7*, 2921-4 (2005).
[110] D.F. Taber, L. Cai, J. Org. Chem. *70*, 4887-8 (2005).
[111] B.W. Fausett, L.S. Liebeskind, J. Org. Chem. *70*, 4851-3 (2005).
[112] Review of 3-component syntheses s. *Reviews* section under *67*, 365.
[113] L.A. Wessjohann, B. Voigt, D.G. Rivera, Angew. Chem. Int. Ed. Engl. *44*, 4785-90 (2005).
[114] A.D. Payne et al., J. Am. Chem. Soc. *127*, 12188-9 (2005).
[115] Y. Yamamoto et al., J. Am. Chem. Soc. *127*, 10804-5 (2005).
[116] C.-D. Wu, W. Lin et al., J. Am. Chem. Soc. *127*, 8940-1 (2005).
[117] J.H. Yoon, C.-H. Jun et al., Org. Lett. *7*, 2889-92 (2005).
[118] Y. Kou et al., J. Am. Chem. Soc. *127*, 9694-5 (2005).
[119] C.M. Crudden, M. Sateesh, R. Lewis, J. Am. Chem. Soc. *127*, 10045-50 (2005).
[120] L.V. Dinh, J.A. Gladysz, Angew. Chem. Int. Ed. Engl. *44*, 4095-7 (2005).
[121] R.A. Houghten, Y. Yu, J. Am. Chem. Soc. *127*, 8582-3 (2005).
[122] X. Fang, T.M. Anderson, C.L. Hill, Angew. Chem. Int. Ed. Engl. *44*, 3540-4 (2005).
[123] A.A. Daemmrich, M.E. Bowden, Chem. Eng. News *83*, No.25, 28-141 (2005).
[124] M.G. Charest, D.R. Siegel, A.G. Myers, J. Am. Chem. Soc. *127*, 8292-3 (2005).

Systematic Survey

Reaction symbol	Page				
HO↕↑N	1	ORem⇓Rem	35	NC⇓OC	83
HO↕↑S	1	ORem↕↑H	35	NC⇓NN	86
HO↕↑Rem	1	ORem↕↑N	36	NC⇓NC	86
HO↕↑C	2	OC⇓HC	36	NC⇓CC	89
HN⇓ON	7	OC⇓ON	37	NC∩HN	93
HN↕↑O	7	OC⇓OC	37	NC∩HC	93
HN↕↑N	8	OC⇓NC	41	NC∩ON	93
HN↕↑C	9	OC⇓CC	41	NC∩OC	93
HN⇑O	11	OC∩HO	49	NC∩CC	94
HS↕↑S	11	OC∩ON	50	NC↕↑H	95
HS↕↑C	11	OC∩CC	50	NC↕↑O	96
HC⇓OC	12	OC↕↑H	52	NC↕↑N	108
HC⇓NC	18	OC↕↑O	55	NC↕↑Hal	111
HC⇓CC	18	OC↕↑N	61	NC↕↑S	117
HC↕↑O	25	OC↕↑Hal	65	NC↕↑Rem	117
HC↕↑N	28	OC↕↑S	67	NC↕↑C	119
HC↕↑Hal	29	OC↕↑Rem	69	NC⇑H	120
HC↕↑Rem	30	OC↕↑C	71	NC⇑O	121
HC↕↑C	30	OC⇑H	74	NC⇑N	123
HC⇑O	31	OC⇑O	78	NC⇑Hal	124
HC⇑N	31	OC⇑N	79	NC⇑S	124
HC⇑C	31	OC⇑Hal	79	NC⇑C	124
OO↕↑O	32	OC⇑S	79	HalC⇓OC	124
ON⇓N	32	OC⇑Rem	80	HalC⇓NC	125
ON↕↑H	32	OC⇑C	80	HalC⇓CC	125
OS⇓S	33	NN⇑H	81	HalC↕↑H	127
OS↕↑O	34	NN⇑O	82	HalC↕↑O	131
OS↕↑N	34	NHal↕↑H	82	HalC↕↑N	133
OS↕↑Hal	34	NS↕↑Hal	82	HalC↕↑Hal	134
ORem⇓HO	35	NS↕↑S	83	HalC↕↑Rem	134
		NS⇑H	83	HalC↕↑C	134
		NS⇑S	83	SS↕↑H	135

Reaction symbol	Page				
		RemC⇓C	148	CC↓↑O	221
		RemC⇓CC	148	CC↓↑N	238
SS↓↑Hal	135	RemC↓↑H	152	CC↓↑Hal	244
SRem↓↑O	135	RemC↓↑O	153	CC↓↑S	266
SC⇓HC	136	RemC↓↑N	153	CC↓↑Rem	269
SC⇓OC	136	RemC↓↑Hal	154	CC↓↑C	299
SC⇓NS	137	RemC↓↑Rem	155	CC↑↑H	305
SC⇓NC	137	RemC↓↑C	155	CC↑↑O	306
SC⇓CC	137	CC⇓OC	156	CC↑↑N	309
SC↓↑H	139	CC⇓NC	170	CC↑↑Hal	309
SC↓↑O	139	CC⇓C	177	CC↑↑S	313
SC↓↑N	142	CC⇓CC	177	CC↑↑Rem	313
SC↓↑Hal	144	CC∩HO	209	CC↑↑C	314
SC↓↑S	145	CC∩HC	209	ElN↑↑O	317
SC↓↑Rem	146	CC∩OC	213	ElN↑↑C	318
SC↓↑C	146	CC∩NC	217	ElS↑↑O	318
SC↑↑H	146	CC∩HalC	218	ElRem↑↑O	318
SC↑↑O	147	CC∩RemC	218	ElRem↑↑Rem	318
SC↑↑Hal	147	CC∩CC	218	Het⇓N	319
RemC⇓OC	147	CC↓↑H	220	Res	319

Abbreviations and Symbols

abs.	absolute
alc.	alcoholic
aq.	aqueous
ar.	aromatic
atm.	atmosphere(s)
compd(s).	compound(s)
deriv(s).	derivative(s)
e.e.	enantiomeric excess
eq(s).	equivalent(s)
E.	Example
F.e.s.	Further example(s) see
M	molar
prepn.	preparation
prim.	primary
s68	supplementary reference in Volume 68
sec.	secondary
startg. m.f.	starting material for (the preparation of ...)
subst.	substituted
sym.	symmetrical
tert.	tertiary
v.i.	via intermediates
w.a.r.	without additional reagents
Y *	Yield
⚡	Electrolysis
⋕	Irradiation
[\\\\]	Microwave irradiation
○	Ring closure
◌	Ring contraction
◯	Ring expansion
C	Ring opening
Ⓗ	Ring hydrogenation
←	'see title or reagent on the left half of the page'

* Yields in parentheses refer to the immediately preceeding step of a multi-step reaction

Formation of H-O Bond

Exchange ⇅

Nitrogen ↑   HO ⇅ N

Palladous hydroxide $Pd(OH)_2$
Alcohols from alkoximes s. *68*, 68   ON=C< → OH

Sulfur ↑   HO ⇅ S

Lithium diisopropylamide $i\text{-}Pr_2NLi$
Phenols from aryl mesylates   OMs → OH
with NaOH cf. *10*, 3; with LDA s. T. Ritter, E.M. Carreira et al., Org. Lett. **6**, 1513-4 (2004).

Tetraethylammonium hydroxide Et_4NOH
Phenols from aryl triflates under mild conditions   OTf → OH

1. $O_2N\text{-}C_6H_4\text{-}OTf \longrightarrow O_2N\text{-}C_6H_4\text{-}OH$

2 eqs. 10% aq. Et_4NOH added to the startg. aryl triflate in dioxane at room temp., and stirred for 1 h → product. Y 99%. Reaction with Bu_4NF was less efficient, and failed with NaOH. Cleavage of aryl tosylates and mesylates was also effected with tetraethylammonium hydroxide, but over a prolonged reaction period. Ketones, halides, amides, silyl ethers, sulfonamides, nitro compds., and methyl esters remained intact. F.e.s. T. Ohgiya, S. Nishiyama, Tetrahedron Lett. **45**, 6317-20 (2004).

Remaining Elements ↑   HO ⇅ Rem

N-Iodosuccinimide   NIS
O-De-*tert*-butyldimethylsilylation $OSiMe_2Bu\text{-}t$ → OH
with NBS cf. *30*, 4s36; preferential cleavage of alkyl *tert*-butyldimethylsilyl ethers with retention of aryl *tert*-butyldimethylsilyl ethers (cf. *51*, 3s55) s. B. Karimi, A. Zamani, D. Zareyee, Tetrahedron Lett. **45**, 9139-41 (2004).

Acetonyltriphenylphosphonium bromide $[MeCOCH_2PPh_3]Br$
Selective and preferential O-de-*tert*-butyldimethylsilylation under mild conditions

2. t-BuPh$_2$SiO~~~~~OSiMe$_2$Bu-t $\xrightarrow{[MeCOCH_2PPh_3]^+Br^-}$ t-BuPh$_2$SiO~~~~~OH

5 Mol% of acetonyltriphenylphosphonium bromide added to a well-stirred soln. of the startg. *tert*-butyldimethylsilyl ether in 5:2 methylene chloride/methanol at room temp., and the mixture stirred for 12 min at the same temp. → product. Y 81%. The method is simple and effective for the deprotection of alkyl *tert*-butyldimethylsilyl ethers in the presence of aryl *tert*-butyldimethylsilyl ethers or *tert*-butyldiphenylsilyl ethers. However, the latter were cleaved with 20 mol% of the reagent, and the former over a prolonged reaction period. Furthermore, a variety of other protective groups, such as O-acetyl, O-benzyl, O-benzoyl, thioketals, esters and O,O-isopropylidene, remained intact. The effective reagent is believed to be *in situ*-generated HBr. F.e. incl. deprotection of nucleosides and carbohydrate derivs. s. A.T. Khan, S. Ghosh, L.H. Choudhury, Eur. J. Org. Chem. **2004**, 2198-204.

Nickel(II) chloride/ethanedithiol $NiCl_2/HSCH_2CH_2SH$
Selective and preferential O-de-*tert*-butyldimethylsilylation s. *68*, 11

Palladium-carbon/methanol   *Pd-C/MeOH*
O-Desilylation   OSi≤ → OH
cleavage of trimethylsilyl ethers cf. *59*, 40s*67*; also mild cleavage of TPS-, TBS-, TBDMS-, TIPS-, and TBDPS-ethers, and selective cleavage of the first four with retention of the latter two, s. S. Kim, J. Rokach et al., Tetrahedron Lett. *45*, 1973-6 (2004).

Carbon ↑   HO ↓↑ C

Irradiation   ⊬
Removal of photo-labile O-protective groups   ←
s. *30*, 5s*64*; liberation of oxo compds. from 2-(6-bromo-7-hydroxycoumarin-4-yl)-1,3-dioxolanes at pH 7.2 s. M. Lu, T.M. Dore et al., Org. Lett. *5*, 2119-22 (2003); liberation of carboxylic acids from 1-subst. 2-(*o*-acetonylphenyl)alkyl esters s. W.N. Atemnkeng, A. Banerjee et al., ibid. 4469-72.

Microwaves s. under TsOH   [\\\\]

Lithium/naphthalene   *Li/C$_{10}$H$_8$*
Selective O-detritylation s. *68*, 14   OCPh$_3$ → OH

tert-Butyllithium   *t-BuLi*
2-Arylallyl as O- and N-protective group   ←

3.

Cleavage of 2-phenylallyl phenolethers. A soln. of the startg. 2-phenylallyl ether in THF treated with 1 eq. *t*-BuLi at -78° for 30 min, and hydrolyzed with aq. acid → product. Y 80%. The 2-arylallyl group can be cleaved simply from protected alcohols, phenols, benzamides, sulfonamides and pivalamides, leaving other allyl protective groups, as well as siloxy, acetal, benzyloxy, chlorine and fluorine, unaffected. Reaction takes place via carbolithiation with subsequent elimination of α-neopentylstyrene. F.e. incl. liberation of prim. amino groups from N,N-bis(2-arylallyl) derivs. s. J. Barluenga et al., Chem. Commun. *2005*, 933-5.

Lithium/ethylenediamine   *Li/H$_2$NCH$_2$CH$_2$NH$_2$*
Cleavage of methyl ethers   OMe → OH
with Li/EtNH$_2$ cf. *31*, 5; of methyl phenolethers with Li/ethylenediamine, also O-debenzylation of allyl benzyl ethers, and application of 2,6-dimethylbenzyl and *m*-xylylmethyl as alternatives to benzyl, s. T. Shindo, Y. Fukuyama, T. Sugai, Synthesis *2004*, 692-700.

Ammonia   *NH$_3$*
O-Decarbobenzoxylation   OCOOBn → OH
with PtO$_2$ on hydrogenation cf. *28*, 118; with methanolic ammonia, retention of *tert*-butyldimethylsilyl and 4-methoxytrityl ethers, s. F. Mouffouk, A. Morère et al., Synth. Commun. *34*, 303-7 (2004).

Triethylamine/methanol   *Et$_3$N/MeOH*
High-pressure O-deacylation   OAc → OH

4.

of hindered steroidal esters. A soln. of the startg. steroidal ester (10 mg), 1% Et$_3$N, and 10% methanol in acetonitrile contained in a Teflon ampoule subjected to a hydrostatic pressure of 6 kbar at room temp. for 6 h → product. Y 84%. Attempts to remove the O-acyl group enzymatically or with Dowex 1x8 100/200 (OH⁻) failed. F.e.s. W. Kroszczynski, J. Jurczak, Helv. Chim. Acta 87, 1488-92 (2004).

Cupric sulfate $CuSO_4$
Cleavage of tetrahydropyran-2-yl ethers s. *49*, 127s68   OThp → OH

Zinc/N-methylimidazole   ←
Protection of carboxyl groups as 2,2,2-trichloroethyl esters $COOCH_2CCl_3$ → COOH
Reductive removal of the protective group
with Zn/AcOH cf. *24*, 9; with Zn/N-methylimidazole in acetone, also N-decarbo-2,2,2-trichloroethoxylation (cf. *27*, 24) and with retention of acid-sensitive groups s. L. Somsak, K. Czifrak, E. Veres, Tetrahedron Lett. *45*, 9095-7 (2004).

Zinc bromide $ZnBr_2$
Cleavage of carboxylic acid *tert*-butyl esters   COOBu-*t* → COOH
with $SnCl_4$ cf. *16*, 201s55; with $ZnBr_2$ (cf. *16*, 201s59), selectivity and preferential cleavage of N-protected α-amino-α,ω-dicarboxylic acid di-*tert*-butyl esters at the α-site, s. R. Kaul, Y. Brouillette, W.D. Lubell et al,. J. Org. Chem. *69*, 6131-3 (2004); with TsOH·H_2O under microwave irradiation in the absence of solvent, also cleavage of carboxylic acid allyl esters, s. J.C. Lee, E.S. Yoo, J.S. Lee, Synth. Commun. *34*, 3017-20 (2004).

Polymer-based phenylboronic acid/hydrogen chloride   ←
Cleavage of cyclic boronic acid esters   C
with $PhB(OH)_2$ cf. *54*, 10; with polymer-based phenylboronic acid/HCl s. T.E. Pennington, K.B. Cynantya, C.A. Hutton, Tetrahedron Lett. *45*, 6657-60 (2004).

Zeolites   ←
Partial O-deacetylation s. *54*, 79s68   OAc → OH

Boron bromide BBr_3
Selective and preferential O-depropargylation $OCH_2C\equiv CH$ → OH

Cleavage of propargyl ethers. A mixture of 1 eq. boron bromide and the startg. propargyl ether in methylene chloride (1 *M*) stirred for 35 min at room temp. under N_2 → product. Y 75%. Benzyl ethers were removed even faster under these conditions, but cleavage of aryl propargyl ethers and propargyl esters was more facile than that of aryl methyl ethers or methyl esters, while N-propargyl derivs. were left intact. Allyl phenolethers, however, underwent a rapid Claisen rearrangement. Reaction is presumed to involve intramolecular delivery of bromide to the propargyl terminus. F.e.s. S. Punna, S. Meunier, M.G. Finn, Org. Lett. *6*, 2777-9 (2004).

1-n-Butyl-3-methylimidazolium heptachloroaluminate   [bmim][Al_2Cl_7]
Cleavage of phenolethers in ionic liquids   OR → OH
s. *24*, 983s67; cleavage of methoxyflavones s. T. Liu, Y.-Z. Hu, Synth. Commun. *34*, 3209-18 (2004); with HBr (47%) in 1-*n*-butyl-3-methylimidazolium fluoroborate cf. S.K. Boovanahalli, D.W. Kim, D.Y. Chi, J. Org. Chem. *69*, 3340-4 (2004).

Indium(III) bromide $InBr_3$
Aldehydes from acylals $CH(OAc)_2$ → CHO
with $InCl_3$ cf. *56*, 63s64; with $InBr_3$ *in polyethylene glycol* for a simplified work-up and catalyst recovery s. Z.-H. Zhang, Y.-M. Wang et al., Green Chem. *6*, 563-5 (2004).

Cerium(III) triflate $Ce(OTf)_3$
Selective cleavage of *p*-methoxybenzyl ethers OCH_2Ar → OH
with CAN cf. *58*, 7s61; with *1 mol%* $Ce(OTf)_3$, selectivity and comparison with $CeCl_3$, s. G. Bartoli, A. De Nino et al., Eur. J. Org. Chem. *2004*, 2176-80.

Imidazolium ionic liquids s. under HBr   ←

Trifluoroacetic acid/pyrrole
Protection of prim. alcohols as 9-aryl-9-xanthyl ethers ←
Removal of the protective group ←
photolysis of 9-phenyl-9-xanthyl [pixyl] ethers cf. *55*, 3; cleavage of 9-phenyl- and 9-*p*-tolyl-9-xanthyl ethers with CF$_3$COOH/pyrrole for liberation of oligonucleotide 5'-hydroxyl groups s. C.B. Reese, H. Yan, Tetrahedron Lett. *45*, 2567-70 (2004).

Ethanedithiol s. under NiCl$_2$ HSCH$_2$CH$_2$SH
Polysulfones or Diphenyl disulfone ←
Radical cleavage of methallyl ethers under mild, neutral conditions   OC-C=C → OH

6.

A mixture of the startg. 2-methylprenyl ether and 10 wt% neutralized polysulfone (prepared as a solid source of sulfonyl radicals from methylenecyclopentane in 1:5 SO$_2$/methylene chloride at 0°; cf. *67*, 342) in cyclohexane refluxed under N$_2$ until reaction complete → product. Y 93%. The order of reactivity of methallyl ethers was 2-methylprenyl > prenyl > methallyl, simple allyl ethers being effectively inert, as also were acetals, esters, silyl ethers, benzyl ethers and free hydroxyl groups. Reaction involves an intermediate allyl radical. F.e.s. D. Markovic, P. Vogel et al., Chem. Commun. *2004*, 2444-5; less efficiently with diphenyl disulfone cf. Org. Lett. *6*, 2693-6 (2004).

Carbon tetrabromide s. under Ph$_3$P   CBr$_4$
Trichloroisocyanuric acid ←
Cleavage of tetrahydropyran-2-yl ethers s. *68*, 69   OThp → OH
Titanium trichloride   TiCl$_3$
Cleavage of tetrahydropyran-2-yl ethers under mild conditions   OThp → OH
with Me$_3$SiI cf. *52*, 10s*64*; with 20 mol% TiCl$_3$, selectivity, s. A. Semwal, S.K. Nayak, Synthesis *2005*, 71-4.

Zirconium tetrachloride   ZrCl$_4$
Cleavage of methoxymethyl ethers s. *48*, 216s*68*   OCH$_2$OMe → OH
Trimethyltin hydroxide   Me$_3$SnOH
Carboxylic acids from esters under mild conditions   COOR → COOH

7.

Selective hydrolysis. 1-10 eqs. Trimethyltin hydroxide added to a soln. of the startg. ester (0.04-0.15 mmol scale) in 1,2-dichloroethane, heated at 80° for 3 h, the solvent replaced by ethyl acetate, the organic layer washed with 0.01 *N* aq. KHSO$_4$ or 5% HCl, and worked up → product. Y 98%. The reagent is superior to LiOH in all departments, being suitable for the cleavage of a range of simple and sensitive ar. or aliphatic methyl, ethyl, allyl or benzyl esters and O-acyl groups *without* epimerization of chiral centres and, notably, leaving Fmoc protective groups unaffected. **Preferential cleavage** of methyl over isopropyl esters and prim. acetate groups was also recorded, but phenolic acetates were more labile than methyl esters. Pure products were obtained without chromatographic work-up. F.e. and from 3-acyl-2-oxazolidones s. K.C. Nicolaou et al., Angew. Chem. Int. Ed. Engl. *44*, 1378-82 (2005).

Triphenylphosphine/carbon tetrabromide Ph_3P/CBr_4
Cleavage of acetals $C(OR)_2 \rightarrow CO$
of 1,3-dioxolanes cf. *45*, 10s*52*; cleavage of aryl methoxymethyl ethers, selectivity, s. Y. Peng et al., Synth. Commun. *34*, 4325-30 (2004).

Diphenyl phosphorazidate/triethylamine $(PhO)_2P(O)N_3/Et_3N$
Protection of phenols as carboxymethyl ethers $OCH_2COOH \rightarrow OH$
Removal of the protective group under mild conditions

PhOCH₂COOH → PhOH

A soln. of phenoxyacetic acid in 10:1 anhydrous toluene/DMF treated with 1-1.15 eqs. Et₃N and 0.9-1.05 eqs. diphenyl phosphorazidate, the mixture refluxed for 3 h, water added, refluxing continued for 1-2 h, then acidified with 2 *N* aq. HCl → product. Y 63%. The method involves conversion of the carboxyl group to azidocarbonyl, followed by Curtius rearrangement and hydrolysis via unstable phenoxymethylamine. The procedure is simple, broad, and reliable, and is notable in that aromatic iodine and *tert*-butyl groups remain unaffected. F.e.s. D. Mirk, S.R. Waldvogel, Tetrahedron Lett. *45*, 7911-4 (2004).

Bismuth trichloride $BiCl_3$
Selective O-detritylation under mild conditions $OCPh_3 \rightarrow OH$
with BCl₃ cf. *49*, 8s*59*; with BiCl₃ s. G. Sabitha, J.S. Yadav et al., Synlett *2004*, 1276-8.

Niobium pentachloride $NbCl_5$
Regiospecific cleavage of phenolethers $OR \rightarrow OH$
cleavage of *o*-alkoxycarbonyl compds. with CeCl₃/NaI or BBr₃ cf. *52*, 4s*59*; with NbCl₅, also regiospecific cleavage of catechol ethers **and partial cleavage** of 1,1'-bi-2-naphthol ethers, s. S. Arai, Y. Sudo, A. Nishida, Synlett *2004*, 1104-6.

Sodium hydrogen sulfate/silica $NaHSO_4/SiO_2$
Heterogeneous cleavage of O-protective groups ←
s. *65*, 6s*66*; O-detritylation in 9:1 methylene chloride/methanol, also N-detritylation, s. B. Das, N. Chowdhury et al., Tetrahedron Lett. *45*, 6709-11 (2004).

Trialkylsilyl triflate/2,6-lutidine ←
Cleavage of acetals under mild conditions $CH(OR)_2 \rightarrow CHO$

with O-triethylsilylation. A soln. of 1 eq. of the startg. acetal in anhydrous methylene chloride treated at 0° under N₂ with 6 eqs. 2,6-lutidine and 4 eqs. triethylsilyl triflate, stirred at the same temp. for 5 min, then quenched with water → product. Y 82%. Most significantly, reaction takes place **with retention of ketal groups**. F.e. incl. cleavage of cyclic acetals, also with trimethylsilyl triflate, s. H. Fujioka, Y. Kita et al., J. Am. Chem. Soc. *126*, 11800-1 (2004).

p-Toluenesulfonic acid/microwaves $TsOH/[\backslash\backslash\backslash\backslash]$
Cleavage of carboxylic acid allyl and *tert*-butyl esters s. *16*, 201s*68* $COOR \rightarrow COOH$

Phosphotungstic acid/silica $H_6P_2W_{13}O_{64}/SiO_2$
Aldehydes from acylals $CH(OAc)_2 \rightarrow CHO$
with zirconium *m*-sulfophenyl phosphonate cf. *51*, 55s*63*; with readily recyclable silica-supported phosphotungstic acid ($H_6P_2W_{13}O_{64}$) (cf. *56*, 63s*64*) s. G.P. Romanelli, H.J. Thomas et al., Synth. Commun. *34*, 3909-14 (2004).

Iodine I_2
Cleavage of acetals $C(OR)_2 \rightarrow CO$
of methoxymethyl ethers cf. *56*, 9s*67*; cleavage of dimethyl acetals/ketals and preferential cleavage

of cyclic acetals, also functional group tolerance, s. J. Sun, Y. Hu et al., J. Org. Chem. **69**, 8932-4 (2004).

*Hydrogen bromide/1-*n-*butyl-3-methylimidazolium fluoroborate*   *HBr/[bmim]BF$_4$*
Cleavage of phenolethers in ionic liquids s. *24*, 983s68   OR → OH

Nickel/sulfuric acid   *Ni/H$_2$SO$_4$*
Reductions with Raney nickel in strongly acidic media   ←

10.   C$_8$H$_{17}$OBn ⟶ C$_8$H$_{17}$OH | PhNHBn ⋯➤ PhNH$_2$ (92%) | [benzyl-C$_6$H$_4$-Br] ⋯➤ [diphenylmethane] (90%)

O-Debenzylation. A stirred mixture of benzyl octyl ether and 0.8 eq. Raney nickel in 2:5 water/methanol treated dropwise at 30° with sulfuric acid (60% w/w in water) over 2 h, any solid residue filtered off, and the filtrate worked up → product. Y 94%. Mechanistically, it appears that hydrogen is consumed both from the surface of the catalyst and from the reaction of nickel with H$_2$SO$_4$ as the metal passes into solution as NiSO$_4$. Hence *no extraneous hydrogen is required*, nor a pressure apparatus. F.e. incl. N-debenzylation, dehydroxylation of benzyl alcohols, and replacement of ar. bromine by hydrogen s. M. Okimoto et al., Bull. Chem. Soc. Jpn. **77**, 1405-6 (2004).

Nickel(II) chloride/ethanedithiol   *NiCl$_2$/HSCH$_2$CH$_2$SH*
Cleavage of tetrahydropyran-2-yl ethers under mild conditions   OThp → OH

11.   [furfuryl-O-THP] ⟶ [Ni(SCH$_2$CH$_2$S)]$_n$ / [HCl] ⟶ [furfuryl-OH] | MeO-C$_6$H$_4$-CH$_2$OSiMe$_2$Bu-t ⋯➤ MeO-C$_6$H$_4$-CH$_2$OH (95%)

0.2 eq. NiCl$_2$-hexahydrate and 0.2 eq. 1,2-ethanedithiol added to the startg. tetrahydropyran-2-yl ether in 5:2 methylene chloride/methanol, stirred at room temp. until completion of the reaction, and chromatographed → product. Y 90%. Functional groups incl. phenolether, halide, carbohydrate, nucleoside, acetal and double bonds remained unaffected. F.e. and **selective cleavage of alkyl *tert*-butyldimethylsilyl ethers** in the presence of aryl ethers and alkyl or aryl THP ethers s. A.T. Khan et al., Tetrahedron Lett. **45**, 9617-21 (2004).

Tris(acetonitrile)cyclopentadienylruthenium(II) hexafluorophosphate/quinaldic acid   ←
Ruthenium-catalyzed O-deallylation   OCH$_2$CH=CH$_2$ → OH
cleavage of allyl esters with [Cp(MeCN)$_2$Ru(PPh$_3$)]PF$_6$ cf. *64*, 12; cleavage of allyl ethers with [CpRu(MeCN)$_3$]PF$_6$/quinaldic acid, selectivity, s. S. Tanaka, M. Kitamura et al., Org. Lett. **6**, 1873-5 (2004).

Palladium-carbon   *Pd-C*
Cleavage of benzyl ethers   OBn → OH
s. *1*, 13; *8*, 22; poisoning of Pd/C and Pd(OH)$_2$/C with bisbenzyl-protected 6-aminocyclitols s. M.B.-U. Surfraz, M. Akhtar, R.K. Allemann, Tetrahedron Lett. **45**, 1223-6 (2004); *in PEG-400* for efficient recycling of the catalyst (four times), also hydrogenation of carbon-carbon multiple bonds (cf. *3*, 46), s. S. Chandrasekhar et al., Synlett *2004*, 522-4.

Palladium-carbon/potassium hydroxide/methanol   *Pd-C/KOH/MeOH*
*(η^3-Allyl)[1,2-bis(*p*-methoxyphenyl)-3,4-bis(2,4,6-tri-*tert*-butylphenylphosphinidene)-1-cyclobutene]palladium(II) triflate/aniline*   ←
Cleavage of allyl ethers   OC-C=C → OH
cleavage of allyl phenolethers with Pd(PPh$_3$)$_4$/K$_2$CO$_3$ cf. *32*, 11s65; cleavage of allyl and subst. allyl phenolethers with Pd-C in methanolic KOH s. M. Ishizaki, A. Tanaka, H. Hara et al., Tetrahedron **60**, 7973-81 (2004); cleavage of allyl ethers with (η^3-allyl)[1,2-bis(*p*-methoxyphenyl)-3,4-bis(2,4,6-tri-*tert*-butylphenylphosphinidene)-1-cyclobutene]palladium(II) triflate and aniline as allyl transfer agent (cf. *32*, 11s66), **also O-decarballyloxylation,** s. H. Murakami, T. Minami, F. Ozawa, J. Org. Chem. **69**, 4482-6 (2004).

Formation of H-N Bond

Uptake ⇓

Addition to Oxygen and Nitrogen   HN ⇓ ON

Samarium diiodide SmI_2
3-Aminoalcohols from isoxazolidines
with Zn/AcOH cf. *61*, 13s*65*; under mild conditions with SmI_2 (and especially useful for 1-β-aminocyclopropanols) s. J. Revuelta, S. Cicchi, A. Brandi, Tetrahedron Lett. *45*, 8375-7 (2004).

Nickel   *Ni*
β-Amino-α,β-ethyleneketones from isoxazoles
s. *24*, 625s*62*; with simultaneous *syn*-selective hydrogenation of β-hydroxy-α-methylenecarboxylic acid esters (Baylis-Hillman adducts) s. R. Saxena, V. Singh, S. Batra, Tetrahedron *60*, 10311-20 (2004).

Palladous hydroxide-carbon/polymethylhydrosiloxane $Pd(OH)_2$-*C/pmhs*
Reductive ring opening of Δ²-isoxazolines
3-aminoalcohols with $LiAlH_4$ cf. *34*, 790; 3-(carbo-*tert*-butoxyamino)alcohols with $Pd(OH)_2$-C/polymethylhydrosiloxane in the presence of di-*tert*-butyl dicarbonate s. S. Chandrasekhar, A. Prabhakar et al., Synlett *2004*, 1303-5.

Exchange ⇅

Oxygen ↑   HN ⇅ O

Zinc/iron/formic acid   *Zn/Fe/HCOOH*
Amines from oximes $C=NOH \rightarrow CHNH_2$
with Zn/CF_3COOH cf. *13*, 27s*52*; α-aminocarboxylic acids with Zn/Fe in formic acid s. T. Kitagawa, M. Asada et al., Chem. Pharm. Bull. *52*, 1137-9 (2004).

Isopropanol s. under Ni   *i-PrOH*
Ammonium formate s. under Pd $HCOONH_4$

Yeast   ←
Ar. hydroxylamines from nitro compds. $NO_2 \rightarrow NHOH$
Enzymatic conversion in aq. medium

$O_2N-C_6H_4-NO_2 \longrightarrow O_2N-C_6H_4-NHOH$

Partial conversion. A mixture of bakers' yeast and glucose in aq. phosphate buffer (0.2 *M*, pH 6.5) incubated at 30° for 0.5 h, a soln. of startg. ar. nitro compd. in ethanol added, and the resulting mixture stirred at 30° until complete consumption of the startg. m. → product. Y 95% (along with 5% ar. amine). The method is mild, efficient and environmentally friendly. F.e.s. F. Li, J. Cui, Chem. Commun. *2004*, 2338-9.

Formic acid s. under Zn   *HCOOH*

Stannous chloride/tetra-n-butylammonium bromide $SnCl_2/Bu_4NBr$
Ar. amines from nitro compds. $NO_2 \rightarrow NH_2$
with $SnCl_2 \cdot 2H_2O$ in ethanol cf. *39*, 14; **in ionic liquids**, e.g. tetra-*n*-butylammonium bromide, s. P. De, Synlett *2004*, 1835-7.

Molybdenum hexacarbonyl $Mo(CO)_6$
Ar. amines from nitro compds. s. *51*, 163s*68*

Tetra-n-butylammonium bromide s. under $SnCl_2$ Bu_4NBr
Iron s. under Zn Fe
Ferrous sulfate/ethylenediaminetetraacetic acid disodium salt $FeSO_4/Na_2EDTA$
Ar. amines from nitro compds. in a 2-phase aq. medium $NO_2 \rightarrow NH_2$

13.   C$_6$H$_5$—NO_2 ⟶ C$_6$H$_5$—NH_2

A mixture of nitrobenzene, 0.08 mol% $FeSO_4\cdot 7H_2O$, 0.4 mol% Na_2EDTA and water stirred under H_2 at 400 psi at 150° in a stainless steel autoclave for 2.4 h → product. Y 99%. By complexing with EDTA, the homogeneous water-soluble iron catalyst is kept in the aqueous phase, thus allowing it to be recycled. The substrate serves as the organic phase, eliminating the need for an organic solvent. The catalyst system is specific for nitro group reduction with no reduction of the aromatic ring or other reducible groups. Thus this provides a low-cost, efficient and environmentally-friendly alternative to the prior art. F.e.s. R.M. Deshpande, R.V. Chaudhari et al., J. Org. Chem. *69*, 4835-8 (2004).

Nickel/mesoporous aluminophosphate/isopropanol/potassium hydroxide   ←
Palladium/mesoporous silica/ammonium formate   ←
Ar. amines from nitro compds.
Heterogeneous transfer-hydrogenation
with Ni(II)-exchanged mesoporous silica/*i*-PrOH/KOH cf. *53*, 9s*65*; with nickel/mesoporous aluminophosphate, also prim. ar. amines from ar. azo compds., and reduction of aryloxo compds., selectivity, s. P. Selvam, R.V. Jayaram et al., Tetrahedron Lett. *45*, 2003-7 (2004); ar. amines from nitro compds. or nitroso compds., cleavage of nitrosamines, reduction of α,β-ethyleneoxo compds., cleavage of ar. azo and hydrazo compds., and replacement of ar. halogen by hydrogen with palladium/mesoporous silica/ammonium formate or *i*-PrOH cf. ibid. 3071-5.

Nitrogen ↑   HN ↓↑ N

Irradiation   ⟿
Amines from triazenes   NN=NR → NH
with CF_3COOH cf. *17*, 32s*58*; liberation of amines from a triazene-linked polymer support by photolysis s. D. Enders et al., Tetrahedron Lett. *45*, 2839-41 (2004).

Zinc/hydrazinium monoformate $Zn/N_2H_4\cdot HCOOH$
Prim. amines from azides $N_3 \rightarrow NH_2$
with $Zn/HCOONH_4$ cf. *29*, 324s*67*; with $Zn/N_2H_4\cdot HCOOH$, selectivity, s. H.S. Prasad, G.R. Srinivasa, D.C. Gowda et al., Indian J. Chem. *43B*, 1787-9 (2004).

Zinc/ammonium chloride Zn/NH_4Cl
Prim. amines from azo compds.   N=N → 2 NH_2
prim. ar. amines with Zn/NH_4OAc cf. *35*, 609s*67*; with Zn/NH_4Cl, selectivity, s. M.B. Sridhara, G.R. Srinivasa, D.C. Gowda, Synth. Commun. *34*, 1441-6 (2004).

Ammonium formate s. under Pd $HCOONH_4$
Hydrazinium monoformate s. under Zn $N_2H_4\cdot HCOOH$

Triphenylphosphine Ph_3P
Amines from azides $N_3 \rightarrow NH_2$
with Ph_3P via phosphine imines cf. *12*, 42; one-pot conversion in refluxing methanol s. B. Pal, P. Jaisankar, V.S. Giri, Synth. Commun. *34*, 1317-23 (2004).

Molybdenum hexacarbonyl $Mo(CO)_6$
Amines from azides
with $[BnNEt_3]_2MoS_4$ cf. *51*, 163; with $Mo(CO)_6$ in refluxing ethanol, also prim. ar. amines from ar. nitro compds., s. S. Iyer, G.M. Kulkarni, Synth. Commun. *34*, 721-5 (2004).

Palladium/mesoporous silica/ammonium formate
Amines from N-nitrosamines
$\geq$NNO → $\geq$NH ←
Also prim. ar. amines from ar. azo or hydrazo compds. s. *53*, 9s68

Carbon ↑   HN ↓↑ C

Lithium/naphthalene
N-Detritylation under mild, non-acidic conditions
$Li/C_{10}H_8$
$NCPh_3$ → NH

14. $(C_8H_{17})_2NCPh_3$ ⟶ $(C_8H_{17})_2NH$

A soln. of di-*n*-octyltritylamine in THF added dropwise under argon to a green suspension of 20 eqs. Li powder and 0.2 eq. naphthalene in the same solvent at 0°, the mixture stirred for 4 h, treated carefully with water, and stirred at 0° to room temp. → product. Y 86%. Reaction is generally applicable to aliphatic and aromatic sec. and tert. tritylamines. However, for sec. tritylamines, deprotection was effected via *in situ*-silylation ($Me_3SiCl/BuLi$). Likewise, substrates containing alcohol groups required prior treatment with BuLi to remove the acidic hydrogen. N-Allyl, N-benzyl, alkoxy and other amino groups remained unaffected. F.e. and **selective O-detritylation** in the presence of N-tritylamines, s. C. Behloul, D. Guijarro, M. Yus, Synthesis *2004*, 1274-80.

Sodium hydroxide
Protection of amino groups as carbo-2-sulfonylethoxyamines
Removal of the protective group
NaOH
NCOOR → NH
protection as carbo-2-(methanesulfonyl)ethoxyamines cf. *29*, 19s*31*; as fluorous carbo-2-sulfonylethoxyamines, and use in purification of peptides, s. P.C. de Visser, H.S. Overkleeft et al., Tetrahedron Lett. *44*, 9013-6 (2003).

tert-Butyllithium
N-De-2-arylallylation s. *68*, 3
t-BuLi
←

Sodium/liq. ammonia/tert-butanol
N-Debenzylation
$Na/NH_3/t$-BuOH
NBn → NH
s. *5*, 32; of N-benzyl-pyrroles and -indoles with added *t*-BuOH, selectivity, s. T.S. Rao, P.S. Pandey, Synth. Commun. *34*, 3121-7 (2004).

Cesium carbonate
N-Detrichloroacetylation
Cs_2CO_3
$NCOCCl_3$ → NH

15. [structure: NHCOCCl$_3$ compound] → [NH$_2$ compound] $\xrightarrow{Ac_2O}$ [NHAc compound]

A mixture of the startg. trichloroacetamide and 2.5 eqs. Cs_2CO_3 in DMSO stirred at 100° for 40 min, cooled to room temp., and poured into satd. aq. $NaHCO_3$ → product (isolated as the N-acetyl deriv.). Y 82%. The method was tolerant of ether, silyl ether, acetal and benzoate groups, but acetate groups were hydrolyzed. F.e., also one-pot conversion to **carbo-*tert*-butoxyamines and carbobenzoxyamines** on subsequent treatment with Boc_2O and CbzCl, respectively, s. D. Urabe, M. Isobe et al., Tetrahedron Lett. *45*, 9405-7 (2004).

Zinc/N-methylimidazole
N-Decarbo-2,2,2-trichloroethoxylation s. *27*, 24s68
←
$NCOOCH_2CCl_3$ → NH

Zeolites
Heterogeneous N-decarbo-*tert*-butoxylation
←
NCOOBu-*t* → NH
with HY-zeolite cf. *66*, 16; with H-β-zeolite, selectivity, s. V.H. Tillu, R.K. Pandey, P. Kumar et al., Indian J. Chem. *43B*, 1004-7 (2004).

Boron chloride BCl_3
Protection of α-aminocarboxylic acids as 5-oxazolidones
Removal of the protective groups
with KOSiMe$_3$ cf. *19*, 471s*66*; cleavage of N-carbobenzoxy-5-oxazolidones with BCl$_3$, **also N-decarbobenzoxylation** of Z-protected α-aminocarboxylic acids, s. P. Allevi, R. Cribiu, M. Anastasia, Tetrahedron Lett. *45*, 5841-3 (2004).

Diisopropyl azodicarboxylate $ROOCN{=}NCOOR$
Selective N-debenzylation NBn → NH
in toluene cf. *59*, 20; improved procedure in THF with retention of azido, OBn and NTs groups s. J. Kroutil, T. Trnka, M. Cerný, Synthesis *2004*, 446-50.

Tyrosinase ←
Protection of *prim*-amino groups as N-(3,4-dihydroxyphenethyl)ureas NHCONHR → NH$_2$
Enzymatic removal of the protective group

16.

A soln. of the startg. protected amine in 1:5 acetonitrile/phosphate buffer sonicated for 20 min at room temp. to effect dissolution, mushroom tyrosinase (0.05 eq. by mass) in phosphate buffer added, and oxygen bubbled through the mixture until reaction complete (tlc monitoring) → product. Y 91%. The novel, enzyme-labile protective group is stable to conditions that are often used to remove other widely used alcohol and amine protective groups. F.e., incl. protection of aliphatic amines, ar. amines and α-aminocarboxylic acid methyl esters, also protection procedure, s. H.M.I. Osborn, N.A.O. Williams, Org. Lett. *6*, 3111-3 (2004).

Triphenyl phosphite/chlorine/pyridine/alcohols ←
N-Deacylation under mild conditions at low temperature NAc → NH

17.

Chlorine gas bubbled into a soln. of 1.1 eqs. triphenyl phosphite in anhydrous methylene chloride at -30° under argon, the bright yellow colour discharged by addition of a few drops of triphenyl phosphite, the startg. *N-monosubst.* amide in the same solvent added, followed by 1.15 eqs. anhydrous pyridine, stirred at the same temp. for 2 h, the cooling bath removed, 6.5 eqs. anhydrous methanol added, stirred for an additional 5 h, the solvent replaced by 1:1 methanol/water, and stirring continued for 12 h → product. Y 90%. *in situ*-Generated triphenoxyphosphine dichloride is the effective cleaving agent, which leaves chiral centres unaffected and tolerates such functional groups as esters, N,N-disubst. amides and the β-lactam ring. A wide variety of N-acyl groups can be removed under these conditions, liberating aliphatic and aromatic amines (as well as amino acids), reaction proceeding by initial formation of the corresponding iminochloride prior to conversion of intermediate iminoesters and hydrolysis. F.e. and comparison of alcohols, also cleavage of urethans, s. A. Spaggiari, L.C. Blaszczak, F. Prati, Org. Lett. *6*, 3885-8 (2004).

Sodium hydrogen sulfate/silica $NaHSO_4/SiO_2$
N-Detritylation s. *65*, 6s*68* NCPh$_3$ → NH

Chromium(III) acetate hydroxide/periodic acid $Cr_3(OAc)_7(OH)_2/H_5IO_6$
Oxidative N-dealkylation of sulfonic acid N-alkyl- and N,N-dialkyl-amides NR → NH

18.

5 Mol% chromium(III) acetate hydroxide added to a mixture of the startg. sulfonic acid N-alkylamide and 6 eqs. periodic acid in acetonitrile, and stirred at room temp. for 7 h → product.

Y 96%. A range of N-*prim*- and N-*sec*-alkyl groups can be removed by this procedure, but N-demethylation required a longer reaction time and higher catalyst loadings, while attempted N-de-*tert*-butylation failed. Undesirable formation of N-acylsulfonamides from N-*prim*-alkyl derivs. by N-α-oxidation is controlled by decreasing the chromium loading and increasing the periodic acid concentration. Reaction is presumed to involve hydrolysis of an intermediate carbinolamide, generated by oxidation with a chromium oxo or peroxo species. F.e. and di-N-dealkylation, also comparison of oxidants, and consideration of **N-propyl as protective group**, s. L. Xu, S. Zhang, M.L. Trudell, Synlett *2004*, 1901-4.

Chlorine s. under (PhO)$_3$P $\qquad Cl_2$

Iodine $\qquad I_2$
Removal of N-protective groups under mild conditions $\qquad \leftarrow$
preferential N-de-9-phenylfluoren-9-ylation cf. *51*, 18s*57*; selective N-decarbo-*tert*-butoxylation of protected 1,2,5-thiadiazolidine 1,1-dioxides by fusion with 0.4 eq. iodine under vacuum s. K. Nadia, N.E. Aouf et al., J. Heterocycl. Chem. *41*, 57-60 (2004).

Periodic acid s. under Cr$_3$(OAc)$_7$(OH)$_2$ $\qquad H_5IO_6$

Nickel/sulfuric acid $\qquad Ni/H_2SO_4$
N-Debenzylation s. *68*, 10 $\qquad NBn \rightarrow NH$

Palladium-carbon $\qquad Pd\text{-}C$
N-Debenzylation
s. *12*, 510; *13*, 103; trifluoromethyl-directed cleavage of diastereomerically pure bis(α-methylbenzyl)amines s. M. Kanai, A. Ishii et al., Org. Lett. *5*, 1007-10 (2003).

Via intermediates $\qquad v.i.$
N-Dephenylation via Birch reduction $\qquad NPh \rightarrow NH$
of N-phenylpiperidines s. *13*, 80s*68*

Elimination $\qquad \Uparrow$

Oxygen ↑ $\qquad$ HN ⇑ O

Stannous chloride $\qquad SnCl_2$
Amidines from amidoximes $\qquad C(NH_2)\!\!=\!\!NOH \rightarrow C(NH_2)\!\!=\!\!NH$
with Pd-C/HCOONH$_4$ cf. *18*, 48s*67*; dehydroxylation of polymer-based amidoximes with SnCl$_2$ s. J. Cesar, K. Nadrah, M.S. Dolenc, Tetrahedron Lett. *45*, 7445-9 (2004).

Formation of H-S Bond

Exchange $\qquad \Updownarrow$

Sulfur ↑ $\qquad$ HS ⇅ S

Samarium diiodide/sodium salt $\qquad SmI_2/Na^+$
Mercaptans from thiolsulfuric acid S-monoesters s. *28*, 28s*68* $\qquad SSO_3Na \rightarrow SH$

Carbon ↑ $\qquad$ HS ⇅ C

Samarium diiodide $\qquad SmI_2$
Mercaptans from thiocyanates $\qquad SCN \rightarrow SH$
with Zn/HCl cf. *28*, 28; cleavage of alkyl thiocyanates with SmI$_2$/*water* in THF, also from thiolsulfuric acid S-monoester sodium salts, s. Z.-P. Zhan et al., Synth. Commun. *34*, 3203-8 (2004).

Formation of H-C Bond

Uptake ⇓

Addition to Oxygen and Carbon   HC ⇓ OC

Microwaves s. under 4-Dimethylaminopyridine	[\\\\]
Sodium formate s. under Ruthenium complexes	HCOONa
Potassium formate s. under Pd-C	HCOOK
4-Dimethylaminopyridine/alumina/microwaves	$DMAP/Al_2O_3/$[\\\\]
Prim. alcohols from aldehydes	CHO → CH_2OH
Selective reduction under microwave irradiation	

19.   p-$NO_2C_6H_4$CHO   ⟶   p-$NO_2C_6H_4CH_2OH$

A soln. of *p*-nitrobenzaldehyde and 10 mol% DMAP in methanol adsorbed over pre-activated basic or neutral alumina in a Petri dish, the latter placed in a domestic microwave oven (KENSTAR, 1000 W capacity), and irradiated at 300 W for 10 min (2 x 5 min) → product. Y 95%. Water does not hamper the reaction, but attempted reduction of substrates bearing phenolic hydroxyl or carboxyl groups failed. F.e. and with Et_3N as base s. P.K. Pradhan, V.S. Giri et al., Synth. Commun. *34*, 2863-72 (2004).

Cupric acetate/(S)-2,2'-bis(diphenylphosphino)-1,1'-binaphthyl/diphenylsilane   ←
Copper-catalyzed asym. hydrosilylation of ketones   CO → CHOH
with CuCl/chiral 2,2'-bis(diarylphosphino)-1,1'-binaphthyls/polymethylhydrosiloxane/NaOBu-*t* cf. *62*, 18s*64*; details s. B.H. Lipshutz et al., J. Am. Chem. Soc. *125*, 8779-89 (2003); with air- and moisture-stable $Cu(OAc)_2·H_2O/$(S)-BINAP/Ph_2SiH_2 for asym. hydrosilylation of ar. ketones s. D. Lee, J. Yun, Tetrahedron Lett. *45*, 5415-7 (2004).

Cupric triflate/borane-tetrahydrofuran or ethyldimethylsilane $Cu(OTf)_2/BH_3$-THF or Me_2EtSiH
Lewis acid-catalyzed ring opening of carbohydrate O^4,O^6-benzylidene derivs.   ⊂
Effect of reductant on regioselectivity

20.

The startg. protected carbohydrate treated with BH_3-THF in the absence of solvent in the presence of 5 mol% $Cu(OTf)_2$ for 4.5 h → O^4-benzyl deriv. Y 87%. With 2 eqs. ethyldimethylsilane and 1 mol% $Cu(OTf)_2$ in acetonitrile the regioisomeric O^6-benzyl deriv. was obtained (Y 71%). Reaction is thought to take place by initial coordination of $Cu(OTf)_2$ with the oxygen at O^6, followed by ring opening to give an O^4-benzyl cation; the latter is readily reduced with BH_3-THF but not with the more bulky silane. Rather, isomerization to the O^6-benzyl cation takes place in the presence of the latter reductant prior to its reduction. Conditions are mild and various protective groups are tolerated. F.e. and comparison of reductants, solvents and concentrations s. C.-R. Shie, C. Hung et al., Angew. Chem. Int. Ed. Engl. *44*, 1665-8 (2005).

Zinc iodide s. under $NaBH_3CN$	ZnI_2
Borane-tetrahydrofuran (s.a. under $Cu(OTf)_2$)	BH_3-THF
1-δ-Hydroxytetrahydroquinolines	
from 1-(tetrahydrofuran-2-yl)-3,4-dihydrocarbostyrils s. *68*, 43	

Borane-tetrahydrofuran/chiral 2-aminoalcohols or α-aminocarboxylic acids   ←
Asym. reduction of ketones   CO → CHOH
s. *33*, 43s*67*; prediction of enantioselectivity based on catalyst structure s. M. Hoogenraad, E.W.P. Damen et al., Tetrahedron:Asym. *15*, 519-23 (2004); with chiral N-squaryl-α-amino-

carboxylic acids as ligand cf. J. Zhang, R.-G. Xie et al., Chinese J. Chem. *22*, 585-9 (2004); chiral 1,4-diols from γ-diketones and conversion to chiral pyrrolidines s. M. Periasamy et al., Synthesis *2003*, 2507-10.

Sodium tetrahydridoborate   *NaBH₄*
Alcohols from oxo compds   CO → CHOH
Ultrasound-promoted reduction under mild, aprotic conditions

21.   PhCHO ⎯⎯⎯→ PhCH₂OH

Reduction of oxo compds. with NaBH₄ can now be conducted in aprotic media as opposed to the customary protic (notably alcoholic) media. E: 1 eq. NaBH₄ added to a soln. of benzaldehyde *in THF*, and stirred *at room temp.* under ultrasonication for 17 min → benzyl alcohol. Y 97%. Reaction is applicable to both aliphatic and aromatic oxo compds., but reduction of ketones required 2-3 eqs. of NaBH₄ and longer reaction times. F.e. and **selective reduction** of aldehydes in the presence of ketones s. B. Zeynizadeh, S. Yahyaei, Z. Naturforsch. B: Anorg. Chem. Org. Chem. *59*, 704-10 (2004).

Hydroxy- from keto-phosphonic acid esters
α-hydroxyphosphonic acid esters cf. *23*, 85; N-protected *syn-* and *anti-*γ-amino-β-hydroxyphosphonic acid esters with asym. induction, effect of N-protective group on diastereoselectivity, s. M. Ordonez, O. Garcia-Barradas et al., Tetrahedron:Asym. *15*, 3035-43 (2004).

Sodium tetrahydridoborate/alumina s. under Lipase   *NaBH₄/Al₂O₃*

Sodium tetrahydridoborate/1-n-butyl-3-methylimidazolium fluoroborate   *NaBH₄/[bmim]BF₄*
Alcohols from oxo compds. in ionic liquids
in 1-*n*-butyl-3-methylimidazolium hexafluorophosphate cf. *62*, 20; improved procedure in 1-*n*-butyl-3-methylimidazolium fluoroborate s. D.Q. Xu et al., Chinese Chem. Lett. *15*, 643-5 (2004).

Sodium tetrahydridoborate/Dowex
Diols from lactones   ←C
with Na[AlH₂(OCH₂CH₂OMe)₂] cf. *30*, 17; 6-thioglycitols from 6-thioaldonolactones with retention of configuration with NaBH₄/Dowex 50X8-100 s. L. Chaveriat, D. Beaupere et al., Carbohydr. Res. *339*, 1817-21 (2004).

Polymer-based tetrahydridoborate
Alcohols from oxo compds.   CO → CHOH
Heterogeneous reduction
with anion exchanger-supported tetrahydridoborate cf. *40*, 19; with high-loading, low-swelling *Ultraresin*-based tetrahydridoborate, also oxidations with Ultraresin-based periodate, s. M. Barth, S.T.A. Shah, J. Rademann, Tetrahedron *60*, 8703-9 (2004).

Sodium trihydridocyanoborate/zinc iodide   *NaBH₃CN/ZnI₂*
Alcohols from epoxides   ⟶ CHC(OH)
regiospecific ring opening with added BF₃ cf. *11*, 59s*37*; 2-arylalcohols from styrene oxides with added ZnI₂ s. L.M. Finkielsztein, G.Y.M. Iglesias et al., Synth. Commun. *34*, 895-901 (2004).

Borane-triethylamine/lithium perchlorate etherate   *BH₃-Et₃N/LiClO₄-Et₂O*
Alcohols from epoxides
regiospecific ring opening with borane-morpholine/BF₃ cf. *10*, 50s*40*; sec. alcohols from terminal epoxides with BH₃-Et₃N/LiClO₄-Et₂O s. A. Heydari et al., Synthesis *2004*, 1563-5.

B-Cyclohexyloxydiisopinocampheylborane   *ROBR'₂*
Prim. alcohols from aldehydes   CHO → CH₂OH

22.   C₅H₁₁CHO [+ C₅H₁₁COMe] ⎯⎯⎯⎯→ C₅H₁₁CH₂OH [+ C₅H₁₁COMe]

Selective reduction with retention of ketones. 1.2 eqs. 1 *M* B-cyclohexyloxydiisopinocampheylborane in THF added with vigorous stirring to a 2 *M* soln. of 1 eq. hexanal and 1 eq. 2-heptanone in the same solvent at 25°, stirring continued for 24 h, the mixture hydrolyzed with 2 N NaOH, the resulting organoborane oxidized with 30% H_2O_2 for 2 h at room temp. with stirring, and the mixture worked up → 1-hexanol (Y 100%) and recovered 2-heptanone (Y 100%). Reaction is applicable to aliphatic, aromatic and α,β-ethylenic aldehydes, ketones being completely inert, as also were carboxylic acid chlorides, esters, epoxides, and nitriles. F.e.s. J.S. Cha et al., Bull. Korean Chem. Soc. 25, 603-4 (2004).

Phenylboron dichloride s. under Et_3SiH $PhBCl_2$
Ethylaluminum dichloride s. under Et_3SiH $EtAlCl_2$

Samarium/iodine/isopropanol $Sm/I_2/i\text{-}PrOH$
Alcohols from oxo compds.   CO → CHOH
reduction of ketones with SmI_2/TMEDA or MeOH cf. 53, 22s64; Meerwein-Ponndorf-Verley-type reduction of oxo compds. with SmI_2 (4-6 mol%) in *i*-PrOH s. S. Fukuzawa, N. Nakano, T. Saitoh, Eur. J. Org. Chem. 2004, 2863-7.

($η^8$-Cyclooctatetraene)(tetrahydrofuran)samarium(I) iodide/(-)-(R,R,R,R)-   ←
N,N,N′,N′-tetrakis(2-hydroxy-2-phenylethyl)-1,3-xylylenediamine/isopropanol
Asym. samarium-mediated Meerwein-Ponndorf-Verley-type reduction of aryl ketones
with a chiral samarium(III) aminodiolate cf. 49, 41; with ($η^8$-cyclooctatetraene)(tetrahydrofuran)-samarium(I) iodide/(-)-(R,R,R,R)-N,N,N′,N′-tetrakis(2-hydroxy-2-phenylethyl)-1,3-xylylene-diamine/*i*-PrOH s. K. Ohno, Y. Kataoka, K. Mashima, Org. Lett. 6, 4695-7 (2004).

Imidazolium ionic liquids s. under $NaBH_4$ and Ru complexes   ←

Lipase/sodium tetrahydridoborate/alumina   ←
Sec. alcohols from ketones
with subsequent kinetic resolution by asym. enzymatic O-acylation
s. 66, 128s67; chiral 2-azidoalcohols s. A. Kamal et al., Tetrahedron:Asym. 15, 935-9 (2004).

Dowex s. under $NaBH_4$ ←
Diphenylsilane s. under $Cu(OAc)_2$ Ph_2SiH_2

Triethylsilane/phenylboron dichloride or ethylaluminum dichloride $Et_3SiH/PhBCl_2$ or $EtAlCl_2$
Regiospecific ring opening of carbohydrate O,O-alkylidene derivs.   C
of O,O-benzylidene derivs. with Et_3SiH/CH_3COOH cf. 39, 33s52; with $Et_3SiH/EtAlCl_2$ s. V. Balakumar, A. Aravind, S. Baskaran, Synthesis 2004, 647-50; of O,O-*p*-methoxybenzylidene derivs. with $Et_3SiH/PhBCl_2$ s. A. Dilhas, D. Bonnaffé, Tetrahedron Lett. 45, 3643-5 (2004).

Triethylsilane/titanium tetrachloride $Et_3SiH/TiCl_4$
α-Alkoxycarboxylic acids from 1,3-dioxolan-4-ones   C
with *t*-BuMgCl cf. 11, 51; chiral products, also with $Et_3SiH/TiCl_4$, notably for substrates with branched alkyl groups, s. L.L. Winneroski, Y. Xu, J. Org. Chem. 69, 4948-53 (2004).

Ethyldimethylsilane s. under $Cu(OTf)_2$ Me_2EtSiH
Triethoxysilane s. under Titanium(IV) complexes $(EtO)_3SiH$

Chiral titanium(IV) bis($Δ^2$-oxazoline) complexes/triethoxysilane   ←
Asym. hydrosilylation of ketones   CO → CHOH
with (R,R)-ethylene-1,2-bis($η^5$-4,5,6,7-tetrahydro-1-indenyl)titanocene difluoride/$PhSiH_3$/polymethylhydrosiloxane cf. 50, 15s57; asym. hydrosilylation of aryl ketones with chiral titanium(IV) bis($Δ^2$-oxazoline) complexes/$(EtO)_3SiH$ s. M. Bandini, A. Bottoni, P.G. Cozzi et al., Eur. J. Org. Chem. 2003, 2972-84.

Titanocene dichloride/manganese/2,4,6-collidine/1-isopropyl-4-methyl-1,4-cyclohexadiene   ←
Alcohols from epoxides   ▽ → CHC(OH)
regiospecific ring opening with Cp_2TiCl/1,4-cyclohexadiene cf. 46, 40; with Cp_2TiCl_2/Mn/2,4,6-collidine/1-isopropyl-4-methyl-1,4-cyclohexadiene s. A. Gansauer, A. Barchuk, D. Fielenbach, Synthesis 2004, 2567-73.

Titanium tetrachloride s. under Et_3SiH $TiCl_4$
Lithium perchlorate s. under $BH_3\text{-}Et_3N$ $LiClO_4$

Manganese s. under Cp_2TiCl_2   Mn

Chiral ruthenium(II) 2,2'-bis(diphenylphosphino)biphenyl complexes ←
Asym. homogeneous hydrogenation of ketones   CO → CHOH
with SYNPHOS as ligand s. *55*, 26s*65*; details s. Eur. J. Org. Chem. *2003*, 1931-41; asym. homogeneous hydrogenation of α-amino-β-ketocarboxylic acid esters s. C. Mordant, J.-P. Genêt et al., ibid. *2004*, 3017-26.

($η^6$-Benzene)dichlororuthenium(II) dimer/chiral β-cyclodextrin-anchored 2-amino- ←
alcohols/sodium formate
Asym. transfer-hydrogenation of ketones in aq. medium
with chiral, supramolecular, water-soluble ruthenium(II) complexes

23.

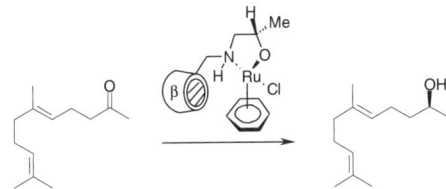

5 Mol% [RuCl$_2$(C$_6$H$_6$)]$_2$ added to a soln. of 10 mol% mono[6-deoxy-6-((S)-2-hydroxypropyl-amino)]-β-cyclodextrin in 3:1 water/DMF, stirred at room temp. for 1 h, treated with 10 eqs. HCOONa, stirring continued for 10 min, 1 eq. startg. ketone injected into the mixture, stirred at the same temp. for 24 h, and extracted with hexane → product. Y 80% (e.e. 95%). Enantioselectivities up to 97% were achieved for the reduction of aromatic, aliphatic and unconjugated ethylenic ketones, the β-cyclodextrin residue enhancing face-selectivity by preorganization of the substrates in the hydrophobic cavity. With chiral 2-aminoalcohols lacking the β-cyclodextrin residue enantioselectivity was significantly lower (ca. 50%). F.e. incl. asym. reduction of α-keto-esters, **also chiral α-deuteriobenzylalcohols** from aryl ketones with DCOONa, s. A. Schlatter, M.K. Kundu, W.-D. Woggon, Angew. Chem. Int. Ed. Engl. *43*, 6731-4 (2004).

Dichloro(p-cymene)ruthenium(II) dimer/chiral N-sulfonyl-1,2-diamines or the polyethylene ←
glycol-based or polymer-based variants/sodium formate
Asym. transfer-hydrogenation of aryl ketones in water

24.

0.5 Mol% [RuCl$_2$(*p*-cymene)]$_2$ and 0.012 eq. (R,R)-N-(*p*-tosyl)-1,2-diphenylethylenediamine in water degassed three times, stirred at 40° for 1 h, 5 eqs. HCOONa and the startg. ketone added, the mixture degassed a further three times with N$_2$, and stirred at the same temp. for another 2 h → (R)-alcohol. Conversion 99% (e.e. 95%). The protocol is environmentally friendly, affording a more rapid conversion with high productivity and only a small decrease in enantioselectivity relative to the established procedure with HCOOH-Et$_3$N azeotrope in methylene chloride (cf. *51*, 26s*68*). F.es. X. Wu, J. Xiao et al., Org. Biomol. Chem. *2*, 1818-21 (2004); with PEG-based (R,R)-N-(*p*-tosyl)-1,2-diphenylethylenediamine for a more efficient recycling of the catalyst (e.e. 85-94%) cf. X. Li, J. Xiao et al., Org. Lett. *6*, 3321-4 (2004); with the polymer-based ligand in the presence of Bu$_4$NBr (e.e. 90-99%) cf. P.N. Liu, S.H. Wang et al., Chem. Commun. *2004*, 2070-1.

Dichloro(p-cymene)ruthenium(II) dimer/chiral N-sulfonyl-1,2-diamines or polymer-based ←
variants/isopropanol/potassium hydroxide or formic acid/triethylamine
Asym. transfer-hydrogenation of ketones
update s. *51*, 26s*67*; of 2-tetralols s. M. Mogi, K. Fuji, M. Node, Tetrahedron:Asym. *15*, 3715-7 (2004); of α-ketocarboxylic acid esters and trifluoromethyl ketones s. D. Sterk, M.S. Stephan,

B. Mohar, Tetrahedron Lett. *45*, 535-7 (2004); of simple aryl ketones with a polymer-based N-sulfonyl-1,2-diamine as ligand s. X. Li, J. Xiao et al., Tetrahedron Lett. *45*, 951-3 (2004).

Dichloro[2,2'-bis(di-p-tolylphosphino)-1,1'-binaphthyl]((1R,2R)-1,2-diphenyl- ←
ethylenediamine)ruthenium(II)/potassium tert-*butoxide*
Dichloro[(R)-4,4'-bis(trimethylsilyl)-2,2'-bis(diphenylphosphino)-1,1'-binaphthyl]- ←
((R)-1,1-dianisyl-2-isopropyl-1,2-ethylenediamine)ruthenium(II)/potassium tert-*butoxide*

Asym. homogeneous hydrogenation of ketones   CO → CHOH

of aryl ketones with chiral 4,4'-disubst. 2,2'-bis(diphenylphosphino)-1,1'-binaphthyl as ligand s. *67*, 22; with dichloro[(R)-4,4'-bis(trimethylsilyl)-2,2'-bis(diphenylphosphino)-1,1'-binaphthyl]-((R)-1,1-dianisyl-2-isopropyl-1,2-ethylenediamine)ruthenium(II) s. A.G. Hu, H.L. Ngo, W.B. Lin, Org. Lett. *6*, 2937-40 (2004); asym. homogeneous hydrogenation of cyclic (incl. N-heterocyclic) ketones **with dynamic kinetic resolution** (cf. *51*, 26s*63*) with dichloro[2,2'-bis(di-*p*-tolylphosphino)-1,1'-binaphthyl]((1R,2R)-1,2-diphenylethylenediamine)ruthenium(II) s. T. Ohkuma, J. Li, R. Noyori, Synlett *2004*, 1383-6.

Chiral dichloro[2,2'-bis(diarylphosphino)-1,1'-dicyclopentane]ruthenium(II) ←
*complexes/2-*tert*-butylthioethylamine/sodium* tert*-butoxide*

Asym. homogeneous hydrogenation of aryl ketones in alcoholic media

25.

2 Mol% 2-*tert*-butylthioethylamine (0.1 M in butanol) and 0.2 mol% dichloro[1S,1'S,2S,2'S)-2,2'-bis[bis(4-methoxy-3,5-dimethylphenyl)phosphino]dicyclopentane](dimethylformamide)-ruthenium(II) (0.007 M in butanol) added under argon to a soln. of 1 eq. startg. aryl ketone in butanol, treated with 4 mol% *t*-BuONa (0.1 M in butanol), then hydrogenated under 7 atm. H_2 at room temp. for 15 h → product. Conversion >99% (e.e. 93%). The method, applicable to a wide range of substituted aryl or heteroaryl ketones, employs a new and low-cost catalyst system based on a readily accessible chiral ligand and an achiral 2-aminothioether or 1,2-diamine as co-ligand. Astonishingly, **reversal of face-selectivity** can be simply achieved on changing the solvent from methanol to ethanol!! F.e.s. D.G. Genov, D.J. Ager, Angew. Chem. Int. Ed. Engl. *43*, 2816-9 (2004).

*Chiral bis[4-aryl-4,5-dihydro-3*H*-dinaphtho[2,1-c;1',2'-e]phosphepine]-* ←
dibromoruthenium(II)

Asym. homogeneous hydrogenation of β-ketocarboxylic acid esters
with chiral, thermally stable, monodentate, cyclic phosphines as ligand

26.

A mixture of dibromobis[4-(4-methoxyphenyl)-4,5-dihydro-3*H*-dinaphtho[2,1-*c*;1',2'-*e*]phosphepine]ruthenium(II) (prepared *in situ* from 1 mol% [Ru(cod)(methallyl)$_2$] and 2 mol% chiral ligand) and the startg. keto ester in ethanol stirred in a Parr stainless-steel autoclave under H_2 (60 bar) *at 100°* for 8 h → product. Y 99% (e.e. 95%). Such chiral, monodentate, cyclic phosphines, apart from displaying a remarkable water- and temperature-tolerance, afford higher enantioselectivities than the corresponding cyclic phosphites, phosphoramidites and phosphinates as ligand. An interesting **deuterium isotope effect** on selectivity was also recorded. F.e. and comparison of ligands s. K. Junge, M. Beller et al., Angew. Chem. Int. Ed. Engl. *43*, 5066-9 (2004).

Chiral dibromo[diamino-2,2'-bis(diphenylphosphino)-1,1'-binaphthyl]- ←
ruthenium(II) bis(hydrobromides)
Asym. hydrogenation of β-ketocarboxylic acid esters in water CO → CHOH
s. *61*, 30; f. complexes, also homogeneous conversion in methanol or ethanol, s. M. Berthod, M. Lemaire et al., Tetrahedron:Asym. *15*, 639-45 (2004).

Dichloro[(R)-2,2'-bis(diphenylphosphino)-1,1'-binaphthyl-4,4'-diphosphonic acid]- ←
ruthenium(II)/1-n-butyl-3-methylimidazolium fluoroborate
**Asym. homogeneous hydrogenation of β-ketocarboxylic acid esters
in ionic liquid-methanol**
s. *66*, 28; chiral β-aryl-β-hydroxycarboxylic acid esters (e.e. 97-99%), comparison of ligands, s. A.G. Hu, H.L. Ngo, W.B. Lin, Angew. Chem. Int. Ed. Engl. *43*, 2501-4 (2004).

Mesoporous silica-supported dibromo[2,2'-bis(diphenylphosphino)-1,1'- ←
binaphthyl]ruthenium(II) complexes
Heterogeneous asym. hydrogenation of ketones
with a polymer-based complex cf. *61*, 29s65, 67; with a readily recyclable mesoporous silica-supported dibromo[2,2'-bis(diphenylphosphino)-1,1'-binaphthyl]ruthenium(II) complex for the asym. hydrogenation of β-alkyl- and β-aryl-subst. β-keto-esters s. B. Kesanli, W. Lin, Chem. Commun. *2004*, 2284-5.

Chiral rhodium(III) 2-aminoalcohol complexes/isopropanol/potassium tert-*butoxide* ←
Asym. transfer-hydrogenation of ketones
with [Cp*RhCl$_2$]$_2$/chiral N-sulfonyl-1,2-diamines/HCOOH/Et$_3$N cf. *46*, 42s63; with chiral rhodium(III) 2-aminoalcohol complexes tethered to an η^5-aryltetramethylcyclopentadienyl residue (with *i*-PrOH/KOBu-*t*) s. D.J. Cross, M. Wills et al., Tetrahedron Lett. *45*, 843-6 (2004).

Palladium-carbon/potassium formate Pd-C/HCOOK
Transfer-hydrogenation of oxo compds.
of α-ketocarboxylic acid esters with Pd-C/Na-hypophosphite/K$_2$CO$_3$ cf. *17*, 65s42; of aldehydes with Pd-C/HCOOK s. M. Baidossi, Y. Sasson et al., Synth. Commun. *34*, 643-50 (2004).

Iridium nanoparticles Ir
Alcohols from oxo compds.
Heterogeneous hydrogenation under mild conditions

27.
$$\underset{Et}{\overset{O}{\|}}{Et} \longrightarrow \underset{Et}{\overset{OH}{|}}{Et}$$

in the absence of solvent. A stirred mixture of 3-pentanone and 0.4 mol% iridium nanoparticles (prepared by hydrogenation of a dispersion of [Ir(cod)Cl]$_2$ in 1-*n*-butyl-3-methylimidazolium hexafluorophosphate at 75° under 4 atm. H$_2$ for 10 min) hydrogenated under 4 atm. H$_2$ at 75° for 3.7 h → product. Conversion 100% (Y 85%). The process was demonstrated with aldehydes and cyclic or acyclic ketones. The nanoparticles can be readily recovered and reused; however, recycling is more efficient if hydrogenation of the substrates is conducted with the same nanoparticles redispersed **in ionic liquids** in a 2-phase system. F.e.s. G.S. Fonseca, J.D. Scholten, J. Dupont, Synlett *2004*, 1525-8.

Dichloro(1,5-cyclooctadiene)hydridoiridium(III) dimer/(1R,2R)-N,N'-bis[2-(diphenyl- ←
phosphino)benzyl]cyclohexane-1,2-diamine/potassium hydroxide/isopropanol
Asym. transfer-hydrogenation of ketones
of ar. ketones with [Ir(cod)Cl]$_2$/chiral diamines or β-aminosulfoxides cf. *46*, 42s66; also of α-arylketones with [HIr(cod)Cl$_2$]$_2$/(1R,2R)-N,N'-bis[2-(diphenylphosphino)benzyl]cyclohexane-1,2-diamine s. J. Chen, J. Gao et al., Tetrahedron Lett. *45*, 8415-8 (2004).

Platinum-alumina/cinchonidines ←
Asym. heterogeneous hydrogenation of functionalized ketones
s. *57*, 27s66; chiral β-trifluoromethyl-β-hydroxyketones from trifluoromethyl β-diketones s. R. Hess, A. Baiker et al., Tetrahedron:Asym. *15*, 251-7 (2004).

Addition to Nitrogen and Carbon HC ⇓ NC

Sodium tetrahydridoborate/boric acid $NaBH_4/H_3BO_3$
Sec. amines from azomethines C=NR → CHNHR
Solid-state reduction
with $NaBH_4$/silica gel cf. *18*, 467s*67*; reduction of aryl and α,β-unsatd. aldimines and ketimines with $NaBH_4/H_3BO_3$, selectivity, s. B.T. Cho, S.K. Kang, Synlett *2004*, 1484-8.

Chiral 1,3,2-oxazaborolidines/borane-tetrahydrofuran or catecholborane   ←
Sec. amines from azomethines by asym. reduction
of ketimines s. *46*, 45s*67*; effect of reducing agent (BH_3-THF cf. catecholborane) on face selectivity s. E.H.M. Kirton, R.A. Field et al., Tetrahedron Lett. *45*, 853-5 (2004).

Trifluoroacetic acid s. under Pd(OH)₂ CF_3COOH

Trichlorosilane/(S)-N-(3,5-xylyl)-2-(N-methylformamido)-3-methylbutyramide   ←
Sec. amines from azomethines via asym. hydrosilylation
with chiral N-formylpyrrolidines cf. *36*, 670s*61*; with (S)-N-(3,5-xylyl)-2-(N-methylformamido)-3-methylbutyramide as ligand (e.e. 87-92%) s. A.V. Malkov, P. Kocovsky et al., Org. Lett. *6*, 2253-6 (2004).

Palladous hydroxide/trifluoroacetic acid $Pd(OH)_2/CF_3COOH$
Amines from aziridines   ⟶ CHC(NH)
with Na/liq. NH_3 cf. *26*, *55*; chiral α-*prim*-aminocarboxylic from aziridine-2-carboxylic acid amides by hydrogenation with $Pd(OH)_2/CF_3COOH$, chiral arylalaninamides, s. N.E. Maguire, A.B. McLaren, J.B. Sweeney, Synlett *2003*, 1898-900.

Chiral cationic iridium(I) 3-(Δ²-oxazolin-2-yl)-2-diphenylphosphino-2-   ←
 azabicyclo[2.2.1]heptane complexes
Sec. amines from azomethines   C=NR → CHNHR
Asym. homogeneous hydrogenation
with chiral iridium(I) 2-(*o*-phosphinoaryl)-Δ²-oxazoline complexes cf. *46*, 47s*53*; with chiral cationic iridium(I) 3-(Δ²-oxazolin-2-yl)-2-diphenylphosphino-2-azabicyclo[2.2.1]heptane complexes (e.e. 66-90%) s. A. Trifonova, P.G. Andersson et al., Org. Lett. *6*, 3825-7 (2004).

Addition to Carbon-Carbon Bonds HC ⇓ CC

Lithium/liq. ammonia/ethanol $Li/NH_3/EtOH$
Birch reduction   ←
partial reduction of the benzene ring s. *13*, 80; of N-phenylpiperidines as part of a 2-step **N-dephenylation** s. N. Girard, L. Toupet et al., Synlett *2004*, 2005-9.

Cesium carbonate s. under Bis(norbornadiene)rhodium(I) hexafluoroantimonate Cs_2CO_3

1,4-Dihydropyridines/chiral 4-imidazolidonium salts   ←
Aldehydes from α,β-ethylenealdehydes   C=C → CHCH
Organocatalyzed asym. transfer-hydrogenation

28.

A soln. of 1 eq. startg. ethylenealdehyde in chloroform treated at -30° with 20 mol% (R)-2-*tert*-butyl-3-methyl-4-imidazolidonium trifluoroacetate and 1.2 eqs. Hantzsch ester, and the resulting suspension stirred at the same temp. for 16 h → product. Y 92% (e.e. 97%). This is the first example of an organocatalyzed asym. hydride reduction, inspired by enzymatic reduction involving co-factors such as NADH. Interestingly, (S)-products were formed irrespective of the geometry of the substrate. Furthermore, the procedure is compatible with functional groups which are ordinarily susceptible to reduction, such as aldehydes and halogen. F.e. incl. asym. reduction of hindered trisubst. enals s. S.G. Ouellet, J.B. Tuttle, D.W.C. MacMillan, J. Am. Chem. Soc. *127*, 32-3 (2005); with (2S,5S)-5-benzyl-2-*tert*-butyl-3-methyl-4-imidazolidonium trichloromethyl peroxide cf. J.W. Yang, B. List et al., Angew. Chem. Int. Ed. Engl. *44*, 108-10 (2005); **achiral procedure** with dibenzylammonium trifluoroacetate s. ibid. *43*, 6660-2 (2004).

Hydrido(triphenylphosphine)copper(I) hexamer/2,3:2′,3′-bis(methylenedioxy)- ←
*6,6′-bis[bis(3,5-di-*tert-*butyl-4-methoxyphenyl)phosphino]biphenyl/*
*polymethylhydrosiloxane/*tert-*butanol*
Carbonyl compds. from α,β-ethylenecarbonyl compds. $C{=}C \rightarrow CHCH$
Copper(I)-catalyzed asym. reduction
of α,β-ethyleneketones with CuCl/polymethylhydrosiloxane/NaOBu-*t* and a chiral ferrocenyl-di(phosphine) as ligand cf. *58*, 32s*66*; of β,β-disubst. α,β-ethylenecarboxylic acid esters and α,β-ethylenelactones with [(Ph$_3$P)CuH]$_6$/polymethylhydrosiloxane/*t*-BuOH and the same ligand or with 2,3:2′,3′-bis(methylenedioxy)-6,6′-bis[bis(3,5-di-*tert*-butyl-4-methoxyphenyl)phosphino]-biphenyl s. B.H. Lipshutz, J.M. Servesko, B.R. Taft, J. Am. Chem. Soc. *126*, 8352-3 (2004).

Cupric acetate/4,5-bis(diphenylphosphino)-9,9-dimethylxanthene/polymethylhydrosiloxane/ ←
tert-*butanol*
Nitriles from α,β-ethylenenitriles under mild conditions

29.

$Ph\diagup\!\!\diagdown\!CN \xrightarrow{\text{Ph}_2\text{P}\quad\text{PPh}_2\text{(Xantphos)}} Ph\diagup\!\!\diagdown\!CN$

4 eqs. Polymethylhydrosiloxane added to a soln. of 3 mol% Cu(OAc)$_2$·H$_2$O and 3 mol% Xantphos in toluene contained in a dry Schlenk tube under N$_2$, stirred for 20-30 min at room temp., (E)-cinnamonitrile added via syringe, followed by 4 eqs. *tert*-butanol, stirred for 1 h at room temp. until TLC or GC indicated completion of reaction, quenched with water, transferred to a flask, 2.5 M NaOH added, and stirred vigorously for 30 min → product. Y 92%. The addition of *tert*-butanol is critical for a rapid conversion. Reaction is presumed to involve initial generation of a copper(I) hydride species which attacks the nitrile in 1,4-fashion, followed by protonation with *tert*-butanol and regeneration of the catalyst with inexpensive polymethylhydrosiloxane. The method is applicable to both aliphatic and aromatic substrates with retention of MeO, Cl, F and cyano groups, but bis[*o*-(diphenylphosphino)phenyl] ether is more suitable as ligand for hindered compds. F.e. and comparison of di(phosphines) s. D. Kim, B.-M. Park, J. Yun, Chem. Commun. *2005*, 1755-7.

Cupric fluoride/(S)-1-[(R)-2-(diphenylphosphino)ferrocenyl]ethyl(dicyclohexyl)phosphine/ ←
*polymethylhydrosiloxane/phenylsilane/tetra-*n-*butylammonium fluoride*
2-Subst. aliphatic nitro compds. from 1,1-nitroethylene derivs.
Copper(I)-catalyzed asym. reduction
with CuOBu-*t*/(S)-2,2′-bis(di-*p*-tolylphosphino)-1,1′-binaphthyl/polymethylhydrosiloxane/PhSiH$_3$ cf. *66*, 34; with CuF$_2$/(R)-(S)-Josiphos/polymethylhydrosiloxane/PhSiH$_3$/Bu$_4$NF s. C. Czekelius, E.M. Carreira, Org. Lett. *6*, 4575-7 (2004).

Zinc/ammonium acetate Zn/NH_4OAc
Ketones from α,β-ethyleneketones
with Zn/AcOH cf. *8*, 87s*61*; dihydrochalcones with Zn/NH$_4$OAc in ethanol/water s. Y.-B. Zhou, Y.-L. Wang, J.-Y. Wang, J. Chem. Res. Synop *2004*, 118-9.

Magnesium bromide s. under Pd-C $MgBr_2$

Sodium tetrahydridoborate $NaBH_4$
trans-2-Ethylenealcohols from 2-acetylenealcohols   C≡C → CH=CH
with Red-Al s. *36*, 45s*41*; also with $NaBH_4$, *trans*-α,β-ethylene-γ-hydroxycarboxylic acid esters, s. C.T. Meta, K. Koide, Org. Lett. *6*, 1785-7 (2004).

Carbon monoxide/water/selenium $CO/H_2O/Se$
Carbonyl compds. from α,β-ethylenecarbonyl compds.   C=C → CHCH
with added dbu in THF cf. *45*, 22; in 20 eqs. DMF without base s. F. Tian, S. Lu, Synlett *2004*, 1953-6.

Ammonium formate s. under Pd $HCOONH_4$
Ammonium acetate s. under Zn NH_4OAc
Chiral 4-imidazolidonium trifluoroacetate or trichloromethyl peroxide s. under 1,4-Dihydropyridines   ←

Nicotiana tabacum *reductase*   ←
Ketones from α,β-ethyleneketones
Asym. reduction
with yeast reductase cf. *35*, 39s*56*; asym. reduction of α-alkyl- and β-alkyl-α,β-ethyleneketones with p44 and p90 reductases, respectively, from *Nicotiana tabacum* (cf. *47*, 34) s. K. Shimoda, N. Kubota, H. Hamada, Tetrahedron:Asym. *15*, 2443-69 (2004).

Phenylsilane s. under CuF_2 $PhSiH_3$
Diethoxymethylsilane s. under Rhodium(III) complexes $(EtO)_2MeSiH$
Polymethylhydrosiloxane s. under $[(Ph_3P)CuH]_6$, $Cu(OAc)_2$ and CuF_2   pmhs
Diethyl 4-(hydrazinosulfonyl)benzylphosphonate $p\text{-}(H_2NNHSO_2)C_6H_4CH_2PO(OEt)_2$
1,1-Diiodides from diiodomethylene compds. under mild conditions $C=CI_2 → CHCHI_2$

30.

A mixture of 1 eq. startg. *gem*-dihaloalkene (1 M) and 1 eq. diethyl 4-(hydrazinosulfonyl)benzylphosphonate **as diazene precursor** in *o*-xylene refluxed for 10 min, and treated at reflux temp. with another 3 eqs. of the hydrazide in three portions over 30 min → product. Y 87%. The polar phosphonate group of the diazene precursor facilitated removal of the by-products. A variety of appended functional groups remained unaffected (ethers, urethans, alcohols, sulfones, carboxylic acid esters, sulfonamides, nitriles, silyl ethers, ar. halides and nitro groups). However, alkene and alkyne derivs. were, predictably, not compatible with these conditions. F.e. and comparison of precursors s. J.-M. Cloarec, A.B. Charette, Org. Lett. *6*, 4731-4 (2004).

Selenium s. under CO   Se
Tetra-n-butylammonium fluoride s. under CuF_2 Bu_4NF

Bis(dinitrogen)[2,6-bis[1-(2,6-diisopropylphenylimino)ethyl]pyridine]iron(0)   ←
Iron(0)-catalyzed hydrogenation under mild conditions   C=C → CHCH

31.

Unusual, high-spin, d^8 square pyramidal iron(0) bis(nitrogen) complexes are useful alternatives to traditional, toxic precious metal complexes for the hydrogenation of a variety of olefins and acetylene derivs. at low catalyst loadings under mild conditions **in non-polar medium. E: Preferential hydrogenation of ethylene derivs.** A mixture of *0.3 mol%* bis(dinitrogen)[2,6-bis[1-(2,6-diisopropylphenylimino)ethyl]pyridine]iron(0) and (R)-limonene in anhydrous *toluene* hydrogenated under 4 atm. H_2 *at 22°* for 3.5 h → product. Conversion >98%. Preparative scale hydrogenation can also be conducted without solvent. F.e. incl. hydrogenation of terminal, internal and *gem*-disubst. olefins as well as internal alkynes, also hydrosilylation of ethylene derivs., s. S.C. Bart, E. Lobkovsky, P.J. Chirik, J. Am. Chem. Soc. *126*, 13794-807 (2004).

Carbonyl(dihydrido)tris(triphenylphosphine)ruthenium(II)/tri-n-butylphosphine ←
α-Subst. vinylstannanes from acetylenestannanes $C\equiv C(Sn\in) \rightarrow C(Sn\in)=CH_2$
Homogeneous hydrogenation with 1,2-stannyl group migration

32.

A soln. of 1 eq. startg. alkynylstannane, 5 mol% $RuH_2(CO)(PPh_3)_3$ and 30 mol% tri-*n*-butylphosphine in anhydrous DMSO degassed by three freeze-pump-thaw cycles, the resulting soln. frozen again, placed under a H_2 atmosphere, and hydrogenated with stirring at 80° for 12 h → product. Y 78%. Reaction is applicable to a range of aromatic and aliphatic acetylenestannanes, leaving hydroxyl, ester, amide and cyano groups unaffected. A ruthenium β-stannylvinylidene complex is invoked as a possible intermediate. F.e.s. E. Shirakawa et al., J. Am. Chem. Soc. *126*, 13614-5 (2004).

Chiral dichlororuthenium(II) di(phosphine) complexes ←
Asym. homogeneous hydrogenation $C=C \rightarrow CHCH$
s. *42*, 45s*64*; of α-aryloxy-α,β-ethylenecarboxylic acids with chiral $Cl_2Ru(BINAP)$ s. P.E. Maligres, S.W. Krska, G.R. Humphrey, Org. Lett. *6*, 3147-50 (2004).

Diacetato(aquo)[2,6-bis(4(S)-isopropyl-Δ²-oxazolin-2-yl)phenyl]rhodium(III)/ ←
  diethoxymethylsilane
Carboxylic from α,β-ethylenecarboxylic acid esters
via asym. hydrosilylation

33.

1.5 eqs. Diethoxymethylsilane added slowly to a soln. of 1 mol% diacetato(aquo)[2,6-bis(4(S)-isopropyl-Δ²-oxazolin-2-yl)phenyl]rhodium(III) and ethyl (E)-3-phenyl-2-butenoate in toluene at 60°, stirred at the same temp. for 1 h, and treated with 1 *N* HCl → (R)-product. Y 96% (e.e. 96%). The face-selectivity is determined by the geometry of the substrate, β-subst. (Z)-enoates affording (S)-esters. The active catalyst is thought to be a (hydrido)(silyl)rhodium(III) bis(Δ²-oxazoline) complex, which delivers hydride to the β-carbon with high enantioselectivity (e.e. 97-8%). F.e., incl. asym. reduction of α,β-ethylenelactones, also comparison of hydridosilanes, s. Y. Tsuchiya, H. Nishiyama et al., Synlett *2004*, 2493-6.

Chiral rhodium(I) di(phosphine) complexes ←
Asym. homogeneous hydrogenation
update s. *27*, 57s*67*; of α- and β-acylamino-α,β-ethylenecarboxylic acid esters with (S)-7,7'-bis[bis(3,5-dimethyl-4-methoxyphenyl)phosphino]-1,1'-spiroindane as ligand (e.e. 97-9%) s. Y. Fu, Q.-L. Zhou et al., J. Org. Chem. *69*, 8157-60 (2004).

Chiral rhodium(I) phosphine-cyclic phosphoramidite complexes
**Asym. homogeneous hydrogenation with
chiral phosphine-cyclic phosphoramidites as ligand**

$C{=}C \rightarrow CHCH$

34.

The asym. hydrogenation of enacylamines, dimethyl itaconate and methyl (Z)-acetamido-cinnamate can be effected **at low catalyst loadings** with 100% conversions and enantioselectivities over 99% by using *robust* rhodium(I) phosphine-cyclic phosphoramidite complexes possessing *both* planar-chiral ferrocenyl and axially-chiral binaphthyl residues. **E:** A mixture of 0.1 mol% [Rh(cod)$_2$]BF$_4$ and 0.11 mol% 4-[N-methyl-N-[1(S)-[2-(diphenylphosphino)ferrocenyl]ethyl]-amino]dinaphtho[2,1-*d*;1′,2′-*f*][1,3,2]dioxaphosphepin in degassed, anhydrous methylene chloride stirred at room temp. for 10 min, a soln. of 1 eq. substrate in the same solvent added, and hydrogenated at the same temp. under 10 atm. H$_2$ for 1 h → product. Y 97% (e.e. 99%). The ligands are easy to prepare and are extraordinarily stable in moist air over a long period of time (6 months). The abs. configuration of the product is determined largely by that of the binaphthyl residue, and high turnover numbers were recorded at loadings as low as 0.01 mol%. F.e.s. X.-P. Hu, Z. Zheng, Org. Lett. *6*, 3585-8 (2004).

Chiral rhodium(I) phosphine-phosphinite or -phosphite complexes
Asym. homogeneous hydrogenation
s. *60*, 36s*64*; of α-acylamino-α,β-ethylenecarboxylic acid esters with (S)-2-diphenylphosphino-2′-diphenylphosphinoxy-3′-phenyl-1,1′-binaphthyl or chiral binaphthyl-based phosphine-phosphites (cf. *60*, 36s*62*) (e.e. >99%) s. Y. Yan, Y. Chi, X. Zhang, Tetrahedron:Asym. *15*, 2173-5 (2004).

Chiral rhodium(I) cyclic phosphite or phosphoromonoamidite complexes
Asym. homogeneous hydrogenation with chiral monodentate P-ligands
s. *60*, 34s*67*; of α-acylamino-α,β-ethylenecarboxylic acid esters with chiral 9,9′-spirobixanthene-1,1′-diyl N,N-dimethylphosphoramidite as ligand s. S. Wu, X. Zhang et al., Org. Lett. *6*, 3565-7 (2004); asym. homogeneous hydrogenation of 1-alkylenolesters with carbohydrate-based 1,1′-binaphthyl-2,2′-diyl phosphites s. M.T. Reetz et al., Org. Lett. *5*, 3099-402 (2003); with chiral acyl 1,1′-binaphthyl-2,2′-diyl phosphites cf. A. Korostylev, A. Börner et al., Tetrahedron:Asym. *15*, 1001-5 (2004); with chiral 2-amino-1,3,2-benzodioxaphospholenes as ligand s. R. Hoen, A.J. Minnaard, B.L. Feringa et al., Org. Lett. *6*, 1433-6 (2004).

Bis(cyclooctadiene)rhodium(I) fluoroborate/P-chiral C$_1$-symmetric cyclic phosphoromonoamidites
**Asym. homogeneous hydrogenation
with P-chiral C$_1$-symmetric cyclic phosphoromonoamidites as ligand**

35.

P-Chiral *C$_1$-symmetric* cyclic phosphoromonoamidites offer enhanced enantioselectivity relative to C$_2$-symmetric variants (cf. *60*, 34s*68*) in Rh-catalyzed asym. homogeneous hydrogenation, and, interestingly can lead to a *reversal* of face-selectivity independent of the P-chirality. **E:** A soln. of methyl α-acetamidoacrylate in methylene chloride hydrogenated under 1.3 atm. H_2 at room temp. in the presence of 0.5 mol% $[Rh(cod)_2]BF_4$ and 1 mol% C_1-symmetric phosphoromonoamidite ligand ($S,S_p/S,R_p$ 1:3) for 20 h → (R)-product. Conversion 100% (e.e. >99%). It is also significant that a mixture of diastereoisomeric ligands can produce *higher* enantioselectivities than the pure homochiral ligand. F.e.s. M.T. Reetz, J.-A. Ma, R. Goddard, Angew. Chem. Int. Ed. Engl. *44*, 412-5 (2005).

Bis(norbornadiene)rhodium(I) hexafluoroantimonate/(R,R)-2,2''-bis[(S)-1- ←
(diphenylphosphino)ethyl]-1,1''-biferrocene/cesium carbonate
Indolines from indoles by asym. homogeneous hydrogenation ←

36.

Chiral 3-subst. N-sulfonylindolines. A mixture of 1 mol% $[Rh(norbornadiene)_2]SbF_6$ and 1 mol% (R,R)-2,2''-bis[(S)-1-(diphenylphosphino)ethyl]-1,1''-biferrocene in isopropanol stirred vigorously at room temp. for 10 min, the soln. added via cannula to a mixture of the startg. indole and 10 mol% Cs_2CO_3 in a stainless steel autoclave, pressurized with H_2 to 50 kg/cm², and heated at 80° for 24 h → product. Y 94% (e.e. 98%). The *trans*-chelating di(phosphine) ligand appears essential for the high enantioselectivity (95-8%), *cis*-chelating BINAP being ineffective. The N-sulfonyl residue also appears to be important as enantioselectivity was poor with N-Boc-derivs. Substrates bearing an alkyl or aryl group at C_3 were reactive, with various functional groups on the alkyl group remaining unaffected (silyl ethers, carbamates and esters). F.e. and enantiomers s. R. Kuwano, Y. Ito et al., Org. Lett. *6*, 2213-5 (2004).

Poly[bis(1,1'-binaphthyl-2,2'-diyl N,N- ←
dimethylphosphoramidite)(cyclooctadiene)rhodium(I) fluoroborate] complexes
Asym. heterogeneous hydrogenation $C{=}C \to CHCH$
with chiral, self-supported polymeric metal complexes

37.

A new breed of chiral, *self-supported*, polymeric, heterogeneous rhodium complexes has been developed, exhibiting permanent porosity and absorption capacity for guest molecules and presenting a dense chiral environment on the surface to effect asym. hydrogenation with high enantioselectivity. **E:** A mixture of 1 eq. methyl α-acetamidoacrylate and 1 mol% poly[bis(1,1'-binaphthyl-2,2'-diyl N,N-dimethylphosphoramidite)(cyclooctadiene)rhodium fluoroborate] complex (prepared as a yellow polymeric solid on treatment of $[Rh(cod)_2]BF_4$ with the monomeric, chiral bis(phosphoramidite) ligand in methylene chloride) in anhydrous toluene pressurized with H_2 to 40 atm., and stirred at room temp. for 10 h → product. Y 99% (e.e. 96%). Such metal-organic assemblies are easy to prepare, are superior to homogeneous counterparts in enantio-selectivity, can be simply removed by filtration and recycled with no significant loss of activity, and are considered superior to classical polymer-based or supported complexes. A further advantage is that there is no detectable leaching of the metal into the medium. F.e.s. X. Wang, K. Ding, J. Am. Chem. Soc. *126*, 10524-5 (2004).

Chloro(1,5-cyclooctadiene)rhodium(I) dimer/di-tert-*butyl-1-[(R)-2-[bis(4-trifluoromethyl-* ←
phenyl)phosphino]ferrocenyl]ethylphosphine
Asym. homogeneous hydrogenation   C=C → CHCH
of N-unsubst. β-amino-α,β-ethylenecarboxylic acid derivs.

38.

A mixture of *0.3 mol%* [RhCl(cod)]$_2$ and *0.31 mol%* di-*tert*-butyl-1-[(R)-2-[bis(4-trifluoromethyl-phenyl)phosphino]ferrocenyl]ethylphosphine in degassed and distilled trifluoroethanol stirred under N$_2$ at room temp. for 40 min, a soln. of 1 eq. startg. enaminoester in the same solvent added, then hydrogenated under H$_2$ (100 psi) at 50° for 24 h → (-)-product. Y 90.5% (e.e. 95.7%). In the past it has been presumed that an N-acyl protective group was essential for high enantioselectivity. Clearly, reaction with *Josiphos-type* ligands proves otherwise, so that the need for protection-deprotection steps is obviated. Enantioselectivity was poor with all other available chiral phosphine ligands. F.e. and amide derivs. s. Y. Hsiao, N.R. Rivera, T. Rosner et al., J. Am. Chem. Soc. *126*, 9918-9 (2004).

Palladium nanoparticles   Pd
Hydrogenation of ethylene derivs.
s. *3*, 46s66; of styrenes with recyclable Pd-nanoparticles prepared from Pd(OAc)$_2$/polymethyl-hydrosiloxane s. B.P.S. Chauhan, J.S. Rathore, T. Bandoo, J. Am. Chem. Soc. *126*, 8493-500 (2004).

Amphiphilic polymer-supported palladium nanoparticles   ←
Heterogeneous hydrogenation in water

39.

of styrenes. A mixture of the startg. styrene and 5 mol% amphiphilic [PEG-based] polymer-supported palladium nanoparticles in water shaken under 1 atm. H$_2$ at 25° for 24 h → product. Y 99%. The readily removable catalyst combines amphiphilic, heterogeneous aqua-catalytic properties with the high catalytic activity presented by the large surface area of the nanoparticles. The procedure is applicable to mono-, di- and tri-subst. styrenes possessing electron-donating or -withdrawing groups, and leaves esters, amides, ketones, aldehydes and carboxylic acids unaffected. F.e., also replacement of ar. chlorine by hydrogen on transfer-hydrogenation with ammonium formate in aq. isopropanol, s. R. Nakao, H. Rhee, Y. Uozumi, Org. Lett. *7*, 163-5 (2005).

Palladium-carbon   Pd-C
Hydrogenation of carbon-carbon multiple bonds in polyethylene glycol s. *3*, 46s68   ←

Hydrogenation of ethylene derivs.   C=C → CHCH
s. *12*, 119; stereospecific hydrogenation of β-(isoxazol-5-yl)-β-hydroxy-α-methylenecarboxylic acid esters s. R. Saxena, V. Singh, S. Batra, Tetrahedron *60*, 10311-20 (2004); of chiral sultam-based fumaric acid amides **with asym. induction** s. S. Jawaid, L.J. Farrugia, D.J. Robins, Tetrahedron:Asym. *15*, 3979-88 (2004).

Hydrogenation of (1,3-diene)diols s. *68,* 41   C═C → CHCH

Palladium-carbon/magnesium bromide   Pd-C/MgBr$_2$
Carboxylic from α,β-ethylenecarboxylic acid esters
from aryl esters cf. *67,* 30; *syn*-α-methyl-γ-hydroxycarboxylic acid ethyl esters s. H. Nagano, M. Yokota, Y. Iwazaki, Tetrahedron Lett. *45,* 3035-7 (2004).

Palladium/mesoporous silica/ammonium formate   ←
Oxo from α,β-ethyleneoxo compds. s. *53,* 9s68

Palladous hydroxide   Pd(OH)$_2$
Piperidines from 2-(2-oxazolidon-3-yl)pyridines with asym. induction s. *68,* 47   ←

Chiral iridium(I) 1-[2-(Δ^2-oxazolin-2-yl)ethyl]imidazol-2-ylidene complexes   ←
Sym. diaryl-subst. hydrocarbons from dienes   ←
Iridium(I)-catalyzed asym. homogeneous hydrogenation

A test-tube containing a soln. of the startg. diene and 2 mol% chiral iridium(I) 1-[2-(Δ^2-oxazolin-2-yl)ethyl]imidazol-2-ylidene complex in methylene chloride placed in a Parr bomb, and stirred under 50 atm. H$_2$ at 25° for 24 h → product. Y 100% (conversion 100%; *ent/meso* 20:1; e.e. 99%; abs. configuration not determined). F.e. incl. asym. hydrogenation of sym. diaryl-subst. dienes possessing two 1,1-disubst. alkene residues s. X. Cui, J.W. Ogle, K. Burgess, Chem. Commun. *2005,* 672-4.

Chiral cationic iridium(I) 4-(o-phosphinophenyl)- or phosphinoxy-Δ^2-oxazoline complexes   ←
Asym. homogeneous hydrogenation   C═C → CHCH
with chiral cationic iridium(I) 2-[*o*-(diarylphosphino)phenyl]-Δ^2-oxazoline complexes cf. *56,* 39s67; of trisubst. styrenes with (1,5-cyclooctadiene)[((4S)-6,6-dimethyl-2-phenyl-4,5,6,7-tetrahydro-1,3-benzoxazol-4-yl) bis(2-methylphenyl)phosphinite] iridium(I) tetrakis[bis(3,5-trifluoromethyl)phenyl]borate s. K. Kallstrom, P.G. Andersson et al., J. Am. Chem. Soc. *126,* 14308-9 (2004); with conformationally rigid chiral cationic iridium(I) 4-(*o*-phosphinophenyl)-Δ^2-oxazoline complexes s. D. Liu, W. Tang, X. Zhang, Org. Lett. *6,* 513-6 (2004).

Chloro(cyclooctadiene)iridium(I) dimer/chiral 2,2′,6,6′-tetramethoxy-4,4′-bis(dicyclohexyl-phosphino)-3,3′-bipyridyl or (S)-2-[2-(diphenylphosphino)ferrocenyl]-4-tert-butyl-Δ^2-oxazoline/iodine   ←
2-Subst. 1,2,3,4-tetrahydroquinolines from quinolines   ←
Asym. homogeneous hydrogenation
with (R)-6,6′-dimethoxy-2,2′-bis(diphenylphosphino)biphenyl as ligand cf. *66,* 42; with chiral 2,2′,6,6′-tetramethoxy-4,4′-bis(dicyclohexylphosphino)-3,3′-bipyridyl s. L. Xu, A.S.C. Chan et al., Chem. Commun. *2005,* 1390-1; with (S)-2-[2-(diphenylphosphino)ferrocenyl]-4-*tert*-butyl-Δ^2-oxazoline s. S.-M. Lu, X.-W. Han, Y.-G. Zhou, Adv. Synth. Catal. *346,* 909-12 (2004).

Exchange ↑   HC ↕ O

Microwaves s. under *PdCl$_2$(dppf)*   [\\\\]
Potassium tert-*butoxide* s. under *Sc(OTf)$_3$*   KOBu-t

Lithium/naphthalene
**Reductive decomplexation of π-allyltricarbonyliron lactone complexes
with simultaneous replacement of acoxy groups by hydrogen
and subsequent hydrogenation of 1,3-dienes**

$Li/C_{10}H_8$
←

41.

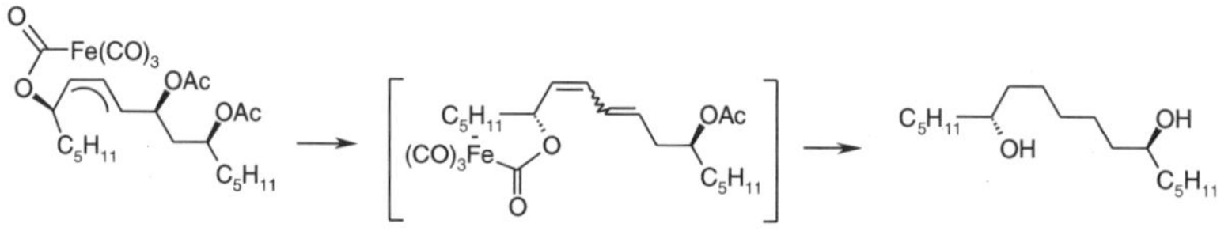

syn-Diols. 10 eqs. Li-naphthalenide [prepared by sonication of a suspension of naphthalene and Li (1:1) in THF] added to a soln. of the startg. iron complex in THF at -78°, stirred overnight, allowed to warm to room temp., methanol added, stirring continued for a further 2 h, filtered, the filtrate concentrated, the purified dienol taken up in ethyl acetate, 10 wt% Pd-C added, purged with H_2 five times, and stirred under 1 atm. H_2 for 2 h → product. Y 81%. There was no epimerization of stereogenic centres. F.e.s. C.J. Hollowood, S.V. Ley, Org. Biomol. Chem. *1*, 3197-207 (2003).

Zinc/ammonium chloride
β-Ketocarboxylic from α-acoxy-β-ketocarboxylic acid amides

Zn/NH_4Cl
OAc → H

42.

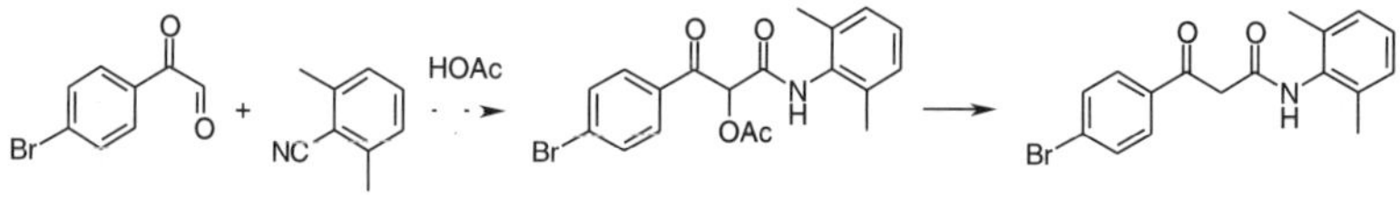

in aq. medium under mild conditions. A soln. of the startg. α-acoxy-β-keto-amide in methanol added to a suspension of 4 eqs. Zn dust in satd. aq. NH_4Cl (preactivated by sonication for 5 min), the mixture stirred at room temp. for 0.5 h, filtered, and water added to precipitate the product → β-keto-amide. Y 95%. Reaction involves initial coordination of zinc with both the keto group and the amide carbonyl prior to formation of a zinc enolate on reduction. The startg. ms. are readily prepared **from** a variety of **α-ketoaldehydes** and isonitriles by Passerini reaction, allowing application in diversity-oriented synthesis. F.e.s. A.G. Neo, J. Delgado, C.F. Marcos et al., Tetrahedron Lett. *46*, 23-6 (2005).

Borane-tetrahydrofuran
**Cyclic amines from lactams
with simultaneous replacement of N-alkoxymethyl by N-methyl groups**

BH_3-THF
←

43.

(98%)

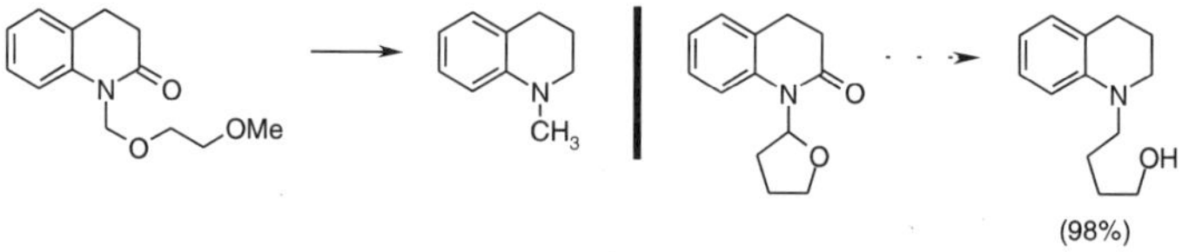

N-Methyl-1,2,3,4-tetrahydroquinolines. 15 eqs. BH_3-THF added to the startg. protected lactam in THF at room temp. under N_2, stirred for 24 h, then quenched with water and worked up → product. Y 94%. In this unusual tandem cleavage, reaction is thought to involve initial reduction of the lactam carbonyl, followed by formation of a 6-membered dioxyborane complex and two consecutive elimination-reduction phases as the second function is removed. F.e. and with cleavage of ethoxymethyl, methoxymethyl, thiomethoxymethyl, 2-(trimethylsilyl)ethoxymethyl, benzyl-oxymethyl, tetrahydrofuranyl and tetrahydrothienyl groups s. W.-P. Hu, J.-J. Wang, J. Org. Chem. *69*, 3983-5 (2004).

Borane-dimethyl sulfide/alcohols $\qquad$ $BH_3\text{-}Me_2S/ROH$
Aminoalcohols from ketocarboxylic acid amides $\qquad$ $CON< \rightarrow CH_2N<$
3-aminoalcohols with BH_3-THF/$TiCl_4$ cf. *62*, 42; 4-aminoalcohols with BH_3-Me_2S/alcohols, retention of carbalkoxy groups, s. C. Schroeder, R. Huddleston, R. Charles, World Intellectual Property Organisation patent WO-2002102776 (Aventis Pharma Deut GmbH).

Sodium tetrahydridoborate/boron fluoride $\qquad$ $NaBH_4/BF_3$
Prim. alcohols from carboxylic acids $\qquad$ $COOH \rightarrow CH_2OH$
s. *27*, 65; *13*, 102; also from carboxylic acid esters or carboxylic acid chlorides, and prim. amines from N-unsubst. carboxylic acid amides or nitriles, s. S.-D. Cho, J.R. Falck, Y.-J. Yoon et al., Bull. Korean Chem. Soc. *25*, 407-9 (2004).

Sodium tetrahydridoborate/hexadecyltrimethylammonium bromide $\qquad$ $NaBH_4/R_4NBr$
Prim. alcohols from carboxylic acid esters in aq. micelles $\qquad$ $COOR \rightarrow CH_2OH$

44. $O_2N\text{-}C_6H_4\text{-}COOC_6H_{13} \longrightarrow O_2N\text{-}C_6H_4\text{-}CH_2OH$

A soln. of 1 eq. startg. ester in acetonitrile added to an aq. micellar soln. containing 10 eqs. hexadecyltrimethylammonium bromide, stirred at room temp. for 10 min, treated with 4 eqs. $NaBH_4$, the mixture stirred at the same temp. for 4-6 h, an aq. soln. of 11 eqs. $NaClO_4$ added to precipitate the surfactant, filtered, and the filtrate worked up → product. Y 84%. Reaction is applicable to aliphatic and aromatic esters, but yields were low with arylcarboxylic acid esters possessing electron-donating groups. F.e. and comparison of surfactants s. D. Das, S. Roy, P.K. Das, Org. Lett. *6*, 4133-6 (2004).

Diisobutylaluminum hydride $\qquad$ $i\text{-}Bu_2AlH$
Aldehydes from acoxylamines s. *68*, 134 $\qquad$ $COON< \rightarrow CHO$

Zeolite s. under Ru-C $\qquad$ ←
Boron fluoride s. under $NaBH_4$ $\qquad$ BF_3

Scandium(III) triflate/1,2-bis(tert-butyldimethylsilyl)hydrazine/potassium tert-butoxide/ tert-butanol $\qquad$ ←
Scandium(III)-catalyzed Wolff-Kishner reduction under mild conditions $\qquad$ $CO \rightarrow CH_2$

45. $Bu\text{-}CH=CH\text{-}(CH_2)_{11}\text{-}CHO \xrightarrow{t\text{-}BuMe_2SiNHNHSiMe_2Bu\text{-}t} [Bu\text{-}CH=CH\text{-}(CH_2)_{11}\text{-}CH=NNHSiMe_2Bu\text{-}t] \longrightarrow Bu\text{-}CH=CH\text{-}(CH_2)_{11}\text{-}CH_3$

via N-silylhydrazones. 1,2-Bis(*tert*-butyldimethylsilyl)hydrazine added via syringe to 0.01 mol% $Sc(OTf)_3$ under argon, chilled to 0°, (Z)-13-octadecenal added dropwise over 15 min via syringe, stirring continued at the same temp. for 15 min, warmed to 23°, stirred again for 15 min, volatiles removed *in vacuo* with stirring at the same temp. over 1 h, heated to 30-35° under vacuum for 6 h, blanketed with argon, a soln. of 20 eqs. KOBu-*t* and 2 eqs. of *tert*-butanol in dry DMSO added via syringe, and stirred for 24 h at room temp. → product. Y 99%. The procedure is significant in that a high temperature is not required and that reduction can be performed in one pot without purification of the intermediate hydrazone. A separate procedure was also detailed, wherein the volatile *tert*-butyldimethylsilanol by-product was not removed. F.e.s. M.E. Furrow, A.G. Myers, J. Am. Chem. Soc. *126*, 5436-45 (2004).

Formic acid s. under $PdCl_2(dppf)$ $\qquad$ HCOOH
1,2-Bis(tert-butyldimethylsilyl)hydrazine s. under Sc(OTf)$_3$ $\qquad$ $t\text{-}BuMe_2SiNHNHSiMe_2Bu\text{-}t$

Tri-n-butyltin hydride/azodiisobutyronitrile $\qquad$ $Bu_3SnH/AIBN$
Deoxygenation of sec. alcohols $\qquad$ $OH \rightarrow OCOCOOMe \rightarrow H$
steroid derivs. via xanthates cf. *31*, 49; 11-subst. androst-5-enes **via oxalic acid esters** s. V. Lecomte, E. Stéphan et al., J. Org. Chem. *69*, 3216-9 (2004); **via phosphorous acid esters** s. L. Zhang, M. Koreeda, J. Am. Chem. Soc. *126*, 13190-1 (2004).

Deoxygenation of alcohols via phosphorous acid esters $OP(OR)OR' \rightarrow H$

46.

R = BzO-[sugar]

via β-scission of cyclic phosphoranyl radicals. A soln. of 1 eq. startg. phosphite [prepared from the corresponding alcohol, methyl dichlorophosphite and 2-(2-iodophenyl)ethanol] in anhydrous benzene (0.02 M) treated under argon with 1.4 eqs. Bu$_3$SnH and a little AIBN, the resulting mixture refluxed for 2 h, cooled to room temp., volatiles stripped off *in vacuo*, the resulting residue redissolved in ether, treated with DBU, and filtered → product. Y 88%. The protocol is versatile for the deoxygenation of sec. and tert. alcohols, including hindered derivs. F.e.s. L. Zhang, M. Koreeda, J. Am. Chem. Soc. *126*, 13190-1 (2004).

Tetraalkylammonium hypophosphites/4,4'-azo(4-cyanovaleric acid) ←
Deoxygenation of sec. alcohols via xanthates in water $OC(S)(SR) \rightarrow H$
with N-ethylpiperidinium hypophosphite/hexadecyltrimethylammonium bromide/4,4'-azo(4-cyanovaleric acid) cf. *64*, 478; with tetraalkylammonium hypophosphites/4,4'-azo(4-cyanovaleric acid), also radical 1,4-addition, s. D.H. Cho, D.O. Jang, Tetrahedron Lett. *46*, 1799-802 (2005).

Hypophosphorous acid/triethylamine/azodiisobutyronitrile/cyclohexene ←
Deoxygenation of sec. alcohols via xanthates
s. *48*, 68s62; deoxygenation of taxane derivs. with cyclohexene or 1-dodecene as sacrificial olefin s. J. Gu, D.L. Yin et al., Chinese Chem. Lett. *15*, 649-51 (2004).

Ammonium chloride s. under Zn NH_4Cl
Hexadecyl(2-hydroxyethyl)dimethylammonium bromide s. under NaBH$_4$ R_4NBr

(S)-[4,4'-Bis(diphenylphosphino)-2,2',5,5'-tetramethyl-3,3'-bithienyl]ruthenium(II) ←
bis(trifluoroacetate)/hydrogen chloride
γ-Lactones from γ-ketocarboxylic acid esters ○
Asym. homogeneous hydrogenation
with Ru(OAc)$_2$[(S)-BINAP]/HCl cf. *46*, 67; with (S)-[4,4'-bis(diphenylphosphino)-2,2',5,5'-tetramethyl-3,3'-bithienyl]ruthenium(II) bis(trifluoroacetate)/HCl (e.e. 97-99%) without isolation of the intermediate hydroxyesters s. T. Benincori, F. Sannicolo et al., Tetrahedron:Asym. *15*, 2289-97 (2004).

Dichloro[1,1'-bis(diphenylphosphino)ferrocene]palladium(II)/potassium carbonate/ ←
formic acid/microwaves
Arenes from aryl perfluoroalkanesulfonates $OSO_2R_f \rightarrow H$
with Pd(PPh$_3$)$_4$/HCOOH·Bu$_3$N cf. *42*, 58; from aryl perfluoroctanesulfonates with PdCl$_2$(dppf)/HCOOH/K$_2$CO$_3$ under microwave irradiation in toluene/acetone/water s. W. Zhang, C.H.T. Chen et al., Tetrahedron Lett. *45*, 4611-3 (2004).

Nitrogen ↑ HC ↓↑ N

Sodium nitrite $NaNO_2$
Arenes from prim. ar. amines via diazotization $NH_2 \rightarrow H$
with NaNO$_2$ in HCl cf. *2*, 103; under mild conditions with NaNO$_2$ in 5:1 ethanol/concd. H$_2$SO$_4$ (for dinitroanilines), or *in ethyl acetate* as pro-reducing agent (for nitroanilines), s. V.A. Bacherikov, T.-L. Su et al., Bull. Chem. Soc. Jpn. *77*, 1027-8 (2004).

Sodium tetrahydridoborate $NaBH_4$
Replacement of nitro groups by hydrogen $NO_2 \rightarrow H$
arenes cf. *24*, 85; (E)-ethylene derivs. from (Z)-1,1-nitroethylene derivs. s. R. Ballini, D. Fiorini, A. Palmieri, Tetrahedron Lett. *45*, 7027-9 (2004).

Diisobutylaluminum hydride $i\text{-}Bu_2AlH$
Aldehydes from N-acyl-N-heterocyclics $RCON{\lt} \rightarrow RCHO$
from N-acylsultams cf. *49*, 638s*53*; chiral α- and β-alkyl-aldehydes from N-acyl-5,5-dimethyl-2-oxazolidones s. S.D. Bull, S.G. Davies et al., Org. Biomol. Chem. *1*, 2886-99 (2003).

Hydrogen peroxide H_2O_2
Arenes from stable diazonium salts $N_2^+ \rightarrow H$
from fluoroborates with $DMF/FeSO_4$ cf. *33*, 71s*51*; from *o*-benzenedisulfonimides with 30% H_2O_2 in THF s. M. Barbero, I. Degani, R. Fochi et al., Synthesis *2004*, 2386-90.

Palladous hydroxide $Pd(OH)_2$
Piperidines from 2-(2-oxazolidon-3-yl)pyridines   ←
Catalytic hydrogenation with chirality transfer

47.

with simultaneous cleavage of the chiral auxiliary. A mixture of 140 mg 20 wt% wet $Pd(OH)_2$/C, 524 mg of the startg. chiral 2-(2-oxazolidon-3-yl)pyridine and 15 ml acetic acid stirred in an autoclave under H_2 (100 bar) at 40° for 22 h, filtered through a short pad of Celite, treated with aq. HCl, and the solvent removed → product. Y 95% (e.e. 96%). The procedure can be applied to the generation of up to *four new chiral centres* in a single operation, offering at the same time a simple extraction of the product (as its hydrochoride) and recycling of the chiral auxiliary. Reaction is presumed to involve initial hydrogenation to give a cyclic aminal, followed by cleavage of the auxiliary and generation of an iminium ion prior to its reduction. F.e. and comparison of catalysts, also with simultaneous reductive N-alkylation, s. F. Glorius et al., Angew. Chem. Int. Ed. Engl. *43*, 2850-2 (2004).

Halogen ↑   HC ↓↑ Hal

n-*Butyllithium*   BuLi
(E)-α,β-Ethylenebromides from dibromomethylene compds. $Br \rightarrow H$
with diethyl phosphite/NaOEt under microwave irradiation cf. *32*, 64s*63*; O-protected β-trifluoromethyl-γ-hydroxy-α,β-ethylenebromides with *n*-BuLi, also trapping the intermediate carbenoids with electrophiles, s. Y. Li, L. Lu, X. Zhao, Org. Lett. *6*, 4467-70 (2004).

Sodium formate s. under Pd-C   HCOONa

Zinc/acetic acid   Zn/AcOH
Replacement of bromine by hydrogen
s. *3*, 62; (E)-α-methylene- from (Z)-α-bromomethyl-α,β-ethylene-carboxylic acid esters (cf. *25*, 59), also with Zn/Cu, s. L. Fernandes, A.J. Bortoluzzi, M.M. Sa, Tetrahedron *60*, 9983-9 (2004).

n-*Butylmagnesium chloride/ferric chloride* $BuMgCl/FeCl_3$
Replacement of ar. chlorine by hydrogen $Cl \rightarrow H$
with $BuMgCl/Cp_2TiCl_2$ cf. *26*, 70s*57*; with $BuMgCl/FeCl_3$, and comparison of metal catalysts, s. H.Q. Guo, K. Kanno, T. Takahashi, Chem. Lett. *33*, 1356-7 (2004).

*Sodium tetrahydridoborate/palladous acetate/2,2'-bis(diphenylphosphino)-
1,1'-binaphthyl/N,N,N',N'-tetramethylethylenediamine* ←
Replacement of ar. halogen by hydrogen Hal → H
with NaBH$_4$/PdCl$_2$ cf. *37*, 49; 4-bromoindoles from 4,5-dibromoindoles with NaBH$_4$/Pd(OAc)$_2$/BINAP/TMEDA s. J.Y. Chae, S.L. Buchwald, J. Org. Chem. *69*, 3336-9 (2004).

Samarium diiodide/amines SmI$_2$/R$_3$N
Replacement of halogen by hydrogen
with SmI$_2$/HMPA/ROH cf. *43*, 69; improved procedure with SmI$_2$/water/amines for reduction of *alkyl* halides s. A. Dahlén, G. Hilmersson, R.A. Flowers II et al., J. Org. Chem. *68*, 4870-5 (2003).

Ammonium formate s. under Pd HCOONH$_4$

Hexabutyldistannane/tetra-n-butylammonium fluoride Bu$_3$SnSnBu$_3$/Bu$_4$NF
Replacement of ar. bromine by hydrogen Br → H
with Et$_3$SiH/*tert*-dodecanethiol/di-*tert*-butyl hyponitrite cf. *45*, 35; with Bu$_3$SnSnBu$_3$/Bu$_4$NF in aq. THF under mild conditions s. D.C. Harrowven, I.L. Guy, M.I.T. Nunn, Chem. Commun. *2004*, 1966-7.

Tetra-n-butylammonium fluoride s. under Bu$_3$SnSnBu$_3$ Bu$_4$NF
Ferric chloride s. under BuMgCl FeCl$_3$

Nickel/sulfuric acid Ni/H$_2$SO$_4$
Replacement of ar. bromine by hydrogen s. *68*, 10

Palladium-carbon/sodium formate Pd-C/HCOONa
Replacement of ar. chlorine by hydrogen in water Cl → H
cf. *33*, 76s*61*; with Pd-C/HCOONa *at room temp.* s. A. Arcadi, D. Zorzan et al., Eur. J. Org. Chem. *2004*, 3040-7.

Palladium/mesoporous silica/ammonium formate ←
Replacement of ar. halogen by hydrogen s. *53*, 9s*68* Hal → H

Amphiphilic polymer-supported palladium nanoparticles/ammonium formate ←
Replacement of ar. chlorine by hydrogen in aq. medium s. *68*, 39 Cl → H

Palladous acetate s. under NaBH$_4$ Pd(OAc)$_2$

Remaining Elements ↑ HC ↓↑ Rem

Potassium carbonate K$_2$CO$_3$
Terminal acetylene derivs. from silylacetylenes C≡C(Si≤) → C≡CH
with NaOH cf. *23*, 656; rapid procedure under microwave irradiation with K$_2$CO$_3$ in methanol s. J. Wettergren, A.B.E. Minidis, Tetrahedron Lett. *44*, 7611-2 (2003).

1,8-Diazabicyclo[5.4.0]undec-7-ene dbu
Ethylene derivs. from enesilanes C=C(Si≤) → C=CH
with KF cf. *39*, 74s*64*; β,γ-ethylenesulfones from β,γ-ethylene-γ-silylsulfones with DBU, *syn*-effect on E/Z-selectivity, s. S.K. Guha, Y. Ukaji, K. Inomata, Chem. Lett. *32*, 1158-9 (2003).

Carbon ↑ HC ↓↑ C

Trifluoroacetic acid CF$_3$COOH
Ketones from β-ketocarboxylic acid esters COOR → H
from methyl esters with AcOH cf. *21*, 805; from *tert*-butyl esters with CF$_3$COOH, α-hetaryl compds. (e.g. azolyl, furyl, thienyl), s. M. Nakatsuka et al., Japanese patent JP-2002212169 (Sumitomo Seiyaku KK).

Ruthenium-carbon/zeolite
Alcohols from cyclic acetals

48.

A mixture of 2-(6-hydroxy-3-oxahexyl)-1,3-dioxane, water, Ru-on-carbon and zeolite heated in an autoclave at 80° under a partial hydrogen pressure of 0.7 MPa, the catalyst filtered off, and the filtrate worked up → 4-oxaheptane-1,7-diol. Y 99%. F.e. and prepn. of the startg. m. from ethylene derivs. s. J. Takahara, Japanese patent JP-2002322113 (Mitsubishi Chem. Corp.).

Dodecacarbonyltriruthenium/ammonium formate $Ru_3(CO)_{12}/HCOONH_4$
Chelation-controlled decarbalkoxylation   COOR → H
by Ru-catalyzed transfer-hydrogenation s. *61*, 42; arenes from arylcarboxylic acid picolinyl esters s. H. Tatamidani, N. Chatani et al., J. Org. Chem. **69**, 5615-21 (2004).

Elimination

Oxygen ↑   HC ⇑ O

Nickel/sulfuric acid Ni/H_2SO_4
Deoxygenation of benzyl alcohols s. *68*, 10   OH → H

Nitrogen ↑   HC ⇑ N

Tris(dibenzylideneacetone)dipalladium/tris(pentafluorophenyl)phosphine $Pd_2(dba)_3/(C_6F_5)_3P$
Allenes from 2-acetyleneamines s. *67*, 485   C≡C-C(N<) → CH=C=C

Carbon ↑   HC ⇑ C

Palladium-carbon   Pd-C
Palladium-catalyzed decarboxylation under hydrothermal conditions   COOH → H

49.

A mixture of the startg. carboxylic acid, 3.3 mol% Pd-on-carbon (10%) and water contained in a Teflon vessel heated in a sealed autoclave under 4-5 MPa at 250° for 14 h → triphenylmethane. Y 99%. The method is believed to proceed through the formation of a hydride species, and is also effective for the **decarbonylation of aldehydes** and decarbamylation of N-unsubst. carboxylic acid amides. F.e., **also decarboxylative and decarbonylative perdeuteriation** in D_2O, s. S. Matsubara, Y. Yokota, K. Oshima, Org. Lett. **6**, 2071-3 (2004).

Pentahydridobis(triisopropylphosphine)iridium $IrH_5(i-Pr_3P)_2$
Nitriles by iridium-catalyzed retro-Michael reaction   ←

50.

of 1,3-dinitriles. A mixture of 20 mol% pentahydridobis(triisopropylphosphine)iridium and the startg. 1,3-dinitrile in toluene heated under argon in a sealed reaction tube with stirring for 12 h at 150° → product. Y 98%. Reaction is presumed to involve iridium-catalyzed C-H bond activation of the primary cyano group to give an alkyliridium species, followed by β-carbon elimination of acrylonitrile and reductive elimination of the metal from an α-cyanoalkyliridium hydride. F.e. and comparison of catalysts, **also from γ-cyanoketones**, s. H. Terai, H. Takaya, S. Murahashi, Synlett *2004*, 2185-7.

Formation of O-O Bond

Exchange ↕

Oxygen ↑ OO ↕ O

Boron fluoride BF_3
1,2,4,5-Tetroxanes
from two different oxo compd. molecules with $H_2O_2/MeReO_3/HBF_4$ cf. *66*, 52; from 1,1-di(hydroperoxides) and acetals with BF_3-etherate s. A.O. Terent'ev, G.I. Nikishina et al., Synthesis *2004*, 2356-66.

Formation of O-N Bond

Uptake ⇓

Addition to Nitrogen ON ⇓ N

Ruthenium trichloride/Bromamine-T $RuCl_3/ArSO_2N(Br)Na$
N-Oxidation $\geqslant N \rightarrow \geqslant NO$
of pyridines and tert. amines with $RuCl_3/O_2$ cf. *63*, 55; with $RuCl_3$/Bromamine-T in aq. medium (pH 8.4) s. V.B. Sharma, S.L. Jain, B. Sain, Tetrahedron Lett. *45*, 4281-3 (2004).

Exchange ↕

Hydrogen ↑ ON ↕ H

*Triphenylphosphine/2,3-dichloro-5,6-dicyanoquinone/tetra-*n*-butylammonium nitrite* ←
Nitrous acid esters from alcohols under mild, neutral conditions OH → ONO

51. $PhCH_2OH \longrightarrow PhCH_2ONO$

2 eqs. Tetra-*n*-butylammonium nitrite added with stirring to a mixture of 2 eqs. triphenylphosphine and 2 eqs. DDQ in anhydrous acetonitrile, benzyl alcohol added, and refluxed until GC indicated completion of reaction (ca. 30 min) → product. Y 98% (conversion 100%). The method is simple, safe and avoids handling gaseous NO. The same products were also obtained **from mercaptans**. **Preferential conversion** of prim. alcohols can be effected in the presence of sec. or tert. alcohols, and **selective conversion** of benzyl alcohols takes place in the presence of non-benzylic alcohols or benzyl mercaptans. F.e.s. B. Akhlaghinia, A.R. Pourali, Synthesis *2004*, 1747-9.

*Tetra-*n*-propylammonium bromate/sulfuric acid* Pr_4NBrO_3/H_2SO_4
Nitro compds. from prim. amines $NH_2 \rightarrow NO_2$
with $NaMnO_4 \cdot H_2O$ cf. *37*, 323; with Pr_4NBrO_3/H_2SO_4 in glacial acetic acid s. S.S. Das, P.J. Das et al., Synth. Commun. *34*, 2359-63 (2004).

Formation of O-S Bond

Uptake ⇓

Addition to Sulfur OS ⇓ S

Iodosobenzene s. under Iron(III) complexes PhIO
Silica-sulfuric acid s. under NaBrO$_3$ SiO_2-OSO_3H

Vanadyl acetoacetonate/(R,R)-1,2-bis(o-hydroxybenzylamino)cyclohexane or (S)-3,3- ←
   dimethyl-2-[(2-hydroxy-2'-pivaloyloxy-1,1'-binaphth-3-yl)methyleneamino]butanol/
   hydrogen peroxide
Sulfoxides from thioethers by asym. oxidation >S → >SO
with chiral salens s. *51*, 46s*67*; with (S)-3,3-dimethyl-2-[(2-hydroxy-2'-pivaloyloxy-1,1'-binaphth-3-yl)methyleneamino]butanol s. Y.-C. Jeong, K.-H. Ahn et al., Tetrahedron Lett. *45*, 9249-52 (2004); with (R,R)-1,2-bis(o-hydroxybenzylamino)cyclohexane as an example of a 'salan' ligand (a reduced salen), reversal of enantioselectivity, cf. J. Sun, C. Zhu et al., J. Org. Chem. *69*, 8500-3 (2004).

Hydrogen peroxide s. under Heteropolyacids, Fe(acac)$_3$ and Iron(II) complexes H_2O_2

Tetra-n-butylammonium phosphomolybdate/fluorapatite/urea-hydrogen peroxide ←
Heteropolyacid pyridinium salt/hydrogen peroxide ←
Sulfoxides from thioethers
with hexadecylpyridinium tungstophosphate cf. *25*, 80s*49*; with a pyridinium molybdovanadophosphate ([PMo$_{11}$VO$_{40}$H$_3$]py), also comparison of heteropolyacids, s. G.P. Romanelli, P.G. Vaquez, P. Tundo, Synlett *2005*, 75-8; **also sulfones** with tetra-*n*-butylammonium phosphomolybdate/fluorapatite/urea-H$_2$O$_2$ in the absence of solvent s. Y. Sasaki, S. Yamaguchi, J. Ichihara et al., Tetrahedron Lett. *45*, 9513-5 (2004).

Sodium bromate/silica-sulfuric acid $NaBrO_3$/SiO_2-OSO_3H
Sulfoxides from thioethers in the absence of solvent s. *29*, 233s*68*

Potassium permanganate/manganese dioxide $KMnO_4$/MnO_2
Sulfoxides from thioethers s. *68*, 130

*Ferric acetoacetonate/(S)-N-(3,5-diiodosalicylidene)-*tert-*leucinol/lithium* ←
   p-methoxybenzoate/hydrogen peroxide
*[(S,S)-N,N'-Bis(3,5-di-*tert-*butylsalicylidene)-2,3-diphenyl-2,3-* ←
   butylenediamino]iron(III) chloride/iodosobenzene
Sulfoxides from thioethers by iron-catalyzed asym. oxidation

52.

A soln. of 2 mol% Fe(acac)$_3$ and 4 mol% (S)-N-(3,5-diiodosalicylidene)-*tert*-leucinol in methylene chloride stirred until the mixture became clear brown, the resulting soln. transferred to a suspension of 1 mol% Li-*p*-methoxybenzoate in the same solvent, stirred for 10 min, treated with a soln. of *p*-bromothioanisole in methylene chloride, followed dropwise by 1.2 eqs. H$_2$O$_2$ (35%), and stirred slowly at room temp. for 16 h in the capped reaction vessel → (S)-product. Y 59% (e.e.

94%). The simple method is mild, inexpensive, environmentally friendly, moderate-to-good yielding, can be conducted in air, and provides enantioselectivities up to 96%. F.e.s. J. Legros, C. Bolm, Angew. Chem. Int. Ed. Engl. *43*, 4225-8 (2004); with [(S,S)-N,N'-bis(3,5-di-*tert*-butyl-salicylidene)-2,3-diphenyl-2,3-butylenediamino]iron(III) chloride/iodosobenzene cf. K.P. Bryliakov, E.P. Talsi, ibid. 5228-30.

5,10,15,20-Tetrakis(pentafluorophenyl)porphyrinatoiron(II)/hydrogen peroxide ←
Sulfoxides or sulfones from thioethers $>$S → $>$SO or $>SO_2$
with *meso*-tetraphenylporphyrinatoiron(III) chloride/PhIO cf. *37*, 80; sulfoxides with 0.03-0.09 mol% 5,10,15,20-tetrakis(pentafluorophenyl)porphyrinatoiron(II) and H_2O_2, also sulfones with 0.09-0.25 mol% of the catalyst, selectivity, s. E. Baciocchi, M.F. Gerini, A. Lapi, J. Org. Chem. *69*, 3586-9 (2004).

Exchange ⇵

Oxygen ↑ OS ⇵ O

Silica chloride ←
O-Tosylation of alcohols OH → OTs
preferential O-tosylation with TsOH/iron-exchanged montmorillonite cf. *59*, 57; O-tosylation of prim. and [more rapidly] sec. alcohols with silica chloride s. B. Das, V.S. Reddy, M.R. Reddy, Tetrahedron Lett. *45*, 6717-9 (2004).

Nitrogen ↑ OS ⇵ N

Triethylamine Et_3N
Aryl triflates from phenols OH → OTf
and a PEG-based bistriflimide cf. *60*, 49; more efficiently and conveniently with a polystyrene-based bistriflimide s. C.W.Y. Chung, P.H. Toy, Tetrahedron *61*, 709-15 (2005).

Halogen ↑ OS ⇵ Hal

Peptides/1,8-bis(dimethylamino)naphthalene ←
Sulfinic acid esters from sulfinic acid chlorides S(O)Cl → S(O)OR
with dynamic kinetic resolution

53.

A mixture of 0.5 mol% Boc-His(Me)-Thr(OBu-*t*)-D-Val-His(trityl)-D-Phe-D-Val-Thr(OBu-*t*)-Ile-OMe, 5 eqs. 2-hydroxymethylnaphthalene and 2.5 eqs. Proton Sponge in anhydrous THF cooled to -78°, treated with a soln. of 1 eq. *racemic tert*-butanesulfinyl chloride in the same solvent under N_2 over 30 min, stirred at the same temp. for 40 h, treated with 80:1 methanol/Et_3N, allowed to warm to room temp., diluted with 2:1 ethyl acetate/hexanes, and washed with 10% citric acid soln. → product. Y 61% (e.e. 99%). Dynamic kinetic resolution takes place through rapid epimerization of the sulfinyl stereo centre, the enantioselectivity being the highest recorded for the preparation of chiral sulfinates. F.e. and comparison with established acyl transfer agents, also structure-activity study with a small library of related peptides, s. J.W. Evans, S.J. Miller, J.A. Ellman et al., J. Am. Chem. Soc. *126*, 8134-5 (2004).

Formation of O-Rem Bond

Uptake ⇓

Addition to Hydrogen and Oxygen   ORem ⇓ HO

Via intermediates   *v.i*
Thiophosphorylation of nucleosides ←
monothiophosphorylation s. *27*, 113s*36*; f. method for monothiophosphorylation of isoprenoid alcohols with 2-(2-cyanoethoxy)-2-thioxo-1,3,2-oxathiaphospholane/dbu s. K. Zmudzka, W.J. Stec et al., Org. Lett. *6*, 1385-8 (2004); dithiophosphorylation via nucleoside S,S-bis(2-cyanoethyl) dithiophosphates s. C.B. Reese, H. Yan, Tetrahedron Lett. *45*, 2653-6 (2004).

Addition to Remaining Elements   ORem ⇓ Rem

Iodine I_2
Oligonucleotide synthesis ←
by the phosphoramidite method s. *17*, 169s*67*; oligodeoxynucleotide synthesis with perfect O-selective internucleotide coupling without base protection s. A. Ohkubo, K. Seio, M. Sekine, Tetrahedron Lett. *45*, 363-6 (2004); **oligonucleotide *H*-phosphonates** s. A. Meyer, F. Morvan, J.-J. Vasseur, ibid. 3745-8.

Exchange ⇅

Hydrogen ↑   ORem ⇵ H

2λ^5-2,2′-Spirobi(1,3,2-benzodioxaphosphole)   ←
Phosphorous acid monoesters from alcohols   OH → OP(H)(O)OH

54.

Nucleoside *H*-phosphonates. A soln. of 5′-O-tritylthymidine and 2 eqs. water in anhydrous pyridine added to a stirred soln. of 1.1 eqs. 2λ^5-2,2′-spirobi(1,3,2-benzodioxaphosphole) in anhydrous dioxane at room temp., and heated to 80° for 1 h → product. Y 89.3% (as the triethylammonium salt). The spirophosphorane is readily available, and reaction applicable to both protected and unprotected nucleosides, as well as simple prim. alcohols. F.e.s. S.B. Tzokov, R.T. Momtcheva, D.D. Petkov, Phosphorus, Sulfur Silicon Relat. Elem. *179*, 1095-111 (2004).

Dichloro(p-cymene)ruthenium(II) dimer   [$RuCl_2$(p-cymene)]$_2$
O-Silylation of alcohols   OH → OSi⋜
with organosilicon hydrides/Grubbs' complex cf. *64*, 52; with [RuCl$_2$(p-cymene)]$_2$ s. R.L. Miller, S.V. Maifeld, D. Lee, Org. Lett. *6*, 2773-6 (2004).

Nitrogen ↑   ORem ↓↑ N

Magnesium triflate $Mg(OTf)_2$
Catalytic O-silylation with hexamethyldisilazane   OH → OSi≤
with $Cu(OTf)_2$ cf. *60*, 55s*65*; of prim. and sec. aliphatic alcohols, benzyl and allyl alcohols, and phenols with $Mg(OTf)_2$ s. H. Firouzabadi, N. Iranpoor et al., J. Organometal. Chem. *689*, 3197-202 (2004).

Palladium-carbon   Pd-C
Nucleoside triphosphates   ←
s. *10*, 125s*56*; f. method from nucleoside phosphoromonoamidic acid benzyl esters via hydrogenolytic O-debenzylation (with Pd-C) and coupling with tris(tetra-*n*-benzylammonium) hydrogen pyrophosphate s. W.D. Wu, C.L.F. Meyers, R.F. Borch, Org. Lett. *6*, 2257-60 (2004).

Formation of O-C Bond

Uptake   ⇓

Addition to Hydrogen and Carbon   OC ⇓ HC

Irradiation s. under Tetraphenylporphyrin
Microwaves s. under $KHSO_5$

Lithium diisopropylamide/triisopropyl borate/potassium peroxymonosulfate   ←
Oxindoles from indoles   ←
with persulfate cf. *15*, 151; one-pot procedure for preparing N-Boc-oxindoles via 2-indolylboronic acid esters (by reaction with LDA/(*i*-PrO)$_3$B) and oxidation of the latter with Oxone s. E. Vazquez, J.F. Payack, Tetrahedron Lett. *45*, 6549-50 (2004).

Sodium nitrite s. under HNO_3 $NaNO_2$

Tetraphenylporphyrin/L-alanine/irradiation   ←
Organocatalyzed asym. α-hydroxylation of ketones with singlet oxygen   H → OH

55.

Cyclohexanone added to a vial containing a mixture of 1 mol% tetraphenylporphyrin and 20 mol% L-alanine in DMSO at room temp., the soln. irradiated with a 250 W high-pressure sodium lamp for 1 h while bubbling O_2 through the mixture, then quenched with brine → product. Y 87% (e.e. 56%). This is the first example of an amino acid-catalyzed asym. incorporation of singlet oxygen into ketones, reaction possibly involving the intermediate formation of a chiral α-hydroperoxyiminium ion. Enantioselectivity was highest with natural alanine or valine (higher than with natural proline!), and the procedure is simple, inexpensive and environmentally friendly. F.e. and solvent effect, also comparison with related chiral organocatalysts, and chiral glycols by *in situ*-reduction of the hydroxyketones s. H. Sundén, A. Córdova et al., Angew. Chem. Int. Ed. Engl. *43*, 6532-5 (2004).

Cumene hydroperoxide/dihydroquinine   ←
Asym. α-hydroxylation of β-ketocarboxylic acid esters
with *t*-BuOOH and cinchona-based auxiliaries s. *66*, 61; f. reagent combinations, incl. cumene hydroperoxide/dihydroquinine, s. M.R. Acocella, K.A. Jørgensen et al., J. Org. Chem. *69*, 8165-7 (2004).

Nitric acid/sodium nitrite $\quad HNO_3/NaNO_2$
Carboxylic acids from aldehydes $\quad CHO \rightarrow COOH$
s. *6*, 170; α,α-dichlorocarboxylic acids s. F. Bellesia, P. Strazzolini et al., Synth. Commun. *34*, 1473-81 (2004).

Potassium peroxymonosulfate s.a. under LDA $\quad KHSO_5$
$\quad \leftarrow$

Potassium peroxymonosulfate/alumina/microwaves
Carboxylic acids from aldehydes
with Oxone in aq. EDTA cf. *54*, 63; arylcarboxylic acids, rapid procedure under microwave irradiation in the absence of solvent with Oxone/Al$_2$O$_3$ and a little water, s. M.M.A. Nikje, M.A. Bigdeli, Phosphorus, Sulfur Silicon Relat. Elem. *179*, 1445-8 (2004).

Iodine/potassium hydroxide $\quad I_2/KOH$
α-Hydroxyacetals from oxo compds. $\quad COCH \rightarrow C(OR)_2C(OH)$

56.

The startg. aldehyde added over several min to a soln. of 2.4 eqs. KOH (85%) in anhydrous methanol at -10°, the mixture aged for 5-10 min, a soln. of 1.1 eqs. I$_2$ in the same solvent added over 1 h, gradually warmed to room temp., and worked up after a further 1 h → product. Y 72%. The procedure is safer, less expensive, cleaner and higher-yielding than routes based on iodine(III) compds. and anodic processes, but apparently limited to aldehydes and 6-membered cyclic ketones. N-Carbo-*tert*-butoxy groups remained unaffected. F.e.s. M.J. Zacuto, D. Cai, Tetrahedron Lett. *46*, 447-50 (2005).

Microencapsulated methylrhenium oxide $\quad \leftarrow$
Heterogeneous oxidation of hydrocarbons in ionic liquids $\quad \leftarrow$

57.

A clean and efficient insertion of environmentally friendly H$_2$O$_2$ into the C-H bond of hydrocarbons can be effected with *heterogenized* methylrhenium oxide in ionic liquids. E: 100 mg microencapsulated MeReO$_3$ (in polystyrene 2% cross-linked with divinylbenzene) and 4-6 eqs. H$_2$O$_2$ added portionwise to a soln. of 1 mmol adamantane in 1-ethyl-3-methylimidazolium triflimide at 60°, and the product extracted with ether after 48 h → adamantanol. Conversion 72% (Y 72%). The supported catalyst is more active and selective than MeReO$_3$ itself, and can be recycled in the ionic liquid several times with no apparent loss of activity. F.e. and comparison of supported catalysts, also ketones from sec. alcohols, s. G. Bianchini, M. Crucianelli, R. Saladino et al., Tetrahedron Lett. *46*, 2427-32 (2005).

Addition to Oxygen and Nitrogen OC ⇓ ON

(S)-2-(Trifluoromethanesulfonylmethyl)pyrrolidine $\quad \leftarrow$
Organocatalyzed asym. α-aminooxylation of ketones $\quad H \rightarrow ONHR$
with L-proline cf. *40*, 57; of acyclic and cyclic ketones with (S)-2-(trifluoromethanesulfonylmethyl)pyrrolidine (e.e. 97-9%), also chiral 2-aminooxyalcohols from aldehydes via *in situ*-reduction with NaBH$_4$, s. W. Wang et al., Tetrahedron Lett. *45*, 7235-8 (2004).

Addition to Oxygen and Carbon OC ⇓ OC

4-Dimethylaminopyridine/p-methoxyphenol $\quad \leftarrow$
Zinc halide/1-n-butyl-3-methylimidazolium halide $\quad ZnHal_2/[bmim]Hal$
1,3-Dioxolan-2-ones from epoxides
with ZnBr$_2$/pyridine cf. *23*, 139s66; with readily recyclable ZnCl$_2$ in 1-*n*-butyl-3-methylimidazolium bromide **as ionic liquid** under 1.5 MPa CO$_2$ s. F. Li, C. Xia et al., Tetrahedron Lett.

45, 8307-10 (2004); styrene carbonate with ZnBr$_2$/1-*n*-butyl-3-methylimidazolium chloride cf. J. Sun, M. Arai et al., Green Chem. *6*, 613-6 (2004); with DMAP/*p*-methoxyphenol under 3.57 MPa CO$_2$ (cf. *23*, 139s67), also 2-oxazolidones from aziridines, and with N,N'-bis(salicylidene)-2,2'-diamino-1,1'-binaphthyl, s. Y.M. Shen, W.L. Duan, M. Shi, Eur. J. Org. Chem. *2004*, 3080-9; with [(1R,2R)-N,N'-bis(3,5-di-*tert*-butylsalicylidene)-1,2-cyclohexanediamine]cobalt(III) chloride/DMAP s. R.L. Paddock, S.T. Nguyen, Chem. Commun. *2004*, 1622-3.

Ion exchanger-supported tetrahydridoborate s. under Ni(OAc)$_2$ BH$_4^-$

Diisobutylaluminum hydride   i-Bu$_2$AlH
Tishchenko reaction   2 CHO → COOCH
with siloxyaluminum alkoxides cf. *58*, 58s67; with *i*-Bu$_2$AlH for coupling of aliphatic aldehydes possessing a sec., tert. or quaternary α-carbon atom s. Y.-S. Hon, C.-P. Chang, Y.-C. Wong, Tetrahedron Lett. *45*, 3313-5 (2004).

Triethylborane s. under RhCl(PPh$_3$)$_3$ Et$_3$B
Montmorillonite s. under P$_2$O$_5$ ←

Indium(III) bromide   InBr$_3$
Acylals from aldehydes   CHO → CH(OAc)$_2$
with CAN cf. *56*, 63s64, with Fe$_2$(SO$_4$)$_3$·xH$_2$O in the absence of solvent s. *38*, 100s66, and with zeolites cf. *51*, 55; with InBr$_3$ in the absence of solvent cf. L. Yin, Y.-M. Wang et al., Synlett *2004*, 1727-30; in the absence of solvent with reusable Mo/TiO$_2$-ZrO$_2$ s. B.M. Reddy, P.M. Sreekanth, A. Khan, Synth. Commun. *34*, 1839-45 (2004); solid-state procedure with P$_2$O$_5$/montmorillonite ('clayphos') s. H. Eshghi, Z. Gordi, Phosphorus, Sulfur Silicon Relat. Elem. *179*, 1341-6 (2004); with Fe$_2$(SO$_4$)$_3$·xH$_2$O, s.a. Chin. Chem. Lett. *15*, 508-10 (2004).

Scandium(III) triflate s.a. under Bi(OTf)$_3$ Sc(OTf)$_3$

Scandium(III) triflate/(R,R)-6,6'-bis(1-hydroxy-2,2-dimethylpropyl)-2,2'-bipyridyl   ←
Nucleophilic ring opening of epoxides with desymmetrization   C.

58.

(Y 95%; e.e. 93%)

Chiral glycol monoethers. A soln. of 10 mol% Sc(OTf)$_3$ and 10 mol% (R,R)-6,6'-bis(1-hydroxy-2,2-dimethylpropyl)-2,2'-bipyridyl in anhydrous methylene chloride stirred under N$_2$ at room temp. for 5 min, treated at the same temp. with 1 eq. *cis*-stilbene oxide and 2 eqs. *p*-methoxybenzyl alcohol, and stirring continued under N$_2$ for 12 h → product. Y 82% (e.e. 97%). High yields and enantioselectivities were recorded with complete diastereoselectivity. F.e., **also chiral 2-arylamino-alcohols** with anilines (aliphatic amines being unreactive), s. C. Schneider, A.R. Sreekanth, E. Mai, Angew. Chem. Int. Ed. Engl. *43*, 5691-4 (2004).

Ytterbium(III) triflate   Yb(OTf)$_3$
2-Alkoxyacylamines from Δ^2-oxazolines
2-acylamino-2-deoxy-β-glycosides with CuCl$_2$ cf. *63*, 63; with Yb(OTf)$_3$ s. C.F. Crasto, G.B. Jones, Tetrahedron Lett. *45*, 4891-4 (2004); from carbohydrate 2-trichloromethyl-Δ^2-oxazolines with Me$_3$SiOTf s. T.J. Donohoe, J.G. Logan, D.D.P. Laffan, Org. Lett. *5*, 4995-8 (2003).

Imidazolium ionic liquids s. under ZnHal$_2$ ←

Hydrolases   ←
Glycols from epoxides with kinetic resolution   ▽O → C(OH)C(OH)
s. *48*, 108s66; enhancement of enantioselectivity with directly evolved *mutant* hydrolases from *Aspergillus niger* s. M.T. Reetz, Org. Lett. *6*, 177-80 (2004).

Glycols from epoxides with enzymatic desymmetrization
Screening of enzymes from environmental libraries

$\overset{O}{\triangle} \rightarrow C(OH)C(OH)$

59.

A diverse library of novel microbial epoxide hydrolases has been discovered from numerous global habitats, exhibiting a wide substrate specificity in the hydrolytic desymmetrization of epoxides, and offering high enantioselectivities for the preparation of both (R,R)- and, *for the first time*, (S,S)-glycols. E: A soln. of the startg. *meso*-epoxide (2 mg/ml) in sodium phosphate buffer (pH 7.5 with 5% v/v acetonitrile) treated with epoxide hydrolase BD8877 (1 mg/ml, as a lyophilized cell lysate), and stirred at 22° for 18 h → product. Y 78% (e.e. 99%; TOF 16.5). F.e. incl. desymmetrization of bulky internal epoxides (such as *cis*-stilbene oxide) s. L. Zhao, D.P. Weiner, M.J. Burk et al., J. Am. Chem. Soc. *126*, 11156-7 (2004).

Chiral 2-aminoureas
α-Acylaminocarboxylic acid esters from Δ²-5-oxazolones
Dynamic kinetic resolution with a bifunctional organocatalyst

C ←

60.

1.5 eqs. Allyl alcohol added to a soln. of 5 mol% chiral 2-aminourea in toluene, followed by a soln. of the startg. azlactone in the same solvent, and stirred at room temp. for 48 h → product. Conversion 96% (e.e. 72%). The carbonyl group of the azlactone is activated by hydrogen-bonding with the urea hydrogens, serving as a *quasi Lewis acid*, while the nucleophilicity of the alcohol is increased by hydrogen-bonding to Brønsted basic sites of the same reagent. Enantioselectivities are the highest recorded for non-enzymatic dynamic kinetic resolution, the rapid interconversion of the azlactone enantiomers being facilitated via preferential formation of one of two possible diastereoisomeric catalyst-azlactone supramolecular aggregates. F.e. and with chiral 2-aminothioureas (with e.e. up to 91%!) s. A. Berkessel et al., Angew. Chem. Int. Ed. Engl. *44*, 807-11 (2005); s.a. Chem. Commun. *2005*, 1898-9.

Titanium-zirconium dioxide s. under Mo — $TiO_2\text{-}ZrO_2$

5,10,15,20-Tetraphenylporphyrinatotin(IV) bis(triflate) — $[Sn(tpp)](OTf)_2$
Regiospecific ring opening of epoxides with O-nucleophiles ←
Metalloporphyrins as mild Lewis acid

61.

1.9 Mol% 5,10,15,20-tetraphenylporphyrinatotin(IV) bis(triflate) added to a soln. of the startg. epoxide in acetic acid, and stirred under reflux for 35 min → product. Y 99%. Reaction is applicable to the ring opening of a wide range of epoxides by acetic acid, prim., sec. and tert. alcohols, and water (aq. acetonitrile), cleavage taking place at the least substituted carbon atom of the epoxide (with the exception of styrene epoxide). Furthermore, *trans*-products were obtained from cyclohexene oxide. F.e., also thiiranes from epoxides, and **1,3-dioxolanes from epoxides**, s. M. Moghadam, S. Tangestaninejad et al., Tetrahedron *60*, 6105-11 (2004).

Phosphorus pentoxide/montmorillonite ←
Acylals from aldehydes by solid-state conversion s. *56*, 63s68 $CHO \rightarrow CH(OAc)_2$

Bismuth(III) triflate [or Scandium(III) triflate] $Bi(OTf)_3$ *[or* $Sc(OTf)_3$*]*
Thiele-Winter reaction ←
with H_2SO_4 cf. *8*, 165; with 2.5 mol% $Bi(OTf)_3$ or $Sc(OTf)_3$ s. J.S. Yadav et al., Tetrahedron Lett. *45*, 6037-9 (2004).

Trimethylsilyl triflate Me_3SiOTf
2-Trichloroacetylamino-2-deoxy-β-glycosides   C
from carbohydrate-fused 2-trichloromethyl-Δ^2-oxazolines s. *63*, 63s68

Sulfamic acid/acetic acid $H_2NSO_2NH_2/AcOH$
Diol esters from cyclic ethers under mild conditions

62.   [structure: tetrahydrofuran + Ac_2O → AcO—/\—OAc]

0.5 ml Tetrahydrofuran added to a mixture of 0.06 g sulfamic acid in 5 ml acetic acid and 5 ml acetic anhydride, and stirred for 4 h at 60° → product. Y 97%. Sulfamic acid is a useful, green alternative to metal-containing acidic reagents, being suitable for the ring opening of tetrahydrofurans and -pyrans, as well as less reactive 1,4-dioxane. The procedure is safe, convenient, simple and amenable to scale-up. F.e., also benzyl acetate from dibenzyl ether, s. B. Wang, L. Yang et al., Tetrahedron Lett. *45*, 6599-602 (2004).

Molybdenum/titanium-zirconium dioxide Mo/TiO_2-ZrO_2
Acylals from aldehydes in the absence of solvent s. *56*, 63s68 $CHO \rightarrow CH(OAc)_2$

*[(1R,2R)-N,N'-Bis(3,5-di-*tert-*butylsalicylidene)-1,2-cyclohexanediamine]cobalt(III)* ←
chloride/4-dimethylaminopyridine
1,3-Dioxolan-2-ones from epoxides s. *23*, 139s68   ○

Nickel(II) acetate/ion exchanger-supported tetrahydridoborate ←
α-Acylaminocarboxylic acid derivs. from 4-alkylidene-Δ^2-5-oxazolones   C
α-acylaminocarboxylic acid amides with Raney nickel cf. *28*, 288; α-acylaminocarboxylic acid esters with $Ni(OAc)_2$/ion exchanger-supported tetrahydridoborate, α-benzyl derivs., s. A.P. Sikdar, A.B. Chetri, P.J. Das, Indian J. Chem. *42B*, 2878-81 (2003).

Chlorotris(triphenylphosphine)rhodium(I)/triethylborane $RhCl(PPh_3)_3/Et_3B$
Glycol monoethers from epoxides and aldehydes $\triangleleft_O \rightarrow C(OH)C(OR)$
Regiospecific reductive ring opening with retention of configuration

63.   [reaction scheme with intermediates involving [Rh]-H, Et_2BCl, Et_2BO, [Rh]Cl, Ph, etc.]

A mixture of 2.6 mol% $RhCl(PPh_3)_3$, 2.2 eqs. (R)-propylene oxide, 1 eq. benzaldehyde, and 2.1 eqs. Et_3B stirred under N_2 at room temp. for 16 h → product. Y 82% (e.e. >99%). This unprecedented reductive coupling is applicable to the ring opening of aliphatic and aromatic epoxides with ar. or heteroar. aldehydes (regioselectivity >95%), yields being low with aliphatic aldehydes and ketones. Unusually, the catalytic cycle is initiated by epoxide ring opening (possible with the intervention of a rhodium hydride complex), followed by reduction of the aldehyde *with the trialkylborane*. F.e.s. C. Molinaro, T.F. Jamison, Angew. Chem. Int. Ed. Engl. *44*, 129-32 (2005).

Addition to Nitrogen and Carbon   OC ⇓ NC

Pyridine N-oxides s. under Ruthenium(IV) complexes

Resin-supported lipase
Aminocarboxylic acids from lactams with enzymatic kinetic resolution

64.

2 g Lipolase adsorbed on a macroporous resin and 0.13 ml water added to 1 g startg. racemic lactam in diisopropyl ether, shaken in an incubator at 70° for 1 day (50% conversion), the enzyme filtered off, the filtrate evaporated, and the residue crystallized → (1S,2R,3S,4R)-β-amino acid (Y 46%; e.e. 99%) and (1S,2R,5S,6R)-epoxide (Y 40%; e.e. 99%). F.e.s. E. Forro, F. Fülöp, Tetrahedron:Asym. *15,* 573-5 (2004); from carbocyclic-fused β-lactams s. Org. Lett. *5,* 1209-12 (2003); with lipase B (from *Candida antarctica*) s. S. Park, F. Fülöp et al., Adv. Synth. Catal. *345,* 986-95 (2003).

Dichloro(5,10,15,20-tetramesitylporphyrinato)ruthenium(IV)/2,6-dichloropyridine N-oxide
Acylaminocarboxylic acids from cyclic N-acylamines

65.

A mixture of 1 eq. N-benzoyl-L-proline (0.16 *M*), 2.5 eqs. 2,6-dichloropyridine N-oxide, and 0.6 mol% dichloro(5,10,15,20-tetramesitylporphyrinato)ruthenium(IV) in anhydrous benzene stirred under argon at 40° overnight → N-benzoyl-L-glutamic acid. Y 91%. The procedure is highly efficient (TONs up to 5000), leaves chiral centres intact, and is not complicated by lactam formation (as takes place with RuO₄). Reaction takes place via initial N-α-hydroxylation, followed by ring opening to the acylaminoaldehyde prior to a second oxidation. F.e., **also dicarboxylic acid imides from lactams**, s. R. Ito, N. Umezawa, T. Higuchi, J. Am. Chem. Soc. *127,* 834-5 (2005).

Addition to Carbon-Carbon Bonds   OC ⇓ CC

Microwaves s. under VO(acac)₂
n-Butyllithium s. under Hydroperoxides

Potassium bis(trimethylsilyl)amide/18-crown-6 polyether
Asym. Michael addition with a chiral lactol as water surrogate
to 1,1-nitroethylene derivs. cf. *66,* 70; to alkylidenemalonic acid esters s. D.J. Buchanan, D.J. Dixon, F.A. Hernandez-Juan, Org. Lett. *6,* 1357-60 (2004).

1,8-Diazabicyclo[5.4.0]undec-7-ene
Amine-catalyzed Michael addition under mild conditions

66.

of alcohols. 5 Mol% 1,8-diazabicyclo[5.4.0]undec-7-ene added via syringe to a soln. of methyl vinyl ketone in excess of isopropanol at room temp., and stirred for 8.5 h → product. Y 97%. The procedure is an improvement on that with triphenylphosphine (cf. *48,* 129s66) in terms of convenience, cost, simpler [acidic] work-up, and experimentation, which can be conducted *in air* without degassing the solvent. It is applicable to the Michael addition of prim. or sec. alcohols to a range of α,β-ethylene-ketones, -nitriles and -esters, as well as the Michael addition of pyrrole, and the double Michael addition of alcohols to α,β-acetyleneoxo compds. to give the corresponding β-dioxo compd. monoacetals. The active nucleophile is alkoxide ion generated *in situ* via initial Michael addition of the amine, followed by deprotonation of the alcohol with the intermediate ammonioenolate. F.e.s. J.E. Murtagh, S.H. McCooey, S.J. Connon, Chem. Commun. *2005*, 227-9.

N-Methylmorpholine N-oxide s. under Manganese(III) complexes and OsO$_4$ R_3NO
Pyridine N-oxides s. under Ruthenium(IV) complexes   ←

Cupric sulfate $CuSO_4$
Protection of hydroxyl groups as tetrahydropyran-2-yl ethers   OH → OThp
with LiBF$_4$ cf. *56*, 73s*64*; of tert. alcohols with LiPF$_6$ s. N. Hamada, T. Sato, Synlett *2004*, 1802-4; general procedure for protection of alkanols and phenols with CuSO$_4$ in acetonitrile (cf. *49*, 127s*52*), also deprotection with CuSO$_4$ in methanol, s. A.T. Khan, L.H. Choudhury, S. Ghosh, Tetrahedron Lett. *45*, 7891-4 (2004).

Cuprous chloride/1-n-butyl-3-methylimidazolium benzenesulfonate $CuCl/[bmim][PhSO_3]$
5,5-Disubst. 4-methylene-1,3-dioxolan-2-ones from 2-acetylene-*tert*-alcohols
with cobaltocene/Et$_3$N cf. *42*, 127; with CuCl immobilized **in ionic liquids**, e.g. 1-*n*-butyl-3-methylimidazolium benzenesulfonate, for efficient recycling of catalyst/medium s. Y. Gu, F. Shi, Y. Deng, J. Org. Chem. *69*, 391-4 (2004).

Cuprous iodide   CuI
1-Alkoxy-3-isochromenes from *o*-acetylenealdehydes
with Pd(OAc)$_2$/benzophenone cf. *63*, 80; with CuI s. N.T. Patil, Y. Yamamoto, J. Org. Chem. *69*, 5139-42 (2004).

Silver triflate s. under Ruthenium(III) complexes   AgOTf

Auric chloride $AuCl_3$
3-α-Functionalized furans from 2-acyl-1,3-enynes under mild conditions

67.

3-α-Alkoxyfurans. A soln. of 1 eq. of the startg. 2-acyl-1,3-enyne and 1.5 eqs. of the startg. alcohol in methylene chloride treated with a soln. of 1 mol% AuCl$_3$ in acetonitrile, and stirred at room temp. for 1 h → product. Y 63% (d.r. 1.2:1). Reaction appears to involve initial activation of the alkyne group by the catalyst, followed by intramolecular oxyauration and quenching of the generated carbocation by the nucleophile prior to protonation. The procedure is applicable to acyclic and cyclic substrates, and the nucleophile may be an alcohol, a β-diketone, an electron-rich arene or an indole. However, the terminal carbon of the alkyne residue can only support an aryl or vinyl group. F.e.s. T. Yao, X. Zhang, R.C. Larock, J. Am. Chem. Soc. *126*, 11164-5 (2004).

Diethylzinc/(R)-1,1'-bi-2-naphthol/cumene hydroperoxide $Et_2Zn/(R)$-BINOL/ROOH
Asym. epoxidation of α,β-ethyleneketones
with Et$_2$Zn/(1R,2R)-N-methylpseudoephedrine/O$_2$ cf. *52*, 68s*60*; with Et$_2$Zn/(R)-BINOL/cumene hydroperoxide s. A. Minatti, K.H. Dötz, Synlett *2004*, 1634-6.

Catecholborane s. under Chiral rhodium(I) complexes   ←

Bis[(R,R)-N,N'-bis(3,5-di-tert-butylsalicylidenato)cyclohexane-1,2-diamine]- ←
(μ-oxo)aluminum
N-Acyl-β-hydroxy-   C=C → CHC(ON=CHAr)
from N-acyl-α,β-ethylene-carboxylic acid amides
via asym. Michael addition of *o*-hydroxyoximes

68.

R = i-PrOCOCH$_2$CH$_2$

A soln. of 1 eq. startg. α,β-unsatd. imide and 1.2 eqs. salicylaldoxime in cyclohexane treated with 5 mol% bis[(R,R)-N,N'-bis(3,5-di-*tert*-butylsalicylidenato)cyclohexane-1,2-diamine](μ-oxo)-aluminum, and stirred at 23° under N$_2$ for 48 h → crude oxime ether, in ethanol treated with 2 eqs. acetic acid and 20% Pd(OH)$_2$/C, and hydrogenated with stirring at 23° under H$_2$ (1 atm.) for 3-6 h until reaction complete → product. Y 88%. The protocol corresponds to a net enantioselective Michael-type hydration, reaction being tolerant of esters, acetals and silyl ethers. F.e. and comparison of chiral aluminum salen complexes, also conversion to chiral β-hydroxycarboxylic acid esters (on ethanolysis with Er(OTf)$_3$), s. C.D. Vanderwal, E.N. Jacobsen, J. Am. Chem. Soc. *126*, 14724-5 (2004).

Dimethylaluminum chloride/(R)-3,3'-diphenyl-1,1'-bi-2-naphthol/cumene ←
  hydroperoxide
Asym. Baeyer-Villiger oxidation ←
with (S)-BINOL as auxiliary cf. *50*, 61s63; chiral γ-lactones with (R)-3,3'-diphenyl-1,1'-bi-2-naphthol s. C. Bolm et al., Synlett *2004*, 1619-21.

Scandium(III) perfluorooctanesulfonimide/hydrogen peroxide   Sc[N(SO$_2$C$_8$F$_{17}$)$_2$]$_3$/H$_2$O$_2$
Baeyer-Villiger oxidation ←
with tin(IV) perfluoroctanesulfonimide cf. *66*, 77; with scandium(III) perfluorooctanesulfonimide *at low catalyst loading* (<<0.1 mol%) **in a microreactor** under nanoflow for *perfect* regio-control s. K. Mikami et al., Tetrahedron Lett. *45*, 3681-3 (2004).

Lanthanum triisopropoxide/(R)-1,1'-bi-2-naphthol/tris(4-fluorophenyl)phosphine ←
  oxide/cumene hydroperoxide
Asym. epoxidation of α,β-ethyleneketones   C=C → \o/
s. *53*, 61s60, 67; improved enantioselectivity (e.e. 92-9%) with tris(4-fluorophenyl)phosphine oxide as additive s. R. Kino, J. Inanaga et al., Org. Biomol. Chem. *2*, 1822-4 (2004).

Ammonium ceric nitrate s. under m-*Chloroperoxybenzoic acid*	CAN
Isobutyraldehyde s. under *RuCl$_3$*	i-*PrCHO*
Imidazolium ionic liquids s. under *CuCl, OsO$_4$ and K$_2$OsO$_4$*	←
tert-*Butyl hydroperoxide* s. under *VO(acac)$_2$*	t-*BuOOH*
Cumene hydroperoxide s. under *Et$_2$Zn, Me$_2$AlCl and La(OPr-i)$_3$*	ROOH

(1S,2S,4R)-2-Hydroperoxy-2-(2-furyl)bicyclo[2.2.1]heptane/n-butyllithium   ROOH/BuLi
Asym. anionic epoxidation
with trityl hydroperoxide/*n*-BuLi/diisopropyl L-tartrate cf. *42*, 115s62; asym. epoxidation of chalcones and 1,4-naphthoquinones with (1S,2S,4R)-2-hydroperoxy-2-(2-furyl)bicyclo[2.2.1]-heptane/BuLi s. A. Lattanzi, A. Scettri et al., Tetrahedron:Asym. *15*, 3751-5 (2004).

Dimethyldioxirane or Methyl(trifluoromethyl)dioxirane
Epoxidation   ←
     C=C → C(O)C
s. *44*, 117; regiospecific epoxidation of 3-cinnamoylcoumarins s. A. Levai, J. Jeko, D.I. Brahmbhatt, J. Heterocycl. Chem. *41*, 707-9 (2004); of 3-cinnamoyl-4-chromones s. ibid. 439-41; **asym. induction** on epoxidation of chiral 1-(α,β-ethyleneacyl)-3-pyrazolidones with methyl(trifluoromethyl)dioxirane (cf. *44*, 117s66), also reversal of face-selectivity with urea-H_2O_2/Ac_2O, s. C.L. Fan, Y.-C. Sun, K. Chen et al., J. Org. Chem. *68*, 9816-8 (2003).

Peroxyacetic acid $MeCOO_2H$
Baeyer-Villiger oxidation   ←
s. *19*, 190s20; of hydroxyadamantanones and conversion to their (meth)acrylates s. K. Inoue, S. Nagano, Japanese patent JP-2002284785 (Daicel Chem. Ind. Ltd.).

m-Chloroperoxybenzoic acid s.a. under Manganese(III) complexes $ArCOO_2H$

m-Chloroperoxybenzoic acid/ammonium ceric nitrate $ArCOO_2H/CAN$
Lewis acid-catalyzed Baeyer-Villiger oxidation   ←
with added $Bi(OTf)_3$ as catalyst cf. *45*, 70s66; with added CAN (6.7 mol%) s. P. Goswami, P. Chowdhury et al., Indian J. Chem. *43B*, 1275-81 (2004).

N-Bromosuccinimide or Trichloroisocyanuric acid   ←
Protection of hydroxyl groups as tetrahydropyran-2-yl ethers   OH → OThp
in the absence of solvent

69.

(94%)

10 Mol% Trichloroisocyanuric acid added to a mixture of 4-chlorobenzyl alcohol and 1.2-1.6 eqs. 3,4-dihydro-2H-pyran, and stirred at 60-80° for 5 h → product. Y 92%. The procedure, based on the *in situ*-generation of HCl, is safe and inexpensive, being suitable for the protection of phenols and alcohols (prim., sec. or tert.), with **preferential protection** of the latter in the presence of the former. **Removal of the protective group** was accomplished using the same catalyst in methanol. F.e. incl. protection of steroidal, cyclic, benzylic, allylic and propargylic alcohols s. H. Firouzabadi, N. Iranpoor, H. Hazarkhani, Synth. Commun. *34*, 3623-30 (2004); protection with NBS cf. B. Das, M.R. Reddy et al., Indian J. Chem. *43B*, 1711-2 (2004).

Phenylsilane s. under Manganese(III) complexes $PhSiH_3$

P4-Phosphazene base   ←
Enolethers from acetylene derivs.   C≡C → C(OR)=CH
(E)-β-alkoxy-α,β-ethylenecarboxylic acid esters with Bu_3P cf. *48*, 129; addition of O- and N-nucleophiles to acetylene derivs. with 10 mol% *t*-Bu-P4 base s. T. Imahori, C. Hori, Y. Kondo, Adv. Synth. Catal. *346*, 1090-2 (2004).

Lithium hexafluorophosphate $LiPF_6$
Protection of hydroxyl groups as tetrahydropyran-2-yl ethers s. *56*, 73s68   OH → OThp

Vanadyl acetoacetonate/tert-butyl hydroperoxide/microwaves   ←
Epoxidation   C=C → C(O)C
s. *24*, 149s31; of hindered 3-ethylenealcohols, rapid procedure under microwave irradiation, and application to polypropionate synthesis, s. G. Torres, W. Torres, J.A. Prieto, Tetrahedron *60*, 10245-51 (2004).

Hydrogen peroxide s. under $Sc[N(SO_2C_8H_{17})_2]_3$, Oxodiperoxymolybdate complexes, H_2O_2
   Manganese(III) complexes, Rhenium(IV) complexes, Ruthenium(II) complexes,
   and K_2OsO_4

p-*Toluenesulfonic acid*   *TsOH*
Ketones from acetylene derivs.   C≡C → CH$_2$CO
with H$_2$SO$_4$ cf. *2*, 818; aryl ketones from electron-rich arylacetylenes with TsOH·H$_2$O in ethanol s. N. Olivi, M. Alami et al., Synlett *2004*, 2175-9; selenolic acid aryl esters from ar. 1-acetylene-1-selenides in methylene chloride (cf. *11*, 87s*64*) s. M. Tiecco, K. Testaferri et al., Eur. J. Org. Chem. *2004*, 3447-58.

Potassium peroxymonosulfate/polyethylene glycol-based 4-hydroxy-   ←
   α,α,α-*trifluoroacetophenone*
Epoxidation with supported ketones as dioxirane precursor   C=C → ⳩
heterogeneous conversion with silica-supported trifluoromethyl ketones cf. *60*, 67; more rapid procedure with readily recoverable, *soluble* polyethylene glycol-based 4-hydroxy-α,α,α-trifluoro-acetophenone in aq. medium s. J.T.W. Kan, P.H. Toy, Tetrahedron Lett. *45*, 6357-9 (2004).

Potassium peroxymonosulfate/2,3,3-trimethyl-7-nitro-3,4-dihydroisoquinolinium   ←
   fluoroborate/sodium hydrogen carbonate
Epoxidation
with Oxone/ketones and NaHCO$_3$ cf. *37*, 128s*57*; general procedure with 2,3,3-trimethyl-7-nitro-3,4-dihydroisoquinolinium fluoroborate in place of the ketone s. L. Bohé, M. Kammoun, Tetrahedron Lett. *45*, 747-51 (2004).

Tetraphenylphosphonium oxodiperoxy(salicylaldoximinato)molybdate/hydrogen peroxide/   ←
   sodium hydrogen carbonate
Improved molybdenum(VI)-catalyzed epoxidation

70.

with hydrogen peroxide as reoxidant. A mixture of 0.25 eqs. NaHCO$_3$, 5 eqs. H$_2$O$_2$, *0.05 mol%* tetraphenylphosphonium oxodiperoxy(salicylaldoximinato)molybdate and norbornene in acetonitrile stirred for 20 min at 25° → product. Y 94%. The oxodiperoxomolybdate, in combination with NaHCO$_3$ *as co-catalyst* and inexpensive H$_2$O$_2$ as reoxidant, offers enormous efficiency (relative to established Mo(VI) complexes) for the rapid, economical and environmentally friendly epoxidation of a wide range of functionalized or non-functionalized benzylic, carbocyclic, aromatic and aliphatic systems at low catalyst loadings with high TONs. However, if reactions were allowed to continue longer than necessary, glycols were obtained as by-products. F.e.s. N. Gharah, R. Bhattacharyya et al., Chem. Commun. *2004*, 2630-2.

Sodium hypochlorite/chiral spirocyclic quaternary ammonium bromides   ←
Asym. epoxidation of *trans*-α,β-ethyleneketones
with 9-O-benzyl-N-(4-methoxy-3,5-di-*tert*-butylbenzyl)cinchonidinium bromide as phase transfer catalyst cf. *18*, 193s*66*; with chiral 1,1'-binaphthyl- or biphenyl-based spirocyclic quaternary ammonium bromides possessing two hydroxyl groups to enhance face-selectivity through H-bonding s. T. Ooi, K. Maruoka et al., J. Am. Chem. Soc. *126*, 6844-5 (2004).

Sodium chlorite s. under K$_2$OsO$_4$ *NaClO$_2$*

Tris(dipivaloylmethanato)manganese(III)/phenylsilane   *Mn(dpm)$_3$/PhSiH$_3$*
α-Hydroxy- from α,β-ethylene-carboxylic acid amides   C=C → CHC(OH)
Regiospecific manganese(III)-catalyzed aerobic hydration with asym. induction

71.

A soln. of the startg. chiral α,β-ethylenecarboxylic acid amide in isopropanol added to a soln. of 5 mol% tris(dipivaloylmethanato)manganese(III) in the same solvent at 0° under 1 atm. O$_2$, treated with 2 eqs. phenylsilane, stirred for 2 h at the same temp., and quenched with satd. aq. $Na_2S_2O_3$ → product. Y 79% (diastereoselectivity 84%). Chiral auxiliaries based on 2-oxazolidones, sultams, and C_2-symmetric cyclic α,α'-diphenylamines gave lower diastereoselectivities, results being optimum with (S,S)-2,5-bis(2-naphthyl)pyrrolidine. F.e.s. M. Sato, T. Yamada et al., Chem. Lett. *33*, 1304-5 (2004).

Manganese(III) porphyrin complexes/hydrogen peroxide/ammonium acetate ←
Epoxidation $C=C → \overset{O}{\triangle}$
s. *39*, 124s67; **of arenes** to provide *anti*-1,2,3,4-diepoxides (from naphthalenes) and the 9,10-epoxide from phenanthrene s. S.L.H. Rebelo, J.A.S. Cavaleiro et al., Chem. Commun. *2004*, 608-9; with readily recyclable PEG-based manganese porphyrin complexes s. M. Benaglia, T. Danelli, G. Pozzi, Org. Biomol. Chem. *1*, 454-6 (2003).

Chiral manganese(II) salen complexes/N-methylmorpholine N-oxide/ ←
  m-*chloroperoxybenzoic acid*
Asym. epoxidation
with chiral, hindered manganese(II) salen complexes and NaOCl as reoxidant cf. *46*, 106s67; with carbohydrate-based complexes for asym. epoxidation of styrenes s. C. Borriello, F. Ruffo et al., Tetrahedron:Asym. *15*, 681-6 (2004).

Chiral mesoporous silica-supported manganese(III) salen complexes/hydrogen peroxide/ ←
  sodium hydrogen carbonate
Heterogeneous asym. epoxidation
with NaOCl as reoxidant cf. *46*, 106s67; with H_2O_2 s. X.M. Zheng, Y.X. Qi et al., Chin. Chem. Lett. *15*, 655-8 (2004).

Pentacarbonylrhenium(I) bromide $ReBr(CO)_5$
2-Subst. enolesters $C≡C → CH=C(OAc)$
from terminal acetylene derivs. and carboxylic acids
Regio- and stereo-specific conversion

72.   Ph—≡ + HOCOPh $\xrightarrow{[Re(CO)_4Br]}_{-HBr}$ [Ph\=/OCOPh, (CO)₄Re] $\xrightarrow{HBr}$ Ph\=/OCOPh

A mixture of phenylacetylene, 1.25 eqs. benzoic acid and 1 mol% $ReBr(CO)_5$ *in toluene* heated under air at 115° in a sealed tube for 15 h → product. Y 67% (regioselectivity 99%; Z/E 87:13). Anti-Markovnikov addition to give the (Z)-product predominates in hydrocarbon media, tetrachloroethane and dibutyl ether, but catalytic activity was lower in polar media with an increase in Markovnikov addition. This is the first example of an early transition metal-catalyzed addition of carboxylic acids to alkynes. Mechanistically, it appears that the catalyst initially decarbonylates to give 16-electron $Re(CO)_4Br$, which activates the triple bond of the alkyne prior to formation of a vinylrhenium species and its protonation. The catalyst can be partly recovered and reused when reactions are run in *n*-heptane. F.e. and with unsatd. carboxylic acids s. R. Hua, X. Tian, J. Org. Chem. *69*, 5782-4 (2004).

Bis(tetraphenylphosphonium) hexakis(thiocyanato)rhenium(IV)/hydrogen peroxide/ ←
  sodium hydrogen carbonate
Epoxidation $C=C → \overset{O}{\triangle}$
with $MeReO_3/H_2O_2$ cf. *47*, 111; with 0.25 mol% bis(tetraphenylphosphonium) hexakis(thiocyanato)rhenium(IV) for improved efficiency s. S. Dinda, R. Bhattacharyya et al., Tetrahedron Lett. *46*, 339-41 (2005).

Tetra-n-propylammonium perruthenate/tetra-n-butylammonium periodate ←
Oxidative ring closure of 1,5-dienes ○
cis-2-α,5-α-dihydroxytetrahydrofurans with $RuO_4/NaIO_4$ cf. *61*, 71s62; *cis*-2-α-hydroxy-5-α-ketotetrahydrofurans with tetra-*n*-propylammonium perruthenate/Bu_4NIO_4 s. V. Piccialli, T. Caserta, Tetrahedron Lett. *45*, 303-8 (2004).

Chiral (2,6-dicarboxylatopyridine)ruthenium(II) 2,2'-(pyridine-2,6-diyl)bis(5,6-dihydro- ←
4H-1,3-oxazine) complexes/hydrogen peroxide
Improved ruthenium-catalyzed asym. epoxidation   C=C → ⟨o⟩

73.

with hydrogen peroxide as reoxidant. A mixture of 5 mol% chiral (2,6-dicarboxylato-pyridine)ruthenium(II) 2,2'-(pyridine-2,6-diyl)bis(5,6-dihydro-4H-1,3-oxazine) complex in *tert*-amyl alcohol stirred at room temp. for 10 min, the startg. olefin added, followed over 12 h with a soln. of 30% H_2O_2 in the same solvent, then quenched with aq. Na_2SO_3 → product. Y >99% (e.e. 79%). The new 'pyboxazine' ligands afford the highest yields and chemoselectivities (e.e. up to 84%) to date for the asym. epoxidation of a range of mono-, di- and tri-subst. styrenes with H_2O_2 as stoichiometric oxidant, this being a useful complement to asym. Mn-catalyzed epoxidation. An intermediate chiral dioxoruthenium species is the presumed active catalyst. F.e. and asym. epoxidation of allyl acetate and chloride, also enhancement of enantioselectivity with added acetic acid, s. M.K. Tse, M. Beller et al., Angew. Chem. Int. Ed. Engl. *43*, 5255-60 (2004).

Acetonitrile(cycopentadienyl)bis[2-(diphenylphosphino)-6-tert-butylpyridine]ruthenium(II) ←
hexafluorophosphate/tetrakis(trimethylsilyl)methane
Aldehydes from terminal acetylene derivs.   C≡C → CH_2CHO
Ruthenium-catalyzed anti-Markovnikov hydration under mild, neutral conditions s. *68*, 118

Dichloro(pentamethylcyclopentadienyl)ruthenium(III) dimer/   [Cp*RuCl_2]_2/AgOTf/dppb
silver triflate/1,4-bis(diphenylphosphino)butane
Acoxy compds. from ethylene derivs.   C=C → CHC(OAc)

74.

A soln. of 1 mol% [Cp*RuCl$_2$]$_2$ in toluene heated at 85° for 15 min, treated with 6 mol% AgOTf, stirred at the same temp. for 3 h, treated with 2 mol% 1,4-bis(diphenylphosphino)butane, stirred again at the same temp. for 1 h, cooled to room temp., 1 eq. *o*-anisic acid and 1 eq. norbornene added, and stirred at 85° for a further 18 h → *exo*-product. Y 91%. This is the first example of such an addition without β-hydride elimination. However, reaction appears limited to arylcarboxylic acids, the highest yields being recorded with substrates possessing electron-withdrawing groups. F.e. and regioselectivity s. Y. Oe, T. Ohta, Y. Ito, Chem. Commun. *2004*, 1620-1.

Dichloro[tetrakis(2,6-dichlorophenyl)porphyrinato]ruthenium(IV)/2,6-dichloro- ←
pyridine N-oxide
Aldehydes from terminal ethylene derivs. under mild conditions   C=CH_2 → CHCHO

75.

β,γ-Ethylenealdehydes. A mixture of 1 eq. startg. alkene, 1.03 eqs. 2,6-dichloropyridine N-oxide and 0.5-2 mol% dichloro[tetrakis(2,6-dichlorophenyl)porphyrinato]ruthenium(IV) in deuteriochloroform stirred in an NMR tube at room temp. for 0.5 h → product. Y 90%. The procedure, which can be conducted in air, is highly regiospecific, devoid of C=C cleavage, and a useful supplement to Wacker oxidation. However, it appears limited to 1,3-dienes and styrenes, vinylcyclohexane, for example, undergoing epoxidation. F.e.s. J. Chen, C.M. Che, Angew. Chem. Int. Ed. Engl. *43*, 4950-4 (2004).

Ruthenium trichloride/1-methyl-2-(2-pyridyl)-4,6-bis(perfluorooctyl)benzimidazole/ ←
isobutyraldehyde
Ruthenium-catalyzed aerobic epoxidation in a fluorous 2-phase medium　　C=C → \\O/

76.

2 Mol% 1-methyl-2-(2-pyridyl)-4,6-bis(perfluorooctyl)benzimidazole in perfluorooctyl bromide and 1 mol% $RuCl_3·xH_2O$ in acetone added to a Schlenk tube, the resulting red soln. stirred for 0.5 h, 1 eq. *cis*-cyclooctene and 2 eqs. isobutyraldehyde in chlorobenzene added, the 2-phase mixture stirred at 40° for 1 h with passage of a gentle stream of O_2, cooled to 10° after 15 min, the organic layer (containing the product) decanted from the fluorous phase (containing the catalyst and fluorous ligand), the washed chlorobenzene, the organic layer and washings concentrated, the residue taken up in methylene chloride, and treated with cold aq. NaOH → product. Y 89%. The fluorous phase was recycled up to ten times with no apparent loss of activity, and there was no leaching of the metal. Esters and halogens were unaffected, but hydroxyl groups required protection. Terminal olefins were only partially converted. F.e. incl. epoxidation of enones s. G. Ragagnin, P. Knochel, Synlett *2004*, 951-4.

(1,5-Cyclooctadiene)(methoxy)rhodium(I) dimer　　　　　　　　　　　*[Rh(cod)(OMe)]₂*
β-Alkoxyketones from α,β-ethyleneketones　　　　　　　　　　　　C=C → CHC(OR)
Rhodium-catalyzed Michael addition of alcohols

77.

A soln. of phenyl vinyl ketone in benzene-d_6 treated with 1 mol% [Rh(cod)(OMe)]₂ and 1.1 eqs. 4-methoxybenzyl alcohol at 60° for 2-10 h → product. Y 92%. Reaction is generally applicable to the addition of prim. or sec. alcohols, incl. electron-rich and -deficient benzyl alcohols, to vinyl ketones, there being no conversion with cyclohexenone or pentenone. Low yields were obtained with phenol, while bulky tert. alcohols were unreactive. The catalyst may be generated *in situ* from methanolic [Rh(cod)Cl]₂ and Na_2CO_3. F.e. and solvent effect s. M.V. Farnworth, M.J. Cross, J. Louie, Tetrahedron Lett. *45*, 7441-3 (2004).

Chiral rhodium(I) phosphine complexes/catecholborane　　　　　　　←
Asym. hydroboration　　　　　　　　　　　　　　　　　　　　　C=C → CHC(OH)
s. *44*, 129s63, 67; chiral sec. benzylalcohols from styrenes with [(R)-1-[2-(diphenylphosphino)-1-naphthyl]-4-(1-phenylethoxy)phthalazine](1,5-cyclooctadiene)rhodium(I) fluoroborate s. T.E. Knopfel, E.M. Carreira et al., Angew. Chem. Int. Ed. Engl. *43*, 5971-3 (2004).

Chiral cationic palladium(II) 2-[o-(diphenylphosphino)phenyl]pyridine complexes　←
Asym. transition metal-catalyzed Baeyer-Villiger oxidation　　　　　　　　←
chiral γ-lactones with chiral cobalt(III) salen complexes/H_2O_2 cf. *62*, 80s65; with chiral cationic palladium(II) 2-[o-(diphenylphosphino)phenyl]pyridine complexes/urea-H_2O_2 (e.e. >99%) s. K. Ito, T. Katsuki et al., Synlett *2003*, 643-6.

Bis(acetonitrile)dichloropalladium(II) $PdCl_2(MeCN)_2$
α-Acoxy-α,β-ethyleneoxo compds. from acoxy-2-acetylenes $C(O)C(OAc)=C$
Palladium-catalyzed oxidative rearrangement

78.

0.2 eq. $PdCl_2(MeCN)_2$ added to a soln. of 1 eq. startg. propargyl acetate in anhydrous toluene under inert conditions, treated with 1 eq. water, and stirred at room temp. for 4-6 h → product. Y 71%. Water is critical to the conversion, but not oxygen. F.e.s. A. Bartels, R. Mahrwald, K. Müller, Adv. Synth. Catal. *346*, 483-5 (2004).

Dendritic osmium tetroxide/N-methylmorpholine N-oxide   ←
Glycols from ethylene derivs. s. *64*, 81s*66* $C≡C → C(OH)C(OH)$

Osmium tetroxide/N-methylmorpholine N-oxide/N-benzyl-1,4-bis(9-O-quinine)-   ←
   phthalazinium bromide/1-n-butyl-3-methylimidazolium hexafluorophosphate
Potassium osmate/N-methylmorpholine/1,3-dimethyl-5-ethyl-5,10-dihydroalloxazine/4-   ←
   dimethylaminopyridine/tetraethylammonium acetate/1-n-butyl-3-methylimidazolium
   hexafluorophosphate/hydrogen peroxide
Glycols from ethylene derivs. in ionic liquids
with OsO_4/N-methylmorpholine N-oxide cf. *64*, 81s*66*; with K_2OsO_4/N-methylmorpholine/1,3-dimethyl-5-ethyl-5,10-dihydroalloxazine/DMAP/Et_4NOAc in 1-*n*-butyl-3-methylimidazolium hexafluorophosphate (containing aq. acetone) with H_2O_2 as terminal oxidant (cf. *58*, 69) for improved recycling of the catalyst s. A. Closson, M. Johansson, J.E. Bäckvall, Chem. Commun. *2004*, 1494-5; **asym. dihydroxylation** with OsO_4/N-methylmorpholine N-oxide and a N-benzyl-1,4-bis(9-O-quinine)phthalazinium bromide in the same ionic liquid **or in polyethylene glycol** cf. R. Jiang, S. Zhang et al., Tetrahedron:Asym. *15*, 743-6 (2004); immobilization of *dendritic* osmium tetroxide **in *tert*-butanol/water/hexane** with catalyst recycling on phase separation with added water s. W.-J. Tang, N.-F. Yang, Q.-H. Fan et al., Chem. Commun. *2004*, 1378-9.

Potassium osmate/1,4-bis(9-O-dihydroquinidine)phthalazine/sodium chlorite/sodium   ←
   chloride
Asym. Sharpless dihydroxylation with sodium chlorite as reoxidant

79.

A mixture of styrene, 1 mol% $(DHQD)_2PHAL$, 0.4 mol% $K_2OsO_4·2H_2O$ and NaCl in 1:1 water/ *tert*-butanol cooled to 0-10°, and treated dropwise via syringe over 2.5 h with *0.5 eq.* 1 *M* aq. $NaClO_2$ (adjusted to pH 11.8 with 0.5 *M* aq. NaOH) → product. Y 73% (e.e. 96%). $NaClO_2$ not only serves as the stoichiometric oxidant but also provides the requisite hydroxide ions without consumption of additional base. Reaction is also *twice* as fast, while offering the same enantioselectivities, as under standard conditions with $K_3Fe(CN)_6$, and can be controlled more simply by observing the violet colouration (of the reduced form) so that the dangerous accumulation of oxidant can be avoided. Reaction is applicable to terminal as well as disubst. olefins and enones. F.e.s. M.H. Junttila, O.E.O. Hormi, J. Org. Chem. *69*, 4816-20 (2004).

Rearrangement   ∩

Hydrogen/Oxygen Type   OC ∩ HO

Dicarbonyl(chloro)rhodium(I) dimer $[RhCl(CO)_2]_2$
Hydroxy-O-heterocyclics from epoxyalcohols
with $Pd(PPh_3)_4/Ph_3P$ cf. *33*, 145s*49*; stereospecific *endo*-mode conversion with $[RhCl(CO)_2]_2$, also N-protected 3-hydroxy-N-heterocyclics from epoxyamines, s. J.D. Ha et al., Tetrahedron Lett. *45*, 4193-5 (2004).

Oxygen/Nitrogen Type   OC ∩ ON

3-ω-(Chlorosulfonyl)imidazolium ionic liquids ←
Beckmann rearrangement in ionic liquids ←
with H_2SO_4 in 1-*n*-butyl-3-methylimidazolium fluoroborate under microwave irradiation cf. *61*, 74s*67*; in task-specific 3-ω-(chlorosulfonyl)imidazolium ionic liquids for rearrangement of ketoximes with a simple aqueous work-up, also nitriles from aldoximes, s. J. Gui, Z. Sun et al., Tetrahedron Lett. *45*, 2681-3 (2004).

Aluminum chloride/zinc chloride/silica/microwaves ←
Ytterbium(III) triflate $Yb(OTf)_3$
Beckmann rearrangement
with $AlCl_3$/NaI cf. *60*, 169s*63*; of ketoximes with $AlCl_3$/$ZnCl_2$ on silica under microwave irradiation without solvent s. F.M. Moghaddam et al., Synth. Commun. *34*, 2071-5 (2004); with $Yb(OTf)_3$ (cf. *63*, 86) s. S.K. De, Org. Prep. Proc. Int. *36*, 383-6 (2004).

Molybdenum trioxide/silica MoO_3/SiO_2
Ruthenium trichloride $RuCl_3$
Beckmann rearrangement ←
of cyclic ketoximes with $H_3PO_4/SiO_2/Al_2O_3$ cf. *25*, 117; with MoO_3/SiO_2, selectivity, s. M.K. Dongare, M.K. Gurjar et al., Tetrahedron Lett. *45*, 4759-62 (2004); of ketoximes with $RuCl_3$ (cf. *61*, 75s*66*) s. S.K. De, Synth. Commun. *34*, 3431-4 (2004).

Carbon/Carbon Type   OC ∩ CC

Microwaves [\\\\]
Ring expansion of alkylidenecyclopropanes by cycloisomerization ○
furans from 2-alkylidenecyclopropyl ketones via halogenopalladation cf. *64*, 85; fused furans from α-cyclopropylideneketones under microwave irradiation in the absence of solvent s. M.A. Chowdhury, H. Senboku, M. Tokuda, Synlett *2004*, 1933-6.

Potassium tert-*butoxide* KOBu-t
Cycloisomerization of allenealcohols ○
cyclic enolethers with Et_3N cf. *36*, 148s*63*; 5- to 9-membered cyclic enolethers substituted by sulfoxide, sulfone, phosphinate or phosphonate groups (with KOBu-*t* as base) s. C. Mukai, M. Ohta, S. Kitagaki et al., J. Org. Chem. *69*, 6867-73 (2004).

Silver nitrate $AgNO_3$
Furan ring by cycloisomerization
furans from β,γ-acetyleneketones with $AuCl_3$ cf. *60*, 74; furo[2,3-*d*]pyrimidin-2(3*H*)-ones from 5-alkynyluracils with $AgNO_3$ s. V. Aucagne, F. Amblard, L.A. Agrofoglio, Synlett *2004*, 2406-8.

Auric chloride $AuCl_3$
Furans from 3-acetyleneepoxides ○
with $Ru(MeCN)Cl(PPh_3)[BH(pyrazolyl)_3]$ cf. *63*, 88; with $AuCl_3$ s. A.S.K. Hashmi, P. Sinha, Adv. Synth. Catal. *346*, 561-5 (2004).

Silica gel SiO_2
Oxazoles from 2-acetyleneacylamines under mild conditions ○

80.

5-β-Ketooxazoles. A mixture of the startg. acetyleneacylamine and silica gel in anhydrous methylene chloride stirred under N_2 at room temp. for 24 h → product. Y 99%. The procedure is simple, inexpensive, tolerant of a wide range of functional groups, and suitable for preparing 2,5-disubst. and 2,4,5-trisubst. derivs. F.e. and 5-oxazolylacetic acid esters s. P. Wipf, Y. Aoyama, T.E. Benedum, Org. Lett. *6*, 3593-5 (2004).

Zirconium tetrachloride $ZrCl_4$
2,3-Dihydrobenzofurans from *o*-allylphenols
with AlCl₃ cf. *23*, 182s*55*; with ZrCl₄ s. H.M. Meshram, J.S. Yadav et al., Synth. Commun. *34*, 3091-7 (2004).

Trifluoromethanesulfonic acid CF_3SO_3H
Regiospecific acid-catalyzed cycloisomerization of 4-ethylenealcohols

81.

Tetrahydropyrans. A mixture of the startg. 4-ethylenealcohol and 5 mol% TfOH in methylene chloride refluxed with stirring for 1.5 h, and quenched with 1 *M* HCl → product. Y 80%. The substitution of the double bond largely dictates the regioselectivity, trisubst. derivs. affording tetrahydropyrans exclusively while terminal and 1,2-disubst. derivs. give **tetrahydrofurans**. Other protic acids (H₂SO₄, CF₃COOH, H₃PO₄ and TsOH) were ineffective. F.e. and in nitromethane or in the absence of solvent s. L. Coulombel, E. Duñach, Green Chem. *6*, 499-501 (2004).

Sulfuric acid/acetic anhydride/potassium carbonate $H_2SO_4/Ac_2O/K_2CO_3$
Isomerization of 2-ethylenealcohols via acoxy-2-ethylenes C≡C-C(OH) → C(OH)C≡C
via Pd-catalyzed isomerization of Baylis-Hillman acetates cf. *35*, 87s*67*; by treatment of Baylis-Hillman adducts with Ac₂O/10 mol% H₂SO₄ and subsequent O-deacylation with K₂CO₃ (without isolation of the intermediate) s. K.Y. Lee, S. GowriSankar, J.N. Kim, Bull. Korean Chem. Soc. *25*, 413-4 (2004).

Tungsten hexacarbonyl/triethylamine/irradiation $W(CO)_6/Et_3N/⫰⫰⫰$
Cyclic enolethers from acetylenealcohols
s. *31*, 135s*64*; *endo*-selective cycloisomerization to 2,3,4,5-tetrahydrooxepins s. E. Alcazar, J.M. Pletcher, F.E. McDonald, Org. Lett. *6*, 3877-80 (2004).

Tris(acetonitrile)cyclopentadienylruthenium(II) hexafluorophosphate $[CpRu(MeCN)_3]PF_6$
Condensed 2-silylpyran ring from ω-silyl-2,(ω-1)-diyn-1-ols
via regiospecific ruthenium-catalyzed cycloisomerization

82.

Condensed 6-silyl-3,4-dihydro-2*H*-pyrans. 5 eqs. Water and 10 mol% tris(acetonitrile)cyclopentadienylruthenium(II) hexafluorophosphate added to a soln. of startg. diynol in distilled acetone under argon, the reaction vessel sealed, and heated in an oil bath at 60° for 2 h → product. Y 69%. The regioisomeric **condensed 6-silyl-2*H*-pyrans** predominated in 3:2 acetone/water or with an oxygen or nitrogen atom in the tether. Reaction involves initial cycloisomerization to an acylsilane, followed by spontaneous 6π-electrocyclization. However, substrates with a sec. propargyl residue failed to react. F.e.s. B.M. Trost et al., Org. Lett. *6*, 4235-8 (2004).

Dichloro(ethylene)platinum(II) dimer/tris[4-(trifluoromethyl)phenyl] phosphine ←
Cyclic ethers from ethylenealcohols
Regio- and stereo-specific platinum-catalyzed cycloisomerization under mild conditions

83.

A soln. of *0.5 mol%* Zeise's dimer, 1 mol% tris[4-(trifluoromethyl)phenyl]phosphine, and 1 eq. startg. ethylenealcohol in anhydrous 1,1,2,2-tetrachloroethane stirred in a sealed glass tube under N_2 at 70° for 24 h → product. Y 60% (cis/trans >50:1). The protocol has been applied to 4-ethylenealcohols possessing an internal or terminal double bond (variously substituted along the chain) and to terminal 5-ethylenealcohols. Mechanistically, it appears that reaction takes place by outer-sphere attack of the pendant hydroxyl group on the Pt-complexed olefin residue to produce a zwitterion, followed by ionization and protonolysis. Pivalates, acetates, amides, silyl and benzyl ethers, and additional hydroxyl and ethylene groups remained unaffected. F.e. incl. fused and spirocyclic ethers s. H. Qian, X. Han, R.A. Widenhoefer, J. Am. Chem. Soc. *126*, 9536-7 (2004).

Exchange ↕

Hydrogen ↑   OC ↕ H

Microwaves s. under PhI(OAc)$_2$ [\\\\]

Sodium hydride   *NaH*
α-(Piperidinyloxylation)   H → ON<
with TEMPO/LDA/ferrocenium hexafluorophosphate cf. *56*, 61; metal-free procedure with 2,2,6,6-tetramethyl-1-oxopiperidinium fluoroborate/NaH s. M. Schamann, H.J. Schafer, Synlett *2004*, 1601-3.

Sodium nitrite/trifluoroacetic acid   *NaNO$_2$/CF$_3$COOH*
Dicarboxylic acids from cyclic alcohols   C
with H_2WO_4/H_2O_2 cf. *66*, 100; with $NaNO_2$ in CF_3COOH under O_2, **also carboxylic acids from prim. alcohols**, s. Y. Matsumura, O. Onomura et al., Tetrahedron Lett. *45*, 8221-4 (2004).

Sodium nitrite/hydrogen chloride   *NaNO$_2$/HCl*
α-Diketones from ketones via α-isonitrosoketones CH_2 → CO

84.

One-pot procedure. A suspension of the startg. ketone and *3 eqs.* $NaNO_2$ in THF cooled to 0°, concd. HCl added slowly via cannula so that the temp. did not exceed 10°, the cooling bath removed, and the mixture worked up when TLC indicated completion of reaction (0.1-12 h) → product. Y 81%. The intermediate (Z)-α-isonitrosoketones were isolated with 1 eq. $NaNO_2$. F.e. incl. medium-to-large ring cyclic α-diketones s. G. Rüedi, H.-J. Hansen et al., Synlett *2004*, 2315-8.

Cuprous chloride s. under N-Hydroxy-3,4,5,6-tetraphenylphthalimide   *CuCl*

Auric chloride/alumina/oxygen   *AuCl$_3$/Al$_2$O$_3$/O$_2$*
Carboxylic acid esters from aldehydes   CHO → COOR

85.

A mixture of freshly prepared $AuCl_3$-on-alumina, methanol and α-methylacrolein aged for 2 h at 80° under O_2 → product. Y 75%. F.e., also from two different alcohol molecules, s. T. Hayashi, T. Inagaki, World Intellectual Property Organisation patent WO-200298558 (Nippon Shokubai Co. Ltd.); s.a. United States patent US-20030060655; European patent EP-1393800.

Zeolites s. under Sulfated tin dioxide   ←

Activated carbon   C
Keto from methylene groups $CH_2 \rightarrow CO$
Carbon-catalyzed benzylic oxidation with molecular oxygen

86.

A mixture of fluorene and 100 wt% activated carbon (Shirasagi KL) in *m*-xylene stirred in a reaction tube under O_2 at 120° for 24 h → product. Y 83%. Reaction is thought to involve initial generation of a benzyl radical, followed by oxidation to an intermediate peroxide prior to its decomposition and further oxidation to the ketone. The procedure is simple, inexpensive and environmentally friendly, and the catalyst can be readily removed for recycling. F.e. incl. oxidation of anthrone, xanthene and thioxanthene, also with Darco KB as source of active carbon, s. H. Kawabata, M. Hayashi, Tetrahedron Lett. *45*, 5457-9 (2004).

N-Hydroxy-3,4,5,6-tetraphenylphthalimide/cuprous chloride/air   ←
Benzylic oxidation
with N-hydroxyphthalimide/Co(acac)$_3$ cf. *51*, 76; with N-hydroxy-3,4,5,6-tetraphenylphthalimide/CuCl at low catalyst loading s. M. Nechab, C. Einhorn, J. Einhorn, Chem. Commun. *2004*, 1500-1.

4-Acetylamino-2,2,6,6-tetramethyl-1-oxopiperidinium fluoroborate/pyridine   ←
Carboxylic acid esters from prim. alcohols $2\ CH_2OH \rightarrow COOCH_2$
with 4-benzoyloxy-2,2,6,6-tetramethylpiperidine nitroxyl/NaBrO$_2$/NaHCO$_3$ cf. *45*, 120; with 4-acetylamino-2,2,6,6-tetramethyl-1-oxopiperidinium fluoroborate/pyridine and added 4 Å molecular sieves s. N. Merbouh, J.M. Bobbitt, C. Bruckner, J. Org. Chem. *69*, 5116-9 (2004).

tert-*Butyl hydroperoxide s.a. under NaOCl and Rhodium(II) complexes*   t-*BuOOH*

tert-*Butyl hydroperoxide/phenyl iodosotrifluoroacetate/sodium hydrogen carbonate*   ←
Quinones from arenes   ←
with CrO$_3$/HIO$_4$ cf. *9*, 254; 1,4-naphthoquinones from unactivated naphthalenes with *t*-BuOOH/PhI(OCOCF$_3$)$_2$/NaHCO$_3$ s. M. Catir, H. Kilic, Synlett *2004*, 2151-4.

Trifluoroacetic acid s. under NaNO$_2$ CF_3COOH

Phenyl iodosoacetate/microwaves $PhI(OAc)_2$/[\\\\]
Protection of alcohols as tetrahydrofuran-2-yl ethers $OH \rightarrow OThf$
with TsCl/NaH cf. *42*, 146s*51*; of prim. and sec. alcohols with PhI(OAc)$_2$ under microwave irradiation s. A.N. French, J. Cole, T. Wirth, Synlett *2004*, 2291-4.

Phenyl iodosotrifluoroacetate s. under t-BuOOH $PhI(OCOCF_3)_2$
Silica-sulfuric acid s. under NaBrO$_3$ $SiO_2\text{-}OSO_3H$

Sulfated tin dioxide/zeolite/perchloric acid/hydrogen peroxide   ←
Carboxylic acid esters from aldehydes $CHO \rightarrow COOR$
heterogeneous oxidation with Ti-silicate/H$_2$O$_2$ cf. *63*, 90; with sulfated SnO$_2$-on-SBA-1 zeolite/HClO$_4$/H$_2$O$_2$ s. G. Qian, Y. Qi et al., Chem. Lett. *33*, 834-5 (2004).

Hydrogen peroxide s. under Sulfated tin dioxide H_2O_2

Potassium peroxymonosulfate $KHSO_5$
Dicarboxylic acid esters by oxidative ring opening under mild conditions   C

87.

of cyclic α-hydroxyketones. 4 eqs. Anhydrous KHSO$_5$ (95%) added in one portion to a soln. of 1 eq. of the startg. startg. cyclic α-hydroxyketone in methanol at room temp., and stirred at the same temp. for 18 h → product. Y 98%. The same products are obtained similarly **from cyclic α- and β-diketones** (incl. α-subst. derivs.), but reaction in ethanol or isopropanol gave a mixture of the diester and monoester, possibly via a peroxyhemiacetal. The protocol is mild, efficient and environmentally benign, and does not require the use of transition metal oxides. F.e. and carboxylic acid esters from acyclic derivs. s. J. Yan, B.R. Travis, B. Borhan, J. Org. Chem. 69, 9299-302 (2004).

Chromium trioxide/periodic acid/acetic anhydride $CrO_3/H_5IO_6/Ac_2O$
N-Acylcarboxylic from N-subst. carboxylic acid amides $CONHCH_2 \rightarrow CONHCO$

88.

A mixture of 6 eqs. H_5IO_6 and 2.5 mol% CrO_3 in acetonitrile stirred at room temp. for 30 min, treated with 6 eqs. acetic anhydride, the resulting mixture cooled to 0°, 1 eq. of the startg. N-alkylamide added in one portion, and quenched with ice-water when TLC indicated completion of reaction (1-2 h) → product. Y 91%. The procedure is rapid and superior to that with RuO_4, having a better functional group tolerance (leaving N-propargyl, carbalkoxy, ethylene, halogen, nitrile and ar. nitro groups unaffected). However, there was no such oxidation with 2,2,2-trichloroethylbenzamide or N-allylbenzamide. Acetic anhydride was required to keep the medium anhydrous so that N-dealkylation was minimized. F.e.s. L. Xu, S. Zhang, M.L. Trudell, Chem. Commun. *2004*, 1668-9.

Hexamethylenetetrammonium fluorochromate   ←
Quinones from arenes s. *42*, 235s68   ←

Iodine I_2
***p*-Alkoxybenzyl ethers from 4-alkylidene-2-cyclohexenones**   ←

89.

A stirred soln. of the startg. cyclic ketone and 1.1 eqs. I_2 in methanol heated gently to 40-50° for 7 h, and poured into cold water → product. Y 64%. Reaction is presumed to involve initial Michael addition of methanol, followed by hemiketal formation, dehydration and oxidative aromatization. Yields were moderate in ethanol or propanol. F.e.s. J.M. Kim, J.N. Kim et al., Bull. Korean Chem. Soc. *24*, 999-1001 (2003); s.a. ibid. *25*, 328-30 (2004); **4-alkoxy-2,3-dihydroxy-2,3-dihydrobenzofuran ring** from α-(1,3-cyclohexadion-2-yl)-α-hydroxyketones under the same conditions s. J.E. Na, J.N. Kim et al., ibid. *24*, 1725-6 (2003).

Iodine/potassium carbonate I_2/K_2CO_3
Carboxylic acid esters from prim. alcohols $CH_2OH \rightarrow COOR$
methyl esters from activated prim. alcohols with $MnO_2/NaCN$ cf. *64*, 86; **2,2,2-trifluoroethyl esters** from a wide range of prim. alcohols with I_2/K_2CO_3 s. N. Mori, H. Togo, Synlett *2004*, 880-2.

Sodium hypochlorite/tert-butyl hydroperoxide   *NaOCl/t-BuOOH*
Keto from methylene groups $CH_2 \rightarrow CO$
Uncatalyzed water-based procedure in the absence of solvent under mild conditions

90.

A simple, economical, waste-free, environmentally friendly procedure for **allylic and benzylic oxidation** has been devised with household laundry bleach and *tert*-butyl hydroperoxide (70%

or less) in the absence of organic solvent, transition metal, surfactant or hydrotropic agent. **E: Steroidal α,β-ethyleneketones.** A mixture of 3β-acetoxyandrost-5-en-17-one and 10 eqs. 70% *tert*-butyl hydroperoxide stirred vigorously at 2-5°, 2 eqs. household bleach (5.25%) added as fine droplets over 9-10 h using a minipulse pump, the mixture satd. with NaHCO₃, the separated organic layer mixed with 20% aq. Na₂SO₃ (4 eqs.), and stirred at 50° for 2 h → 3β-acetoxyandrost-5-ene-7,17-dione. Y 60% (99% purity). Reaction can also be conducted in water, quite concentrated, and can be adapted for large-scale preparations. F.e. and **aryl ketones from alkylarenes** s. P. Marwah, A. Marwah, H.A. Lardy, Green Chem. *6*, 570-7 (2004).

Sodium bromate/silica-sulfuric acid $NaBrO_3/SiO_2$-OSO_3H
Keto from methylene groups $CH_2 \rightarrow CO$
with NaBrO₃/ion exchanger cf. *29*, 233s*65*; with NaBrO₃/silica-sulfuric acid on wet SiO₂ in the absence of solvent, also sym. disulfides from mercaptans, and sulfoxides from thioethers, s. A. Shaabani, K. Soleimani, A. Bazgir, Synth. Commun. *34*, 3303-15 (2004).

Periodic acid s. under CrO₃ HIO_4

Pyridinium hydrobromide perbromide $C_5H_5NH \cdot Br_3$
Carboxylic acid esters from aldehydes $CHO \rightarrow COOR$
with Br₂/NaHCO₃ in aq. methanol cf. *44*, 149; general procedure with pyridinium hydrobromide perbromide in water, **also from two prim. alcohol molecules**, s. S. Sayama, T. Onami, Synlett *2004*, 2739-45.

Potassium permanganate/manganese dioxide $KMnO_4/MnO_2$
Aryloxo compds. from alkylarenes s. *68*, 130 $CH_2 \rightarrow CO$

Rhodium(II) caprolactamate/tert-butyl hydroperoxide/potassium carbonate   ←
Cyclic α,β-ethyleneketones from ethylene derivs.

91.

Rhodium(II) caprolactamate offers unique selectivity and unprecedented turnover numbers and frequency (at catalyst loadings as low as 0.1 mol%) for allylic oxidation of cyclic ethylene derivs. **E:** A mixture of 1 eq. startg. olefin, *0.5 eq. K₂CO₃*, and 0.1 mol% rhodium(II) caprolactamate in anhydrous methylene chloride treated at room temp. under air with 5 eqs. *tert*-butyl hydroperoxide in one portion (oxygen evolution), and stirred at the same temp. for 1 h → product. Y 92%. The high activity of the catalyst is ascribed to the facile Rh_2^{4+}-Rh_2^{5+} redox equilibrium which facilitates the intermediate generation of a reactive dirhodium *tert*-butoxy peroxyether complex. There was no such reaction with $Rh_2(OAc)_4$ or $Rh_2(pfb)_4$. F.e.s. A.J. Catino, R.E. Forslund, M.P. Doyle, J. Am. Chem. Soc. *126*, 13622-3 (2004).

Oxygen ↑   OC ↓↑ O

Microwaves s. under NaOAc, 1,8-Diazabicyclo[5.4.0]undec-7-ene, ZnCl₂,   [\\\\]
Montmorillonite, Silica-sulfuric acid, and NiCl₂

Sodium acetate/microwaves $NaOAc$/[\\\\]
O-Acetylation under microwave irradiation in the absence of solvent $OH \rightarrow OAc$
of phenols s. *55*, 79; of α-hydroxyphosphonic acid esters s. H. Firouzabadi, N. Iranpoor et al., Synthesis *2004*, 1771-4; β-acyl glycosides from aldoses with added NaOAc, also α-acyl glycosides with added ZnCl₂ s. B.S. Patil, V.V.S. Babu, Indian J. Chem. *43B*, 1288-91 (2004).

Potassium fluoride   *KF*
Selective and preferential O-acetylation   OH → OAc

92.

A mixture of *p*-chlorobenzyl alcohol, ca. 1.2 eqs. KF, and acetic acid heated at 80° for 3 h → product. Y 97%. The method is high-yielding and selective for the acetylation of prim. and sec. alcohols, while reaction with tert. alcohols is sluggish and accompanied by undesirable elimination. The procedure is simple, clean, inexpensive, and environmentally friendly; furthermore, it does not require dry glassware, an inert atmosphere, molecular sieves as drying agent or a Dean-Stark trap. Phenol groups were not acetylated under these conditions, and a variety of functional groups remained unaffected, notably ethylene groups, halides, ethers, thiols and nitro groups. F.e. and with retention of chiral centres s. J.W.J. Bosco, B.R. Raju, A.K. Saikia, Synth. Commun. *34*, 2849-55 (2004).

Lithium bromide   *LiBr*
O-Acetylation
with LiCl cf. *57*, 80; of camptothecins and mappicines with LiBr s. N. Ravindranath, B. Das et al., Synth. Commun. *33*, 4029-35 (2003).

Sodium iodide s. under AlCl₃   *NaI*

1,8-Diazabicyclo[5.4.0]undec-7-ene/microwaves   *dbu*/[\\\\]
O-Methylation of phenols with dimethyl carbonate   OH → OMe
with K₂CO₃ cf. *41*, 325s66; with dbu, rapid procedure under microwave irradiation in DMF, also methylation of carboxylic acids (cf. *41*, 325s65), and with added BF₃ or KOH, s. F. Rajabi, M.R. Saidi, Synth. Commun. *34*, 4179-88 (2004).

4-Dimethylaminopyridine s. under Boc₂O, Di-2-thienyl carbonate and   *DMAP*
     Tetramethylfluoroformamidinium hexafluorophosphate

Polymer-based 4-dimethylaminopyridine s. under Polymer-based 2-chloropyridinium triflate ←

Cuprous alkoxides/chloro(1,5-cyclooctadiene)iridium(I) dimer/chiral cyclic ←
     phosphoromonoamidites
Regiospecific iridium-catalyzed asym. O-allylation of cuprous alkoxides   OH → OC-C=C

93.

The first general and highly selective asym. allylation of primary and secondary alkoxides with *achiral* allyl carbonates is reported. E: A suspension of 2 eqs. of the startg. chiral lithium alkoxide and 2.1 eqs. CuI in anhydrous THF stirred for 30 min, the resulting suspension treated with a soln. of 2 mol% [Ir(cod)Cl]₂ and 4 mol% chiral cyclic phosphoromonoamidite in the same solvent, cooled to 0°, the reaction vial sealed with a septum, 1 eq. of the startg. allyl carbonate added via syringe, allowed to warm to room temp. over 4 h, and stirring continued until reaction complete → product. Y 88% (d.e. 96%; regioselectivity 98:1). Reaction with tertiary alkoxides was much slower and enantioselectivities were lower. F.e. and asym. O-allylation of achiral alkoxides s. C. Shu, J.E. Hartwig, Angew. Chem. Int. Ed. Engl. *43*, 4794-7 (2004).

Zinc chloride/microwaves   *ZnCl₂*/[\\\\]
α-Acyl glycosides from aldoses s. *55*, 79s68   OH → OAc

Diisobutylaluminum hydride s. under CAN   i-Bu_2AlH
Boric acid $B(OH)_3$
Carboxylic acid esters from acids   COOH → COOR
arylcarboxylic acid aryl esters with $B(OAc)_3$ cf. *39*, 157, and with boric acid esters/H_2SO_4 cf. *13*, 236; α-hydroxycarboxylic acid esters with $B(OH)_3$ (10-20 mol%) s. T.A. Houston, B.L. Wilkinson, J.T. Blanchfield, Org. Lett. *6*, 679-82 (2004).

Montmorillonite/microwaves
Alkoxy-2-ethylenes from 2-ethylenealcohols with allyl rearrangement   C=C-C(OR) ←
with $PtCl_2(Ph_3P)_2/SnCl_2$ and acetonitrile as nucleophile cf. *34*, 165; with montmorillonite under microwave irradiation and methyl orthoformate as nucleophile s. P. Shanmugam, P. Rajasingh, Tetrahedron *60*, 9283-95 (2004).

Zeolite
Heterogeneous O-acetylation   OH → OAc ←
with zeolites s. *54*, 79s67; partial O-acetylation of diols with acetic acid or ethyl acetate and HY-zeolite, also partial O-deacetylation with the same zeolite in methanol, s. K.V.N.S. Srinivas, I. Mahender, B. Das, Synlett *2003*, 2419-21.

Lithium fluoroborate $LiBF_4$
Acetals from oxo compds. and orthoformic acid esters   CO → C(OR)$_2$
from aldehydes with HCl cf. *31*, 123; also from ketones with $LiBF_4$ s. N. Hamada, T. Sato et al., Synlett *2004*, 1074-6.

Aluminum chloride/sodium iodide $AlCl_3/NaI$
Carboxylic acid esters from acids   COOH → COOR
with polymer-based $AlCl_3$ cf. *29*, 186; arylcarboxylic acid esters with $AlCl_3/NaI$ in acetonitrile s. N.N. Karade et al., Synth. Commun. *34*, 391-6 (2004).

Indium(III) chloride (s.a. under o-Iodoxybenzoic acid) $InCl_3$
Acetalation   CO → C(OR)$_2$
s. *58*, 78s65; 1,3-dioxolanes in cyclohexane s. B.C. Ranu, R. Jana, S. Samanta, Adv. Synth. Catal. *346*, 573-8 (2004).

Scandium(III) triflate/1,2-bis(tert-butyldimethylsilyl)hydrazine/iodobenzene difluoride/ ←
2-chloropyridine
Carboxylic acid esters from acids and oxo compds.   COOH → COOR
O-Alkylation under neutral conditions
with diazo compds. generated *in situ* from N-(*tert*-butyldimethylsilyl)hydrazones

94.

O-Alkylation of carboxylic acids with diazo compds. has been greatly extended by a novel and safe procedure for their generation *in situ* by oxidation of N-(*tert*-butyldimethylsilyl)hydrazones with iodobenzene difluoride. E: A freshly prepared soln. of 0.03 mol% Sc(OTf)$_3$ in anhydrous acetonitrile evaporated to dryness *in vacuo* and treated with 3 eqs. 1,2-bis(*tert*-butyldimethylsilyl)-hydrazine, the resulting soln. chilled to 0°, treated dropwise over 15 min with a soln. of 3 eqs. of the startg. oxo compd. (freshly prepared) in anhydrous methylene chloride, stirred at the same temp. for 15 min, allowed to warm to room temp. over 15 min, the solvent removed *in vacuo*, the residue stirred *in vacuo* for 1 h at 23° and then for 2 h at 30-35°, cooled to room temp., taken up in anhydrous methylene chloride, the soln. added dropwise over 2 min to the startg. carboxylic acid in the same solvent containing iodobenzene difluoride (prepared *in situ* at -78° from 4.6 eqs. iodosobenzene and 48% HF) and 10 eqs. 2-chloropyridine [added over 1 min in the dark], stirring continued at -78° for 4 h, warmed to 23° over 3.5 h, the resulting yellow soln. stirred again at 23° for 6 h, diluted with hexane, quenched with a 1:1 mixture of half-satd. aq. $Na_2S_2O_3$ and half-satd. aq. $NaHCO_3$, and the 2-phase mixture stirred vigorously for 20 min → product. Y 92%. The procedure appears generally applicable, and leaves a variety of functional groups unaffected, e.g. hydroxyl and phenol groups, ketones, nitro compds., lactones, alkenes, acetals and ketals. F.e.s. M.E. Furrow, A.G. Myers, J. Am. Chem. Soc. *126*, 12222-3 (2004).

Ammonium ceric nitrate/diisobutylaluminum hydride $CAN/i\text{-}Bu_2AlH$
Regiospecific protection of glycols as mono(methoxymethyl) ethers   OH → OCH_2OMe
via 2-alkoxy-1,3-dioxolanes

95.

A soln. of the startg. glycol in anhydrous methylene chloride treated under argon with 1.4 eqs. methyl orthoformate in the presence of a little ammonium cerium(IV) nitrate, stirred at room temp. for 2 h, the mixture cooled to -78°, 7 eqs. diisobutylaluminum hydride added, stirred again for 1 h, allowed to warm to 0°, stirring continued for 10 min, then quenched with 1 *N* aq. HCl and satd. aq. sodium potassium tartrate → product. Y 90%. The adjacent ethereal oxygen atom dictates the high regioselectivity; a nitrogen atom in the same position, however, prevented formation of the intermediate orthoester and gave none of the desired methoxymethyl ether, while 1-phenylglycol gave a mixture of regioisomers. The ceric salt functions as a Lewis acid in both the orthoester formation and in the subsequent hydride reduction. F.e.s. M.J. Comin, E. Elhalem, J.B. Rodriguez, Tetrahedron *60*, 11851-60 (2004).

Imidazolium ionic liquids s.a. under TsOH   ←

1-Methylimidazolium fluoroborate or 1-Chlorosulfinyl-3-methylimidazolium chloride   ←
Acetalation in ionic liquids   CO → $C(OR)_2$

96.

A mixture of *o*-nitrobenzaldehyde and 1 eq. neopentyl glycol in *Brønsted acidic* 1-methylimidazolium fluoroborate heated at 90° for 6 h → product. Conversion 100% (selectivity 100%). The acetals, being immiscible in the medium, were simply removed by decanting, and the ionic liquid was recycled after drying *in vacuo* and reused up to eight times with no loss of activity. The procedure is simple, mild and efficient, and generally applicable to aldehydes and ketones. F.e.s. H.-H. Wu, J. Tang et al., Tetrahedron Lett. *45*, 4963-5 (2004); cyclic acetals with 1-chlorosulfinyl-3-methylimidazolium chloride as a *functional* ionic liquid cf. D. Li, Y. Deng et al., J. Org. Chem. *69*, 3582-5 (2004).

tert-*Butoxyformic anhydride/4-dimethylaminopyridine* $Boc_2O/DMAP$
Carboxylic acid esters from acids   COOH → COOR
with Boc_2O/pyridine cf. *48*, 164; stoichiometric esterification with prim. or sec. alcohols using Boc_2O/DMAP s. L.J. Gossen, A. Döhring, Synlett *2004*, 263-6.

Di-2-thienyl carbonate/4-dimethylaminopyridine/iodine   ←
Carboxylic acid esters from acids
with di-2-pyridyl carbonate/DMAP cf. *40*, 99; with di-2-thienyl carbonate/DMAP s. T. Mukaiyama, Y. Oohashi, K. Fukumoto, Chem. Lett. *33*, 552-3 (2004); improved procedure with added I_2 s. ibid. 968-9.

Iodosobenzene s. under $Sc(OTf)_3$ PhIO

o-*Iodoxybenzoic acid/indium(III) chloride* $ArIO_2/InCl_3$
Protected α,β-ethylene-2,3-dideoxyaldonolactones from glycals   ←

97.

A mixture of 10 mol% $InCl_3$, 2.5 eqs. o-iodoxybenzoic acid and the startg. protected glycal in 9:1 acetonitrile/water stirred for 6 h at 80° → product. Y 79%. The procedure is simple and convenient, and generally applicable to acetyl-, benzyl-, benzoyl- and allyl-glycals. Reaction involves initial $InCl_3$-catalyzed Ferrier-type displacement with water, followed by oxidation. F.e.s. J.S. Yadav, B.V.S. Reddy, C.S. Reddy, Tetrahedron Lett. *45*, 4583-5 (2004).

2-Chloropyridine s. under Sc(OTf)$_3$ ←

N,N,N′,N′-Tetramethylfluoroformamidinium hexafluorophosphate/   ←
triethylamine/4-dimethylaminopyridine
N,N,N′,N′-Tetramethylhalogenoformamidinium salts as condensing agent   ←
carboxylic acid anhydrides from acids with N,N,N′,N′-tetramethylchloroformamidinium chloride cf. *39*, 162; carboxylic acid esters from acids, and thiolic acid esters from mercaptans, with crystalline, easy-to-handle N,N,N′,N′-tetramethylfluoroformamidinium hexafluorophosphate and Et$_3$N/DMAP s. M. Pittelkow, J.B.Christensen et al., Synthesis *2004*, 2485-92.

Silica-sulfuric acid/microwaves $SiO_2\text{-}OSO_3H/[\backslash\backslash\backslash\backslash]$
Persulfated zirconia   ←
Heterogeneous acetalation $CO \rightarrow C(OR)_2$
with sulfated zirconia cf. *28*, 141s62; 5,5′-spirobis(1,3-dioxanes) with persulfated zirconia (cf. *58*, 78s65) s. T.-S. Jin, T.-S. Li et al., J. Chem. Res. Synop *2004*, 203-5; with silica-sulfuric acid under microwave irradiation in benzene s. Synth. Commun. *34*, 2993-9 (2004); dimethyl acetals with sulfonic acid-functionalized silica s. K. Shimizu, Y. Kitayama et al., Tetrahedron Lett. *45*, 5135-8 (2004); cyclic acetals with P$_2$O$_5$/silica s. B.F. Mirjalili, M.A. Zolfigol et al., Phosphorus, Sulfur Silicon Relat. Elem. *179*, 1397-401 (2004).

1,2-Bis(tert-butyldimethylsilyl)hydrazine s. under Sc(OTf)$_3$ t-$BuMe_2SiNHNHSiMe_2Bu$-t
Hafnium(IV) perfluorooctanesulfonimide $Hf[N(SO_2C_8F_{17})_2]_4$
Carboxylic acid esters from acids   COOH → COOR
stoichiometric esterification with HfCl$_4$ cf. *61*, 85; with readily recoverable Hf[N(SO$_2$C$_8$F$_{17}$)$_2$]$_4$ **in a fluorous 2-phase medium**, also transesterification with Sn[N(SO$_2$C$_8$F$_{17}$)$_2$]$_4$, s. X. Hao, A. Yoshida, J. Nishikido, Tetrahedron Lett. *45*, 781-5 (2004).

Phosphorus pentoxide/silica P_2O_5/SiO_2
Sulfonic acid-functionalized silica   ←
Heterogeneous acetalation s. *28*, 141s68 $CO \rightarrow C(OR)_2$

Thionyl chloride/sodium carbonate $SOCl_2/Na_2CO_3$
Carboxylic acid esters from acids   COOH → COOR
with SOCl$_2$/Amberlyst A-21 cf. *4*, 214s60; isopropyl esters with SOCl$_2$/Na$_2$CO$_3$ s. F. Kazemi, A.R. Kiasat, B. Mombaini, Phosphorus, Sulfur Silicon Relat. Elem. *179*, 1187-91 (2004).

Sodium hydrogen sulfate/silica $NaHSO_4/SiO_2$
Benzyl ethers from benzylalcohols and alcohols   OH → OBn
with FeCl$_3$ cf. *54*, 83; with NaHSO$_4$/SiO$_2$, also benzyl thioethers from mercaptans, s. R. Ramu, M.R. Reddy, B. Das et al., Synth. Commun. *34*, 3135-45 (2004).

p-Toluenesulfonic acid/1-methyl-3-octylimidazolium fluoroborate $TsOH/[omim]BF_4$
Carboxylic acid esters from acids   COOH → COOR
with TsOH in chloroform cf. *7*, 246; with TsOH **in ionic liquids** (cf. *65*, 93), e.g. 1-methyl-3-octylimidazolium fluoroborate, also under microwave enhancement, s. H.-P. Nguyen, S. Znifeche, M. Baboulène, Synth. Commun. *34*, 2085-93 (2004).

Sulfamic acid $H_2NSO_2NH_2$
Acetalation under mild conditions $CO \rightarrow C(OR)_2$

Diethyl acetals. 10 Mol% sulfamic acid added with stirring to a soln. of 4-chlorobenzaldehyde and 1.5 eqs. ethyl orthoformate, and stirring continued for 1 h at 25° → product. Y 95%. The procedure is mild, cost-effective, and environmentally friendly, and the *insoluble* reagent can be simply removed by filtration and recycled without loss of activity. Protection of ketones required a slightly longer reaction time. F.e.s. W. Gong, J. Suo et al., Synth. Commun. *34*, 4243-7 (2004).

Persulfate s. under Persulfated zirconia $S_2O_8^{2-}$
Iodine s. under Di-2-thienyl carbonate I_2

Lithium perchlorate $LiClO_4$
O-Acetylation $OH \rightarrow OAc$
s. *55*, 81s*65*; per-O-acylation of carbohydrates s. K.-C. Lu, C.-C. Lin et al., Tetrahedron *60*, 8967-73 (2004).

Perchloric acid/silica gel $HClO_4/SiO_2$
Heterogeneous Ferrier reaction ←
α-selectivity with montmorillonite under microwave irradiation cf. *59*, 76s*64*; with $HClO_4/SiO_2$ s. A. Agarwal, S. Rani, Y.D. Vankar, J. Org. Chem. *69*, 6137-40 (2004).

Polymer-based 2-chloropyridinium triflate/polymer-based 4-dimethylaminopyridine/ ←
  triethylamine
Carboxylic acid esters from acids $COOH \rightarrow COOR$
with 2-halogenopyridinium salts s. *32*, 148; for a simple work-up with polymer-based 2-chloropyridinium triflate/polymer-based 4-dimethylaminopyridine/Et$_3$N, also carboxylic acid amides with amines, s. S. Crosignani, J. Gonzalez, D. Swinnen, Org. Lett. *6*, 4579-82 (2004).

Cobalt(II) chloride $CoCl_2$
Selective acetalation of aldehydes s. *68*, 99 $CHO \rightarrow CH(OR)_2$

Nickel(II) chloride/microwaves $NiCl_2/[\backslash\backslash\backslash\backslash]$
O-Acylation $OH \rightarrow OAc$
with CoCl$_2$ cf. *42*, 164; of prim. and sec. alcohols with NiCl$_2$, rapid procedure under microwave irradiation, **also preferential O-acylation** at less hindered sites, s. V. Constantinou-Kokotou, A. Peristeraki, Synth. Commun. *34*, 4227-32 (2004).

Carbonyl(η^3-2-methallyl)[1,1'-bis(diphenylphosphino)ferrocene]ruthenium(II) ←
  hexafluoroantimonate
Alkoxy-2-acetylenes from 2-acetylenealcohols and alcohols $OH \rightarrow OR$
with Re(O)Cl$_3$[CH$_2$(PPh$_2$)$_2$] cf. *65*, 97; with carbonyl(η^3-2-methallyl)[1,1'-bis(diphenylphosphino)-ferrocene]ruthenium(II) hexafluoroantimonate s. V. Cadierno, J. Diez, J. Gimeno et al., Chem. Commun. *2004*, 2716-7.

Ruthenium trichloride $RuCl_3$
Ruthenium-catalyzed acetalation under mild conditions $CHO \rightarrow CH(OR)_2$

of aldehydes. A mixture of the startg. aldehyde, excess of propylene diol and *0.1 mol%* hydrated RuCl$_3$ stirred at room temp. for 10 h, then diluted with water → product. Y 95%. The method is operationally simple and highly selective at low catalyst loading for the protection of aliphatic and ar. aldehydes as lower alkyl acetals or cyclic acetals, proceeding **with retention of keto groups**. Addition of anhydrous Na$_2$SO$_4$ as dehydrating agent is recommended for the acetalation of aromatic aldehydes. F.e. incl. acetalation of acid-sensitive aldehydes s. J.-Y. Qi, A.S.C. Chan et al., Tetrahedron Lett. *45*, 7719-21 (2004); s.a. S.K. De, R.A. Gibbs, ibid. 8141-4; **ruthenium-**

catalyzed acylation (of alcohols, phenols, mercaptans and amines) s. ibid. 2919-22; selective acetalation of aldehydes with CoCl$_2$ cf. S. Velusamy, T. Punniyamurthy, ibid. 4917-20.

Tetrakis(triphenylphosphine)palladium(0)   Pd(PPh$_3$)$_4$
O-Allylation with 2-ethylenealcohols   OH → OC-C=C
of phenols with Pd(OAc)$_2$/Ph$_3$P/Ti(OPr-i)$_4$ cf. 53, 79; of alcohols with Pd(PPh$_3$)$_4$ s. Y. Kayaki, T. Koda, T. Ikariya, J. Org. Chem. 69, 2595-7 (2004).

Bis(benzonitrile)dichloropalladium(II)   PdCl$_2$(PhCN)$_2$
2-Alkoxy-6-vinyltetrahydropyrans
from O-protected ζ-hydroxy-δ,ε-ethylenealdehydes
Stereospecific palladium-catalyzed ring closure

100.

2.2 eqs. Abs. ethanol and a soln. of the startg. aldehyde in THF added to a soln. of ca. 5 mol% PdCl$_2$(PhCN)$_2$ in the same solvent at room temp. under argon, and stirred for 16 h → product. Y 70%. Reaction involves initial hemiacetal formation, followed by diastereoselective nucleophilic attack of the generated hydroxyl group onto the palladium-coordinated allyl alcohol residue. F.e. and comparison of palladium catalysts, also with sec. or tert. alcohols and cyclohexanol as the alcohol component, s. M. Miyazawa, Y. Hirai et al., Tetrahedron Lett. 45, 2883-6 (2004).

Nitrogen ↑   OC ↓↑ N

Irradiation s. under Platinum complexes   ///
Microwaves s. under CuCl$_2$, NBS, N,N'-Dibromo-N,N'-propylenebis(p-   [\\\\]
   toluenesulfonamide), Bi(NO$_3$)$_3$, (Bu$_4$N)$_2$Cr$_2$O$_7$ and CrO$_3$
Triethylenediamine s. under Bi(NO$_3$)$_3$ dabco
4-Dimethylaminopyridine   DMAP
O-Acylation with 3-acylthiazolidine-2-thiones   OH → OAc
s. 43, 162; of benzyl alcohols with added DMAP s. Y.-K. Wu, Q. Zhang et al., J. Org. Chem. 69, 6141-4 (2004).

Cupric chloride/microwaves   CuCl$_2$/[\\\\]
Oxo compds. from their N-derivs.   C=N- → CO
with CuCl$_2$ cf. 47, 146s53; from oximes and semicarbazones, rapid procedure under microwave irradiation in the absence of solvent with a little water, s. N. Karchaudhuri, A. De, A.K. Mitra, J. Indian Chem. Soc. 81, 79-81 (2004).

Zinc/acetic acid   Zn/AcOH
Ketones from alkoximes   C=NOR → CO

101.

α,β-**Diketocarboxylic acid esters**. A soln. of ethyl 2-(benzyloxyimino)-3-oxohexanoate in acetic acid treated with 9 eqs. zinc powder in one portion, and stirred at room temp. for 1 h → product. Y 72%. The method is convenient, mild and inexpensive, being suitable for the cleavage of α-alkoximino-β-ketocarboxylic acid esters and amides. F.e. incl. cleavage of O-methyl- and O-propargyl-oxime derivs. as well as unprotected α-oximino derivs. s. H. Ryu, S. Kim et al., Bull. Chem. Soc. Jpn. 77, 1407-8 (2004).

Methylmagnesium bromide   MeMgBr
Carboxylic acid esters from 3-acyl-2-oxazolidones s. 68, 262   ←

Magnesium bromide s. under Ti(OPr-i)$_4$ MgBr$_2$

Mercuric nitrate/silica gel   Hg(NO$_3$)$_2$/SiO$_2$

Oxo compds. from their N-derivs.   C=N- → CO

from hydrazones with HgCl$_2$/NaOH cf. *12*, 252; also from semicarbazones and oximes with Hg(NO$_3$)$_2$/silica gel in aq. THF s. S.K. De, Synth. Commun. *34*, 2289-94 (2004).

Zeolites s. under CrO$_3$ ←

Samarium s. under TiCl$_4$ Sm

Lanthanum(III) triflate   La(OTf)$_3$

1,3-Dioxolan-2-ones from epoxides   ○

102.

40.8 g *n*-Octyl glyceryl ether, 16.5 g methyl carbamate and a little La(OTf)$_3$ mixed at 80° until homogeneous, heated to 120° under N$_2$, and worked up after 24 h → product. Y 80%. F.e. and metal triflates incl. copper or zinc triflate s. T. Okutsu, T. Kitsuki, Japanese patent JP-2004168674 (Kao Corp.).

β-Cyclodextrin s. under NBS   ←

Silica-supported imidazolium ionic liquids   ←

Oxo compds. from their N-derivs.   C=N- → CO

from dimethylhydrazones in aq. media cf. *45*, 95; **from oximes** in aq. acetone with added silica gel-confined imidazolium ionic liquids at room temp. s. D. Li, Y. Deng et al., Tetrahedron Lett. *45*, 265-8 (2004).

Dimethyldioxirane   ←

Oxidative cleavage of diazo compds.   CN$_2$ → CO

α-ketoaldehyde hydrates cf. *47*, 147; β-hydroxy-α-ketocarboxylic acid esters s. M. Liao, W. Yao, J. Wang, Synthesis *2004*, 2633-6.

(S)-(1-Naphthyl)glycolic acid   ←

Regiospecific Brønsted acid-catalyzed asym. condensation of enamines with nitroso compds.   ←

103.

(Y 63%; e.e. 91%)

In the novel asym. Brønsted acid-catalyzed condensation of enamines with nitroso compds., the nature of the acid plays a significant part in determining the regioselectivity of the substitution (O *vs.* N). **E: Chiral α-(aminooxy)ketones.** A mixture of 1 eq. nitrosobenzene and 30 mol% (S)-(1-naphthyl)glycolic acid in anhydrous ether stirred at room temp. for 30 min, the mixture chilled to -88 to -78°, treated dropwise over 1 h with a soln. of 1 eq. of the startg. enamine in the same solvent, stirring continued at -78° for 1 h, then quenched with chilled brine → O-nitroso aldol. Y 83% (e.e. 93%). With a less acidic chiral TADDOL deriv. as Brønsted acid, the corresponding **chiral α-hydroxylaminoketones** were obtained. The nature of the amino residue also controls the regioselectivity to a large extent: pyrrolidine and homopyrrolidine enamines generally favouring O-adducts, while morpholine and thiomorpholine derivs. favour N-adducts. F.e.s. N. Momiyama, H. Yamamoto, J. Am. Chem. Soc. *127*, 1080-1 (2005).

Di-2-pyridyl diselenide s. under Me$_3$P   ArSeSeAr

N-Bromosuccinimide/microwaves   NBS/[\\\\]
N-Bromosuccinimide/β-cyclodextrin   ←
Oxo compds. from oximes   C=NOH → CO
with NBS in aq. media s. *31*, 185s*59*; enhanced cleavage with added β-cyclodextrin s. M.S. Reddy, M. Narender, K.R. Rao, Synth. Commun. *34*, 3875-81 (2004); under microwave irradiation cf. A. Khazaei, A.A. Manesh, Synthesis *2004*, 1739-40.

N-Bromobis(p-toluenesulfonyl)amine   Ts$_2$NBr
N,N'-Dibromo-N,N'-propylenebis(p-toluenesulfonamide)/microwaves   ←
Oxo compds. from oximes
with N,N-dibromobenzenesulfonamide cf. *62*, 102s*67*; with readily recyclable N-bromobis(*p*-toluenesulfonyl)amine s. R. Ghorbani-Vaghei, A. Khazaei, Phosphorus, Sulfur Silicon Relat. Elem. *179*, 1169-73 (2004); with N,N'-dibromo-N,N'-propylenebis(*p*-toluenesulfonamide), rapid procedure under microwave irradiation in acetone/water or methylene chloride/water, s. A. Khazaei, A.A. Manesh, A.H. Ghasemi, Synthesis *2004*, 2784-6.

Titanium tetraisopropoxide/ethylmagnesium bromide   Ti(OPr-i)$_4$/EtMgBr
β-Hydroxyketones from Δ^2-isoxazolines   C
with Ti(III) s. *39*, 418; with Ti(OPr-*i*)$_4$/EtMgBr, also β-amino-α,β-ethyleneketones from isoxazoles, s. D.H. Churykau, V.G. Zinovich, O.G. Kulinkovich, Synlett *2004*, 1949-52.

Silicon tetrabromide/silica gel   SiBr$_4$/SiO$_2$
Heterogeneous cleavage of oxo compd. N-derivs.   C=N- → CO
with silica chloride/silica cf. *52*, 96s*66*; with SiBr$_4$/wet silica gel for cleavage of oximes, hydrazones and semicarbazones s. S.K. De, Tetrahedron Lett. *44*, 9055-6 (2003).

Titanium tetrachloride/samarium   TiCl$_4$/Sm
Oxo compds. from oximes   C=NOH → CO
with TiCl$_4$/NaI cf. *32*, 610s*47*; with TiCl$_4$/Sm s. X.-S. Fan, X.-Y. Zhang, Y.-M. Zhang, J. Chem. Res. Synop *2004*, 290-1.

tert-Butyl nitrite   t-BuONO
O-Alkylation with glycol monocarbamates under mild conditions   OH → OR

104.

Carboxylic acid ethyl esters. A mixture of 3 eqs. 2-hydroxy-1,1,2-trimethylpropyl ethylcarbamate and 3 Å molecular sieves in 1,2-dichloroethane treated with 3.3 eqs. *tert*-butyl nitrite, stirred at room temp. for 30 min, 1 eq. of the startg. carboxylic acid added, and stirring continued at 60° overnight → product. Y 99%. Reaction involves initial N-nitrosation of the carbamate, followed by elimination of 4,4,5,5-tetramethyl-1,3-dioxolan-2-one with generation of ethyldiazonium ion as the effective alkylating agent. Chiral α-alkoxy- and N-protected α-amino-carboxylic acids reacted with retention of configuration, but simple aliphatic carboxylic acids required harsher conditions. F.e., also O-ethylation of an α,β-ethylene-β-hydroxyketone and *p*-nitrophenol, s. M. Suzuki, T. Sugai, Bull. Chem. Soc. Jpn. *77*, 1217-27 (2004).

Trimethylphosphine/di-2-pyridyl diselenide   Me$_3$P/PySeSePy
Ketones from ketoximes   C=NOH → CO
with Bu$_3$P/PhSSPh cf. *39*, 172; from hindered and/or conjugated substrates with Me$_3$P/di-2-pyridyl diselenide s. M. Martin, G. Martinez, J. Vilarrasa et al., Tetrahedron Lett. *45*, 5559-61 (2004).

Bismuth(III) nitrate/silica/triethylenediamine/microwaves $Bi(NO_3)_3/SiO_2/dabco/$[\\\\]
Bismuth(III) nitrate/phosphotungstic acid $Bi(NO_3)_3/H_3PW_{12}O_{40}$
Oxo compds. from oximes   C=NOH → CO
ketones with $Bi(NO_3)_3/Cu(OAc)_2$/montmorillonite cf. *39*, 171s67; aryloxo compds. with $Bi(NO_3)_3$-on-silica/dabco, rapid procedure under microwave irradiation in the absence of solvent, s. T.T. Niaki, M.M. Heravi, B. Miralaee et al., J. Chem. Res. Synop *2004*, 488-9; with $Bi(NO_3)_3/H_3PW_{12}O_{40}$ s. *40*, 107s68.

Tetra-n-butylammonium dichromate/microwaves $(Bu_4N)_2Cr_2O_7/$[\\\\]
Imidazolium dichromate   ←
Oxo compds. from oximes
with pyridinium dichromate cf. *34*, 172s67; with tetra-*n*-butylammonium dichromate, rapid procedure under microwave irradiation in methylene chloride, s. R. Murugan, B.S.R. Reddy, Chem. Lett. *33*, 1038-9 (2004); **also from hydrazones and semicarbazones** with imidazolium dichromate s. S.K. De, Synth. Commun. *34*, 2751-5 (2004).

Chromium trioxide/zeolite/microwaves   ←
Oxo compds. from oximes
with CrO_3/silica gel cf. *39*, 231s58; rapid procedure under microwave irradiation in the absence of solvent with CrO_3/H-ZSM-5 zeolite s. M.M. Heravi, M. Ghassemzadeh et al., J. Chem. Res. Synop *2004*, 137-8.

Phosphotungstic acid s. under $Bi(NO_3)_3$ and $Fe(NO_3)_3$ $H_3PW_{12}O_{40}$

Hydrochlorides   ←
α-Acoxylation of aldehydes with N-(*tert*-butyl)acoxylamines   H → OAc

105.

Isovaleraldehyde added to a soln. of 1 eq. N-*tert*-butyl-O-benzoylhydroxylamine hydrochloride in 9:1 THF/water, and warmed to 50° for 14 h → product. Y 79%. A variety of acoxy groups, incl. benzoyloxy, acetoxy and pivaloyloxy, can be transferred by this procedure, which can be conducted in the presence of moisture and air without the need for purification of the solvent or special apparatus. However, there was no reaction with ketones. The air-stable acoxylamine hydrochlorides are also easy to prepare and can be stored at room temp. for long periods. A pericyclic mechanism is invoked. F.e. and with α-subst. aldehydes s. C.S. Beshara, N.C.O. Tomkinson et al., Chem. Commun. *2005*, 1478-80.

Hydrogen bromide   HBr
Ketones from N-carbalkoxyketimines s. *68*, 253   C=NCOOR → CO

Ferric nitrate/phosphotungstic acid $Fe(NO_3)_3/H_3PW_{12}O_{40}$
Oxo compds. from oximes   C=NOH → CO
with $Fe(NO_3)_3$-clay cf. *40*, 107s59; **solid-state conversion** with $Fe(NO_3)_3 \cdot H_2O$ or $Bi(NO_3)_3 \cdot 5H_2O$ and 5 mol% phosphotungstic acid s. H. Firouzabadi, N. Iranpoor, K. Amani, Synth. Commun. *34*, 3587-93 (2004).

Cationic terpyridylplatinum acetylide complexes/irradiation
Oxo compds. from oximes
Photosensitized cleavage with singlet oxygen

$\leftarrow$
C=NOH → CO

106.

Oxygen bubbled for 1 h into a soln. of the startg. oxime and 0.2 mol% cationic terpyridylplatinum acetylide complex in acetonitrile (contained in a Pyrex reactor) while irradiating with a 500 W high-pressure Hanovia Hg-lamp fitted with a glass filter to block light with wavelengths below 400 nm → product. Y 94% (conversion 95%). The protocol is environmentally friendly and permits recovery and reuse of the cationic sensitizer without loss of activity. It is generally applicable to the cleavage of aliphatic and ar. aldoximes as well as aliphatic, cycloaliphatic and ar. ketoximes. F.e.s. Y. Yang, L.-Z. Wu, C.-H. Tung et al., J. Org. Chem. *69*, 4788-91 (2004).

Halogen ↑   OC ↓↑ Hal

Microwaves (s.a. under NaOH, K$_2$CO$_3$, Zn and Bu$_2$SnO)   [\\\\]
α-Tosyloxyketones from alcohols   CH(OH)CH → COC(OTs)
with PhIO/TsOH cf. *66*, 97; from sec. benzylalcohols with PhI(OH)OTs, rapid procedure under microwave irradiation, s. J.C. Lee, J.Y. Lee, S.J. Lee, Tetrahedron Lett. *45*, 4939-41 (2004).

Sodium hydroxide/bentonite/microwaves $\leftarrow$
Potassium carbonate/microwaves   K$_2$CO$_3$/[\\\\]
Phenolethers from phenols under microwave irradiation   OH → OR
with NaOH in the absence of solvent cf. *41*, 199s54; with NaOH/bentonite and a little water s. H.M.A. Hamid, E.S.H. El Ashry et al., Synth. Commun. *34*, 377-82 (2004); with K$_2$CO$_3$ in methanol cf. J. Sarju, T.N. Danks, G. Wagner, Tetrahedron Lett. *45*, 7675-7 (2004).

Sodium/alcohol   NaOR
α-Alkoxy-ω-amino-α,β-ethylenecarboxylic acid esters   C
from 3-alkoxy-4-ω-halogeno-2-azetidinones

107.

(Z)-α-Alkoxy-δ-amino-α,β-ethylenecarboxylic acid esters. 4 eqs. 2 N Na-methoxide in methanol added to cis-4-[(2-bromo-1,1-dimethyl)ethyl]-1-cinnamyl-3-methoxy-2-azetidinone in methanol, and refluxed for 4 h → (Z)-methyl 5-cinnamylamino-4,4-dimethyl-2-methoxypent-2-enoate. Y 68%. Reaction involves intermediate formation of azetidine derivs. which are isolable. F.e., **also (Z)-α-alkoxy-γ-amino-α,β-ethylenecarboxylic acid esters** from 4-α-halogeno-2-azetidinone derivs. via aziridines, s. Y. Dejaegher, N. De Kimpe, J. Org. Chem. *69*, 5974-85 (2004).

Potassium fluoride   KF
Carbohydrate orthocarboxylic acid esters from O^2-acylglycosyl bromides   O
high-pressure conversion with Bu$_4$NF/i-Pr$_2$NEt/molecular sieves cf. *46*, 192; with KF/molecular sieves s. S. Shoda, M. Noguchi et al., Tetrahedron Lett. *45*, 8847-8 (2004).

Triethylamine $\qquad Et_3N$
Carboxylic acid esters from acid chlorides via ketenes with asym. induction COCl → COOR
with chiral α-hydroxycarboxylic acid esters as auxiliary cf. *45*, 100; chiral α-bromo-β,γ-ethylene-
carboxylic acid esters from α-bromo-α,β-ethylenecarboxylic acid chlorides with (R)-pantolactone
as auxiliary s. G. Cardillo et al., Tetrahedron:Asym. *15*, 593-601 (2004).

Triethylenediamine/tetra-n-*butylammonium bromide* $\qquad dabco/Bu_4NBr$
Preferential O-tritylation of nucleoside *prim*-hydroxyl groups $\qquad$ OH → OCPh$_3$
with imidazole/MeSO$_3$H/*i*-Pr$_2$NEt cf. *12*, 288s58; O-tritylation, O-monomethoxy- and O-
dimethoxy-tritylation with dabco in a melt of Bu$_4$NBr **as ionic liquid** at 140° s. A. Khalafi-
Nezhad, B. Mokhtari, Tetrahedron Lett. *45*, 6737-9 (2004).

Copper-bronze/triethylamine $\qquad ←$
Diaryl ethers from diaryliodonium salts and phenols $\qquad$ ArOH → ArOAr'
from Na-aroxides cf. *46*, 186; with copper-bronze/Et$_3$N s. C. Schmeck et al., German patent DE-
10115408 (Bayer AG).

Cuprous bromide/dimethyl sulfide/potassium carbonate $\qquad CuBr-Me_2S/K_2CO_3$
Ullmann diaryl ether synthesis
update s. *54*, 90s67; **polymer-based synthesis** with supported [triazene-linked] ar. bromides with
CuBr·Me$_2$S/K$_2$CO$_3$ s. K. Knepper, M.E.P. Lormann, S. Brase, J. Comb. Chem. *6*, 460-3 (2004).

Zinc/dimethylformamide/microwaves $\qquad Zn/DMF/[\backslash\backslash\backslash\backslash]$
Zinc-catalyzed Williamson ether synthesis $\qquad$ OH → OR
under microwave irradiation in the absence of solvent and base

108. Cl—C$_6$H$_4$—OH + BuBr → Cl—C$_6$H$_4$—OBu

Phenolethers. 2.5 eqs. DMF added to 1 eq. 4-chlorophenol, 1 eq. *n*-butyl bromide and 0.25 eqs.
commercial Zn-powder contained in a borosil beaker, mixed thoroughly with a glass rod for 10
sec, and irradiated in a microwave oven (LG Chef MS 192) at 640 W for 2.5 min → product. Y
92%. The method avoids the use of base or phase transfer catalyst. The reaction also proceeds
with oil-bath heating but the yields are slightly lower and the reaction times longer (85% after 3
h in this example). The zinc can be recovered and reused up to six times after washing with ether
and dil. HCl. F.e. incl. alkyl, allyl and benzyl phenolethers and diaryl ethers s. S. Paul, M. Gupta,
Tetrahedron Lett. *45*, 8825-9 (2004).

Bentonite s. under NaOH $\qquad ←$

Ytterbium(III) triflate $\qquad Yb(OTf)_3$
Monothioacetals from 1,1-halogenothioethers $\qquad$ C(SR)Hal → C(SR)(OR')
with AgOTf/Ag$_2$CO$_3$ cf. *53*, 198; from 1,1-fluorothioethers with Yb(OTf)$_3$ s. M. Inoue, S.
Yamashita, M. Hirama, Tetrahedron Lett. *45*, 2053-6 (2004).

2-Phenyl-6,7-dihydro-5H-pyrrolo[2,1-c][1,2,4]triazol-2-ium chloride/sodium hydride/ $\qquad ←$
triethylamine
Acylation with α-halogenaldehydes under nucleophilic carbene catalysis $\qquad ←$

109. [reaction scheme: Bn-CH(Br)-CHO + Ph-triazolium ylide → tetrahedral intermediate with Br and triazolium → enol intermediate (−Br⁻) → acyl azolium + HO-CH(COOEt) → Bn-CH$_2$-C(=O)-O-CH(COOEt)]

O-Acylation. A mixture of 20 mol% 2-phenyl-6,7-dihydro-5*H*-pyrrolo[2,1-*c*][1,2,4]triazol-2-
ium chloride, 1 eq. each of NaH and Et$_3$N, and 1 eq. of the startg. alcohol (e.e. 99%) in anhydrous
toluene (final substrate concentration 0.15 M) stirred under argon at room temp. for 10 min,
treated with 1 eq. of the startg. α-halogenaldehyde, and stirring continued at the same temp.
under argon for 24 h → product. Y 56% (e.e. 94%). The startg. bromide may be primary,

secondary or tertiary, the latter requiring a longer reaction time (24 h). Reaction proceeds through a Stetter-type manifold with generation of an active 5-acyl-4H-1,2,4-triazolium halide which returns the catalyst on displacement with the nucleophile. F.e. incl. O-acylation of phenols, and **N-acylation** of anilines, **also desymmetrization of glycols** with a chiral carbene as catalyst, s. N.T. Reynolds, J.R. de Alaniz, T. Rovis, J. Am. Chem. Soc. *126*, 9518-9 (2004).

Tris(trimethylsilyl)silane/di-tert-butyl hyponitrite $\qquad\qquad (Me_3Si)_3SiH/t\text{-}BuON{=}NOBu\text{-}t$
Alkoxylamines from N-oxide radicals $\qquad\qquad\qquad\qquad\qquad$ N-O· → N-OR

with CuBr/Cu/pentamethylethylenetriamine in ionic liquids cf. *65*, 107; with $(Me_3Si)_3SiH$/di-*tert*-butyl hyponitrite, selectivity, s. R. Braslau, A. Tsimelzon, J. Gewandter, Org. Lett. *6*, 2233-5 (2004).

Zirconyl [or Bismuth oxide] chloride $\qquad\qquad\qquad\qquad\qquad\qquad ZrOCl_2\ [or\ BiOCl]$
Zirconium-catalyzed acylation $\qquad\qquad\qquad\qquad\qquad\qquad\qquad$ ←

110.

in the absence of solvent. 1.5 eqs. Acetyl chloride added with stirring at room temp. to a mixture of ca. 1 eq. cholesterol and 0.1 mol% $ZrOCl_2 \cdot 8H_2O$, and worked up after 15 min → product. Y 97%. The reagent is readily available and inexpensive, and, unlike $ZrCl_4$, is moisture-resistant and easy to handle. It can also be easily recovered after aqueous work-up, and reused without loss of activity. The procedure was effective for the acylation of prim., sec. and tert. aliphatic alcohols, allyl and propargyl alcohols, phenols, amines, mercaptans and thiophenols, leaving ethylene, acetylene, carbalkoxy, acyl and nitro groups unaffected. It can also be carried out in methylene chloride, but reaction was faster without solvent and required less catalyst. F.e. incl. per-O-acylation of carbohydrates s. R. Ghosh, S. Maiti, A. Chakraborty, Tetrahedron Lett. *46*, 147-51 (2005); **bismuth-catalyzed acylation** of alcohols, mercaptans and amines with $BiCl_3$ generated *in situ* from BiOCl cf. ibid. *45*, 6775-8 (2004).

Di-n-butyltin oxide/tetra-n-butylammonium iodide/microwaves $\qquad Bu_2SnO/Bu_4NI/[\backslash\backslash\backslash\backslash]$
Regiospecific O-alkylation of diols via cyclic dialkoxystannanes $\qquad$ OH → OR

s. *34*, 187s67; of disaccharides, rapid procedure under microwave irradiation in 5:1 benzene/acetonitrile, s. L. Ballell, R.M.J. Liskamp, R.J. Pieters et al., Tetrahedron Lett. *45*, 6685-7 (2004).

Di-tert-butyl hyponitrite s. under $(Me_3Si)_3SiH$ $\qquad\qquad\qquad$ $t\text{-}BuON{=}NOBu\text{-}t$
Bismuth oxide chloride s. under $ZrOCl_2$ $\qquad\qquad\qquad\qquad\qquad$ *BiOCl*
Tetra-n-butylammonium bromide s. under Triethylenediamine $\qquad$ Bu_4NBr
Tetra-n-butylammonium iodide s. under Bu_2SnO $\qquad\qquad\qquad$ Bu_4NI

Palladium-carbon/sodium hydroxide $\qquad\qquad\qquad\qquad\qquad\qquad$ *Pd-C/NaOH*
Arylcarboxylic acids from benzyl halides by aerobic oxidation $\qquad CH_2Hal →$ COOH

111.

6-Chloromethylquinoxaline added to a little Pd-C (0.5%) and 1.29 g NaOH in water, and refluxed with air-sparging for 48 h → product. Y 80%. Work-up is straightforward. F.e.s. J. Burdeniuc, European patent EP-1277739 (Air Prod. & Chem. Inc.).

Sulfur ↑ $\qquad\qquad\qquad\qquad\qquad\qquad\qquad\qquad\qquad\qquad\qquad$ OC ↓↑ S

Electrolysis $\qquad\qquad\qquad\qquad\qquad\qquad\qquad\qquad\qquad\qquad\qquad\qquad\qquad$ ⇄
Glycosides from aryl thioglycosides $\qquad\qquad\qquad\qquad\qquad\qquad$ SAr → OR′

by anodic oxidation s. *46*, 194; β-glycosides with added CF_3SO_3H s. S. Suzuki, K. Matsumoto et al., Org. Lett. *6*, 3755-8 (2004).

Microwaves s. under Dichromates and Chlorochromates [\\\\]
N-(Phenylthio)caprolactam s. under Tf$_2$O ←

Trifluoromethanesulfonic anhydride/N-(phenylthio)caprolactam ←
Glycosides from thioglycosides SR → OR′
with Tf$_2$O/N-benzenesulfinylpiperidine/2,4,6-tri-*tert*-butylpyrimidine cf. 62, 117s67; with N-(phenylthio)caprolactam as activator s. S.G. Durón, T. Polat, C.-H. Wong, Org. Lett. 6, 839-42 (2004).

Camphorsulfonic acid RSO$_3$H
Spiroorthocarboxylic acid esters from cyclic 1-(arylthio)enolethers and diols

112.

A soln. of the startg. ketene thioacetal and 1.1 eqs. 2,2-dimethyl-1,3-propanediol in methylene chloride treated with 1 mol% camphorsulfonic acid, warmed to 40°, and stirred for 2 h → product. Y 88%. The procedure is mild and generally applicable to variously substituted 1,2-, 1,3- and 1,4-diols. Yields were lower with the corresponding cyclic 1-(methylthio)enolethers. F.e.s. T.E. La Cruz, S.D. Rychnovsky, Synlett *2004*, 2013-5.

n-Butyltriphenylphosphonium dichromate/microwaves [BuPPh$_3$]$_2$Cr$_2$O$_7$/[\\\\]
Quinolinium fluorochromate ←
2-Carboxypyridinium or 2,2′-dipyridinium chlorochromate/microwaves ←
Replacement of carbonyl sulfur by oxygen CS → CO

113.

A mixture of thioacetamide and 2.5 eqs. *n*-butyltriphenylphosphonium dichromate in acetonitrile subjected to microwave irradiation at 900 W for 2 min → acetamide. Y 95%. The procedure is applicable to thioamides, thioureas, thionoesters and thioketones. F.e. and thermal procedure in refluxing acetonitrile s. I. Mohammadpoor-Baltork et al., Bull. Korean Chem. Soc. *24*, 1002-4 (2003); with 2-carboxypyridinium or 2,2′-dipyridinium chlorochromate under the same conditions or in the absence of solvent cf. Monatsh. Chem. *135*, 411-8 (2004); conversion of thioamides and thioureas with quinolinium fluorochromate in refluxing acetonitrile s. Indian J. Chem. *42B*, 2638-40 (2003).

Zinc dichromate ZnCr$_2$O$_7$
Sodium chlorite/sodium dihydrogen phosphate/2-methyl-3-butene ←
Oxo compds. from mercaptals C(SR)$_2$ → CO
from cyclic mercaptals with HIO$_4$ in THF cf. *52*, 108; with NaClO$_2$/NaH$_2$PO$_4$/2-methyl-2-butene in aq. methanol for cleavage of 1,3-dithianes derived from ketones s. T. Ichige, M. Nakata et al., Synlett *2004*, 1686-90; general procedure with ZnCr$_2$O$_7$·3H$_2$O in acetonitrile s. H. Firouzabadi, N. Iranpoor et al., Synth. Commun. *34*, 1967-72 (2004).

Remaining Elements ↑ OC ↕ Rem

Without additional reagents
**Unsatd. glycol monoaryl ethers
from epoxides and boric acid aryl esters**
Regio- and stereo-specific ring opening under neutral conditions

w.a.r.
△O → C(OH)C(OAr)

114.

Aryl borates serve as activating nucleophiles in the regiospecific *syn*-selective ring opening of styrene oxides and 3-ethyleneepoxides. **E:** 1.2 eqs. Triphenyl borate added with stirring to a soln. of the startg. epoxide in THF at room temp., quenched with 5% aq. HCl after 1 h (TLC monitoring), diluted with ether, and washed with 5% NaOH → product. Y 65% (*syn/anti* 92:8). Reaction is presumed to involve initial coordination of boron to the epoxide oxygen, which enhances the carbocationic character of the adjacent carbon atom [further stabilized by the unsaturation] prior to intramolecular delivery of the phenoxy anion. N-Carbobenzoxy- and N-tosyl-aziridines generally reacted similarly to give the corresponding **N-protected *syn*-2-aminoethers.** F.e.s. M. Pineschi et al., Chem. Commun. *2005*, 1426-8.

Sodium/alcohol
(E)-Enolethers from (Z)-1-fluoroenestannanes

NaOR
C=C(F)Sn≤ → C=CH(OR)

115.

(E)-2-(Trifluoromethyl)enolethers. 1.25 eqs. Clean Na metal added under N_2 to anhydrous methanol, followed by the startg. 1-fluoroenestannane, and the mixture refluxed for 4 h → product. Y 91%. Reaction, which is facilitated by the strongly electron-withdrawing CF_3 group or F, takes place with retention of configuration by an Ad_N-E mechanism, involving nucleophilic addition of alkoxide ion, followed by defluorination and destannylation. F.e. and with phenoxide ion s. Y. Shen, G. Wang, Synthesis *2004*, 2637-40.

Cesium carbonate
Phenolethers from aryloxysilanes and halides

Cs_2CO_3
ArOSi≤ → ArOR

with CsF cf. *43*, 187s*53*; diaryl ethers with Cs_2CO_3 s. S.L. Cui, Z.Y. Jiang, Y.G. Wang, Synlett *2004*, 1829-31.

Cupric acetate/pyridine
Copper-catalyzed O-vinylation

$Cu(OAc)_2/C_5H_5N$
OH → OC=C

with K-ene(trifluoro)borates cf. *61*, 100s*65*; aryl vinyl ethers with 2,4,6-trivinylcyclotriboroxane-pyridine complex/$Cu(OAc)_2$ s. N.F. McKinley, D.F. O'Shea, J. Org. Chem. *69*, 5087-92 (2004).

Polymer-based copper(II) carboxylate/triethylamine
Heterogeneous O-arylation of phenols s. **68**, 193

←
OH → OAr

Tris(pentafluorophenyl)borane s. under Polymethylhydrosiloxane

$(C_6F_5)_3B$

Polymethylhydrosiloxane/tris(pentafluorophenyl)borane
Ethers from oxo compds. and alkoxysilanes

$pmhs/(C_6F_5)_3B$
CO → CHOR

with $Et_3SiH/Cu(OTf)_2$ cf. *41*, 176s*67*; with polymethylhydrosiloxane/$(C_6F_5)_3B$ s. S. Chandrasekhar, K.V. Reddy et al., Tetrahedron Lett. *45*, 5497-9 (2004).

Tetrakis(trimethylsilyl)methane s. under Ruthenium complexes (Me$_3$Si)$_4$C
Stannic chloride SnCl$_4$
Glucuronides from glucurono-1,6-lactones and alkoxysilanes
Stereospecific tin(IV)-catalyzed ring opening

116.

α-Glucuronides. 1 eq. SnCl$_4$ and 4 eqs. of the startg. alkoxysilane added to a soln. of startg. 1,6-lactone in anhydrous methylene chloride under N$_2$, the mixture stirred at room temp. for 18 h, diluted with methylene chloride, quenched with satd. aq. NaHCO$_3$ soln., and stirred for 30 min → α-product. Y 71%. The method is highly stereospecific, depending on the substitution at C$_2$: O^2-acetates gave the α-glucuronide predominantly [*without* neighbouring group participation], as also did 2-deoxy derivs., whereas *trans*-2-iodo-2-deoxy-derivs. favoured β-anomers via intramolecular displacement of the carboxylate group through formation of a 3-membered iodonium ring. F.e.s. M. Poláková, P.V. Murphy et al., Angew. Chem. Int. Ed. Engl. *43*, 2518-21 (2004).

Hydrogen peroxide s. under Rhodium complexes H$_2$O$_2$
p-*Toluenesulfonic acid* TsOH
Protection of carbonyl groups as acid-stable 1,2,4-trioxepanes

117.

Robust, acid-resistant 1,2,4-trioxepanes are useful alternatives to 1,3-dithianes for the protection of carbonyl groups. E: A soln. of 1 eq. of the startg. oxo compd. in methylene chloride treated with 1.8 eqs. of the startg. neat silylperoxyalkanol and 1 eq. *p*-TsOH·monohydrate, and stirred for 1-2 h → product. Y 91%. The 1,2,4-trioxepane system is stable to a variety of reagents and reaction conditions (e.g. amines, NaH, aq. HCl, methanolic NaOH, NaBH$_4$, DDQ, and palladium catalysis), but is sensitive to *n*-BuLi, and **removal of the protective group** can be effected with Zn/HOAc or Mg/MeOH. F.e.s. A. Ahmed, P.H. Dussault, Org. Lett. *6*, 3609-11 (2004).

Tetra-n-butylammonium fluoride Bu$_4$NF
Carboxylic acid esters from chromium alkoxycarbene complexes ←
with dimethyldioxirane cf. *48*, 194; with Bu$_4$NF s. J. Barluenga et al., J. Org. Chem. *69*, 7352-4 (2004).

Acetonitrile(cyclopentadienyl)bis[2-(diphenylphosphino)-6-tert-butylpyridine]- ←
ruthenium(II) hexafluorophosphate/tetrakis(trimethylsilyl)methane
Aldehydes from terminal acetylene derivs. C≡C(Si≤) → CH$_2$CHO
Ruthenium-catalyzed anti-Markovnikov hydration under mild, neutral conditions

118.

of *in situ*-generated terminal acetylene derivs. A mixture of 2 mol% acetonitrile(cyclopentadienyl)bis[2-(diphenylphosphino)-6-*tert*-butylpyridine]ruthenium(II) hexafluorophosphate, 5 eqs. water, 1 eq. startg. protected alkyne, and ca. 0.6 mol% tetrakis(trimethylsilyl)methane in deoxygenated acetone-d$_6$ heated in a J-Young NMR tube at 70° for 66 h → product. Y 100% (by

NMR). The *enzyme-like*, bifunctional catalyst, possessing both a metal centre and a basic site, is the most active and selective to date for the *exclusive* anti-Markovnikov hydration of both alkylacetylenes (*at room temp.*!) and [ordinarily unreactive] arylacetylenes. Significantly, Thp-ethers, nitriles, sulfonylamino and *tert*-hydroxyl groups remained unaffected. F.e. and from preformed terminal acetylene derivs. s. D.B. Grotjahn, D.A. Lev, J. Am. Chem. Soc. *126*, 12232-3 (2004).

Bis(norbornadiene)rhodium(I) fluoroborate/(R,aR)-1-[1-[bis[3,5-bis(trifluoromethyl)- ←
phenyl]phosphino]ethyl]-2-[2-(diphenylphosphino)phenyl]ferrocene/
hydrogen peroxide/sodium hydroxide
Glycols from ene-1,2-di(boronic acid esters)   CH(OH)CH(OH)
via asym. homogeneous hydrogenation

119.

A mixture of 2 mol% bis(norbornadiene)rhodium(I) fluoroborate and *4 mol%* (R,aR)-1-[1-[bis-[3,5-bis(trifluoromethyl)phenyl]phosphino]ethyl]-2-[2-(diphenylphosphino)phenyl]ferrocene ((R,R)-Walphos-W001) in anhydrous *toluene* stirred under argon at 23° for 10 min, 1 eq. of the startg. enedi(boronate) added, hydrogenated with stirring under 20 atm. H_2 in a Parr bomb at the same temp. for 24 h, diluted with anhydrous THF, treated successively with 3 *M* aq. NaOH and 30% aq. H_2O_2 (dropwise), stirring continued at the same temp. for 3 h, and quenched with satd. aq. $Na_2S_2O_3$ → (S)-product. Y 90% (e.e. 93%). Interestingly, the (R)-enantiomer predominated with *1.6-2 mol%* of the chiral ligand. The method is significant in that attempts to generate 1,2-di(boronic acid esters) by asym. diborylation of monosubst. olefins are problematic. F.e. incl. conversions of alkyl- and cycloalkyl-subst. enedi(boronates) with the 2-[2-(dicyclohexylphosphino)phenyl]ferrocene analog (Walphos-W008) as ligand s. J.B. Morgan, J.P. Morken, J. Am. Chem. Soc. *126*, 15338-9 (2004).

Carbon↑   OC ↓↑ C

Microwaves s. under Lipase	[\\\\]
Cupric chloride s. under $PdCl_2$	$CuCl_2$
Sodium tetrahydridoborate s. under $RuCl_3$	$NaBH_4$
Zeolite	←
Heterogeneous partial O-acetylation with ethyl acetate s. *54*, 79s68	OH → OAc
Trifluoroperoxyacetic acid/trifluoroacetic acid	CF_3COO_2H/CF_3COOH
Carbonic acid diaryl esters from trityl alcohols	$Ar_3COH → (ArO)_2CO$

120.

A soln. of trityl alcohol in dry Freon 113 added to a soln. of 10 eqs. trifluoroperoxyacetic acid in trifluoroacetic acid at -25°, stirred for 1 h, then quenched with water → product. Y 96%. Reaction takes place by **consecutive Criegee rearrangement** involving a *triple* O-insertion. F.e., also carbonic acid diaryl and alkyl aryl esters from diaryl ketone diaryl or dialkyl ketals, respectively, s. P.A. Krasutsky et al., Org. Lett. *6*, 2539-42 (2004).

Indium(III) chloride s. under NIS $InCl_3$
Scandium(III) triflate s. under NIS $Sc(OTf)_3$

Ammonium ceric nitrate/diisobutylaluminum hydride $CAN/i\text{-}Bu_2AlH$
Regiospecific protection of glycols as methoxymethyl ethers s. 68, 95   OH → OCH_2OMe

Imidazol-2-ylidenes   ←
Transesterification under nucleophilic carbene catalysis   COOR → COOR'
with prim. alcohols cf. 64, 120; with sec. alcohols s. R. Singh, S.P. Nolan et al., J. Org. Chem. 69, 209-12 (2004).

Diisopropyl azodicarboxylate s. under Triphenylphosphine   ROOCN=NCOOR

Lipase/1-n-butyl-3-methylimidazolium hexafluorophosphate   ←
Kinetic resolution of alcohols by asym. enzymatic O-acylation in ionic liquids   OH → OAc
s. 44, 214s67; kinetic resolution of glycols s. A. Kamal, G. Chouhan, Tetrahedron Lett. 45, 8801-5 (2004).

Amberlite IR-120   ←
Cyclic orthocarboxylic acid esters by transesterification   ○
with $MeSO_3H$ cf. 21, 270; bicyclic orthoesters from triols with Amberlite IR-120 and 4 Å molecular sieves in DMF s. E. Stanoeva, N. De Kimpe et al., Tetrahedron 60, 5077-84 (2004).

N-Iodosuccinimide/scandium(III) or indium(III) triflate $NIS/Sc(OTf)_3$ or $In(OTf)_3$
Glycosides from pent-4-enyl glycosides   OR → OR'
with NIS/TfOH cf. 45, 116; oligosaccharide synthesis with added $Sc(OTf)_3$ or $In(OTf)_3$ s. K.N. Jayaprakash, B. Fraser-Reid, Synlett 2004, 301-5.

Trimethylsilyl iodide Me_3SiI
Trimethylsilyl iodide/triphenylphosphine oxide Me_3SiI/Ph_3PO
Glycosides from acyl glycosides   OAc → OR
with Me_3SiOTf cf. 34, 209s44; via glycosyl iodides (cf. 43, 404s59; 45, 88s52) with Me_3SiI, 2-amino-2-deoxy-β-glycosides, s. N. Miquel, L. Lay et al., Synlett 2004, 341-3; α-disaccharides with added Ph_3PO and 5 Å molecular sieves s. Y. Kobashi, T. Mukaiyama, Chem. Lett. 33, 874-5 (2004).

Zirconium tetrachloride $ZrCl_4$
Protection of alcohols as methoxymethyl ethers under neutral conditions   OH → OCH_2OMe
with $Sc(OTf)_3$ cf. 48, 216s66, and with $MoO_2(acac)_2$ cf. 48, 216; with $ZrCl_4$ in the absence of solvent, also deprotection in isopropanol, s. G.V.M. Sharma, P.R. Krishna et al., Tetrahedron Lett. 45, 9229-32 (2004); regiospecific protection of glycols s. 68, 95

Stannic perfluorooctanesulfonimide $Sn[N(SO_2C_8F_{17})_2]_4$
Transesterification in a fluorous 2-phase medium s. 61, 85s68   COOR → COOR'

Triphenylphosphine/diisopropyl azodicarboxylate $Ph_3P/ROOCN$=NCOOR
Interchange of N-carbalkoxy groups by transesterification   NCOOR → NCOOR'
with $Ti(OPr\text{-}i)_4$ cf. 54, 100; transesterification of polymer-based N''-(carbo-9-fluorenylmethoxy)-guanidines with triphenylphosphine/diisopropyl azodicarboxylate *en route* to N-aryl-N''-carbalkoxyguanidines s. D.E. Robinson, P.P. Seth, E.A. Jefferson, Synth. Commun. 34, 2743-9 (2004).

Triphenylphosphine oxide s. under Me_3SiI Ph_3PO

Trimethylsilyl triflate Me_3SiOTf
Acoxy compds. from ethers   OR → OAc
s. 38, 211s48; phenol acetates from isopropyl phenolethers, guaicol derivs., s. C.M. Williams, L.N. Mander, Tetrahedron Lett. 45, 667-9 (2004).

p-Toluenesulfonic acid or Nafion SAC-13   ←
Protection of alcohols as methoxymethyl ethers   OH → OCH_2OMe
by transacetalation with TsOH s. 39, 214s46; also with pyridinium tosylate, notably for protection of sec. alcohols, s. Y. Watanabe, T. Ikemoto, Tetrahedron Lett. 45, 5795-7 (2004); protection **as ethoxymethyl ethers** with TsOH or ion exchangers s. E. Dilk, I. Reiss, German patent DE-

10332229 (Symrise GmbH); f. alkoxymethyl ethers with TsOH, Nafion-SAC-13 or BF$_3$-etherate s. I. Ledneczki, A. Molnár, Synth. Commun. 34, 3683-90 (2004).

Potassium peroxymonosulfate $\qquad$ $KHSO_5$
Dicarboxylic acid esters from cyclic β-diketones s. 68, 87

Sodium periodate s. under $RuCl_3$ and OsO_4 $\qquad$ $NaIO_4$

Ruthenium trichloride/sodium periodate/sodium tetrahydridoborate $\qquad$ $RuCl_3/NaIO_4/NaBH_4$
Prim. alcohols from terminal ethylene derivs. with C-cleavage $\qquad$ $CH{=}CH_2 \to CH_2OH$

121.

One-pot procedure. A soln. of 1.5 eqs. NaIO$_4$ in water (1 part) chilled to 0°, 7 mol% RuCl$_3$·xH$_2$O, ethyl acetate (3 parts) and acetonitrile (3 parts) added sequentially, stirred for 5 min at the same temp., the startg. alkene added, the resulting slurry stirred for 1.5 min, quenched with satd. aq. Na$_2$S$_2$O$_3$, extracted with ethyl acetate, the organic layers combined, dried with anhydrous Na$_2$SO$_4$ and concentrated *in vacuo*, the residue dissolved in 1:1 THF/water, 1 eq. NaBH$_4$ added, stirred 20 min at room temp., water added, extracted with methylene chloride, the organic layer rinsed with aq. NaHCO$_3$, dried and concentrated *in vacuo*, the residue dissolved in 1:1 THF/water at 0-5°, 2 eqs. NaIO$_4$ added in small portions, stirred for 20 min, ethylene glycol added, diluted with water, extracted with ethyl acetate, dried and again concentrated, the residue dissolved in 1:1 THF/water, 3 eqs. NaBH$_4$ added, and stirred at room temp. for 1 h → product. Y 72%. The procedure is an improvement on osmium- or ozone-based methodologies in that: the catalyst is relatively inexpensive, safe and easy to handle; the conversion is rapid; all steps are aqueous, and work-up is easy. The reductive step prior to the diol cleavage removes by-products and improves the yield significantly. F.e.s. P.K. Sharma, P. Nielsen, J. Org. Chem. 69, 5742-5 (2004).

Ruthenium trichloride/sodium periodate/benzyltriethylammonium chloride ←
Aldehydes from ethylene derivs. by oxidative cleavage $\qquad$ $CH{=}C \to CHO$
with RuCl$_3$/NaIO$_4$ s. 30, 154s62; cleavage of 3-aryl-1-propenes with added BnEt$_3$NCl as phase transfer catalyst (cf. 30, 154s42) s. Y. Yuasa, S. Shibuya, Y. Yuasa, Synth. Commun. 33, 3947-52 (2003).

Palladous chloride/cupric chloride $\qquad$ $PdCl_2/CuCl_2$
Preferential and selective heterogeneous O-acetylation under mild conditions $\qquad$ $OH \to OAc$

122.

via palladium-catalyzed transesterification. A mixture of the startg. alcohol, 2 eqs. vinyl acetate, 0.3 mol% PdCl$_2$, and 7.8 mol% CuCl$_2$ in anhydrous toluene stirred at room temp. for 3 h → product. Y 93%. The procedure is specific for O-acetylation of prim. and sec. (incl. hindered) alcohols, there being no reaction with tert. alcohols, phenols, mercaptans, and aliphatic or ar. amines. Methoxy, benzyloxy, and alkylthio groups and ar. chlorine were also unaffected. As the catalyst is heterogeneous, work-up is simple and the only by-product is volatile acetaldehyde. There was reaction with acetic anhydride or acetic acid as acetylating agent. F.e.s. J.W.J. Bosco, A.K. Saikia, Chem. Commun. 2004, 1116-7.

Bis(1,5-cyclooctadiene)iridium(I) fluoroborate $\qquad$ $[Ir(cod)_2]BF_4$
Iridium-catalyzed allylation under neutral conditions $\qquad$ $OH \to OC{-}C{=}C$

123.

O-Allylation of phenols. *p*-Cresol and 10 eqs. allyl acetate added to a soln. of 2 mol% bis(1,5-cyclooctadiene)iridium(I) fluoroborate in toluene under argon, and heated at 100° for 15 h →

product. Y 90%. The procedure is also applicable to the O-allylation of carboxylic acids and prim., sec. or tert. alcohols, S-allylation of mercaptans, and N,N-diallylation of prim. amines, bifunctional substrates undergoing bisallylation. Reaction appears to involve nucleophilic attack on an intermediate iridium π-allyl complex, and is not complicated by transesterification. F.e.s. H. Nakagawa, Y. Ishii et al., J. Org. Chem. *69*, 3474-7 (2004).

Chlorobis(cyclooctene)iridium(I) dimer/(1S,4R,8R)-2-(4-tert-butylphenyl)-8-methoxy- ←
1,8-dimethylbicyclo[2.2.2]octa-2,5-diene
Kinetic resolution of 2-ethylenecarbonic acid esters by asym. O-allylation of phenols ←
Chiral bicyclo[2.2.2]octadienes as ligand

124.

A new family of chiral bicyclo[2.2.2]octadienes, readily prepared on the large-scale in either enantiomeric form from inexpensive (R)- or (S)-carvone, are highly efficient for the kinetic resolution of allyl carbonates by asym. O-allylation of phenols. **E:** A mixture of 1.5 mol% [IrCl(coe)$_2$]$_2$ and 3.6 mol% (1S,4R,8R)-2-(4-*tert*-butylphenyl)-8-methoxy-1,8-dimethyl-bicyclo[2.2.2]octa-2,5-diene in methylene chloride stirred at room temp. under argon for 8 h, racemic 3-carbomethoxyoxy-3-(*p*-nitrophenyl)prop-1-ene and 0.5 eq. phenol added at the same temp., and allowed to react for 24 h → (S)-3-(*p*-nitrophenyl)-3-phenoxyprop-1-ene (Y 49%; e.e. 86%) and unreacted (R)-3-carbomethoxyoxy-3-(*p*-nitrophenyl)prop-1-ene (Y 45%; e.e. 95%). Reaction is generally applicable to allyl carbonates substituted by alkyl or aryl groups, which may be electron-rich or -deficient. F.e.s. C. Fischer, E.M. Carreira et al., J. Am. Chem. Soc. *126*, 1628-9 (2004).

Osmium tetroxide/sodium periodate/2,6-lutidine ←
Aldehydes from ethylene derivs. by oxidative C-cleavage CH=C → CHO
with OsO$_4$/KIO$_4$/Et$_3$N/dibenzo-18-crown-6 cf. *39*, 223; improved procedure with OsO$_4$/NaIO$_4$/2,6-*lutidine* in aq. dioxane for acid-sensitive substrates s. W. Yu, Z. Jin et al., Org. Lett. *6*, 3217-9 (2004).

Elimination ⇑

Hydrogen ↑ OC ⇑ H

Irradiation s. under HgO ⫽
Microwaves s. under Chloramine-T [\\\\]
Sodium bromide/sodium hydrogen sulfite NaBr/NaHSO$_3$
Lactones from diols under mild conditions in water ○

125.

Hydroxylactones. A mixture of 131 g 3-methylpentane-1,3,5-triol and 202 g NaBr in pure water added to 16.7 wt.% aq. NaHSO$_3$ at 40-50° over 2 h, left for 4 h, cooled to room temp., and treated with 10% aq. Na-sulfate → product. Y 70%. Reaction is applicable to both γ- and δ-lactones, and is thought to involve *in situ*-generation of HBr. F.e.s. S. Nagano, Japanese patent JP-2002173491 (Daicel Chem. Ind. Ltd.).

Mercuric oxide/irradiation   *HgO/ℎν*
Oxo compds. from alcohols   CHOH → CO
with Hg(OAc)$_2$/DMSO cf. *25*, 182; aryloxo compds. with HgO under irradiation s. M.H. Habibi, S. Farhadi, Pol. J. Chem. *78*, 741-4 (2004).

Hydroxyapatite s. under Palladium nanoparticles ←

Indium(III) chloride or bromide/silica gel   *InCl$_3$ or InBr$_3$/SiO$_2$*
Flavones from *o'*-hydroxychalcones
with I$_2$ cf. *2*, 288s*66*; with InCl$_3$ or InBr$_3$ on silica gel in the absence of solvent s. N. Ahmed, H. Ali, J.E. van Lier, Tetrahedron Lett. *46*, 253-6 (2005).

Imidazolium ionic liquids s. under Imidazolium decatungstates ←

4-[4,6-Bis[bis(heptadecafluoroundecyl)amino]-1,3,5-triazin-2-yloxy]-2,2,6,6- ←
tetramethylpiperidine nitroxyl/phenyl iodosoacetate
Oxo compds. from alcohols   CHOH → CO
aldehydes with TEMPO/PhI(OAc)$_2$ cf. *45*, 120s*64*; also ketones with 4-[4,6-bis[bis(heptadecafluoroundecyl)amino]-1,3,5-triazin-2-yloxy]-2,2,6,6-tetramethylpiperidine nitroxyl s. G. Pozzi, I. Shepperson et al., Tetrahedron Lett. *45*, 4249-51 (2004).

Methyl(trifluoromethyl)dioxirane ←
Epoxyketones from epoxyalcohols under mild, neutral conditions

126.

(d.r. 7:3)

A stirred soln. of 4,5-epoxy-2-pentanol (d.r. 7:3) in methylene chloride treated in one portion at 0° with a soln. of 1.1 eqs. methyl(trifluoromethyl)dioxirane in methyl trifluoromethyl ketone, and stirred at the same temp. for 20 min → (4S)-4,5-epoxy-2-pentanone. Conversion >98% (Y >90%; e.e. 40%). Reaction is applicable to open-chain and cyclic epoxyalcohols, and proceeds **with retention of configuration** at the 2-position. F.e. incl. α,β-epoxyketones, also with dimethyldioxirane (more slowly), s. L. D'Accolti, R. Curci et al., J. Org. Chem. *69*, 8510-3 (2004).

Dimethyl sulfoxide s. under N$_2$H$_4$·H$_2$O   *DMSO*

Bis(2,4,6-triisopropylphenyl) telluroxide   *Ar$_2$TeO*
Oxo compds. from alcohols
benzylic oxidation with diaryl tellurones cf. *37*, 86; with bis(2,4,6-triisopropylphenyl) telluroxide s. M. Oba, K. Nishiyama, W. Ando et al., Chem. Commun. *2004*, 1672-3.

o-Iodoxybenzoic acid   *ArIO$_2$*
Cyclic α,β-ethyleneketones from 2-ethylene-*tert*-alcohols   CH=C-C(OH) → COC=C

127.

Oxidative rearrangement. 1.2 eqs. *o*-Iodoxybenzoic acid added to a soln. of the startg. cyclic alcohol in DMSO, and heated at 55° for 1 h under argon → product. Y 85%. Reaction is generally applicable to cyclohexene and cyclopentene derivs., alkyl-subst. derivs. requiring the addition of pyridine to prevent undesirable dehydration. The procedure is practical and environmentally friendly, and leaves OAc, OMOM and phenolic OTBS groups intact. F.e. and comparison of high-valent iodine oxidants s. M. Shibuya, Y. Iwabuchi et al., Org. Lett. 6, 4303-6 (2004).

Phenyl iodosoacetate (s.a. under Piperidine nitroxyls)   PhI(OAc)$_2$
Chloramine-T/microwaves   p-TolSO$_2$N(Cl)Na/[\\\\]
1,3,4-Oxadiazoles from acylhydrazones
solid-state conversion with PhI(OAc)$_2$ s. *44*, 301s62; s.a. V.S. Rao, K.V.G.C. Sekhar, Synth. Commun. *34*, 2153-7 (2004); rapid procedure under microwave irradiation in ethanol with Chloramine-T s. K. Mogilaiah, G.R. Reddy, J. Chem. Res. Synop *2004*, 477-9.

Bromobenzene s. under Pd(OAc)$_2$ PhBr
Hydrazine hydrate/iodine/dimethyl sulfoxide   N$_2$H$_4$/I$_2$/DMSO
Ketones from sec. alcohols in aq. medium   CHOH → CO

128.

1 eq. Hydrazine hydrate and 2 eqs. iodine in 5:1 acetonitrile/water stirred at room temp. under N$_2$ for 15 min, 1 eq. of the startg. alcohol added, stirred for an additional 5 min at the same temp., treated with 5 eqs. DMSO, and refluxed at 80° for 2.5 h → product. Y 95%. **Preferential oxidation** of *sec*-hydroxyl groups takes place in the presence of non-benzylic *prim*-hydroxyl groups. The procedure is simple, inexpensive and environmentally friendly, being insensitive to moisture and not requiring toxic or basic reagents. It is thought that reaction involves initial formation of HI by reduction of iodine with hydrazine hydrate, followed by generation of a carbocation and oxidation by DMSO. F.e.s. P. Gogoi, G.K. Sarmah, D. Konwar, J. Org. Chem. *69*, 5153-4 (2004).

Hydrogen peroxide s.a. under Imidazolium decatungstates   H$_2$O$_2$
Hydrogen peroxide/hydrogen bromide   H$_2$O$_2$/HBr
Ketones from sec. alcohols in aq. medium under very mild conditions

129.

20 Mol% 48% HBr added dropwise to a stirred soln. of the startg. alcohol and 2 eqs. 30% H$_2$O$_2$ in acetonitrile, refluxed for 2.5 h, and excess of the oxidant destroyed with aq. bisulfite → product. Y 80%. The method is inexpensive, environmentally friendly and applicable to the oxidation of both *activated and non-activated* sec. alcohols. Reaction is thought to involve initial formation of HOBr, which converts the alcohol to a hypobromite prior to abstraction of hydrogen. F.e. and **preferential oxidation** with retention of *prim*-hydroxyl groups s. V.B. Sharma, S.L. Jain, B. Sain, Synlett *2005*, 173-5.

Nicotinium dichromate   ←
Oxo compds. from alcohols
aldehydes with pyridinum dichromate cf. *25*, 185; acylphosphonic from α-hydroxyphosphonic acid esters with nicotinium dichromate s. H. Firouzabadi, N. Iranpoor, S. Sobhani, Synth. Commun. *34*, 1463-71 (2004).

Barium dichromate   BaCr$_2$O$_7$
Oxo compds. from alcohols
ketones with ZnCr$_2$O$_7$ cf. *41*, 240; also aldehydes with BaCr$_2$O$_7$ s. E. Mottaghinejad, E. Shaafi, Z. Ghasemzadeh, Tetrahedron Lett. *45*, 8823-4 (2004).

Hexamethylenetetrammonium fluorochromate   ←
Oxo compds. from alcohols
with tetramethylammonium fluorochromate cf. *42*, 235s66; with hexamethylenetetrammonium fluorochromate, also quinones from arenes, pyridines from 1,4-dihydropyridines, and sym. disulfides from mercaptans, s. E. Turunc, F. Aydin, Org. Prep. Proced. Int. *36*, 363-6 (2004).

4-Aminopyridinium chlorochromate/silica gel
Oxo compds. from alcohols   CHOH → CO
with pyridinium chlorochromate/silica cf. *45*, 122; with 4-aminopyridinium chlorochromate/
silica gel s. M.M. Hashemi, D. Ghazanfari, M. Akhbari, Monatsh. Chem. *135*, 793-7 (2004).

1-n-Butyl-3-methylimidazolium decatungstate/hydrogen peroxide/1-n-*butyl-3-*
 methylimidazolium fluoroborate
Oxo compds. from alcohols
with $Na_2WO_4/H_2O_2/Bu_4NHSO_4$ under microwave irradiation without organic solvent cf. *54*,
109s58; with 1-*n*-butyl-3-methylimidazolium decatungstate/H_2O_2 **in ionic liquids,** e.g. 1-*n*-butyl-
3-methylimidazolium fluoroborate, for oxidation of benzyl and aliphatic sec. alcohols s. B.S.
Chhikara, S. Tehlan, A. Kumar, Synlett *2005*, 63-6.

Iodine s. under $N_2H_4 \cdot H_2O$ I_2

Tetraalkylammonium bromate $[R_4N]BrO_3$
Oxo compds. from alcohols
with $NaBrO_3$/ion exchanger cf. *29*, 233s65; with tetraalkylammonium bromate in ethanol s. D.
Deb, P.J. Das et al., Indian J. Chem. *43B*, 1360-2 (2004).

Hydrogen bromide s. under H_2O_2 HBr

Potassium permanganate/manganese dioxide $KMnO_4/MnO_2$
Oxidations with potassium permanganate-on-active manganese dioxide

130.   Ph⌢OH → Ph⌢O | PhCH₂Pr ⋯→ PhCOPr
                                                     (92%)

Oxo compds. from alcohols in the absence of solvent. A mixture of benzyl alcohol and $KMnO_4$-
on-active MnO_2 irradiated at room temp. with ultrasound for 63 min, the product washed with
methylene chloride, the spent oxidant filtered off, and the filtrate worked up → benzaldehyde. Y
94% (78% after 60 min without ultrasonication). The process is infinitely sustainable as the
recoverable MnO_2 can be simply reoxidized to $KMnO_4$ by established means. Reaction can also
be performed **under heterogeneous conditions** in methylene chloride. F.e. incl. oxidation of
aliphatic, ar. and α,β-ethylenic aldehydes, also aryloxo compds. from alkylarenes, and sulfones
from thioethers, s. A. Shaabani et al., Tetrahedron *60*, 11415-20 (2004).

Ruthenium hydride complexes/silica gel
Oxo compds. from alcohols   CHOH → CO
ketones with an *in situ*-generated Shvo complex (*53*, 500) cf. *65*, 128; also aldehydes with a
stable, easy-to-handle, readily recoverable ruthenium hydride complex-on-silica gel s. J.H. Choi,
J. Park et al., Tetrahedron Lett. *45*, 4607-10 (2004).

Palladium nanoparticles/hydroxyapatite/oxygen
Oxo compds. from alcohols
Heterogeneous aerobic oxidation
with $PdCl_2(PhCN)_2$-on-hydroxyapatite cf. *55*, 113s67; with palladium nanoparticles-on-hydroxy-
apatite in trifluoromethylbenzene or **in water** s. K. Mori, T. Hara, K. Kaneda et al., J. Am. Chem.
Soc. *126*, 10657-66 (2004).

Palladous acetate/triphenylphosphine/bromobenzene/potassium carbonate
Aldonolactones from aldoses

131.   [BnO-furanose-OH with BnO, OBn]   →   [BnO-lactone=O with BnO, OBn]

A soln. of 2 mol% $Pd(OAc)_2$ and 4 mol% triphenylphosphine in dry THF stirred under argon for
2 min, 2,3,5-tri-O-benzyl-β-D-arabinofuranoside, 2 eqs. K_2CO_3 and 2 eqs. bromobenzene (as H-

acceptor) added sequentially, and refluxed with vigorous stirring for 4 h → product. Y 98%. The method is applicable to perbenzylated furanoses and pyranoses, but the corresponding acyl glycosides were not oxidized under these conditions. The choice of base and Pd(OAc)$_2$ as catalyst is critical, while tri-*o*-tolylphosphine and (R)-BINAP were equally effective as ligand. The aqueous work-up was straightforward. F.e. and with 4-bromobiphenyl as H-acceptor s. A. Bessmertnykh, F. Hénin, J. Muzart, Carbohydr. Res. *339*, 1377-80 (2004).

Diacetatobis(2,3,4,5-tetraphenyl-3-pyridylbenzene)palladium(II)/sodium acetate/oxygen ←
Oxo compds. from alcohols CHOH → CO
Aerobic oxidation under mild conditions at low catalyst loading
with a diacetatopalladium(II) imidazol-2-ylidene complex cf. *67, 119*; with diacetatobis(2,3,4,5-tetraphenyl-3-pyridylbenzene)palladium(II), also comparison of pyridylpolyaryl ligands (avoiding formation of Pd-black), s. T. Iwasawa, Y. Tsuji et al., J. Am. Chem. Soc. *126*, 6554-5 (2004).

Bis(acetonitrile)(η^5-pentamethylcyclopentadienyl)(1,2,3,4-tetramethylimidazol-2-ylidene)iridium(III) triflate/acetone/potassium carbonate ←
Oxo compds. from alcohols
with an iridium(III) dihydride complex and 3,3-dimethylbutene as H-acceptor cf. *42, 241s62*; Oppenauer-type oxidation with bis(acetonitrile)(η^5-pentamethylcyclopentadienyl)(1,2,3,4-tetramethylimidazol-2-ylidene)iridium(III) triflate s. F. Hanasaka, K.I. Fujita, R. Yamaguchi, Organometallics *23*, 1490-2 (2004).

Oxygen ↑   OC ⇑ O

Zirconium tetrachloride $ZrCl_4$
1,3,4-Oxadiazoles from N,N'-diacylhydrazines O
with TsCl/polymer-based iminophosphorotriamide under microwave irradiation cf. *19, 563s61*; with 0.1 eq. ZrCl$_4$ s. G.V.M. Sharma, A. Begum, P.R. Krishna, Synth. Commun. *34*, 2387-91 (2004).

Bismuth(III) triflate/1-n-butyl-3-methylimidazolium fluoroborate $Bi(OTf)_3$/[bmim]BF_4
Furans from γ-diketones in ionic liquids s. *67, 159s68*

Tetrakis(triphenylphosphine)palladium(0) $Pd(PPh_3)_4$
***trans*-4-Vinyl-1,3-dioxolan-2-ones from 2-ene-1,4-diol monocarbonates**

132.

The startg. chiral enediol monocarbonate treated under N$_2$ at room temp. with a soln. of 5 mol% Pd(PPh$_3$)$_4$ in methylene chloride, and stirred at the same temp. for 1 h → (4S,4'R,5S)-4-(2,2-dimethyl-1,3-dioxolan-3-yl)-5-vinyl-1,3-dioxolan-2-one. Y 61%. The products serve as **chiral O-protected *syn*-3-ene-1,2-diols**, and are obtained under thermodynamic control irrespective of the geometry of the startg. carbonate. F.e.s. Y. Georges, X. Ariza, J. Garcia et al., J. Org. Chem. *69*, 7387-90 (2004).

Nitrogen ↑

OC ⇑ N

Sodium nitrite/acetic acid
1,3-Dioxolan-2-ones from glycol monocarbamates

$NaNO_2/AcOH$

133.

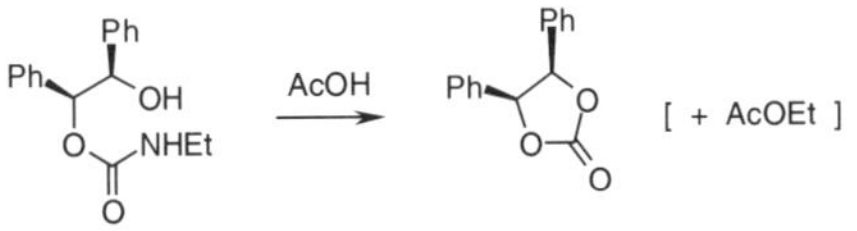

with retention of configuration. A mixture of the startg. ethyl carbamate and 3 Å molecular sieves in acetic acid treated with 8.6 eqs. NaNO$_2$, and stirred at 80° overnight → product. Y 72%. F.e. and application of the substrate as an ethylating agent (*68*, 104) s. M. Suzuki, T. Sugai, Bull. Chem. Soc. Jpn. *77*, 1217-27 (2004).

m-Chloroperoxybenzoic acid
Oxo compds. from halides via 1-alkoxy-2,2,6,6-tetramethylpiperidines

$ArCOO_2H$
$CH(ON<) \to CO$

134.

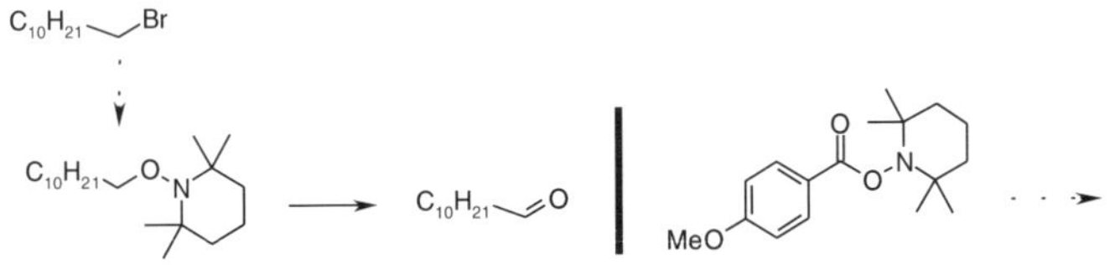

2,2,6,6-Tetramethylpiperidine nitroxyl (TEMPO) serves *as nucleophile* in the overall conversion of alkyl halides to oxo compds. **E**: A soln. of the startg. 1-alkoxy-2,2,6,6-tetramethylpiperidine (readily prepared from undecyl bromide and TEMPO in the presence of Na-metal and a little naphthalene) in methylene chloride treated portionwise over 10 min with 1.2 eqs. *m*-chloroperoxybenzoic acid (70-5%), stirred for 30 min, then quenched with cold aq. Na$_2$S$_2$O$_3$ → product. Y 88%. F.e., **also aldehydes from carboxylic acid chlorides or anhydrides via** chelation-controlled reduction of **1-acoxy-2,2,6,6-tetramethylpiperidines** with DIBAL, s. T. Inokuchi, H. Kawafuchi, Tetrahedron *60*, 11969-75 (2004).

Halogen ↑

OC ⇑ Hal

Potassium fluoride
Δ^2-Oxazolines from 2-chloroacylamines

KF

135.

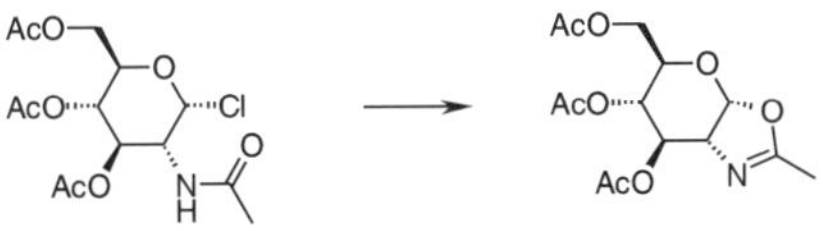

Carbohydrate Δ^2-oxazolines. A soln. of 1.8 g of the startg. glycosyl chloride in DMF added to a soln. of 5 eqs. KF in acetonitrile under argon, and stirred for 72 h at 60° → product. Y 81%. The process is both simple and high-yielding. F.e.s. S. Shoda et al., World Intellectual Property Organisation patent WO-2003004508 (Seikagaku Corp.).

Sulfur ↑

OC ⇑ S

Microwaves s. under NH$_4$OAc

[\\\\]

Lithum anilide   *PhNHLi*
Cyclic α-aminoaldehydes from spirocyclic 2-sulfinylaziridines   C̹

136.

A soln. of 5.5 eqs. Li-anilide and the startg. 2-sulfinylaziridine (readily prepared from the corresponding α-chloro-α,β-ethylenesulfoxide and Li-*o*-methoxyanilide) in THF stirred for 4 h at room temp., then quenched with satd. aq. NH$_4$Cl → product. Y 90%. Reaction failed with lithium *p*-nitroanilide and lithium alkylamides. F.e. and reactions of the product, also one-pot procedure from the α-chloro-α,β-ethylenesulfoxides, s. H. Ota, T. Satoh et al., Tetrahedron Lett. 45, 3903-7 (2004).

Ammonium acetate/microwaves   *NH$_4$OAc/*[\\\\]
Aldehydes from α-hydroxysulfonic acids (bisulfite adducts)   CH(OH)SO$_3$H → CHO
with Na$_2$CO$_3$ cf. *22*, 268; rapid procedure under microwave irradiation in the absence of solvent with NH$_4$OAc, also cleavage of ar. acylals, s. A.K. Mitra, N. Karchaudhuri, A. De, J. Chem. Res. Synop *2004*, 237-9.

p-Toluenesulfonyl chloride/sodium hydroxide   *TsCl/NaOH*
1,3-N,O-Heterocyclics from hydroxythioureas   ○
with KO$_2$ cf. *38*, 239s*54*; 5- and 6-membered 2-arylimino-1,3-O,N-heterocyclics with TsCl/ NaOH s. U. Heinelt, H.S.G. Beckmann et al., Tetrahedron *60*, 9883-8 (2004).

Remaining Elements ↑   OC ⇅ Rem

Bismuth(III) nitrate/montmorillonite/microwaves   ←
Zinc dichromate   *ZnCr$_2$O$_7$*
Chromium trioxide/zeolites or montmorillonite/microwaves   ←
Manganese(III) salen complexes/iodosobenzene   ←
Oxo compds. from alkoxysilanes   CH(OSi≤) → CO
with CrO$_3$/Al$_2$O$_3$ cf. *41*, 261s*57*, and with CrO$_3$/H$_2$SO$_4$ cf. *37*, 265s*39*; with CrO$_3$ on zeolites or montmorillonite, rapid procedure under microwave irradiation in the absence of solvent, s. M.M. Heravi et al., Phosphorus, Sulfur Silicon Relat. Elem. *179*, 1473-5 (2004); with Bi(NO$_3$)$_3$/ montmorillonite (cf. *63*, 129s*64*) s. J. Chem. Res. Synop *2004*, 129-30; with ZnCr$_2$O$_7$ in the absence of solvent, also oxidative cleavage of tetrahydropyran-2-yl ethers, s. H. Firouzabadi, H. Hassani, M. Gholizadeh, Phosphorus, Sulfur Silicon Relat. Elem. *179*, 1417-22 (2004); ketones with [N,N'-bis(*o*-hydroxybenzylidene)ethylenediamine]manganese(III) chloride/PhIO s. S.I. Murahashi, N. Komiya et al., Synlett *2004*, 1739-42.

Carbon ↑   OC ⇅ C

Microwaves s. under Hexamethylenetetramine-bromine   [\\\\]

Zinc/acetic acid   *Zn/AcOH*
Protection of oxo compds. as 1,2,4-trioxepanes   C̹
Removal of the protective group s. *68*, 117

β-Cyclodextrin s. under NBS   ←
Dimethyl sulfoxide s. under I$_2$ *DMSO*

N-Bromosuccinimide/β-cyclodextrin ←
Hexamethylenetetramine-bromine/silica gel/microwaves ←
Oxo compds. from tetrahydropyran-2-yl ethers $\quad$ CH(OThp) → CO
with AgBrO$_3$/AlCl$_3$ in acetonitrile cf. *57*, 120; with NBS/β-cyclodextrin **in aq. media** s. M. Narender, M.S. Reddy, K.R. Rao, Synthesis *2004*, 1741-3; with hexamethylenetetramine-bromine on silica gel, rapid procedure under microwave irradiation in the absence of solvent, s. M.B. Dehkordi, M.M. Heravi et al., Phosphorus, Sulfur Silicon Relat. Elem. *179*, 1493-6 (2004).

Methanesulfonic acid $\quad$ MeSO$_3$H
γ-Lactones from cyclopropanecarboxylic acid esters
with (Me$_3$SiO)$_2$SO$_2$ cf. *37*, 270; *cis*-fused 2,8-dioxabicyclo[3.3.0]octan-3-ones s. C. Kim, E.A. Theodorakis et al., Synth. Commun. *34*, 1951-65 (2004).

Zinc dichromate $\quad$ ZnCr$_2$O$_7$
Oxo compds. from tetrahydropyran-2-yl ethers s. *41*, 261s68 $\quad$ CH(OThp) → CO

Iodine/dimethyl sulfoxide $\quad$ I$_2$/DMSO
Flavones from *o'*-allyloxychalcones

137.

1 eq. Iodine added to a soln. of the startg. *o'*-allyloxychalcone in DMSO, the mixture heated in an oil bath at 130° for 30 min, cooled, diluted with water, and washed with satd. aq. Na$_2$S$_2$O$_3$ → product. Y 86%. Cleavage of the allyl group and ring closure is effected by the same reagent under mild, neutral conditions, leaving O-benzyl and O-methyl groups unaffected. F.e.s. P.D. Lokhande et al., Tetrahedron Lett. *46*, 1573-4 (2005).

Palladium-carbon $\quad$ Pd-C
Spiroketals from α,β-acetylene-ω-benzyloxy-ω'-hydroxyketones

138.

A soln. of 1 eq. of the startg. alkynone in anhydrous ethyl acetate treated with a little 10% Pd-C, and stirred at room temp. under 1 atm. H$_2$ for 24 h → product. Y 84% [(5S,7S)(5R,7S) 7:4]. The procedure is suitable for preparing [4.4]-, [4.5]-, [5.5]- and [5.6]-spirocyclics, reaction taking place in one pot **under neutral conditions** by a sequence involving initial hydrogenation of the triple bond, followed by hydrogenolytic O-debenzylation and spiroketalization. F.e.s. J. Doubsky, B. Koutek et al., Org. Lett. *6*, 4909-11 (2004).

Formation of N-N Bond

Elimination $\quad$ ⇑

Hydrogen ↑ $\quad$ NN ⇑ H

Calcium hypochlorite $\quad$ Ca(OCl)$_2$
1,2,4-Triazoline-3,5-diones from 1,2,4-triazolidine-3,5-diones $\quad$ NHNH → N=N
heterogeneous conversion with HIO$_4$/NaNO$_2$/silica gel cf. *19*, 356s62; with Ca(OCl)$_2$ in methylene chloride s. M.A. Zolfigol, M. Torabi et al., Russ. J. Org. Chem. *40*, 914-6 (2004).

Oxygen ↑   NN ⇑ O

Acetophenone/sodium/alcohol   PhCOMe/NaOR
Reductive cinnoline ring closure
benzo[c]cinnolines from o,o'-dinitrodiaryls with Ni/N_2H_4 cf. *14*, 366; with PhCOMe as reductant and ethanolic NaOEt, or the N-oxide in aq. NaOH, s. H.R. Bjorsvik, R.R. González, L. Liguori, J. Org. Chem. *69*, 7720-7 (2004).

Formation of N-Hal Bond

Exchange   ⇵

Hydrogen ↑   NHal ⇵ H

Trichloroisocyanuric acid
N-Chlorination of amines   NH → NCl

139.

PhCH$_2$NH$_2$ ⟶ PhCH$_2$NCl$_2$ ⋯⟶ PhCN (95%)

Ph–CH(NH$_2$)–COOH ⋯⟶ Ph–CN (98%)

N,N-Dichloramines from prim. amines. 1 eq. Trichloroisocyanuric acid added to a soln. of benzylamine in methylene chloride at 0°, warmed to room temp., stirred for 1 h, filtered over Celite, and the solvent removed → product. Y 98%. Sec. amines were similarly N-chlorinated, but prim. ar. amines failed to react. N,N-Dichloramine products were isolated without further purification. The procedure is mild, non-toxic, simple in application, and can be scaled up. Interestingly, sec. N,N-dichloramines were converted with triethylamine to **N-chloroketimines**, hydrolyzable to ketones, while prim. N,N-dichloramines gave the corresponding **nitriles**. Furthermore, the latter were also obtained **from α-*prim*-aminocarboxylic acids** with trichloroisocyanuric acid in aq. NaOH in a racemization-free procedure (s. *68*, 202). F.e.s. L. De Luca, G. Giacomelli, Synlett *2004*, 2180-4.

Formation of N-S Bond

Exchange   ⇵

Halogen ↑   NS ⇵ Hal

Without additional reagents   w.a.r.
Microwaves   [\\\\]
Triethylamine/N,O-bis(trimethylsilyl)acetamide $Et_3N/CH_2=C(OSiMe_3)NHSiMe_3$
N-Sulfonylation   NH → NSO$_2$R
under microwave irradiation in the absence of solvent with silica gel cf. *2*, 312s58; of anilines and hetar. amines without added silica gel s. A.K. Sharma, S.K. Das, Synth. Commun. *34*, 3807-19 (2004); **solid-state N-tosylation** of ar. amines on grinding in a mortar s. N. Zhao, Y.L. Wang, J. Chem. Res. Synop *2004*, 366-7; N-(*p*-hydroxybenzenesulfonyl)ation with *in situ*-O-silylation-desilylation (using Et$_3$N/N,O-bis(trimethylsilyl)acetamide) s. J.I. Levin, M.T. Du, K. Park, Synth. Commun. *34*, 2773-81 (2004).

Sulfur ↑   NS ↓↑ S

Silver nitrate $AgNO_3$
Sulfenamides from disulfides   RSSR → RSN<
s. *28*, 258; S-glycosylsulfenamides s. T.Z. Illyes, D. Molnar-Gabor, L. Szilagyi, Carbohydr. Res. *339*, 1561-4 (2004).

Elimination   ⇈

Hydrogen ↑   NS ⇈ H

Hydrogen peroxide or Bromine H_2O_2 or Br_2
Isothiazoles from β-amino-α,β-ethylenethiooxo compds.
from aldehyde derivs. with *m*-chloroperoxybenzoic acid cf. *45*, 150; also from ketone derivs., and with H_2O_2 or Br_2 as oxidant (cf. *18*, 354s*37-8*), s. M. Mishra, S.K.D. Chowdhury, K.K. Mahalanabis, Synth. Commun. *34*, 2681-9 (2004).

Sulfur ↑   NS ⇈ S

O-Methylhydroxylamine hydrochloride/pyridine $MeONH_2 \cdot HCl/C_5H_5N$
1,2-Benzisothiazol-3-ones
from *o,o'*-dicarbamyldisulfides with I_2/pyridine cf. *10*, 258; with O-methylhydroxylamine hydrochloride/pyridine s. T. Sano, M. Shimizu et al., Synthesis *2004*, 1585-8.

Formation of N-C Bond

Uptake   ⇓

Addition to Oxygen and Carbon   NC ⇓ OC

Without additional reagents   w.a.r.
2-Aminoalcohols from epoxides   ▽O → C(OH)C(N<)
s. *12*, 376; regiospecific ring opening **in the absence of solvent** s. G. Huerta, R.A. Toscano et al., Synth. Commun. *34*, 2393-406 (2004).

N-Silyldicarboxylic acid amide silyl esters from dicarboxylic acid anhydrides

A mixture of hexamethyldisilazane and 1 eq. tetrachlorophthalic anhydride stirred at 130-140° until homogeneous → product. Y 96%. Succinic anhydride and 4-nitrophthalic anhydride reacted in the same manner, but other anhydrides gave the corresponding N-silyldicarboxylic acid anhydrides. F.e.s. S.V. Basenko, M.G. Voronkov, Russ. J. Gen. Chem. *74*, 545-7 (2004).

2-Oxazolidone ring opening with amines
α-ureidoketones from 5-alkylidene-2-oxazolidones cf. *63*, 140; N-β-glycosylureas from carbohydrate-fused 2-oxazolidones in aq. media s. Y. Ichikawa, Y. Matsukawa, M. Isobe, Synlett *2004*, 1019-22.

Sodium azide NaN_3
2-Azidoalcohols from epoxides $\overset{\triangledown}{\circ}{}^{\!\!/} \to C(OH)C(N_3)$
with NaN_3/zeolite s. *40*, 176s*42*; with NaN_3/3 Å molecular sieves in acetonitrile, regiospecific ring opening, s. J. Boruwa, N.C. Barua et al., Tetrahedron Lett. *45*, 7355-8 (2004).

Lithium bromide $LiBr$
2-Aminoalcohols from epoxides $\overset{\triangledown}{\circ}{}^{\!\!/} \to C(OH)C(N{<})$
with $LiNTf_2$ cf. *46*, 267s*64*; with LiBr **in the absence of solvent** s. A.K. Chakraborti, S. Rudrawar, A. Kondaskar, Eur. J. Org. Chem. **2004**, 3597-600.

Boron fluoride BF_3
2-Acylaminoalcohols from epoxides and nitriles $\overset{\triangledown}{\circ}{}^{\!\!/} \to C(OH)C(NHAc)$
s. *23*, 348; *anti*-β-acylamino-α-hydroxycarboxylic acid amides s. M.V. Voronkov, H.C. Kolb et al., Tetrahedron *60*, 9043-8 (2004).

Indium(III) bromide $InBr_3$
2-(Arylamino)alcohols from epoxides $\overset{\triangledown}{\circ}{}^{\!\!/} \to C(OH)C(NHAr)$
with $InCl_3$ cf. *61*, 132; regiospecific ring opening with $InBr_3$ s. J.R. Rodriguez, A. Navarro, Tetrahedron Lett. *45*, 7495-8 (2004).

Scandium(III) triflate/(R,R)-6,6'-bis(1-hydroxy-2,2-dimethylpropyl)-2,2'-bipyridyl ←
2-Aminoalcohols from epoxides with desymmetrization s. *68*, 58 $\overset{\triangledown}{\circ}{}^{\!\!/} \to C(OH)C(N{<})$

Samarium diiodide SmI_2
2-Aminoalcohols from epoxides
with SmI_2 cf. *50*, 146; with $SmI_2(THF)_2$, stereoselectivity, s. F. Carree, R. Gil, J. Collin, Tetrahedron Lett. *45*, 7749-51 (2004).

1,1,3,3-Tetramethylguanidine $(Me_2N)_2C{=}NH$
Hydroxycarboxylic acid amides from lactones
with Me_2NH cf. *10*, 263; racemization-free ring opening of chiral pantolactones with chiral α-amino-acids using 1,1,3,3-tetramethylguanidine s. M. Wlostowski, T. Rowicki, L. Synoradzki, Tetrahedron:Asym. *15*, 2333-8 (2004).

Silica gel SiO_2
2-Aminoalcohols from epoxides in the absence of solvent $\overset{\triangledown}{\circ}{}^{\!\!/} \to C(OH)C(N{<})$
under microwave irradiation cf. *13*, 361s*58*; at room temp. without irradiation, regio- and stereoselectivity, s. A.K. Chakraborti, S. Rudrawar, A. Kondaskar, Org. Biomol. Chem. *2*, 1277-80 (2004).

Zirconium tetrachloride $ZrCl_4$
Bismuth(III) triflate $Bi(OTf)_3$
Potassium cobaltotungstate $K_5CoW_{12}O_{40}$
2-Aminoalcohols from epoxides
with $ZrCl_4$ s. *49*, 254s*66*; 2-(arylamino)alcohols s. N.R. Swamy, Y. Venkateswarlu et al., Synth. Commun. *34*, 727-34 (2004); with $Bi(OTf)_3$ **in water** (with or without surfactant) (cf. *49*, 254s*67*) s. T. Ollevier, G. Lavie-Compin, Tetrahedron Lett. *45*, 49-52 (2004); with $Al(OTf)_3$ **in the absence of solvent** for ring opening with 2-picolylamine s. F. Fringuelli et al., J. Org. Chem. *69*, 7745-7 (2004); with K-cobaltotungstate for regiospecific ring opening with weakly nucleophilic ar. amines s. E. Rafiee, S. Tangestaninejad et al., Synth. Commun. *34*, 3673-81 (2004).

[(R,R)-N,N'-Bis(3,5-di-tert-butylsalicylidenato)-1,2-cyclohexanediamine]-
   chromium(III) chloride
[(R,R)-N,N'-Bis(3,5-di-tert-butylsalicylidenato)-1,2-cyclohexanediamine]cobalt(II)/
   p-nitrobenzoic anhydride
2-(Arylamino)alcohols from epoxides $\triangledown_0\!\!\nearrow \rightarrow C(OH)C(NHAr)$
Regiospecific ring opening with kinetic resolution

141.

The first completely regio- and *anti*-selective aminolysis of racemic *trans*-styrene oxides with anilines is reported with enantioselectivities up to 99%. **E:** A 2 *M* soln. of the startg. racemic styrene epoxide and 4 mol% [(R,R)-N,N'-bis(3,5-di-*tert*-butylsalicylidenato)-1,2-cyclohexanediamine]chromium(III) chloride in methylene chloride stirred at room temp. for 5 min, cooled to 0°, and treated with 0.4 eq. *p*-anisidine for 24 h → *anti*-aminoalcohol (Y 95%; e.e. 86%) and unreacted epoxide enantiomer (e.e. 53%). The presence of coordinating functional groups and Lewis basic residues did not affect the catalytic activity of the system. **Desymmetrization** of *meso*-stilbene oxide was also effected. F.e. and cleavage of the protective group s. G. Bartoli, P. Melchiorre et al., Org. Lett. *6*, 2173-6 (2004); **chiral N-protected 2-aminoalcohols** (NBoc derivs.) from terminal epoxides by asym. aminolysis in the presence of [(R,R)-N,N'-bis(3,5-di-*tert*-butylsalicylidenato)-1,2-cyclohexanediamine]cobalt(II)/*p*-nitrobenzoic anhydride s. ibid. 3973-5.

[(S,S)-N,N'-Bis(3,5-di-tert-butylsalicylidenato)-1,2-cyclohexanediamine]cobalt(III)
   acetate/pyridinium tosylate
N-Sulfonylaziridines from epoxides
Regiospecific asym. conversion via N-protected 2-sulfonylaminoalcohols

142.

A mixture of 2 mol% [(S,S)-N,N'-bis(3,5-*tert*-butylsalicylidenato)-1,2-cyclohexanediamine]-cobalt(III) acetate and 1 eq. epichlorhydrin in anhydrous THF cooled to 0°, treated with 0.55 eq. water, stirred for 3 h, a soln. of 0.4 eq. N-Boc-2-(trimethylsilyl)ethanesulfonamide in the same solvent added, stirring continued at 0° for 3 h, 4.8 mol% pyridinium tosylate in anhydrous methylene chloride added, and allowed to react to completion → intermediate alcohol, in anhydrous methylene chloride cooled to 0°, treated dropwise with trifluoroacetic acid while warming to room temp., stirred for 1.5 h, cooled to 0°, diluted with ether and satd. aq. NaHCO₃, worked up, the resulting residue taken up in anhydrous methylene chloride, treated with 2 eqs. pyridine, 1.5 eqs. methanesulfonic anhydride and 0.1 eq. DMAP, stirred under N₂ at room temp. for 30 min, diluted with ether, treated with satd. aq. CuSO₄ then worked up, the obtained mesylate taken up in anhydrous THF, cooled to 0°, treated under N₂ with a suspension of 1.1 eqs. NaH in the same solvent, warmed to room temp., stirred for 30 min, cooled to 0°, and quenched with a mixture of ether and water → product. Y 91% (e.e. 99.2%). Carboxylic acid esters, halides, ar. nitro groups and phenolethers remained unaffected. F.e.s. S.K. Kim, E.N. Jacobsen, Angew. Chem. Int. Ed. Engl. *43*, 3952-4 (2004).

Addition to Nitrogen-Nitrogen Bonds   NC ⇓ NN

(3R,4S,8R,9S)-10,11-Dihydro-3,9-epoxy-6′-hydroxycinchonan [β-Isocupreidine]   ←
Asym. organocatalyzed α-amination   H → N(COOR)NHCOOR
with azodicarboxylic acid esters

143.

of α-cyanocarboxylic acid esters. A mixture of toluene, 1.1 eqs. startg. α-cyanocarboxylic acid ester (0.1 M), and 5 mol% β-isocupreidine stirred at room temp. for 15 min, cooled to -78°, treated dropwise with 1 eq. di-*tert*-butyl azodicarboxylate over 0.5 min, and stirred at the same temp. for 16-20 h → (S)-product. Y 99% (e.e. 98%). The chiral quaternary centre is created with high enantioselectivity and TONs up to 1000 and at catalyst loadings as low as 0.5 mol%. F.e. incl. 2-thienyl derivs., also asym. α-amination **of β-ketocarbonyl compds.**, and cleavage of the N-N bond in the products, s. S. Saaby, M. Bella, K.A. Jørgensen, J. Am. Chem. Soc. *126*, 8120-1 (2004).

Indium trichloride/silica gel/microwaves $InCl_3/SiO_2/[\backslash\backslash\backslash\backslash]$
Methylmanganese(II) amides   MeMnN<
Hydrazodicarbonyl compds. by substituting addition to azodicarbonyl compds.
N-aryl derivs. with InCl$_3$/silica gel under microwaves cf. *21*, 439s62; addition of β-dicarbonyl compds. s. J.S. Yadav, B.V.S. Reddy et al., Tetrahedron Lett. *45*, 7507-9 (2004); of ketones with methylmanganese(II) amides via manganese(II) enolates, also addition of S-chiral N-sulfinylimines **with asym. induction,** s. G. Dessole, A. Ricci et al., J. Org. Chem. *69*, 8525-8 (2004).

Rhodium(II) acetate $Rh_2(OAc)_4$
Rhodium-catalyzed hydroacylation of nitrogen-nitrogen double bonds   ←

144.

N-Acylhydrazodicarboxylic acid esters. A soln. of 20 mol% Rh$_2$(OAc)$_4$, 1 eq. diisopropyl azodicarboxylate and 2,6-dichlorobenzaldehyde *in ethyl acetate* stirred for 24 h at room temp. → product. Y 78%. Reaction is notably applicable to unsatd. and ethylenic aldehydes (without associated ene-reaction), but ar. aldehydes (especially electron-rich derivs.) reacted much more slowly. Other transition metal catalysts and solvents were less effective. A radical mechanism is invoked. F.e.s. D. Lee, R.D. Otte, J. Org. Chem. *69*, 3569-71 (2004).

Addition to Nitrogen and Carbon   NC ⇓ NC

Microwaves s. under KOH and Me$_3$SiCl   [\\\\]
Potassium hydroxide/microwaves   KOH/[\\\\]
Potassium hydroxide/1-n-butyl-3-methylimidazolium hexafluorophosphate/microwaves   ←
2,4-Diamino-1,3,5-triazines from nitriles   ○
and cyanoguanidine with piperidine cf. *5*, 247; rapid procedure in DMSO under microwave irradiation with KOH s. Á. Díaz-Ortiz, G. Valiente et al., New J. Chem. *28*, 952-8 (2004); **in ionic liquids,** e.g. 1-*n*-butyl-3-methylimidazolium hexafluorophosphate, s. Y.Q. Peng, G.H. Song, Tetrahedron Lett. *45*, 5313-6 (2004).

n-*Butyllithium*   *BuLi*
Addition of chiral lithium amides to heterocumulenes with retention of configuration ←

145.

Chiral 2-aminothioureas. 1 eq. *n*-BuLi (1.6 *M* in *n*-hexane) added slowly under an inert atmosphere to a stirred soln. of 1 eq. of (S)-2-(pyrrolidin-1-ylmethyl)pyrrolidine in anhydrous THF at -30°, the yellow mixture warmed to room temp., stirred for 1 h, 1 eq. phenyl isothiocyanate added slowly, and stirring continued for 2 h at room temp. → product. Y 94.4%. The procedure is mild and racemization-free. F.e. and chiral 2-amino-guanidines and -ureas from carbodiimides and isocyanates, respectively s. U. Köhn, E. Anders et al., Tetrahedron:Asym. *15*, 1419-26 (2004).

1,8-Diazabicyclo[5.4.0]undec-7-ene   *dbu*
Quinazoline-2,4-diones from *o*-aminonitriles
and CO_2 with dbu s. *24*, 601s59; in supercritical CO_2 s. T. Mizuno, T. Iwai, Y. Ishino, Tetrahedron Lett. *45*, 7073-5 (2004).

Sodium azide s.a. under Phosphomolybdic acid NaN_3
4-Dimethylaminopyridine s.a. under Chromium(III) complexes   *DMAP*

4-Dimethylaminopyridine/p-methoxyphenol   *DMAP/ArOH*
2-Oxazolidones from aziridines and CO_2 s. *23*, 139s68

Boron fluoride BF_3
Δ²-Imidazolines from aziridines and nitriles
s. *30*, 217; 1-tosyl-Δ²-imidazolines under mild conditions, also with [Et₃O]BF₄, s. B.A.B. Prasad, G. Pandey, V.K. Singh, Tetrahedron Lett. *45*, 1137-41 (2004).

1-Tosyl-1,4,5,6-tetrahydropyrimidines from -azetidines and nitriles

146.

Ar = m-BrC₆H₄

1 eq. Benzonitrile added to a soln. of the startg. N-tosylazetidine in anhydrous methylene chloride under argon at room temp., followed by slow addition of 0.2 eq. freshly distilled BF_3-etherate, and quenched with satd. aq. $NaHCO_3$ after 3 h → product. Y 49%. Reaction is thought to involve initial coordination of the Lewis acid to a sulfonyl oxygen, followed by attack of the nitrile at the activated benzylic center in Ritter-fashion prior to ring closure. F.e. and preparation of the startg. azetidines s. B.A.B. Prasad, A. Bisai, V.K. Singh, Org. Lett. *6*, 4829-31 (2004).

Cerium(III) chloride s. under Pd₂(dba)₃ $CeCl_3$
Imidazolium ionic liquids s. under KOH   ←
p-*Methoxyphenol s. under 4-Dimethylaminopyridine*   *ArOH*

Hexamethyldisilazane/ammonium sulfate/dimethylformamide $(Me_3Si)_2NH/(NH_4)_2SO_4/DMF$
Phthalocyanines from *o*-dinitriles
with (Me₃Si)₂NH/ZnBr₂ cf. *27*, 435s64; under mild conditions with (Me₃Si)₂NH/(NH₄)₂SO₄/DMF s. H. Uchida, T. Toru et al., Bull. Chem. Soc. Jpn. *77*, 1401-4 (2004).

Trimethylsilyl azide/hydrogen chloride Me_3SiN_3/HCl
Tetrazoles from isonitriles
and HN₃ cf. *13*, 365; with HN₃ generated *in situ* from Me₃SiN₃/HCl, also with Lewis acids, s. T.N. Jin, S. Kamijo, Y. Yamamoto, Tetrahedron Lett. *45*, 9435-7 (2004).

Trimethylsilyl chloride/isopropanol/microwaves $Me_3SiCl/i\text{-}PrOH/[\backslash\backslash\backslash\backslash]$
Biguanides from amines ←
1,5-diarylbiguanides s. *16*, 395; 1-arylbiguanides from dicyanodiamide with Me₃SiCl/*i*-PrOH, rapid procedure under microwave irradiation, s. S. Mayer, M.G. Organ et al., J. Comb. Chem. *6*, 776-82 (2004).

Tantalum pentachloride/silica gel $TaCl_5/SiO_2$
Phosphomolybdic acid/silica ←
Phosphomolybdic acid/silica/sodium azide ←
Nucleophilic ring opening of N-tosylaziridines C
N-tosyl-1,2-diamines without reagent and 2-tosylaminoalcohols with CAN cf. *50*, 151s*65*; **heterogeneous conversion** with TaCl₅-on-silica gel, regio- and stereo-specific addition of ar. amines, s. S. Chandrasekhar, S.J. Prakash et al., Synth. Commun. *34*, 3865-73 (2004); 2-tosylaminoalcohols with phosphomolybdic acid-on-silica in aq. acetonitrile, also ring opening with NaN₃ and NaCN, s. G.D.K. Kumar, S. Baskaran, Synlett *2004*, 1719-22.

N-Sodiosaccharin/tetra-n-butylammonium iodide ←
Isocyanurates from isocyanates by trimerization O
with *p*-MeC₆H₄S(O)ONa/Bu₄NI cf. *21*, 358s*63*; with Na-saccharin/Bu₄NI in the absence of solvent s. F.M. Moghaddam, G.R. Koozehgiri, M.G. Dekamin, Monatsh. Chem. *135*, 849-51 (2004).

Trifluoromethanesulfonic anhydride Tf_2O
Melamines from cyanamides by trimerization
with Et₃N cf. *31*, 296; with Tf₂O under mild conditions, also sym. 1,3,5-triazines from nitriles, s. A. Herrera, R. Martínez-Alvarez et al., Synthesis *2004*, 503-5.

*[N,N'-Bis(3,5-di-*tert*-butylsalicylidenato)-1,2-cyclohexanediamine]chromium(III)* ←
 chloride/4-dimethylaminopyridine
2-Oxazolidones from aziridines O

147.

Regiospecific ring expansion. A mixture of the startg. aziridine, 1 mol% [N,N'-bis(3,5-di-*tert*-butylsalicylidenato)-1,2-cyclohexanediamine]chromium(III) chloride and 2 mol% DMAP in methylene chloride stirred in a Parr high-pressure reactor under 400 psi CO₂ at 100° for 5 h → product. Y 93%. Carbon dioxide inserts at the more subst. N-C bond of the aziridine ring to give 5-subst. 2-oxazolidones, reaction taking place by initial coordination of chromium to aziridine nitrogen, followed by Lewis base-assisted ring opening prior to ring closure. F.e. and with N-arylaziridines and 2,3-disubst. N-alkylaziridines s. A.W. Miller, S.T. Nguyen, Org. Lett. *6*, 2301-4 (2004).

Tetra-n-butylammonium iodide s. under N-Sodiosaccharin Bu_4NI

Tris(dibenzylideneacetone)dipalladium/(S)-2,2'-bis(diphenylphosphino)-1,1'-binaphthyl/cerium(III) chloride
4-Vinyl-2-imidazolidones from 2-vinylaziridines and isocyanates
Dynamic kinetic asym. cycloaddition
with bis(η^3-allylpalladium chloride) and Trost's ligand/AcOH cf. *66*, 155; with Pd$_2$(dba)$_3$/(S)-BINAP and *10 mol% CeCl$_3$* s. C. Dong, H. Alper, Tetrahedron:Asym. *15*, 1537-40 (2004).

Addition to Carbon-Carbon Bonds   NC ⇓ CC

Without additional reagents   w.a.r.
2-Amino-2-deoxy-β-glycosides from glycals
via 1,3-dipolar cycloaddition with azides

148.

A mixture of 1 eq. tri-O-acetyl-D-glucal and 1.3 eqs. benzyl azide in anhydrous methyl orthoformate heated at 120° for 30 h in a sealed tube → intermediate triazoline, in anhydrous acetone (as both solvent and sensitizer) UV-irradiated in a closed quartz reaction vessel at room temp. for 15 h, the resulting soln. treated immediately with a soln. of 2 eqs. methanol and 20 mol% Sc(OTf)$_3$ in anhydrous THF, and stirred at room temp. for 2 h → product. Y 94%. The method, featuring regiospecific, Lewis acid-catalyzed nucleophilic ring opening of an intermediate aziridine-fused carbohydrate, is only applicable to glycals possessing electron-withdrawing protecting groups and electron-rich alkyl azides. Reaction in methyl or ethyl orthoformate facilitates isolation of the unstable 1,2,3-triazoline derivs. F.e. and with sec. alcohols, complex alcohols, azides and mercaptans as nucleophile s. R.S. Dahl, N.S. Finney, J. Am. Chem. Soc. *126*, 8356-7 (2004).

Lithium amides/lithium diisopropylamide   LiNHR/i-Pr$_2$NLi
Catalyzed Haller-Bauer reaction

149.

Haller-Bauer reaction of cyclic and acyclic α-arylketones with lithium N-alkylamides is catalyzed efficiently with a little LDA or Li-2,2,6,6-tetramethylpiperidide. **E: ω-Arylcarboxylic acid amides.** 1.2 eqs. *n*-BuLi (1.58 *M* in hexane) added dropwise to a mixture of 1.1 eqs. isopropylamine and *0.1 eq.* diisopropylamine in dry THF at 0° under N$_2$, stirred for 15 min, treated with a soln. of the startg. oxo compd. in the same solvent, stirred again for 0.5 h at 0° then for 5 h at room temp., and quenched with 1 *M* HCl → product. Y 92%. *in situ*-Generated LDA facilitates cleavage of the carbon-carbon bond, possibly by formation of a stable 6-membered intermediate or a dianionic species, reaction being applicable to both *enolizable* and non-enolizable ketones. **Carboxylic acid amides** can also be obtained (*with prim. alcohols*) **from aldehydes by Cannizzaro reaction** with Li- or Na-alkylamides or -dialkylamides, the procedure being most facile with ar. aldehydes. F.e. and Haller-Bauer reaction **with kinetic resolution** s. K. Ishihara, T. Yano, Org. Lett. *6*, 1983-6 (2004).

Potassium fluoride/natural phosphate
Heterogeneous Michael addition of amines   C=C → CHC(N<)
to α,β-ethyleneketones s. *63*, 147s68

1,8-Diazabicyclo[5.4.0]undec-7-ene   dbu
Michael addition of amines s. *68*, 66

Cupric triflate/2,2-bis(4(S)-tert-butyl-Δ²-oxazolin-2-yl)propane ←
Lewis acid-catalyzed asym. Michael addition of urethans   C=C → CHC(NHCOOR)

150. HO-C(=O)-CH=CH-Pr-i + H₂NCOOBu-t →[t-Bu, Bu-t oxazoline ligand] HO-C(=O)-CH(NHCOOBu-t)-CH₂-Pr-i

to α,β-ethylene-α′-hydroxyketones. A mixture of 11 mol% 2,2-bis(4(S)-*tert*-butyl-Δ²-oxazolin-2-yl)propane and 10 mol% Cu(OTf)₂ in anhydrous methylene chloride stirred under N₂ at room temp. for 3 h, a soln. of 1 eq. of the startg. enone in the same solvent added, stirred at the same temp. for 30 min, treated with a soln. of 2 eqs. *tert*-butyl carbamate in the same solvent, and stirring continued under N₂ at the same temp. for 22 h → product. Y 87% (e.e. 98%). This is the first example of a highly enantioselective Lewis acid-catalyzed asym. Michael addition of urethans. The hydroxyl group of the substrate, however, appears essential for coordination purposes, there being no reaction with N-(α,β-ethyleneacyl)-2-oxazolidines while alkylidenemalonates gave a racemic product. F.e. and conversion to chiral N-protected β-alkyl-β-aminocarboxylic acids s. C. Palomo et al., J. Am. Chem. Soc. *126*, 9188-9 (2004).

Cuprous iodide/trimethylsilyl azide   CuI/Me₃SiN₃
1,2,3-Triazoles from terminal acetylene derivs.   ○
N-subst. derivs. from azides s. *64*, 141s66; N-unsubst. derivs. with Me₃SiN₃ s. T. Jin, S. Kamijo, Y. Yamamoto, Eur. J. Org. Chem. *2004*, 3789-91.

Zinc chloride s. under Bis(indenyl)dimethyltitanium(IV)   ZnCl₂
Sodium trihydridocyanoborate s. under Bis(indenyl)dimethyltitanium(IV) NaBH₃CN

Tetraethylammonium carbonate   (Et₄N)₂CO₃
5-Alkylidene-2-oxazolidones from 2-acetyleneamines
5-methylene derivs. with 7-methyl-1,5,7-triazabicyclo[4.4.0]dec-5-ene and CO₂ cf. *52*, 137; 5-alkylidene derivs. with tetraethylammonium carbonate s. A. Arcadi, L. Rossi et al., Synlett *2005*, 67-70.

Phenylsilane s. under Manganese(III) complexes   PhSiH₃

Bis(cyclopentadienyl)(η²-bis(trimethylsilyl)acetylene)titanium(II)   ←
Regiospecific hydroamination of terminal acetylene derivs.   C≡C → CH₂C(=NR)
with prim. amines
aldehydes with alkylamines cf. *64*, 143; methyl N-arylketimines from anilines s. A. Tillack, M. Beller et al., Chem. Eur. J. *10*, 2409-20 (2004).

Silica gel   SiO₂
Heterogeneous Michael addition of amines   C=C → CHC(N<)
in the absence of solvent s. *63*, 147s68

Bis(indenyl)dimethyltitanium(IV)/sodium trihydridocyanoborate/zinc chloride ←
Bis[2-(dimethylaminomethyl)pyrrol-1-yl]bis(dimethylamino)titanium(IV)   ←
Regiospecific hydroamination of acetylene derivs. with prim. amines
ketimines with (phenylimino)bis(anilino)titanium(IV) cf. *58*, 126s67; α,β-ethyleneketimines from 1,3-enynes s. C.S. Cao, A.L. Odom et al., Chem. Commun. *2004*, 2002-3; **sec. amines** with bis(indenyl)dimethyltitanium(IV)/NaBH₃CN/ZnCl₂ s. A. Heutling, F. Pohlki, S. Doye, Chem. Eur. J. *10*, 3059-71 (2004).

[2-(Pyrrol-2-yl)-2-(η⁵-pyrrolyl)propane-N,N'-diyl][bis(dimethylamino)]titanium(IV)
**Pyrroles from 1,4(5)-diynes and prim. amines
via regiospecific titanium-catalyzed hydroamination**

151.

1,2,5-Trisubst. pyrroles. A mixture of 10 mol% [2-(pyrrol-2-yl)-2-(η⁵-pyrrolyl)propane-N,N'-diyl][bis(dimethylamino)]titanium(IV) and equimolar amounts of benzylamine and 1-phenylhexa-1,4-diyne in chlorobenzene heated at 100° for 30 h in a sealed pressure tube → product. Y 53%. Reaction takes place via regiospecific hydroamination of the least encumbered alkyne residue, followed by 5-*endo-dig* cyclization. 1,5-Diynes reacted similarly via 5-*exo-dig* cyclization. This is a useful alternative to the classical Paal-Knorr pyrrole synthesis, but reaction failed with 1,4-pentadiyne, 1,6-diphenyl-1,5-hexadiyne and 1-phenyl-1,4-pentadiyne. F.e. and titanium(IV) tetraamide complexes s. B. Ramanathan, A.L. Odom et al., Org. Lett. *6*, 2957-60 (2004).

Trimethylsilyl azide s. under CuI Me_3SiN_3
Trimethylsilyl chloride s. under Bu_3P and $PdCl_2(MeCN)_2$ Me_3SiCl

Tri-n-butylphosphine/trimethylsilyl chloride Bu_3P/Me_3SiCl
β-(Carbalkoxyamino)ketones C≡C → CHC(NHCOOR)
from α,β-ethyleneketones and urethans
with BF_3/Bu_4NBr cf. *66*, 160s67; with Bu_3P/Me_3SiCl s. L. Xu, C. Xia, Tetrahedron Lett. *45*, 4507-10 (2004).

Natural phosphate s. under KF

Tetramethylammonium fluoride Me_4NF
Fluoride ion-catalyzed Michael addition C≡C → CHC(N<)
of amines with Bu_4NF cf. *63*, 147; of 2-oxazolidone and mercaptans with Me_4NF s. M.L. Menand, V. Dalla, Synlett *2005*, 95-8; **heterogeneous Michael addition of amines** to enones with KF/natural phosphate (cf. *29*, 752s67) s. M. Zahouily, S. Sebti et al., Tetrahedron Lett. *45*, 4135-8 (2004); Michael addition of amines with silica gel **in the absence of solvent** s. B. Basu, P. Das, I. Hossain, Synlett *2004*, 2630-2.

Amberlyst A-26 diazidoiodate
Carbamyl azides from aldehydes CHO → NHCON₃
with NaN_3/ICl cf. *43*, 264s66; more safely with Amberlyst A-26 diazidoiodate (or the Amberlite IR-900 variant), also 1-aryl-1,1-azidoethers (from benzyl ethers), s. L.G. Marinescu, C.M. Pedersen, M. Bols, Tetrahedron *61*, 123-7 (2005).

Tris(dipivaloylmethanato)manganese(III)/phenylsilane $Mn(dpm)_3/PhSiH_3$
Regiospecific hydrohydrazination of ethylene derivs. C≡C → CHCN(COOR)NHCOOR
with Na-bis(N-salicylidene-2-aminoisobutyrato)cobaltate(III)/PhSiH₃ cf. *67*, 146; improved yields with tris(dipivaloylmethanato)manganese(III) s. J. Waser, E.M. Carreira, Angew. Chem. Int. Ed. Engl. *43*, 4099-102 (2004).

Ferric chloride $FeCl_3$
Lewis acid-catalyzed Michael addition of amines in water C≡C → CHC(N<)
with $InCl_3$ cf. *56*, 129; of prim. amines with $FeCl_3$ (cf. *45*, 171) s. L. Xu, L. Li, C. Xia, Helv. Chim. Acta *87*, 1522-6 (2004).

Bis(acetonitrile)[hydridotris(pyrazolyl)borato](triphenylphosphine)ruthenium(II) ←
hexafluorophosphate
2-α-Functionalized pyrroles from 2-en-4-ynaldimines   ○

152.

[M]⁺ = [TpRu(PPh₃)(MeCN)₂]⁺

A mixture of the startg. enynaldimine (1.5 M), 1 mol% bis(acetonitrile)[hydridotris(pyrazolyl)-borato](triphenylphosphine)ruthenium(II) hexafluorophosphate and 1.2 eqs. methanol in dichloroethane heated at 50° for 6 h → product. Y 89%. The reaction is presumed to involve initial activation of the alkyne residue by the metal, followed by 5-*exo-dig* cyclization to a ruthenium (2-pyrrolyl)carbenoid, which then undergoes nucleophilic attack by the alcohol. Water and certain amines [not diethyl- or diisopropyl-amine] also served as nucleophile, but reaction failed with more acidic phenol. The ene residue may be substituted by an alkyl or aryl group, but internal alkynes resisted ring closure. F.e. and comparison of catalysts and solvents s. H.-C. Shen, C.-W. Li, R.-S. Liu, Tetrahedron Lett. *45*, 9245-7 (2004).

Ruthenium trichloride/trimethylsilyl chloride $RuCl_3/Me_3SiCl$
Palladium-catalyzed Michael addition of urethans   C=C → CHC(NHCO-)
to α,β-ethyleneketones s. *61*, 143s68

Tetrakis(triphenylphosphine)palladium(0)/benzoic acid $Pd(PPh_3)_4/PhCOOH$
N-Allylation with acetylene derivs.   NH → NC-CH=CH
of sec. amines cf. *51*, 131s57; of anilines s. N.T. Patil, Y. Yamamoto et al., J. Org. Chem. *69*, 8745-50 (2004).

Hydroxy[(R)-2,2′-bis(diphenylphosphino)-1,1′-binaphthyl]palladium(II) ←
triflate dimer/hydrotriflates
Palladium-catalyzed asym. Michael addition of ar. amines   C=C → CHC(NHAr)
N-carbalkoxy-α,β-ethylenecarboxylic acid amides with bis(acetonitrile)[(R)-2,2′-bis(diphenyl-phosphino)-1,1′-binaphthyl]palladium(II) bis(triflate) cf. *67*, 149; of ar. amines (as *TfOH salts*) to 3-(α,β-ethyleneacyl)-2-oxazolidones with hydroxy[(R)-2,2′-bis(diphenylphosphino)-1,1′-binaphthyl]palladium(II) triflate dimer s. Y. Hamashima, M. Sodeoka et al., Org. Lett. *6*, 1861-4 (2004).

Bis(acetonitrile)dichloropalladium(II)/trimethylsilyl chloride $PdCl_2(MeCN)_2/Me_3SiCl$
Bis(benzonitrile)dichloropalladium(II) $PdCl_2(PhCN)_2$
Palladium-catalyzed Michael addition of acylamines   C=C → CHC(NHCO-)
to α,β-ethyleneketones
of urethans with PdCl₂(PhCN)₂ cf. *61*, 143; of alkyl carbamates and 2-oxazolidone with PdCl₂(MeCN)₂/Me₃SiCl, also with RhCl₃·3H₂O, s. L. Xu, C. Xia, Synthesis *2004*, 2191-5; Michael addition of prim. acylamines s. K. Takasu, N. Nishida, M. Ihara, Synlett *2004*, 1844-6.

Potassium osmate/polyethylene glycol-linked bis[1-(9-O-dihydroquinine)phthalazine]/ ←
lithium hydroxide
Regiospecific asym. Sharpless oxyamination   C=C → C(OH)C(NHAc)
of α,β-ethylenecarboxylic acid esters with AcNHBr s. *51*, 132s64; with a readily recyclable, *soluble*, polyethylene glycol-linked bis[1-(9-O-dihydroquinine)phthalazine] as ligand in the presence of LiOH s. X.-W. Yang, M.-H. Xu, G.-Q. Lin et al., Tetrahedron:Asym. *15*, 1915-8 (2004).

Rearrangement

Hydrogen/Nitrogen Type   NC ∩ HN

Sodium/alcohol   *NaOR*
5-Carbamylhydantoins from 5-aminobarbituric acids

153.

The startg. 5-aminobarbituric acid added to 4 eqs. 0.3 *M* ethanolic NaOEt, and refluxed for 3 h under argon → 1-benzyl-5-phenyl-5-(N-phenylcarbamyl)hydantoin. Y 85%. 3-Unsubst. barbituric acids react via an intermediate isocyanate which is trapped by the amino function; with 3-subst. barbituric acids, however, reaction takes place by ring closure of an intermediate N-(α-aminoacyl)-urethan [isocyanate formation being blocked]. F.e. and bases (NaOBu, NaH) s. M. Meusel, M. Gütschow, J. Org. Chem. *68*, 4684-92 (2003); **1-acylaminohydantoins** via cycloisomerization of N^1-acyl-N^2-α-cyanosemicarbazides (with NaOEt) s. I. Bélai, Tetrahedron Lett. *44*, 7475-7 (2003).

Hydrogen/Carbon Type   NC ∩ HC

Bis(tricyclohexylphosphine)palladium(0) $Pd(PCy_3)_2$
N-Tosylimines from N-tosylaziridines
Palladium-catalyzed isomerization under mild conditions

154.   R = CH_2=$CHCH_2C(COOEt)_2CH_2$

A soln. of the startg. aziridine in toluene added to 2 mol% $Pd(PCy_3)_2$ contained in a Schlenk tube under N_2, and stirred at 70° for 34 h → product. Y 73%. The method tolerates a variety of functional groups (e.g. esters, olefins, acetals, and ketones), but reaction failed with 1,2-disubst. aziridines. F.e.s. J.P. Wolfe, J.E. Ney, Org. Lett. *5*, 4607-10 (2003).

Oxygen/Nitrogen Type   NC ∩ ON

Sodium/alcohol   *NaOR*
α-Cyanoketones from isoxazoles
s. *4*, 756s*39*; s.a. K. Harada et al., Japanese patent JP-2002275145 (Ube Ind. Ltd.).

Oxygen/Carbon Type   NC ∩ OC

Dicarbonyl(chloro)rhodium(I) dimer $[RhCl(CO)_2]_2$
N-Protected 3-hydroxy-N-heterocyclics from epoxyamines s. *33*, 145s*68*

Hexafluoroacetoacetonato[η^5-(S)-2-[(4-isopropyl-Δ^2-oxazolin-2-yl)cyclo-   ←
pentadienyl](η^4-tetraphenylcyclobutadiene)cobalt]palladium
2-Ethyleneacylamines from 2-ethyleneiminoesters   ←
Asym. [3.3]-sigmatropic rearrangement
with chiral ferrocenylbis(palladacyclics) cf. *54*, 138s*65*; with hexafluoroacetoacetonato[η^5-(S)-2-[(4-isopropyl-Δ^2-oxazolin-2-yl)cyclopentadienyl](η^4-tetraphenylcyclobutadiene)cobalt]-palladium and f. Pd-Co complexes s. S.F. Kirsch, L.E. Overman, M.P. Watson, J. Org. Chem. *69*, 8101-4 (2004).

Carbon/Carbon Type

NC ∩ CC

Silver nitrate/microwaves
Pyrroles from 1-amino-1,4-enynes
via intramolecular hydroamination under microwave irradiation

$AgNO_3$/[\\\\]

155.

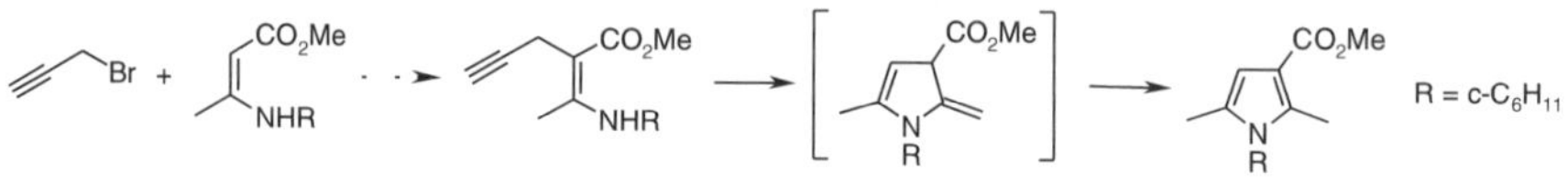

A mixture of the startg. 1-amino-1,4-enyne (prepared by propargylation of the corresponding vinylogous amide with propargyl bromide in the presence of *n*-BuLi) and 0.2 eq. $AgNO_3$ in acetonitrile irradiated in a sealed tube inside a microwave oven at 700 W for ca. 1 min → product. Y 96%. 2-Carbethoxy derivs. were unreactive. F.e. and at room temp. overnight without irradiation, also one-pot procedure from the startg. vinylogous amide (with *n*-BuLi alone), s. R.S. Robinson, M.C. Dovey, D. Gravestock, Tetrahedron Lett. *45*, 6787-9 (2004).

Sodium tetrachloroaurate
Indoles from *o*-acetyleneamines

$NaAuCl_4$

with KOBu-*t* cf. *59*, 137s*65*; with $NaAuCl_4$ in ethanol or aq. ethanol s. A. Arcadi, G. Bianchi, F. Marinelli, Synthesis *2004*, 610-8.

Auric chloride
Δ³-Pyrrolines from 2-alleneamines

$AuCl_3$

with $AgNO_3$ cf. *58*, 129s*62*; N-sulfonyl derivs. with $AuCl_3$, stereoselectivity, s. N. Morita, N. Krause, Org. Lett. *6*, 4121-3 (2004).

(β-Diketiminato)calcium bis(trimethylsilyl)amide complexes
Calcium-mediated intramolecular hydroamination

←

156.

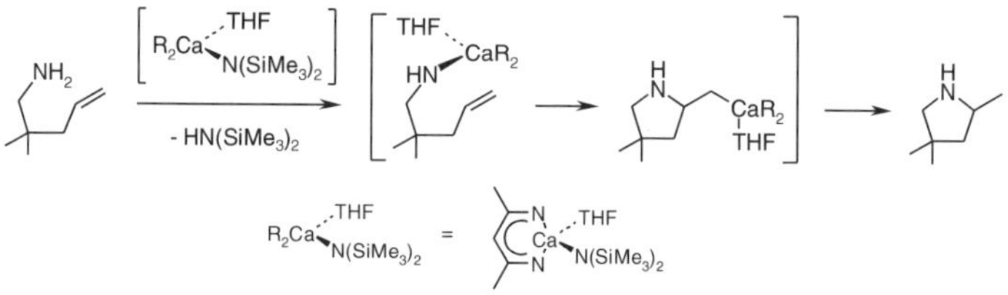

The first efficient alkaline earth-catalyzed intramolecular hydroamination is reported. E: A soln. of the startg. ethyleneamine in benzene-d_6 treated with 10 mol% (β-diketiminato)calcium bis-(trimethylsilyl)amide complex at 25° for 15 min on an NMR scale → product. Conversion >99% (by ¹H NMR). Reaction takes place by initial transamination of the bis(trimethylsilyl)amino residue, followed by the novel insertion of the ethylene residue into the Ca-N bond. The low cost and benign nature of the readily available complex offers significant advantages over more familiar lanthanide-based methodologies. F.e.s. M.R. Crimmin, I.J. Casely, M.S. Hill, J. Am. Chem. Soc. *127*, 2042-3 (2005).

Methyl[2,2,6,6-tetramethyl-3,5-N,N-bis(2,6-diisopropylphenyl)-3,5-diiminatoheptane]scandium methyltris(pentafluorophenyl)borate
Cyclic amines from ethyleneamines

←

with lanthanide(III) complexes cf. *46*, 287s*67*; with methyl[2,2,6,6-tetramethyl-3,5-N,N-bis(2,6-diisopropylphenyl)-3,5-diiminatoheptane]scandium methyltris(pentafluorophenyl)borate, also cyclic azomethines from acetyleneamines, s. F. Lauterwasser, W.E. Piers, L.L. Schafer, Organometallics *23*, 2234-7 (2004).

Exchange
Hydrogen ↑   NC ↕ H

Without additional reagents   w.a.r.
Sym. thioureas from amines   2 >NH → (>N)$_2$CS
and CS$_2$ with lac sulfur cf. *30*, 243s*53*; from prim. amines, uncatalyzed procedure **in the absence of solvent** with retention of α-chirality, also under microwave irradiation, s. J. Vazquez, R. Gutierrez et al., Synthesis *2004*, 1955-8.

3-Alkoxy-4-imino-2-oxazolidones from cyanohydrins and hydroxylamines

157.

A suspension of 1.08 eqs. 1,1'-carbonyldiimidazole in anhydrous methylene chloride treated dropwise over 10 min at 0° with a soln. of 1 eq. of the startg. cyanohydrin in the same solvent, stirred at room temp. for 10 min, 1 eq. of the startg. alkoxylamine added, and stirring continued at the same temp. for 1 h → product. Y 90%. Ring opening to **α-hydroxyamidoximes** was effected by cleavage with NaOMe, followed by catalytic hydrogenation over Pd-C. F.e. incl. O-phenyl derivs., and catalytic hydrogenation to 3-hydroxy derivs., s. T. Kurz, K. Widyan, Org. Lett. *6*, 4403-5 (2004); **3-amino-4-imino-2-imidazolidones** from α-aminonitriles and hydrazines s. Tetrahedron Lett. *45*, 7049-51 (2004).

Microwaves (s.a. under ZnO)   [\\\\]
Sym. thioureas from amines in the absence of solvent   2 >NH → (>N)$_2$CS
with retention of α-chirality s. *30*, 243s*68*

Lithium amides/lithium diisopropylamide   LiN<$/i$-Pr$_2$NLi
N-Subst. carboxylic acid amides from aldehydes s. *68*, 149   CHO → CON<

Sodium nitrite/hydrogen chloride   NaNO$_2$/HCl
α-Diketone monoximes from ketones s. *68*, 84   CH$_2$ → C=NOH

Potassium fluoride/alumina   KF/Al$_2$O$_3$
N-Formylation with chloroform   NH → NCHO
with NaOH/[BnNEt$_3$]Cl cf. *31*, 395; of sec. amines with KF/Al$_2$O$_3$ s. M. Mihara, Y. Ishino, M. Komatsu et al., Synthesis *2003*, 2317-20.

1,8-Diazabicyclo[5.4.0]undec-7-ene s. under Bu$_3$P   dbu

Cupric trifluoroacetoacetonate/phenyl iodosoacetate   Cu(CF$_3$COCHAc)$_2$/PhI(OAc)$_2$
Cupric triflate/iodosobenzene   Cu(OTf)$_2$/PhIO
N-Functionalized aziridines from ethylene derivs.
N-sulfonylaziridines with Cu(MeCN)$_4$PF$_6$/PhIO cf. *62*, 159; with Cu(CF$_3$COCHAc)$_2$/PhI(OAc)$_2$ in the presence of 4 Å molecular sieves s. H. Han, S. Chang et al., Org. Lett. *6*, 4109-12 (2004); N-(N-acyliminosulfinyl)aziridines with Cu(OTf)$_2$/PhIO and 3 Å molecular sieves s. D. Leca, M. Malacria et al., ibid. 3573-5.

Calcium oxide   CaO
Sym. ureas from amines   2 >NH → (>N)$_2$CO
and ethylene carbonate with NaOR cf. *56*, 137; from aliphatic amines with 22 mol% CaO s. S. Fujita, B.M. Bhanage, M. Arai, Chem. Lett. *33*, 742-3 (2004).

Zinc oxide/microwaves   ZnO/[\\\\]
Cyclic ureas and urethans from diamines and aminoalcohols, respectively
with urea under reduced pressure cf. *66*, 165; rapid procedure under microwave irradiation using ZnO in DMF s. Y.J. Kim, R.S. Varma, Tetrahedron Lett. *45*, 7205-8 (2004).

Di-tert-*butyl azodicarboxylate s. under Bu₃P*   ROOCN=NCOOR
Iodosobenzene s. under Cu(OTf)₂   PhIO
Phenyl iodosoacetate s. under Cu(CF₃COCHAc)₂   PhI(OAc)₂
Carbon tetrachloride s. under Ph₃P   CCl₄

Bis(trichloromethyl) carbonate $(Cl_3CO)_2CO$
Isocyanates from amines $NH_2 \rightarrow N{=}C{=}O$
with di-*tert*-butyl tricarbonate/Et₃N cf. *51*, 133s*64*; N-arylisocyanates with bis(trichloromethyl) carbonate s. Z. Xu, X. Du, W. Su, J. Indian Chem. Soc. *79*, 962-3 (2002).

Oxalyl chloride/hydrogen chloride $(COCl)_2/HCl$
Isocyanates from amines
s. *27*, 361; with added 4 *N* HCl via carbamyl chlorides, selectivity, s. L.M. Oh, P.G. Spoors, R.M. Goodman, Tetrahedron Lett. *45*, 4769-71 (2004).

Guanidinium nitrate/sulfuric acid   ←
Ar. mononitration $H \rightarrow NO_2$
of activated arenes with [Ph₃PBn]NO₃/Ms₂O cf. *37*, 316s*67*; also of deactivated arenes with guanidinium nitrate/H₂SO₄ s. M.M.V. Ramana, S.S. Malik, J.A. Parihar, Tetrahedron Lett. *45*, 8681-3 (2004).

Tri-n-butylphosphine/di-tert-*butyl azodicarboxylate/1,8-diazabicyclo[5.4.0]undec-7-ene*   ←
Triphenylphosphine/carbon tetrachloride/triethylamine   Ph₃P/CCl₄/Et₃N
Mitsunobu carboxylation
urethans with Ph₃P/dimethyl azodicarboxylate cf. *66*, 169; 2-oxazolidones from 2-aminoalcohols with Bu₃P/di-*tert*-butyl azodicarboxylate/dbu, stereoselectivity, s. C.J. Dinsmore, S.P. Mercer, Org. Lett. *6*, 2885-8 (2004); **sym. ureas** from prim. amines with Ph₃P/CCl₄/Et₃N s. S. Porwanski, S. Menuel, A. Marsura et al., Tetrahedron Lett. *45*, 5027-9 (2004).

Amberlyst A-26 diazidoiodate   ←
α-Azidation of benzyl ethers s. *43*, 264s*68* $H \rightarrow N_3$

Nickel(II) acetate/dimethylphenanthroline   ←
N-Subst. urethans from prim. amines and alcohols $NH_2 \rightarrow NHCOOR$

158.   t-BuNH₂ + CO₂ $\xrightarrow[-H_2O]{[LnNiOH]}$ [t-BuNHCOONiLn] $\xrightarrow{-[LnNiOH]}$ t-BuNCO] $\xrightarrow{MeOH}$ t-BuNHCOOMe

Liquid CO₂ (6.5 MPa), *tert*-butylamine, 2 mol% Ni(OAc)₂, 6 mol% dimethylphenanthroline, 10 eqs. methanol and an internal standard introduced into a stainless steel autoclave under argon, the initial pressure adjusted to 30 MPa, and heated with stirring at 200° for 24 h → methyl *tert*-butylcarbamate. Conversion 49% (selectivity 98%). The strong coordinating ability of the bidentate ligand is essential for efficient catalysis. It is thought that reaction involves intermediate formation of an isocyanate as there was no conversion with sec. amines. The procedure avoids handling toxic and corrosive phosgene. F.e. and with 2,2'-bipyridyls as ligand s. M. Abla, J.-C. Choi, T. Sakakura, Green Chem. *6*, 524-5 (2004).

Oxygen ↑   NC ↓↑ O

Without additional reagents   w.a.r.
Azomethines from aldehydes in the absence of solvent   CHO → CH=NR
under microwave irradiation cf. *1*, 391s*64*; N-arylaldimines under IR-irradiation s. M.A. Vazquez, F. Delgado et al., Synth. Commun. *34*, 2705-18 (2004).

Dicarboxylic acid imides from anhydrides   ←
phthalimides s. *5*, 341; naphthalene-1,8-dicarboximides under ultrasonication **in water** s. E.R. Triboni, M.J. Politi et al., Synth. Commun. *34*, 1989-99 (2004); maleimide ring under microwave irradiation (cf. *54*, 157s*64*) in the absence of solvent with montmorillonite K10 or silica gel s. A. Mortoni, S. Gagliardi et al., Tetrahedron Lett. *45*, 6623-7 (2004).

Microwaves (s.a. under (NH$_4$)$_2$CO$_3$, Montmorillonite, Dicyclohexylcarbodiimide and Polyethylene glycol bis(dichlorophosphate)) [\\\\]

Δ^2-Pyrazolines from α,β-ethyleneketones ←
s. *8*, 927; rapid procedure under microwave irradiation in the absence of solvent, also indole analogs, s. E. Karthikeyan, S. Perumal, S. Selvaraj, Indian J. Chem. *43B*, 1565-8 (2004); with simultaneous N-acylation with acetic acid s. H.M. Kanjariya, H. Parekh et al., ibid. 1569-73.

Pyrazoles from β-alkoxy-α,β-ethylenecarbonyl compds. ○
from β-alkoxy-α,β-ethyleneketones s. *66*, 181; chiral 4-(polyoxyalkyl)pyrazoles from C$_2$-formylglycals s. J.S. Yadav et al., Tetrahedron Lett. *45*, 8587-90 (2004); chiral 5-(polyoxyalkyl)-derivs. from carbohydrate-based 2,3-dihydro-4-pyrones with montmorillonite or TsOH s. ibid. 6033-6.

1,3,4-Oxadiazoles from acylhydrazines and orthocarboxylic acid esters
s. *11*, 424; rapid procedure under microwave irradiation in the absence of solvent, 2-aryl-derivs., s. R. Natero, D.O. Koltun, J.A. Zablocki, Synth. Commun. *34*, 2523-9 (2004).

4H-1,2-Diazepines from pyrylium salts under microwave irradiation in water ○

159.

3,5,7-Triaryl-4H-1,2-diazepines. 2.5 eqs. Hydrazine hydrate added to a suspension of 2,4,6-triphenylpyrylium salt in water, and irradiated with microwaves at 225 W for 30-60 sec in an open flask → product. Y 90%. This is a simple, mild, inexpensive, eco-friendly, practical and rapid method. F.e. **and from thiopyrylium salts** s. J.X. Wang et al., Chin. Chem. Lett. *15*, 284-5 (2004).

Sodium/alcohol NaOR
5,6-Dihydro-2-thiouracils from α,β-ethylenecarboxylic acid esters ○
with ethanolic NaOEt cf. *3*, 322; improved procedure with methanolic NaOMe s. J.-T. Li, J.-F. Han, T.-S. Li, J. Chem. Res. Synop *2004*, 160-2.

Potassium tert-butoxide KOBu-t
Uracil ring from *o*-aminocarboxylic acid esters
and chlorosulfonyl isocyanate/KOH cf. *40*, 225; **and urethans** with KOBu-*t*, xanthines, s. I.A. Zavialov, D.R. Andrews et al., Org. Lett. *6*, 2237-40 (2004).

Hindered lithium amides LiNR$_2$
Enamines from terminal epoxides via α-lithiation

160.

R = PhCH$_2$CH$_2$

1.25 eqs. *n*-BuLi (1.6 *M* in hexanes) added dropwise to a soln. of 1.25 eqs. 2,2,6,6-tetramethylpiperidine in anhydrous THF at 0° under argon, the mixture warmed to 25° over 15 min, treated with a soln. of 1 eq. of the startg. epoxide in the same solvent, stirred at 25° for 1 h, and filtered through a pad of Et$_3$N-deactivated silica before work-up → product. Y 72%. Reaction takes place by the novel insertion of the lithiated epoxide into the lithium amide, rather than by condensation of the isomeric aldehyde with 2,2,6,6-tetramethylpiperidine during work-up. A range of functional groups is tolerated, e.g. ethylenic groups, protected alcohols, amines and ketones, as well as aryl substitution. Interestingly, thus-generated N-*tert*-butyl-N-isopropylenamines are *sufficiently nucleophilic* to react with *sec*-alkyl iodides and activated prim. bromides to give the corresponding α-subst. aldehydes. F.e.s. D.M. Hodgson, C.D. Bray, N.D. Kindon, J. Am. Chem. Soc. *126*, 6870-1 (2004).

Potassium carbonate s. under I_2	K_2CO_3
Sodium hydrogen sulfite s. under Ethyl propiolate	$NaHSO_3$
Lithium salt s. under BF_3	Li^+
Ammonium salt	NH_4^+
N-Formylation with formic acid	NH → NCHO

in diisopropyl ether cf. *13*, 442s*36*; racemization-free N-formylation of α-aminocarboxylic acid esters with NH_4-formate in acetonitrile s. S. Kotha, M. Behera, P. Khedkar, Tetrahedron Lett. *45*, 7589-90 (2004).

Triethylenediamine s. under Iridium(I) complexes	dabco
N-Methylmorpholine s. under Ethyl propiolate	$O(CH_2CH_2)_2NMe$
4-Dimethylaminopyridine s. under Dicyclohexylcarbodiimide and 2-Methyl-6-nitrobenzoic anhydride	DMAP
Polymer-based 4-dimethylaminopyridine s. under Polymer-based 2-chloropyridinium triflate	←
Auric chloride s. under Ruthenium complexes	$AuCl_3$
Zinc s.a. under $TiCl_4$	Zn
Zinc/ammonium formate/microwaves	$Zn/HCOONH_4/[\backslash\backslash\backslash\backslash]$
Formanilides from ar. nitro compds.	NO_2 → NHCHO
under microwave irradiation in the absence of solvent	

161.

A mixture of *p*-methoxynitrobenzene, 1.5 eqs. zinc and excess of ammonium formate irradiated in a 2450 MHz domestic microwave oven at 300 W for 2.5 min → product. Y 84%. The protocol is simple and mild. F.e. and reductive ring closures, **also from ar. azides,** and prim. amines from aliphatic or ar. azides without irradiation, s. A. Kamal et al., Tetrahedron Lett. *45*, 6517-21 (2004).

Magnesium or Zinc salts s.a. under Perchlorates	Mg^{2+} or Zn^{2+}
Sodium tetrahydridoborate s.a. under Chiral 2-(arenesulfonylaminomethyl)pyrrolidines	$NaBH_4$
Sodium tetrahydridoborate/acetic acid/trimethylsilyl chloride	$NaBH_4/AcOH/Me_3SiCl$
Sodium hydridotriacetoxoborate	$NaBH(OAc)_3$
Reductive N-alkylation	NH → NR

of urethans s. *46*, 317s*54*; also of thioureas with ar. aldehydes using $NaBH_4/AcOH/Me_3SiCl$ s. L. Ciszewski, T.J. Blacklock et al., Tetrahedron Lett. *45*, 8091-3 (2004); racemization-free mono-N-alkylation and **N,N-dialkylation** of *prim*-aminocarboxylic acids with $NaBH(OAc)_3$ s. M.K. Levadala, S.R. Banerjee, J. Zubieta et al., Synthesis *2004*, 1759-66.

Tris(pentafluorophenyl)borane	$(C_6F_5)_3B$
Stereospecific Ferrier reaction with N-nucleophiles	←

using $ZrCl_4$ cf. *67*, 82; with sulfonamides, urethans and NaN_3 as nucleophile using $(C_6F_5)_3B$, α-selectivity, s. S.S. Chandrasekhar, C.R. Reddy, G. Chandrashekar, Tetrahedron Lett. *45*, 6481-4 (2004).

Borane-α-picoline/acetic acid
Reductive N-alkylation with oxo compds. in the absence of solvent   NH → NR

162.

of prim. amines. 1 eq. Borane-α-picoline added over 5 min to equivalent amounts of benzylamine and acetophenone in the presence of a little acetic acid, stirred for 72 h at room temp., 10% aq. HCl added, stirring continued for 30 min at room temp., diluted with water, and made alkaline with Na_2CO_3 → product. Y 87%. This is the first environmentally friendly reductive N-alkylation without solvent. The reagent is a commercially available, thermally stable, transparent solid, storable for months without deactivation, and a useful alternative to classical $NaBH_3CN$, $NaBH(OAc)_3$ and borane-pyridine which often present problems. F.e. and N-alkylation of sec. amines, **also in water** (for reductive N-alkylation of poorly water-soluble substrates) or in methanol, s. S. Sato, Y. Kikugawa et al., Tetrahedron *60*, 7899-906 (2004).

Arylboronic acids $ArB(OH)_2$
N-Acylation with carboxylic acids   NH → NAc
of amines with 3,5-bis(trifluoromethyl)phenylboronic acid cf. *52*, 146s*63*; **of ureas** with arylboronic acids bearing electron-withdrawing groups s. T. Maki, K. Ishihara, H. Yamamoto, Synlett *2004*, 1355-8.

Montmorillonite (s.a. under Silica gel and Iron(III)-exchanged montmorillonite)
5-α-Hydroxypyrazoles from 2,3-dihydro-4-pyrones s. *66*, 181s*68*

Montmorillonite/microwaves
Nitriles from aldehydes under microwave irradiation in the absence of solvent   CHO → CN
with $NH_2OH·HCl/NaHSO_4$-SiO_2 cf. *55*, 146s*58*; with $NH_2OH·HCl$/montmorillonite for preparing [het]ar. and α,β-unsatd. nitriles s. S.K. Dewan, R. Singh, A. Kumar, Synth. Commun. *34*, 2025-9 (2004).

Maleimide from maleic anhydride ring s. *54*, 157s*68*

Borosilicate
Nitriles from carboxylic acid esters   COOR → CN
and dimethylaluminum amide cf. *35*, 348; and ammonia, **gas-phase conversion** over boro-, gallo- or ferro-silicate, also from acids, s. T. Shoji et al., Japanese patent JP-2002284754 (Koei Chem. Ind. Co. Ltd.); over TiO_2 or ZrO_2 cf. JP-2002284753.

Boron fluoride/lithium salt BF_3/Li^+
Simultaneous protection and activation
of α-aminocarboxylic acids as 2,2-difluoro-1,3,2-oxazaborolidin-5-ones

163.

α-Aminocarboxylic acid amides. 2 eqs. BF_3-etherate added to a suspension of Li-N-benzylglycinate in dry THF, stirred for 4 h at 50° with TLC monitoring, and the intermediate condensed with benzylamine → product. Y 92%. Steric hindrance in either the nucleophile or at the α-site of the α-amino acid does, however, result in lower yields. F.e. and with isolation of the intermediate s. S.H. van Leeuwen, R.M.J. Liskamp et al., Tetrahedron Lett. *46*, 653-6 (2005).

Ytterbium(III) triflate $Yb(OTf)_3$
Benzimidazoles from o-diamines and aldehydes
with $SOCl_2$/silica cf. *46*, 321s*66*; with 5 mol% $Yb(OTf)_3$, selectivity, s. M. Curini, S. Taccone et al., Synlett *2004*, 1832-4.

Ring closures of dinucleophiles with oxalic acid esters   ○
2,8-dioxaquinolizidine-3,4-diones cf. *21*, 416; quinoxaline-2,3-diones from *o*-diamines with Yb(OTf)$_3$ in the absence of solvent s. L. Wang, C. Qian et al., Synth. Commun. *34*, 1349-57 (2004).

Cerium(III) chloride/tetra-n-butylammonium bromide $\qquad$ $CeCl_3/Bu_4NBr$
(Z)-β-Amino-α,β-ethylene- from β-keto-carbonyl compds. $\qquad$ COCH → C(N<)=C
Cerium(III)-catalyzed conversion in ionic liquids under mild conditions

164.   EtO-CO-CH$_2$-CO-CH$_3$ $\xrightarrow{CeCl_3}$ [Ce(III) chelate of EtO-CO-CH=C(O⁻)-CH$_3$] $\xrightarrow{PhNH_2}$ EtO-CO-CH=C(NHPh)-CH$_3$

10 Mol% CeCl$_3$·7H$_2$O added to 0.5 eq. molten tetra-*n*-butylammonium bromide, the mixture stirred at room temp., equimolar amounts of ethyl acetoacetate and aniline added, stirring continued at the same temp. for 7 min, and extracted with ethyl acetate → product. Y 80%. The procedure is simple, rapid, non-toxic and clean, and generally applicable to the condensation of aliphatic and ar. amines with β-ketocarboxylic acid esters and β-diketones. Furthermore, the catalyst can be easily recovered and reused, along with the ionic liquid, at least three times without loss of activity. F.e. **and in the absence of solvent** (over a slightly longer reaction period) s. M.M. Khodaei, A.R. Khosropour, M. Kookhazadeh, Synlett *2004*, 1980-4.

Samarium diiodide $\qquad$ SmI_2
Carboxylic acid anilides from esters and ar. nitro compds. $\qquad$ COOR → CONHAr

165.   Cl-C$_6$H$_4$-NO$_2$ $\xrightarrow{SmI_2}$ [Cl-C$_6$H$_4$-N(SmI$_2$)$_2$] $\xrightarrow{EtO-CO-Ph}$ Cl-C$_6$H$_4$-NH-CO-Ph

under mild, neutral conditions. A mixture of the startg. nitroarene and 1.1 eqs. ethyl benzoate in anhydrous THF added via syringe to 6 eqs. SmI$_2$ in the same solvent under N$_2$, and treated with 0.1 *N* HCl after ca. 30 min → product. Y 95%. The procedure is simple and generally applicable to aliphatic, aromatic and α,β-ethylenic aldehydes. F.e. and γ-hydroxycarboxylic acid anilides from γ-lactones s. X. Wang et al., Synth. Commun. *34*, 3001-8 (2004).

Ammonium formate s. under Zn $\qquad$ $HCOONH_4$

Ammonium carbonate/microwaves $\qquad$ $(NH_4)_2CO_3/[\backslash\backslash\backslash\backslash]$
Glycosylamines from aldoses $\qquad$ OH → N<
s. *64*, 151; prim. glycosylamines with (NH$_4$)$_2$CO$_3$ under microwave irradiation in DMSO s. M. Bejugam, S.L. Flitsch, Org. Lett. *6*, 4001-4 (2004).

Imidazolium ionic liquids s. under Bi(OTf)$_3$ $\qquad$ ←
Diethyl azodicarboxylate s. under Ph$_3$P $\qquad$ ROOCN=NCOOR
Polymeric azodicarboxylates s. under Polymeric phosphines $\qquad$ ←

Dicyclohexylcarbodiimide $\qquad$ RN=C=NR
Polymer-based synthesis of N-heterocyclics $\qquad$ ○
update s. *43*, 316s*67*; of 1,5-disubst. 2-amino-Δ^2-4-imidazolones s. J. Li, Z. Zhang, E. Fan, Tetrahedron Lett. *45*, 1267-9 (2004); of functionalized imidazo[1,2-*b*]pyrazol-2-ones s. B.E. Blass et al., ibid. 1275-7; of 2-arylamino-3,4-dihydroquinazolines s. A. Song, J. Marík, K.S. Lam, ibid. 2727-30; of benzimidazoles and benzothiazoles s. H. Matsushita, B. Clapham, K.D. Janda et al., ibid. 313-6; of 2-amino-D^2-pyrrolones s. A. Detsi, O. Igglessi-Markopoulou et al., Synlett *2004*, 353-5; of 2-aminobenzimidazoles from *o*-diamines and isothiocyanates under microwave irradiation (using HgCl$_2$) s. Y.-S. Su, M.-J. Lin, M.-C. Sun, Tetrahedron Lett. *46*, 177-80 (2005); of *N*-alkylated naltrindoles via Fischer indole synthesis using a 3-nitrobenzyl safety-catch linker s. H. Ohno, H. Tanaka, T. Takahashi, Synlett *2004*, 508-11; of bis(benzimidazoles) under microwave irradiation s. M.-J. Lin, C.-M. Sun, ibid. 663-6.

Dicyclohexylcarbodiimide $RN{=}C{=}NR$
1-Ethyl-3-(3-dimethylaminopropyl)carbodiimide hydrochloride/1-hydroxybenzotriazole ←
1,2,4-Oxadiazoles from amidoximes and carboxylic acids
polymer-based synthesis using dicyclohexylcarbodiimide cf. *50*, 182s58; soln.-phase route with chiral α-amino acid derivs. s. A.L. Braga et al., Synthesis *2004*, 1589-94; using 1-ethyl-3-(3-dimethylaminopropyl)carbodiimide hydrochloride/1-hydroxybenzotriazole s. B. Pipik, D.A. Conlon et al., Synth. Commun. *34*, 1863-70 (2004); with benzotriazolyloxytris(dimethylamino)-phosphonium hexafluorophosphate/ethyldiisopropylamine s. T. Wunberg et al., German patent DE-10148598 (Bayer AG).

Dicyclohexylcarbodiimide/microwaves $RN{=}C{-}NR[\setminus\setminus\setminus\setminus]$
4(3*H*)-Quinazolones from *o*-acylaminocarboxylic acids and prim. amines
with PCl₃ cf. *3*, 341; 2-aryl-derivs. s. S. Xue, J. Repic et al., J. Org. Chem. *69*, 6474-7 (2004); rapid procedure under microwave irradiation in the absence of solvent with dicyclohexyl-carbodiimide, also in ethanol with acidic alumina, s. M. Kidwai, R. Rastogi, S. Rastogi, Indian J. Chem. *43B*, 423-5 (2004).

Dicyclohexylcarbodiimide/4-dimethylaminopyridine $RN{=}C{=}NR/DMAP$
N-Acylation   NH → NAc
of 2-oxazolidones cf. *41*, 339s67; of indoles with electron-withdrawing groups at C₅ s. J.B. Bremner, S. Samosorn, J.I. Ambrus, Synthesis *2004*, 2653-8.

Lipase   ←
Enzymatic N-carbalkoxylation with carbonic acid esters   NH → NCOOR
with subtilisin cf. *51*, 146; regiospecific N-carbalkoxylation of prim. amines (in pyrimidine 3′,5′-diaminodideoxynucleosides) s. I. Lavandera, V. Gotor et al., J. Org. Chem. *69*, 1748-51 (2004).

Ethyl propiolate/N-methylmorpholine/sodium hydrogen sulfite   ←
Peptide synthesis   COOH → CON<

166.

Inexpensive and commercially available ethyl propiolate compares favourably with PyBOP as a peptide coupling agent, significant advantages being that a large excess of amine is not required and that the co-cocatalyst, NaHSO₃, is environmentally friendly. E: A soln. of 1 eq. of the startg. N-protected α-amino acid in chloroform treated at room temp. in succession with 1.3 eqs. ethyl propiolate and 1.5 eqs. N-methylmorpholine, stirred at the same temp. for 2 h, 1.3 eqs. *tert*-butyl prolinate hydrochloride and ca. 11 mol% NaHSO₃ added in succession, and stirring continued for 1 h → product. Y 90%. To minimize racemization a catalytic procedure was devised, wherein the intermediate active vinyl ester is first generated *in situ* by reaction of the amino acid with ethyl propiolate in the presence of *20 mol%* base. Standard N-protective groups were tolerated (e.g. Boc, Fmoc, Cbz). F.e., also condensation of simple carboxylic acids with amines and hydroxyl-amines, s. B. Iorga, J.-M. Campagne, Synlett *2004*, 1826-8.

2-Methyl-6-nitrobenzoic anhydride/4-dimethylaminopyridine $(ArCO)_2O/DMAP$
N-Subst. carboxylic acid amides from acids
with Ac₂O cf. *24*, 408; with 2-methyl-6-nitrobenzoic anhydride/DMAP s. I. Shiina, Y.I. Kawakita, Tetrahedron *60*, 4729-33 (2004).

Amberlyst 15   ←
3(4*H*)-Quinazolones from *o*-aminocarboxylic acids and orthocarboxylic acid esters
3-unsubst. derivs. in the absence of solvent under microwave irradiation cf. *66*, 178s67; 3-subst. derivs. with Amberlyst 15 or NaHSO₄/silica s. B. Das, J. Banerjee, Chem. Lett. *33*, 960-1 (2004).

Formic acid   HCOOH
4-Imidazolidones from α-aminocarboxylic acid amides and aldehydes
with β-naphthalenesulfonic acid cf. *17*, 451; 2-unsubst. derivs. with formaldehyde/formic acid, also from hindered substrates with Eschweiler-Clarke methylation, s. F.L. Chen, K.S. Sung, J. Heterocycl. Chem. *41*, 697-700 (2004).

Acetic acid   AcOH
(Z)-β-Amino-α,β-ethylenecarboxylic acid esters   COCH → C(N<)=C
from β-ketocarboxylic acid esters under ultrasonication s. *17*, 784s68

N-Bromosuccinimide s. under Ph_3P NBS
Silica gel s.a. under Hydrochlorides SiO_2

Silica gel/montmorillonite/microwaves   ←
β-Amino-α,β-ethylenecarbonyl compds. from β-ketocarbonyl compds.
on silica gel s. *30*, 463s67; ethyl β-arylaminocrotonates on various inorganic supports, e.g. silica gel/montmorillonite, under microwave irradiation in the absence of solvent s. Z.Y. Song, J.B. Meng et al., Chinese Chem. Lett. *15*, 127-30 (2004); (Z)-β-amino-α,β-ethylenecarboxylic acid esters with 0.1 eq. acetic acid (cf. *17*, 784) under ultrasonication s. C.A. Brandt, M.A.B. da Silveira et al., Synthesis *2004*, 1557-9; α-(aminomethylene)-γ-lactones s. P. Krajewski, L. Kozerski, Synth. Commun. *34*, 3737-42 (2004).

Titanium dioxide TiO_2
Nitriles from carboxylic acid esters in the gas phase s. *35*, 348s68   COOR → CN

Zirconium(IV) triflate/p-toluenesulfonamide $Zr(OTf)_4/TsNH_2$
$Δ^1$-Pyrrolines from cyclopropyl ketones

167.

via γ-tosylaminoketones. A mixture of the startg. aryl cyclopropyl ketone, 2 eqs. *p*-toluenesulfonamide and 50 mol% $Zr(OTf)_4$ in 1,2-dichloroethane heated at 60° for 48 h → product. Y 82%. Reaction is presumed to involve initial activation of the carbonyl group with the Lewis acid, followed by nucleophilic cyclopropane ring opening with the sulfonamide to give a zwitterionic intermediate prior to ring closure with elimination of *p*-toluenesulfonic acid. F.e. and isolation of the intermediate tosylaminoketones (with 1 eq. of the catalyst over a shorter period) s. M. Shi, Y.-H. Yang, B. Xu, Synlett *2004*, 1622-4.

Trimethylsilyl chloride s. under $NaBH_4$ Me_3SiCl

Titanium tetrachloride/zinc $TiCl_4/Zn$
2,3-Dihydro-4(1H)-quinazolones from *o*-nitrocarboxylic acid amides and ketones
with $TiCl_4$/Sm cf. *65*, 169s67; with $TiCl_4$/Zn s. D. Shi, Chinese J. Chem. *22*, 743-6 (2004); 3,4-dihydroquinazolines from *o*-nitrobenzylamines and ethyl orthoformate (cf. *65*, 169), also imidazo[1,2-*c*]quinazolines, s. Synlett *2004*, 1098-100.

Zirconium tetrachloride $ZrCl_4$
N-Carbo-*tert*-butoxylation   NH → NCOOBu-*t*

168.   HO∼∼NH₂ + (t-BuOCO)₂O ⟶ HO∼∼NHCOOBu-t

Selective N-carbo-*tert*-butoxylation. A soln. of 2-aminoethanol in acetonitrile treated dropwise with 1 eq. *tert*-butoxyformic anhydride, followed by 10 mol% $ZrCl_4$ at room temp., and stirred at room temp. for 5 min → product. Y 96%. Reaction is applicable to the protection of prim. and sec. amines, incl. cyclic sec. amines and α- or β-*prim*-amino esters, and proceeds with retention of hydroxyl and sulfhydryl groups. F.e.s. G.V.M. Sharma et al., Tetrahedron Lett. *45*, 6963-5 (2004); with $Zn(ClO_4)_2$ cf. G. Bartoli et al., Synlett *2004*, 1794-8.

Nicotinoyl azide s. under Ph_3P $RCON_3$

Triphenylphosphine/diethyl azodicarboxylate/nicotinoyl azide   ←
Azides from alcohols $OH \rightarrow N_3$
with $Ph_3P/DDQ/[Bu_4N]N_3$ cf. *32*, 333s67; with Ph_3P/diethyl azodicarboxylate/nicotinoyl azide s. G. Papeo, M. Varasi et al., Synthesis *2004*, 2886-92.

Triphenylphosphine/N-bromosuccinimide/pyridine $Ph_3P/NBS/C_5H_5N$
N-Acylation with carboxylic acids $NH \rightarrow NAc$
N-subst. carboxylic acid amides with Ph_3P/NCS cf. *50*, 185; partial N-acylation of diamines with $Ph_3P/NBS/C_5H_5N$ s. B.P. Bandgar, S.V. Bettigeri, Synth. Commun. *34*, 2917-24 (2004).

Polymeric triarylphosphines/polymeric azodicarboxylates   ←
Mitsunobu reaction with polymeric reagents   ←

169.

N-Alkylation. A mixture of 1.05 eqs. phthalimide, 1 eq. of the startg. alcohol, and 2.03 eqs. oligomeric phosphine in anhydrous THF treated under argon at room temp. with 2.06 eqs. oligomeric azodicarboxylate, stirred at the same temp. for 2 h, and worked up after filtration of the spent reagent → product. Y 69%. The procedure offers a more facile product isolation than traditional methods. F.e.s. A.M. Harned, P.R. Hanson et al., J. Am. Chem. Soc. *127*, 52-3 (2005).

Tetra-n-butylphosphonium bromide (s.a. under $CeCl_3$) Bu_4PBr
N-Benzylation with dibenzyl carbonate $NH \rightarrow NBn$
of N-heterocyclics with triethylenediamine/Bu_4NCl under microwave irradiation cf. *41*, 325s67; **N,N-dibenzylation** of aliphatic prim. amines with Bu_4PBr in the absence of solvent s. A. Loris, A. Perosa, M. Selva et al., J. Org. Chem. *69*, 3953-6 (2004).

Benzotriazolyloxytris(dimethylamino)phosphonium hexafluorophosphate/
  ethyldiisopropylamine   ←
1,2,4-Oxadiazoles from amidoximes and carboxylic acids s. *50*, 182s68   ○

Polyethylene glycol bis(dichlorophosphate)/microwaves   ←
1,3,4-Oxadiazoles from acylhydrazines and carboxylic acids
under microwave irradiation with $POCl_3$ cf. *44*, 301s66; with readily recoverable polyethylene glycol bis(dichlorophosphate) in the absence of solvent s. Z. Li, X.-C. Wang et al., Synth. Commun. *34*, 2981-6 (2004).

Bismuth(III) triflate/1-n-butyl-3-methylimidazolium fluoroborate $Bi(OTf)_3/[bmim]BF_4$
Paal-Knorr pyrrole synthesis in ionic liquids
in 1-*n*-butyl-3-methylimidazolium iodide without additive cf. *67*, 159; in 1-*n*-butyl-3-methylimidazolium fluoroborate with added 5 mol% $Bi(OTf)_3$, also furans by cyclodehydration, and thiophenes [with 2,4-bis(*p*-methoxyphenyl)-1,3,2,4-dithiadiphosphetane 2,4-disulfide], s. J.S. Yadav et al., Tetrahedron Lett. *45*, 5873-6 (2004).

p-Toluenesulfonamide s. under $Zr(OTf)_4$ $TsNH_2$

Chiral 2-(arenesulfonylaminomethyl)pyrrolidines/sodium tetrahydridoborate/
sodium hydroxide
3-(Carbalkoxyamino)-2-oxazolidones from aldehydes
via organocatalyzed asym. α-amination with azodicarboxylic acid esters

170.

One-pot procedure. 1 Mol% (S)-2-(N-tosylaminomethyl)pyrrolidine (readily prepared from L-proline) added to a suspension of diethyl azodicarboxylate and 1.5 eqs. propanal in methylene chloride (cf. *63*, 142s67), stirred at room temp. for 3 h, methanol and 1.32 eqs. NaBH₄ added, stirring continued 20 min, treated with 0.5 M NaOH, and stirred again for 2 h at the same temp. → (R)-product. Y 58% (e.e. 87%). Linear aldehydes gave moderate to high yields in up to 87% e.e., whereas reaction with a branched substrate (*i*-PrCHO) resulted in a poor yield and lower enantioselectivity. F.e. and comparison of ligands s. N. Dahlin, A. Bøgevig, H. Adolfsson, Adv. Synth. Catal. *346*, 1101-5 (2004).

Methanesulfonyl chloride/triethylamine $MeSO_2Cl/Et_3N$
Hydroxamic acid esters from hindered carboxylic acids COOH → CONOR
with Cl₃COCOCl/Et₃N cf. *13*, 441s67; with MeSO₂Cl/Et₃N, notably for the conversion of hindered carboxylic acids, s. J.C.S. Woo, E. Fenster, G.R. Dake, J. Org. Chem. *69*, 8984-6 (2004).

Trifluoromethanesulfonic anhydride/triethylamine Tf_2O/Et_3N
1,2-Di-*tert*-amines from 2-*tert*-aminoalcohols and sec. amines OH → N<
via regiospecific ring opening of intermediate aziridinium triflates

171.

1.3 eqs. Triethylamine added to a soln. of (S)-N-allyl-N-benzylalaninol in anhydrous methylene chloride at -78°, followed by 1.1 eqs. triflic anhydride, the resulting mixture stirred for 1 h at the same temp., warmed to room temp., 1.1 eqs. (S)-N-benzyl-2-amino-3-methylbutan-1-ol in the same solvent added, stirring continued for 2 h at room temp., then quenched with 1 M aq. NaOH → product. Y 69% (d.e. >99%; single regioisomer). The intermediate aziridinium ion was ring opened with *complete* regiospecificity and with exclusive N-alkylation of the *sec*-aminoalcohol. An **iterative synthesis of stereo-defined polyamines** can be effected by cleavage of both the N-allyl and N-benzyl groups of the product and subsequent coupling with another 2-*tert*-aminoalcohol molecule. F.e.s. C. McKay, R.J. Wilson, C.M. Rayner, Chem. Commun. *2004*, 1080-1.

N,N-Disubst. amidines from oximes and sec. amines s. *67*, 371   NH → NC(=NR)R'

Pyridinium tosylate s. under Cobalt(III) complexes C_5H_5NHOTs

p-*Toluenesulfonic acid*   TsOH
N-Alkoxymethylation with formals   NH → NCH₂OR

172.

of N-subst. carboxylic acid amides. A mixture of the startg. N-subst. amide, 15 eqs. dibutoxymethane and 0.2 eq. *p*-toluenesulfonic acid refluxed for 5 h with azeotropic distillation of the liberated butanol and unreacted dibutoxymethane, cooled, and neutralized with satd. aq. NaHCO$_3$ → product. Y 77%. The equilibrium is shifted to the right by the azeotropic distillation. However, the method is impractical for methoxymethylation because of extensive removal of dimethoxymethane with the liberated methanol. Methanesulfonic acid and Nafion-H SAC-13 were equally effective, but Lewis acids were less so. F.e. incl. **N-alkoxymethylation** of N-arylamides s. I. Ledneczki, P.M. Agocs, A. Molnar, Synlett *2003*, 2255-7; N-methoxymethylation of N-subst. amides, sulfonamides, imides and phosphinylamines with BF$_3$-etherate s. R. Szmigielski, W. Danikiewicz, ibid. 372-6.

Polymer-based 2-chloropyridinium triflate/polymer-based 4-dimethylaminopyridine/ ←
triethylamine
N-Subst. carboxylic acid amides from acids s. *32*, 148s*68*   COOH → CON<

Selenium/sodium acetate   *Se/NaOAc*
Sym. ureas from nitro compds. and carbon monoxide   NO$_2$ → NHCONH
sym. N,N'-diarylureas with Pd-Al$_2$O$_3$/FeCl$_3$ cf. *32*, 345; with Se/NaOAc/water *at atm. pressure* s. X.-F. Wang, S. W. Lu, Z.-K. Yu, Adv. Synth. Catal. *346*, 929-32 (2004).

Iodine/potassium carbonate I_2/K_2CO_3
4(3H)-Quinazolones from *o*-aminocarboxylic acid amides and aldehydes
Oxidative ring closure under mild conditions

173.

1.2 eqs. Iodine and 1 eq. anhydrous K$_2$CO$_3$ added with stirring to equivalent amounts of 3,4,5-trimethoxybenzaldehyde and anthranilamide in anhydrous DMF, heated at 60-80° for 6 h, and poured into ice-water → product. Y 75.3%. **2,3-Disubst. 4(3H)-quinazolones** were also prepared **by 3-component condensation** of aldehydes, prim. amines and isatoic anhydride. F.e. and with DDQ s. B.A. Bhat, D.P. Sahu, Synth. Commun. *34*, 2169-76 (2004).

Magnesium perchlorate $Mg(ClO_4)_2$
Azomethines from oxo compds.   CO → C=NR
with TiCl$_4$ cf. *50*, 187s*61*; with Mg(ClO$_4$)$_2$ from *less* electrophilic aryloxo compds. and poorly nucleophilic amines, **also phenylhydrazones**, s. A.K. Chakraborti, S. Bhagat, S. Rudrawar, Tetrahedron Lett. *45*, 7641-4 (2004).

Zinc perchlorate $Zn(ClO_4)_2$
N-Carbo-*tert*-butoxylation s. *68*, 168   NH → NCOOBu-*t*

Hydrochlorides/sodium hydroxide/silica gel   ←
Nitrones from aldehydes   CHO → CH=N(O)R
and hydroxylamine hydrochlorides with molecular sieves cf. *54*, 153; with silica gel and 0.5 eq. NaOH in the absence of solvent s. M.M.A. Nikje, M.A. Bigdeli, H. Imanieh, Phosphorus, Sulfur Silicon Relat. Elem. *179*, 1465-8 (2004).

Hydrochlorides/silica gel   ←
Oximes from oxo compds.   CO → C=NOH
solid-state conversion with NH$_2$OH·HCl and molecular sieves cf. *57*, 145s*63*; with silica gel s. A.R. Kiasat, F. Kazemi, K. Nourbakhsh, Phosphorus, Sulfur Silicon Relat. Elem. *179*, 1193-6 (2004).

Manganese dioxide MnO_2
Benzimidazoles from *o*-diamines and activated prim. alcohols   O

174.

15 eqs. Activated MnO_2 added to a mixture of benzyl alcohol, 2.5 eqs. N-methyl-1,2-phenylenediamine, 15 mol% HCl (2 *M* in ether) and 4 Å molecular sieves in anhydrous toluene, stirred at 105° for 18 h, cooled to 50°, filtered (to remove spent oxidant), and worked up → product. Y 90%. The procedure involves a tandem oxidation: the prim. alcohol is initially oxidized to the aldehyde, which couples with the diamine to give the corresponding benzimidazoline prior to a second oxidation with the same reagent to give the product. The method is limited, however, to benzyl alcohols and heterocyclic analogs. F.e. and preliminary application to the synthesis of benzoxazoles and benzothiazoles s. C.D. Wilfred, R.J.K. Taylor, Synlett *2004*, 1628-30.

Iron(III)-exchanged montmorillonite   ←
Heterogeneous N-acylation   NH → NAc
N-acetylation with acetic anhydride on montmorillonite K10 s. *54*, 79; N-acylation of sulfonic acid amides with carboxylic acid anhydrides on iron(III)-exchanged montmorillonite s. D.U. Singh, P.R. Singh, S.D. Samant, Tetrahedron Lett. *45*, 4805-7 (2004).

Dodecacarbonyltriruthenium/acenaphthoquinone diimines/carbon monoxide   ←
Ar. 2-ethyleneamines from ethylene derivs. and ar. nitro compds.   CH(NHR)C≡C
with $[Cp^*Fe(CO)_2]_2$/CO under irradiation cf. *56*, 152s63; with $Ru_3(CO)_{12}$/acenaphthoquinone diimines/CO s. F. Ragaini, S. Cenini, A. Caselli et al., Tetrahedron *60*, 4989-94 (2004).

Thiolate-bridged diruthenium complex/auric chloride/ammonium fluoroborate   ←
Oxazoles from 2-acetylenealcohols and N-unsubst. carboxylic acid amides   O

175.

Dual catalysis. Anhydrous 1,2-dichloroethane, the startg. propargyl alcohol and 5 eqs. of the startg. amide added to a mixture of 5 mol% [Cp*RuCl(μ^2-SMe)$_2$RuCp*Cl] (*66*, 365) and 10 mol% ammonium fluoroborate under N_2, stirred for 1 h at 60°, 10 mol% auric chloride and the same anhydrous solvent added, and heated at 80° for 18 h → product. Y 88%. The ruthenium complex is thought to catalyze the intermediate formation of the corresponding N-propargylamide, prior to Au(III)-catalyzed isomerization to the allene and ring closure. Reaction is completely regiospecific but limited to 1-aryl- and 1-vinyl-propargyl alcohols. F.e.s. M.D. Milton, Y. Nishibayashi, S. Uemura et al., Chem. Commun. *2004*, 2712-3.

Ruthenium trichloride $RuCl_3$
Ruthenium-catalyzed N-acylation s. *68*, 99   NH → NAc

(4,7-Diphenyl-1,10-phenanthroline)palladium(II) bis(trifluoroacetate)   ←
Palladium-catalyzed N-vinylation with vinyl ethers   NH → NCH=CH$_2$

176.

of amides. A mixture of startg. 2-oxazolidone, 10 eqs. butyl vinyl ether, and 5 mol% (4,7-diphenyl-1,10-phenanthroline)palladium(II) bis(trifluoroacetate) heated with stirring at 75° under open air for 4 h → product. Y 92%. Reaction is thought to involve initial aminopalladation of the vinyl ether, followed by β-alkoxide elimination. The procedure is generally applicable to the N-vinylation of amides, lactams, urethans and sulfonylamines, there being no reaction with simple prim. or sec. amines which presumably coordinate too strongly to palladium. F.e. and comparison of catalysts s. J.L. Brice, J.E. Meerdink, S.S. Stahl, Org. Lett. 6, 1845-8 (2004).

Bis(η^3-allylpalladium chloride)/(1R,2R)-N,N'-bis[2-(diphenylphosphino)-benzoyl]-1,2-diaminocyclohexane/potassium tert-butoxide ←
Desymmetrization of 1,2-di(sulfonylamines)   NH → N-C-C=C
by palladium-catalyzed N-allylation

177.

1 eq. Startg. 1,2-di(sulfonylamine) added to a suspension of 1 eq. *t*-BuOK in toluene under argon, stirred at room temp. for 5 min, treated at -15° with a soln. of 3.7 mol% [(η^3-allyl)PdCl]$_2$, 7.3 mol% (R,R)-Trost ligand and 1 eq. allyl acetate in dioxane, stirring continued at -15 to 0° for 23 h, and quenched with 2% aq. HCl → (1R,2S)-product. Y 69% (e.e. 90%). F.e. and comparison of ligands, bases and solvents s. O. Kitagawa, T. Taguchi et al., Org. Lett. 6, 3605-7 (2004).

Bis(η^3-allylpalladium chloride)/1,2-bis(diphenylphosphino)ethane/potassium carbonate ←
N-Allylation of indoles s. *68,* 376

Bis(acetonitrile)dichloropalladium(II)/triphenylphosphine $PdCl_2(MeCN)_2/Ph_3P$
Regiospecific ring closures of (Z)-2-ene-1,4-diol O-derivs. with dinucleophiles
with Pd$_2$(dba)$_3$/(*i*-PrO)$_3$P cf. *46,* 335; 2-vinyl-1,2,3,4-tetrahydroquinoxalines from *o*-diamines with PdCl$_2$(MeCN)$_2$/Ph$_3$P s. S.-C. Yang, P.-C. Liu, W.H. Feng, Tetrahedron Lett. *45,* 7951-4 (2004).

Bis(1,5-cyclooctadiene)iridium(I) fluoroborate $[Ir(cod)_2]BF_4$
Iridium-catalyzed N-allylation s. *68,* 123

Chloro(1,5-cyclooctadiene)iridium(I) dimer/chiral cyclic phosphoromonoamidites/triethylenediamine   ←
Regiospecific asym. iridium-catalyzed N-allylation of ar. amines

178.

A mixture of 10 mol% dabco, 0.5 mol% [Ir(cod)Cl]$_2$, and 1 mol% chiral binaphthyl-based phosphoromonoamidite in anhydrous THF treated with 1.06 eqs. startg. aniline and 1 eq. startg. allyl carbonate, and stirred *at room temp.* for 10 h → product. Y 92% (e.e. 96%). Reaction is applicable to a broad range of achiral, linear allyl carbonates to give *branched* chiral N-allylarylamines in excellent yield with high regio- and enantio-selectivity. The conversion of electron-deficient ar. amines, however, required more forcing conditions. F.e. and method s. C. Shu, A. Leitner, J.F. Hartwig, Angew. Chem. Int. Ed. Engl. *43,* 4797-800 (2004).

Dichloro(pentamethylcyclopentadienyl)iridium(III) dimer/sodium carbonate
Cyclic tert. amines from diols and prim. amines

179.

A mixture of 1.5 eqs. benzylamine, 1 eq. startg. diol, 1 mol% [Cp*IrCl$_2$]$_2$, and 1 mol% Na$_2$CO$_3$ in toluene stirred under argon at 110° for 17 h → product. Y 94% (*cis/trans* 73:27). This environmentally benign method produces only water as by-product, affording 5-, 6-, or 7-membered cyclic amines in high yield. F.e.s. K. Fujita, T. Fujii, R. Yamaguchi, Org. Lett. *6*, 3525-8 (2004).

Via intermediates   *v.i.*
β-Amino-α,β-ethylene- from β-keto-carbonyl compds.   COCH → C(N<)=C
β-amino-α,β-ethyleneketones via complexation with BF$_3$-etherate s. *63*, 167; β-amino-α,β-ethylenecarboxylic acid amides, also β-hydrazonocarboxylic acid esters with hydrazines, s. B. Stefane, S. Polanc, Synlett *2004*, 698-702.

Nitrogen ↑   NC ↓↑ N

Without additional reagents   *w.a.r.*
N-Acylation with N-acylsulfonic acid amides   NH → NAc
polymer-based N-acylation cf. *56*, 154; **preferential N-acylation** of prim. amino over sec. amino groups with N-acylmethanesulfonamides s. S. Coniglio, M. Allegretti et al., Tetrahedron Lett. *45*, 5375-8 (2004).

Hydrazones from oximes   C=NOH → C=NN<
N-subst. hydrazones s. *12*, 497; N-unsubst. hydrazones from ar. aldoximes, diaryl and alkyl aryl ketoximes with hydrazine hydrate s. M.A. Pasha, H.M. Nanjundaswamy, Synth. Commun. *34*, 3827-31 (2004).

Polymer-based synthesis of guanidines from prim. amines   NH$_2$ → NHC(=NH)NH$_2$
s. *60*, 147; f. method for preparing **N-monosubst. guanidines** from a cellulose-supported, triazene-linked N-amidinylating agent s. A. Porcheddu, S. Masala et al., Org. Lett. *6*, 4925-7 (2004).

Microwaves s. under Hydrochlorides   [\\\\]
Sodium hydroxide   *NaOH*
(Aminoaryl)phosphine oxides from (sulfonyloxyaryl)phosphines and azides   N$_3$ → NHR
via intramolecular Staudinger ligation

180.

Chiral 2'-amino-1,1'-binaphthyl-2-phosphine oxides. 1 eq. Startg. chiral phosphine added to a soln. of 1.52 eqs. startg. azide in 1:1 anhydrous toluene/THF, stirred at 115° for 17 h, cooled to room temp., concentrated, and the resulting phosphonium salt stirred at 65° for 2 h in 1:1:1 THF/ethanol/0.1 M aq. NaOH → product. Y 39%. This is the first instance of an intramolecular S$_N$Ar reaction with an iminophosphorane as nucleophile. F.e. and *prim*-amino derivs. with Me₃SiN₃, also coupling with ar. azides s. P.N.M. Botman, H. Hiemstra, J.H. van Maarseveen et al., Angew. Chem. Int. Ed. Engl. *43*, 3471-3 (2004).

Sodium azide/cerium(III) chloride $NaN_3/CeCl_3$
Azides from diazo compds. $C{=}N_2 \rightarrow CHN_3$
s. *36*, 266; α-azidoketones with $NaN_3/CeCl_3$ or $Ce(OTf)_3$ s. J.S. Yadav, B.V.S. Reddy, M. Srinivas, Chem. Lett. *33*, 882-3 (2004).

Sodium iodide   *NaI*
Acylamines from azides $N_3 \rightarrow NHCOR$
and carboxylic acids with $Bu_3P/PhSeSePh$ cf. *48*, 346; ar. acylamines with NaI, also lactams (3,4-dihydro-1*H*-1,4-benzodiazepine-2,5-diones) from azidocarboxylic acid esters, and fused 4(3*H*)-quinazolones from N-(*o*-azidoaroyl)lactams, s. A. Kamal et al., Tetrahedron Lett. *45*, 8187-90 (2004); acylamines **from carboxylic acid esters** with SmI_2 cf. X.X. Wang, J. Chem. Res. Synop *2004*, 484-5; **N-glycosylamines** from α-glycosyl azides with retention of configuration by Staudinger ligation (cf. *40*, 254s67) with (*o*-acetoxyphenyl)diphenylphosphine or 1-acetyl-2-(diphenylphosphino)imidazole s. A. Bianchi, A. Bernardi, Tetrahedron Lett. *45*, 2231-4 (2004).

1,8-Diazabicyclo[5.4.0]undec-7-ene s. under CO   *dbu*

Cuprous iodide   *CuI*
N'-Sulfonylamidines $C{\equiv}C \rightarrow CH_2C({=}NSO_2R)N{<}$
from terminal acetylene derivs., azides and amines

181.
$$Ph{-}{\equiv} \xrightarrow{Cu(I)} \left[Ph{-}{\equiv}{-}Cu \xrightarrow{TsN_3} \underset{Ph}{\overset{Cu}{>}}{=}NTs \right] \xrightarrow{i\text{-}Pr_2NH} Ph\underset{NPr\text{-}i_2}{\overset{NTs}{>}}$$

A mixture of phenylacetylene, 1.2 eqs. tosyl azide, 1.2 eqs. diisopropylamine and 10 mol% CuI in THF stirred at room temp. for 1 h → (E)-product. Y 89%. This mild, highly efficient 3-component synthesis is broadly applicable to the coupling of aromatic or [somewhat more slowly] aliphatic terminal alkynes with aliphatic or [het]ar. azides and a broad range of prim., sec., aliphatic, aromatic, acyclic or cyclic amines, reaction with chiral α-amino esters proceeding *without racemization*. The procedure can also be scaled up, performed with other copper(I) or copper(II) salts, is efficient at the 1 mol% level (after 8-12 h), and leaves a number of functional groups unaffected, notably halides, alcohols, silyl groups, and conjugated ester and ethylenic groups. Reaction possibly involves initial formation of a cuprous acetylide, followed by generation of a cuproketenimine prior to addition of the amine. F.e. and solvent effect s. I. Bae, H. Han, S. Chang, J. Am. Chem. Soc. *127*, 2038-9 (2005).

Zinc/ammonium formate $Zn/HCOONH_4$
Formanilides from ar. azides s. *68*, 161 $N_3 \rightarrow NHCHO$

Cerium(III) chloride s. under NaN_3 $CeCl_3$

Samarium diiodide SmI_2
Acylamines from azides and carboxylic acid esters s. *48*, 346s68 $N_3 \rightarrow NHCOR$

Carbon monoxide/selenium/1,8-diazabicyclo[5.4.0]undec-7-ene/triethylamine   ←
Carboxylic acid anilides $NH \rightarrow NAr$
from N-unsubst. carboxylic acid amides and ar. nitro compds.

182.
$$O_2NAr \xrightarrow[-CO_2]{[SeCO]} \left[:NAr \xrightarrow[-Se]{[SeCO]} O{=}C{=}NAr \xrightarrow{PhCONH_2} PhCONHCONHAr \right] \xrightarrow{-[HN{=}C{=}O]Se} PhCONHAr$$

Ar = 5-methoxy-2-pyridyl (N-OMe)

A mixture of 5 mol% elemental selenium, 1 eq. each of benzamide and 2-methoxy-5-nitropyridine, 2 eqs. triethylamine and 1 eq. dbu in toluene pressurized in a stainless steel autoclave to 1 MPa with CO, the latter carefully vented, the purging process repeated twice, the autoclave pressurized to 3 MPa with CO, heated to 160° for 4 h, cooled to room temp., CO carefully vented, and the mixture poured into 1 N aq. HCl → product. Y 76%. Reaction is presumed to involve initial reduction of the nitro compd. to the nitrene with *in situ*-generated SeCO, followed by isocyanate formation and addition of the amide prior to elimination of isocyanic acid (possibly coordinated to Se). The selenium catalyst was recovered after reaction by quenching with 1 N aq. HCl in air. F.e.s. J. Chen, Z. Yu, S. Lu et al., Adv. Synth. Catal. *346*, 1267-70 (2004).

Chiral α,α,α',α'-Tetraaryl-1,3-dioxolane-4,5-dimethanols ←
α-Hydroxylaminoketones from enamines and nitroso compds. C(N<)=C → CO-C-N(OH)R
Brønsted acid-catalyzed asym. conversion s. *68*, 104

Thioacetamide MeCSNH$_2$
Δ^2-Imidazolines from 1,2-diamines and nitriles in the absence of solvent
with S$_8$ under microwave irradiation cf. *4*, 316s67; thermal procedure with a little thioacetamide s. J.A. Parihar, P. Dash, D.P. Kudav, J. Chem. Res. Synop *2004*, 220-2.

N-Bromosuccinimide NBS
N-Subst. carboxylic acid amides from carboxylic acid hydrazides   CONHNH$_2$ → CON<
peptide synthesis with NBS cf. *26*, 398; polymer-based synthesis of peptide *p*-nitroanilides s. Y. Kwon, J.A. Camarero et al., Org. Lett. *6*, 3801-4 (2004).

Selenium s. under CO Se

Hydrochlorides ←
Hydrazonoesters from iminoesters   C(OR)=NR → C(OR)=NN<
N-carbalkoxyhydrazonoesters cf. *18*, 416; N-arylhydrazonoesters s. G.S. Zhang, Z. Suo, Synth. Commun. *34*, 673-8 (2004).

Hydrochlorides/microwaves ←
N-Acetylation with acetamide   NH → NAc
of amine hydrochlorides s. *10*, 296; **selective N-acylation** of aminophenols with bisacetamide hydrochloride under microwave irradiation in the absence of solvent s. Y.Q. Peng, G.H. Song, F. Ding, Indian J. Chem. *43B*, 2021-3 (2004).

Hydrogen chloride HCl
γ-Acylaminoketones from Δ^1-pyrrolines
and carboxylic acid chlorides/NaOH cf. *13*, 487; and N-acetylpyridinium chloride with HCl s. V.G. Nenajdenko, E.S. Balenkova et al., Tetrahedron *60*, 11719-24 (2004).

Palladium-carbon Pd-C
Sec. from prim. amines and nitriles   NH$_2$ → NHR

183.

Reductive mono-N-alkylation under mild conditions. A stirred mixture of 10% Pd-C, 5 eqs. acetonitrile and the startg. prim. amine in methanol hydrogenated for 12 h under a H$_2$ balloon at 20° → product. Y 97% (selectivity 99%). Only minor amounts of the corresponding tert. amine were isolated. The procedure is applicable to the reduction of ar. or aliphatic nitriles [the latter preferably over Rh-C] with prim., sec. or tert. nitriles, being supportive of electron-withdrawing and -donating groups in the benzene ring and leaving alcohols and acetals unaffected. It is also relatively mild and avoids handling traditional, less friendly alkylating agents, such as alkyl halides. The process appears to involve initial formation of an amidine, followed by reductive elimination of ammonia and subsequent hydrogenation of the resulting aldimine. F.e., also one-pot conversion **from nitro compds.**, and indoles by intramolecular reductive N-alkylation, s. H. Sajiki, T. Ikawa, K. Hirota, Org. Lett. *6*, 4977-80 (2004).

Halogen ↑   NC ↓↑ Hal

Microwaves s. under NaN_3 and $Pd(OAc)_2$ [\\\\]

Sodium hydride   *NaH*
Regiospecific N-alkylation of the imidazole ring   NH → NR
s. *9*, 512s*39*; of N^α-protected histidines s. N. Kaur, V. Monga, R. Jain, Tetrahedron Lett. *45*, 6883-5 (2004).

Potassium hydroxide/1-n-butyl-3-methylimidazolium hexafluorophosphate $KOH/[bmim]PF_6$
N-Alkylation in ionic liquids
s. *56*, 159s*67*; of sulfonic acid amides s. Y. Hu, Q.-G. Zheng et al., Org. Prep. Proced. Int. *36*, 347-51 (2004); **of pyrroles,** also N-acylation and -sulfonylation, s. Z.-G. Le, Q.-G. Zheng et al., Synthesis *2004*, 1951-4; of dicarboxylic acid imides with KF as base cf. J. Chem. Res. Synop *2004*, 276-8.

Potassium hydroxide/tetra-n-butylammonium hydrogen sulfate KOH/Bu_4NHSO_4
N-Alkylation under solid-liq. phase transfer catalysis
s. *33*, 412; of N-carbalkoxyhydrazones in toluene, also conversion to N-monosubst. hydrazines, s. K.G. Meyer, Synlett *2004*, 2355-6.

Cesium hydroxide   *CsOH*
N-Arylation of amines   NH → NAr
diarylamines with Cs_2CO_3 cf. *17*, 490s*44*; cyclic tert. ar. amines with CsOH (cf. *59*, 164) s. R. Varala, S.R. Adapa et al., Synlett *2004*, 1747-50.

Lithium dialkylamides $LiNR_2$
Replacement of ar. halogen by amino groups
s. *24*, 955; 2-amino- from 2-fluoro-pyridines (cf. *66*, 204) s. L. Pasumansky, B. Singaram et al., Tetrahedron Lett. *45*, 6417-20 (2004).

Lithium bis(trimethylsilyl)amide/hexamethylphosphoramide $LiN(SiMe_3)_2/HMPA$
Potassium carbonate/tetra-n-butylammonium iodide K_2CO_3/Bu_4NI
N-Carbalkoxylation   NH → NCOOR
with NaOH cf. *9*, 507; of chiral α-(carbalkoxyamino)carboxylic acid esters with $LiN(SiMe_3)_2$/HMPA s. J.N. Hernandez, V.S. Martin, J. Org. Chem. *69*, 3590-2 (2004); of the electron-deficient pyrrole ring with K_2CO_3/Bu_4NI (cf. *30*, 297) s. S.T. Handy, I. Vulfova et al., Tetrahedron Lett. *45*, 5057-60 (2004).

Rubidium carbonate s. under $[Cu(MeCN)_4]PF_6$ Rb_2CO_3
Cesium acetate s. under CuI   *CsOAc*

Potassium thiocyanate/N,N,N',N'-tetramethylethylenediamine   *KSCN/tmeda*
Ammonium thiocyanate/polyethylene glycol NH_4SCN/PEG
Acylthioureas from carboxylic acid chlorides and amines   NH → NC(S)NHAc
under microwave irradiation cf. *22*, 470s*63*; **solid-state procedure, also N^1,N^4-diacylthiosemicarbazides** from acylhydrazines, s. Z. Zhang, X.-C. Wang, Z. Li, Synth. Commun. *34*, 1407-14 (2004); s.a. T.-B. Wei et al., Phosphorus, Sulfur Silicon Relat. Elem. *179*, 1539-44 (2004); N-carbalkoxythioureas from halogenoformic acid esters with KSCN/TMEDA s. Synth. Commun. *34*, 2205-13 (2004).

Sodium azide/L-proline/sodium carbonate/sodium ascorbate/cupric sulfate   ←
Sodium azide/copper/cupric sulfate/microwaves   ←
1,2,3-Triazoles from terminal acetylene derivs. and halides   ○
via regiospecific 1,3-dipolar cycloaddition with *in situ*-generated azides

184.   PhI $\xrightarrow{NaN_3}$ [PhN=$\overset{+}{N}$=$\overset{-}{N}$] $\xrightarrow{\equiv\!\!-\!\!OC_6H_4Cl\text{-}p}$ Ph-N,N,N-triazole-OC_6H_4Cl-p

1,4-Disubst. 1,2,3-triazoles. 0.2 eq. L-proline, 0.2 eq. Na_2CO_3, 1.2 eqs. NaN_3, 0.1 eq. Na-ascorbate, 0.05 eq. $CuSO_4 \cdot 5H_2O$ and 9:1 DMSO/water added to an equimolar mixture of iodobenzene and 1-chloro-4-prop-2-ynyloxybenzene in a scintillation vial, stirred overnight at 65°, poured into ice-cold water, and the off-white precipitate filtered off → product. Y 83%. *Caution*: Copper azides are explosive when dry and traces must be removed from the product. The procedure is simple, safe and clean, avoids handling potentially unstable azides, and is generally applicable to ar., hetar. and aliphatic halides. F.e.s. A.K. Feldman, B. Colasson, V.V. Fokin, Org. Lett. 6, 3897-9 (2004); with NaN$_3$/Cu/CuSO$_4$ in aq. *tert*-butanol under microwave irradiation cf. P. Appukkuttan, E. Van der Eycken et al., ibid. 4223-5.

Potassium fluoride-alumina s. under CuI KF-Al$_2$O$_3$

Potassium fluoride/1-n-butyl-3-methylimidazolium hexafluorophosphate KF/[bmim]PF$_6$
N-Alkylation in ionic liquids NH → NR
of dicarboxylic acid imides s. *56*, 159s68

Triethylamine Et$_3$N
N-Arylation with ar. fluorides F → N<
with K$_2$CO$_3$ cf. *8*, 563s49; **high-pressure N-arylation** with nitrofluorobenzenes in the presence of Et$_3$N s. C.L. Brown, I.W. Muderawan, D.J. Young, Synthesis *2003*, 2511-7.

2-Ethylenephosphorylamines from 2-ethylenealcohols and azides ←
via [3.3]-sigmatropic rearrangement

185.

1.25 eqs. Cyclohex-2-enol, 1.25 eqs. triethylamine and a soln. of 1.25 eqs. 2-chloro-5,5-dimethyl-1,3,2-dioxaphosphorinane in dry, degassed ether added to a chilled flask containing the same dry, degassed solvent, stirred for 20 min, triethylamine hydrochloride removed using Schlenck filtration, solvent removed *in vacuo*, the residue taken up in xylene, added dropwise to a soln. of benzyl azide in the same solvent at 0°, warmed to room temp. over 1 h, heated at 80° for 1 h, diluted with the same solvent, and refluxed for 4 h → product. Y 65%. Reaction proceeds via a novel allylic phosphorimidate-phosphoramidate rearrangement, being tolerant of substitution on the allyloxy residue, and providing the same product irrespective of the (Z)/(E)-geometry of the substrate. Coupling with allyl azide was performed with excess of the compd. (3 eqs.) due to its volatility. F.e. incl. generation of quaternary stereo centres and (E)-products with high selectivity, also N-dephosphorylation, s. B. Chen, A.K. Mapp, J. Am. Chem. Soc. *126*, 5364-5 (2004).

Ethyldiisopropylamine/tetra-n-butylammonium iodide i-Pr$_2$NEt/Bu$_4$NI
α-Amino- from α-bromo-carboxylic acid esters Br → N<
with dynamic kinetic resolution
with Et$_3$N/Bu$_4$NI cf. *65*, 171s66; polymer-based synthesis with a supported amine using i-Pr$_2$NEt as base s. Y. Valenrod, J. Myung, R.N. Ben, Tetrahedron Lett. *45*, 2545-9 (2004).

N,N,N',N'-Tetramethylethylenediamine s. under KSCN tmeda
Copper s. under NaN$_3$ Cu

Tetrakis(acetonitrile)copper(I) hexafluorophosphate/tetramethyl-1,10-phenanthroline/ ←
rubidium carbonate
Copper(I)-catalyzed N-vinylation NH → NC=C
α-Acylamino-α,β-ethylenecarboxylic acid esters s. *47*, 337s68

Cupric acetoacetonate/1-n-butyl-3-methylimidazolium fluoroborate Cu(acac)$_2$/[bmim]BF$_4$
Cuprous triflate/triethylamine CuOTf/Et$_3$N
N-Tosylaziridines from ethylene derivs.
with phenyl(tosylimino)iodinane and [hydridotris(1-pyrazolyl)borato]copper(I) complexes cf. *55*, 159s61; with Cu(acac)$_2$ **in ionic liquids**, e.g. 1-*n*-butyl-3-methylimidazolium fluoroborate,

for a simple recycling of catalyst and medium s. M.L. Kantam, V. Neeraja et al., Synlett *2004*, 525-7; from electron-deficient ethylene derivs. with CuOTf·C$_6$H$_6$/Et$_3$N and N,N-dichloro-*p*-toluenesulfonamide s. D.-J. Chen, C. Timmons, G.-G. Li et al., Synthesis *2004*, 2479-84; with phosphomolybdic acid/hexadecyltrimethylammonium bromide and inexpensive Chloramine-T (cf. *55*, 159s*67*) s. G.D.K. Kumar, S. Baskaran, Chem. Commun. *2004*, 1026-7; with 5,10,15,20-tetraphenylporphyrinatoiron(III) chloride and Bromamine-T s. R. Vyas, X.-P. Zhang et al., Org. Lett. *6*, 1907-10 (2004).

Cupric triflate/(S,S)-1,8-bis(4-isopropyl-Δ^2-oxazolin-2-yl)anthracene
N-Sulfonylaziridines from ethylene derivs.
Improved copper-catalyzed asym. conversion

186.

A novel chiral, bidentate bis(Δ^2-oxazoline) ligand, based on the anthracene skeleton (AnBOX) affords the highest enantioselectivities to date (up to >99%) for the copper-catalyzed asym. aziridination **of chalcones**, the face selectivity being opposite to that recorded with Evan's (S,S)-2,2-bis(4-phenyl-Δ^2-oxazolin-2-yl)propane. **E:** A stirred soln. of 1.5 eqs. of chalcone, 6 mol% (S,S)-1,8-bis(4-isopropyl-Δ^2-oxazolin-2-yl)anthracene and 5 mol% [CuOTf]$_2$·(C$_6$H$_6$) in methylene chloride treated portionwise with 1 eq. phenyl(tosylimino)iodinane under N$_2$ at 24° over 2 h, then stirred at the same temp. for 3 h → product. Y 80% (e.e. 96%). Reaction is facilitated by electron-donating groups in the benzene ring, the high enantioselectivity being associated with coordination of the carbonyl oxygen with copper. F.e.s. J. Xu, L. Ma, P. Jiao, Chem. Commun. *2004*, 1616-7.

Cupric sulfate s.a. under NaN$_3$ CuSO$_4$

Cupric sulfate/1,10-phenanthroline/potassium phosphate   ←
N-Alk-1-ynylation with α,β-acetylenebromides   NH → NC≡C
s. *65*, 172s*67*; of sultams s. S. Hirano, H. Urabe, F. Sato et al., Org. Lett. *6*, 727-30 (2004).

Cuprous iodide/cesium acetate   CsI/CsOAc
Cuprous iodide/ethylenediamine/potassium phosphate   ←
Cuprous iodide/1,10-phenanthroline/potassium fluoride-alumina
Copper(I)-catalyzed N-arylation   NH → NAr
of 2-oxazolidones with CuI/1,2-diaminocyclohexane/K$_2$CO$_3$ cf. *62*, 171s*65*; with CuI/ethylenediamine/K$_3$PO$_4$, also partial conversion, s. M.V. Nandakumar, Adv. Synth. Catal. *346*, 954-8 (2004); of 2-pyridones s. C.S. Li, D.D. Dixon, Tetrahedron Lett. *45*, 4257-60 (2004); of carboxylic acid amides with CuI/1,10-phenanthroline/KF$_2$-Al$_2$O$_3$ s. R. Hosseinzadeh, H. Mehdinejad et al., Synlett *2004*, 1517-20; of sulfoximines with CuI/CsOAc s. G.-Y. Cho, C. Bolm et al., Org. Lett. *6*, 3293-6 (2004).

Cuprous iodide/N,N-dimethylglycine/cesium carbonate   ←
Copper(I)-catalyzed N-vinylation   NH → NC≡C
of acylamines with CuI/N,N'-dimethylethylenediamine/K$_2$CO$_3$ cf. *47*, 337s*66*; with CuI/N,N-dimethylglycine/Cs$_2$CO$_3$ s. X.-H. Pan, Q. Cai, D.-W. Ma, Org. Lett. *6*, 1809-12 (2004); α-acylamino-α,β-ethylenecarboxylic acid esters with [Cu(MeCN)$_4$]PF$_6$/tetramethyl-1,10-phenanthroline/Ru$_2$CO$_3$ s. C. Han, J.A. Porco Jr. et al., Org. Lett. *6*, 27-30 (2004); s.a. R.S. Coleman, P.-H. Liu, ibid. 557-80.

Cuprous iodide/1,2-diphenyl-3,4-bis[(2,4,6-tri-tert-*butylphenyl)phosphinidene]-* ←
cyclobutene/potassium tert-*butoxide*
Ar. amines from halides NH → NAr
Copper(I)-catalyzed N-arylation in the absence of solvent

187.

Air- and moisture-resistant sp^2-*hybridized* phosphorus ligands have been used for the first time in copper-catalyzed N-arylation. **E:** Bromobenzene and 1 eq. 1,2,3,4-tetrahydroisoquinoline added to a mixture of 1 eq. *t*-BuOK, 2 mol% CuI, and 2 mol% 1,2-diphenyl-3,4-bis[(2,4,6-tri-*tert*-butylphenyl)phosphinidene]cyclobutene at room temp. under argon, and stirred at 100° for 12 h → product. Y 94%. The method is applicable to the N-arylation of aliphatic prim. amines and cyclic sec. amines, and of certain prim. and sec. ar. amines (incl. *o*-methoxyaniline), with ar. bromides or chlorides. Ar. amines and ar. bromides possessing electron-withdrawing groups, however, failed to react. F.e. and intramolecular N-arylation, **also tert. diarylamines** from prim. amines (with 2 eqs. ar. iodide), s. A.S. Gajare, M. Yoshifuji, F. Ozawa et al., Chem. Commun. *2004*, 1994-5.

Silver nitrate $AgNO_3$
Aliphatic nitro compds. from halides Hal → NO_2
with $AgNO_3/(MeO)_3P$ cf. *37*, 369; from prim. halides **in water** with $AgNO_3$ s. R. Ballini, L. Barboni, G. Giarlo, J. Org. Chem. *69*, 6907-8 (2004).

Boron fluoride BF_3
3,1,5-Benzoxadiazepines from *o*-diamines and two carboxylic acid chloride molecules

188.

The startg. *o*-phenylenediamine added to a soln. of *2 eqs.* benzoyl chloride in dry dioxane at 0°, warmed to room temp., stirred for 30 min, a soln. of BF_3-etherate in the same dry solvent added, and refluxed for 1-2.5 h at 130° → product. Y 92%. Isolation of the intermediate N,N'-diacyl derivs. is not required. The corresponding **benzimidazoles** were generated using 1 eq. of the acid chloride reactant. F.e.s. V.K. Tandon, M. Kumar, Tetrahedron Lett. *45*, 4185-7 (2004).

α-*Pinene* ←
2,5-Oxazolidiones from α-aminocarboxylic acids
and phosgene in toluene cf. *6*, 461; in ethyl acetate with α-pinene, retention of configuration, s. F. Cornille et al., European patent EP-1201659 (Isochem SA).

Imidazolium ionic liquids s. under *KOH, KF*, and $Cu(acac)_2$ ←
N,N-Dimethylglycine s. under *CuI* Me_2NCH_2COOH
L-*Proline* s. under NaN_3 *Pro-OH*

Trimethylsilyl chloride Me_3SiCl
N-Acylation of nucleoside bases via O-trimethylsilylation NH → NAc
N-benzoylation cf. *1*, 374s66; N-acylation of the guanosine amino group at C_6 (without base) s. Y. Fan, B.L. Gaffney, R.A. Jones, Org. Lett. *6*, 2555-7 (2004).

Zirconyl chloride or Bismuth oxide chloride $ZrOCl_2$ or $BiOCl$
N-Acylation s. *68*, 110

Hydrogen peroxide/hydrogen bromide/N-sodio compd.
N-Tosylaziridines from ethylene derivs.
Metal-free procedure in aq. medium

189.

A stirred soln. of 20 mol% H_2O_2 (30% aq.) in acetonitrile treated under N_2 with 20 mol% HBr (48% aq.), 4-methylstyrene, 1.2 eqs. Chloramine-T trihydrate and $MgSO_4$ at 25°, and stirring continued for 3.5 h → product. Y 80%. The procedure is simple, mild, inexpensive and environmentally friendly, being facilitated by electron-donating groups on the benzene ring. The presence of $MgSO_4$ as dehydrating agent is essential. Reaction appears to involve initial generation of HOBr as a source of bromonium ions. F.e.s. S.L. Jain, V.B. Sharma, B. Sain, Tetrahedron Lett. *45*, 8731-2 (2004).

Phosphomolybdic acid/hexadecyltrimethylammonium bromide
1-Tosylaziridines from ethylene derivs. s. *55*, 159s68

Hexadecyltrimethylammonium bromide s. under *Phosphomolybdic acid* $[C_{16}H_{33}NMe_3]Br$
Hydrogen bromide s. under H_2O_2 HBr

5,10,15,20-Tetraphenylporphyrinatoiron(III) chloride
1-Tosylaziridines from ethylene derivs. s. *55*, 159s68

Palladous acetate/N,N'-bis(2,6-diisopropylphenyl)imidazolidin-2-ylidene/sodium hydride/tert-butanol
Benzo-condensed N-aryl-N-heterocyclics from ω-(o-halogen)amines and ar. halides via palladium-catalyzed intramolecular-intermolecular N-arylation

190.

3 eqs. NaH in anhydrous dioxane treated sequentially with 2 mol% $Pd(OAc)_2$ and 4 mol% N,N'-bis(2,6-diisopropylphenyl)imidazolidin-2-ylidene at room temp. under N_2, heated to 100°, 3 eqs. *tert*-butanol in dioxane injected into the mixture dropwise, stirred at 100° for 15 min, the startg. *o*-chloroamine in the same solvent injected, allowed to react at the same temp. for 2 h (with TLC monitoring), 1.2 eqs. chlorobenzene in dioxane injected, heating continued at 100° for 8 h, then cooled, treated with silica and concentrated → product. Y 91%. This novel intramolecular-intermolecular adaptation of Hartwig-Buchwald N-arylation is based on a robust catalyst [not requiring an excess of the ligand], and is generally applicable to the synthesis of a wide range of N-arylated 5-, 6- and 7-membered heterocyclics. F.e.s. R. Omar-Amrani, R. Schneider, Y. Fort, Synthesis *2004*, 2527-34.

Palladous acetate/2-(dicyclohexylphosphino)-2',4',6'-triisopropylbiphenyl/sodium tert-butoxide/microwaves
N-Arylation under microwave irradiation   NH → NAr
of amines with 2-(dicyclohexylphosphino)-2'-(dimethylamino)biphenyl cf. *65*, 17s66; diarylamines with 2-(dicyclohexylphosphino)-2',4',6'-triisopropylbiphenyl s. T.A. Jensen, N.M. Skjaerbaek et al., J. Org. Chem. *69*, 4936-47 (2004); N-arylation of sulfoximines with ar. chlorides using BINAP as ligand and Cs_2CO_3 as base s. M. Harmata, X.C. Hong, S.K. Ghosh, Tetrahedron Lett. *45*, 5233-6 (2004).

Palladous acetate/2-(di-tert-butylphosphino)-1-phenylindole/sodium tert-butoxide
Ar. amines from chlorides s. *51*, 171s68   NH → NAr

Palladous acetate/9,9-dimethyl-4,6-bis(diphenylphosphino)xanthene/cesium carbonate
**Imidazole ring from *o*-dihalides and *o*-amino-N-heterocyclics
via intermolecular-intramolecular N-arylation**

191.

Dipyrid[1,2-a;3',2'-d]imidazoles. A mixture of 1 eq. 2-chloro-3-iodopyridine, 1 eq. of the startg. cyclic amidine, 6 mol% Pd(OAc)$_2$, 12 mol% xantphos and *4 eqs.* Cs$_2$CO$_3$ in anhydrous toluene refluxed for 17 h → product. Y 82%. This is the first example of a tandem intermolecular-intramolecular Hartwig-Buchwald N-arylation. F.e. incl. benzo- and aza-analogs, also with BINAP as ligand, s. K.J.T. Loones, B.U.W. Maes et al., Chem. Commun. *2004*, 2466-7.

***meso*-Acylaminoporphyrins** s. *64*, 175s68

Palladous acetate or bis(dibenzylideneacetone)palladium(0) or tris(dibenzylideneacetone)-dipalladium/dicyclohexyl(5-methyl-2-p-tosyl)phosphine or bis[2-(diphenylphosphino)-phenyl] ether or 2,2'-bis(diphenylphosphino)-1,1'-binaphthyl or 1,3,5,7-tetramethyl-6-phenyl-2,4,8-trioxa-6-phosphaadamantane or 2-(dicyclohexylphosphino)-2'-(dimethyl-amino)biphenyl/cesium carbonate or sodium tert-*butoxide*
Ar. amines from halides   NH → NAr
updates s. *51*, 171s66; *52*, 171s66; tert. ar. amines with dicyclohexyl(5-methyl-2-*p*-tosyl)-phosphine as ligand s. R.A. Singer, W.M. Simon et al., Tetrahedron Lett. *45*, 4715-8 (2004); diarylamines with bis[2-(diphenylphosphino)phenyl] ether as ligand s. R. Csuk, A. Barthel, C. Raschke, Tetrahedron *60*, 5735-50 (2004); 2,2'-di(2-pyridyl)amines with BINAP as ligand s. C. Bolm et al., Tetrahedron Lett. *45*, 5019-21 (2004); general procedure with 1,3,5,7-tetramethyl-6-phenyl-2,4,8-trioxa-6-phosphaadamantane s. D. Gerristma, A. Capretta et al., ibid. 8319-21; N-[het]arylpiperazines with 2-(dicyclohexylphosphino)-2'-(dimethylamino)biphenyl s. D. Michalik, M. Beller et al., ibid. 2057-61.

*Tris(dibenzylideneacetone)dipalladium/tri-*tert-*butylphosphine or 9,9-dimethyl-4,6-bis(diphenylphosphino)xanthene/cesium carbonate*
N-Arylation
of ureas and lactams cf. *59*, 173s62, and of O-alkylamidoximes cf. *59*, 173s64; of **sulfamides** s. L. Alcaraz, S.M. Thom et al., Org. Lett. *6*, 2705-8 (2004); with *t*-Bu$_3$P as ligand s. K. Muniz, M. Nieger, Synlett *2005*, 149-51; N-arylation of a fluorous benzophenone imine *en route* to **prim. ar. amines** (with BINAP as ligand) s. C.L. Cioffi, M.L. Berlin, R.J. Herr, ibid. *2004*, 841-5.

Tris(dibenzylideneacetone)dipalladium/bis[2-(diphenylphosphino)phenyl] ether/cesium carbonate
**Indoles from *o*-bromo-β-styryl triflates and prim. amines
Palladium-catalyzed cascade ring closure**

192.

A mixture of 2.5 mol% Pd$_2$(dba)$_3$, 6 mol% bis[2-(diphenylphosphino)phenyl] ether and 2.5 eqs. Cs$_2$CO$_3$ suspended in anhydrous toluene under N$_2$, 2-(2-bromophenyl)cyclohexen-1-yl triflate and 1.2 eqs. aniline added under N$_2$, and heated at 100° for 20 h → product. Y 83%. The same catalyst facilitates coupling of the amine with both the triflate group and the aromatic bromide. N-Acyl-, N-carbalkoxy-, N-sulfonyl- and N-alkylideneamino-indoles were obtained similarly with the appropriate N-unsubst. nucleophile in the presence of xantphos as ligand. F.e. incl. N-alkylindoles and 7-azaindoles s. M.C. Willis, G.N. Brace, I.P. Holmes, Angew. Chem. Int. Ed. Engl. *44*, 403-6 (2005).

Tris(dibenzylideneacetone)dipalladium/2-(dicyclohexylphosphino)-2'- ←
(dimethylamino)biphenyl/sodium tert-*butoxide*
Palladium-catalyzed N-vinylation NH → NC═C
of sec. amines with α,β-ethylenebromides using BINAP as ligand cf. *64*, 175; with α,β-ethylenechlorides using 2-(dicyclohexylphosphino)-2'-(dimethylamino)biphenyl as ligand, also azomethines from prim. amines, s. J. Barluenga et al., Chem. Commun. *2004*, 1400-1; *meso*-acylaminoporphyrins with Pd(OAc)$_2$/xanthos/Cs$_2$CO$_3$ s. G.-Y. Gao, Y. Chen, X.-P. Zhang, Org. Lett. *6*, 1837-40 (2004).

Palladacyclic sec. phosphine complexes ←
Ar. amines from chlorides NH → NAr
with palladacyclic phosphine-phosph[in]ite complexes cf. *51*, 171s*66*; with a palladacyclic bis(2-norbornyl)phosphine complex for coupling non-activated or deactivated ar. chlorides with prim. or sec. [incl. hindered] amines s. U. Nettekoven, H.-U. Blaser et al., Synlett *2004*, 2549-52; coupling of activated or unactivated ar. and hetar. chlorides with Pd(OAc)$_2$/2-(di-*tert*-butylphosphino)-1-phenylindole as ligand s. F. Rataboul, M. Beller et al., Chem. Eur. J. *10*, 2983-90 (2004).

Sulfur ↑   NC ↓↑ S

Without additional reagents w.a.r.
Replacement of hydroxyl by carbalkoxyamino groups OH → NHCOOR
N-glycosylurethans from aldoses with Burgess'-type reagents cf. *67*, 187; β-carbalkoxyamino-α-methylenecarboxylic acid esters from Baylis-Hillman adducts, also regioisomeric α-(carbalkoxyaminomethyl)-α,β-ethylenecarboxylic acid esters with added NaH, s. M. Mamaghani, A. Badrian, Tetrahedron Lett. *45*, 1547-50 (2004).

Replacement of sulfonyl by amino groups SO$_2$R → N<
preferential replacement s. *16*, 505; 2-aminopyrimidines s. R. Green et al., World Intellectual Property Organisation patent WO-2002296886 (Glaxo Group, Ltd.); 3-amino-1,2,4-triazine ring and f. nucleophiles s. M. Mojzych, A. Rykowski, Heterocycles *63*, 1829-38 (2004).

Guanidines from isothioureas N-C(═N-)SR → N-C(═N-)N<
s. *5*, 346; N,N''-bis(*o*-halogenocarbobenzoxy)guanidines with added DMAP s. T. Gers, J. Izdebski et al., Synthesis *2004*, 37-42; cyclic guanidines from isothiouronium salts, enhanced procedure under microwave irradiation, s. H. Sandin, M.-L. Swanstein, E. Wellner, J. Org. Chem. *69*, 1571-80 (2004); N-acylguanidines s. Vol *61* (p. 93).

4*H*-1,2,4-Triazoles from acylhydrazines and thioiminoesters ○
from thioiminoester hydroiodides under microwave irradiation with NH$_4$OAc/SiO$_2$ cf. *28*, 404s*65*; from crude thioiminoesters in refluxing *n*-butanol s. M.H. Klingele, S. Brooker, Eur. J. Org. Chem. *2004*, 3422-34.

Microwaves [\\\\]
Cyclic guanidines from isothiouronium salts s. *5*, 346s*68* ←

4*H*-1,2-Diazepines from thiopyrylium salts s. *68*, 159 ○

Polymer-based 2-chloropyridinium halide/triethylamine ←
N,N''-Di(carbo-*tert*-butoxy)guanidines from amines NH(C═NCOOBu-*t*)NHCOOBu-*t*
and N,N'-di(carbo-*tert*-butoxy)thiourea with polymer-based carbodiimide cf. *48*, 367s*65*, and with Et$_3$N cf. *49*, 343s*52*; with polymer-based 2-chloropyridinium halide/Et$_3$N s. E. Convers, H. Tye, M. Whittaker, Tetrahedron Lett. *45*, 3401-4 (2004).

Remaining Elements ↑   NC ↓↑ Rem

Without additional reagents w.a.r.
N-Protected ar. 2-aminoethers from aziridines and triaryl borates s. *68*, 114 ○

Microwaves s. under Cu(OAc)$_2$ [\\\\]

Cupric acetate/potassium fluoride/alumina/microwaves   Cu(OAc)$_2$/KF-Al$_2$O$_3$/[\\\\]
Cupric acetate/air   Cu(OAc)$_2$/O$_2$
N-Arylation with arylboronic acids   NH → NAr
of imides with Cu(OAc)$_2$/O$_2$ s. *55*, 166s66; of amines, amides, imides and sulfonamides s. J.-B. Lan, X.-Q. Yu, R.-G. Xie et al., Synlett *2004*, 1095-7; of aliphatic amines and prim. ar. amines with Cu(OAc)$_2$/KF-Al$_2$O$_3$, rapid procedure under microwave irradiation in the absence of solvent, also with Na-tetraphenylborate, s. P. Das, B. Basu, Synth. Commun. *34*, 2177-84 (2004).

Polymer-based copper(II) carboxylate/triethylamine ←
Heterogeneous arylation with arylboronic acids under mild conditions ←

193.

Selective N-arylation. 1.5 eqs. Polymer-based Cu(II)-acetate, 3 eqs. *p*-tolylboronic acid, crushed 4 Å molecular sieves, 2.6 eqs. Et$_3$N and anhydrous methylene chloride added to the startg. amine, and agitated vigorously for 24 h with exposure to air → product. Y 75% (purity 85%). The immobilized complex, based on a modified Wang resin, is air-stable, inexpensive, and can be simply recycled with minimal loss of activity. Electron-donating and -withdrawing groups in the aromatic ring were tolerated, and acylamino and hydroxyl groups were left intact. Reaction is presumed to involve generation of an active polymer-based copper(III) species. F.e., **also O-arylation of phenols**, s. G.C.H. Chiang, T. Olsson, Org. Lett. *6*, 3079-82 (2004).

Silver(I) triflate/(R)-2,2'-bis(diphenylphosphino)-1,1'-binaphthyl   AgOTf/(R)-BINAP
α-(Hydroxylamino)ketones from enoxystannanes   C(OSn≤)=C → CO-C-N(OH)R
Asym. conversion

194.

A soln. of nitrosobenzene in 1,2-diethoxyethane and 1 eq. of the startg. tri-*n*-butyltin enolate added sequentially to 4 mol% [AgOTf]$_2$·(R)-BINAP complex (generated in 1,2-diethoxyethane by mixing AgOTf with (R)-BINAP in *5:2* proportion) under argon at -78° [out of direct sunlight], stirred for 2 h at the same temp., then quenched by addition of chilled brine → product. Y 97% (regiospecificity >99%, e.e. 98%). Interestingly, the regioisomeric chiral α-(aminooxy)ketones were obtained predominantly with the 1:1 complex, [AgOTf]·(R)-BINAP (cf. *66*, 119, 119s67). F.e. and comparison of silver salts, also characterization of the complexes, s. N. Momiyama, H. Yamamoto, J. Am. Chem. Soc. *126*, 5360-1 (2004).

Trimethylsilyl chloride s. under NH$_4$NO$_3$ *Me$_3$SiCl*

Ammonium nitrate/trimethylsilyl chloride
Ar. nitro compds. from arylboronic acids
ipso-**Nitration under mild conditions**

NH_4NO_3/Me_3SiCl
$B(OH)_2 \rightarrow NO_2$

195.

A soln. of 4-bromophenylboronic acid in methylene chloride treated with 2.2 eqs. NH_4NO_3 and 2.2 eqs. trimethylsilyl chloride, the mixture stirred vigorously at room temp. for 48 h, then filtered → product. Y 96%. The active nitrating agent is thought to be *in situ*-generated trimethylsilyl nitrate, reaction being applicable to a range of functionalized arylboronic acids and uncomplicated by further nitration. F.e. and with $AgNO_3$ s. G.K.S Prakash, G.A. Olah et al., Org. Lett. *6*, 2205-7 (2004).

Dichlorotris(triphenylphosphine)ruthenium(II)
N-Tosylaldimines from aldehydes under mild conditions

$RuCl_2(PPh_3)_3$
$CHO \rightarrow CH{=}NTs$

196.

5 Mol% $RuCl_2(PPh_3)_3$ added to a stirred suspension of benzaldehyde and 1 eq. triphenylphosphine N-tosylimine in anhydrous methylene chloride at 20° under N_2, and stirring continued for 6 h at the same temp. → product. Y 75%. Reaction is thought to involve generation of a ruthenium imido species, and is favoured by electron-withdrawing substituents in the benzene ring. F.e.s. S.L. Jain, V.B. Sharma, B. Sain, Tetrahedron Lett. *45*, 4341-3 (2004).

Carbon ↑   NC ↓↑ C

Without additional reagents
Sec. from tert. amines via urethans
s. *23*, 479; via N-carbopropargyloxyamines s. R.G. Bhat, Y. Ghosh, S. Chandrasekaran, Tetrahedron Lett. *45*, 7983-5 (2004).

w.a.r.
$>NR \rightarrow >NCOOR'$
←

Microwaves s. under Na_2CO_3, KF and TsOH

[\\\\]

Lithium amides/lithium diisopropylamide
Carboxylic acid amides from α-arylketones s. *68*, 149

$LiNR_2/i\text{-}Pr_2NLi$
$CO\text{-}C(Ar) \rightarrow CON{<}$

Sodium carbonate/microwaves
4(3H)-Quinazolones from 3,1-benzoxazine-2,4-diones
and carboxylic acid amides s. *28*, 418; rapid procedure under microwave irradiation with Na_2CO_3 in aq. DMF s. J. Azizian, A.R. Karimi et al., J. Chem. Res. Synop *2004*, 435-7; N-condensed 4(3H)-quinazolones from lactams with $KF\text{-}Al_2O_3$ in dimethylacetamide under microwave irradiation s. Heterocycles *63*, 791-5 (2004); **from prim. amines and orthocarboxylic acid esters** under microwave irradiation in the absence of solvent with TsOH s. M. Dabiri, A.A. Mohammadi et al., ibid. 1417-21.

$NaCO_3/[\\\\]$

Potassium carbonate
Replacement of chlorine by dimethylamino groups
with DMF s. *24*, 491; replacement of activated chlorine, e.g. in *o*-nitrochlorides, with K_2CO_3 s. A. Agarwal, P.M.S. Chauhan, Synth. Commun. *34*, 2925-30 (2004).

K_2CO_3
$Cl \rightarrow NMe_2$

Cesium carbonate
Urethans from trichloroacetylamines s. *68*, 15

Cs_2CO_3
$NCOCCl_3 \rightarrow NCOOR$

Potassium fluoride/alumina/microwaves KF/Al$_2$O$_3$/[\\\\]
N-Condensed 4(3H)-quinazolones from 3,1-benzoxazine-2,4-diones and lactams ←
s. *28*, 418s68

1,8-Diazabicyclo[5.4.0]undec-7-ene *dbu*
N-Sulfonylureas from sulfonylamines and imidodicarbonates N(COOR)$_2$ → NHCONHSO$_2$R'

197.

A soln. of 23.4 g dbu in acetonitrile added dropwise at 20° to a stirred soln. of 32.7 g startg. sulfonamide and 53.2 g startg. diphenyl imidodicarbonate in the same solvent, and stirred for 1 h at room temp. → 36.9 g product. Y 60%. F.e. with retention of ether groups s. K. Müller et al., German patent DE-10111649 (Bayer AG); s.a. World Intellectual Property Organisation patent WO-2002072560; United States patent US-20040097375.

Trimethylsilyl chloride/triethylamine Me$_3$SiCl/Et$_3$N
Replacement of trichloromethyl by amino groups CCl$_3$ → N<
with Al$_2$O$_3$ under microwave irradiation cf. *22*, 493s66; unsym. oxamides from trichloropyruvamide hydrates (prepared from isonitriles and trichloroacetic anhydride) with Me$_3$SiCl/Et$_3$N s. L. El Kaim, L. Gaultier, L. Grimaud et al., Tetrahedron Lett. *45*, 8047-8 (2004).

p-Toluenesulfonic acid/microwaves TsOH/[\\\\]
4(3H)-Quinazolones from 3,1-benzoxazine-2,4-diones, orthocarboxylic acid esters ○
and prim. amines under microwave irradiation in the absence of solvent s. *28*, 418s68

Elimination ⇑

Hydrogen ↑ NC ⇑ H

Microwaves s. under Chloramine-T [\\\\]

Carbon/acetic acid/oxygen C/AcOH/O$_2$
Pyridines from 1,4-dihydropyridines ←
heterogeneous conversion with polymer-based phenyl iodosoacetate cf. *25*, 649s67; with 50% activated carbon in acetic acid under O$_2$, also pyrazoles from Δ^2-pyrazolines, s. N. Nakamichi, Y. Kawashita, M. Hayashi, Synthesis *2004*, 1015-20.

Phenyl iodosoacetate s. under Rhodium(II) carboxylates PhI(OAc)$_2$

Chloramine-T/microwaves p-TolSO$_2$N(Cl)Na/[\\\\]
N-Condensed 1,2,4-triazole ring from hydrazones ○
with PhI(OAc)$_2$ cf. *19*, 554s67; rapid procedure under microwave irradiation in ethanol with Chloramine-T s. K. Mogilaiah, G.R. Reddy, J. Chem. Res. Synop *2004*, 145-7.

Hexamethyleneammonium fluorochromate ←
Pyridines from 1,4-dihydropyridines s. *42*, 235s68 ←

Chiral rhodium(II) α-imidocarboxylates/phenyl iodosoacetate/magnesium oxide ←
Regiospecific asym. intramolecular amination of unactivated hydrocarbon groups ○
with sulfamic acid esters using chiral carbonylruthenium(II) porphyrin complexes/PhI(OAc)$_2$/Al$_2$O$_3$ cf. *64*, 183; with chiral naphthalene-1,8-dicarboxylic acid-based rhodium(II) α-imidocarboxylates/PhI(OAc)$_2$/MgO, also intramolecular aziridination (cf. *66*, 214), s. C. Fruit, P. Müller, Tetrahedron:Asym. *15*, 1019-26 (2004); intramolecular asym. amination **with sulfonic acid amides** s. Helv. Chim. Acta *87*, 1607-15 (2004).

Dichloro(pentamethylcyclopentadienyl)rhodium(III) dimer/acetone/potassium carbonate
Benzolactams from ω-(o-aminoaryl)alcohols
Rhodium(III)-catalyzed oxidative ring closure

198.

Oxindoles. A mixture of 10 mol% K_2CO_3, 3.2 mol% [Cp*RhCl$_2$]$_2$ and the startg. *o*-aminophenethyl alcohol in acetone refluxed for 20 h under argon → product. Y 52%. Reaction, which is facilitated by electron-withdrawing groups, is applicable to 5-, 6- and 7-membered benzolactams and is highly selective with no evidence of intramolecular N-alkylation. An Oppenauer-type oxidation is invoked with acetone as H-acceptor, the same catalyst facilitating both dehydrogenation of the alcohol as well as the intermediate hemiaminal. F.e. and comparison of Rh-catalysts and bases s. K. Fujita, R. Yamaguchi et al., Org. Lett. *6*, 2785-8 (2004).

Oxygen ↑   NC ⇑ O

Microwaves s. under K_2CO_3, Zn and $(EtO)_3P$ [\\\\]

Sodium hydride   NaH
N-Sulfonylaziridines from 2-(sulfonylamino)mesylates
Chiral N-sulfonylaziridines s. *68*, 142

Potassium hydroxide   KOH
Pyridine ring by cyclodehydration
s. *13*, 526; quinolines from *o*-aminoarylethynylcarbinols via β-(*o*-aminoaryl)-α,β-ethyleneketones with KOH s. C.S. Cho, S.C. Shim et al., J. Heterocycl. Chem. *41*, 409-11 (2004).

Potassium hydroxide/tetra-n-butylammonium iodide/benzyl bromide   ←
Aldoximes from prim. nitro compds. under mild conditions $CH_2NO_2 \rightarrow CH{=}NOH$

199.

Chiral aldoximes. A soln. of 1 eq. of the startg. chiral nitroalkane in anhydrous THF treated successively under argon at room temp. with 5 mol% *n*-Bu$_4$NI, 1.1 eqs. benzyl bromide, and 1.05 eqs. KOH, and stirred at the same temp. for 3 h → product. Y 80%. This mild, inexpensive and environmentally friendly procedure [without a heavy metal!] is applicable to a wide range of electron-deficient and -rich nitroarenes, hetar. nitro compds., and branched and unbranched (incl. quaternary) aliphatic nitro compds., reaction taking place *without racemization* of chiral centres. A one-pot preparation of **chiral nitriles** was also effected by *in situ*-dehydration of the aldoximes on addition of trifluoroacetic anhydride or SOCl$_2$ (4.5 eqs.) with 9 eqs. Et$_3$N as base (at -20° over 12 h). F.e.s. C. Czekelius, E.M. Carreira, Angew. Chem. Int. Ed. Engl. *44*, 612-5 (2005).

Potassium carbonate/microwaves K_2CO_3/[\\\\]
Hydantoins from α-ureidocarboxylic acid esters
polymer-based synthesis cf. *31*, 452s*53*; soln.-phase procedure with PEG-based substrates under microwave irradiation in methylene chloride with K_2CO_3 s. M.-J. Lee, C.-M. Sun, Tetrahedron Lett. *45*, 437-40 (2004).

Lithium chloride s. under Cp_2ZrMe_2   LiCl

Zinc/acetic acid Zn/AcOH
Zinc/ammonium chloride/microwaves Zn/NH$_4$Cl/[\\\\]
Lactams from nitrocarboxylic acid esters O
2-pyrrolidones cf. *19*, 561; 2*H*-1,4-benzoxazin-3(4*H*)-ones s. T. Bird, World Intellectual Property Organisation patent WO-200285868 (Astra Zeneca UK Ltd.); soln.-phase polymer-based synthesis of chiral 3,4-dihydro-2(1*H*)-quinoxalones from PEG-supported substrates with Zn/NH$_4$Cl under microwave irradiation in methanol s. C.-L. Tung, C.-M. Sun, Tetrahedron Lett. *45*, 1159-62 (2004).

N,N'-Carbonyldiimidazole (Im)$_2$CO
Azetidines from 3-aminoalcohols
with Ph$_3$PBr$_2$ cf. *26*, 471s*30*; with N,N'-carbonyldiimidazole, also higher cyclic amines, s. A. Munch, B. Wendt, M. Christmann, Synlett *2004*, 2751-5.

Acetic acid AcOH
Imidazole ring from N-acyl-*o*-diamines O
with H$_3$PO$_4$/P$_2$O$_5$ cf. *21*, 543; soluble polymer-based synthesis of benzimidazoles from PEG-supported substrates with acetic acid, also benzoxazoles from *o*-acylaminophenols, and benzothiazoles from *o*-acylaminomercaptans, s. C. Chen, Y.-J. Chen, Tetrahedron Lett. *45*, 113-5 (2004).

S,S-Dimethyl dithiocarbonate/triethylamine (MeS)$_2$CO/Et$_3$N
Pivaloyl chloride/pyridine t-BuCOCl/C$_5$H$_5$N
Nitriles from aldoximes CH=NOH → CN
with PhCOCl in pyridine cf. *4*, 457; with *t*-BuCOCl in pyridine, also from carboxylic acid amides, s. A.V. Narsaiah, K. Nagaiah, Adv. Synth. Catal. *346*, 1271-4 (2004); general procedure with (MeS)$_2$CO/Et$_3$N (cf. *42*, 416s*49*) s. T.A. Khan, H. Ila, H. Junjappa et al., Synlett *2004*, 2019-21; with 2-chloropyridine methiodide s. K. Lee, S. Hong et al., Synth. Commun. *34*, 1775-82 (2004).

Bromobenzene s. under KOH PhBr
Chloranil s. under Trifluoroacetic anhydride ←

Trimethylsilyl bromide/ammonium sulfate/hexamethyldisilazane ←
Δ^2-1,2,4-Triazolines O
from acylureas and hydrazines cf. *20*, 320; f. method from N^1-formylsemicarbazides with hexamethyldisilazane and Me$_3$SiBr/(NH$_4$)$_2$SO$_4$ s. X.H. Huang, N.Y. Shih et al., Org. Lett. *6*, 4795-8 (2004).

Dimethylzirconocene/lithium chloride Cp$_2$ZrMe$_2$/LiCl
Nitriles from N-unsubst. carboxylic acid amides CONH$_2$ → CN

200.

A mixture of 1 eq. LiCl, 1 eq. of the startg. amide, and 1.1 eqs. dimethylzirconocene in anhydrous THF-d$_8$ heated in a sealed NMR tube under N$_2$ at 105° for 15 h → product. Y 93%. Chloride ion is essential to convert the intermediate methylzirconium amide to the corresponding N-acylimidozirconium complex prior to reductive elimination. F.e. incl. aliphatic nitriles s. R.T. Ruck, R.G. Bergman, Angew. Chem. Int. Ed. Engl. *43*, 5375-7 (2004).

Stannous chloride SnCl$_2$
Cyclic hydroxylamines from nitroketones O
with Pd-C cf. *24*, 525s*66*; polymer-based synthesis of 1-hydroxyindoles from α-(*o*-nitroaryl)-ketones with SnCl$_2$ s. A.D. Roy, S. Sharma et al., Org. Lett. *6*, 4763-6 (2004).

Triethyl phosphite/microwaves $(EtO)_3P/[\\\\]$
Indoles from *o*-nitrostyrenes
with $(EtO)_3P$ s. *40*, 315; rapid procedure under microwave irradiation in the absence of solvent, carbazoles and condensed indoles, s. P. Appukkuttan, E. Van der Eycken, W. Dehaen, Synlett *2005*, 127-33.

Phosphorus oxide chloride/triethylamine $POCl_3/Et_3N$
2-Azetidinones from β-aminocarboxylic acids
with Ph_2POCl cf. *42*, 420s*43*; with $POCl_3/Et_3N$ s. S.D. Sharma, R.D. Anand, G. Kaur, Synth. Commun. *34*, 1855-62 (2004).

3-ω-(Chlorosulfonyl)imidazolium ionic liquids   ←
Nitriles from aldoximes in ionic liquids s. *61*, 74s*68*   CH=NOH → CN

Tetra-n-*butylammonium iodide* s. under KOH Bu_4NI

2-Chloropyridine methiodide
Nitriles from aldoximes s. *4*, 457s*68*   ←

Iron   Fe
Quinolines by reductive ring closure
of (Z)-*o*-nitrocinnamaldehydes with $FeSO_4/NH_3$ cf. *10*, 394; of *o*-nitroaryl(vinyl)carbinols with F.e.s. D. Basavaiah, J.S. Rao, R.J. Reddy, J. Org. Chem. *69*, 7379-82 (2004).

Tetrakis(triphenylphosphine)palladium(0)/triethylamine $Pd(PPh_3)_4/Et_3N$
**Imidazoles from N-allyl-O-acylamidoximes
via palladium-catalyzed intramolecular amination**

201.

A soln. of 1 eq. of the startg. N-allyl-O-(pentafluorobenzoyl)amidoxime and 5 eqs. Et_3N in anhydrous DMF treated under argon at room temp. with 10 mol% $Pd(PPh_3)_4$, stirred at 80° for 30 min, then quenched with water → product. Y 70%. This is the first example of an imidazole synthesis involving a metal-catalyzed C-N bond formation, reaction taking place by initial oxidative addition of Pd(0) to the N-O bond, followed by olefin insertion, elimination of palladium hydride and isomerization. There was no racemization of chiral centres. F.e.s. S. Zaman, K. Mitsuru, A.D. Abell, Org. Lett. *7*, 609-11 (2005).

Bis(η³-allylpalladium chloride)/chiral polymer-based N,N'-bis[o-(diphenylphosphino)-   ←
benzoyl]-1,2-diamines
Palladium-catalyzed intramolecular N-allylation with desymmetrization
s. *51*, 188s*63*; heterogeneous procedure with chiral polymer-based N,N'-bis[*o*-(diphenylphosphino)benzoyl]-1,2-diamines s. B.M. Trost et al., Angew. Chem. Int. Ed. Engl. *41*, 4691-3 (2002).

Nitrogen ↑   NC ⇑ N

Sodium iodide   NaI
Lactams from azidocarboxylic acid esters
Also fused 4(3H)-quinazolones from N-(*o*-azidoaroyl)lactams s. *48*, 346s*68*.

Zinc/ammonium formate $Zn/HCOONH_4$
Cyclic azomethines from azidoaldehydes
with Al/NH_4Cl cf. *13*, 539s*67*; with $Zn/HCOONH_4$ s. A. Kamal, K.S. Reddy et al., Tetrahedron Lett. *45*, 6517-21 (2004).

Halogen ↑ NC ⇑ Hal

Sodium hydride NaH
Lactams from halogenocarboxylic acid amides ○
s. *22*, 528; 2-piperidones from γ-bromocarboxylic acid amides s. L.T. Liu et al., United States patent US-2002169323.

Potassium tert-*butoxide* KOBu-t
N-Heterocyclics from bromamines
with NaOMe cf. *11*, 573; pyrroles from 1-amino-4-bromo-1,4-dienes with KOBu-*t* s. A.S. Demir, D.M. Akhmedov, O. Sesenoglu, Tetrahedron *58*, 9793-9 (2002).

Triethylamine Et_3N
Nitriles from prim. N,N-dichloramines s. *68,* 139 $CH_2NCl_2 \rightarrow CN$

Palladous acetate/2,2'-bis(diphenylphosphino)-1,1'-binaphthyl/cesium carbonate ←
Palladium-catalyzed intramolecular N-arylation ○
with $Pd_2(dba)_3$/BINAP/Cs_2CO_3 cf. *51*, 190s*61*; dibenzo[*b,e*][1,4]diazepinones with $Pd(OAc)_2$ s. E.M. Beccalli, C. Zoni et al., Tetrahedron *61*, 61-8 (2005); N-sulfonylindazoles with $Pd_2(dba)_3$/*o*-Tol_3P/Cs_2CO_3 (cf. *51*, 190s*63*) s. K. Inamoto, T. Sakamoto et al., Chem. Lett. *33*, 1026-7 (2004).

Sulfur ↑ NC ⇑ S

Cuprous chloride/ethyldiisopropylamine/Celite ←
2-Aminobenzimidazoles from *o*-aminothioureas ○
with MeI cf. *29*, 476s*30*; with CuCl/*i*-Pr_2NEt/Celite s. X.-J. Wang, C.H. Senanayake et al., Tetrahedron Lett. *45*, 7167-70 (2004).

Carbon ↑ NC ⇑ C

Trichloroisocyanuric acid/sodium hydroxide or pyridine ←
Nitriles from α-aminocarboxylic acids $CH(NH_2)COOH \rightarrow CN$
Oxidative decarboxylation

202.

1 eq. Solid trichloroisocyanuric acid added over 30 min through a funnel to a stirred soln. of 1.17 eqs. L-isoleucine and ca. 3 eqs. pyridine in water (exothermic), stirred at room temp. for 3 h, and quenched with solid $NaHSO_3$ → product. Y 77% (GC purity 99.9%). F.e. and in methanol s. G.A. Hiegel, J.C. Lewis, J.W. Bae, Synth. Commun. *34*, 3449-53 (2004); with aq. NaOH as base s. *68,* 139.

Formation of Hal-C Bond

Uptake ⇓

Addition to Oxygen and Carbon HalC ⇓ OC

o-Phenylenediamine [or Phenylhydrazine] o-$C_6H_4(NH_2)_2$ *[or $PhNHNH_2$]*
1,2-Halogenhydrins from epoxides $\overset{\diagdown_O\diagup}{} \rightarrow C(Hal)C(OH)$
Regio- and stereo-specific ring opening under mild conditions
1,2-bromo- and 1,2-iodo-hydrins with macrocyclic crown dilactams cf. *55*, 175; with *o*-phenylenediamine s. H. Eshghi, S.F. Tayyari, E. Sanchuli, Monatsh. Chem. *135*, 1101-11 (2004); 1,2-

bromohydrins with phenylhydrazine as catalyst, also with simultaneous ar. bromination, s. M. Soroka et al., Synthesis *2003*, 2341-4.

Magnesium bromide $MgBr_2$
1,2-Bromohydrins from epoxides ▽O → C(Br)C(OH)
regio- and stereo-specific ring opening with $Mg(NO_3)_2/Bu_4NBr$ cf. *49*, 398; with $MgBr_2$ s. J.D. Ha et al., Tetrahedron Lett. *45*, 5969-72 (2004).

Zirconium tetrachloride $ZrCl_4$
1,2-Chlorohydrins from epoxides ▽O → C(Cl)C(OH)
with $TiCl_4$ cf. *41*, 457s*67*; with $ZrCl_4$ s. G. Smitha, C.S. Reddy, J. Chem. Res. Synop *2004*, 300-1.

Phenylhydrazine s. under o-Phenylenediamine $PhNHNH_2$

Addition to Nitrogen and Carbon HalC ⇓ NC

Boron fluoride/isopropanol $BF_3/i\text{-}PrOH$
2-Fluoramines from aziridines ▽N → C(F)C(N<)
regio- and stereo-specific ring opening of N-aryl-, N-sulfonyl- and N-acyl-aziridines with KF/ Bu_4NHSO_4 cf. *24*, 582s*67*; details s. J. Org. Chem. *69*, 335-8 (2004); with BF_3-etherate/*i*-PrOH s. C.-H. Ding, L.-X. Dai, X.-L. Hou, Synlett *2004*, 2218-20.

Bis(trichloromethyl) carbonate/dimethylformamide $(Cl_3CO)_2CO/DMF$
Phosphorus tribromide/dimethylformamide PBr_3/DMF
Tetra-n-butylammonium halides/β-cyclodextrin ←
2-Halogenosulfonylamines from N-sulfonylaziridines ▽N → C(Hal)C(NHTs)
with hydrogen halides and β-cyclodextrin cf. *67*, 207; with tetra-*n*-butylammonium halides and β-cyclodextrin, regio- and stereo-specific ring opening, s. M. Narender, K.R. Rao et al., Tetrahedron Lett. *45*, 7995-7 (2004); with triphosgene-, oxalyl chloride- or PBr_3-DMF complexes s. M.K. Pandey, A. Bisai, V.K. Singh, ibid. 9661-3.

Addition to Carbon-Carbon Bonds HalC ⇓ CC

Without additional reagents *w.a.r.*
1,2-Ethylene-1,2-diiodides from acetylene derivs. in water C≡C → C(I)=C(I)
with CO_2 as catalyst cf. *13*, 561s*67*; without additive, also replacement of hydrogen by iodine with added H_2O_2, s. M. Jereb, M. Zupan, S. Stavber, Chem. Commun. *2004*, 2614-5.

1,2-Ethylene-1,2-chloroiodides from acetylene derivs. C≡C → C(Cl)=C(I)
via addition of $TeCl_4$ cf. *37*, 446; regiospecific formation of (E)-isomers by addition of ICl, also iodinative ring closures, s. F. Bellina et al., J. Org. Chem. *68*, 10175-7 (2003).

Polymer-based synthesis of (E)-2-halogenenol tosylates C≡C → C(Hal)=C(OTs)
from acetylene derivs.

203.   Ph—≡ + (P)—⟨⟩—I(OH)OTs →[I_2] Ph\C=C/I with TsO

2 eqs. Polymer-based phenyl iodoso(hydroxy)tosylate added in one portion to a stirred mixture of the startg. acetylene deriv. and 0.6 eq. iodine in anhydrous methylene chloride at room temp., and worked up after 12 h by washing with 5% Na_2SO_3 → product. Y 95%. The protocol is simple and mild, and the supported reagent can be simply recovered and regenerated without loss of activity. F.e., also bromo- and chloro-derivs. with NBS and NCS, respectively, s. J.-M. Chen, X. Huang, Synthesis *2004*, 1577-80.

Cuprous triflate *CuOTf*
2-Chlorosulfonylamines from ethylene derivs. C=C → C(Cl)C($NHSO_2R$)
with CuOTf/N-chloro-N-sodio-2-nitrobenzenesulfonamide cf. *24*, 555s*62*; with CuOTf/N,N-dichloro-*p*-toluenesulfonamide, *anti*-β-chloro-α-tosylaminoketones from α,β-ethyleneketones,

effect of substitution on regioselectivity, s. D.-J. Chen, C. Timmons, G.E. Li et al., Eur. J. Org. Chem. *2004*, 3097-101.

Cuprous triflate/1-n-butyl-3-methylimidazolium fluoroborate   *CuOTf/[bmim]BF$_4$*
2-Chlorosulfonylamines from ethylene derivs. in ionic liquids   C=C → C(Cl)C(NHSO$_2$R)

204.

Regiospecific conversion with asym. induction. 1.1 eqs. N,N-Dichloro-*p*-toluenesulfonamide added to a mixture of the startg. chiral N-(α,β-ethyleneacyl)-2-oxazolidone, 10 mol% CuOTf, 4 Å molecular sieves, and anhydrous 1-*n*-butyl-3-methylimidazolium fluoroborate, the reaction vial capped, stirred at room temp. for 12 h, then quenched with satd. aq. Na$_2$SO$_3$ → product. Y 70% (d.r. 7:1). Reaction is presumed to involve nucleophilic ring opening of an intermediate aziridinium ion, a non-chelation model being advanced to explain the stereoselectivity. Interestingly, there was no conversion in traditional organic solvents. F.e.s. X. Xu, J.F. Cannon, A. D. Headley et al., Org. Lett. *6*, 4881-4 (2004); *anti*-β-chloro-α-tosylaminocarboxylic acid esters in the same solvent s. S.R.S.S. Kotti, A.D. Headley et al., Tetrahedron Lett. *45*, 7209-12 (2004).

*Silver triflate/2,6-di-*tert-*butyl-4-methylpyridine*   ←
α-Iodoacetals from enolethers   C=C(OR) → C(I)C(OR)(OR')
with NIS cf. *44*, 154; improved procedure with I$_2$/AgOTf/2,6-di-*tert*-butyl-4-methylpyridine, oligosaccharide derivs., s. I. Cumpstey, C.M.P. Seward et al., Tetrahedron:Asym. *15*, 3207-21 (2004).

Cadmium acetate or Ammonium acetate   *Cd(OAc)$_2$ or NH$_4$OAc*
1,2-Acoxyiodides from ethylene derivs.   C=C → C(I)C(OAc)

205.

Regiospecific conversion. A soln. of 1 eq. iodine in glacial acetic acid added dropwise to a mixture of 0.5 eqs. Cd(II)-acetate and 1-hexene in the same solvent at 25°, stirred for 15 min, and the ethereal extract rinsed with satd. aq. NaHCO$_3$ and aq. 5% Na$_2$S$_2$O$_3$ → product. Y 91%. The procedure is convenient, economical and generally applicable to acyclic and cyclic ethylene derivs., the latter affording *trans*-adducts. F.e.s. Y.Y. Myint, M.A. Pasha, J. Chem. Res. Synop *2004*, 333-5; with I$_2$/NH$_4$OAc in acetic acid (cf. *43*, 456), regio- and stereo-selectivity, s. Synth. Commun. *34*, 4477-82 (2004); with tetraphenylphosphonium iodide cf. A.Y. Koposov, V.V. Boyarskikh, V.V. Zhdankin, Org. Lett. *6*, 3613-5 (2004).

Imidazolium ionic liquids s. under CuOTf   ←
Diethyl azodicarboxylate s. under Titanium tetrahalides   ROOCN=NCOOR

4,4'-Bis(dichloroiodo)biphenyl   *ArICl$_2$*
1,2-Alkoxyhalides from ethylene derivs.   C=C → C(OR)C(Hal)
1,2-alkoxychlorides with PhICl$_2$ cf. *46*, 432s64; also 1,2-alkoxyiodides, 1,2-iodohydrins and 1,2-iodochlorides with added I$_2$ s. M.S. Yusubov et al., Synth. Commun. *34*, 443-50 (2004); 1,2-alkoxyiodides with I$_2$/4,4'-bis(dichloroiodo)biphenyl, and addition to acetylene derivs., s. M.S. Yusubov, L.A. Drygunova, V.V. Zhdankin, Synthesis *2004*, 2289-92.

N-Halogenosuccinimides   *NCS or NBS*
Polymer-based synthesis of (E)-2-halogenenol tosylates   C≡C → C(Hal)=C(OTs)
from acetylene derivs. s. *68*, 203

N-Bromosuccinimide (s.a. under $Cp_2Zr(H)Cl$) NBS
δ-Bromo-γ-tosylaminosulfoxides from γ,δ-ethylene-*N*-tosylsulfilimines ←
via stereospecific 1,4-S→C-tosylamino group migration with inversion of S-chirality

206.

Chiral δ-bromo-β-hydroxy-γ-tosylaminosulfoxides. A mixture of the startg. sulfilimine, 1.3 eqs. NBS and 1.2 eqs. water in toluene stirred at room temp. until reaction complete → product. Y 90% (*syn/anti* >95:<5). Regio- and stereo-specific functionalization of the allyl alcohol is thereby achieved, reaction taking place via intramolecular nucleophilic attack of the nitrogen function on an intermediate bromonium ion. The procedure is fast, clean and high-yielding. F.e.s. S. Raghavan et al., Tetrahedron Lett. *45*, 7231-4 (2004).

Chlorobis(cyclopentadienyl)hydridozirconium/N-bromosuccinimide $Cp_2Zr(H)Cl/NBS$
α,β-Ethylenehalides from acetylene derivs. via hydrozirconation   C≡C → CH=C(Hal)
α,β-ethylenebromides from terminal acetylene derivs. with $Cp_2Zr(H)Cl/NBS$ cf. *43*, 625s*46*; (E)-1-iodoenestannanes and (Z)-1-bromoenestannanes from acetylenestannanes with I_2 and NBS, respectively, s. M.Z. Cai et al., Chin. Chem. Lett. *15*, 257-60 (2004); (Z)-α,β-ethylene-α-halogeno- from α,β-acetylene-phosphonic acid esters s. ibid. 386-8.

Titanium tetrahalides/diethyl azodicarboxylate $TiHal_4/ROOCN=NCOOR$
3,4-Ethylene-1,3-dihalides from alkylidenecyclopropanes   C̋
diiodides with CuI (or CuI_2) and dibromides with $CuBr_2$ cf. *66*, 225; also dihalides with the appropriate Ti(IV) halides and DEAD, and f. methods, s. L.-X. Shao, L.-J. Zhao, M. Shi, Eur. J. Org. Chem. *2004*, 4894-900.

Tetraphenylphosphonium iodide Ph_4PI
1,2-Acoxyiodides from ethylene derivs. s. *68*, 205   C=C → C(I)C(OAc)

Exchange   ⇅

Hydrogen ↑   HalC ⇅ H

Without additional reagents   w.a.r.
α-Bromination of ketones   H → Br
in ether cf. *4*, 486; of acetophenones *in methanol* s. J. Goswami, A. Goswami, J. Indian Chem. Soc. *79*, 469-71 (2002).

2-α-Iodo-2,3-dihydrofurans from γ,δ-ethyleneketones   ○
with Na_2CO_3 cf. *44*, 414s*65*; improved procedure in dry acetonitrile *without base*, *trans*-selectivity, s. R. Antonioletti, S. Malancona, P. Bovicelli, Heterocycles *63*, 1573-6 (2004).

Lithium hydride   LiH
Halogeno-N-heterocyclics by intramolecular halogenamination
s. *48*, 434s*60*, *64*; of N-(ethyleneacyl)ureas with LiH/I_2, asym. induction, s. M.H. Shen, C.Z. Li, J. Org. Chem. *69*, 7906-9 (2004); 6-iodomethyl-5,6-dihydro-4*H*-1,3-thiazines from 3-ethylenethioacylamines, stereoselectivity, s. T. Murai, H. Niwa, F. Shibahara et al., Chem. Lett. *33*, 508-9 (2004); 5-α-iodo-Δ²-oxazolines from carboxylic acid N-allylamides with NIS s. R. Galeazzi, S. Rinaldi et al., Org. Lett. *6*, 2571-4 (2004).

sec-Butyllithium/hexachloroethane $s\text{-}BuLi/CCl_3CCl_3$
Regiospecific ar. halogenation via lithiation   H → Hal
s. *55*, 182s*67*; 5-chlorination of 4-halogeno-7-azaindoles with s-BuLi/CCl_3CCl_3, also f. electrophiles, s. A. L'Heureux, C. Thibault, R. Ruel, Tetrahedron Lett. *45*, 2317-9 (2004).

Lithium acetate
4-Halogeno-5-hydroxy-2(5H)-furanones from α-allenecarboxylic acids LiOAc

207.

A mixture of the startg. allenecarboxylic acid, 1.2 eqs. LiOAc·2H$_2$O and 2 eqs. iodine in THF stirred at room temp. for 3 h, and the resulting 4-iodo-2(5H)-furanone heated in DMF at 40° under O$_2$ (1 atm.) for 36 h → product. Y 87%. Reaction is thought to involve an intermediate 5-hydroperoxy-4-iodo-2(5H)-furanone. F.e. and with CsOAc, also 4-bromo- and 4-chloro-analogs via halolactonization with CuBr$_2$ and CuCl$_2$, respectively, s. S. Ma, B. Wu, Z. Shi, J. Org. Chem. 69, 1429-31 (2004).

Potassium bromide s. under N′-Chloromethyl-N-fluoro-1,4-diazonia- KBr
  bicyclo[2.2.2]octane bis(fluoroborate)
Sodium iodide s. under H$_2$O$_2$ NaI
Potassium iodide s. under H$_2$O$_2$, H$_2$SO$_4$ and [BnPPh$_3$]HSO$_5$ KI
Cupric triflate/N-halogenosuccinimide/2,2-bis(4(S)-tert-butyl-Δ^2-oxazolin-2-yl)propane ←
Asym. α-halogenation of β-ketocarboxylic acid esters H → Hal

208.

A soln. of 10 mol% Cu(OTf)$_2$ and 10 mol% 2,2-bis(4(S)-*tert*-butyl-Δ^2-oxazolin-2-yl)propane in ether stirred under N$_2$ for 1 h at room temp., the startg. β-keto ester and 1.2 eqs. N-chlorosuccinimide added, and stirring continued for 16 h → product. Y 98% (e.e. 77%). The procedure is generally applicable to the asym. α-chlorination and -bromination [with NBS] of acyclic and cyclic β-keto esters. The face-selectivity derives from bidentate coordination of the substrate (in enolate form) to the metal in such a way that the *Si*-face is exposed to the incoming halogenating agent. F.e.s. M. Marigo, N. Kumaragurubaran, K.A. Jørgensen, Chem. Eur. J. *10*, 2133-7 (2004).

Calcium carbonate s. under 1-Benzyl-4-aza-1-azoniabicyclo[2.2.2]octane tribromide CaCO$_3$
Lithium triisobutyl(2,2,6,6-tetramethylpiperidino)aluminate Li[i-Bu$_3$AlNR$_2$]
o-**Alumination under mild conditions** ←

209.

1 eq. 4-iodobenzonitrile added dropwise to a soln. of 2.2 eqs. Li-triisobutyl(2,2,6,6-tetramethyl-piperidino)aluminate [prepared by treating 2.2 eqs. 2,2,6,6-tetramethylpiperidine in dry THF at -78° under argon with 2 eqs. 2.17 M *n*-BuLi in hexane, stirring at 0° for 10 min, adding 0.95 M *i*-Bu$_3$Al at -78° and stirring at 0° for 30 min] at -78°, stirred at room temp. for 3 h, a soln. of 8 eqs. iodine in dry THF added at -78°, allowed to warm to 0° over 1 h, and quenched with satd. aq. NaHS$_2$O$_3$ and satd. aq. NH$_4$Cl → product. Y 90%. *o*-Alumination takes place exclusively with phenolethers, ar. nitriles, ar. amides, and ar. halides, *o*- and *m*-dichlorobenzenes leading to **1,2,3-**

trisubst. benzenes *without* formation of benzyne intermediates. Trifluoromethylarenes, however, underwent *m*-alumination. Reaction proceeds **via lithium aryl(triisobutyl)aluminates,** which were characterized, and converted to a variety of substituted arenes by quenching with electrophiles, and by subsequent Cu- and Pd-catalyzed cross-coupling. F.e. and conversion to **phenols,** also regiospecific alumination of π-rich heteroarenes, s. M. Uchiyama et al., J. Am. Chem. Soc. *126,* 10526-7 (2004).

2-Nitrobenzoic acid s. under NCS	*ArCOOH*
Diphenyl diselenide s. under NBS	*PhSeSePh*
Hexachloroethane s. under s-BuLi	*CCl₃CCl₃*
N-Halogenosuccinimide s.a. under Cu(OTf)₂	*NCS*

N-Chlorosuccinimide/(4R,5R)-4,5-diphenylimidazolidine/2-nitrobenzoic acid   ←
Organocatalyzed asym. α-chlorination of ketones   H → Cl
with NCS/(R,R)-2,5-diphenylpyrrolidine cf. *67,* 212; with NCS/(4R,5R)-4,5-diphenylimidazolidine/2-nitrobenzoic acid s. M. Marigo, K.A. Jørgensen et al., Angew. Chem. Int. Ed. Engl. *43,* 5507-10 (2004).

N-Chlorosuccinimide/benzeneselenyl chloride   *NCS/PhSeCl*
Replacement of hydrogen by chlorine
(E)-β,γ-ethylenechlorides cf. *67,* 213; α-chlorination of ketones and β-ketocarboxylic acid esters s. C. Wang, J. Tunge, Chem. Commun. *2004,* 2694-5.

N-Bromosuccinimide   *NBS*
3-Halogenoindoles from *o*-acetyleneamines   ○
3-iodo-1-tosyl-derivs. with I₂/K₂CO₃ cf. *65,* 197s67; N-unsubst. derivs. with Br₂ or NBS, s. A. Arcadi, G. Bianchi, F. Marinelli, Synthesis *2004,* 610-8.

N-Bromosuccinimide/diphenyl diselenide   *NBS/PhSeSePh*
Halogenolactonization
s. *33,* 477s57, *60;* β-bromo-γ-lactones from β,γ- or γ,δ-ethylenecarboxylic acids with NBS and *a little* PhSeSePh (cf. *67,* 213) s. S.R. Mellegaard, J.A. Tunge, J. Org. Chem. *69,* 8979-81 (2004).

N-Iodosuccinimide (s.a. under Ti(OPr-i)₄)   *NIS*
5-α-Iodo-Δ²-oxazolines from carboxylic acid N-allylamides s. *48,* 434s68

N,N-Dibromobenzenesulfonamide   *PhSO₂NBr₂*
Replacement of hydrogen by bromine   H → Br
ar. and benzylic bromination with N,N'-dibromo-N,N'-1,2-ethylenebis(2,5-dimethylbenzenesulfonamide) cf. *22,* 565s58; bromination of carbonyl compds., nitro compds. and alkynes with N,N-dibromobenzenesulfonamide s. M. Tajbakhsh, A. Khazaei et al., Phosphorus, Sulfur Silicon Relat. Elem. *179,* 1159-63 (2004).

Trichloroisocyanuric acid/phosphorus trichloride   ←
α-Chlorination of carboxylic acids   H → Cl
with LDA/CCl₄ cf. *42,* 463; with trichloroisocyanuric acid and *a little* PCl₃ s. G.A. Hiegel et al., Synth. Commun. *34,* 889-93 (2004).

N'-Chloromethyl-N-fluoro-1,4-diazoniabicyclo[2.2.2]octane bis(fluoroborate)/   ←
potassium bromide
α-Bromination of α,β-ethyleneoxo compds. in aq. medium s. *38,* 669s68   H → Br

Benzeneselenyl chloride s. under NBS   *PhSeCl*

Titanium tetraisopropoxide/(R)-1,1'-bi-2-naphthol/N-iodosuccinimide   ←
Asym. intramolecular 1,2-iodooxylation   ○
asym. iodolactonization with Ti(OPr-i)₄/chiral TADDOLs/pyridine/I₂ cf. *48,* 440; chiral 2-(α-iodo)tetrahydrofurans from 4-ethylenealcohols with Ti(OPr-i)₄/(R)-BINOL/NIS s. S.H. Kang, M. Kim et al., Synlett *2004,* 1279-81.

Phosphorus trichloride s. under Trichloroisocyanuric acid   *PCl₃*

Hydrogen peroxide   *H₂O₂*
Replacement of hydrogen by iodine s. *13,* 561s68   H → I

Hydrogen peroxide/sodium iodide/sulfuric acid $H_2O_2/NaI/H_2SO_4$
α-Iodoketones from sec. alcohols   CH(OH)CH → C(O)C(I)
Metal-free procedure in water

210. [reaction scheme: cyclododecanol → [cyclododecanone] → α-iodocyclododecanone, reagents [IOH], −HI, then HI, H_2O_2]

A mixture of 1.05 eqs. NaI, 20 eqs. H_2O_2 (33% aq. soln.), 1.25 eqs. sulfuric acid and cyclododecanol in water stirred for 16 h at 60° → product. Y 90%. The procedure is inexpensive, environmentally friendly, simple and generally applicable to acyclic and cyclic ketones, acylophenones reacting sluggishly. F.e. and acidic reagents (H_3PO_4 or Amberlyst-15), **also from** the intermediate **ketones**, s. J. Barluenga et al., Chem. Commun. *2004*, 2616-7.

Hydrogen peroxide/ammonium bromide H_2O_2/NH_4Br
Oxidative ar. bromination   H → Br
monobromination with $KHSO_5/NH_4Br$ cf. *44*, 420s67, and with $PhI(OAc)_2/LiBr$ cf. *47*, 431s67; with H_2O_2/NH_4Br s. K.V.V.K. Mohan, K.V. Raghavan et al., Synth. Commun. *34*, 2143-52 (2004); ar. bromination of electron-rich arenes with $(Bu_4N)_2S_2O_8/LiBr$ or Br_2 s. M.Y. Park, Y.H. Kim et al., Tetrahedron Lett. *45*, 4887-90 (2004); **ar. chlorination** with $KHSO_5/NH_4Cl$ (cf. *43*, 431s63) s. N. Narender, S.J. Kulkarni et al., Indian J. Chem. *43B*, 1335-8 (2004).

Hydrogen peroxide/hydrogen chloride H_2O_2/HCl
α,α-Dihalogenoketones from ketones CH_2 → $CHal_2$
with phosphorus/hydrogen halides cf. *8*, 602; α,α-dichloroacetophenones with H_2O_2/HCl s. A.O. Terent'ev, G.I. Nikishin et al., Synthesis *2004*, 2845-8.

Hydrogen peroxide/potassium iodide/sulfuric acid $H_2O_2/KI/H_2SO_4$
Sulfuric acid/potassium iodide H_2SO_4/KI
Poly(4-vinylpyridinium) persulfate   ←
Benzyltriphenylphosphonium peroxymonosulfate/potassium iodide $[BnPPh_3]HSO_5/KI$
Oxidative ar. iodination   H → I
with $KHSO_5/KI$ cf. *47*, 431, and with $[BuPPh_3]_2S_2O_8$ (and I_2) cf. *38*, 669s65; with $H_2O_2/KI/H_2SO_4$ s. J. Iskra, S. Stavber, M. Zupan, Synthesis *2004*, 1869-73; of electron-rich arenes with KI and concd. H_2SO_4 *as oxidant* s. M.A. Pasha, Y.Y. Myint, Synth. Commun. *34*, 2829-33 (2004); with poly(4-vinylpyridinium) persulfate cf. H. Tajik, I. Mohammadpoor-Baltork, H.R. Rasht-Abadi, ibid. 3579-85; monoiodination of phenols with benzyltriphenylphosphonium peroxymonosulfate/KI cf. A.R. Hajipour, H. Adibi, J. Chem. Res. Synop *2004*, 294-5.

Potassium peroxymonosulfate/ammonium chloride $KHSO_5/NH_4Cl$
Oxidative ar. chlorination s. *43*, 431s68   H → Cl

Potassium peroxymonosulfate/hydrogen halides/triethylamine $KHSO_5/HHal/Et_3N$
α-Halogenation of α,β-ethylenecarbonyl compds.   H → Hal
of α,β-ethyleneketones with Na-halides/Amberlyst/dimethyldioxirane cf. *38*, 699s57; also of α,β-ethylene-aldehydes and -carboxylic acid esters with $KHSO_5/HCl$ (or HBr)/Et_3N s. K.M. Kim, I.H. Park, Synthesis *2004*, 2641-4; α-bromination of α,β-ethyleneoxo compds. in aq. media with N'-chloromethyl-N-fluoro-1,4-diazoniabicyclo[2.2.2]octane bis(fluoroborate)/KBr s. C.F. Ye, J.M. Shreeve, J. Org. Chem. *69*, 8561-3 (2004).

Sodium iodate/sulfuric acid $NaIO_3/H_2SO_4$
Ar. iodination   H → I
with $KIO_3/KI/HCl$ cf. *47*, 431s66; of deactivated arenes with $NaIO_3/I_2/H_2SO_4$, also diiodination s. L. Kraszkiewicz, M. Sosnowski, L. Skulski, Tetrahedron *60*, 9113-9 (2004).

Ammonium chloride s. under $KHSO_5$ NH_4Cl
Ammonium bromide s. under H_2O_2 NH_4Br

1-Methyl- or 1-Butyl-3-methyl-imidazolium tribromide   *[Hmim]Br$_3$ or [bmim]Br$_3$*
Ar. bromination in ionic liquids   H → Br
in N-pentylpyridinium tribromide cf. *67*, 215; in 1-methylimidazolium or 1-*n*-butyl-3-methylimidazolium tribromide, also benzylic bromination, s. C. Chiappe, E. Leandri, D. Pieraccini, Chem. Commun. *2004*, 2536-7; of ar. amines in 1-*n*-butyl-3-methylimidazolium tribromide s. Z.-G. Le, Q.-G. Zheng et al., Synthesis *2004*, 2809-12.

1-Benzyl-4-aza-1-azoniabicyclo[2.2.2]octane tribromide/calcium carbonate   ←
Ar. bromination of ar. amines
with pyridinium tribromide cf. *48*, 447; with 1-benzyl-4-aza-1-azoniabicyclo[2.2.2]octane tribromide/CaCO$_3$ s. A.R. Hajipour, H. Imanieh, S.A. Pourmousavi, Synth. Commun. *34*, 4597-604 (2004).

Benzyltrimethylammonium dichloroiodate   *[BnNMe$_3$]ICl$_2$*
Ar. iodination   H → I
with [Me$_4$N]ICl$_2$ cf. *43*, 421s65; with benzyltrimethylammonium dichloroiodate for 6-iodination of 5,7-dioxyflavones s. J. Quintin, G. Lewin, Tetrahedron Lett. *45*, 3635-8 (2004).

Bis(pyridine)iodine(I) fluoroborate/fluoroboric acid   *[Py$_2$I]BF$_4$/HBF$_4$*
Regio- and stereo-specific synthesis of benzo-condensed iodoheterocyclics   O
via iodocarbocyclization

211.

3-Iodochromans from allyl phenolethers. 1 eq. Bis(pyridine)iodine fluoroborate in methylene chloride stirred at room temp. under N$_2$ for 5 min, cooled to -40°, 1.5 eqs. HBF$_4$ in ether added, the mixture stirred for an additional 10 min, treated with the startg. allyl phenolether, stirring continued for 3 h (with TLC monitoring), then quenched with a mixture of crushed ice and water → product. Y 95%. Interestingly, *at -90°* the intermediate iodonium ion rearranged to give the isomeric 2-phenyl derivs., the rearranged products also being obtained directly from allyl phenolethers possessing a trisubst. ethylenic residue. F.e., **also 3-iodo-1-sulfonyl-1,2,3,4-tetrahydroquinolines** from N-aryl-2-ethylenesulfonylamines, and benzo-condensed bicyclics by double ring closure, s. J. Barluenga et al., J. Am. Chem. Soc. *126*, 3416-7 (2004).

Hydrogen halides s. under H$_2$O$_2$ and KHSO$_5$ *HHal*

Oxygen↑   HalC ↓↑ O

Microwaves s. under KI and Ph$_3$P   [\\\\]

Lithium halides/sodium hydrogen sulfate/silica gel   *LiHal/NaHSO$_4$/SiO$_2$*
β,γ-Ethylenehalides from 2-ethylenealcohols   C=C-C(Hal)
Regio- and stereo-specific conversion with allyl shift s. *62*, 194s68

Sodium iodide s.a. under ZrCl$_4$ *NaI*

Sodium iodide/Amberlyst 15   ←
Potassium iodide/p-toluenesulfonic acid/microwaves   *KI/TsOH/*[\\\\]
Iodides from alcohols   OH → I
with NaI/MeSO$_3$H cf. *62*, 195; with NaI/Amberlyst 15, selectivity, s. M. Tajbakhsh, R. Hosseinzadeh, Z. Lasemi, Synlett *2004*, 635-8; benzyl iodides with KI/TsOH under microwave

irradiation in the absence of solvent (cf. *60*, 180s66) s. J.C. Lee, J.Y. Park, E.S. Yoo, Synth. Commun. *34*, 2095-9 (2004); β,γ-ethylene-bromides and -iodides from 2-ethylenealcohols with allyl shift (cf. *62*, 194) with LiBr or LiI/NaHSO$_4$-on-silica gel, stereoselectivity, s. B. Das, J. Banerjee, N. Ravindranath, Tetrahedron *60*, 8357-61 (2004).

Indium trichloride or tribromide   *InCl$_3$ or InBr$_3$*
2-Halogeno-1,3-dienes from 2-allenealcohols   C(OH)C=C=C → C=C-C(Hal)=C
with PBr$_3$ cf. *19*, 630; chloro- and bromo-derivs. with InCl$_3$ and InBr$_3$, respectively, s. Y.S. Cho et al., Synthesis *2004*, 2620-4.

Bis(trichloromethyl) carbonate/diisopropylamine   *(Cl$_3$CO)$_2$CO/i-Pr$_2$NH*
Halogeno-N-heterocyclics from cyclic N-oxides   ←
with CF$_3$COOH/AcCl cf. *33*, 491; (chloromethyl)pyridines with triphosgene/*i*-Pr$_2$NH s. P. Narendar, V.J. Rao et al., Synth. Commun. *34*, 1097-103 (2004).

Amberlyst 15 s. under NaI   ←
Carbon tetrachloride s. under Triphenylphosphine   *CCl$_4$*
N-Bromosuccinimide s. under Triphenylphosphine   *NBS*
Zirconium tetrachloride/sodium iodide   *ZrCl$_4$/NaI*
Iodides from alcohols   OH → I

212.   BnOH ⟶ BnI

0.5 eq. ZrCl$_4$ added portionwise to a mixture of benzyl alcohol and 1.5 eqs. NaI in anhydrous acetonitrile, stirred at room temp. for 10 min, diluted with 1:1 ether/water, and worked up → product. Y 95%. The procedure is simple, efficient, based on relatively non-toxic reagents, and generally applicable to structurally diverse prim., sec., tert., allylic and benzylic alcohols with straightforward work-up. Diols underwent **partial conversion** under these conditions, and complete conversion to the diiodides with excess of the reagent. F.e.s. H. Firouzabadi, N. Iranpoor, M. Jafarpour, Tetrahedron Lett. *45*, 7451-4 (2004).

Triphenylphosphine/carbon tetrachloride   *Ph$_3$P/CCl$_4$*
5-Chloroimidazoles from α-acylaminonitriles

213.

A mixture of the startg. α-acylaminonitrile and 2.5 eqs. triphenylphosphine in degassed acetonitrile treated with 2.5 eqs. carbon tetrachloride at 45°, and allowed to react for 4.5 h → product. Y 74%. The protocol accommodates a range of functionalized aromatic and aliphatic substrates. F.e.s. Y.-L. Zhong, D. Askin et al., Org. Lett. *6*, 929-31 (2004).

Triphenylphosphine/N-bromosuccinimide/microwaves   *Ph$_3$P/NBS/[\\\\]*
Bromides from alcohols   OH → Br
with Ph$_3$P/NBS cf. *34*, 371; benzyl bromides, rapid procedure under microwave irradiation in the absence of solvent, s. J.C. Lee, E.Y. Hwang, Synth. Commun. *34*, 2959-63 (2004).

Triphenylphosphine dihalides   *Ph$_3$PHal$_2$*
α,β-Ethylenehalides from enol phosphates   C=C(OPO(OR)$_2$) → C=C(Hal)

214.

1.2 eqs. Triphenylphosphine dichloride added to a stirred soln. of 4-methyl-1,4-benzoxazepin-5(4*H*)-on-3-yl diethyl phosphate in anhydrous acetonitrile at room temp. under argon, and stirring continued for 2 h → product. Y 91%. The method is applicable to acyclic and cyclic enol phosphates, and work-up is simple. Reaction appears to involve intermediate formation of an O-phosphoryloxonium species. F.e. and α,β-ethylenebromides s. K. Kamei, N. Maeda, T. Tatsuoka, Tetrahedron Lett. *46*, 229-32 (2005).

Bismuth oxide chloride/thionyl chloride   *BiOCl/SOCl$_2$*
α-Glycosyl chlorides from acyl glycosides   OAc → Cl
with BiCl$_3$/Me$_3$SiCl cf. *25*, 396s*53*; with BiOCl/SOCl$_2$ s. R. Ghosh, A. Chakraborty, S. Maiti, Tetrahedron Lett. *45*, 9631-4 (2004).

Thionyl chloride s. under BiOCl   *SOCl$_2$*
Sodium hydrogen sulfate/silica gel s. under LiHal   *NaHSO$_4$/SiO$_2$*
p-Toluenesulfonic acid s. under KI   *TsOH*

Tungsten hexachloride   *WCl$_6$*
Cyclic α,β-ethylenechlorides from ketones   COCH → C(Cl)=C

215.

1-Chlorocyclohexene ring. 2 eqs. WCl$_6$ added to a soln. of the startg. cyclic ketone in methylene chloride, refluxed for 20 min at 45°, diluted with ether, and poured into 2 *N* NaOH → product. Y 94%. Reaction is notably applicable to hindered cyclohexanone rings, cyclohexanone itself and adamantanone affording the corresponding **cyclic 1,1-dichlorides**. F.e. and with simultaneous formation of **1,2-dichlorides from epoxides,** also with skeletal rearrangement, s. M.E. Jung, J.I. Wasserman, Tetrahedron Lett. *44*, 7273-5 (2003).

1-Methylimidazolium bromide   *[Hmim]Br*
Halides from alcohols in ionic liquids   OH → Hal
in 1-methyl-3-propylimidazolium halides cf. *60*, 182s*65* and with added TsOH under microwave irradiation cf. *62*, 196s*65*; conversion of prim. alcohols, benzyl alcohols and diols in 1-methylimidazolium bromide s. H.-H. Wu, M.-Y. He et al., Chinese J. Chem. *22*, 619-21 (2004).

Nitrogen ↑   HalC ↓↑ N

Ferrous chloride/trimethylsilyl chloride   *FeCl$_2$/Me$_3$SiCl*
5-α-Chloro-2-pyrrolidones
from γ,δ-ethylenecarboxylic acids via acid chlorides and acid azides
Regio- and stereo-specific radical chlorolactamization

216.

One-pot procedure. A soln. of 2-(cyclohex-2-enyl)acetic acid in methylene chloride treated with 1.1 eqs. oxalyl chloride and one drop of DMF, stirred at room temp. for 20 min, the solvent and excess of oxalyl chloride removed *in vacuo*, the resulting acid chloride dissolved in acetone, treated with 2 eqs. aq. NaN$_3$ at -15°, stirring continued for 1.5 h, the solvent removed again *in vacuo*, the resulting acyl azide dissolved in isopropanol, treated with a soln. of 0.2 eq. FeCl$_2$ and 2 eqs. trimethylsilyl chloride in the same solvent, and stirred at -15° for 5 h then at room temp. for 8 h → product. Y 75% (*all-cis*-isomer). *cis*-Addition to the double bond is prevalent, reaction proceeding via a carbon-centred radical generated by 5-*exo-trig* cyclization. F.e. incl. isolated 2-pyrrolidone derivs. s. J. Kluegge, E. Herdtweck, T. Bach, Synlett *2004*, 1199-202.

Halogen ↑   HalC ↓↑ Hal

Potassium fluoride/N''-(1,3-dimethylimidazolidin-2-yl)-N,N,N',N'-tetramethyl-   ←
guanidinium chloride
Potassium fluoride/poly(diallyldimethylammonium chloride)/microwaves   ←
Ar. fluorides from chlorides   Cl → F
with KF/18-crown-6 cf. *4*, 513s67; with KF and 1 mol% N''-(1,3-dimethylimidazolidin-2-yl)-N,N,N',N'-tetramethylguanidinium chloride s. A. Pleschke, G.-V. Röschenthaler et al., J. Fluorine Chem. *125*, 1031-8 (2004); with KF and poly(diallyldimethylammonium chloride), rapid procedure under microwave irradiation in DMSO, cf. J. Luo, W.-C. Qu et al., ibid. 701-4.

Remaining Elements ↑   HalC ↓↑ Rem

Bis[(1S,2R)-2-(1-naphthyl)cyclohexyl] 2,2-dichloromalonate/zirconium tetrachloride   ←
α-Chloroketones from enoxysilanes   C=C(OSi≤) → C(Cl)CO
Asym. conversion under mild conditions

217.

A soln. of 1 eq. bis[(1S,2R)-2-(1-naphthyl)cyclohexyl] 2,2-dichloromalonate in anhydrous methylene chloride cooled to -78°, treated sequentially under N_2 with 1 eq. $ZrCl_4$ and a soln. of 1 eq. of the startg. silyl enolate in the same solvent, stirred at the same temp. for 2 h, then quenched with satd. aq. $NaHCO_3$ → product. Y 90% (e.e. 88%). The Lewis acid significantly enhances the electrophilicity of the chlorine atoms of the chiral reagent, and the diastereoselectivity and face-selectivity is notably dependent on the size of the ester groups. The protocol, applicable to both cyclic and acyclic substrates, is efficient and highly enantioselective, reaction apparently proceeding through a C_2-symmetric 6-membered ring in which zirconium is coordinated to both carbonyl groups of the reagent. F.e. and regeneration of the reagent s. Y. Zhang, K. Shibatomi, H. Yamamoto, J. Am. Chem. Soc. *126*, 15038-9 (2004).

N'-Chloromethyl-N-fluoro-1,4-diazoniabicyclo[2.2.2]octane bis(fluoroborate)/   ←
polymeric dihydroquinines
α-Fluoroketones from enoxysilanes   C=C(OSi≤) → C(F)CO
Asym. conversion
with N-fluorocinchoninium salts in ionic liquids cf. *60*, 186s67; with Selectfluor and readily recyclable polymeric dihydroquinines for improved work-up s. B. Thierry, D. Cahard et al., Synlett *2004*, 856-60.

Zirconium tetrachloride s. under Bis[(1S,2R)-2-(1-naphthyl)cyclohexyl] $ZrCl_4$
2,2-dichloromalonate

Carbon ↑   HalC ↓↑ C

Without additional reagents   w.a.r.
Halogenative ring closure of *o*-functionalized arylacetylenes   ○
3-iodoindoles cf. *62*, 203s67; 1-ethoxy-4-iodo-1*H*-2,1-benzoxaphosphorin P-oxides from *o*-acetylenephosphonic acid esters s. A.Y. Peng, Y.X. Ding, Org. Lett. *6*, 1119-21 (2004).

Formation of S-S Bond

Exchange	↓↑
Hydrogen ↑	**SS ↓↑ H**

Cuprous chloride/kieselguhr/oxygen	←
1,3-Dibromo-5,5-dimethylhydantoin	←
Silica-phosphoric acid/silica/sodium nitrite	←
1,4-Diazabicyclo[2.2.2]octane 1,4-dioxide bis(hydrogen peroxide)	←
Sulfuryl chloride	SO_2Cl_2
1-Butyl-4-aza-1-azoniabicyclo[2.2.2]octane dichromate	←
Hexamethylenetetrammonium fluorochromate	←
γ-Picolinium chlorochromate/silica	←
Sodium bromate/silica-sulfuric acid/silica	$NaBrO_3/SiO_2$-OSO_3H/SiO_2
Sym. disulfides from mercaptans	2 RSH → (RS)$_2$

with Cu(NO$_3$)$_2$ cf. *4, 274s55*; with CuCl-on-kieselguhr under O$_2$ s. M.M. Hashemi, Z. Karimi-Jaberi, D. Ghazanfari, J. Chem. Res. Synop *2004*, 364-5; **solid-state reaction** with 1,3-dibromo-5,5-dimethylhydantoin (cf. *47, 468*) s. A. Khazaei, M.A. Zolfigol, A. Rostami, Synthesis *2004*, 2959-61; with stable, easily-handled 1,4-diazabicyclo[2.2.2]octane 1,4-dioxide bis(hydrogen peroxide) **under** neutral **heterogeneous conditions** s. P. Salehi, M.A. Zolfigol, L.B. Tolami, Phosphorus, Sulfur Silicon Relat. Elem. *179*, 1777-81 (2004); heterogeneously with silica-phosphoric acid (from silica chloride/H$_3$PO$_4$)/wet silica/NaNO$_2$ (2 eqs.) s. M.A. Zolfigol et al., ibid. 2177-82; general procedure with SO$_2$Cl$_2$ **in the absence of solvent** (cf. *22, 588s52*) s. R. Leino, J.E. Lonnqvist, Tetrahedron Lett. *45*, 8489-91 (2004); with 1-butyl-4-aza-1-azoniabicyclo-[2.2.2]octane dichromate (cf. *54, 108s67*) s. A.R. Hajipour, H. Bagheri, A.E. Ruoho, J. Chem. Res. Synop *2004*, 286-7; with γ-picolinium chlorochromate/silica (cf. *39, 480s67*) s. M.M. Khodaei, A. Yazdanipour et al., Synth. Commun. *34*, 3661-6 (2004); with hexamethylenetetrammonium fluorochromate s. *42, 235s68*; with NaBrO$_3$/SiO$_2$-OSO$_3$H/SiO$_2$ s. *29, 233s68*.

Halogen ↑	**SS ↓↑ Hal**
Zinc/sulfuric acid	Zn/H_2SO_4
Sym. disulfides from sulfonic acid chlorides	2 RSO$_2$Cl → (RS)$_2$

with AlI$_3$ cf. *26, 564s41*; with Zn/H$_2$SO$_4$ in toluene/water s. K. Abe, M. Yuguchi, Japanese patent JP-2002241361 (Ube Ind. Ltd.).

Formation of S-Rem Bond

Exchange	↓↑
Oxygen ↑	**SRem ↓↑ O**

Phosphorus pentasulfide/hexamethyldisiloxane/microwaves	$P_2S_5/(Me_3Si)_2O/[\backslash\backslash\backslash\backslash]$
Replacement of P-oxygen by P-sulfur	P=O → P=S

with P$_2$S$_5$ s. *22, 594*; thionophosphoromonoamidates and aminothiophosphoryl dichlorides, rapid procedure under microwave irradiation in the absence of solvent with P$_2$S$_5$/hexamethyldisiloxane s. M. Nivsarkar, A.K. Gupta, M.P. Kaushik, Tetrahedron Lett. *45*, 6863-6 (2004).

Formation of S-C Bond

Uptake ⇓

Addition to Hydrogen and Carbon SC ⇓ HC

Via intermediates v.i.
Replacement of hydrogen by sulfhydryl groups H → SH
via isothioureas cf. *31*, 522; aryl mercaptans via arylbis[2-(carbomethoxy)ethyl]sulfonium triflates and methyl 3-(arylthio)propionates s. J.-M. Becht, A. Wagner, C. Mioskowski, J. Org. Chem. *68*, 5758-61 (2003).

Addition to Oxygen and Carbon SC ⇓ OC

Microwaves s. under NaOH [\\\\]

Sodium hydride NaH
1,3-Oxathiolan-2-ones from epoxides

218. $C_{10}H_{21}$—△—O —CO/S→ $C_{10}H_{21}$—(O-S ring with C=O)

Regiospecific conversion. A mixture of the startg. epoxide, 5 eqs. sulfur and 0.25 eq. NaH in THF heated to 60° under 10 atm. CO for 3 h → product. Y 95%. The method was effective with mono- and 2,2-di-subst. oxiranes, trisubst. derivs. affording low yields. Reaction is presumed to involve insertion of *in situ*-generated COS, which attacks the 3-membered ring from the less hindered face. F.e. and enhanced procedure with added selenium as catalyst s. Y. Nishiyama, C. Katahira, N. Sonoda, Tetrahedron Lett. *45*, 8539-40 (2004).

Sodium hydroxide/microwaves *NaOH/*[\\\\]
2-Hydroxythioethers from epoxides in water ▽_O → C(OH)C(SR)
with aq. NaOH (pH 9) cf. *2*, 532s*67*; under microwave irradiation s. V. Pironti, S. Colonna, Green Chem. *7*, 43-5 (2005).

Ammonium thiocyanate/5,10,15,20-tetrakis(4-hydroxyphenyl)porphyrinatocobalt(II) ←
2-Hydroxythiocyanates from epoxides ▽_O → C(OH)C(SCN)
with NH$_4$SCN/2,6-bis(*o*-aminophenoxymethyl)-4-bromoanisole cf. *59*, 203s*67*; regiospecific ring opening with added 5,10,15,20-tetrakis(4-hydroxyphenyl)porphyrinatocobalt(II) (1 mol%), also f. catalysts, and isolation of thiiranes (cf. *55*, 205s*68*), s. H. Sharghi, A.H. Nejad, M.A. Nasseri, New J. Chem. *28*, 946-51 (2004).

Zinc/cerium(III) chloride/tetra-n-butylphosphonium bromide *Zn/CeCl$_3$/Bu$_4$PBr*
2-Hydroxythioethers from epoxides ▽_O → C(OH)C(SR)
and disulfides with Zn/AlCl$_3$ cf. *59*, 219s*66*; with Zn/CeCl$_3$ in tetra-*n*-butylphosphonium bromide as ionic liquid, regio- and stereo-selectivity, s. A.R. Khosropour, M.M. Khodaei, K. Ghozati, Chem. Lett. *33*, 1378-9 (2004).

1-n-Butyl-3-methylimidazolium fluoroborate *[bmim]BF$_4$*
Sulfonylquinols from quinones and sulfinic acids ←
in water cf. *18*, 638; **in ionic liquids**, e.g. 1-*n*-butyl-3-methylimidazolium fluoroborate, as readily recyclable medium and catalyst s. J.S. Yadav et al., Synthesis *2004*, 1849-53.

Tetrakis(4-hydroxyphenyl)porphyrinatocobalt(II) s. under NH$_4$SCN ←

Addition to Nitrogen and Sulfur SC ⇓ NS

Chloro(1,5-cyclooctadiene)rhodium(I) dimer/potassium iodide [Rh(cod)Cl]$_2$/KI
Tetrahydro-2H-1,3-thiazin-2-ones from isothiazolidines
Rhodium-catalyzed regiospecific carbonylative ring expansion

219.

A mixture of 1 eq. of the startg. N-alkylisothiazolidine, 5 mol% [Rh(cod)Cl]$_2$, and 5 mol% KI in anhydrous toluene purged in an autoclave a few times with CO, pressurized to 1000 psi CO, and stirred at 130° for 24 h → product. Y 85%. Ruthenium and palladium catalysts were effectively unsuitable. Reaction is thought to involve initial oxidative addition of rhodium(I) to the N-S bond, followed by insertion of CO and reductive elimination. F.e.s. C. Dong, H. Alper, Org. Lett. *6*, 3489-92 (2004).

Addition to Nitrogen and Carbon SC ⇓ NC

Ammonium sulfide/microwaves (NH$_4$)$_2$S/[\\\\]
Ammonium sulfide/triethylamine/pyridine (NH$_4$)$_2$S/Et$_3$N/C$_5$H$_5$N
Carboxylic acid thioamides from nitriles CN → CSNH$_2$
with Et$_3$N/H$_2$S cf. *19*, 378; with Et$_3$N/(NH$_4$)$_2$S in pyridine s. L.J. Crane, M. Payard et al., Tetrahedron *60*, 5325-30 (2004); with (NH$_4$)$_2$S in aq. methanol under microwave irradiation s. M.C. Bagley, E.A. Merritt et al., Synlett *2004*, 2615-7.

Bismuth(III) triflate Bi(OTf)$_3$
N-Protected 2-aminothioethers from aziridines and mercaptans ▽$_N$ → C(SR)C(NH-)

220.

Stereospecific ring opening of bicyclic N-sulfonylaziridines. A mixture of the startg. aziridine, 1.5 eqs. thiophenol and 5 mol% Bi(OTf)$_3$ in anhydrous acetonitrile stirred at room temp. for 4.5 h, then quenched with water → product. Y 92%. N-Protected 2-alkylaziridines underwent **regiospecific ring opening** at the *least* substituted position, while aziridines derived from styrene oxides were cleaved at the benzylic site. The procedure is mild, clean, simple and generally applicable to the ring opening of N-sulfonyl- and N-Boc-aziridines with alkyl or aryl mercaptans. F.e. and with readily recoverable Sc(OTf)$_2$ s. J.S. Yadav et al., Synthesis *2004*, 1854-8.

Addition to Carbon-Carbon Bonds SC ⇓ CC

Potassium thiocyanate/ferric chloride KSCN/FeCl$_3$
1,2-Di(thiocyanates) from ethylene derivs. C=C → C(SCN)C(SCN)
with Me$_3$SiNCS/PhI(OAc)$_2$ cf. *18*, 647s55; with KSCN/FeCl$_3$ s. J.S. Yadav, B.V.S. Reddy, M.K. Gupta, Synthesis *2004*, 1983-6.

Triethylborane Et$_3$B
Thioethers from ethylene derivs. C=C → CHC(SR)
radical addition with 9-BBN cf. *47*, 488; with Et$_3$B s. G. Gros et al., European patent EP-1260500 (Aventis Animal Nutrition SA).

Boron fluoride BF_3
3-(β-Mercaptoacyl)-2-oxazolidones ←
from 3-(α,β-ethyleneacyl)-2-oxazolidinethiones
Michael-type addition with asym. induction
via intramolecular sulfur transfer with SnCl$_4$ cf. *61*, 209; formation of quaternary carbon centres with BF$_3$-etherate s. C. Palomo et al., Angew. Chem. Int. Ed. Engl. *43*, 3307-10 (2004).

Dimethylaluminum chloride/pentafluorobenzoic acid $Me_2AlCl/ArCOOH$
Sec. alcohols from α,β-ethyleneketones ←
via asym. Michael addition-intramolecular Meerwein-Ponndorf-Verley reduction
s. *53*, 213; from α-subst. enones with stereocontrol of the three contiguous chiral centres, enhanced stereoselectivity with added pentafluorobenzoic acid, s. K. Nishida, M. Node et al., Angew. Chem. Int. Ed. Engl. *42*, 4515-7 (2003).

Indium(I) iodide InI
1,4-Addition with reductively generated metal mercaptides $C≡C → CHC(SR)$
general procedure from disulfides with Zn/ZrCl$_4$ cf. *50*, 305s*65*; with InI s. B.C. Ranu, T. Mandal, Synlett *2004*, 1239-42.

Ammonium ceric nitrate CAN
2-Deoxythioglycosides from glycals ←
s. *47*, 106; with CAN in acetonitrile s. S. Paul, N. Jayaraman, Carbohydr. Res. *339*, 2197-204 (2004).

Pentafluorobenzoic acid s. under Me$_2$AlCl $ArCOOH$

Chiral hafnium(IV) salen complexes ←
Lewis acid-catalyzed asym. Michael addition of mercaptans $C≡C → CHC(SR)$
to 3-(α,β-ethyleneacyl)-2-oxazolidones with Hf(OTf)$_4$/chiral N-acyl-2-α-methoxypyrrolidines cf. *58*, 194s*62*; with pentagonal bipyramidal chiral hafnium(IV) salen complexes s. K. Matsumoto, T. Katsuki et al., Tetrahedron Lett. *45*, 2385-8 (2004).

p-Toluenesulfonic acid $TsOH$
β-Hydroxysulfones $C≡C → C(OH)C(SO_2R)$
from ethylene derivs. and sulfonic acid chlorides

221. Ph—CH=CH$_2$ + p-TolSO$_2$Cl $\xrightarrow{H^+}$ [HO-S(=O)-Tol-p / Ph-CH$^+$-CH$_2$-Cl $\xrightarrow{-H^+}$ Ph-(O-S(Tol-p)=O)-CH$_2$Cl] $\xrightarrow[-HCl]{H_2O}$ Ph-CH(OH)-CH$_2$-SO$_2$Tol-p

Regiospecific conversion. Styrene and 1.2 eqs. water added to a soln. of 1.5 eqs. benzenesulfonyl chloride and 20 mol% TsOH in THF at room temp., the mixture warmed to 50°, stirred for 36 h, then quenched with water → product. Y 75%. Reaction is applicable to the addition of mesyl and tosyl chloride to terminal or 1,1-disubst. alkenes, the hydroxyl groups being introduced at the benzylic site with styrenes. 2-Chloro-1,2-oxathietane S-oxides are invoked as intermediates. F.e.s. C. Xi et al., Synlett *2004*, 1595-7.

Ferric chloride s. under KSCN $FeCl_3$

Nickel(II) chloride/quinoline/pyridine ←
Nickel(II)-catalyzed Michael addition of mercaptans $C≡C → CHC(SR)$
asym. conversion with chiral Ni(II)-bis(Δ^2-oxazoline) complexes cf. *58*, 194; achiral process with NiCl$_2$/quinoline/pyridine for Michael addition to α,β-ethylenecarboxylic acids s. S. Gogia, B.C. Joshi et al., Indian J. Chem. *43B*, 1008-11 (2004).

Exchange

Hydrogen ↑ SC ↓↑ H

Zeolite
Ar. sulfonation H → SO₃H

222.

A mixture of zeolite 5A-supported sulfur trioxide and toluene heated at 50° for 22 h under N₂ → *p*-methylbenzenesulfonic acid. Y 46% (and 7.7% *o*-methylbenzenesulfonic acid). F.e.s. S. Jacobson, D. Corbin, United States patent US-6462215; with silica-sulfuric acid for enhanced *p*-selectivity s. A.R. Hajipour et al., Tetrahedron Lett. *45*, 6607-9 (2004).

Phenyl iodosotrifluoroacetate PhI(OCOCF₃)₂
Oxidative 3-sulfenylation of indoles H → SR
with NCS cf. *26, 592s67*; with PhI(OCOCF₃)₂ s. J.A. Campbell, J.H. Wang et al., Tetrahedron Lett. *45*, 4073-5 (2004).

Silica-sulfuric acid SiO₂-OSO₃H
Ar. sulfonation s. *68, 222* H → SO₃H

Oxygen ↑ SC ↓↑ O

Without additional reagents w.a.r.
**2,3-Dihydrobenz[e][1,4]oxathiepin-5-ones
from *o*-mercaptocarboxylic acids and epoxides**

223.

in the absence of solvent. A mixture of thiosalicylic acid and 1 eq. of the startg. epoxide stirred at 50° in a closed vessel for 6 h then heated in the air at 200° for 1 h → product. Y 89%. The procedure, requiring neither catalyst nor solvent, is environmentally friendly. F.e.s. F. Fringuelli et al., J. Org. Chem. *69*, 8780-5 (2004).

Microwaves (s.a. under i-Pr₂NEt, AcOH, SiO₂ and P₂S₅) [\\\\]
4-Thiazolidones from azomethines
s. *4, 552; 14, 666*; rapid procedure under microwave irradiation in benzene s. A. Bolognese, V. Barone et al., Org. Biomol. Chem. *2*, 2809-13 (2004).

Potassium carbonate K₂CO₃
Benzothiazoles from *o*-aminomercaptans and carboxylic acid esters
s. *16, 652*; from carboxylic acid aryl esters with 5 mol% K₂CO₃ s. A.K. Chakraborti, S. Rudrawar, L. Sharma et al., Synlett 2004, 1533-6.

Potassium thiocyanate s. under β-Cyclodextrin KSCN
Ammonium thiocyanate s. under TiO₂ and Sn(IV) complexes NH₄SCN

Ethyldiisopropylamine/microwaves i-Pr₂NEt/[\\\\]
3-Component synthesis of 4-thiazolidones s. *9, 672s68*

Calcium chloride/hydrogen chloride CaCl₂/HCl
Mercaptals from aldehydes s. *60, 194s68* CHO → CH(SR)₂

Montmorillonite
1,3-Oxathiolanes from oxo compds. s. *51, 226s68*

Lithium fluoroborate $LiBF_4$
1,3-Dithianes from oxo compds. in the absence of solvent s. *60*, 194s68 $CO \rightarrow C(SR)_2$
Zinc fluoroborate $Zn(BF_4)_2$
Cyclic mercaptals from oxo compds. in aq. medium s. *60*, 194s68
Aluminum chloride/silica gel $AlCl_3/SiO_2$
Neodymium(III) or praseodymium(III) triflate $Nd(OTf)_3$ or $Pr(OTf)_3$
Mercaptals from oxo compds.
with Yb(OTf)$_3$ cf. *60*, 194s67; from aldehydes with Nd(OTf)$_3$ s. S.K. De, J. Chem. Res. Synop *2004*, 230-1; with Pr(OTf)$_3$, also 1,3-oxathiolanes (cf. *51*, 226s68), s. Synthesis *2004*, 2837-40; 1,3-dithianes from aldehydes and [more slowly] ketones with LiBF$_4$ **in the absence of solvent** s. K. Kazahaya, S. Tsuji, T. Sato, Synlett *2004*, 1640-2; cyclic mercaptals with Zn(BF$_4$)$_2$ **in aq. organic media** s. S. Islam, A.T. Khan et al., Synth. Commun. *34*, 2911-6 (2004); from aldehydes with anhydrous CaCl$_2$ and a little concd. HCl s. J.H. Zaidi et al., ibid. 2641-53; 1,3-dithianes with AlCl$_3$-on-silica gel, selective conversion of aldehydes, s. B. Tamami, K.P. Borujeny, ibid. *33*, 4253-8 (2003).

Ytterbium(III) triflate/1-n-*butyl-3-methylimidazolium hexafluorophosphate* ←
1,3-Oxathiolanes from oxo compds. in ionic liquids ○
from aldehydes s. *66*, 242; also [more slowly] from ketones with added Yb(OTf)$_3$ (1 mol%) s. A. Kumar, S.M.S. Chauhan et al., Synlett *2004*, 2785-7.

β-Cyclodextrin/potassium thiocyanate or thiourea ←
Thiiranes from epoxides in aq. medium s. *55*, 205s68

Ammonium acetate/alumina s. *under* P_2S_5 NH_4OAc/Al_2O_3
Imidazolium ionic liquids s. *under* $Yb(OTf)_3$ *and* $Bi(OTf)_3$ ←

2-(1H-Benzotriazol-1-yl)-1,1,3,3-tetramethyluronium hexafluorophosphate/ ←
  ethyldiisopropylamine
Acetic acid/microwaves $AcOH/[\backslash\backslash\backslash\backslash]$
3-Component synthesis of 4-thiazolidones ○
with dicyclohexylcarbodiimide cf. *9*, 672s64; with 2-(1*H*-benzotriazol-1-yl)-1,1,3,3-tetramethyluronium hexafluorophosphate/*i*-Pr$_2$NEt, also tetrahydro-1,3-thiazin-4-ones from 3-mercaptopropionic acid, s. R.K. Rawal, T. Srivastava et al., J. Chem. Res. Synop *2004*, 368-9; with a little AcOH under microwave irradiation in ethanol s. P. Venkateswarlu, N.R. Vasireddy, ibid. 288-9; with *i*-Pr$_2$NEt in the absence of solvent s. V. Gududuru, D.D. Miller et al., Synlett *2004*, 2357-8.

Thiourea s. *under β-Cyclodextrin and Tin(IV) complexes* $(NH_2)_2CS$

N,N,N′,N′-Tetramethylfluoroformamidinium hexafluorophosphate/ ←
  triethylamine/4-dimethylaminopyridine
Thiolic acid esters $COOH \rightarrow COSR$
from carboxylic acids and mercaptans s. *39*, 162s68

Silica gel SiO_2
2,3-Dihydro-1,5-benzothiazepines from *o*-aminomercaptans ○
on montmorillonite under microwave irradiation cf. *13*, 896s65; 2,4-diaryl-derivs. from chalcones on heating with silica gel, also 2,3-dihydro-1*H*-1,5-benzodiazepines from *o*-diamines, s. M. Kodomari, T. Noguchi, T. Aoyama, Synth. Commun. *34*, 1783-90 (2004).

Silica gel/microwaves $SiO_2/[\backslash\backslash\backslash\backslash]$
Benzothiazoles from *o*-aminomercaptans and aldehydes
under microwave irradiation in ionic liquids cf. *19*, 674s67; on silica gel in the absence of solvent s. M. Kodomari, Y. Tamaru, T. Aoyama, Synth. Commun. *34*, 3029-36 (2004).

Hexamethyldisiloxane s. *under* P_2S_5 $(Me_3Si)_2O$

Titanium dioxide/ammonium thiocyanate TiO_2/NH_4SCN
5,10,15,20-Tetraphenylporphyrinatotin(IV) bis(triflate)/ammonium thiocyanate or thiourea ←
Thiiranes from epoxides
with LiBF$_4$/NH$_4$SCN cf. *55*, 205s64; with 5 mol% TiO$_2$/NH$_4$SCN s. B. Yadollahi, S.

Tangestaninejad, M.H. Habibi, Synth. Commun. *34*, 2823-7 (2004); with 5,10,15,20-tetraphenyl-porphyrinatotin(IV) bis(triflate)/NH$_4$SCN or thiourea (cf. *55*, 205s67) s. M. Moghadam, S. Tangestaninejad et al., Tetrahedron *60*, 6105-11 (2004); with β-cyclodextrin and thiourea **in aq. medium** (cf. *67*, 231) s. K. Surendra, N.S. Krishnaveni, K.R. Rao, Tetrahedron Lett. *45*, 6523-6 (2004); with β-cyclodextrin/KSCN cf. N.S. Krishnaveni, K.R. Rao et al., Adv. Synth. Catal. *346*, 539-41 (2004); with P$_2$S$_5$/NH$_4$OAc/Al$_2$O$_3$, rapid procedure under microwave irradiation in the absence of solvent, s. B. Kaboudin, H. Norouzi, Synthesis *2004*, 2035-9.

2,4-Bis(p-methoxyphenyl)-1,3,2,4-dithiadiphosphetane 2,4-disulfide s. under Bi(OTf)$_3$ ←

Polyphosphoric acid/silica gel   PPA/SiO$_2$
1,3-Oxathiolanes and 1,3-dithiolanes from oxo compds. s. *51*, 226s68   O

Phosphorus pentasulfide/alumina   P$_2$S$_5$/Al$_2$O$_3$
Phosphorus pentasulfide/hexamethyldisiloxane/microwaves   P$_2$S$_5$/(Me$_3$Si)$_2$O/[\\\\]
Replacement of carbonyl oxygen by sulfur   C=O → C=S
with P$_2$S$_5$/(Me$_3$Si)$_2$O cf. *34*, 525s64; rapid procedure under microwave irradiation in the absence of solvent for preparing thioketones, thiono-esters and -amides s. V. Polshettiwar, M.P. Kaushik et al., J. Chem. Res. Synop *2004*, 474-6; thioketones with P$_2$S$_5$/Al$_2$O$_3$ s. Tetrahedron Lett. *45*, 6255-7 (2004).

Phosphorus pentasulfide/ammonium acetate-alumina/microwaves
Thiiranes from epoxides
under microwave irradiation in the absence of solvent s. *55*, 205s68

Bismuth(III) triflate/2,4-bis(p-methoxyphenyl)-1,3,2,4-dithiadiphosphetane 2,4-disulfide/ ←
1-n-butyl-3-methylimidazolium fluoroborate
Thiophenes from β-diketones in ionic liquids s. *67*, 159s68   O

Sodium hydrogen sulfate/silica   NaHSO$_4$/SiO$_2$
Benzyl thioethers from benzylalcohols and mercaptans s. *54*, 83s68   OH → SR

p-Toluenesulfonic acid/azodiisobutyronitrile/irradiation   TsOH/AIBN/∰
6-α-Arylthio-1,2,4-trioxanes   O
from 2-ethylenealcohols, ketones and arylmercaptans

224.

6-α-Arylthio-3-spiro-1,2,4-trioxanes. A soln. of 1 eq. 2-methyl-2-propen-1-ol and 0.68 eq. AIBN in acetonitrile flushed with O$_2$ for several min at 0°, the stoppered flask kept under a positive O$_2$ pressure, irradiated with a 100 W BLAK-RAY UV lamp with vigorous stirring at 0° while simultaneously adding 1.25 eqs. of the startg. thiophenol in the same solvent over 30 min, the resulting soln. stirred at the same temp. for 4-6 h, cooled to -10° and flushed with N$_2$, a soln. of 2.5 eqs. startg. ketone in methylene chloride and a little TsOH added in succession, and stirring continued overnight at room temp. → product. Y 46%. Reaction is initiated by Markovnikov addition of arylthiiyl radical to the unsaturation, followed by oxygenation and condensation of the intermediate 2-hydroxyhydroperoxide with the ketone. F.e.s. P.M. O'Neill et al., Org. Lett. *6*, 3035-8 (2004).

Iodine   I$_2$
1,3-Oxathiolanes from oxo compds.
with I$_2$ in methylene chloride cf. *51*, 226s67; in water s. B.P. Bandgar, S.V. Bettigeri, J. Chem.

Res. Synop *2004*, 389-91; **heterogeneous conversion** with montmorillonite, selectivity, s. S. Gogoi, J.C. Borah, N.C. Barua, Synlett *2004*, 1592-4; with polyphosphoric acid/silica gel, also 1,3-dithiolanes (cf. *44*, 460s*60*), s. T. Aoyama, T. Takido, M. Kodomari, ibid. 2307-10.

Bromodimethylsulfonium bromide   *[Me$_2$SBr]Br*
Tetra-n-butylammonium tribromide   *Bu$_4$NBr$_3$*
Mercaptals from oxo compds.   CO → C(SR)$_2$

from aldehydes with acetonyltriphenylphosphonium bromide cf. *46*, 162s*67*; also from ketones with bromodimethylsulfonium bromide, and cyclic acetals from oxo compds., s. A.T. Khan, E. Mondal, S. Islam et al., Eur. J. Org. Chem. *2004*, 2002-9; cyclic mercaptals from oxo compds. **or cyclic acetals** (cf. *44*, 460s*65*) with Bu$_4$NBr$_3$ s. S. Naik, B.K. Patel et al., Org. Biomol. Chem. 2, 1670-7 (2004).

Ruthenium trichloride   *RuCl$_3$*
S-Acylation s. *68*, 99   SH → SAc

Tris(dibenzylideneacetone)dipalladium/9,9-dimethyl-4,5-bis(diphenylphosphino)xanthene/ ←
ethyldiisopropylamine
Ar. thioethers from aryl triflates and mercaptans   OTf → SR
with Pd(OAc)$_2$/(R)-Tol-BINAP/NaOBu-*t* cf. *56*, 211; from ar. and alkyl mercaptans with Pd$_2$(dba)$_3$/ 9,9-dimethyl-4,5-bis(diphenylphosphino)xanthene/*i*-Pr$_2$NEt, also from ar. halides (cf. *36*, 561s*68*), s. T. Itoh, T. Mase, Org. Lett. *6*, 4587-90 (2004).

Bis(1,5-cyclooctadiene)iridium(I) fluoroborate   *[Ir(cod)$_2$]BF$_4$*
S-Allylation s. *68*, 123   SH → SC-C=C

Nitrogen ↑   SC ↓↑ N

Without additional reagents   *w.a.r.*
Thioureas from N-amidinylbenzotriazoles   >NC(Bt)=NR → >NCSNHR

225.

N-Acylthioureas. H$_2$S bubbled into acetic acid for 5 min under anhydrous conditions, the startg. benzotriazole deriv. added, and stirring continued at room temp. with continuous H$_2$S bubbling until TLC indicated completion of reaction → product. Y 80%. The procedure is mild and avoids handling toxic reagents (such as isothiocyanates) and heavy metals. A further advantage is that recyclable benzotriazole is the only by-product. F.e. incl. simple thioureas and N-carbamylthioureas s. A.R. Katritzky et al., Synthesis *2004*, 1799-805.

Potassium thiocyanate/cerium(III) chloride   *KSCN/CeCl$_3$*
2-Ketothiocyanates from α-diazoketones s. *36*, 266s*68*   C=N$_2$ → CH(SCN)

Triethylamine   *Et$_3$N*
S-Acylation with N-acylbenzotriazoles under mild conditions   SH → SAc

226.

A soln. of N-2-pyridylcarbonylbenzotriazole and 10-20 mol% Et$_3$N in methylene chloride treated with 1 eq. ethyl 2-mercaptoacetate, and stirred at 25° for 2 h → product. Y 90%. Reaction was applied to the condensation of moisture-resistant N-aroyl-, N-hetaroyl- and N-(α-aminoacyl)-benzotriazoles with such substrates as thiophenol, benzyl mercaptan, mercaptoacetic acid and ethyl mercaptoacetate, and is especially useful where the corresponding acyl chorides are inaccessible or unstable. The conditions are also sufficiently mild to avoid racemization of stereogenic centers. F.e. incl. peptidyl derivs. s. A.R. Katritzky, A.A. Shestopalov, K. Suzuki, Synthesis *2004,* 1806-13.

1,8-Diazabicyclo[5.4.0]undec-7-ene   *dbu*
Thiolic acid esters from N-acyl-N-heterocyclics   CON< → COSR
from 3-acyl-2-oxazolones with Me$_3$Al cf. *46,* 494s57; from 3-acyl-2-oxazolidinethiones with dbu s. Y. Wu et al., Tetrahedron Lett. *45,* 7715-7 (2004).

Sodium tetrahydridoborate s. under (S)-[Bis[3,5-bis(trifluoromethyl)phenyl]-   *NaBH$_4$*
(trimethylsiloxy)methyl]pyrrolidine

Ytterbium(III) triflate/trimethylsilyl chloride   *Yb(OTf)$_3$/Me$_3$SiCl*
β,γ-Ethylenesulfoxides from ethylene derivs. and sulfinic acid amides   C=C-C-S(O)R

227.

Regiospecific conversion. 0.5 eq. Yb(OTf)$_3$, 3 eqs. startg. ethylene deriv., and 1 eq. trimethylsilyl chloride added sequentially to a soln. of 1 eq. p-toluenesulfinamide in anhydrous methylene chloride, stirred at room temp. for 16 h, inorganic salts removed by filtration, and the filtrate worked up → product. Y 90%. The sulfinyl group is always introduced at the *less* substituted position of the alkene double bond, the more electron-rich one being functionalized where two exist in the same molecule. The startg. sulfinamides are readily available, stable and easy to handle. F.e. and with trimethylsilyl triflate s. M. Alajarin, A. Pastor, J. Cabrera, Synlett *2004,* 995-8.

(S)-2-[Bis[3,5-bis(trifluoromethyl)phenyl](trimethylsiloxy)methyl]pyrrolidine/sodium   ←
tetrahydridoborate
Organocatalyzed asym. α-sulfenylation of aldehydes   H → SR

228.

Chiral 2-hydroxythioethers. A mixture of 10 mol% (S)-2-[bis[3,5-bis(trifluoromethyl)phenyl]-(trimethylsiloxy)methyl]pyrrolidine and 1 eq. 3-phenylpropionaldehyde in toluene stirred at room temp. for 5 min, treated with 1.2 eqs. 1-benzylthio-1,2,4-triazole, stirred at the same temp. for 3 h, diluted with methanol, further treated at the same temp. with 1.2 eqs. NaBH$_4$, stirred for 20 min, and quenched with 1 *M* aq. KHSO$_4$ → product. Y 94% (e.e. 97%). Work-up is simplified if the intermediate aldehyde is reduced *in situ* to the corresponding alcohol. Reaction is generally applicable to the asym. sulfenylation of straight-chain, α-branched, and hindered α,α-disubst. aldehydes (incl. α-aryl derivs.), and the product can be simply debenzylated to give the corresponding mercaptans. The (S)-configuration is compatible with *Si*-face attack of the electrophile on an intermediate (E)-configured enamine. F.e. and comparison of sulfenylating agents s. M. Marigo, K.A. Jørgensen et al., Angew. Chem. Int. Ed. Engl. *44,* 794-7 (2005); asym. sulfenylation **of oxo compds.** with N-(phenylsulfenyl)phthalimide in the presence of (S)-2-(trifluoromethanesulfonylaminomethyl)pyrrolidine cf. W. Wang et al., Tetrahedron Lett. *45,* 8229-31 (2004).

Trimethylsilyl chloride s. under Yb(OTf)$_3$ *Me$_3$SiCl*

Halogen ↑   SC ↓↑ Hal

Microwaves s. under P_2S_5 [\\\\]

Sodium hydroxide   *NaOH*
2-Imino-4-thiazolidones from thioureas
and α-halogenocarboxylic acid esters cf. *38*, 523; and 2,2,2-trichloroalcohols with NaOH s. J. Blanchet, J.P. Zhu, Tetrahedron Lett. *45*, 4449-52 (2004).

Cesium hydroxide   *CsOH*
Ar. thioethers from ar. halides and mercaptans   Hal → SR

229. O_2N–⟨⟩–I + HSBn ⟶ O_2N–⟨⟩–SBn

A mixture of *p*-iodonitrobenzene, 1.2 eqs. benzyl mercaptan, and 2 eqs. CsOH·H₂O in DMSO allowed to react in a sealed tube at room temp. for 2.5 h → product. Y 90%. The method is rapid and direct, and does not require a transition metal catalyst. In general, reaction is facilitated by electron-withdrawing groups on the aromatic ring of the aryl halide, there being no arylation at all with *p*-hydroxy- and *p*-methoxy-phenyl halides. Reaction is also applicable to ar. iodides and ar. chlorides or fluorides possessing electron-withdrawing groups. F.e. incl. coupling with ar. mercaptans s. R. Varala, S.R. Adapa et al., Chem. Lett. *33*, 1614-5 (2004).

*Methyllithium s. under 3-*tert-*Butyl-3-methyl-2-(phenylsulfonyl)oxaziridine*   *MeLi*

Sodium sulfide Na_2S
Ar. mercaptans from chlorides   Cl → SH
with aq. Na₂S cf. *20*, 458; with Na₂S/S₈ in DMF s. A. Schnyder, M. Passafaro, T. Rapold, World Intellectual Property Organisation patent WO-200294760 (Syngenta Participations AG).

*Sodium salt/1-*n-*butyl-3-methylimidazolium fluoroborate* $Na^+/[bmim]BF_4$
Sulfones from sulfinic acids and halides   S(O)OH → SO₂R
from lithium salts/Bu₄NBr under phase transfer catalysis cf. *58*, 51; from sodium salts in **ionic liquids**, e.g. 1-*n*-butyl-3-methylimidazolium fluoroborate containing 20 vol% water, s. Y. Hu, O.-G. Zheng et al., J. Chem. Res. Synop *2004*, 267-9.

Bis(triphenylphosphine)(1,10-phenanthroline)copper(I) nitrate/potassium phosphate   ←
Thioenolethers from α,β-ethyleneiodides and mercaptans   C=C(I) → C=C(SR)

230.   Ph~~~I + HS(CH₂)₄OH ⟶ Ph~~~S(CH₂)₄OH

with retention of configuration. Toluene and equimolar amounts of the startg. mercaptan and β-styryl iodide added via syringe to a mixture of 5 mol% bis(triphenylphosphine)(1,10-phenanthroline)copper(I) nitrate and 1.5 eqs. K-phosphate in a septum-sealed reaction tube under argon, and heated at 110° for 8 h → product. Y 97%. The procedure does not involve expensive additives (notably palladium catalysts), and is generally applicable to the coupling of prim., sec., and tert. aliphatic mercaptans, as well as aryl and hetaryl mercaptans (incl. hindered derivs.), and tolerates both electron-withdrawing and -donating, as well as base-sensitive groups, leaving ar. halogen, isolated hydroxyl groups and esters unaffected. F.e. and comparison of copper catalysts and bases s. C.G. Bates, D. Venkataraman et al., Org. Lett. *6*, 5005-8 (2004).

Cuprous iodide/N-methylglycine/potassium hydroxide   *CuI/MeNHCH₂COOH/KOH*
Ar. thioethers from ar. halides and mercaptans   ArHal → ArSR
with CuI/K₂CO₃/py cf. *31*, 522s66; with CuI/N-methylglycine/KOH s. W. Deng, Q.-X. Guo et al., Synlett *2004*, 1254 8; with NiCl₂ in quinoline/pyridine cf. S. Gogia, S. Gupta, B.C. Joshi et al., J. Indian Chem. Soc. *81*, 515-7 (2004).

Bentonite s. under Iron(III)   ←
Ammonium acetate/alumina s. under P_2S_5 NH_4OAc/Al_2O_3
Imidazolium ionic liquids s. under Na^+ ←
N-Methylglycine s. under CuI   *MeNHCH₂COOH*

Phosphorus pentasulfide/ammonium acetate-alumina/microwaves ←
Dithiophosphoric acid O,O-diesters from halides   Hal → $P(S)(OR)_2(SR')$
and alcohols via O,O-dialkyl hydrogen dithiophosphates with P_2S_5 s. *17*, 165; one-pot conversion with added NH_4OAc/Al_2O_3 under microwave irradiation in the absence of solvent s. B. Kaboudin, H. Norouzi, Synthesis *2004*, 2035-9.

Bismuth oxide chloride or Zirconyl chloride $BiOCl$ or $ZrOCl_2$
S-Acylation s. *68*, 110   SH → SAc

Antimony or bismuth trichloride/trifluoromethanesulfonic acid $SbCl_3/TfOH$ or $BiCl_3/TfOH$
Antimony pentachloride/benzyltriethylammonium chloride $SbCl_5/BnEt_3NCl$
Aryl sulfones from arenes and sulfonic acid chlorides   ArH → $ArSO_2R$
with Fe(III)-exchanged montmorillonite cf. *57*, 207; from activated and weakly activated arenes and hetarenes with Fe(III)-pillared bentonite clay in the absence of solvent s. D.U. Singh, P.R. Singh, S.D. Samant, Tetrahedron Lett. *45*, 9079-82 (2004); with $SbCl_3$ or $BiCl_3/TfOH$ cf. M. Peyronneau, C. Le Roux et al., Eur. J. Org. Chem. *2004*, 4636-40; with 2:1 $SbCl_5/BnEt_3NCl$ cf. *54*, 413s*68*.

trans-3-tert-Butyl-3-methyl-2-(phenylsulfonyl)oxaziridine/methyllithium ←
1-Sulfinylthioenolethers from dithiocarboxylic acid esters   CHCSSR → C=C(SR)S(O)R'

231.

One-pot procedure. A soln. of 1.1 eqs. methyllithium in ether (1.6 *M*) added dropwise to a soln. of the startg. dithioester in anhydrous THF at -78°, stirred at the same temp. for 15 min, a soln. of 1 eq. *trans*-3-*tert*-butyl-3-methyl-2-(phenylsulfonyl)oxaziridine in the same solvent added dropwise (exothermic), stirred for 20 min, slowly warmed to -15°, 1.1-2 eqs. benzyl bromide added, stirring continued at the same temp. for 5 h, and quenched with satd. aq. NaCl → product. Y 66% ((E)-selectivity 78%). The procedure affords the (Z)-isomers predominantly at -78° as a result of trapping of the intermediate lithium sulfenates, but isomerization to the thermodynamically more stable (E)-isomers takes place on warming. Other bases were ineffective. F.e.s. F. Sandrinelli, S. Perrio et al., J. Org. Chem. *69*, 6916-9 (2004).

Trifluoromethanesulfonic acid s. under $SbCl_3$ CF_3SO_3H

Iron(III)-pillared bentonite ←
Aryl sulfones from arenes and sulfonic acid chlorides s. *57*, 207s*68*   ArH → $ArSO_2R$

Nickel(II) chloride/quinoline/pyridine
Ar. thioethers from halides s. *31*, 522s*68*   ArHal → ArSR

Palladous acetate/1,1'-bis(diisopropylphosphino)ferrocene/sodium tert-butoxide ←
Ar. thioethers from halides
with $Pd_2(dba)_3$/bis[2-(diphenylphosphino)phenyl] ether/NaOBu-*t* cf. *36*, 561s*61*; condensation of ar. bromides or chlorides (incl. hindered compds.) with aliphatic or ar. mercaptans using $Pd(OAc)_2$/1,1'-bis(diisopropylphosphino)ferrocene/NaOBu-*t*, also tert. arylphosphines from ar. halides (cf. *38*, 584s*64*), s. M. Murata, S.L. Buchwald, Tetrahedron *60*, 7397-403 (2004).

Sulfur ↑   SC ↓↑ S

Magnesium/cuprous iodide/2,2'-bipyridyl   Mg/CuI/bipy
Zinc/aluminum chloride $Zn/AlCl_3$
Zinc/nickel(II) bromide/2,2'-bipyridyl $Zn/NiBr_2$/bipy
Thioethers from disulfides and halides   Hal → SR
with $Zn/ZrCl_4$ cf. *53*, 230s*65*; **ar. thioethers** from ar. halides with $Zn/NiBr_2$/bipy s. N. Taniguchi, J. Org. Chem. *69*, 6904-6 (2004); **from tosylates** with $Zn/AlCl_3$ (cf. *12*, 686s*60*) s. B. Movassagh, A. Mossadegh, Synth. Commun. *34*, 1685-90 (2004); with Mg/CuI/bipy (10 mol%) (cf. *12*, 686), also ar. selenides from diselenides with Mg/Cu_2O/bipy, s. N. Taniguchi, T. Onami, J. Org. Chem. *69*, 915-20 (2004).

Aluminum chloride s. under Zn $\qquad AlCl_3$

Indium(I) iodide $\qquad InI$
Samarium/methanol $\qquad Sm/MeOH$
Thioethers from disulfides and halides $\qquad Hal \rightarrow SR$
allyl thioethers with SmI$_2$/HMPA cf. *53*, 230s56; with Sm/MeOH s. Z.-P. Zhan, K. Lang, Chem. Lett. *33*, 1370-1 (2004); ar. thioethers from diaryl disulfides with InI, also thiolic acid aryl esters from acyl chlorides, s. B.C. Ranu, T. Mandal, J. Org. Chem. *69*, 5793-5 (2004).

Nickel(II) bromide s. under Zn $\qquad NiBr_2$

Remaining Elements ↑ $\qquad$ SC ↓↑ Rem

Cupric acetate/potassium carbonate/sodium salt $\qquad Cu(OAc)_2/K_2CO_3/Na^+$
Aryl sulfones from arylboronic acids and sulfinic acids $\qquad B(OH)_2 \rightarrow SO_2R$
under mild conditions

232. Ph-C$_6$H$_4$-B(OH)$_2$ + NaOS(O)Me $\longrightarrow$ Ph-C$_6$H$_4$-SO$_2$Me

1.1 eqs. Cu(OAc)$_2$, 1.5 eqs. Na-methylsulfinate, 2 eqs. K$_2$CO$_3$ and 4 Å molecular sieves added to a 0.25 M soln. of the startg. boronic acid in DMSO, stirred at room temp. for 16 h, filtered, and the filtrate worked up → product. Y 97%. Reaction is generally applicable to the coupling of electron-deficient or -rich arylboronic acids (incl. hindered derivs.) with sodium alkyl- or aryl-sulfinates, leaving ar. bromine and chlorine unaffected. Yields were lower, however, with hetarylboronic acids, and the presence of oxygen appears essential. F.e. and comparison of bases and solvents s. C. Beaulieu, D.A. Evans et al., Tetrahedron Lett. *45*, 3233-6 (2004).

tert-Butyldimethylsilyl triflate/bromine $\qquad t\text{-}BuMe_2SiOTf/Br_2$
α-Sulfonylcarbonyl compds. from enoxysilanes $\qquad C{=}C(OSi{\leqslant}) \rightarrow C(SO_2R)CO$
and halides cf. *63*, 219; β-ketosulfonic acid amides and esters via halides (with Br$_2$, Cl$_2$, NBS or NCS), s. L.C. Bouchez, P. Vogel et al., J. Org. Chem. *69*, 6413-8 (2004).

Carbon ↑ $\qquad$ SC ↓↑ C

Samarium/methanol $\qquad Sm/MeOH$
Thioethers from thiocyanates and halides $\qquad SCN \rightarrow SR$
with Mg cf. *23*, 628; allyl thioethers with Sm/MeOH (cf. *50*, 335) s. Z.P. Zhan, K. Lang, Chem. Lett. *33*, 1370-1 (2004).

Acetyl chloride $\qquad AcCl$
1,3-Dithianes from oxo compds. $\qquad \bigcirc$
and 2-ene-1,3-dithianes s. *66*, 240; from f. odourless 1,3-propanedithiol equivalents with added AcCl s. L. Jun, D. Dong et al., Synth. Commun. *34*, 4545-56 (2004); s.a. H.-F. Yu, Q. Lin, D. Dong et al., Synlett *2004*, 999-1002.

Bromine/acetic acid $\qquad Br_2/AcOH$
Acylthio compds. from thioethers and carboxylic acid chlorides $\qquad SR \rightarrow SAc$
from 2-(trimethylsilyl)ethyl thioethers with AgBF$_4$ cf. *56*, 223; from *tert*-butyl thioethers with Br$_2$/AcOH s. A. Blaszczyk, M. Elbing, M. Mayor, Org. Biomol. Chem. *2*, 2722-4 (2004).

Elimination $\qquad$ ⇑

Hydrogen ↑ $\qquad$ SC ⇑ H

Microwaves s. under I$_2$ $\qquad$ [\\\\]
Montmorillonite s. under TsOH $\qquad \leftarrow$

p-Toluenesulfonic acid/montmorillonite/oxygen
2-Aminobenzothiazoles from N-arylthioureas
with [Me₃NBn]Br₃ cf. *8*, 688s*66*; thiazolo[4,5-*c*]carbazoles with TsOH/montmorillonite K10 in the absence of solvent s. M. Chakrabarty, N. Ghosh, Y. Harigaya, Tetrahedron Lett. *45*, 4955-7 (2004).

Iodine/microwaves $I_2/$[\\\\]
Benzo[*b*]thiophenes from β-mercaptostyrenes
with I_2/PhNO₂ cf. *12*, 689; rapid procedure with I_2 in dioxane (in a sealed tube) under microwave irradiation at 160° s. D. Allen, V.A. Wood et al., Tetrahedron Lett. *45*, 9645-7 (2004).

Oxygen↑   SC ⇑ O

Acetic acid   *AcOH*
Soluble polymer-based synthesis of benzothiazoles from *o*-acylaminomercaptans B
s. *21*, 543s*68*

Triphenylphosphine/diethyl azodicarboxylate   *Ph₃P/EtOOCN=NCOOEt*
Cyclic thioiminoesters from thioacylaminoalcohols
Δ²-thiazolines s. *25*, 458s*54*; 5,6-dihydro-4*H*-1,3-thiazines s. N. Leflemme, P. Dallemagne, S. Rault, Tetrahedron Lett. *45*, 1503-5 (2004).

Halogen↑   SC ⇑ Hal

Cuprous iodide/1,10-phenanthroline/cesium carbonate
2-Aminobenzothiazoles from *o*-halogenothioureas

233.

A mixture of the startg. thiourea, 2 eqs. Cs₂CO₃, 5 mol% CuI, and 10 mol% 1,10-phenanthroline in dimethoxyethane heated at 80° for 24 h under N₂ → product. Y 85% (conversion >98%). The procedure is more economical than that under palladium catalysis, and yields were higher than with Pd(PPh₃)₄. Reaction tolerates electron-withdrawing and -donating groups. F.e. and from *o*-iodothioureas s. L.L. Joyce, G. Evindar, R.A. Batey, Chem. Commun. *2004*, 446-7.

Formation of Rem-C Bond

Uptake   ⇓

Addition to Oxygen and Carbon   RemC ⇓ OC

Microwaves   [\\\\]
Sym. α,α'-dihydroxyphosphinic acids from aldehydes   2 CHO → [CH(OH)]₂P(O)OH
under microwave irradiation in the absence of solvent

234.

0.3 eq. Hypophosphorous acid (50%) added to *p*-fluorobenzaldehyde, the mixture irradiated at 180 W *for 1 min* in a commercial microwave oven, cooled, treated with ethyl acetate, stirred for 5 min, hexane added, and the precipitate collected → product. Y 88%. The procedure is simple, mild and clean, and generally applicable to ar. aldehydes (except *p*-nitrobenzaldehyde). There was no reaction with hetar. aldehydes. F.e.s. B. Kaboudin, N. As-habei, Tetrahedron Lett. *45*, 9099-101 (2004).

Tris(trimethylsilyl) phosphite $(Me_3SiO)_3P$
1-Hydroxy-1,1-diphosphonic acid esters from carboxylic acids or derivs. ←
from carboxylic acids cf. *29*, 593, and review s. *28*, 584s*60*; large-scale procedure with H_3PO_3/PCl_3 in nonylphenol ethoxylate s. K. Dabak et al., World Intellectual Property Organisation patent WO-200290367 (EOS Eczacibasi Ozgun Kimyasal Urunler SA); ω-carboxy-derivs. from anhydrides with tris(trimethylsilyl) phosphite s. E. Guenin, M. Lecouvey et al., Eur. J. Org. Chem. *2004*, 2983-7; from acylphosphonic acid esters cf. Y.L. Xie et al., Chinese Chem. Lett. *14*, 25-8 (2003); from carboxylic acid chlorides in the absence of solvent cf. E. Migianu, M. Lecouvey et al., Tetrahedron Lett. *45*, 4511-3 (2004).

Addition to Carbon RemC ⇓ C

1,8-Diazabicyclo[5.4.0]undec-7-ene *dbu*
Monoselenoiminocarbonic acid esters N≡C: → N=C(OR)(SeR')
from isonitriles, alcohols and halides

235.

A mixture of cyclohexyl isocyanide, 2.1 eqs. methanol, 1 eq. selenium and 1 eq. 1,8-diazabicyclo[5.4.0]undec-7-ene in THF stirred at room temp. for 20 h, 2 eqs. *n*-butyl iodide added, stirring continued for 1 h, diluted with hexane, filtered, and the filtrate worked up → product. Y 92%. Reaction is generally applicable to coupling of aromatic and aliphatic isocyanides with prim. alcohols, incl. benzyl and allyl alcohol. F.e., also **4-alkylidene-2-imino-1,3-oxaselenolanes** from 2-acetylenealcohols, s. Y. Asanuma, S. Fujiwara, N. Kambe et al., J. Org. Chem. *69*, 4845-8 (2004).

Addition to Carbon-Carbon Bonds RemC ⇓ CC

Microwaves [\\\\]
Tert. phosphines from ethylene derivs. C=C → CHC(PR$_2$)
under irradiation cf. *25*, 466; tert. phosphine-borane complexes under microwave irradiation or by thermal conversion (cf. *67*, 245) s. D. Mimeau, A.-C. Gaumont et al., Compt. Rend. Chim. *7*, 845-54 (2004).

Potassium tert-*butoxide* *KOBu*-t
Phosphine oxides from ethylene derivs. C=C → CHC(POR$_2$)
and phosphinous acids s. *38*, 557; bridged bicyclic phosphine oxides with asym. induction using KOBu-*t* as base (cf. *25*, 466s*64*) s. T. Bunlaksananusorn, P. Knochel, J. Org. Chem. *69*, 4595-601 (2004).

Michael-type addition of dialkyl phosphites C=C → CHC(PO(OR)$_2$)
to enones with NaOMe cf. *9*, 710; 2-nitro-2-deoxy-β-glycosylphosphonic acid esters with KOBu-*t* s. K. Pachamuthu, R.R. Schmidt et al., Eur. J. Org. Chem. *2004*, 3959-61.

tert-*Butylmagnesium chloride s. under Silyllithium compds.* t-BuMgCl
Zinc chloride s. under Silyllithium compds. ZnCl$_2$

Sodium tetrahydridoborate $NaBH_4$
Enetellurides from acetylene derivs.   C≡C → CH=C(TeR)
s. *50*, 343s*66*; α,β-ethylene-β-(organotelluro)sulfoxides s. Q. Xu, X. Huang, J. Ni, Tetrahedron Lett. *45*, 2981-4 (2004).

Dicyclohexylborane/oxygen Cy_2BH/O_2
(E)-α,β-Ethyleneboronic acid esters   C≡CH → CH=CB(OR)$_2$
from terminal acetylene derivs.

236.

in the absence of solvent. The solvent removed from a suspension of 5 mol% dicyclohexylborane in THF, 1-hexyne and 1 eq. pinacolborane added at 0°, the mixture stirred at room temp. for 2 h, and air bubbled through the mixture for 2 h → product. Y 94%. Reaction proceeds via initial hydroboration with dicyclohexylborane, followed by exchange with pinacolborane. The procedure is notably tolerant of acid- and base-labile O-protecting groups, but only applicable to terminal acetylene derivs. F.e. and method s. K. Shirakawa, A. Arase, M. Hoshi, Synthesis *2004*, 1814-20.

Triethylborane/oxygen Et_3B/O_2
Radical hydrophosphinylation of ethylene derivs.   C=C → CHC(P(O)<)
phosphine oxides s. *53*, 240s*66*; β-alkoxyphosphonic acid esters and thionophosphate analogs from enolethers, also radical ring closure-hydrophosphinylation of dienes, s. C.M. Jessop, D.J. Irvine et al., Tetrahedron Lett. *45*, 5095-8 (2004); phosphonic acid esters with Mn(OAc)$_2$/O$_2$ cf. O. Tayama, Y. Ishii et al., J. Org. Chem. *69*, 5494-6 (2004).

Phenyl iodosoacetate/trimethylsilyl azide $PhI(OAc)_2/Me_3SiN_3$
2-Azidoselenides from ethylene derivs.   C=C → C(N$_3$)C(SeR)
and diselenides, regiospecific conversion with asym. induction using AgOTf/Br$_2$, cf. *65*, 223; 1,2-*cis*-2-azido-2-deoxyselenoglycosides with PhI(OAc)$_2$/Me$_3$SiN$_3$ s. Y.V. Mironov, A.A. Sherman, N.E. Nifantiev, Tetrahedron Lett. *45*, 9107-10 (2004).

p-Methyliodobenzene difluoride $ArIF_2$
2-Fluoroselenides from ethylene derivs.   C=C → C(F)C(SeR)
and selenenyl chlorides, regiospecific conversion with AgF, cf. *45*, 290; regio- and stereo-specific addition of diselenides with *p*-methyliodobenzene difluoride, also (E)-2-fluoroeneselenides from acetylene derivs., s. B. Panunzi, A. Picardi, M. Tingoli, Synlett *2004*, 2339-42.

Silyllithium compds./zinc chloride/tert-butylmagnesium chloride/2,2'-dihydroxybiphenyl   ←
Enesilanes from terminal acetylene derivs.   ←
Regiospecific conversion via 2-silylvinylzincates

237.

A mixture of 1 eq. 2,2'-biphenol in anhydrous THF and 1.1 eqs. ZnCl$_2$ (0.5 *M* in THF) treated at -78° under argon with 3.3 eqs. *tert*-butylmagnesium chloride (1 *M* in THF) and 1.1 eqs. dimethylphenylsilyllithium (0.82 M in THF), stirred at 0° for 30 min, 1 eq. startg. terminal alkyne added dropwise, stirring continued at room temp. for 12 h, and quenched with satd. aq. NH_4Cl → product. Y 99% (branched/linear 81:19). Reaction proceeds via 2-silylvinylzincates which can be trapped by electrophiles other than proton to give the corresponding **trisubst. enesilanes,** or undergo transition metal-catalyzed cross-coupling. The regioselectivity is markedly dependent on the nature of the alkyne substituent: alkyl, chloroalkyl, carbamylalkyl, carbalkoxyalkyl, carboxyalkyl and hydroxyalkyl derivs. gave the branched isomer predominantly, while silyl-, aryl-, hetaryl-, methoxymethyl-, hydroxymethyl-, and aminomethyl-acetylenes favoured formation of the linear isomer. Alkene and internal alkyne residues remained unaffected. F.e.s. S. Nakamura, M. Uchiyama, T. Ohwada, J. Am. Chem. Soc. *126*, 11146-7 (2004).

Trimethylsilyl azide s. under PhI(OAc)$_2$ Me_3SiN_3

Tricarbonyltris(tert-butyl isocyanide)molybdenum $Mo(CO)_3(t\text{-}BuNC)_3$
2-Ethylene-4-hydroxystannanes from 2-allenealcohols   C=C=C → C=CHC(Sn≤)
Regiospecific molybdenum-catalyzed hydrostannylation

238.

A mixture of 2 mol% tricarbonyltris(*tert*-butyl isocyanide)molybdenum, 3 eqs. tri-*n*-butyltin hydride and the startg. 2-allenealcohol in THF heated at 55° until reaction complete (TLC monitoring) → product. Y 74% ((Z)-selectivity 67%). Regioselectivity is towards formation of the sterically least hindered stannyl deriv. Reaction appears to involve initial dissociation of one of the isocyanide ligands leaving a free coordination site on molybdenum prior to oxidative addition of the tin hydride and coordination of the allene. F.e.s. U. Kazmaier, M. Klein, Chem. Commun. *2005*, 501-3.

Tetra-n-butylammonium fluoride Bu_4NF
Regiospecific hydrophosphination with silylphosphines under mild conditions ←

239.

(75%; E/Z ~5:1)

of ethylene derivs. A soln. of 1.2 eqs. startg. silylphosphine in DMF and 1 eq. tetra-*n*-butyl-ammonium fluoride (1 M in THF) added to styrene at room temp., and the mixture stirred for an additional 15 min at the same temp. → product. Y 89%. This reaction required an aryl substituent or an electron-withdrawing group on the alkene residue, which directs the incoming diphenyl-phosphide anion to the β-site. Simple alkenes failed to react. Interestingly, the intermediate carbanion can be trapped by electrophiles in a **3-component synthesis** to give more highly substituted phosphines. F.e., **also hydrophosphination of acetylene derivs.,** s. M. Hayashi, Y. Matsuura, Y. Watanabe, Tetrahedron Lett. *45*, 9167-9 (2004).

Manganese(II) acetate/oxygen $Mn(OAc)_2/O_2$
Phosphonic acid esters from ethylene derivs. s. *53*, 240s68   C=C → CHC(PO(OR)$_2$)

Bis(dinitrogen)[2,6-bis[1-(2,6-diisopropylphenylimino)ethyl]pyridine]iron(0) ←
Regiospecific iron-catalyzed hydrosilylation under mild conditions ←

240.

of ethylene derivs. Equivalent amounts of the startg. olefin and phenylsilane added to *0.3 mol%* bis(dinitrogen)[2,6-bis[1-(2,6-diisopropylphenylimino)ethyl]pyridine]iron(0) in anhydrous pentane under N_2 at 22°, and stirred at the same temp. for 2 h → product. Conversion >98%. Conversions are ca. 100% **at low catalyst loading**, and reaction favours the anti-Markovnikov product. Terminal alkenes and styrene reacted the most rapidly, followed by 1,1-disubst. and internal olefins. F.e., also enesilanes from acetylene derivs., and homogeneous hydrogenations, s. S.C. Bart, E. Lobkovsky, P.J. Chirik, J. Am. Chem. Soc. *126*, 13794-807 (2004).

Tris(acetonitrile)(pentamethylcyclopentadienyl)ruthenium(II)   *[Cp*Ru(MeCN)$_3$]PF$_6$*
hexafluorophosphate
Regiospecific hydrosilylation of acetylene derivs.   C≡C → CH=C(Si≤)
with Cp*RuH$_3$(PPh$_3$)/Et$_3$N cf. *62*, 230s*64*; cyclic (E)-ethylene derivs. with [Cp*Ru(MeCN)$_3$]PF$_6$ s. F. Lacombe, A. Fürstner et al., Tetrahedron *60*, 7315-24 (2004).

Chloro(1,5-cyclooctadiene)rhodium(I) dimer/triisopropylphosphine/triethylamine ←
α,β-Ethyleneboronic acid esters from acetylene derivs.   C≡C → CH=CB(OR)$_2$
(E)-isomers with Ru(CO)H(Cl)(PPh$_3$)$_3$ cf. *59*, 221s*63*; with [Rh(cod)Cl]$_2$/*i*-Pr$_3$P/Et$_3$N s. T. Lee, J. Ko et al., Organometallics *23*, 4569-75 (2004).

Palladous acetate/1,1,3,3-tetramethylbutyl isocyanide   *Pd(OAc)$_2$/RNC*
Tris(dibenzylideneacetone)dipalladium/tricyclohexyl- or triphenyl-phosphine   *Pd$_2$(dba)$_3$/R$_3$P*
2-Silylenestannanes from acetylene derivs.   C≡C → C(Si≤)=C(Sn≤)
regio- and stereo-selectivity with Pd(PPh$_3$)$_4$ cf. *41*, 564; (Z)-selective addition to acetylene itself with Pd(OAc)$_2$/1,1,3,3-tetramethylbutyl isocyanide s. M. Murakami, M. Terayama et al., Synthesis *2004*, 1522-6; preferential conversion with Pd$_2$(dba)$_3$/Cy$_3$P s. S. Apte, T.V. RajanBabu et al., Org. Lett. *6*, 4053-6 (2004); 2'-alkoxy- and 2'-hydroxy-2-silylenestannanes with Ph$_3$P as ligand s. T.E. Nielsen, S. Le Quement, D. Tanner, Synthesis *2004*, 1381-90.

Bis(dibenzylideneacetone)palladium(0)/3-iodo-2-methylcyclohex-2-enone ←
β,γ-Ethylene-β-silylboronic acid esters from allenes   C=C(Si≤)C-B(OR')$_2$
via regio- and stereo-selective 1,2-silaboration

241.

A mixture of 10 mol% 3-iodo-2-methylcyclohex-2-enone, 5 mol% Pd(dba)$_2$, 1 eq. 2-(dimethylphenylsilyl)-4,4,5,5-tetramethyl-1,3,2-dioxaborolane and 2 eqs. of the startg. allene in anhydrous acetonitrile stirred under N_2 at 80° for 5 h → product. Y 87% (E/Z 99:1). F.e.s. K.-J. Chang, C.-H. Cheng et al., J. Am. Chem. Soc. *127*, 126-31 (2005).

Tris(dibenzylideneacetone)dipalladium/polymer-based 4,6-bis(diphenylphosphino)- ←
phenoxazine-10-carboxamide
Phosphonous acids from terminal ethylene derivs.   C=CH$_2$ → CHCH$_2$P(OH)$_2$
regiospecific addition of H$_3$PO$_2$ with 9,9-dimethyl-4,5-bis(diphenylphosphino)xanthene as ligand cf. *64*, 210; with air- and moisture-tolerant, recyclable polymer-based 4,6-bis(diphenylphosphino)-

phenoxazine-10-carboxamide as ligand s. S. Deprele, J.L. Montchamp, Org. Lett. *6*, 3805-8 (2004).

Tris(dibenzylideneacetone)dipalladium/chiral cyclic phosphoromonoamidites ←
1-Methylene-1,2-di(boronic acid esters) from terminal allenes $CH_2=C(B(OR)_2)C(B(OR)_2)$
via regiospecific asym. 1,2-diboration

242.

A mixture of 2.6 mol% $Pd_2(dba)_3$ and 6 mol% (R,R)-2,2-dimethyl-α,α,α′,α′-tetraphenyl-1,3-dioxolane-4,5-dimethyl N,N-dimethylphosphoramidite in anhydrous toluene stirred at room temp. for 30 min, treated under N_2 with 1.2 eqs. bis(pinacolato)diboron and a soln. of 1 eq. 1,2-butadiene in the same solvent, and stirring continued at the same temp. for 14 h → product. Y 68% (e.e. 92%). The procedure is rapid and generally applicable to aryl- and alkyl-allenes affording single regioisomers with high enantioselectivities. F.e. and comparison of ligands s. N.F. Pelz, J.P. Morken et al., J. Am. Chem. Soc. *126*, 16328-9 (2004).

Bis(η³-allylpalladium chloride)/chiral cyclic phosphoromonoamidites ←
Regiospecific asym. hydrosilylation of styrenes $C=C → CHC(Si⩽)$
with a chiral 1,1′-binaphthyl-based ligand cf. *64*, 211; with (R,R,R)-2,2′,3,3′-tetrahydro-1,1′-spiro-(1H-indene)-7,7′-diyl N,N-bis(1-phenylethyl)phosphoramidite s. X. Guo, Q.-L. Zhou et al., Tetrahedron:Asym. *15*, 2231-4 (2004).

[Bis(phenylimino)acenaphthene](dimethyl fumarate)platinum(0) ←
Addition of tetraalkoxydiboranes to multiple bonds
1,2-diborylation of terminal ethylene derivs. with $Pt(cod)Cl_2$ cf. *49*, 518s60; of α,β-ethylene-carbonyl compds. with [bis(phenylimino)acenaphthene](dimethyl fumarate)platinum(0) s. N.J. Bell, R.P. Tooze et al., Chem. Commun. *2004*, 1854-5.

Exchange ↕

Hydrogen ↑   RemC ↕ H

Dodecacarbonyltriruthenium/norbornene ←
Chelation-controlled benzylic silylation $H → Si⩽$

243.

of o-subst. hydrazones. A mixture of 6 mol% $Ru_3(CO)_{12}$, 1 eq. of the startg. hydrazone, 5 eqs. triethylsilane, and 5 eqs. norbornene (as H-acceptor) in anhydrous toluene refluxed under N_2 for 20 h → product. Y 40% (and 15% disilyl deriv.). Silylation at the benzylic site [the least substituted if two are available] is directed by the *o*-imino nitrogen, which may also be N-heterocyclic (pyridyl and pyrazolyl). There was no reaction, however, with simple *o*-subst. aldimines, benzylamines or alkoximes. F.e. and comparison of silicon hydrides, olefinic H-acceptors, and transition metal complexes s. F. Kakiuchi et al., J. Am. Chem. Soc. *126*, 12792-3 (2004).

Cationic iridium complexes
Ar. deuteriation H → D
with di(acetone)dihydridobis(triphenylphosphine)iridium fluoroborate cf. 39, 555s47; of unactivated arenes with [Cp*(PMe₃)Ir(Me)(CH₂Cl₂)][BAr_f] or Cp*(PMe₃)Ir(H₃)OTf, **also ar. tritiation**, s. M.B. Skadden, C.M. Yung, R.G. Bergman, Org. Lett. 6, 11-4 (2004).

Oxygen ↑   RemC ↓↑ O

Gallium/iodine Ga/I_2
*Chloroaluminum tetra-*tert-*butylphthalocyanine complexes* ←
Ammonium ceric nitrate or Ceric triflate CAN or $Ce(OTf)_4$
3-Component synthesis [Kabachnick-Fields reaction]   CO → CH(NHR)PO(OR')₂
of α-aminophosphonic acid esters
with SmI₂ cf. 33, 593s67; with 33 mol% CAN s. K. Ravinder, Y. Venkateswarlu et al., Synth. Commun. 34, 1677-83 (2004); with 10 mol% Ce(OTf)₄, Mg(OTf)₂, Cu(OTf)₂ or LiOTf **in the absence of solvent** s. H. Firouzabadi, N. Iranpoor, S. Sobhani, Synthesis 2004, 2692-6; with 10 mol% Ga/I₂ s. P.-P. Sun, Z.-X. Hu, Z.-H. Huang, Synth. Commun. 34, 4293-9 (2004); with 10 mol% chloroaluminum tetra-*tert*-butylphthalocyanine complexes s. E.D. Matveeva, S. Zefirov et al., Synlett 2003, 2321-4.

Thiolate-bridged diruthenium complexes/ammonium tetrafluoroborate ←
1-Methylene-1,2-bis(phosphine oxides) from ethynylcarbinols   CH₂=C(POR₂)C(POR₂)
via palladium-catalyzed 1,2-diphosphinylation

244.

A stirred mixture of 5 mol% thiolate-bridged diruthenium complex (cf. 61, 343) and 10 mol% NH₄BF₄ in anhydrous 1,2-dichloroethane treated at room temp. under N₂ with 1 eq. of the startg. propargyl alcohol and 5 eqs. diphenylphosphine oxide, and stirred at 60° for 18 h → product. Y 96%. Reaction is highly selective for 1-aryl-2-propyn-1-ols, being tolerant of ar. halogen and phenolethers. There was no reaction, however, with simple terminal alkynes, nor alkyl-substituted ethynylcarbinols, and yields were low with substrates possessing electron-withdrawing groups in the aromatic ring. Allenylphosphine oxides are invoked as intermediates. F.e.s. M.D. Milton, Y. Nishibayashi, S. Uemura et al., Org. Lett. 6, 3993-5 (2004).

Nitrogen ↑   RemC ↓↑ N

(L)-*Prolinamide*   Pro-NH₂
Organocatalyzed α-selenylation of aldehydes   H → SeR

245.

1.2 eqs. N-(phenylseleno)phthalimide added at room temp. to a soln. of 2 *mol*% L-prolinamide and the startg. aldehyde in methylene chloride, and treated with water after 10 min → product. Y 95%. This is the first example of a high-yielding organocatalyzed α-selenenylation, reaction being generally applicable to a range of straight-chain and [with added molecular sieves] α-subst.

aldehydes at catalyst loadings as low as 1 mol%. F.e. and comparison of solvents, organocatalysts and selenylating agents s. W. Wang, J. Wang, H. Li, Org. Lett. *6*, 2817-20 (2004).

Silyllithium compds.   LiSi≤
Acylsilanes from N,N-disubst. carboxylic acid amides   CON< → COSi≤
from N,N-dimethylamides cf. *49*, 530; from carboxylic acid morpholides s. C.T. Clark, B.C. Milgram, K.A. Scheidt, Org. Lett. *6*, 3977-80 (2004).

Halogen ↑   RemC ↓↑ Hal

Without additional reagents   w.a.r.
Intramolecular oxyselenation   ○
s. *29*, 180s*66*; polymer-based synthesis of 5-α-arylseleno-2-alkylidenetetrahydrofurans and 2-α-arylseleno-2,3-dihydrofurans from γ,δ-ethyleneketones and a supported ar. selenenyl bromide s. E. Tang, X.-A. Huang, W.-M. Xu, Tetrahedron *60*, 9963-9 (2004).

Irradiation s. under Na/NH₃   ⚡

Lithium   Li
Arylboronic acids from ar. halides   Hal → B(OH)₂
with BuLi cf. *43*, 531s*64*; from ar. chlorides with Li/trimethyl borate s. A. Meudt, M. Erbes, K. Forstinger, European patent EP-1236730 (Clariant Gmbh).

sec-Butyllithium/3,7-di-n-butyl-3,7-diazabicyclo[3.3.1]nonane or (-)-sparteine   ←
1,2-Epoxysilanes via lithiation of epoxides   ←
with Li-2,2,6,6-tetramethylpiperidide cf. *33*, 786s*64*; 1,2-epoxy-1,1-di(silanes) from terminal epoxides via lithiation at the least subst. (terminal) carbon atom with *s*-BuLi/(-)-sparteine, also lithiation with *s*-BuLi/3,7-dibutyl-3,7-diazabicyclo[3.3.1]nonane, s. D.M. Hodgson, E.H.M. Kirton, Synlett *2004*, 1610-2; 1,2-epoxystannanes s. D.M. Hodgson, N.J. Reynolds, S.J. Coote, Org. Lett. *6*, 4187-9 (2004).

Sodium/liq. ammonia/irradiation   Na/NH₃/⚡
Enestannanes   C=C(OPO(OR)₂) → C=C(Sn≤)
from enol phosphates and halogenostannanes

246.   Ph—C(OPO(OEt)₂)=CH₂ + Me₃SnCl ⟶ Ph—C(SnMe₃)=CH₂

A mixture of 1.2 eqs. trimethylstannyl chloride and 2.9 eqs. Na metal in anhydrous liq. ammonia stirred until the blue colour was dispelled, the startg. vinyl phosphate added, the stirred mixture irradiated in a Pyrex reactor with four 200 W UV lamps emitting maximally at 350 nm for 2 h, then quenched with NH₄Cl → product. Y 82%. This is the first example of a vinylic $S_{RN}1$ process involving organostannyl anions as nucleophile, supported by the fact that there was no reaction in the dark. The procedure is stereospecific, but limited to conjugated (phenyl-substituted) enol phosphates. F.e.s. A.B. Chopa et al., J. Org. Chem. *69*, 3801-5 (2004).

1,8-Diazabicyclo[5.4.0]undec-7-ene   dbu
Monoselenoiminocarbonic acid esters from isonitriles s. *68*, 235   RN=C: → RN=C(SeR)OR'

Magnesium   Mg
Arylsilanes from ar. halides   ArHal → ArSi≤
aryl(trimethyl)silanes with Me₃SiCl/Mg cf. *9*, 720; aryl(dialkoxy)methylsilanes with MeSi(OEt)₃/Mg s. S. Jacob et al., German patent DE-10159859 (Fraunhofer Ges Foerderung Angewandten); aryl(trialkoxy)silanes with (EtO)₄Si/Mg s. A.S. Manoso, P. DeShong et al., J. Org. Chem. *69*, 8305-14 (2004).

Boron chloride/aluminum chloride
3,4-Benzocoumarins from *o*-hydroxybiphenyls via 10-hydroxy-10,9-boroxarophenanthrenes

$BCl_3/AlCl_3$

247.

The startg. *o*-hydroxybiphenyl in anhydrous hexane treated with 1.5 eqs. BCl₃ (1 *M* in hexane), stirred for 10 min at room temp., 4% AlCl₃ added quickly, heated at 75° for 6 h, cooled, and quenched with ice-water → intermediate cyclic boronic acid monoester (Y 98%), in 2:1 DMSO/methanol treated with 1 eq. Pd(OAc)₂, stirred at 25° under CO for 3 h, then quenched with water → product. (Y 100%). The protocol is highly regiospecific, clean and proceeds under mild conditions without the use of strong oxidizing agents. However, there was effectively no reaction with substrates possessing electron-withdrawing groups on the pendant aryl ring. F.e.s. Q.J. Zhou, K. Worm, R.E. Dolle, J. Org. Chem. *69*, 5147-9 (2004).

Palladous acetate/1,3-bis(diphenylphosphino)propane/triethylenediamine/ tetra-n-butoxysilane
Palladous acetate/1,1'-bis(diphenylphosphino)ferrocene/sodium tert-*butoxide*
Palladium-catalyzed P-arylation   Hal → P(O)<
arylphosphinic acid esters with PdCl₂(PPh₃)₂/*i*-Pr₂NEt cf. *38*, 584s*64*; *H*-arylphosphonates from Si(OBu)₄/anilinium hypophosphite with Pd(OAc)₂/dppp/dabco, also from aminotrialkoxysilanes, s. Z.H. Huang, K. Bravo-Altamirano, J.L. Montchamp, Compt. Rend. Chim. *7*, 763-8 (2004); tert. arylphosphines s. *36*, 561s*68*.

Palladous acetate/bis[2-(diphenylphosphino)phenyl] ether/triethylamine
Chloro[2,6-bis(2,5-diphenylphosphol-1-ylmethyl)pyridine]palladium(II) fluoroborate/ triethylamine
Arylboronic acid esters from ar. halides   Hal → B(OR)₂
with PdCl₂(dppf)/Et₃N cf. *54*, 244; with chloro[2,6-bis(2,5-diphenylphosphol-1-ylmethyl)-pyridine]palladium(II) fluoroborate/Et₃N s. M. Melaimi, P. Le Floch et al., J. Organomet. Chem. *689*, 2988-94 (2004); with Pd(OAc)₂/bis[2-(diphenylphosphino)phenyl] ether cf. P.E. Broutin, F. Colobert et al., Org. Lett. *6*, 4419-22 (2004).

Remaining Elements ↑   RemC ↓↑ Rem

Magnesium/cuprous oxide/2,2'-bipyridyl $Mg/Cu_2O/bipy$
Ar. selenides from halides *53*, 230s*68*   Hal → SeR

Palladous acetate/1,1,3,3-tetramethylbutyl isocyanide/potassium fluoride/18-crown-6 polyether
***o*-Disubst. arenes from benzynes**
o-(arylthio)stannanes from stannyl sulfides with KF/18-crown-6 cf. *67*, 255; *o*-di(stannanes) with Pd(OAc)₂/1,1,3,3-tetramethylbutyl isocyanide/KF/18-crown-6 s. H. Yoshida, A. Kunai et al., Angew. Chem. Int. Ed. Engl. *43*, 5052-5 (2004).

Carbon ↑   RemC ↓↑ C

Without additional reagents   w.a.r.
β,γ-Ethylenephosphorus(V) acid esters   C=C-CP(O)<
from 2-ethylene-*tert*-amines via N-quaternization

248.

α-Methylene-β-phosphonylcarboxylic acid esters. 1.3 eqs. Methyl iodide added to a soln. of ethyl 2-(morpholin-4-ylmethyl)acrylate in methanol, and stirred for 4 h at 40° → intermediate quaternary ammonium salt, in anhydrous benzene treated with 1 eq. trimethyl phosphite, and refluxed for 2 h → product. Y 82% (overall). F.e. and with phosphonous acid esters s. H. Mrabet, H. Zantour, Phosphorus, Sulfur Silicon Relat. Elem. *179*, 25-33 (2004).

Sodium iodide s. under Pd-C	NaI
Cuprous chloride s. under Ruthenium complexes	CuCl

Lithium perchlorate/p-toluenesulfonic acid $\qquad\qquad\qquad\qquad\qquad$ LiClO$_4$/TsOH
3-Component synthesis of α-aminophosphonic acid esters $\quad$ CHO → CH(NHR)PO(OR')$_2$
with prim. amines cf. *59*, 234s67; α-*prim*-aminophosphonic acid esters with (Me$_3$Si)$_2$NH/LiClO$_4$/TsOH s. N. Azizi, F. Rajabi, M.R. Saidi, Tetrahedron Lett. *45*, 9233-6 (2004).

Carbonyl(chloro)(hydrido)bis(tricyclohexylphosphine)- $\qquad\qquad$ RuH(Cl)(CO)(PCy$_3$)$_2$/CuCl
  ruthenium(II)/cuprous chloride
Regiospecific C-silylation with vinylsilanes $\qquad\qquad\qquad\qquad\qquad$ H → Si≤

249.

α,β-Ethylene-α-silylboronic acid esters. 1 Mol% carbonyl(chloro)(hydrido)bis(tricyclohexylphosphine)ruthenium(II) and 5 mol% cuprous chloride added to a mixture of the startg. α,β-ethyleneboronic acid ester and 2 eqs. dimethyl(phenyl)vinylsilane in benzene (containing dodecane) under argon at 0°, and worked up after 1 h → product. Y 85% (regioselectivity 100%). A mixture of regioisomers was obtained above 20°. Reaction is thought to involve initial insertion of the vinylsilane into the Ru-H bond, followed by migration of silyl to the metal, elimination of ethylene, and regiospecific addition of the silylruthenium species across the double bond prior to elimination of the catalyst. F.e.s. M. Jankowska, B. Marciniec et al., Tetrahedron Lett. *45*, 6615-8 (2004); silylation of enacylamines s. B. Marciniec, D. Chadyniak, S. Krompiec, ibid. 4065-8.

Palladium-carbon/sodium iodide $\qquad\qquad\qquad\qquad\qquad\qquad\qquad\qquad$ Pd-C/NaI
Unsym. triarylphosphines from ar. halides $\qquad\qquad\qquad\qquad\qquad$ ArHal → ArPAr'$_2$
with PdCl$_2$(PPh$_3$)$_2$/Bu$_3$SnCl/NaNH$_2$ cf. *65*, 237s66; from ar. chlorides with Pd-C/NaI s. Y.-C. Wang, S.-C. Kin et al., Tetrahedron *60*, 9433-9 (2004).

Formation of C-C Bond

Uptake ⇓

Addition to Oxygen and Carbon $\qquad\qquad$ CC ⇓ OC

Electrolysis
Electrochemical Henry reaction s. *39*, 578s68 $\qquad\qquad$ CO → C(OH)C(NO$_2$)

Lithium/naphthalene $\qquad\qquad\qquad\qquad\qquad\qquad\qquad\qquad\qquad$ Li/C$_{10}$H$_8$
Syntheses with 2-methylenepropane 1,3-dicarbanion equivalents $\qquad\qquad$ ←
2,8-dioxabicyclo[3.3.0]octanes cf. *47*, 576s55; 1,7-dioxaspiro[4.4]nonanes from ketones and epoxides s. F. Alonso, J. Melenez, M. Yus, Tetrahedron Lett. *45*, 1717-20 (2004).

Sodium/alcohol $\qquad\qquad\qquad\qquad\qquad\qquad\qquad\qquad\qquad\qquad$ NaOR
Baylis-Hillman reaction s. *39*, 593s68 $\qquad\qquad\qquad$ CHO → CH(OH)C(=C)CO

Organolithium compds./zirconocene dichloride RLi/Cp_2ZrCl_2
Reactions of zirconocene η²-olefin complexes with cyclic enolethers   ←

250.

Stereospecific synthesis of 3-(cyclobutyl)alcohols from 3,4-dihydro-2H-pyrans. A soln. of 1 eq. zirconocene dichloride in anhydrous THF treated with a soln. of 2 eqs. *n*-butyllithium at -78° under argon, stirred at the same temp. for 1 h, 1 eq. of dihydropyran added, stirring continued for 15 min, warmed to room temp., stirred again for 3 h, and quenched with D_2O → product. Y 63%. Reaction with 6-membered cyclic enolethers proceeds diastereoselectively via a novel intramolecular migratory insertion, whereas **6-subst. (Z)-3-ethylenealcohols** were obtained from 2,3-dihydrofurans via the anticipated insertion of the double bond of the enolether between the secondary carbon centre and zirconium of the startg. η²-complex. F.e. and electrophiles s. J. Barluenga et al., Angew. Chem. Int. Ed. Engl. *43*, 3932-5 (2004).

n-*Butyllithium*   *BuLi*
Aldol condensation with N-protected α-aminoaldehydes   CHO → CH(OH)C-CO
using LDA cf. *63*, 195; with chiral α-(carbalkoxyamino)aldehydes using *n*-BuLi, asym. induction, s. D.L.J. Clive, M.L. Yu, M. Sannigrahi, J. Org. Chem. *69*, 4116-25 (2004).

2-Hydroxythioethers from oxo compds.   CO → C(OH)C(SR)
with *n*-BuLi cf. *29*, 262s*30*; 1-(1-benzotriazolyl)-2-hydroxythioethers, also subsequent conversion to 2-ketothioethers with $ZnBr_2$ via 1,2-alkyl migration, s. A.R. Katritzky et al., J. Org. Chem. *69*, 4269-71 (2004).

Stereospecific Baylis-Hillman-type reaction with 2,3-dienol 2-monocarbamates   ←

251.

with 1,4-O-carbamyl group migration. 1 eq. Startg. allenyl carbamate in anhydrous THF chilled to -78°, treated under N_2 with 1.1 eqs. *n*-BuLi (1.6 *M* in hexane), stirred at the same temp. for 20 min, 1.2 eqs. *p*-nitrobenzaldehyde added, allowed to warm rapidly to -40°, stirring continued for 2.5 h, and quenched with water → (Z)-product. Y 83%. Reaction involves intermediate formation of an allenolate, (E)-products being obtained at room temp. via a retro-aldol-type reaction. F.e.s. N. Gudimalla, R. Fröhlich, D. Hoppe, Org. Lett. *6*, 4005-8 (2004).

tert-*Butyllithium/hexamethylphosphoramide*   *t-BuLi/HMPA*
Syntheses with 2-lithio-1,3-dithianes   ←
ring opening of epoxides with *n*-BuLi cf. *25*, 483; ring opening of ethyleneepoxides with *t*-BuLi/HMPA, effect of 2-substitution on regio- and stereo-selectivity, s. A.B. Smith III et al., J. Am. Chem. Soc. *124*, 14516-7 (2002).

Phenyllithium/lithium bromide   *PhLi/LiBr*
α-Metalation of α,β-ethylenesulfones with retention of configuration   ←
using MeLi/LiBr cf. *36*, 798; α,β-ethylene-β'-hydroxysulfones from aldehydes with PhLi/LiBr s.
D. Rotulo-Sims, L. Grimaud, J. Prunet, Compt. Rend. Chim. *7*, 941-4 (2004).

Lithium cyanide-acetone   *LiCN·Me$_2$CO*
β-Hydroxynitriles from epoxides   ▽○ → C(OH)C-CN
with LiCN cf. *47*, 584; more rapidly with LiCN-acetone complex, regio- and stereo-selectivity, s.
J.A. Ciaccio, D. Rucando et al., Tetrahedron Lett. *45*, 7201-4 (2004).

Potassium cyanide s. under Titanium(IV) salen complexes   *KCN*
Sodium fluoride s. under Zinc   *NaF*

N-Methylmorpholine N-oxide or o-Hydroxy-N,N-dimethylbenzylamine N-oxide   ←
or Triethanolamine N-oxide/dibenzyldimethylammonium bromide
α-Siloxynitriles from oxo compds.   CO → C(OSi≤)CN
from ketones with N-methylmorpholine N-oxide cf. *65*, 253s67; from aldehydes s. S.S. Kim, G.
Rajagopal, D.H. Song et al., Synth. Commun. *34*, 2973-80 (2004); from ketones with *o*-hydroxy-
N,N-dimethylbenzylamine N-oxide s. Y. Li, G.-L. Zhang et al., Synlett *2004*, 1598-600; with
triethanolamine N-oxide/dibenzyldimethylammonium bromide s. H. Zhou, G.-L. Zhang et al.,
ibid. 1077-9; from oxo compds. with D-sodium gluconate in ether, or K$_2$CO$_3$ in the absence of
solvent, s. B. He, G.-L. Zhang et al., ibid. 1776-8; from ketones with CsF (cf. *28*, 610) s. S.S.
Kim, G. Rajagopal, D.H. Song, J. Organomet. Chem. *689*, 1734-8 (2004); from aldehydes with
1,3-dibenzyl-Δ^2-imidazolinium-2-dithiocarboxylate s. A. Blanrue, R. Wilhelm, Synlett *2004*,
2621-3; from ketones **with asym. induction** using [Bu$_4$N]CN cf. I. Amurrio, R. Cordoba, J.
Plumet et al., Tetrahedron *60*, 10521-4 (2004).

Lithium bromide s. under PhLi   *LiBr*

Hexadecyltrimethylammonium hydroxide   *[Me$_3$NC$_{16}$H$_{33}$]OH*
Henry reaction in water s. *52*, 247s67   CHO → CH(OH)C(NO$_2$)

Ethyldiisopropylamine s. under TiCl$_4$, CrCl$_2$, Mg(ClO$_4$)$_2$ and Cobalt(II) complexes   *i-Pr$_2$NEt*
Piperidine s. under MgI$_2$ *(CH$_2$)$_5$NH*

Triethylenediamine   *dabco*
Triethylenediamine/polyethylene glycol   *dabco/PEG*
Triethylenediamine/1-n-butyl-2,3-dimethylimidazolium hexafluorophosphate   ←
Triethylenediamine/(1S,2R)-N-methyl-N-octylephedrinium triflate   ←
Triethylenediamine/phenol   *dabco/PhOH*
N,N,N',N'-Tetramethylpropylenediamine   *Me$_2$NCH$_2$CH$_2$CH$_2$NMe$_2$*
Baylis-Hillman reaction   CHO → CH(OH)C(=C)CO
update s. *39*, 593s67; γ,δ-epoxy-β-hydroxy-α-methylenecarbonyl compds. with dabco, **asym. induction**, s. P.R. Krishna, K.R. Lopinti, V. Kannan, Tetrahedron Lett. *45*, 7847-50 (2004); β-hydroxy-α-methylenecarboxylic acid esters **with double asym. induction** s. P.R. Krishna, R. Sachwani, V. Kannan, Chem. Commun. *2004*, 2580-1; accelerated Baylis-Hillman reaction with isoxazole-3-carboxaldehydes s. A.K. Roy, S. Batra, Synthesis *2003*, 2325-30; with dabco in PEG-400 for facile recycling of the catalyst s. S. Chandrasekhar, S.S. Sultana et al., Tetrahedron Lett. *45*, 5865-7 (2004); in readily recyclable 1-*n*-butyl-2,3-dimethylimidazolium hexafluorophosphate **as ionic liquid** cf. J.-C. Hsu, Y.-H. Yen, Y.-H. Chu, ibid. 4673-6; **asym. Baylis-Hillman reaction** (cf. *58*, 233s68) in readily recoverable (1S,2R)-N-methyl-N-octylephedrinium triflate **as chiral ionic liquid** s. B. Pegot, G. Vo-Thanh, A. Loupy et al., ibid. 6425-8; with dabco/phenol **in aq. medium** s. C. Faltin, E.M. Fleming, S.J. Connon, J. Org. Chem. *69*, 6496-9 (2004); Baylis-Hillman reaction **with cyclic α,β-ethyleneketones** using N,N,N',N'-tetramethylpropylenediamine s. K.Y. Lee, S. GowriSankar, J.N. Kim, Tetrahedron Lett. *45*, 5485-8 (2004); with hexamethylenetetramine in DMSO (cf. *39*, 593s67) s. R.O.M.A. de Souza, M.L.A.A. Vasconcellos et al., Synthesis *2004*, 1595-600; with 1,2,3- or 1,2,4-triazole and NaHCO$_3$ in aq. media cf. S.-Z. Luo, J.-P. Cheng et al., Tetrahedron Lett. *45*, 5171-4 (2004); Baylis-Hillman reaction of 1,1-nitroethylene derivs. with aq. formaldehyde using imidazole/anthranilic acid s. N. Rastogi, I.N.N. Namboothiri,

M. Cojocaru, ibid. 4745-8 (2004); with 50 mol% *NaOMe* in methanol cf. S.-Z. Luo, J.-P. Cheng et al., J. Org. Chem. *69*, 8413-22 (2004).

Triethylenediamine/tri-n-butylethylphosphonium tosylate   dabco/[EtPBu$_3$]OTs
Co-catalytic Baylis-Hillman reaction in the absence of solvent   CHO → CH(OH)C=CH$_2$

252.

A mixture of benzaldehyde and 1.1 eqs. methyl acrylate added to 0.5 eq. triethylenediamine and 0.1 eq. tri-*n*-butylethylphosphonium tosylate, stirred in a stoppered flask at room temp. for 24 h, diluted with methylene chloride, and washed with 2 *M* aq. HCl and 2 *M* aq. NaOH → product. Y 88%. High yields were obtained for the reaction of acrylic acid esters and acrylonitrile with aliphatic and ar. aldehydes (except anisaldehydes), while methyl vinyl ketone and vinyl sulfones or vinylphosphonates gave low yields or were inactive. The added phosphonium salt is thought to facilitate reaction by stabilizing the intermediate aza-enolate. Lewis acids had a deleterious effect. F.e.s. C.L. Johnson, N. Karodia et al., Tetrahedron Lett. *45*, 7359-61 (2004).

1,8-Diazabicyclo[5.4.0]undec-7-ene s.a. under Ruthenium complexes   dbu

1,8-Diazabicyclo[5.4.0]undec-7-ene/1-ethyl-3-methylimidazolium fluoroborate dbu/[emim]BF$_4$
Henry reaction in ionic liquids   CHO → CH(OH)C(NO$_2$)
in tetramethylguanidinium lactate cf. *34*, 610s67; with dbu in 1-ethyl-3-methylimidazolium fluoroborate s. W.-X. Quian, Y.-M. Zhang et al., J. Chem. Res. Synop *2004*, 154-5.

(S)-1-Methyl-2-(1-pyrrolidinylmethyl)pyrrolidine   ←
Asym. Baylis-Hillman reaction   CHO → CH(OH)C(=C)CO
with (S)-N-methylprolinol cf. *58*, 233s67; with (S)-1-methyl-2-(1-pyrrolidinylmethyl)pyrrolidine s. Y. Hayashi, T. Tamura, M. Shoji, Adv. Synth. Catal. *346*, 1106-10 (2004); with (R,R)-N,N'-bis[N-[3,5-bis(trifluoromethyl)phenylthiocarbamyl]]cyclohexane-1,2-diamine/DMAP in the absence of solvent cf. Y. Sohtome, Y. Hashimoto, K. Nagasawa et al., Tetrahedron Lett. *45*, 5589-92 (2004).

Amine oxides s. under CsF   R$_3$NO

Chiral polymer-based copper(II) bis(Δ^2-oxazoline) complexes   ←
Asym. carbonyl-ene reaction   ←
with chiral copper(II) bis(Δ^2-oxazoline) complexes s. *56*, 242s57; with readily recoverable chiral polymer-based copper(II) bis(Δ^2-oxazoline) complexes for batch-wise or continuous flow conversion s. A. Mandoli, S. Orlandi, P. Salvadori et al., Tetrahedron:Asym. *15*, 3233-44 (2004); with chiral *self-assembled* polymeric titanium(IV) bis(1,1'-bi-2-naphthoxide) complexes (cf. *44*, 568s49) cf. H. Guo, X. Wang, K. Ding, Tetrahedron Lett. *45*, 2009-12 (2004); with [dichloro[(S)-2,3:2',3'-bis(methylenedioxy)-6,6'-bis(diphenylphosphino)]biphenyl]palladium(II)/AgSbF$_6$ for (E)-selective and *anti*-diastereoselective asym. carbonyl-ene reaction with ethyl trifluoropyruvate s. K. Aikawa, K. Mikami et al., ibid. 183-5.

Tetrakis(acetonitrile)copper(I) perchlorate/(1R,2R)-N,N'-bis(4-bromobenzylidene)-   ←
1,2-cyclohexanediamine
α-Hydroxy-γ-ketocarboxylic acid esters from eneurethans   CH(OH)C-C(=NCOOR)
via γ-(N-carbalkoxyimino)-α-hydroxycarboxylic acid esters
Asym. synthesis with addition of two C-atoms

253.

11 Mol% (1R,2R)-N,N'-bis(4-bromobenzylidene)-1,2-cyclohexanediamine in methylene chloride added to 10 mol% [Cu(MeCN)$_4$]ClO$_4$ under argon, stirred for 12 h, cooled to 0°, treated sequentially

with 2 eqs. freshly distilled ethyl glyoxylate in the same solvent and 1 eq. startg. enecarbamate in methylene chloride, stirring continued at the same temp., quenched with satd. aq. NaHCO$_3$, and warmed to room temp. → intermediate imine, in ethanol treated with ca. 28 eqs. 48% aq. HBr, stirred at room temp. for 1.5 min, quenched with satd. aq. NaHCO$_3$ at 0°, and warmed to room temp. → product. Y 79% (e.e. 98%; syn/anti 99:1). The protocol, which is efficient even at the *0.1 mol%* level, illustrates a rare example of utilizing eneurethans as nucleophile, reaction being highly diastereo- and enantio-selective and stereospecific: (Z)-enecarbamates affording *syn*-products while (E)-enecarbamates afford *anti*-isomers. A concerted aza-ene-type mechanism is invoked. F.e.s. R. Matsubara, Y. Nakamura, S. Kobayashi, Angew. Chem. Int. Ed. Engl. *43*, 3258-60 (2004).

Silver(I) acetylides/zirconocene dichloride/silver(I) triflate   ←
α,β-Acetylene-γ-hydroxycarboxylic acid esters from oxo compds.   C(OH)C≡C-COOR
Synthesis with addition of three C-atoms under mild conditions

254.

d.r. 6:1

1.6 eqs. Methyl propiolate (as the silver salt) and 1.2 eqs. Cp$_2$ZrCl$_2$ added to a soln. of the startg. aldehyde in anhydrous methylene chloride under N$_2$ at 23°, treated with 0.2 eq. AgOTf, stirred for 2-7 h at the same temp., quenched with satd. NaHCO$_3$, and stirring continued for 5 min → product. Y 76% (d.r. 6:1). The procedure avoids handling the traditional lithium acetylides, and, accordingly, is applicable to *base-sensitive* compds. Significantly, epoxides and N-Fmoc groups remained unaffected, as also were cyclic ketals. Reaction is generally applicable to aliphatic, ar. and α,β-ethylenic aldehydes and ketones, and is thought to involve intermediate formation of a chlorobis(cyclopentadienyl)zirconium acetylide. F.e.s. S.P. Shahi, K. Koide, Angew. Chem. Int. Ed. Engl. *43*, 2525-7 (2004).

Silver hexafluoroantimonate s. under Palladium complexes   AgSbF$_6$

Magnesium   *Mg*
Grignard synthesis with asym. induction   CO → C(OH)R
s. *9*, 741s62; chiral 2-pyrrolidinylcarbinols s. J. Bejjani, F. Chemla, M. Audouin, J. Org. Chem. *68*, 9747-52 (2003); chiral N-carbalkoxy-1-α-hydroxy-3-azabicyclo[4.4.0]decan-8-one ketals s. J. Christoffers, A. Baro et al., Org. Lett. *6*, 1171-3 (2004); chiral 2-hydroxythioethers s. L. Chacon-Garcia, L.G. Zepada et al., Tetrahedron Lett. *45*, 2141-5 (2004); asym. addition to 2-uloses s. E. Cleator, S.V. Ley et al., ibid. 3077-80.

Grignard synthesis with arylmagnesium halides   CO → C(OH)Ar
s. *3*, 560; *10*, 520; with 3- or 4-carbethoxyphenylmagnesium iodide generated from *active* Mg (prepared from MgCl$_2$ and Li/C$_{10}$H$_8$) s. O. Sugimoto, K. Aoki, K. Tanji, Tetrahedron Lett. *45*, 1915-7 (2004).

Reformatsky-type synthesis   CO → C(OH)C-CO
β-hydroxycarboxylic acid esters cf. *1*, 677; β-hydroxyketones s. J.M. Castro, A. Sanchez et al., Tetrahedron Lett. *45*, 2619-22 (2004).

Magnesium/titanium tetraisopropoxide $Mg/Ti(OPr\text{-}i)_4$
(Z)-3-Ethylene-1,6-diols from two oxo compd. molecules $2\ CO \rightarrow C(OH)C\text{-}C{=}C\text{-}C\text{-}C(OH)$
Synthesis with insertion of four C-atoms via titanacyclopentenes

255.

A soln. of 2.5 eqs. 3-butenylmagnesium chloride in ether (2 M) added dropwise to a soln. of 1 eq. Ti(OPr-i)$_4$ in the same solvent at -70° under N$_2$, warmed to -50°, a soln. of 2 eqs. valeraldehyde in the same solvent added dropwise, allowed to warm to -30° over 1 h with stirring, and quenched by pouring into ice-cold aq. 1 N HCl → product. Y 82% (d.r. 1.3:1; (Z)-selectivity 95%). When unsym. homoallylmagnesium halides were used, the anticipated 1,2-addition took place to give a mixture of regioisomers. Yields were generally better for cyclic ketones and aldehydes. Reaction is thought to involve initial formation of a titanacyclopentene, followed by sequential insertion of two molecules of the oxo compd. via Ti,O-heterocyclics. F.e., **also (Z)-β,γ-ethylene-ε-hydroxyketones from two nitrile molecules**, s. A. Goeke, D. Mertl, S. Jork, Chem. Commun. *2004*, 166-7.

Magnesium/zirconocene dichloride/diisopropyl ketone   ←
Syntheses with zirconocene η^2-olefin complexes   ←
generated from alkylmagnesium bromides s. *66*, 272; 3-ethylenealcohols and 3-ethyleneamines from aldehydes and aldimines, respectively, with added diisopropyl ketone for generation of intermediate alkoxy(allyl)zirconocene complexes, diastereoselectivity, s. K. Fujita, K. Oshima et al., J. Org. Chem. *69*, 3302-7 (2004).

Zinc/oxalic acid $Zn/(COOH)_2$
Pinacolization   2 CHO → CH(OH)CH(OH)
with Zn/H$_3$PO$_4$ under ultrasonication cf. *20*, 501s*67*; with aq. oxalic acid as additive s. J.-T. Li, T.-S. Li et al., J. Chem. Res. Synop *2004*, 494-5.

Zinc/stannous chloride [or Gallium or Indium or Titanocene dichloride/zinc or Stannous   ←
   chloride or Bismuth/potassium fluoride or Bismuth nanoparticles/hexadecyltrimethyl-
   ammonium bromide or Iron/sodium fluoride]
Barbier-type synthesis of 3-ethylenealcohols   CO → C(OH)C-C=C
update s. *40*, 567s*67*; cyclic 1-bromo-1,5-dien-3-ols with In in DMF (cf. *43*, 564s*54*) s. S.K. Mal, D. Ray, J.K. Ray, Tetrahedron Lett. *45*, 277-9 (2004); Barbier-type reaction with *active* indium(0) (generated from InCl$_3$/Sm) in the presence of a little water s. H.-Y. Wu, J. Gao et al., J. Indian Chem. Soc. *81*, 160-2 (2004); chiral *anti*-3-ene-1,2-diols via Barbier-type addition of 3-bromopropenyl acetate to (S)-Garner aldehyde with In in THF s. M. Lombardo, S. Licciulli, C. Trombini, Tetrahedron Lett. *44*, 9147-9 (2003); with Ga metal **in the absence of solvent under ultrasonication**, also 3-ethyleneamines from aldimines (cf. *48*, 626s*66*), s. P.A. Andrews, A.C. Peatt, C.L. Raston, ibid. *45*, 243-8 (2004); with Zn/SnCl$_2$ **in water**, selectivity, s. C.-L. Zhou, H. Yin et al., ibid. 5537-40; with SnCl$_2$ in water under ultrasonication cf. J. Wang, G. Yuan, C.-Q. Dong, Chem. Lett. *33*, 286-7 (2004); with Fe/NaF in water cf. T.-C. Chan, C.-P. Lau, T.-H. Chan, Tetrahedron Lett. *45*, 4189-91 (2004); with Bi-powder in aq. KF s. K. Smith, N. Miyoshi et al., Org. Biomol. Chem. *2*, 935-8 (2004); with Bi-*nanoparticles* (prepared from Bi(NO$_3$)$_3$/KBH$_4$) in aq. hexadecyltrimethylammonium bromide, general procedure from aldehydes or ketones, s. X.-L. Xu, Z.-Y. Wang et al., Synlett *2004*, 1171-4; with Cp$_2$TiCl$_2$/Zn in THF, regioselectivity, s. S. Jana, C. Guin, S.C. Roy, Tetrahedron Lett. *45*, 6575-7 (2004).

Zinc/iodine Zn/I_2
Reformatsky synthesis $CO \to C(OH)C\text{-}COOR$
under ultrasonication cf. 38, 624; **with ketones** in benzene/ether s. S.P. Chavan, K. Shivasankar, R. Sivappa, J. Chem. Res. Synop 2004, 406-7.

Methylmagnesium bromide s. under $Mg(ClO_4)_2$ *MeMgBr*

Diethylzinc/chiral 2-aminoalcohols or 2-(1'-α-hydroxyferrocenyl)-   ←
Δ^2-oxazolines
Diethylzinc/titanium tetraisopropoxide/(S)-3,3'-bis(morpholinomethyl)-   ←
5,5',6,6',7,7',8,8'-octahydro-1,1'-bi-2-naphthol
Zinc triflate/chiral 2-aminoalcohols or fiber-supported variants/triethylamine   ←
Asym. synthesis of 2-acetylenealcohols from aldehydes $CHO \to CH(OH)C\equiv C$
update s. 58, 236s67; with (S)-3-methyl-2-[(2-pyridylmethyl)amino]-1,1-diphenylbutan-1-ol as ligand s. Y.-F. Kang, Y.-F. Zhou et al., Tetrahedron:Asym. 15, 3155-9 (2004); with 2-(1'-α-hydroxyferrocenyl)-Δ^2-oxazolines as ligand s. M. Li, X.-L. Hou et al., ibid. 219-22; with Et_2Zn/Ti(OPr-i)$_4$/(S)-3,3'-bis(morpholinomethyl)-5,5',6,6',7,7',8,8'-octahydro-1,1'-bi-2-naphthol, notably for addition to *o*-subst. benzaldehydes, s. L. Liu, L. Pu, Tetrahedron 60, 7427-30 (2004); with Zn(OTf)$_2$/(1S,2S)-2-(dimethylamino)-4-(4-nitrophenyl)-3-(*tert*-butyldimethylsiloxy)propan-1-ol (cf. 58, 236s64) for preparing chiral 2'-acetylene-2,2,2-trichloroalcohols s. B. Jiang, Y.-G. Si, Adv. Synth. Catal. 346, 669-74 (2004); with readily recyclable chiral fiber-supported 2-aminoalcohols cf. S. Degni, C.-E. Wilén, R. Leino, Tetrahedron:Asym. 15, 231-7 (2004).

Diethylzinc/titanium tetraisopropoxide/(S)-1,1'-bi-2-naphthol
Asym. synthesis of 2-acetylene-*tert*-alcohols from ketones $CO \to C(OH)C\equiv C$
with Me_2Zn/chiral camphorsulfonamides cf. 66, 275s67; with Et_2Zn/Ti(OPr-i)$_4$/(S)-BINOL s. Y.-F. Zhou, Z.-J. Han et al., Org. Lett. 6, 4147-9 (2004).

Diarylzinc compds./diethylzinc/(R)-1-piperidino-1,2,2-triphenylethanol   ←
Asym. synthesis of sec. benzylalcohols from aldehydes $CHO \to CH(OH)Ar$
with chiral ferrocenyl-Δ^2-oxazolines as ligand cf. 55, 239s60; with (R)-1-piperidino-1,2,2-triphenylethanol and Et_2Zn as additive s. M. Fontes, M.A. Pericas, A. Riera et al., J. Org. Chem. 69, 2532-43 (2004).

Magnesium iodide s.a. under Me_3SiI MgI_2

Magnesium iodide/piperidine or Magnesium bromide/ $MgI_2/(CH_2)_5NH$ or $MgBr_2/Et_3N$
triethylamine
Stereospecific aldol condensation via magnesium enolates $CO \to C(OH)C\text{-}CO$
with $MgBr_2/Me_3SiCl/Et_3N$ cf. 63, 248s65; *anti*-β-hydroxyketones with MgI_2/piperidine s. H.-X. Wei, P.W. Pare et al., Tetrahedron 60, 11829-35 (2004); 6-bromo-6-α-hydroxypenicillanates with $MgBr_2/Et_3N$ s. T. Abe, T.S. Mansour et al., J. Org. Chem. 69, 5850-60 (2004).

Zinc fluoride s. under Bi ZnF_2
Aluminum s. under $TiCl_3$ *Al*
Gallium or Indium s. under $Zn/SnCl_2$ *Ga or In*

Trimethylaluminum/(R)-2,2'-bis(trifluoromethanesulfonylamino)-1,1'-binaphthyl   ←
Asym. carbonyl-ene reaction   ←
chiral 4-hydroxy-2-methylenesilanes s. 68, 477

Alumina or Tetra-n-butylammonium fluoride Al_2O_3 or Bu_4NF
Heterogeneous Henry reaction $CHO \to CH(OH)C(NO_2)$
with silica-based diethylpropylamine cf. 34, 610s65; with Al_2O_3, asym. induction on reaction with chiral glyoxylic acid derivs., also with Bu_4NF, s. I. Kudyba, J. Raczko, J. Jurczak, Helv. Chim. Acta 87, 1724-36 (2004).

Chiral N-condensed 1,3,2-oxazaborolidinium triflimides/triphenylphosphine oxide ←
Cyanohydrins from aldehydes   CHO → CH(OSi≤)CN
Asym. conversion via α-siloxynitriles

256.

A soln. of 10 mol% (S)-3,3-bis(3,5-dimethylphenyl)-1-o-tolyltetrahydropyrrolo[1,2-c][1,3,2]-oxazaborolidinium triflimide in toluene added under N_2 at 0° with stirring to 20 mol% triphenylphosphine oxide, stirred until complete dissolution of the latter, treated with 1.13 eqs. trimethylsilyl cyanide in one portion, followed dropwise by a soln. of 1 eq. *p*-cyanobenzaldehyde in toluene at 0° over 1 h, and stirring continued at the same temp. for 144 h → intermediate cyanohydrin trimethylsilyl ether, stirred with a 1:1 mixture of 2 *M* HCl and ethyl acetate → (R)-product. Y 98% (e.e. 97%). The protocol is applicable to both aliphatic and ar. aldehydes, advantages being scalability, predictable face-selectivity, and the fact that the ligand can be easily recycled. The phosphine oxide, serving as a Lewis base, is thought to facilitate the reaction by converting trimethylsilyl cyanide to more reactive isocyano(trimethylsiloxy)triphenylphosphorane. F.e. and comparison of ligands and additives s. D.H. Ryu, E.J. Corey, J. Am. Chem. Soc. *126*, 8106-7 (2004).

Indium(III) triflate $In(OTf)_3$
Friedel-Crafts α-hydroxyalkylation   CO → C(OH)Ar
with $Ga(OTf)_3/CF_3SO_3H$ cf. *43*, 563s*65*; with $In(OTf)_3$ **in water** for reaction of electron-rich arenes with methyl trifluoropyruvate s. R. Ding, D. Wang, C.J. Li et al., Synlett *2004*, 555-7.

Indium(I) bromide   InBr
Reformatsky-type synthesis   ←
α,α-dichloro-β-hydroxynitriles cf. *46*, 592s*62*; α-chloro-β-hydroxyketones, **also sym. and unsym. γ-diketones** from α,α-dichloroketones, s. C. Peppe, R.P. das Chagas, Synlett *2004*, 1187-90.

Lanthanum(III) triflate/(R)-1,1'-bi-2-naphthol/n-butyllithium   ←
Catalytic asym. aldol-Tishchenko reaction under mild conditions   RCH(OH)C-CH(OH)R'

257.

A mixture of 1 eq. of the startg. ar. ketone and 2.5 eqs. *p*-bromobenzaldehyde in anhydrous THF treated slowly with 10 mol% $La(OTf)_3$/(R)-BINOL/BuLi (as a preformed 1:3:5.6 complex; 0.2 *M* in THF) over 1 min at 4°, stirred under argon for 90 h at room temp., diluted with ether, and quenched with aq. 1 *M* HCl → intermediate 1,3-diol monoester, in anhydrous methanol treated with 1 eq. NaOMe, stirred under argon at room temp. until reaction complete (20 min to 2 h) → product. Y 90% (e.e. 88%). This aldol-type coupling is significant as the classical aldol condensation with acylophenones and ar. aldehydes normally suffers from poor catalyst turnover and is often complicated by retro-aldol cleavage. F.e. and with acetophenones and butyrophenones s. V. Gnanadesikan, M. Shibasaki et al., J. Am. Chem. Soc. *126*, 782-3 (2004).

Ytterbium(III) triflate/(S,S)-1,2-dihydroxy-1,2-diphenylethane/ethyldiisopropylamine   ←
Catalyzed asym. aldol-Tishchenko reaction   ←
with chiral yttrium salen complexes cf. *60*, 236; with $Yb(OTf)_3/(S,S)$-1,2-dihydroxy-1,2-

diphenylethane/i-Pr$_2$NEt for preparing chiral 1,2-*anti*-1,3-*anti*-1,3-diol monoesters s. J. Mlynarski, M. Mitura, Tetrahedron Lett. *45*, 7549-52 (2004).

Silica-supported o-*(propylaminomethyl)phenoxyscandium(III) bis(triflate)* ←
α-Siloxynitriles from oxo compds. CO → C(OSi≤)CN
with Yb(OTf)$_3$ cf. *43*, 573s*54*; with thermally stable, readily recyclable silica-supported *o*-(propylaminomethyl)phenoxyscandium(III) bis(triflate) s. B. Karimi, L. Ma'Mani, Org. Lett. *6*, 4813-5 (2004).

*Samarium diiodide/*tert-*butanol or Bis(cyclopentadienyl)-* SmI$_2$/t-BuOH or Cp$_2$TiPh
  phenyltitanium(III)
Cyclic glycols from dioxo compds. ○
with SmI$_2$/*t*-BuOH s. *43*, 571; N-heterocyclic glycols, also reversal of selectivity with Cp$_2$TiPh, s. S. Handa, M.S. Kachala, S.R. Lowe, Tetrahedron Lett. *45*, 253-6 (2004).

Imidazolium ionic liquids s. under Triethylenediamine, 1,8-Diazabicyclo[5.4.0]- ←
  undec-7-ene and 2-(Prolylamino)alcohols

*Tetra-*n-*butylammonium cyanide* [Bu$_4$N]CN
α-Siloxynitriles from ketones with asym. induction s. *65*, 235s*68* CO → C(OSi≤)CN

Imidazole/anthranilic acid ←
1,2,3- or 1,2,4-Triazole/sodium hydrogen carbonate ←
Baylis-Hillman reaction s. *39*, 593s*68* CHO → CH(OH)C(=C)CO

(R,R)-N,N'-Bis[N-[3,5-bis(trifluoromethyl)phenylthiocarbamyl]]cyclohexane-1,2- ←
  diamine/4-dimethylaminopyridine
Asym. Baylis-Hillman reaction in the absence of solvent s. *58*, 233s*68*

1,3-Dibenzyl-Δ^2-imidazolinium-2-dithiocarboxylate ←
α-Siloxynitriles from aldehydes s. *65*, 253s*68* CHO → CH(OSi≤)CN

Phenol s. under Triethylenediamine PhOH
Oxalic acid s. under Zn (COOH)$_2$

L-*Proline or N-Prolylpeptides* Pro-OH or Pro-NHR
Organocatalyzed asym. aldol condensation CHO → CH(OH)C-CO
s. *58*, 245s*66*; with fluoroacetone s. G.-F. Zhong, J.-H. Fan, C.F. Barbas, Tetrahedron Lett. *45*, 5681-4 (2004); with tetrahydro-4*H*-thiopyrones, and desulfurization to chiral, branched aldol adducts, s. D.E. Ward, V. Jheengut, ibid. 8347-50; **asym. α-hydroxymethylation** of oxo compds. with aq. or gaseous formaldehyde s. J. Casas, H. Sunden, A. Cordova, ibid. 6117-9; f. high-pressure asym. aldol condensations (induced in an autoclave by freezing water) s. Y. Hayashi, N. Suzuki et al., ibid. 4353-6; with N-prolylpeptides **in aq. medium** (cf. *58*, 245s*67*) s. Z. Tang, Y.-Z. Jiang et al., Org. Lett. *6*, 2285-7 (2004).

L- *or* D-*Proline* Pro-OH
Asym. synthesis of hexoses from three aldehyde molecules ○
by iterative organocatalyzed aldol condensation

258.

A mixture of isobutanal and propional in DMF treated with 10 mol% L-proline according to *63*, 250 → intermediate chiral β-hydroxyaldehyde, in DMF allowed to react with a second equivalent of propional in the presence of 10 mol% D-proline at 4° for 16 h, and worked up after 24 h at room temp. → product. Overall Y 42% (e.e. 99%). Out of the 16 possible stereoisomers only one is produced, the chirality being simply adjusted by appropriate use of L- or D-proline in the two steps. The procedure is simple, inexpensive, and applicable on the gram scale. F.e. and conversion to chiral δ-lactones s. J. Casas, A. Cordova et al., Angew. Chem. Int. Ed. Engl. *44*, 1343-5 (2005).

Chiral 2-(prolylamino)alcohols/1-n-butyl-3-methylimidazolium fluoroborate ←
Organocatalyzed asym. aldol condensation in ionic liquids CHO → CH(OH)C-CO

259.

Improved procedure. The enantioselectivity of organocatalyzed asym. aldol condensation in ionic liquids (cf. *64, 239s65*) can be significantly enhanced (to 99% for aliphatic aldehydes and 91->99% for aromatic aldehydes), and the range of aldehydes widened, by using a chiral L-prolinamide in place of L-proline. E: A soln. of 4-nitrobenzaldehyde (0.5 mmol scale) in acetone treated with 20 mol% (S,S,S)-pyrrolidine-2-carboxylic acid 2-hydroxy-1,2-diphenylethylamide in 1-*n*-butyl-3-methylimidazolium fluoroborate at 0° for 24 h → product. Y 82% (e.e. 94%). The improvement is attributed to enhanced stabilization of the intermediate iminium ion or the enhanced nucleophilicity of the corresponding enamine. The catalyst can be reused at least twice without loss of efficiency. F.e.s. H.-M. Guo, L.-Z. Gong, Y.-Z. Jiang et al., Chem. Commun. *2005*, 1450-2; with 10 mol% L-proline **in polyethylene glycol** (e.e. 58-84%) cf. S. Chandrasekhar, S.S. Sultana et al., Tetrahedron Lett. *45*, 4581-2 (2004).

*(2S,5S)-5-Benzyl-2-*tert-*butyl-3-methyl-4-imidazolidone/trifluoroacetic acid/Amberlyst 15* ←
Organocatalyzed asym. self-aldol condensation CHO + CHCHO → CH(OH)C-CHO
of α-oxyaldehydes with L-proline cf. *67, 276*; chiral β-hydroxyacetals with (2S,5S)-5-benzyl-2-*tert*-butyl-3-methyl-4-imidazolidone/trifluoroacetic acid/Amberlyst 15, also asym. cross-aldol condensation, s. I.K. Mangion, A.B. Northrup, D.W.C. MacMillan, Angew. Chem. Int. Ed. Engl. *43*, 6722-4 (2004).

Anthranilic acid s. under Imidazole ←
Bis(cyclopentadienyl)phenyltitanium(III) s. under SmI₂ *Cp₂TiPh*
Titanium tetraisopropoxide s.a. under Mg and Et₂Zn *Ti(OPr-i)₄*

Titanium tetraisopropoxide/chiral N-(o-hydroxybenzyl)-2-aminoalcohols ←
α-Siloxynitriles from aldehydes – Asym. conversion CHO → CH(OSi≤)CN
with N,N'-bis(1(S)-ketopinoyl)-1,2-diphenylethylenediamine as ligand cf. *43*, 576s63; with chiral N-(*o*-hydroxybenzyl)-2-aminoalcohols s. Y. Li, X. Feng, G. Zhang et al., J. Org. Chem. *69*, 7910-3 (2004).

Chiral polymeric titanium(IV) bis(1,1'-bi-2-naphthoxide) complexes ←
Asym. carbonyl-ene reaction s. *44*, 568s68 ←

Chiral polymeric titanium(IV) salen complexes/potassium cyanide ←
Cyanohydrin acetates from aldehydes – Asym. conversion CHO → CH(OAc)CN
with chiral binuclear titanium(IV) salen complexes cf. *63*, 253; with readily recyclable chiral polymeric titanium(IV) salen complexes s. W. Huang, Z. Zheng et al., Tetrahedron Lett. *45*, 4763-7 (2004).

Trimethylsilyl chloride s. under Cp₂TiCl₂, TiCl₄ and CrCl₂ *Me₃SiCl*

Trimethylsilyl iodide/magnesium iodide *Me₃SiI/MgI₂*
(E)-α,β-Ethylene-β'-hydroxy-β-iodoketones ←
from α,β-acetyleneketones and aldehydes
with Me₃SiI/BF₃ cf. *64*, 240; with Me₃SiI/MgI₂ s. H.-X. Wei, G. Li et al., Org. Biomol. Chem. *2*, 2893-6 (2004).

Titanocene dichloride s.a. under Zn *Cp₂TiCl₂*

Titanocene dichloride/manganese/trimethylsilyl chloride/2,4,6-collidine
Titanium(III)-catalyzed Barbier-type synthesis under mild conditions

260.

of 3-ethylenealcohols. A suspension of 20 mol% titanocene dichloride and 8 eqs. manganese dust in thoroughly-deoxygenated THF stirred for 15 min under argon at room temp. until it turned lime green, a soln. of 4 eqs. trimethylsilyl chloride, 7 eqs. 2,4,6-collidine and decanal in the same solvent added, followed slowly with stirring over 3 h by 2.5 eqs. allyl bromide, stirring continued for 16 h at the same temp., then quenched with aq. 2 M HCl → product. Y 90%. Reaction is generally applicable to the coupling of aliphatic, unsatd. and aromatic aldehydes and ketones with allyl halides, and propargyl or benzyl bromides, and is more selective than the Sm-mediated route (notably in leaving esters unaffected). The active catalyst is presumed to be Cp$_2$TiCl generated *in situ*. F.e. and asym. synthesis with a chiral Brintzinger-type complex s. A. Rosales, J.E. Oltra, J.M. Cuerva et al., Chem. Commun. *2004*, 2628-9.

Zirconocene dichloride s. under RLi, Silver(I) acetylides and Mg Cp$_2$ZrCl$_2$

Titanium trichloride/aluminum TiCl$_3$/Al
Pinacolization 2 CO → C(OH)C(OH)
with TiCl$_4$/Zn cf. *30*, 561s59; with TiCl$_3$/Al in dil. HCl/ethanol under ultrasonication s. J.-T. Li, T.-S. Li et al., Synth. Commun. *34*, 4339-48 (2004).

Titanium tetrachloride/triethylamine or ethyldiisopropylamine TiCl$_4$/Et$_3$N or i-Pr$_2$NEt
Aldol condensation via titanium(IV) enolates CHO → CH(OH)C-CO
asym. induction with chiral 3-acyl-2-oxazolidones s. *45*, 383; also with chiral 3-acyl-2-oxazolid-inethiones and 3-acylthiazolidine-2-thiones s. M.T. Crimmins, J. She, Synlett *2004*, 1371-4; with chiral 3-acyltetrahydro-1,3,4-oxadiazin-2-ones s. J.F. Vaughn, S.R. Hitchcock, Tetrahedron:Asym. *15*, 3449-55 (2004); with chiral 2-ketoselenides s. M. Tiecco, L. Testaferri et al., ibid. 783-91.

Titanium tetrachloride-bis(tetrahydrofuran)/manganese/(1S,2S)-N,N'-bis(2-pyridylmethylene)-1,2-diphenylethylenediamine/trimethylsilyl chloride
Asym. pinacolization 2 CHO → CH(OH)CH(OH)
with chiral titanium(IV) salen complexes/Zn/Me$_3$SiCl cf. *66*, 280; with TiCl$_4$(THF)$_2$/Mn/(1S,2S)-N,N'-bis(2-pyridylmethylene)-1,2-diphenylethylenediamine/Me$_3$SiCl s. Y.-G. Li, T.-P. You et al., Tetrahedron:Asym. *15*, 1707-10 (2004).

Titanium tetrachloride/tetra-n-butylammonium iodide TiCl$_4$/Bu$_4$NI
Lewis acid-catalyzed Baylis-Hillman reaction CHO → CH(OH)C(=C)CO
with Et$_2$AlI cf. *56*, 253s65; with TiCl$_4$/Bu$_4$NI, **asym. induction** on reaction with carbohydrate-based 3-pyrones, s. R. Sager, C.S. Pant, A.K. Shaw et al., Tetrahedron *60*, 11399-406 (2004).

Titanium tetraiodide TiI$_4$
Reformatsky-type synthesis
β-hydroxy- from α-iodo-oxo compds. cf. *57*, 243s62; β-hydroxy- from α-iodo-alkoximes s. M. Shimizu, T. Toyoda, Org. Biomol. Chem. *2*, 2891-2 (2004).

Stannous chloride s. under Zn $SnCl_2$
Triphenylphosphine oxide s. under Chiral N-condensed 1,3,2-oxazaborolidinium Ph_3PO
    triflimides
Bismuth s.a. under Zn   *Bi*

Bismuth/zinc fluoride Bi/ZnF_2
Reformatsky-type synthesis in aq. medium   CHO → CH(OH)C-CO
β-hydroxyketones with $BiCl_3$/Sm cf. *49*, 591s63; with Bi/ZnF_2 s. Y.J. Lee, T.H. Chan, Can. J. Chem. *81*, 1406-12 (2003).

Tri-n-butylethylammonium tosylate s. under Triethylenediamine $[Bu_3NEt]TsO$

*Chiral [1,1'-binaphthyl-2,2'-diyl-bis(7-*tert-*butyl-8-quinolinolato)]chromium(III)*   ←
    chloride/manganese
Chromium(III)-catalyzed asym. pinacolization   2 CHO → CH(OH)CH(OH)

261.

A mixture of 3 mol% chiral [1,1'-binaphthyl-2,2'-diyl-bis(7-*tert*-butyl-8-quinolinolato)]chromium(III) chloride and 3 eqs. Mn powder (50 mesh) in anhydrous acetonitrile stirred under argon at room temp. for 10 min, the resulting mixture treated with 1 eq. cyclohexanecarboxaldehyde, followed dropwise by 3 eqs. trimethylsilyl chloride, stirred at the same temp., and quenched with satd. aq. $NaHCO_3$ → crude 1,2-diol silyl ether, in dioxane treated at room temp. with 50% aq. H_2SO_4 and ethylene glycol, and stirred at 90° for 24 h → product. Y 44% (*dl/meso* 93:7; e.e. 84%). This highly enantio- and diastereo-selective protocol is applicable to both aromatic aldehydes [incl. those with electron-withdrawing groups] and [for the first time] to aliphatic aldehydes. Reaction is insensitive to steric effects. F.e.s. N. Takenaka, G. Xia, H. Yamamoto, J. Am. Chem. Soc. *126*, 13198-9 (2004).

Chromous chloride $CrCl_2$
Nozaki-Hiyama synthesis of 3-ethylenealcohols   CHO → CH(OH)C-C=C
s. *34*, 614s*47*, 49; polymer-based synthesis of γ-hydroxy-α-methylenecarboxylic acid esters and stereospecific conversion to α-methylene-γ-lactones s. K. Breitenstein, A. Llebaria, A. Delgado, Tetrahedron Lett. *45*, 1511-3 (2004).

Chromous chloride/manganese/chiral bis(Δ^2-oxazolines) or 2-[o-(sulfonylamino)-   ←
    phenyl]-Δ^2-oxazolines/trimethylsilyl chloride/ethyldiisopropylamine
3,4-Unsatd. alcohols from aldehydes   ←
Catalytic asym. Nozaki-Hiyama reaction
chiral 3-ethylenealcohols with chiral 4,5-bis(Δ^2-oxazolin-2-yl)carbazoles as ligand cf. *64*, 244s*67*; with chiral 1,8-bis(Δ^2-oxazolin-2-yl)carbazoles s. M. Inoue, M. Nakada, Org. Lett. *6*, 2977-80 (2004); synthesis of **chiral 3-ethylene-3,1-halogenhydrins** with addition of 3 C-atoms using chiral 2-[*o*-(sulfonylamino)phenyl]-Δ^2-oxazolines as ligand s. M. Kurosu, M.-H. Lin, Y. Kishi, J. Am. Chem. Soc. *126*, 12248-9 (2004).

Copper(I) perchlorate s. under Copper salts $CuClO_4$

Magnesium perchlorate/2,6-bis((R)-4-phenyl-Δ²-oxazolin-2-yl)pyridine/ ethyldiisopropylamine
N,O-Protected β-aryl-α-amino-β-hydroxycarboxylic acid esters from ar. aldehydes via asym. aldol condensation with a glycine equivalent

262.

A mixture of 10 mol% Mg(ClO$_4$)$_2$, 11 mol% 2,6-bis((R)-4-phenyl-Δ²-oxazolin-2-yl)pyridine, 1 eq. 3-(isothiocyanatoacetyl)-2-oxazolidone, and activated powdered 4 Å molecular sieves (to prevent degradation of the magnesium salt) in anhydrous methylene chloride stirred at room temp. under N$_2$ for 1 h, the temperature lowered to -78°, the mixture stirred for 15 min, 1.1 eqs. of the startg. aldehyde and 20 mol% ethyldiisopropylamine added, stirring continued at -78° for 24 h, then quenched with satd. aq. NH$_4$Cl → crude aldol intermediate, dissolved in anhydrous THF, cooled to 0°, treated via cannula with a soln. of 1.3 eqs. MeMgBr (3 M in ether) in excess of ethanol, stirred at the same temp. for 3 min, and quenched with aq. phosphate buffer (pH 7) → product. Y 86% (d.r. 85:15; e.e. of major diastereomer 90%). The procedure is simple and highly enantioselective for the preparation of *syn*-adducts from ar. aldehydes possessing a variety of substituents in the *m*- or *p*-position. F.e.s. M.C. Willis et al., Angew. Chem. Int. Ed. Engl. *44*, 1543-5 (2005).

Tetra-n-butylammonium fluoride s. under Al$_2$O$_3$	Bu$_4$NF
Tetra-n-butylammonium iodide s. under TiCl$_4$	Bu$_4$NI
Dibenzyldimethylammonium bromide s. under CsF	Bn$_2$Me$_2$NBr
Hexadecyltrimethylammonium bromide s. under Zn	C$_{16}$H$_{33}$Me$_3$NBr

Manganese (s.a. under Cp$_2$TiCl$_2$, TiCl$_4$ and CrCl$_2$) — Mn
Reformatsky-type synthesis — CO → C(OH)C-COOR
with Mn/PbCl$_2$/Me$_3$SiCl cf. *52*, 273; with activated Mn (from MnI$_2$ and Li/naphthalene) s. Y.S. Suh, R.D. Reike, Tetrahedron Lett. *45*, 1807-9 (2004).

Iron s. under Zinc — Fe

Iron pentacarbonyl — Fe(CO)$_5$
Reformatsky-type synthesis
of β-hydroxyphosphonic acid esters using [Co(PMe$_3$)$_4$] cf. *55*, 249; α-bromo-β-hydroxynitriles from oxo compds. with addition of 2 C-atoms using Fe(CO)$_5$ s. T.T. Vasil'eva, A.B. Terent'ev et al., Russ. J. Org. Chem. *40*, 174-7 (2004).

*(S,S)-N,N'-[1,2-Bis(3,5-xylyl)ethylene]bis[3-oxo-2-(2,4,6-trimethylbenzoyl)-
butaniminato]cobalt(II)/ethyldiisopropylamine*
Chiral cobalt(II) salen complexes/ethyldiisopropylamine
Asym. Henry reaction $\quad CHO \to CH(OH)CH_2NO_2$

263.

A mixture of 1 eq. *o*-fluorobenzaldehyde, 37 eqs. nitromethane, 5 mol% (S,S)-N,N'-[1,2-bis(3,5-xylyl)ethylene]bis[3-oxo-2-(2,4,6-trimethylbenzoyl)butaniminato]cobalt(II), and 2.5 eqs. ethyldiisopropylamine in methylene chloride allowed to react at -78° for 40 h → product. Y 98% (e.e. 92%). High enantioselectivity was recorded, notably with *o*-halogenobenzaldehydes. F.e. and comparison of β-ketoiminatocobalt(II) complexes and bases, also reaction with aliphatic and α,β-ethylenic aldehydes, s. Y. Kogami, T. Yamada et al., Chem. Lett. *33*, 614-5 (2004); with chiral cobalt(II) salen complexes/ethyldiisopropylamine cf. Synthesis *2004*, 1947-50.

*Bis(acetonitrile)(triphenylphosphine)(cyclopentadienyl)ruthenium(II) hexafluoro-
phosphate/1,8-diazabicyclo[5.4.0]undec-7-ene/sodium hexafluorophosphate*
β-Hydroxynitriles from aldehydes $\quad CHO \to CH(OH)CH_2CN$
Synthsis with addition of 2 C-atoms s. *68*, 276

Tetrakis(triphenylphosphine)palladium(0)/1,3-bis(diphenylphosphino)propane
2,6-Enynols from 3-ethyleneepoxides and allenes

264.

Regiospecific synthesis. Equivalent amounts of the startg. vinyloxirane and allene added to a soln. of 10 mol% Pd(PPh$_3$)$_4$ and 20 mol% dppp in dry, degassed THF (premixed for 30 min), and heated in an autoclave under 5 psi N$_2$ at 70° for 24 h → product. Y 80% (Z/E 61:39). There was no reaction at room temp., or in the absence of ligand or palladium complex, and monosubst. and disubst. allenes were unreactive. 1,4-Addition was exclusive, and (Z)-selectivity was highest with substrates possessing electron-withdrawing groups in the aromatic ring. A variety of functional groups was tolerated, e.g. esters, phenolethers, and halides. F.e.s. P. Nanayakkara, H. Alper, J. Org. Chem. *69*, 4686-91 (2004).

Palladous chloride/stannous chloride $\quad PdCl_2/SnCl_2$
Palladium-catalyzed Barbier-type reaction $\quad CHO \to CH(OH)C-C \equiv C$
heterogeneous conversion with a silica-supported palladium complex s. *52*, 273s53; s.a. M.-Z. Cai et al., J. Organomet. Chem. *689*, 2436-40 (2004); with PdCl$_2$/SnCl$_2$ **in water** s. X.-H. Tan, Q.-X. Guo et al., Tetrahedron Lett. *45*, 5525-8 (2004).

*Dichloro[(S)-2,3:2',3'-bis(methylenedioxy)-6,6'-bis(diphenylphosphino)biphenyl]-
palladium(II)/silver hexafluoroantimonate*
Asym. carbonyl-ene reaction s. *56*, 242s68

Addition to Nitrogen and Carbon CC ⇓ NC

Without additional reagents w.a.r.
N-Protected 2-carbamyl-1,2-dihydropyridine ring ←
from pyridine ring and isonitriles s. *26*, 648s68

n-*Butyllithium/cuprous triflate* BuLi/CuOTf
Regiospecific ring opening of N-functionalized aziridines C̣
of N-tosylaziridines with arylmagnesium bromides/CuI cf. *49*, 610s65, 3-acetylenesulfonylamines from terminal acetylene derivs. with BuLi/CuOTf, regio- and stereo-selectivity, s. C.-H. Ding, L.-X. Dai, X.-L. Hou, Synlett *2004*, 1691-4.

Aryllithium compds./(R,R)-N,N,N′,N′-tetramethyl-1,2-cyclohexanediamine ←
Asym. synthesis of sec. amines from aldimines CH=NR → CH(NHR)R′
with chiral bis(Δ^2-oxazolines) as ligand cf. *50*, 379, asym. addition of aryllithium compds. with inexpensive, readily recoverable (R,R)-N,N,N′,N′-tetramethyl-1,2-cyclohexanediamine as ligand s. N. Cabello, J.C. Kizirian, A. Alexakis, Tetrahedron Lett. *45*, 4639-42 (2004).

Lithium diisopropylamide/hexamethylphosphoramide i-Pr_2NLi/HMPA
α-Diazo-β-(sulfonylamino)carboxylic acid amides $C(NHSO_2R)C(N_2)CON<$
from N-sulfonylimines
Synthesis with addition of two C-atoms with asym. induction

265.

1.2 eqs. Diisopropylamine and 1.1 eqs. *n*-BuLi (2 *M* in hexane) added sequentially at -98° under N_2 to anhydrous THF, the resulting soln. treated dropwise at the same temp. with 1 eq. startg. α-diazocarbonyl compd. over 30 min, stirred at the same temp. for 10 min, *5 eqs. HMPA* added, stirring continued at the same temp. for 5 min, a soln. of 1.1 eqs. startg. N-tosylimine in anhydrous THF added dropwise over 2 h, stirred again for 0.5-3 h until complete consumption of the startg. diazo compd., then quenched with satd. aq. NH_4Cl → product. Y 84% (d.r. >95:5). This the first example of a highly diastereoselective nucleophilic addition of an anion derived from an α-diazocarbonyl compd. to a carbon-nitrogen double bond. Reaction is applicable to aromatic and *in situ*-generated aliphatic N-tosylimines, and is presumed to proceed through a non-chelated open transition state in which the tosylimine approaches from the less hindered side of the anion. F.e. and conversion to **chiral *anti*- and *syn*-β-amino-α-hydroxycarboxylic acid derivs.** s. Y. Zhao, J. Wang et al., Angew. Chem. Int. Ed. Engl. *43*, 5977-80 (2004).

Lithium bis(trimethylsilyl)amide $LiN(SiMe_3)_2$
Asym. Mannich-type reaction CH=N- → CH(NH-)C-CO
of N-phosphinylimines with chiral N-acylsultams cf. *60*, 245; chiral β-(sulfinylamino)ketones with S-chiral N-sulfinylimines s. A. Kennedy, A. Nelson, A. Perry, Synlett *2004*, 967-70.

Chiral 1,2-diamines s. under ArLi ←

(S)-1-(2-Pyrrolidinylmethyl)pyrrolidine ←
(S)-2-(Trifluoromethanesulfonylamino)pyrrolidine ←
Organocatalyzed asym. Mannich reaction C=NR → C(NHR)C-CO
with 5-((S)-pyrrolidin-2-yl)tetrazole cf. *67*, 275, and with L-proline cf. *63*, 266; chiral *β-subst.* γ-aldehydo-α-aminocarboxylic acid esters (with L-proline) s. N.S. Chowdari, J.T. Suri, C.F. Barbas, Org. Lett. *6*, 2507-10 (2004); chiral *α-subst.* products with (S)-1-(2-pyrrolidinylmethyl)-pyrrolidine s. W. Zhuang, S. Saaby, K.A. Jørgensen, Angew. Chem. Int. Ed. Engl. *43*, 4476-8 (2004); chiral α-amino-γ-ketocarboxylic acid esters with (S)-2-(trifluoromethanesulfonylamino)-pyrrolidine s. W. Wang, J. Wang, H. Li, Tetrahedron Lett. *45*, 7243-6 (2004).

1,8-Diazabicyclo[5.4.0]undec-7-ene s. under Ruthenium(II) complexes   *dbu*
Cuprous triflate s. under BuLi   *CuOTf*
Cupric triflate/2,6-bis((3aS,8aR)-8,8a-dihydro-3aH-indeno[1,2-d]oxazol-2-yl)pyridine   ←
Catalytic asym. Passerini reaction   CHO → CH(OAc)CONHR

266.

1.05 eqs. Benzyloxyacetaldehyde added to a soln. of 20 mol% Cu(OTf)$_2$ and 20 mol% 2,6-bis((3aS,8aR)-8,8a-dihydro-3a*H*-indeno[1,2-*d*]oxazol-2-yl)pyridine in methylene chloride under argon, chilled to 0° and aged for 30 min, AW-300 molecular sieves added, followed via syringe pump over 4 h by 1.05 eqs. benzoic acid and *tert*-butyl isonitrile in the same solvent (previously agitated over AW-300 molecular sieves for 30 min), stirred for 18 h at the same temp., quenched by addition of aq. Na-hypochlorite, and stirring continued for 1 h → product. Y 95% (e.e. 98%). Reaction is applicable to aliphatic and aromatic aldehydes and isonitriles. F.e. and comparison of ligands s. P.R. Andreana, C.C. Liu, S.L. Schreiber, Org. Lett. *6*, 4231-3 (2004).

Silver triflate s. under AuCl$_3$ and [IrCl(cod)]$_2$ *AgOTf*
Auric chloride/silver triflate   *AuCl$_3$/AgOTf*
Co-catalytic imino-Friedel-Crafts reaction   H → CH(NHSO$_2$R)R'

267.

α-Aryl-α-(sulfonylamino)carboxylic acid esters. A soln. of furan and 1 eq. startg. N-tosylimine in methylene chloride treated with 2 mol% AuCl$_3$ and 6 mol% AgOTf with exposure to air, the reaction vessel capped, and stirred at 0° for 12 h → product. Y 73%. The protocol is applicable to a range of electron-rich arenes and hetarenes (not indole). Yields were noticeably lower without the silver salt. F.e. and comparison of catalysts s. Y. Luo, C.-J. Li, Chem. Commun. *2004*, 1930-1.

Magnesium   *Mg*
Synthesis of 2-subst. 1-carbalkoxy-1,2-dihydropyridines from pyridines   ←
s. *26*, 884; synthesis of polymer-based 2-(alk-1-ynyl) derivs. and conversion to 2-vinylpyridines s. C. Chen, B. Wang, B. Munoz, Synlett *2003*, 2404-6; 1-carbalkoxy-2-carbamyl-1,2-dihydropyridine ring from isonitriles without reagent, also N-acyl- and N-tosyl-derivs., and polymer-based synthesis s. J.L. Diaz, M. Miguel, R. Lavilla, J. Org. Chem. *69*, 3550-3 (2004).

Magnesium/zirconocene dichloride/diisopropyl ketone   *Mg/Cp$_2$ZrCl$_2$/i-Pr$_2$CO*
3-Ethyleneamines   CH=NR → CH(NHR)C-C=C
from aldimines and zirconocene η^2-olefin complexes s. *66*, 272s68

Zinc   *Zn*
Synthesis of 3-ethyleneamines from azomethines   C=NR → C(NHR)C-C=C
with Zn/CeCl$_3$ cf. *49*, 611; *51*, 292s56; with Zn, regiospecific synthesis with asym. induction, s. C.-L.K. Lee, H.Y. Ling, T.-P. Loh, J. Org. Chem. *69*, 7787-9 (2004).

Dialkylzinc/cupric triflate/chiral bis(Δ^2-oxazolines)
Asym. synthesis of sulfonylamines from N-sulfonylimines   CH(R')NHSO$_2$R
with chiral 2-amino-2'-thiophosphinylamino-1,1'-binaphthyls as ligand cf. *60*, 247s66; with chiral bis(Δ^2-oxazolines), e.g. (R,R)-2,6-bis(4-phenyl-Δ^2-oxazolin-2-yl)pyridine, in the presence of 4 Å molecular sieves for enhanced enantioselectivity s. X. Li, L.-Z. Gong, A.-Q. Mi et al., Tetrahedron:Asym. *14*, 3819-21 (2003).

Magnesium iodide s. under [IrCl(cod)]₂ MgI₂
Zinc triflate/chiral 2-aminoalcohols /triethylamine ←
Asym. synthesis of 2-acetyleneamines from azomethines C=N → C(NH)C≡C
and zinc acetylides with dipeptide amides as chiral auxiliary in the presence of Zr(OPr-i)₄ cf. *66,* 290; chiral 4-(alk-1-ynyl)-3,4-dihydro-2(1*H*)-quinazolones with chiral 2-aminoalcohols as auxiliary, e.g. (1R,2R)-3-*tert*-butoxy-2-dimethylamino-1-(4-nitrophenyl)propan-1-ol, s. B. Jiang, Y.G. Si, Angew. Chem. Int. Ed. Engl. *43,* 216-8 (2004).

Gallium Ga
Synthesis of 3-ethyleneamines from azomethines C=N → C(NH)C-C=C
in the absence of solvent under ultrasonication s. *48,* 626s68

Indium/indium(III) triflate In/In(OTf)₃
Synthesis of 3-ethylenehydrazines from hydrazones C(NHN<)C-C=C
with In cf. *60,* 249; reductive allylation with In/In(OTf)₃, asym. induction, s. G.R. Cook, B.C. Maity, R. Kargbo, Org. Lett. *6,* 1741-3 (2004).

Trialkylaluminum compds./tris(2,2,6,6-tetramethylheptane-3,5-dionato)europium(III) ←
Lanthanide(III)-catalyzed synthesis of sec. benzylamines CH=NAr → CH(NHAr)R
from ar. aldimines

268.

A mixture of 5 mol% Eu(dpm)₃ and the startg. ar. N-arylaldimine in dry benzene treated with 1 eq. Et₃Al (1 *M* in hexane) at room temp. under argon, the mixture stirred for 24 h, then quenched with methanol and powdered NaOH → product. Y 99%. Reaction is thought to involve intermediate formation of an alkyllanthanide as the effective nucleophilic agent, the rate being largely dependent on the nature of the lanthanide metal and the ligand. F.e. and substituent effects, also asym. synthesis with a chiral europium(III) complex s. D. Tsvelikhovsky, G.A. Molander, J. Blum et al., Org. Lett. *6,* 1995-7 (2004).

Diethylaluminum chloride/(R$_S$,S$_S$)-3,3'-bis(benzenesulfinylmethyl)-1,1'-bi- ←
2-naphthol/trimethylsilyl cyanide
Catalytic asym. Reissert reaction of pyridine-3-carboxylic acid derivs. ←

269.

A soln. of 10 mol% predried (R$_S$,S$_S$)-3,3'-bis(benzenesulfinylmethyl)-1,1'-bi-2-naphthol in anhydrous methylene chloride treated under argon with 5 mol% Et₂AlCl (0.98 *M* in *n*-hexane), stirred at room temp. for 1 h, the resulting mixture chilled to -60°, treated successively with 1 eq. of the startg. pyridine (0.4 *M* in methylene chloride), 14 eqs. 9-fluorenylmethyl chloroformate, and 20 eqs. trimethylsilyl cyanide, and stirring continued at the same temp. under argon for 5 h → product. Y 98% (e.e. 96%). This is the first example of a catalytic asym. Reissert reaction with a pyridine deriv., being facilitated by the *bifunctional* nature of the reagent: Lewis acidic aluminum activating the intermediate N-carbalkoxypyridinium ion while the Lewis basic sulfinyl residues of the ligand serve to activate trimethylsilyl cyanide. The chiral sulfinyl residues also stabilize the intermediate complex by coordination to the metal and combine with the axial chirality of the binaphthyl system to effect high face selectivity. Enantioselectivity was lower, however, with pyridine-3-carboxylic acid esters. F.e. and with chiral ligands possessing phosphine sulfide residues s. E. Ichikawa, M. Kanai, M. Shibasaki et al., J. Am. Chem. Soc. *126*, 11808-9 (2004).

Indium(I) iodide InI
Ketimines from nitriles $CN \rightarrow C(=NH)R$
with Mg cf. *21*, 719; 1,2-addition of allyl and benzyl bromides with InI under ultrasonication s. B.C. Ranu, A. Das, Tetrahedron Lett. *45*, 6875-7 (2004).

Gadolinium(III) isopropoxide/(2S,3S,4R)-3-hydroxy-4-(2-hydroxy-4,5-difluorophenoxy)- ←
2-(diphenylphosphinylmethyl)tetrahydropyran/trimethylsilyl cyanide
α-(Phosphinylamino)nitriles from N-phosphinylketimines $C=NPOR_2 \rightarrow C(NHPOR_2)CN$
Asym. Strecker synthesis
with 1.5 eqs Me$_3$SiCN cf. *66*, 292; improved procedure at lower catalyst loading (*0.1 mol%*) with 1.5 eqs HCN and 2.5-5 mol% Me$_3$SiCN s. N. Kato, M. Kanai, M. Shibasaki et al., Tetrahedron Lett. *45*, 3153-5 (2004).

Tris(2,2,6,6-tetramethylheptane-3,5-dionato)europium(III) s. under R_3Al ←

Samarium diiodide SmI$_2$
N-Protected β'-amino-β-hydroxyketones
from N-protected 2-acylaziridines and aldehydes

270.

Stereospecific ring opening. A mixture of 1 eq. of the startg. N-tosylaziridine and 1.1 eqs. of the startg. aldehyde in THF treated at -78° under argon with 2.5 eqs. 0.1 *M* SmI$_2$ in the same solvent, stirred at the same temp. for 1 h, then quenched with satd. aq. NH$_4$Cl → product. Y 99% (*anti,anti* isomer >95%). The substituent at C$_3$ of the aziridine ring, which may be alkyl or aryl, largely determines the stereoselectivity. However, yields were lower with ar. aldehydes, which were partly reduced under these conditions. Samarium enolates are invoked as intermediates. F.e.s. T. Mukaiyama, Y. Ogawa, K. Kuroda, Chem. Lett. *33*, 1472-3 (2004).

Samarium diiodide/tert-butanol SmI$_2$/*t-BuOH*
2-(Hydroxylamino)sulfinylamines C(N(OH)R)C(NHS(O)R')
from nitrones and N-sulfinylimines with asym. induction

271.

A mixture of 3 eqs. Sm powder and 2 eqs. methylene iodide in anhydrous THF stirred at room temp. under argon for 1 h, then cooled to -78°, the resulting mixture treated dropwise at the same temp. with a mixture of 2 eqs. *tert*-butanol, 1.4 eqs. startg. nitrone, and 1 eq. startg. chiral N-*tert*-butylsulfinylimine in the same solvent, stirring continued at the same temp. for 4 h, then quenched with satd. aq. Na$_2$S$_2$O$_3$ → product. Y 85% (d.r. 15:1). This the first example of a highly diastereo- and enantio-selective cross-coupling between two different imine components. Reaction is presumed to involve initial 2-electron reduction of the nitrone to an α-aza-nucleophilic species which then adds preferentially to the *Si*-face of the chiral sulfinylimine. There was no coupling, however, if both substrates were aromatic or aliphatic. F.e. and substituent effects, also conversion to **chiral 1,2-diamines**, s. Y.-W. Zhong, M.-H. Xu, G.-Q. Lin, Org. Lett. *6*, 3953-6 (2004); **2-hydroxylaminoalcohols from nitrones and oxo compds.** s. M. Chavarot, S. Py et al., Chem. Commun. *2004*, 2330-1.

1,1,3,3-Tetramethylguanidine (Me₂N)₂C=NH
2-Nitrophosphinylamines CH(NHPOR₂)C(NO₂)
from N-phosphinylimines and aliphatic nitro compds.
asym. synthesis with lithium aluminum bis((R,R)-1,1′-bi-2-naphthoxide)/KOBu-*t* cf. *62,* 274; *anti*-selective aza-Henry reaction in the absence of solvent with 5 mol% 1,1,3,3-tetramethylguanidine s. L. Bernardi, A. Ricci et al., J. Org. Chem. *69,* 8168-71 (2004).

(S)-3-[N-Isopropyl-N-(3-pyridyl)aminomethyl]-1,1′-bi-2-naphthol ←
Organocatalyzed asym. aza-Baylis-Hillman reaction COCH=CH₂ → COC(=CH₂)CHNHTs

272.

A soln. of methyl vinyl ketone and the startg. ar. N-tosylaldimine in 1:9 toluene/cyclopentyl methyl ether treated with 10 mol% (S)-3-[N-isopropyl-N-(3-pyridyl)aminomethyl]-1,1′-bi-2-naphthol at -15° for 168 h → product. Y 93% (e.e. 87%). The bifunctional activity of the catalyst is apparent: the Brønsted acidic phenolic groups serving to activate the carbonyl group, while the *tert*-amino group serves to generate an enolate by Michael addition (*à la* Baylis-Hillman) prior to the imino-aldol-type addition to the imine and retro-Michael cleavage. The distance between the two activating groups, however, is critical for high enantioselectivity. Reaction tolerates electron-withdrawing and -donating groups in the aromatic ring of the aldimine, which may also be heteroaromatic. F.e. and with acrolein s. K. Matsui, S. Takizawa, H. Sasai, J. Am. Chem. Soc. *127,* 3680-1 (2005).

Chiral dipeptidylthiazolium salts/1,2,2,6,6-pentamethylpiperidine ←
Organocatalyzed asym. synthesis of α-acylaminoketones CHO → CO-C(NHCOR)
from aldehydes and *in situ*-generated N-acylimines

273.

A mixture of 1 eq. of the startg. α-acylaminosulfone (as N-acylimine precursor) and 5.2 eqs. *p*-chlorobenzaldehyde treated under N₂ at 23° successively with a soln. of 15 mol% chiral dipeptidylthiazolium iodide in anhydrous methylene chloride and 10 eqs. 1,2,2,6,6-pentamethylpiperidine, and stirred at the same temp. for 2 h → product. Y 86% (e.e. 85%). The base fulfils a dual role: to assist initial generation of the N-acylimine and for deprotonation of the thiazolium salt to liberate the nucleophilic carbene required to activate the aldehyde (*à la* Stetter). The dipeptidyl side-chain is probably critical in activating the imine through H-bonding. There was minimal racemization under these conditions, and even less with deuterated imines. F.e.s. S.M. Mennen, S.J. Miller et al., J. Am. Chem. Soc. *127,* 1654-5 (2005).

Chiral salen-functionalized α-thioureidocarboxylic acid amides
Asym. Strecker synthesis s. *64*, 429s67 ← C≡N → C(NH)CN

Trimethylsilyl cyanide s. under Et₂AlCl and Gd(OPr-i)₃   Me₃SiCN
Zirconocene dichloride s. under Mg   Cp₂ZrCl₂

Methyldiphenyl- or Dimethylphenyl-phosphine   Ph₂PMe or PhPMe₂
Aza-Baylis-Hillman reaction with N-sulfonylimines   ←
with Bu₃P/DMAP cf. *62*, 271; with Ph₂PMe or PhPMe₂ s. Y.-L. Shi, Y.-M. Xu, M. Shi, Adv. Synth. Catal. *346*, 1220-30 (2004).

(R)-3,3′-Bis(3,5-dimesitylphenyl)-1,1′-binaphthyl-2,2′-diyl hydrogen phosphate   ←
N-Protected 2-α-aminofurans from aldimines   H → CH(NH-)
via organo-Brønsted acid-catalyzed asym. imino-Friedel-Crafts reaction

274.

A soln. of 2 mol% (R)-3,3′-bis(3,5-dimesitylphenyl)-1,1′-binaphthyl-2,2′-diyl hydrogen phosphate in anhydrous 1,2-dichloroethane treated under N₂ with 1 eq. of the startg. imine and 1.2 eqs. 2-methoxyfuran at -35°, and stirred at the same temp. for 24 h → product. Y 88% (e.e. 97%). The procedure is applicable to a wide range of electronically diverse *o-*, *m-* and *p-*subst. N-carbo-*tert*-butoxyaldimines at catalyst loadings as low as 0.5 mol% and on the gram scale. It is also highly enantioselective, high yielding and atom economical. F.e.s. D. Uraguchi, K. Sorimachi, M. Terada, J. Am. Chem. Soc. *126*, 11804-5 (2004).

(S)-2-(Trifluoromethanesulfonylaminomethyl)pyrrolidine   ←
Organocatalyzed asym. Mannich reaction s. *67*, 275s68   C=NR → C(NHR)C-CO

Lithium triflate   LiOTf
β-Acoxycarboxylic acid amides   ▽O → C(OAc)C-CONHR
from epoxides, isonitriles and carboxylic acids
Passerini-type reaction

275.

1 eq. LiOTf, 1 eq. *tert*-butyl isocyanide and 1 eq. benzoic acid added in succession to a soln. of 1 eq. styrene oxide in THF under N₂, and the mixture refluxed for 3 h → product. Y 77%. Aliphatic, aromatic and α,β-unsaturated carboxylic acids can all be used, and remote alkene or alkyne functionalities remained unaffected. Yields were lower, however, with alkyl-subst. epoxides as stabilization of the incipient carbonium ion is lower. F.e. with amino acids, **also β-acylaminocarboxylic acid amides from aziridines**, s. O.T. Kern, W.B. Motherwell, Chem. Commun. *2003*, 2988-9.

Bis(acetonitrile)(cyclopentadienyl)(triphenylphosphine)ruthenium(II) hexafluoro-
phosphate/1,8-diazabicyclo[5.4.0]undec-7-ene/sodium hexafluorophosphate
N-Protected β-aminonitriles from aldimines   CH=N- → CH(NH-)CH$_2$CN
Synthesis with addition of two C-atoms under mild conditions

276.

10 mol% NaPF$_6$ (0.2 M in acetonitrile), 5 mol% [CpRu(PPh$_3$)(MeCN)$_2$]PF$_6$ (0.06 M in acetonitrile), 5.7 eqs. anhydrous acetonitrile and anhydrous HMPA added sequentially to pre-dried 4 Å molecular sieves under argon at room temp., the resulting mixture stirred at the same temp., treated with 1 eq. of the startg. N-protected imine, the soln. degassed via three freeze-pump-thaw cycles, allowed to warm to room temp., 5 mol% dbu (0.5 M in acetonitrile) added, stirring continued at 50° for 48 h, then quenched with aq. 1 M HCl → product. Y 86%. Each of the three reagents is uniquely effective in the catalytic cycle: ruthenium first activates acetonitrile, which is then deprotonated by dbu prior to 1,2-addition to the imine; Ru-Na exchange with NaPF$_6$ then generates the N-sodio deriv. which yields the product on protonation with dbu·H⁺. F.e., **also β-hydroxynitriles from aldehydes**, s. N. Kumagai, S. Matsunaga, M. Shibasaki, J. Am. Chem. Soc. *126*, 13632-3 (2004).

Bis(aquo)[(R)-2,2'-bis(diphenylphosphino)-1,1'-binaphthyl]palladium(II)
bis(triflate)
Palladium-catalyzed asym. Mannich-type reaction   H → CH(NH-)
with β-ketocarboxylic acid esters

277.

Startg. β-keto ester and 2.5 mol% bis(aquo)[(R)-2,2'-bis(diphenylphosphino)-1,1'-binaphthyl]-palladium(II) bis(triflate) added successively to a soln. of 1.5 eqs. startg. N-protected imine in THF at 0°, stirred for 5 h at the same temp., and quenched with ethyl acetate and brine → product. Y 93% (d.r. 88:12; e.e. major isomer 99%; e.e. of minor isomer 97%). The reactivity of the imine is greatly enhanced by triflic acid liberated *in situ* by the initial condensation of the keto ester with the bis(aquo) complex. The procedure is operationally convenient (without recourse to a dry or inert atmosphere) and generates vicinal tertiary-quaternary centres with high diastereo- and enantio-selectivity. Reaction is also applicable to imines derived from simple aldehydes. F.e. incl. N-tosyl derivs., also comparison of chiral di(phosphine) ligands, s. Y. Hamashima, M. Sodeoka et al., Angew. Chem. Int. Ed. Engl. *44*, 1525-9 (2005).

Chloro(1,5-cyclooctadiene)iridium(I) dimer/magnesium iodide $[IrCl(cod)]_2/MgI_2$
2-Acetyleneamines from azomethines $C{\equiv}CH \rightarrow C{\equiv}C\text{-}C(NHR)$

278.

A mixture of 1 mol% [IrCl(cod)]$_2$ and 3 mol% MgI$_2$ in THF stirred for 10 min at room temp. under argon, the startg. imine, 1.2 eqs. trimethylsilylacetylene and further THF added, and stirring continued for 24 h at the same temp. → product. Y 94%. Yields were lower without MgI$_2$ and slightly lower **in the absence of solvent**. Reaction is clean (requiring no work-up procedure) and applicable to a wide range of aliphatic, aromatic and heteroaromatic aldimines and ketimines possessing N-benzyl, N-benzhydryl or N-*p*-methoxyphenyl protective groups. F.e. and iridium catalysts s. C. Fischer, E.M. Carreira, Synthesis *2004*, 1497-503; **2-(alk-1-ynyl)-1-carbalkoxy-1,2-dihydroquinolines** from quinolines with added AgOTf/2,6-lutidine s. Y. Yamazaki, K. Fujita, R. Yamaguchi, Chem. Lett. *33*, 1316-7 (2004).

Addition to Carbon   CC ⇓ C

Bis(η^5-pentamethylcyclopentadienyl)dimethylthorium(IV) $Cp^*_2ThMe_2$
α,β-Acetylenealdimines $C{\equiv}CH \rightarrow C{\equiv}C\text{-}CH{=}NR$
from terminal acetylene derivs. and isonitriles

279.

A mixture of 1 mol% (Cp*)$_2$ThMe$_2$, 2 eqs. startg. alkyne, and 1 eq. *tert*-butyl isocyanide in anhydrous benzene-d$_6$ heated with stirring in a sealed NMR tube at 90° under N$_2$ for 17 h → product. Y 95%. Reaction is presumed to involve 1,1-insertion of the isonitrile into the metal-acetylide bond of an intermediate actinide bis(acetylide). F.e. and with [(Et$_2$N)$_3$U][BPh$_4$] or Cp$_2$UMe$_2$ s. E. Barnea, M.S. Eisen et al., J. Am. Chem. Soc. *126*, 10860-1 (2004).

Addition to Carbon-Carbon Bonds   CC ⇓ CC

Without additional reagents   w.a.r.
Asym. synthesis of quaternary hydrocarbon groups via Michael addition $C{=}C \rightarrow CHC(R)$
with chiral azomethines s. *40*, 458; asym. Michael addition of chiral α,β-dimethyl-β-enamino-esters to α-subst. acrylates s. F. Hendra, M. Nour, C. Cavé et al., Tetrahedron:Asym. *15*, 1027-32 (2004).

3-Component synthesis via zwitterionic addition of isonitriles   ←
to acetylenedicarboxylic acid esters
α-aminoketenimines s. *59*, 279s65; α-acylaminoketenimines s. I. Yavari, H. Djahaniani, F. Nasiri, Collect. Czech. Chem. Commun. *69*, 1499-505 (2004).

Diels-Alder reaction with 1,1-nitroethylene derivs.
s. *35*, 454; with α,β-ethylene-β-nitrophosphonic acid esters s. V.M. Berestovitskaya, L.I. Deiko et al., Russ. J. Gen. Chem. *74*, 523-9 (2004).

Diels-Alder reaction with 2-siloxy-1,3-dienes
s. *31*, 622s*67*; *exo*-selective cycloaddition with a 1-phthalimido-4-(3-indolyl)-2-siloxy-1,3-butadiene s. E. Caballero et al., Tetrahedron Lett. *45*, 1631-4 (2004).

Diels-Alder reaction with 2-pyrones
s. *22*, 877s*63*; with 3-phenylamino-5-bromo-2-pyrone *en route* to constrained α-amino acid derivs. s. W.-S. Kim, C.-G. Cho et al., Tetrahedron Lett. *45*, 1683-7 (2004).

High-pressure Diels-Alder reaction
s. *34*, 626s*67*; of (+)-nopadiene with cyclic enones s. L. Minuti, A. Taticchi et al., Tetrahedron: Asym. *15*, 1187-92 (2004).

N-Subst. 2-amino-5-imidopyrrole-3,4-dicarboxylic acid esters
from acetylenedicarboxylic acid esters, dicarboxylic acid imides and isonitriles

280.

E = COOMe R = c-C_6H_{11}

2 eqs. Cyclohexyl isocyanide added via a syringe to a mixture of succinimide and 1 eq. dimethyl acetylenedicarboxylate in methylene chloride, and refluxed for 48 h → product. Y 72%. Densely functionalized pyrroles are thereby secured from simple and readily available substrates. Reaction appears to involve intermediate formation of a bis(ketenimine), to which the imide adds prior to ring closure. F.e.s. A. Shaabani, M.B. Teimouri, S. Arab-Ameri, Tetrahedron Lett. *45*, 8409-13 (2004).

N-Condensed 1,2-dihydro-4(3*H*)-pyrimidinones
from cyclic imines, acetylene derivs. and isocyanates

281.

E = COOMe Ar = 3-chloro-4-methylphenyl

A soln. of 1 eq. DMAD in methylene chloride added dropwise over 10 min to a stirred soln. of isoquinoline and 1 eq. startg. isocyanate in the same solvent at -5°, allowed to warm to room temp., and stirring continued for 1 h → dimethyl 2-oxo-1-(3-chloro-4-methylphenyl)-1,11b-dihydro-2*H*-pyrimido[2,1-*a*]isoquinoline-3,4-dicarboxylate. Y 99%. The method is simple and mild, and does not require an activation process. Mechanistically, it is possible that the isoquinoline first adds to the acetylenic ester to give a 1:1 adduct, which then combines with the isocyanate prior to ring closure. F.e. and with isoquinoline s. M. Adib et al., Synthesis *2004*, 861-4; with pyridines s. Tetrahedron Lett. *45*, 1803-5 (2004); with imidazoles s. Synlett *2004*, 1086-8.

1,3-Dipolar cycloaddition with nitrile oxides
s. *16*, 888s*54*; cycloaddition to exocyclic glycals with excellent regio- and diastereo-selectivity s. P.A. Colinas, R.D. Bravo et al., Tetrahedron Lett. *44*, 1071-4 (2003); cycloaddition to allyl glycosides s. T. Tamai, K. Tadano et al., Synlett *2003*, 1865-7; synthesis of dideoxynucleoside Δ^2-isoxazolines via cycloaddition with bromonitrile oxide s. E. Coutouli-Argyropoulou, P. Pilanidou, Tetrahedron Lett. *44*, 3755-8 (2003); polymer-based synthesis of a liquid crystalline isoxazole library (cf. *16*, 888s*67*) s. T. Haino, Y. Fukazawa et al., ibid. *45*, 2277-9 (2004).

1,3-Dipolar cycloaddition with nitrones
s. *16*, 735s*66, 54*; with prop-1-ene-1,3-sultone as ene component, regio- and stereo-selectivity, s. L. Tian, L.-Z. Liu et al., Synthesis *2003*, 1329-34; s.a. Tetrahedron Lett. *44*, 395-7 (2003); with γ-enollactones s. C. Roussel, K. Ciamala et al., Org. Biomol. Chem. *1*, 2689-98 (2003); cycloaddition to 2-phenylisatin and its phenylimino deriv. s. P. Astolfi, L. Greci et al., Eur. J. Org. Chem. *2003*, 2626-34; cycloaddition to chiral allyl fluorides with asym. induction s. L. Bernardi, M. Comes-Franchini et al., Tetrahedron:Asym. *15*, 245-50 (2004); synthesis of chiral 3-(C-glycosyl)isoxazolidines s. P. Merino et al., ibid. *14*, 3731-43 (2003); cycloaddition to a D-glyceraldehyde-based cyclic nitrone with asym. induction s. R. Alibés, M. Figueredo et al., Tetrahedron Lett. *44*, 523-5 (2003); with a camphor-derived Δ^2-oxazoline-N-oxide s. A. Voituriez, Y. Langlois et al., Synthesis *2003*, 1419-26.

1,3-Dipolar cycloaddition with nitrile oxides in supercritical carbon dioxide
Effect of solvent density on regioselectivity

282. Ar—N⁺-O⁻ + ≡—COOMe $\xrightarrow{ScCO_2}$ [isoxazole with Ar and COOMe] + [isoxazole regioisomer] Ar = 2,4,6-Me$_3$C$_6$H$_2$

An equimolar (0.016 M) mixture of methyl propiolate and mesitonitrile oxide heated in supercritical carbon dioxide (d 0.765 g/ml) for 21 h at 40° under 2045 psi → product. Y 97% (2.9:1 mixture of regioisomers). The ratio of isomers decreased to 2.5:1 at a density of 0.814 g/ml (2540 psi), and increased to 3.8:1 at a density of 0.611 g/ml (1420 psi). Reaction is also efficient with a range of electron-deficient, electron-rich and hindered ethylenic dipolarophiles, while cycloaddition with chelating α-subst. allyl alcohols is highly *syn*-selective with added MgBr$_2$ (5 eqs.). F.e.s. C.K.Y. Lee, A.B. Holmes et al., Chem. Commun. *2004*, 2622-3.

Hetero-Diels-Alder reaction of α,β-ethyleneazomethines with allenes
s. *16*, 733s*62*; 2-amino-3-methylene-1-sulfonyl-1,2,3,4-tetrahydropyridines from N-sulfonyl-α,β-ethyleneimines with asym. induction s. C.R. Berry, R.P. Hsung, Tetrahedron *60*, 7629-36 (2004).

Irradiation (s.a. under Ph$_2$CO and Cobalt(I) complexes)
Photochemical [2+2]-cycloaddition
s. *22*, 705s*66*; polymer-based [2+2]-cycloaddition of ethylene to chiral PEG-grafted Wang resin-supported 2-cyclohexenones with asym. induction s. T. Shintani, K. Kakiuchi et al., Tetrahedron Lett. *45*, 1849-51 (2004).

Oxetane ring from ethylene derivs. and oxo compds.
s. *19*, 764s*58*; regiospecific solid-state [2+2]-cycloaddition of diaryl ketones to 2-pyrones on grinding in a mortar s. T. Shimo, R. Yamaguchi, K. Somekawa et al., Heterocycles *63*, 1541-5 (2004); cycloaddition to furans s. M. D'Auria, L. Emanuele, R. Racioppi, Tetrahedron Lett. *45*, 3877-80 (2004).

Electrolysis
Michael addition of electrochemically-generated carbanions   C≡C → CHC(R)
of aliphatic nitro compds. cf. *39*, 578s*49*; of active methylene compds., **also electrochemical Henry reaction** (cf. *39*, 578), s. L. Palombi, A. Inesi et al., Chem. Commun. *2004*, 1846-7.

Microwaves (s.a. under ZnCl₂, Tungsten complexes and Pd(PPh₃)₄)
Hetero-Diels-Alder reaction with N-sulfonyl-α,β-ethyleneimines
s. *33*, 627s*49*; N-sulfonyl-1,2,3,4-tetrahydropyridines under microwave enchancement s. B.-C. Hong, M.S. Hallur, J.H. Liao et al., Org. Lett. *6*, 3453-6 (2004).

Potassium hydroxide/N-(9-anthracenylmethyl)cinchonidium bromide
2-Alkylidene-1,5-diketones from α,β-ethyleneketones
Asym. dimerization under phase transfer catalysis

283.

50% Aq. KOH added to a mixture of 1-phenyl-2-buten-1-one and 5 mol% N-(9-anthracenylmethyl)cinchonidium bromide in toluene at -40°, and the mixture stirred at the same temp. for 12 h → product. Y 87% (e.e. 89%). The procedure is high-yielding and highly enantioselective with a range of enones, enantioselectivity increasing with electron-withdrawing groups in the aromatic ring and bulky substituents at the β-carbon atom. Reaction involves an initial asym. Michael addition, followed by base-induced isomerization. F.e.s. F.-Y. Zhang, E.J. Corey, Org. Lett. *6*, 3397-9 (2004).

tert-*Butyllithium/zinc chloride/trimethylsilyl chloride/cuprous chloride*
Stereospecific 3-component synthesis of δ-hydrazonoboronic acid esters
via Michael addition of zincated (Z)-enehydrazines
to α,β-ethyleneboronic acid esters

284.

A soln. of 1 eq. of the startg. N,N-dimethylhydrazone in anhydrous hexane treated slowly at -78° with 2 eqs. *t*-BuLi (1.59 *M* in pentane), stirred at 0° for 1.5 h, 1 eq. ZnCl₂ added, stirring continued for 15 min, solvent removed *in vacuo*, the residue treated at 0° with a soln. of 0.95 eq. startg. α,β-ethyleneboronic acid ester in anhydrous ether, a mixture of 4 eqs. 2-cyclohexenone, 4 eqs. trimethylsilyl chloride and 2 eqs. CuCl added, stirred at the same temp. for 2 h, allowed to warm to 20°, stirred again for 2 h, and quenched at 0° with satd. aq. NaHCO₃ and 10% aq. ammonia until the copper salt dissolved → product. Y 69% (d.s. >95%). *Four contiguous carbon centres* are created with high diastereoselectivity, the latter inverting with cyclic hydrazones. F.e. and electrophiles, also from (Z)-α,β-ethyleneboronic acid esters, and conversion of the product to **1,4-diols** s. M. Nakamura, E. Nakamura et al., J. Am. Chem. Soc. *126*, 14344-5 (2004).

Lithium diisopropylamide   i-Pr_2NLi
Michael addition of enolates   C=C → CHC(R)
to α-chloro-α,β-ethylenesulfoxides s. *36*, 652s*63*; of amide enolates s. T. Satoh, Y. Kamide, S. Sugiyama, Tetrahedron *60*, 11805-12 (2004).

Potassium carbonate/sodium tetrahydridoborate/hydrogen peroxide $K_2CO_3/NaBH_4/H_2O_2$
1,4-Diols from α,β-ethyleneketones and aliphatic nitro compds.   CH(OH)CH-C-C(OH)

285.

via **Michael addition in water**. An aq. soln. of nitroethane and 2 eqs. K_2CO_3 stirred at room temp. for 5 min, 1 eq. methyl vinyl ketone added, stirring continued for 3 h at room temp., treated with 30% H_2O_2, stirred overnight at room temp., excess of $NaBH_4$ added, and stirring continued at room temp. for 2 h → product. Y 60%. The procedure is inexpensive and environmentally friendly. F.e. and isolation of **4-nitroalcohols**, also γ-lactols and γ-diketones, s. R. Ballini, L. Barboni, G. Giarlo, J. Org. Chem. *68*, 9173-6 (2003).

Cesium carbonate/chiral quaternary ammonium salts   ←
Asym. Michael addition under phase transfer catalysis
s. *23*, 700s*67*; of prim. nitro compds. with 2,6-bis[3,5-bis[3,5-bis(trifluoromethyl)phenyl]phenyl]-4,4'-spirobi[dinaphtho[2,1-*c*:1',2-*e*]azepinium] bromide s. T. Ooi, S. Fujioka, K. Maruoka, J. Am. Chem. Soc. *126*, 11790-1 (2004); of fluoromalonic acid esters with cinchonidinium salts (cf. *23*, 700s*62*) s. D.Y. Kim, K. Lee et al., Bull. Korean Chem. Soc. *24*, 1425-6 (2003).

Potassium fluoride/alumina KF/Al_2O_3
Double Michael addition   ←
of azomethines with pyridine as base cf. *29*, 668; sym. 4-acyl-1,7-dicarboxylic acid esters from methyl ketones with KF/Al_2O_3 (cf. *38*, 668s*42*) in the absence of solvent s. B. Basu, P. Das, I. Hossain, Synlett *2004*, 2224-6.

Lithium chloride s. under Pd(PPh$_3$)$_4$ LiCl
Sodium iodide s. under CeCl$_3$ NaI
Triton X-100 s. under Co$_4$(CO)$_{12}$ ←

1,8-Diazabicyclo[5.4.0]undec-7-ene (s.a. under 1,3-Dimesitylimidazolium chloride)   dbu
Michael addition   C=C → CHC(R)
s. *38*, 668; of nickel(II)-complexed N-arylideneglycinates to α,β-ethylenecarboxylic acid amides with asym. induction s. C. Cai, V.J. Hruby, V.A. Soloshonok et al., Tetrahedron Lett. *45*, 6855-8 (2004).

Baylis-Hillman reaction-Michael addition   ←

286.

A soln. of benzaldehyde in THF treated sequentially with 1 eq. 1,8-diazabicyclo[5.4.0]undec-7-ene and 1.1 eqs. methyl acrylate, stirred at room temp. for 16 h, treated slowly with 1.2 eqs. 2-

nitropropane, and stirring continued at the same temp. for 3 h → product. Y 60% (*syn/anti* 1:1; conversion >95%). Complex mixtures were obtained from *prim*-nitroalkanes, and reaction failed with β-subst. acrylates or less reactive ar. aldehydes, such as 4-methoxybenzaldehyde. DBU was fifty times more active than triethylenediamine. F.e. and with dimethyl methylmalonate as nucleophile s. W. Wang, M. Yu, Tetrahedron Lett. *45*, 7141-3 (2004).

(S)-1-(Pyrrolidin-2-ylmethyl)pyrrolidine/trifluoroacetic acid ←
(S)-4-Pyrrolidino-2-(pyrrolidin-2-ylmethyl)pyridine/2,4-dinitrobenzenesulfonic acid ←
Organocatalyzed asym. Michael addition to 1,1-nitroethylene derivs.   C=C → CHC(R)
with chiral diamines s. *62*, 282s66; *64*, 260; chiral γ-nitroaldehydes with (S)-1-(pyrrolidin-2-ylmethyl)pyrrolidine/CF$_3$COOH s. N. Mase, C.F. Barbas III et al., Org. Lett. *6*, 2527-30 (2004); γ-nitroketones with (S)-4-pyrrolidino-2-(pyrrolidin-2-ylmethyl)pyridine/2,4-dinitrobenzenesulfonic acid s. T. Ishii, H. Kotsuki et al., J. Am. Chem. Soc. *126*, 9558-9 (2004); with (S)-5-(pyrrolidin-2-yl)tetrazole, out-performing L-proline (cf. *60*, 267s62), s. A.J.A. Cobb, S.V. Ley et al., Chem. Commun. *2004*, 1808-9.

6'-O-Demethylquin[id]ine derivs. ←
Asym. Michael addition to 1,1-nitroethylene derivs.
with chiral diamines cf. *64*, 260; of malonates and β-keto-esters with bifunctional 6'-O-demethylquin[id]ine derivs. s. H. Li, L. Deng et al., J. Am. Chem. Soc. *126*, 9906-7 (2004); generation of chiral quaternary and tertiary centres s. Angew. Chem. Int. Ed. Engl. *44*, 105-8 (2005).

2-Amino-3-picoline s. under RhCl(PPh$_3$)$_3$ ←

Triphenylphosphinecopper(I) hydride hexamer/hexamethyldisilazane ←
Stereospecific intramolecular reductive aldol condensation   ○
of α,β-acetylene-ω-diketones

287.

cis-**Fused cyclic α,β-ethylene-β'-hydroxyketones.** A mixture of the startg. diketone, 10 mol% [Cu(H)PPh$_3$]$_6$ and 2 eqs. hexamethyldisilazane in anhydrous toluene stirred at -40° for 30 min → product. Y 53% (*cis/trans* 3:1). The method is effective for five- and six-membered cycloalkene ring closure, and notably applicable to β-subst. enones and ketones which ordinarily make poor Michael acceptors and electrophiles, respectively, for the Baylis-Hillman reaction. There was no reaction with the corresponding α,β-ethylenecarboxylic acid esters. F.e.s. P. Chiu, S.K. Leung, Chem. Commun. *2004*, 2308-9.

Chiral copper(II) α-di(azomethine) complexes ←
endo-**Specific asym. 1,3-dipolar cycloaddition with nitrones** s. *54*, 296s68

Chiral copper(II) bis(Δ^2-oxazoline) complexes ←
Chiral copper(II) bis(Δ^2-oxazoline) complexes/silica ←
Asym. Diels-Alder reaction
s. *46*, 662s65; asym. cycloaddition of cyclic and acyclic 1,3-dienes to N-(α,β-ethyleneacyl)-2-oxazolidones s. M.P. Sibi, H. Matsunaga, Tetrahedron Lett. *45*, 5925-9 (2004); reversal of face-selectivity with recyclable, chiral silica-supported copper(II) bis(Δ^2-oxazoline) complexes s. P. O'Leary, J.M. Klein Gebbink et al., ibid. 3177-80.

Silver acetate
Δ^1-Pyrroline-5-carboxylic acid esters
from Δ^2-5-oxazolones and ethylene derivs.
via *exo*-specific 1,3-dipolar cycloaddition

AgOAc
←

288.

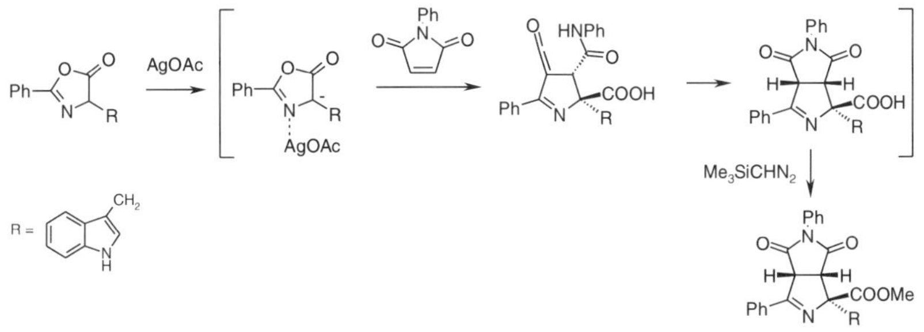

A soln. of 1 eq. of the startg. azlactone, 10 mol% AgOAc, and 1.2 eqs. N-phenylmaleimide in anhydrous THF stirred under argon at room temp. in the dark for 60 h, treated with excess of trimethylsilyldiazomethane, and stirring continued at the same temp. for 2 h → product. Y 70%. Electron-deficient *cis*-olefins afford *exo*-adducts exclusively, there being no isomerization to the corresponding Δ^2-pyrrolines or decarboxylation to pyrroles. Furthermore, the stereoselectivity complements the *endo*-cycloaddition of acyclic azomethinium ylids. There was no reaction with electron-rich olefins. F.e. and isomerization to 3,4-*trans*-products s. S. Peddibhotla, J.J. Tepe, J. Am. Chem. Soc. *126*, 12776-7 (2004).

Cupric triflate s. under R_2Zn	$Cu(OTf)_2$
Cuprous chloride s. under t-BuLi	CuCl
Cuprous bromide s. under Mg	CuBr
Cuprous iodide s. under Mg	CuI
Cupric halides s. under $PdHal_2$	$CuHal_2$

Silver triflimide
2-Siloxycyclobut-2-enecarbonyl compds.
from siloxyacetylenes and α,β-ethylenecarbonyl compds.

$AgNTf_2$
□

289.

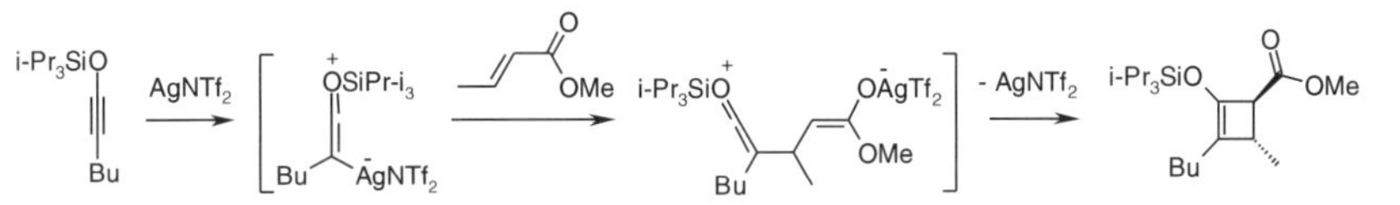

via stereospecific [2+2]-cycloaddition. A soln. of 1.2 eqs. of the startg. siloxyacetylene in anhydrous methylene chloride treated sequentially with 1 eq. methyl crotonate and 5 mol% $AgNTf_2$, stirred at 20° for 5 min, and quenched with satd. aq. $NaHCO_3$ → product. Y 81%. The (Z)-crotonate gave the same stereoisomer, suggesting a stepwise pathway during which the siloxyacetylene is first activated by the silver salt, followed by 1,4-addition and trapping of an intermediate keteninium ion. Reaction is applicable to α,β-ethylenic ketones, esters and nitriles, and the triflimide anion appears essential for high yields. Other Lewis acid gave low yields or were inactive. F.e.s. R.F. Sweis, M.P. Schramm, S.A. Kozmin, J. Am. Chem. Soc. *126*, 7442-3 (2004).

Silver salts s.a. Silver fluoroborate

Ag^+

Methyl(triphenylphosphine)gold(I)/tricyclohexylphosphine/fluoroboric acid
Exocyclic alkoxy-3-ethylenes from enynes

290.

Gold(I)-catalyzed ring closure of enynes (*68*, 351) can be elaborated under acidic conditions by quenching the intermediate carbonium ion with an alcohol to provide additional functionality. **E:** A mixture of the startg. enyne, 3 mol% Au(PPh$_3$)Me, 3 mol% tricyclohexylphosphine and 6 mol% HBF$_4$ in methanol stirred at 23° for 12 h → product. Y 85%. The methoxycyclization is almost exclusively *exo*-selective, reaction being more facile than with platinum(II) catalysts. F.e. and stereoselectivity, also exocyclic 3-ethylenealcohols with water as nucleophile, s. C. Nieto-Oberhuber, A.M. Echavarren et al., Angew. Chem. Int. Ed. Engl. *43*, 2402-6 (2004).

Sodium tetrachloroaurate(III)   *NaAuCl$_4$*
Michael-type addition with indoles   C=C → CHC(R)
addition to enones with Bi(NO$_3$)$_3$ cf. *11*, 770s65; with NaAuCl$_4$·2H$_2$O under neutral conditions s. A. Arcadi, F. Marinelli et al., Synlett *2004*, 944-50; 3-subst. indoles by Michael-type addition to 1,1-nitroethylene derivs. with Amberlyst-15 s. M. Bandini, M. Fagioli, A. Umani-Ronchi, Adv. Synth. Catal. *346*, 439-45 (2004); continuous and semi-continuous process s. ibid. 545-8; **organocatalyzed Michael-type addition** of indoles and arenes to 1,1-nitroethylene derivs. (cf. *17*, 880s68) using *H-bonding* N,N'-bis[3,5-bis(trifluoromethyl)phenyl]thiourea s. D. Gabriella, R.P. Herrera, A. Riccia, Synlett *2004*, 2374-8.

Magnesium   *Mg*
1,4-Addition of Grignard compds. with asym. induction
s. *37*, 657s67; *9*, 770s65; diastereoselective 1,4-addition to chiral N,N'-fumaroylbis(sultams) and conversion to chiral succinic acids s. G.P. Reid, K.W. Brear, D.J. Robins, Tetrahedron:Asym. *15*, 793-801 (2004).

Magnesium/cuprous bromide-dimethyl sulfide/(R)-1-(2-(diphenylphosphino)-
ferrocenyl)ethyldicyclohexylphosphine
Asym. 1,4-addition of Grignard compds. to acyclic α,β-ethyleneketones

291.

A soln. of 5 mol% CuBr·SMe$_2$ and 6 mol% JosiPhos in anhydrous *tert*-butyl methyl ether stirred under argon at room temp. for 20 min, 1 eq. of the startg. enone added, stirred at the same temp. for 5 min, chilled to -75°, treated dropwise over 5 min with 1.1 eqs. methylmagnesium bromide (0.1 *M*) in the same solvent, stirring continued for 2 h, diluted with methanol, allowed to warm to room temp., and quenched with 1 *M* aq. NH$_4$Cl → (R)-product. Y 86% (e.e. 98%; conversion >98%; 99% regio-purity). Enantioselectivities are the highest recorded for the 1,4-addition of an alkylmetal to an acyclic enone. The opposite enantiomer can be secured by judicious selection of complementary enones and Grignard compds. without changing the configuration of the chiral phosphine. F.e. and comparison of chiral phosphines, also from (Z)-enones and β-arylenones, s. F. Lopez, B.L. Feringa et al., J. Am. Chem. Soc. *126*, 12784-5 (2004).

Magnesium/cuprous iodide/lithium chloride/trimethylsilyl chloride ←
1,4-Addition to α,β-acetylenecarboxylic acid esters   C≡C → CH=C(R)
s. *23*, 693s*36*; via Me₃SiCl-mediated catalytic carbocupration of Grignard compds. with CuI·2LiCl, effect of catalyst loading on (E)-selectivity, s. M.P. Jennings, K.B. Sawant, Eur. J. Org. Chem. *2004*, 3201-4.

Zinc s. under CoI₂(PPh₃)₂   Zn
Isopropylmagnesium chloride s. under Ti(OPr-i)₄   i-*PrMgCl*
Isobutylmagnesium bromide s. under Cp₂TiCl₂   i-*BuMgBr*

Dialkylzinc compds./cupric triflate/triethyl phosphite   R₂Zn/Cu(OTf)₂/(EtO)₃P
Stereospecific copper-catalyzed 1,4-addition-intramolecular electrophile trapping   ○
with zinc enolates

292.

Ketones, esters and nitriles have been used for the first time as terminal electrophiles for intramolecular trapping with enolates generated by copper-catalyzed 1,4-addition. **E: 1,4-Addition-intramolecular aldol condensation.** A mixture of the startg. α,β-ethyleneketone, 2.5 mol% Cu(OTf)₂ and triethyl phosphite in anhydrous methylene chloride stirred at room temp. for 15 min, cooled to -20°, treated with 1.5 eqs. Et₂Zn (1 *M* in hexanes), stirring continued for 24 h at the same temp., then quenched with satd. aq. NH₄Cl → product. Y 99% (d.r. >95:1). **1,4-Addition-intramolecular Dieckmann condensation** was equally facile with esters as electrophile, as also was **1,4-addition-intramolecular Blaise reaction** with nitriles as electrophile. F.e. and asym. variant with a chiral cyclic phosphoromonoamidite (1 example) s. K. Agapiou, D.F. Cauble, M.J. Krische, J. Am. Chem. Soc. *126*, 4528-9 (2004).

Dialkylzinc/cupric triflate/chiral cyclic phosphites or phosphoromonoamidites and polymer- ←
based variants or (R)-2-(diphenylphosphino)-2-(p-toluenesulfonylamino)-1,1'-binaphthyl
or chiral cyclic 2-α-(phosphinoamino)-Δ²-oxazolines
Catalytic asym. 1,4-addition   C=C → CHC(R)
update s. *52*, 297s*67*; to chalcone and cyclic enones with chiral 1,1'-binaphthyl-2,2'-diyl 1,2-diphenyl-2-benzyloxyethyl phosphites as ligand s. P. Scafato, C. Rosini et al., Tetrahedron:Asym. *14*, 3873-7 (2003); asym. 1,4-addition to enones and 1,1-nitroethylene derivs. with chiral biphenyl-2,2'-diyl N,N-bis(1(R)-phenylpropyl)phosphoramidites s. A. Alexakis et al., J. Org. Chem. *69*, 5660-7 (2004); s.a. H. Choi, Z.H. Hua, I. Ojima, Org. Lett. *6*, 2689-91 (2004); asym. 1,4-addition to 5,6-dihydro-2-pyridones with chiral 1,1'-binaphthyl-2,2'-diyl phosphoramidites as ligand s. M. Pineschi, B.L. Feringa et al., Chem. Commun. *2004*, 1244-5; iterative asym. synthesis of β-subst. malonic acid esters via asym. 1,4-addition to acyclic alkylidenemalonic acid esters s. J. Schuppan, A.J. Minnaard, B.L. Feringa, ibid. 792-3; asym. 1,4-addition to 2-cyclohexenone with a chiral polymer-based 1,1'-binaphthyl-2,2'-diyl phosphoramidite s. A. Mandoli, B.L. Feringa et al., Tetrahedron:Asym. *14*, 3647-50 (2003); asym. addition to *acyclic* enones with cyclic 2-α-(phosphinoamino)-Δ²-oxazolines as ligand s. T. Morimoto, N. Mochizuki, M. Suzuki, Tetrahedron Lett. *45*, 5717-22 (2004); to chalcone and 2-cyclohexenone with chiral (R)-2-(diphenylphosphino)-2-(*p*-toluenesulfonylamino)-1,1'-binaphthyl as ligand s. C. Blanc, F. Agbossou-Niedercorn, Tetrahedron:Asym. *15*, 757-61 (2004).

Diethylzinc/(S,S)-3,3'-oxydimethylenebis(1,1'-bi-2-naphthol) ←
Asym. Michael addition with α-hydroxyketones   C=C → CHC(R)
s. *63*, 281; details s. J. Am. Chem. Soc. *125*, 2582-90 (2003); asym. Michael addition to N-(α,β-ethyleneacyl)pyrroles as highly reactive monodentate α,β-ethylenecarboxylic acid ester equivalents s. S. Matsunaga, M. Shibasaki et al., ibid. *126*, 7559-70 (2004).

Chiral zinc bis(Δ^2-oxazoline) complexes
Isoxazolidines from ethylene derivs. and nitrones
***endo*-Specific asym. 1,3-dipolar cycloaddition**
with Sc(OTf)$_3$/chiral bis(Δ^2-oxazolines) cf. *54*, 296; with chiral zinc or nickel(II) bis(Δ^2-oxazoline) complexes for cycloaddition to α,β-ethylenealdehydes s. M. Shirahase, S. Kanemasa, M. Hasegawa, Tetrahedron Lett. *45*, 4061-3 (2004); with chiral copper(II) α-di(azomethine) complexes cf. T. Saito, T. Yamada, T. Otani et al., ibid. 9585-7.

Magnesium bromide   MgBr
(Z)-α-Bromo-α,β-ethylene-β'-hydroxyketones
from α,β-acetyleneketones and aldehydes s. *54*, 307s68

Magnesium iodide   MgI$_2$
Tetrahydro-1,2-oxazines from cyclopropanes and nitrones
with Yb(OTf)$_3$ cf. *66*, 314; with MgI$_2$, notably for reaction with formaldehyde nitrone, also one-pot procedure with *in situ*-generated nitrones, s. M.D. Ganton, M.A. Kerr, J. Org. Chem. *69*, 8554-7 (2004).

Ring expansion of methylenecyclopropanes with N-functionalized imines
3-methylene-N-tosylpyrrolidines from N-sulfonylimines cf. *63*, 282; **asym. induction** on ring expansion of 2-methylenecyclopropanecarboxylic acid diphenylamides with S-chiral N-sulfinyl-imines s. M.E. Scott, W. Han, M. Lautens, Org. Lett. *6*, 3309-12 (2004); 3-methylene-Δ^1-pyrrolines from nitriles with CF$_3$SO$_3$H s. J.-W. Huang, M. Shi, Synlett *2004*, 2343-6.

Zinc triflate/triethylamine   Zn(OTf)$_2$/Et$_3$N
Michael addition of terminal acetylene derivs.   C≡C → CHC-C≡C
via cuprous acetylides in aq. medium cf. *65*, 266; via zinc acetylides (with Zn(OTf)$_2$/Et$_3$N) with asym. induction on Michael addition to α-alkylidene-β-dicarbonyl compds. s. T.F. Knopfel, D. Boyall, E.M. Carreira, Org. Lett. *6*, 2281-3 (2004).

Zinc triflate/1-ethyl-3-methylimidazolium triflate   Zn(OTf)$_2$/[emim]OTf
Catalytic Michael addition in ionic liquids   C≡C → CHC(R)
with Ni(acac)$_2$ in 1-*n*-butyl-3-methylimidazolium fluoroborate cf. *35*, 476s63; Michael addition to α-trifluoromethyl-α,β-ethylenecarboxylic acid esters with Zn(OTf)$_2$ or L-proline in 1-ethyl-3-methylimidazolium triflate s. A.M. Salaheldin, Z. Yi, T. Kitazume, J. Fluorine Chem. *125*, 1105-10 (2004).

Zinc chloride s.a. under t-*BuLi*   ZnCl$_2$

Zinc chloride/silica/microwaves   ZnCl$_2$/SiO$_2$/[\\\\]
Phenols from furans and acetylene derivs. via Diels-Alder reaction
Heterogeneous conversion under microwave irradiation in the absence of solvent

293.

A mixture of the startg. acetylene deriv. (1.5 mmol), 6 eqs. 2-methoxyfuran and 0.5 g silica-supported ZnCl$_2$ contained in a hermetically sealed Teflon PTFE tube irradiated in a Miele Electronic M720 microwave oven at 450 W for 30 min, cooled, methylene chloride added, filtered, and the filtrate worked up → product. Y 81%. Et$_2$AlCl/SiO$_2$ and TiCl$_4$/SiO$_2$ were less effective. The method is simple and based on readily available substrates and catalyst. F.e. and regioselectivity s. A. Moreno, A. de la Hoz et al., Synlett *2004*, 1259-63.

Sodium tetrahydridoborate s. under K_2CO_3 NaBH$_4$
9-Borabicyclo[3.3.1]nonane s. under PdCl$_2$(dppf)   BBN

Diisobutylaluminum hydride/dichloro[bis[2-(diphenylphosphino)phenyl] ether]palladium/ tri-2-furylphosphine/indium(III) chloride
(E,E)-1-Halogeno-1,3-dienes from terminal acetylene derivs.
Regiospecific synthesis with addition of two C-atoms

294.

via **hydroalumination-cross-coupling.** A soln. of 1-octyne in heptane treated under argon with 1.05 eqs. diisobutylaluminum hydride at 23°, the mixture heated at 50° for 4 h, cooled to 0°, treated with a suspension of 0.34 eq. dry $InCl_3$ in THF, allowed to react for 30 min, the mixture added via cannula to a soln. of 1.2 eqs. (E)-1-bromo-2-iodoethylene, 1 mol% dichloro[bis[2-(diphenylphosphino)phenyl] ether]palladium, 2 mol% tri-2-furylphosphine and 2 mol% diisobutylaluminum hydride (1 M in hexane) in THF at 0°, stirred at the same temp. for 4 h, and quenched with water → product. Y 81%. Reaction involves intermediate formation of a trivinyl-indium compd., which undergoes Pd-catalyzed cross-coupling with the ethylenedihalide. The choice of palladium catalyst and phosphine ligand is critical as yields were low with other combinations. F.e., also via hydrozirconation-cross-coupling or via zirconocene-catalyzed carbo-alumination, and **synthesis of (E)-β-styryl bromides from arylzinc bromides,** s. M. Qian, Z. Huang, E. Negishi, Org. Lett. *6*, 1531-4 (2004).

Triethylborane Et_3B
3-α-Chloro-1-sulfonylpyrrolidines
from N-chloro-2-ethylenesulfonylamines and ethylene derivs.

295.

3-α,β-Dichloro-1-sulfonylpyrrolidines. A soln. of the N-chlorosulfonamide, 2-3 eqs. styrene and 10 mol% Et_3B in benzene allowed to react at room temp. for 3 h → product. Y 96%. This is part of a simple 2-step **radical synthesis from 1,3-dienes.** Reaction with aliphatic alkenes, however, required a large excess (9 eqs.) of the latter. F.e. and preparation of the startg. m., also with ethyl vinyl ether, s. T. Tsuritani, H. Shinokubo, K. Oshima, J. Org. Chem. *68*, 3246-50 (2003).

Trimethylaluminum/methylaluminum dichloride $Me_3Al/MeAlCl_2$
Lewis acid-catalyzed Diels-Alder reaction with asym. induction s. *36*, 667s68

Sodium dihydridobis(2-methoxyethoxo)aluminate/boron fluoride $NaAlH_2(OCH_2CH_2OMe)_2/BF_3$
β-Hydroxymercaptals $CHO \rightarrow CH(OH)C\text{-}CH(SR)_2$
from aldehydes and ketene mercaptals

296.

anti-β-**Hydroxymercaptals.** A soln. of cinnamaldehyde and 1.2 eqs. startg. ketene mercaptal in methylene chloride treated with 2.4 eqs. BF_3-etherate at -94°, stirred for 0.5 h, a soln. of 1.2 eqs. Red-Al in toluene added, stirring continued for 1 h, then quenched with phosphate buffer (pH 7) → product. Y 65% (*anti/syn* 90:10). Trimethylsilyl triflate predominantly gave the *syn*-isomers. F.e.s. T. Saitoh, N. Jimbo, J. Ichikawa, Chem. Lett. *33*, 1032-3 (2004).

Indium(III) acetate/phenylsilane
Reductive aldol condensation
with Co(II)-hexamethylacetoacetonate/PhSiH$_3$ cf. *45*, 417; β-hydroxyketones with In(OAc)$_3$/ PhSiH$_3$, also intramolecular process, s. K. Miura, Y. Yamada, A. Hosomi et al., Synlett *2004*, 1985-9.

In(OAc)$_3$/PhSiH$_3$
CHO → CH(OH)C-CH

Zeolites
Heterogeneous Diels-Alder reaction
s. *36*, 674s*49*; with α,β-ethylenecarbonyl compds. **in the absence of solvent** using zeolite NaY s. S. Imachi, M. Onaka, Tetrahedron Lett. *45*, 4943-6 (2004).

Dicyclohexylborinyl chloride s. under Rh(CO)$_2$(acac)   Cy$_2$BCl

Boron fluoride (s.a. under Sodium dihydridobis(2-methoxyethoxo)aluminate)   BF$_3$
Lewis acid-catalyzed Diels-Alder reaction-intramolecular carbonyl-ene reaction

297.

under mild conditions. 1.1 eqs. BF$_3$-etherate added to 1.1 eqs. α-bromoacrolein in ether at 0°, stirred for 10 min, treated via cannula with the startg. triene in the same solvent, stirring continued for 1 h at the same temp., warmed to room temp., stirred again for 6 h, and quenched with satd. aq. NH$_4$Cl → product. Y 82% (single stereoisomer). The protocol creates up to five stereogenic centers in a single operation. F.e.s. G.A. Kraus, J. Kim, Org. Lett. *6*, 3115-7 (2004).

Tetrahydrofurans from cyclopropanes and oxo compds.
with SnCl$_4$ cf. *28*, 641s*59*; from electron-deficient ar. aldehydes with BF$_3$-etherate s. S.D.R. Christie, G.J. Pritchard et al., Chem. Commun. *2004*, 2474-5.

Silver fluoroborate s. under [RhCl(CO)$_2$]$_2$ AgBF$_4$
Fluoroboric acid s. under Au(PPh$_3$)Me   HBF$_4$

Diethylaluminum iodide   Et$_2$AlI
Tetrahydrofuran-3-carboxylic acid amides
from cyclopropanecarboxylic acid amides and aldehydes
via β'-hydroxy-γ-iodocarboxylic acid amides with asym. induction

298.

1.2 eqs. Et$_2$AlI added to a mixture of the startg. cyclopropane and 2 eqs. cinnamaldehyde in methylene chloride at 0° under N$_2$, and the mixture stirred at the same temp. for 1 h → intermediate iodohydrin (Y 93%; d.e. 90%), in methylene chloride treated with 5 eqs. Et$_3$N at room temp., and allowed to react for 12 h → product. (Y 84%). Comparable results were obtained in toluene for the first step, but other bases, such as K$_2$CO$_3$ and basic alumina, were either ineffective or required longer reaction times for the ring closure. There was no epimerization during the latter step. F.e.s. C. Timmons et al., Org. Lett. *6*, 2075-8 (2004).

Aluminum chloride   AlCl$_3$
β-Arylcarbonyl compds.
from α,β-ethylenecarbonyl compds. and arenes
C=C → CHC(Ar)
s. *17*, 880s*67*; addition of activated arenes to highly active, *captodative* 1-acetylvinyl *p*-nitrobenzoate s. R. Aguilar, A. Benavides, J. Tamariz, Synth. Commun. *34*, 2719-35 (2004).

Gallium(III) chloride/2,6-di-tert-butyl-4-methylpyridine
Regiospecific addition of ketones to terminal acetylene derivs. $C{\equiv}C \to CH{=}C(R)$
with In(OTf)$_3$ cf. 66, 311; (E)-β-silylvinylation with GaCl$_3$/2,6-di-*tert*-butyl-4-methylpyridine (cf. 53, 302) s. R. Amemiya, Y. Nishmura, M. Yamaguchi, Synthesis 2004, 1307-14.

Indium(III) bromide $InBr_3$
Regiospecific dimerization of α-methylstyrenes under mild conditions s. 63, 304s68

Scandium(III) triflate/1-n-butyl-3-methylimidazolium hexafluoroantimonate
Friedel-Crafts vinylation with acetylene derivs. in ionic liquids $H \to C{=}CH$

299.

10 mol% Sc(OTf)$_3$ added to a soln. of 1-phenyl-1-propyne in 6:1 benzene/1-*n*-butyl-3-methylimidazolium hexafluoroantimonate under N$_2$, and the 2-phase mixture heated to reflux for 4 h → 1,1-diphenyl-1-propene. Y 91%. The upper organic layer, containing the product, was extracted with benzene, while the lower ionic liquid layer, containing the catalyst, was readily recovered by simple decantation and recycled. The catalytic efficiency of the metal triflate, and the yield, were significantly enhanced in the ionic liquid, notably with electron-deficient alkynes which ordinarily fail to react in conventional solvents. This is attributed to increased stabilization of the intermediate vinyl cationic species by the highly polar medium. F.e. with alkyl- or aryl-acetylenes, also comparison of metal triflates, and intramolecular Friedel-Crafts vinylation (with Hf(OTf)$_4$), s. C.E. Song, S. Lee et al., Angew. Chem. Int. Ed. Engl. 43, 6183-5 (2004).

Scandium(III) triflate/sulfoalkylcyclopentadienylium triflates
Friedel-Crafts alkylation with ethylene derivs. in ionic liquids $H \to C\text{-}CH$
with imidazolium salts as ionic liquids cf. 59, 293; improved conversion with sulfoalkylcyclopentadienylium triflates s. K. Qiao, C. Yokoyama, Chem. Lett. 33, 472-3 (2004).

Cerium(III) chloride/sodium iodide $CeCl_3/NaI$
Stereospecific synthesis of α-(halogenomethylene)-β-hydroxycarbonyl compds.
from terminal α,β-acetylenecarbonyl compds. and aldehydes
(Z)-α-(iodomethylene)-β-hydroxycarboxylic acid esters with MgI$_2$/Me$_3$SiI cf. 54, 307s66; ketone derivs. with CeCl$_3$/NaI s. J.S. Yadav, B.V.S. Reddy, B. Eeshwaraiah et al., Synthesis 2005, 57-60; (Z)-β-bromo-α,β-ethylene-β'-hydroxyketones with MgBr$_2$ s. H.-X. Wei, P.W. Pare et al., Tetrahedron 60, 10233-7 (2004).

Benzophenone/irradiation $Ph_2CO/h\nu$
Radical 1,4-addition with 1,3-dioxolanes $C{=}C \to CHC(R)$
s. 35, 474s62; to 2(5H)-furanones s. A.K. Ghosh, S. Leshchenkop, M. Noetzel, J. Org. Chem. 69, 7822-9 (2004).

Imidazolium ionic liquids s.a. under Zn(OTf)$_2$, Sc(OTf)$_3$, L-Proline, Thiazolium salts,
and Tungsten complexes

1-n-Butyl-3-methylimidazolium fluoroborate [bmim]BF$_4$
3-Component synthesis of 2-aminofurans in ionic liquids

300.

A mixture of the startg. aldehyde, 1 eq. dimethyl acetylenedicarboxylate and 1 eq. cyclohexyl isocyanide in 1-*n*-butyl-3-methylimidazolium fluoroborate stirred at room temp. for 1 h (with

TLC monitoring), and the product extracted with ether → dimethyl 2-cyclohexylamino-5-(2-furyl)-3,4-furandicarboxylate. Y 89%. The remaining ionic liquid was readily removed and recycled 5-6 times without loss of activity. Yields are significantly higher, and reaction rates higher, by comparison with the same conversion in traditional organic solvents. Reaction is presumed to involve initial generation of a zwitterionic species which adds to the aldehyde prior to ring closure. F.e. and with aliphatic aldehydes s. J.S. Yadav et al., Synthesis *2004*, 2376-80.

1,3-Dimesitylimidazolium chloride/1,8-diazabicyclo[5.4.0]undec-7-ene
**γ-Lactones from α,β-ethylenealdehydes and aldehydes
under nucleophilic carbene catalysis**

301.

Aldehyde homoenolate equivalents as intermediates. A mixture of 1 eq. cinnamaldehyde (0.5 M), 2 eqs. *p*-bromobenzaldehyde, and 8.1 mol% 1,3-dimesitylimidazolium chloride in anhydrous THF/*t*-butanol (10:1) treated under argon with 7.2 mol% dbu, and stirred under argon at room temp. for 15 h → product. Y 79% (d.r. 4:1). The generated N-heterocyclic carbene reacts with the enal to provide a homoenolate equivalent, which adds to the aldehyde prior to ring closure with release of the catalyst. The latter is sufficiently bulky to prevent the classical Stetter-type benzoin condensation, prevents deprotonation, and in the final phase is incorporated as an activated carboxylate function. The protocol is both simple and mild, but only applicable to ar. aldehydes.
F.e.s. S.S. Sohn, E.L. Rosen, J.W. Bode, J. Am. Chem. Soc. *126*, 14370-1 (2004).

Azodiisobutyronitrile   AIBN
**Regiospecific thiiyl-mediated ring closures of acetylene derivs.
via 1,5-hydrogen atom transfer**

302.

E = MeO$_2$C

under mild conditions. 2 eqs. Thiophenol and 2 eqs. AIBN added over 20 h via syringe pump to a soln. of the startg. acetylene deriv. in refluxing *tert*-butanol → product. Y 89% (d.r. 62:38). Yields are consistently higher, and reaction more environmentally friendly, than by the standard Curran procedure via tin hydride-mediated ring closure of α,β-ethylenebromides which is often complicated by direct reduction of the bromide. Further advantages are that an additional functionality is introduced for subsequent elaboration, and that hydrogen can be transferred from *unactivated* sites, such as a *tert*-alkyl groups. F.e.s. F. Beaufils, F. Dénès, P. Renaud, Org. Lett. *6*, 2563-6 (2004).

4,4'-Azobis(4-cyanovaleric acid) s.a. under Tetraalkylammonium hypophosphites   RN=NR
4,4'-Azobis(4-cyanovaleric acid)/hexadecyltrimethylammonium bromide
Radical ring closures of dienes with functionalization
with addition of H-phosphonates cf. *46*, 451s65; with addition of sec. phosphines or phosphinous acids **in water** with 4,4'-azobis(4-cyanovaleric acid)/hexadecyltrimethylammonium bromide s. D.-Y. Cho, D.-O. Jang, Synlett *2005*, 59-62.

1,1,3,3-Tetramethylguanidine s. under Chiral thioureas $(Me_2N)_2C═NH$

(S)-5-(Pyrrolidin-2-yl)tetrazole   ←
Organocatalyzed asym. Michael addition of ketones   C═C → CHC(R)
to 1,1-nitroethylene derivs. s. *60*, 267s68

Albumin s. under Rh(CO)$_2$(acac)   ←

Amberlyst 15   ←
Michael-type addition with indoles s. *11*, 770s68

Formic acid s. under Pd(PPh$_3$)$_4$ *HCOOH*
Trifluoroacetic acid s. under Chiral diamines CF_3COOH

L-*Proline/1-ethyl-3-methylimidazolium triflate*   *Pro-OH/[emim]OTf*
Michael addition in ionic liquids s. *35*, 476s68

Dimethyl sulfoxide s. under Mo(CO)$_6$ *DMSO*

*3-Benzyl-5-(2-hydroxyethyl)-4-methylthiazolium chloride/triethylamine/1-*n-*butyl-3-*   ←
    methylimidazolium hexafluorophosphate
Polymer-based thiazolium iodides/triethylamine   ←
Stetter hydroacylation   C═C → CHC-COR
under microwave enhancement on alumina cf. *28*, 648s67; **in ionic liquids**, e.g. 1-*n*-butyl-3-methylimidazolium hexafluorophosphate, as readily recyclable media s. S. Anjaiah, S. Chandrasekhar, R. Gree, Adv. Synth. Catal. *346*, 1329-34 (2004); with readily recoverable polymer-based thiazolium iodides s. A.G.M. Barrett, A.C. Love, L. Tedeschi, Org. Lett. *6*, 3377-80 (2004).

N,N'-Bis[3,5-bis(trifluoromethyl)phenyl]thiourea $(ArNH)_2CS$
Organocatalyzed Michael-type addition of indoles   C═C → CHC(R)
to 1,1-nitroethylene derivs. – Also addition of arenes s. *11*, 770s68

(R,R)-N-[3,5-Bis(trifluoromethyl)phenyl]-N'-[2-(dimethylamino)-   *ArNHCSNHR*
    cyclohexyl]thiourea
Organocatalyzed asym. Michael addition of β-dicarbonyl compds.
to 1,1-nitroethylene derivs.

303.

A stirred soln. of 2 eqs. startg. β-dicarbonyl compd. and 10 mol% (R,R)-N-[3,5-bis(trifluoromethyl)phenyl]-N'-[2-(dimethylamino)cyclohexyl]thiourea in anhydrous toluene treated at room temp. with 1 eq. startg. 1,1-nitroethylene deriv., and stirred at -50° for 24 h → product. Y 96% (2R/2S 93:7, e.e. 93%). The environmentally friendly organocatalyst is bifunctional in nature: the thiourea residue activates the electrophile by hydrogen bonding to the nitro group, while the basic amino residue simultaneously activates the dicarbonyl compd. by deprotonation. F.e. incl. Michael addition to alkyl- and hetaryl-subst. nitroolefins, **also** generation of **quaternary hydrocarbon groups,** s. T. Okino, Y. Takemoto et al., J. Am. Chem. Soc. *127*, 119-25 (2005).

(R,R)-N-[3,5-Bis(trifluoromethyl)phenyl]-N'-[2-(dimethylamino)cyclohexyl]thiourea/
1,1,3,3-tetramethylguanidine
**4-Nitrocyclohexanones from α,β-ethyleneketones and 1,1-nitroethylene derivs.
via organocatalyzed asym. Michael addition-intramolecular Michael addition**

304.

Chiral 4-nitrocyclohexanone-2-carboxylic acid esters. A mixture of β-nitrostyrene and the startg. β-ketoester in toluene treated with 1,1,3,3-tetramethylguanidine and 0.1 eq. (R,R)-N-[3,5-bis(trifluoromethyl)phenyl]-N'-[2-(dimethylamino)cyclohexyl]thiourea at -20° → product. Y 87% (d.e. >99%; e.e. 92%). The method creates *three contiguous stereocenters* with high enantioselectivity, reaction benefiting from the bifunctional nature of the catalyst (cf. 68, 303). F.e.s. Y. Hoashi, T. Yabuta, Y. Takemoto, Tetrahedron Lett. 45, 9185-8 (2004).

Phenylsilane s. under In(OAc)₃ $PhSiH_3$

Titanium tetraisopropoxide/isopropylmagnesium chloride $Ti(OPr-i)_4/i-PrMgCl$
Synthesis of 1,4-enynes from acetylene derivs. and 1-funtionalized allenes

305.

via propargyltitanation. 2.5 eqs. Isopropylmagnesium chloride (1.54 *M* in ether) added under argon at -78° to a soln. of 5-decyne and 1.25 eqs. Ti(OPr-*i*)₄ in ether, the mixture warmed to -50° over 30 min, stirred at the same temp. for 3 h, 0.8 eq. 1-bromo-1-(trimethylsilyl)propadiene in ether added, stirring continued for 5 h, treated with 1.2 eqs. benzaldehyde, the cooling bath removed, the mixture stirred at room temp. overnight, then quenched with water → product. Y 63%. Reaction is facilitated by an allenyl hetero-substituent (Br or PhS), which is transferred to titanium prior to quenching with the electrophile. F.e. and electrophiles, also regiospecificity with unsym. alkynes, s. R. Tanaka, F. Sato, H. Urabe et al., Tetrahedron Lett. 46, 329-32 (2005).

Zirconium tetrapropoxide/(R)-3,3'-diiodo-1,1'-bi-2-naphthol/n-propanol
1-Acylpyrazolidines from ethylene derivs. and N-acylhydrazones via asym. [3+2]-cycloaddition

306.

A suspension of 12 mol% (R)-3,3'-diiodo-1,1'-bi-2-naphthol in anhydrous toluene treated at room temp. under argon with a soln. of 10 mol% Zr(OPr)$_4$ in the same solvent, stirred for 0.5 h, a soln. of 0.5 eq. *n*-propanol in toluene added, stirred at the same temp. for 0.5 h, the resulting catalyst soln. (and toluene washings) added to 1 eq. startg. N-acylhydrazone, stirred at 0°, treated with a soln. of the startg. ethylene deriv. in toluene, stirring continued for 18 h, and quenched with water → product. Y 87% (e.e. 97%). Reaction is high yielding and highly enantioselective, and generally applicable to a range of aldehydes, incl. α- and β-subst., enolizable, functionalized, and hindered derivs. Chiral 1-acyl-5-alkoxypyrazolidines were obtained similarly from enolethers, and converted to **chiral 1-acyl-Δ^2-pyrazolines.** A concerted mechanism is invoked. F.e. and with thioenolethers (in lower yield) s. Y. Yamashita, S. Kobayashi, J. Am. Chem. Soc. *126*, 11279-82 (2004).

Trimethylsilyl chloride s. under t-BuLi, Mg and Pd(PPh$_3$)$_4$ Me$_3$SiCl
Chlorobis(cyclopentadienyl)hydridozirconium s.a. under Pd(PPh$_3$)$_4$ CpZr(H)Cl

Chlorobis(cyclopentadienyl)hydridozirconium/trimethylsilyl triflate   Cp$_2$Zr(H)Cl/Me$_3$SiOTf
Synthesis of 2-ethylenealcohols   CO → C(OH)CH=CH
from terminal acetylene derivs. and oxo compds.
via regio- and stereo-specific hydrozirconation
(E)-2-ethylenealcohols from aldehydes s. *52*, 310s66; from ketones with added Me$_3$SiOTf s. T. Murakami, K. Furusawa, Synthesis *2004*, 1566-72.

1,1-Bis(η^5-cyclopentadienyl)-1,3,4-triaryl-1,2-zirconacyclobut-3-enes
(E,E)-α,β-Ethyleneketimines from acetylene derivs. and aldimines   CH=C-C(=NR)R'
Zirconium-catalyzed carboamination

307.

Imidozirconium-catalyzed 'carboamination' of acetylene derivs. with aldimines has been reported for the first time. **E:** A soln. of 10 mol% 1,1-bis(η^5-cyclopentadienyl)-3,4-diphenyl-N-*p*-tolyl-

1,2-zirconacyclobut-3-ene and 1 eq. startg. aldimine in anhydrous benzene-d_6 treated under N_2 with 1 eq. diphenylacetylene, and heated at 145° in a sealed tube for 80 h → product. Y 82%. Reaction is presumed to involve insertion of the imine into the azazirconacyclobutene to give a 6-membered diazazirconacyclic prior to elimination. However, it appears limited to *all-aryl* substrates. Reaction is also effective with methylzirconocene (*p*-methoxyphenyl)amide so that a more generalized procedure is feasible. F.e. and substituent effects s. R.T. Ruck, R.G. Bergman et al., Angew. Chem. Int. Ed. Engl. *43*, 5372-4 (2004).

Titanocene dichloride/isobutylmagnesium bromide/tetrakis- Cp_2TiCl_2/i-BuMgBr/Pd(PPh_3)_4$
(triphenylphosphine)palladium(0)
Synthesis of (Z)-enesilanes from silylacetylenes ←
via regio- and stereo-specific hydromagnesiation s. *66*, 318; 2-silyl-1(Z),4-dienes from β,γ-ethylenechlorides s. H. Zhao, M.Z. Cai, Z. Zhou et al., J. Chem. Res. Synop *2003*, 780-1; 2-silyl-1(Z),3-enynes from α,β-acetyleneiodides with added Pd(PPh_3)_4 s. ibid. 485-6.

Zirconocene dichloride/n-butyllithium $Cp_2ZrCl_2/BuLi$
Ring closures of unsatd. azomethines ○
via condensed 1,2-azatitanacyclopent(a,e)nes with Ti(OPr-*i*)_4/*i*-PrMgCl cf. *51*, 315; ring closures of acetyleneazomethines via condensed 1,2-azazirconacyclopentenes with Cp_2ZrCl_2/BuLi s. M. Makabe, Y. Sato, M. Mori, Synthesis *2004*, 1369-74; stereospecific ring closures of ethyleneazomethines s. J. Org. Chem. *69*, 6238-43 (2004).

Titanium tetrachloride $TiCl_4$
Lewis acid-catalyzed Diels-Alder reaction with asym. induction
s. *44*, 622s63; **polymer-based synthesis** with a chiral resin-supported 3-acryloyloxy-2-pyrrolidone s. R. Akkari, M. Calmes, J. Martinez et al., Tetrahedron:Asym. *15*, 2515-25 (2004); achiral polymer-based process, also comparison of Lewis acids, s. Eur. J. Org. Chem. *2004*, 2441-50; soln.-phase method with Me_3Al/MeAlCl_2 (cf. *36*, 677s68), asym. induction with a bridged N-(α,β-ethyleneacyl)lactam, s. R.K. Boeckman, L.M. Reeder, Synlett *2004*, 1399-403.

4-(Silylmethyl)cyclopent-2-enyl ketones ○
from 2-(silylmethyl)cyclopropyl ketones and terminal acetylene derivs.
Regio- and stereo-specific [3+2]-cycloaddition

308.

2-Aryl-4-(silylmethyl)cyclopent-2-enyl ketones. A soln. of 1.3 eqs. TiCl_4 in anhydrous methylene chloride added slowly under N_2 to a stirred soln. of 1 eq. of the startg. cyclopropyl ketone and 1.3 eqs. phenylethyne in the same solvent at 78°, stirred for 3 h, warmed slowly over 1 h to -40°, and stirring continued for another 2 h at the same temp. → product. Y 75% (*cis/trans* 85:15). Reaction of such donor-acceptor cyclopropanes is facilitated by stabilization of the intermediate dipole, the positive charge by the β-silyl effect and the negative charge by the keto group. The method is highly regio- and stereo-specific, but not applicable to simple alkylacetylenes. F.e. and with added K_2CO_3 (for arylacetylenes possessing electron-donating groups), also intramolecular [3+2]-cycloaddition, s. V.K. Yadav, V. Sriramurthy, Angew. Chem. Int. Ed. Engl. *43*, 2669-71 (2004).

Cyclic (E)-3-ene-1,6-chlorhydrins from (aldehydo)vinylcyclopropanes
Stereospecific intramolecular Prins-type cyclization under mild conditions

309.

A soln. of 1.1 eqs. TiCl$_4$ in anhydrous methylene chloride added via syringe over 10 min to a stirred soln. of the startg. cyclopropylvinylic aldehyde in the same solvent at -78° under N$_2$, stirred for 2 h at -78°, allowed to warm to 0°, and quenched with aq. NaHCO$_3$ → product. Y 82%. This is the first instance of a cyclopropylvinyl moiety serving as an electrophile for capturing an incoming nucleophile, reaction taking place with remarkably high *cis*-diastereoselectivity, and being suitable for preparing 5- and 6-membered carbo- and N-hetero-cyclics. F.e. and solvent effect s. C.-M. Yu et al., Chem. Commun. *2004*, 1840-1.

Zirconium tetrachloride $ZrCl_4$
3,4-Fused 1,2,3,4-tetrahydroquinolines from N-arylaldimines
via stereospecific hetero-Diels-Alder reaction
with InCl$_3$ cf. *53*, 301; with 10 mol% ZrCl$_4$ s. M. Mahesh, V.V.N. Reddy et al., Synth. Commun. *34*, 4089-104 (2004); with triphenylphosphonium perchlorate s. Y. Zulykama, R. Nagarajam, P.T. Perumal, ibid. 1309-15.

Tert. phosphines s.a. under Transition metal complexes R_3P

Triphenylphosphine/sodium acetate/acetic acid $Ph_3P/NaOAc/AcOH$
Anti-Michael addition of activated ketones   C≡C → CH=C(R)
to α,β-acetylenecarboxylic acid esters

310.

0.5 eq. Acetic acid added under argon in one portion to a refluxing mixture of 2,4-pentanedione, 0.1 eq. triphenylphosphine and 0.5 eq. NaOAc in toluene, 1 eq. ethyl propiolate added dropwise, stirring continued at reflux for 0.5 h, cooled, filtered, and worked up → product. Y 88%. Reaction is facilitated by initial 1,4-addition of the phosphine, followed by Michael-type addition to the generated enephosphonium ion. There were no α-O-adducts or Michael adducts. F.e. and with β-keto esters and β-ketophosphonic acid esters, also **4-acyl-5-alkylthio-2,3-dihydrothiophene-3-carboxylic acid esters** from β-ketodithiocarboxylic acid esters, s. M. Hanédanian, F. Taran, C. Mioskowski et al., Tetrahedron Lett. *45*, 7035-8 (2004).

Bis(triphenylphosphoranylidene)iminium chloride s. under Ru$_3$(CO)$_{12}$ $[Ph_3P=N=PPh_3]Cl$

Tetraalkylammonium hypophosphites/4,4'-azo(4-cyanovaleric acid)   ←
Radical 1,4-addition in water s. *64*, 478s68   C=C → CHC(R)

N-Ethylpiperidinium hypophosphite/triethylborane   ←
Radical 1,4-addition
of iodides using added Yb(OTf)$_3$/AIBN cf. *62*, 300s67; rapid radical addition to pentafluorophenyl acrylate with added Et$_3$B s. S. Caddick et al., Tetrahedron Lett. *45*, 2363-6 (2004).

Tri-n-butyl phosphate s. under Fe $(BuO)_3PO$
Trimethylsilyl triflate s. under Cp$_2$Zr(H)Cl Me_3SiOTf

Trifluoromethanesulfonic acid CF_3SO_3H
3-Methylene-Δ¹-pyrrolines
from methylenecyclopropanes and nitriles s. *63*, 282s68

2,4-Dinitrobenzenesulfonic acid s. under (S)-4-Pyrrolidino-2-(pyrrolidin-2-yl)- $ArSO_3H$
pyridine

Molybdenum hexacarbonyl/dimethyl sulfoxide $Mo(CO)_6/DMSO$
***cis*-Fused α-methylene-γ-lactones from alleneoxo compds.
via intramolecular oxa-Pauson-Khand reaction**

311.

A soln. of 1.2 eqs. Mo(CO)₆ in toluene treated dropwise under N₂ at room temp. with 1 eq. startg. alleneoxo compd. and 10 eqs. DMSO, and stirred at 100° for 6 h → product. Y 83%. The accelerating influence of DMSO is attributed to a favourable ligand exchange with carbon monoxide, thereby generating a vacant orbital on molybdenum to accommodate the allene residue. The linking residue between the two functional groups may be all-carbon, oxygen or nitrogen. F.e. and comparison of molybdenum catalysts, solvents and additives s. C.-M. Yu, Y.-T. Hong, J.-H. Lee, J. Org. Chem. *69*, 8506-9 (2004).

Carbonylbis(nitrosyl)[tris(2-pyridyl)phosphine oxide]tungsten bis(tetrafluoroborate)/   ←
1-n-butyl-3-methylimidazolium hexafluorophosphate/microwaves
Tungsten-catalyzed Diels-Alder reaction in ionic liquids under microwave irradiation

312.

Equimolar amounts of 1-methoxy-1,3-butadiene and methyl vinyl ketone added to a soln. of 3 mol% carbonylbis(nitrosyl)[tris(2-pyridyl)phosphine oxide]tungsten bis(tetrafluoroborate) in 1-*n*-butyl-3-methylimidazolium hexafluorophosphate contained in a sealed vial, the mixture irradiated in a microwave oven at a 20% power setting (300 W) at 50° for 1 min, and extracted with ether → product. Y 75% (single *endo-syn* isomer). The catalyst can be readily recovered in the ionic liquid layer and was reused 10 times with no significant loss of activity. Reaction is also facile **in water,** but 20% of the catalytic activity was lost after the 6th cycle. The complex is stable in air for months without decomposition, and compares with AlCl₃ in Lewis acidity. F.e.s. I.-H. Chen, J.-N. Young, S.J. Yu, Tetrahedron *60*, 11903-9 (2004).

Triphenylphosphonium perchlorate $[Ph_3PH]ClO_4$
3,4-Fused 1,2,3,4-tetrahydroquinolines from N-arylaldimines
via stereospecific hetero-Diels-Alder reaction s. *53*, 301s68

Hexadecyltrimethylammonium bromide s. under RN=NR $[C_{16}H_{33}NMe_3]Br$
Chiral quaternary ammonium halides s. under KOH R_4NHal

Iron/ferric chloride/tri-n-butyl phosphate $Fe/FeCl_3/(BuO)_3PO$
Addition of polyhalides to ethylene derivs.
with ruthenium complexes cf. *18*, 776s*67*; large-scale synthesis of 1,1,1,3,3-pentachlorides with $Fe/FeCl_3/(BuO)_3PO$ and a little water s. L. Branan, World Intellectual Property Organisation patent WO-2002102750 (Vulcan Chem.).

Chiral (pentamethylcyclopentadienyl)[7-(pyrrolidin-1-yl)-4-azaindenyl]iron(II)
β-Lactones from ketenes and aldehydes
via iron(II)-catalyzed asym. [2+2]-cycloaddition

Chiral α,α-disubst. β-lactones. A soln. of 1.2 eqs. startg. disubst. ketene and 1 eq. startg. aldehyde in anhydrous THF cooled to -78°, treated dropwise over 5 min with a soln. of 5 mol% chiral (pentamethylcyclopentadienyl)[7-(pyrrolidin-1-yl)-4-azaindenyl]iron(II) in the same solvent, and stirred at the same temp. for 5.5 h → product. Y 76% (e.e. 81%). This is the first example of a catalytic asym. synthesis with subst. ketenes, unsym. derivs. affording products with adjacent quaternary and tertiary chiral centres. F.e.s. J.E. Wilson, G.C. Fu, Angew. Chem. Int. Ed. Engl. *43*, 6358-60 (2004).

Cobalt carbonyl $Co_2(CO)_8$
Reductive intramolecular Pauson-Khand reaction
with $Co_2(CO)_8$/silica under dry-state absorption conditions cf. *49*, 675; with $Co_2(CO)_8$ or $Co_4(CO)_{12}$ in DME/*water* s. H.-Y. Lee, M. An, J.-H. Sohn, Bull. Korean Chem. Soc. *24*, 539-40 (2003).

Cobalt carbonyl/N-methylmorpholine N-oxide $Co_2(CO)_8/R_3NO$
Pauson-Khand reaction with allenes
s. *53*, 318; with N-sulfonyl- and N-acyl-alleneamines, regioselectivity, s. L. Anorbe, J. Perez-Castells et al., Tetrahedron Lett. *45*, 4441-4 (2004).

Cobalt carbonyl/molecular sieves
Heterogeneous Pauson-Khand reaction at atmospheric pressure
s. *59*, 304s*64*; of indole-tethered enynes with preactivated 4 Å molecular sieves *without CO* s. L. Perez-Serrano, G. Dominguez, J. Perez-Castells, J. Org. Chem. *69*, 5413-8 (2004); of fullerene-tethered enynes s. N. Martin, A. Martin-Domenech et al., Chem. Commun. *2004*, 1338-9.

Cobalt carbonyl/N-methylmorpholine N-oxide/Triton X-100
Tetracobalt dodecacarbonyl/Triton X-100
Pauson-Khand reaction in water
with hexadecyltrimethylammonium bromide as surfactant cf. *40*, 475s*67*; bicyclo[3.3.0]oct-1-en-2-ones with Triton X-100 as surfactant s. M.E. Krafft, J.A. Wright, L.V.R. Bonaga, Synlett *2005*, 71-4; with $Co_4(CO)_{12}$/Triton X-100 s. Chem. Commun. *2004*, 1746-7.

Dicarbonyl(cyclopentadienyl)cobalt(I)/irradiation $CpCo(CO)_2/h\nu$
Pyridine ring by [2+2+2]-cycloaddition
from diynes and nitriles s. *37*, 674s*40*; chiral 2,2′-bis(4,5-polymethylene-2-pyridyl)-1,1′-binaphthyls s. T. Hoshi, H. Hagiwara et al., Tetrahedron Lett. *45*, 3489-91 (2004).

(1,5-Cyclooctadiene)(1-neomenthylindenyl)cobalt(I)/irradiation
Atropoisomeric 2-arylpyridines by cobalt(I)-catalyzed asym. [2+2+2]-cycloaddition

314.

A stirred mixture of 1 eq. startg. diyne, 2 eqs. benzonitrile, and 1 mol% (1,5-cyclooctadiene)(1-neomenthylindenyl)cobalt(I) in anhydrous THF irradiated with two 460 W Phillips HPM 12 lamps (ca. 420 nm) at 3° under argon for 24 h → product. Y 57% (e.e. >98% after recrystallization). Face-selectivity arises on addition of the nitrile to the intermediate chiral cobaltacyclopentadiene, the *ent*-complex affording the opposite enantiomer. Reaction is independent of the nature of the solvent, and the yield independent of the temperature. F.e. and from nitriles and two acetylene deriv. molecules s. A. Gutnov, B. Heller et al., Angew. Chem. Int. Ed. Engl. *43*, 3795-7 (2004).

Chiral cationic bis(β-ketoiminato)cobalt(III) complexes
Transition metal-catalyzed *endo*-specific asym. 1,3-dipolar cycloaddition with nitrones
with chiral aquanickel(II) bis(Δ²-oxazoline) complexes cf. *56*, 294; with chiral cationic bis(β-ketoiminato)cobalt(III) complexes for asym. cycloaddition to α-subst. α,β-ethylenealdehydes s. N. Ohtsuki, T. Yamada et al., Synthesis *2003*, 1462-6.

Diiodobis(triphenylphosphine)cobalt(II)/zinc $CoI_2(PPh_3)_2/Zn$
[2+2+2]-Cycloaddition
fused benzene ring from diynes and acetylene derivs. with $Co_2(CO)_8$ s. *33*, 658s60; arylboronic acid esters s. V. Gandon, K.P.C. Vollhardt, M. Malacria et al., Org. Lett. *6*, 3405-7 (2004); condensed 1,3-cyclohexadienes from diynes and norbornene or benzonorbornene with $CoI_2(PPh_3)_2/Zn$ s. M.-S. Wu, D.K. Rayabarapu, C.-H. Cheng, Tetrahedron *60*, 10005-9 (2004).

Diiodobis(triphenylphosphine)cobalt(II)/zinc/triphenylphosphine $CoI_2(PPh_3)_2/Zn/Ph_3P$
Regiospecific dimerization of styrenes
with cyanocobalamin/Ti(III)-citrate/Bu_4NOH cf. *63*, 304; head-to-tail dimerization with $CoI_2(PPh_3)_2/Zn/Ph_3P$, and reductive dimerization of electron-deficient ethylene derivs. (cf. *24*, 709), s. C.-C. Wang, P.-S. Lin, C.-H. Cheng, Tetrahedron Lett. *45*, 6203-6 (2004); with $RuCl_3$ (cf. *24*, 711) s. M. Higashimura, K. Imamura, T. Sakakibara et al., Chem. Lett. *33*, 728-9 (2004); dimerization of α-methylstyrenes with $InBr_3$ s. C. Peppe, L.B. Castro et al., Synlett *2004*, 1732-6.

Bis(1,5-cyclooctadiene)nickel(0)/N,N'-bis(2,6-diisopropylphenyl)imidazol-2-ylidene
2-Pyridone ring from diynes and isocyanates
by nickel-catalyzed [2+2+2]-cycloaddition under mild conditions

315.

Nickel-catalyzed synthesis of the 2-pyridone ring by [2+2+2]-cycloaddition is highly efficient **with hindered imidazol-2-ylidenes as ligand** in place of the traditional tert. phosphines with which cyclotrimerization of the alkyne component is often a complication. E: A soln. of the startg. diyne and 1 eq. of the startg. isocyanate in toluene stirred at 80° for a few min, treated with a soln. of 5 mol% Ni(cod)$_2$ and 5 mol% N,N'-bis(2,6-diisopropylphenyl)imidazol-2-ylidene in the same solvent, and stirring continued for 30 min → product. Y 84%. Reaction is applicable to both alkyl- and aryl-isocyanates, incl. hindered derivs., although substrates with electron-withdrawing substituents require a higher temp. F.e. incl. cycloheptene-fused analogs and with internal alkynes, also comparison of carbene ligands, and synthesis of isolated 2-pyridones from nitriles and and two alkyne molecules, s. H.A. Duong, M.J. Cross, J. Louie, J. Am. Chem. Soc. *126*, 11438-9 (2004).

Bis(1,5-cyclooctadiene)nickel(0)/5,5-bis(Δ^2-imidazolin-2-yl)nonane ←
α,β-Ethylenecarboxylic acids $C \equiv C \rightarrow CH = C\text{-}COOH$
from acetylene derivs. by regiospecific hydrocarboxylation
electrochemical procedure with added NiBr$_2$ as mediator cf. *45*, 397; from terminal acetylene derivs. by carboxylation at the less hindered site with Ni(cod)$_2$, also from internal acetylene derivs. with added 5,5-bis(Δ^2-imidazolin-2-yl)nonane as ligand, s. M. Aoki, N. Iwasawa et al., Chem. Commun. *2004*, 2568-9.

Bis(1,5-cyclooctadiene)nickel(0)/trimethylphosphine Ni(cod)$_2$/Me$_3$P
Tetrasubst. (Z)-cinnamonitriles from acetylene derivs. and ar. nitriles C(Ar)=C(CN)
by nickel-catalyzed 1,2-arylcyanation

1 eq. startg. nitrile treated under argon with a soln. of 10 mol% Ni(cod)$_2$ and 20 mol% trimethylphosphine in anhydrous toluene, the resulting mixture further treated with 1 eq. startg. alkyne, and stirred under argon at 100° for 86 h → (Z)-product. Y 59% (99:1 mixture of regioisomers). Reaction is presumed to involve initial oxidative addition of the C-CN bond to Ni(0), followed by insertion of the alkyne to give a vinylnickel(II) species, which undergoes reductive elimination with regeneration of the catalyst. Other mono- and bi-dentate phosphine ligands, and other transition metal catalysts, were less effective. A wide range of aryl nitriles participated in the conversion, and a variety of functional groups, incl. fluorides, ketones, esters and aldehydes, remained unaffected. F.e.s. Y. Nakao, S. Oda, T. Hiyama, J. Am. Chem. Soc. *126*, 13904-5 (2004).

Bis(1,5-cyclooctadiene)nickel(0)/tri-tert-butylphosphine Ni(cod)$_2$/t-Bu$_3$P
1,3-Enynes from two terminal acetylene deriv. molecules ←
by head-to-head dimerization under palladium catalysis cf. *48*, 694s62; with Ni(cod)$_2$/t-Bu$_3$P s. S. Ogoshi, H. Kurosawa et al., Chem. Commun. *2004*, 2735-3.

Bis(1,5-cyclooctadiene)nickel(0)/triphenylphosphine $Ni(cod)_2/Ph_3P$
**5-Carbalkoxymethylene-1,3-cycloheptadienes
from cyclopropylideneacetic acid esters and acetylene derivs.
via nickel-catalyzed [3+2+2]-cycloaddition**

A soln. of 1 eq. ethyl cyclopropylideneacetate and 5 eqs. trimethylsilylethyne in anhydrous toluene added dropwise under argon over 5 h to a mixture of 10 mol% Ni(cod)$_2$ and 20 mol% triphenylphosphine in the same solvent at room temp. → product. Y 70%. Yields were highest with bulky terminal alkynes, the reactivity of internal alkynes being much lower. However, it appears that the electron-withdrawing carbalkoxy (or acyl) group of the cyclopropane is essential as there was no cycloaddition with alkylcyclopropanes. Reaction may involve rearrangement of an intermediate spirocyclic nickelacycloheptadiene. F.e.s. S. Saito, M. Masuda, S. Komagawa, J. Am. Chem. Soc. *126*, 10540-1 (2004).

Bis(1,5-cyclooctadiene)nickel(0)/[o-(dimethylamino)phenyl]diphenylphosphine $Ni(cod)_2/Ar_3P$
Regio- and stereo-specific Ni-catalyzed 3-component synthesis   C≡C(Sn≤)C-C≡C-C≡C
**of 2-stannyl-1,4,6-dienynes from acetylenestannanes
via sequential insertion of allenes and acetylene derivs.**

(1Z,4Z)-2-Stannyl-1,4,6-dienynes. A soln. of 1 eq. startg. acetylenestannane, ca. 5 mol% Ni(cod)$_2$ and ca. 5 mol% *[o-(dimethylamino)phenyl]diphenylphosphine* in anhydrous dibutyl ether treated with 3 eqs. startg. allene and 6 eqs. startg. alkyne, and stirred under N$_2$ at 50° for 24 h → product. Y 49%. This is the first example of such a tandem carbostannylation, reaction involving initial oxidative addition of the acetylenestannane to nickel(0), followed by sequential insertion of the allene and alkyne molecules prior to reductive elimination. The procedure is applicable to both terminal and internal alkynes and to monosubst. and 1,1-disubst. allenes. With tris(*p*-trifluoromethylphenyl)phosphine and 2-(diphenylphosphino)pyridine as ligand, however, the corresponding (1E,4Z)-isomers were obtained. F.e.s. E. Shirakawa, T. Hiyama et al., Angew. Chem. Int. Ed. Engl. *43*, 3448-51 (2004).

Chiral nickel(II) bis(Δ^2-oxazoline) complexes ←
endo-Specific asym. 1,3-dipolar cycloaddition with nitrones s. *54*, 296s68   ○

Dodecacarbonyltriruthenium/bis(triphenylphosphoranylidene)iminium chloride ←
Transition metal-catalyzed Michael addition of terminal acetylene derivs.   C≡C-C-CHCO
to enones with [RuCl$_2$(*p*-cymene)]$_2$ cf. *62*, 306; to enoates with Ru$_3$(CO)$_{12}$/bis(triphenylphosphoranylidene)iminium chloride s. T. Nishimura, S. Uemura et al., Chem. Commun. *2004*, 1312-3; to enones with Rh(CO)$_2$(acac)/tri(*o*-methoxyphenyl)phosphine cf. R.V. Lerum, J.D. Chisholm, Tetrahedron Lett. *45*, 6591-4 (2004).

Chiral (η^6-arene)(N-sulfonyl-1,2-diaminato)ruthenium(II) complexes ←
Ruthenium-catalyzed asym. Michael addition   C=C → CHC(R)
s. *48*, 687s67; of β-dicarbonyl compds. to 1,1-nitroethylene derivs. with ((1S,2S)-N-pentamethylbenzenesulfonyl-1,2-diphenylethylene-1,2-diaminato)(η^6-hexamethylbenzene)ruthenium(II) s. M. Watanabe, T. Ikariya et al., J. Am. Chem. Soc. *126*, 11148-9 (2004).

Dichloro(norbornadiene)bis(triphenylphosphine)ruthenium(II) $RuCl_2(PPh_3)_2(nbd)$
Homo-Diels-Alder reaction with acetylene derivs.   ○
and norbornadiene using Co(acac)$_3$/dppe/Et$_2$AlCl cf. *45*, 416; with internal acetylene derivs. using RuCl$_2$(PPh$_3$)$_2$(nbd) s. A. Tenaglia, L. Giordano, Tetrahedron Lett. *45*, 171-4 (2004).

Chloro(1,5-cyclooctadiene)(η^5-pentamethylcyclopentadienyl)ruthenium(II) $Cp^*Ru(cod)Cl$
Ruthenium-catalyzed [2+2]-cycloaddition with acetylene derivs.   □
s. *60*, 288s67; cycloaddition of norbornenes to α,β-acetylenehalides s. K. Villeneuve, W. Tam et al., Org. Lett. *6*, 4543-6 (2004).

Carbonyl(chloro)bis(tricyclohexylphosphine)(3,3-dimethylprop-2-enylidene)- ←
   ruthenium(II) fluoroborate
1,4-Dienes from 1,3-dienes
Regiospecific ruthenium-catalyzed hydrovinylation   C=C → CHC-C=C
with RhH(Cl)(CO)(PCy$_3$)$_2$/HBF$_4$ cf. *65*, 298; with carbonyl(chloro)bis(tricyclohexylphosphine)-(3,3-dimethylprop-2-enylidene)ruthenium(II) fluoroborate s. Z. He, C.S. Yi, W.A. Donaldson, Synlett *2004*, 1312-4.

Chiral chloro(2-isopropoxy-3-phenylbenzylidene)[1-(2'-oxy-1,1'-binaphthyl-2-yl)-3- ←
   mesitylimidazolidin-2-ylidene]ruthenium(II)
2,6-Divinyltetrahydropyrans from 8-oxabicyclo[3.2.1]oct-6-enes and ethylene derivs.   C
Ring-opening metathesis-cross metathesis with desymmetrization

319.

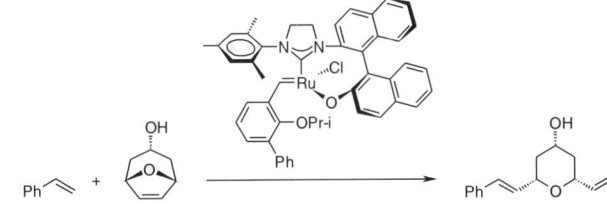

5 Mol% chiral chloro(2-isopropoxy-3-phenylbenzylidene)[1-(2'-oxy-1,1'-binaphthyl-2-yl)-3-mesitylimidazolidin-2-ylidene]ruthenium(II) added to a mixture of the startg. 8-oxabicyclo[3.2.1]-oct-6-ene and 4.5 eqs. styrene in THF under N$_2$, stirred for 1.5 h at 22°, and the mixture concentrated → product. Y 80% (conversion >98%, e.e. 94%). Reaction was faster and yields

higher **in the absence of solvent,** and the *air-stable* catalyst can be recycled five times without appreciable loss of activity. Yields and enantioselectivity were lower with aliphatic olefins, but improved somewhat with the corresponding iodoruthenium complex. Both *exo-* and *endo-* alkoxy and -hydroxy substituents were tolerated at the 3-position. F.e.s. D.G. Gillingham, A.H. Hoveyda et al., J. Am. Chem. Soc. *126*, 12288-90 (2004).

Ruthenium trichloride $RuCl_3$
Regiospecific dimerization of styrenes s. *63*, 304s68 ←

Carbonyl(hydrido)tris(triphenylphosphine)rhodium(I)/9,9-dimethyl-4,5- ←
bis(diphenylphosphino)xanthene
Polymer-based hydroformylation C═C → CHC-CHO
s. *4*, 667s54; of ester-linked polymer-based ethylene derivs. with HRh(CO)(PPh$_3$)$_3$ and Xantphos as ligand for enhanced formation of linear aldehydes (>99%) s. M. Marchetti et al., Adv. Synth. Catal. *345*, 1229-36 (2003).

Bis(1,5-cyclooctadiene)rhodium(I) fluoroborate/9,9-dimethyl-4,5- ←
bis(diphenylphosphino)xanthene
α-Unsubst. amines from ethylene derivs. via hydroformylation C═C → CHC-CH$_2$N<
2-arylamines from styrenes with zwitterionic rhodium(I) complexes s. *61*, 344; linear α-unsubst. amines from terminal ethylene derivs. with [Rh(cod)$_2$]BF$_4$/9,9-dimethyl-4,5-bis(diphenylphosphino)xanthene, effect of P-ligand on regioselectivity, s. M. Ahmed, M. Beller et al., J. Am. Chem. Soc. *125*, 10311-8 (2003).

Bis(1,5-cyclooctadiene)rhodium(I) triflate/2,2'-bis(diphenylphosphino)biphenyl ←
Alkylidenecyclopentanes from 1,6-enynes ○
via stereospecific hydrogenative carbocyclization under mild conditions

320.

E = CO$_2$Me

The first example of the use of elemental hydrogen as terminal reductant in a metal-catalyzed reductive carbocyclization is reported. **E:** A soln. of the startg. 1,6-enyne in dichloroethane (0.1 *M*) treated under argon at room temp. with 5 mol% [Rh(cod)$_2$]OTf and 5 mol% 2,2'-bis(diphenylphosphino)biphenyl, the mixture purged with H$_2$ gas, and stirred *under 1 atm. H$_2$ at room temp.* until completion of reaction → product. Y 89% (E-isomer). It appears that reaction is initiated by *heterolytic* activation of hydrogen with formation of an active rhodium(I) hydride complex; addition of the latter to the enyne ensues to give a fused rhodacyclopentene which cleaves to a vinylrhodium species prior to hydrogenative demetalation. The method is applicable to carbon-, nitrogen-, and oxygen-tethered enynes, and the alkyne residue may be terminal or internal. **Exocyclic 1,3-dienes** were obtained similarly from non-terminal 1,6-diynes via fused rhodacyclopentadienes. F.e. and ligands s. H.-Y. Jang, M.J. Krische, J. Am. Chem. Soc. *126*, 7875-80 (2004).

Acetoacetonato(dicarbonyl)rhodium(I)/albumin ←
Hydroformylation in aq. medium C═C → CHC-CHO
s. *48*, 686s64; environmentally friendly procedure with the water-soluble complex derived from Rh(CO)$_2$(acac) and human serum albumin in a 2-phase (water/pentane) medium s. C. Bertucci, M. Marchetti et al., Adv. Synth. Catal. *344*, 556-62 (2002).

Acetoacetonato(dicarbonyl)rhodium(I)/tri(o-methoxyphenyl)phosphine $Rh(CO)_2(acac)/Ar_3P$
γ,δ-Ethyleneketones C≡C-C-CHCO
from α,β-ethyleneketones and terminal acetylene derivs. – Rhodium-catalyzed Michael addition s. *62*, 306s68

Acetoacetonato(dicarbonyl)rhodium(I)/2,2'-bis(diphenylphosphinomethyl)- ←
1,1'-binaphthyl
Enamines from ethylene derivs. and amines $C=CH \rightarrow CHC=CHN<$
via regio- and stereo-specific hydroaminomethylenation under mild conditions

321.

A mixture of 1-pentene, 0.1 mol% $Rh(CO)_2(acac)$, 0.2 mol% 2,2'-bis(diphenylphosphinomethyl)-1,1'-binaphthyl (naphos), 1 eq. (S)-2-methoxymethylpyrrolidine, and toluene pressurized with CO (5 bar) and H_2 (5 bar) in an autoclave, and stirred at 65° for 16 h → (S)-product. Y 98% (n/iso 98%, conversion 100%; 100% E-isomer). The method is atom-economical, environmentally friendly, highly selective, and based on inexpensive and readily available starting materials. The high selectivity, notably with aliphatic olefins, is attributed to the choice of ligand (the conversion and regioselectivity being much lower with triphenylphosphine). However, regiospecificity is somewhat lower with styrene (n/iso 63:37). F.e. and comparison of ligands s. M. Ahmed, M. Beller et al., Angew. Chem. Int. Ed. Engl. *42*, 5615-9 (2003).

Acetoacetonato(dicarbonyl)rhodium(I)/9,9-dimethyl-4,5-bis(diphenylphosphino)xanthene/ ←
dicyclohexylborinyl chloride/triethylamine
Regio- and stereo-specific hydroformylation-intramolecular aldol condensation ○
via enol borinates

322.

Cyclic β'-hydroxy-β-ketocarboxylic acid esters. 1.05 eqs. Triethylamine pre-complexed with 1.05 eqs. dicyclohexylborinyl chloride in dry methylene chloride under argon at 0° for 15 min, the startg. ethylene deriv. in the same solvent added slowly via syringe, stirred for 0.5 h, the mixture transferred to an autoclave containing 0.9 mol% $Rh(CO)_2(acac)$, 1.8 mol% Xantphos and further solvent, pressurized to 60 bar with equal pressures of CO and H_2, heated at 80° overnight, cooled, concentrated under reduced pressure, the residue taken up in methanol, concd. phosphate buffer (pH 7) and 30% H_2O_2 added, and stirred again overnight → product. Y 89% (6:1 mixture of diastereomers). Reaction proceeds by initial enolboration, followed by regiospecific hydroformylation and diastereoselective intramolecular aldol condensation, the procedure being suitable for preparing 5-, 6- and 7-membered carbocyclics bearing *functionalized quaternary carbon centers* from easily available substrates. F.e.s. M.D. Keranen, P. Eilbracht, Org. Biomol. Chem. *2*, 1688-90 (2004).

Rhodium(I) phosphine complexes ←
Hydroformylation $C=C \rightarrow CHC-CHO$
s. *4*, 667s67; with 2,7-dialkyl-4,5-bis(10-phenoxaphosphino)-9,9-dimethylxanthenes as ligand, solubility study, s. R.P.J. Bronger, P.W.N.M. van Leeuwen et al., Adv. Synth. Catal. *346*, 789-99 (2004); with highly active rhodium(I) phosphabarrelene complexes for isomerization-free hydroformylation of internal alkenes s. B. Breit, E. Fuchs, Chem. Commun. *2004*, 694-5; synthesis of β-formylmetalloporphyrins s. A. Peixoto, M.M. Pereira et al., Tetrahedron Lett. *44*, 5593-5 (2003).

Chiral polymer-based cyclic rhodium(I) phosphine-phosphites ←
Asym. hydroformylation
with (R,S)-BINAPHOS as ligand cf. *49*, 683; **heterogeneous asym. hydroformylation** with a highly cross-linked chiral polystyrene-based Rh(I)-BINAPHOS complex s. F. Shibahara, K. Nozaki, T. Hiyama, J. Am. Chem. Soc. *125*, 8555-60 (2003).

Dicarbonyl(chloro)rhodium(I) dimer [RhCl(CO)$_2$]$_2$
Rhodium-catalyzed Pauson-Khand reaction with 1,3-dienes ○
5-vinyl-2-cyclopentenones by intermolecular reaction with acetylene derivs. cf. *67*, 330; fused 2-vinylcyclopentanones from 1,3,n-trienes by intramolecular conversion s. P.A. Wender, M.P. Croatt, N.M. Deschamps, J. Am. Chem. Soc. *126*, 5948-9 (2004).

6-Vinyl-2-pyrones from cyclobutenones ○
via stereospecific rhodium-catalyzed ring-opening dimerization

323.

A mixture of 1 eq. 2,3-dipropylcyclobutenone and 5 mol% [RhCl(CO)$_2$]$_2$ in anhydrous *toluene* stirred under argon at 110° for 12 h, and distilled in a Kugelrohr apparatus → 6-(2-methyl-1-propylpent-1-enyl)-3,4-dipropyl-2-pyrone. Y 84% (100% E-isomer). Reaction is presumed to proceed by initial formation of an η^4-vinylketene which dimerizes by hetero-Diels-Alder reaction prior to isomerization. E/Z-selectivity was variable under ruthenium catalysis. F.e. and comparison of rhodium and ruthenium complexes, also reactions with norbornene, s. T. Kondo, T. Mitsudo et al., Angew. Chem. Int. Ed. Engl. *43*, 5369-72 (2004).

Dicarbonyl(chloro)rhodium(I) dimer/triphenylphosphine/silver fluoroborate ←
Rhodium-catalyzed intramolecular Pauson-Khand reaction ○
of enynes cf. *55*, 296; of N-protected 5-aza-1,2-dien-7-ynes with added AgBF$_4$/Ph$_3$P s. K.M. Brummond, B. Mitasev, Org. Lett. *6*, 2245-8 (2004); double ring closure **of 1,2-dien-n-ynes**, also with [RhCl(CO)dppp]$_2$, s. C. Mukai, I. Nomura, S. Kitagaki, J. Org. Chem. *68*, 1376-85 (2003).

Chloro(1,5-cyclooctadiene)rhodium(I) dimer [Rh(cod)Cl]$_2$
Tricyclic 2,4-cycloheptadienones from enediynes
by intramolecular carbonylative cycloaddition

324.

E = CO$_2$Et

CO bubbled into a 0.1 *M* soln. of the startg. enediyne in anhydrous 1,2-dichloroethane at room temp. for 15 min at atm. pressure, treated with 5 mol% [Rh(cod)Cl]$_2$ under CO, stirred at the same temp. for another 5 min, and again at 50° for 16 h with continued bubbling of CO → product. Y 66%. This novel intramolecular [2+2+2+2]-cycloaddition is highly selective and high-yielding, and presumed to involve intermediate formation of a series of rhodacyclics. Oxygen, nitrogen and carbon atoms are acceptable in the tether, and ethers, sulfonamides, carbamates, esters and ketal groups are tolerated. F.e. and with silyl-substituted alkyne residues, also comparison of catalysts, s. B. Bennacer, M. Fujiwara, I. Ojima, Org. Lett. *6*, 3589-91 (2004).

*Chloro(1,5-cyclooctadiene)rhodium(I) dimer/(S)-2,2′-bis(di-p-tolylphosphino)-
1,1′-binaphthyl/tris(m-sulfophenyl)phosphine trisodium salt/sodium octadecyl sulfate*
**Asym. Pauson-Khand reaction of 1,6-enynes in water
with formaldehyde as carbon monoxide substitute**

325.

A mixture of 5 mol% [RhCl(cod)]$_2$, 0.1 eq. (S)-2,2′-bis(di-*p*-tolylphosphino)-1,1′-binaphthyl and 0.15 eq. *water-soluble* tris(*m*-sulfophenyl)phosphine trisodium salt in water stirred under N$_2$ at room temp. for 15 min, 0.5 eq. sodium octadecyl sulfate, 5 eqs. 37% aq. formalin, 1 eq. of the startg. 1,6-enyne and more water added, the mixture degassed, charged with N$_2$, and stirred at 100° for 6 h → product. Y 83% (e.e. 81%). The combination of achiral hydrophilic phosphine and chiral hydrophobic phosphine is essential for high enantioselectivity, and avoidance of carbon monoxide is an obvious bonus. F.e. and comparison of chiral ligands s. K. Fuji, T. Morimoto et al., Tetrahedron Lett. *45*, 9163-6 (2004).

Chlorotris(triphenylphosphine)rhodium(I)/2-amino-3-picoline/benzoic acid
**α,β-Ethyleneketones from terminal acetylene derivs.
by regiospecific chelation-controlled hydrative dimerization**

326.

A mixture of 1 eq. oct-1-yne, 5 mol% RhCl(PPh$_3$)$_3$, 1 eq. 2-amino-3-picoline, 5 mol% benzoic acid and 1 eq. water in anhydrous THF stirred at 110° for 2 h → product. Y 82% (as a 78:22 mixture of regioisomers). Reaction is thought to involve initial generation of a rhodium(I) vinylidene complex, which adds to the 2-aminopyridine to give an iminoacylrhodium(III) hydride complex prior to insertion of the second alkyne molecule, reductive elimination and hydrolysis. Regioselectivity is largely dependent on the bulk of the alkyl substituent, *tert*-butylethyne, for example, affording the linear isomer exclusively. However, the protocol is ineffective for internal as well as functionalized alkynes. F.e.s. Y.J. Park, C.-H. Jun et al., J. Am. Chem. Soc. *126*, 13892-3 (2004).

Palladous acetate/norbornadiene
[n+4]-Oxabicyclo[n.4.0]alka-1,3,(n+2),(n+5)-tetraene-2,3-dicarboxylic acid esters from cyclic 2-en-4-ynals

327.

1.5 eqs. Dimethyl acetylenedicarboxylate added to a soln. of 5 mol% Pd(OAc)$_2$, 5 mol% norbornadiene and the startg. enynal in toluene at room temp. under argon, heated with stirring at 100° for 30 min, cooled to room temp., and quenched with satd. aq. NH$_4$Cl → product. Y 71%. Reaction involves deprotonation of a palladated pyrylium deriv., followed by [2+2]-cycloaddition of the alkyne and ring expansion. F.e. incl. bicyclics with 7-10 and 14-membered carbocyclic rings, and with 1,5-cyclooctadiene as additive, s. K. Sato, N. Asao, Y. Yamamoto et al., Synthesis *2004*, 1409-12.

Palladous acetate/trimethylphosphine $Pd(OAc)_2/Me_3P$
γ,δ-Acetyleneketones   C≡C → CHC-C≡C
from α,β-ethyleneketones and terminal acetylene derivs.
Palladium-catalyzed 1,4-addition in water

328.

A mixture of 1 eq. phenylethyne, 2 eqs. ethyl vinyl ketone, 5 mol% Pd(OAc)$_2$, and 20 mol% trimethylphosphine in water stirred at 60° in air for 40 h → product. Y 91%. Reaction appears to involve 1,4-addition of a palladium acetylide, followed by reductive elimination of palladium(0) with the solvent or alkyne molecule as source of hydrogen. The procedure is applicable to alkynes possessing silyl, vinyl, aryl, alkyl and chloroalkyl groups. However, the choice of a small electron-rich phosphine as ligand is critical. F.e. and in acetone s. L. Chen, C.-J. Li, Chem. Commun. *2004*, 2362-4.

Tetrakis(triphenylphosphine)palladium(0) s.a. under Cp_2TiCl_2 $Pd(PPh_3)_4$
Tetrakis(triphenylphosphine)palladium(0)/lithium chloride/trimethylsilyl chloride/ organozinc halides
Synthesis of γ-diketones from α,β-ethyleneketones   C≡C → CHC-COR
via palladium-catalyzed carbonylative 1,4-addition

329.

δ-Aryl-γ-diketones. 3.5 eqs. Trimethylsilyl chloride and 1.5 eqs. methyl vinyl ketone added to a stirred mixture of 5 eqs. LiCl and 1.5 mol% Pd(PPh$_3$)$_4$ in THF under 1 atm. CO, aged for 10 min, a soln. of benzylzinc chloride (1.82 M) in the same solvent added dropwise over 30 min with vigorous stirring at 30°, and quenched with 2 N aq. HCl after 5 min → product. Y 59%. Carbonylation of an intermediate η^3-1-siloxyallylpalladium complex is thought to be a key step in this interesting 4-component coupling. Reaction is also possible, but in lower yield, with alkyl- and phenyl-zinc chloride, but there was no conversion with α,β-ethylenic esters and nitriles. F.e. and with o-subst. benzylzinc chlorides, also comparison of complexes, s. M. Yuguchi, M. Tokuda, K. Orito, J. Org. Chem. *69*, 908-14 (2004).

Tetrakis(triphenylphosphine)palladium(0)/formic acid $Pd(PPh_3)_4/HCOOH$
1,2-Di(alkylidene)cyclopentanes from 1,2,6-dienynes

330.

A mixture of the startg. 1,2,6-dienyne and 5 mol% $Pd(PPh_3)_4$ in dry DMF treated under argon with 1.2 eqs. formic acid at room temp., stirred for 10 min, then heated at 50° for 1 h → product. Y 97%. Reaction proceeds via regiospecific hydropalladation of the allene residue (rather than the alkyne residue), the electron-withdrawing carbalkoxy group being essential for high yields. F.e. and solvent effect s. C.H. Oh et al., Tetrahedron Lett. *45*, 2499-502 (2004).

Tetrakis(triphenylphosphine)palladium(0)/acetic acid/microwaves $Pd(PPh_3)_4/AcOH/[\backslash\backslash\backslash\backslash]$
Tetrakis(triphenylphosphine)palladium(0)/benzoic acid $Pd(PPh_3)_4/PhCOOH$
C-α-Allylation with acetylene derivs.   H→C-CH=CH
s. *67*, 335; of aldehydes with added PhCOOH in place of AcOH s. N.T. Patil, Y. Yamamoto et al., J. Org. Chem. *69*, 8745-50 (2004); rapid procedure under microwave irradiation in the absence of solvent, also O- and N-allylation, s. Tetrahedron Lett. *45*, 8497-9 (2004); of β-diketones and β-keto-esters with $Pd_2(dba)_3$/Ph_3P/PhCOOH s. J. Org. Chem. *69*, 6478-81 (2004).

Tetrakis(triphenylphosphine)palladium(0)/benzoic acid $Pd(PPh_3)_4/PhCOOH$
Stereospecific C-α-allylation with allenes   H→C-CH=C

331.

10 Mol% Benzoic acid added to a mixture of 1.2 eqs. diethyl malonate, 5 mol% $Pd(PPh_3)_4$ and phenylallene in anhydrous dioxane, and stirred for 12 h at 100° → product. Y 90%. Reaction proceeds by hydropalladation of the allene residue to give a π-allyl complex, which duly couples with the nucleophile. (E)-Products were obtained exclusively, and there was no diallylation. However, reaction is only applicable to activated allenes, e.g. aryl- and carbalkoxy-allenes. F.e. incl. allylation of active methylenes and methynes s. N.T. Patil, N.K. Pahadi, Y. Yamamoto et al., Synthesis *2004*, 2186-90.

Tetrakis(triphenylphosphine)palladium(0)/chlorobis(cyclopenta- $Pd(PPh_3)_4/Cp_2Zr(H)Cl$
dienyl)hydridozirconium
Hydrozirconation-cross-coupling with acetylene derivs.   C≡C→CH=C(R)
2-arylseleno-1,3-dienes cf. *52*, 419s*66*; 2-stannyl-1,3-dienes s. M.-Z. Cai, C.-S. Song et al., J. Organomet. Chem. *687*, 462-5 (2003).

Bis(η³-allylpalladium chloride) $[(\eta^3\text{-}allyl)PdCl]_2$
Regio- and stereo-specific intramolecular carbopalladation of bis(allenes)
with 1,4-silylstannylation using $Pd(PPh_3)_4$ cf. *60*, 300; with 1,4-germylstannylation using

[(η³-allyl)PdCl]₂, Pd(PPh₃)₄ or Pd₂(dba)₃ s. Y.T. Hong, S.K. Kang, C.-M. Yu et al., Eur. J. Org. Chem. *2004*, 4628-35.

(η³-Allyl)(η⁵-cyclopentadienyl)palladium(II)/1,3-bis(dicyclohexylphosphino)propane ←
C-α-Allylation with 1,3-dienes H → C-C=C
with [(π-allyl)PdCl]₂/dppp/NaOMe cf. *48*, 691; of carbonyl compds. and nitriles with (η³-allyl)(η⁵-cyclopentadienyl)palladium(II)/1,3-bis(dicyclohexylphosphino)propane, **also asym. variant** with a chiral ferrocenylphosphine as ligand, s. A. Leitner, J.F. Hartwig et al., J. Org. Chem. *69*, 7552-7 (2004).

Palladous halides/cupric halides PdHal₂/CuHal₂
Sym. 1,4-dihalogeno-1,3-dienes from acetylene derivs. C(Hal)=C-C=C(Hal)
diiodo-derivs. via zirconacyclopentadienes with CuCl cf. *53*, 199; dichloro- and dibromo-derivs. with PdHal₂/CuHal₂ s. J.-H. Li, Y. Liang, Y.-X. Xie, J. Org. Chem. *69*, 8125-7 (2004).

Palladous chloride/cupric chloride/carbon dioxide PdCl₂/CuCl₂/CO₂
Benzene ring from three acetylene deriv. molecules ○
cyclotrimerization with PdCl₂/Me₃SiCl cf. *42*, 676; sym. subst. benzenes with PdCl₂/CuCl₂ **in water** with CO₂ as promoter s. J.-H. Li, Y.-X. Xie, Synth. Commun. *34*, 1737-43 (2004).

Dichlorobis(triphenylphosphine)palladium(II)/sodium hydroxide PdCl₂(PPh₃)₂/NaOH
Regio- and stereo-specific hydroboration-Suzuki coupling C≡C → CH=C(R)
with acetylene derivs.
s. *49*, 836; trisubst. α-(polyfluoroalkyl)styrenes with PdCl₂(PPh₃)₂/NaOH s. T. Konno et al., Chem. Commun. *2004*, 690-1.

Dichloro[bis[o-(diphenylphosphino)phenyl] ether]palladium(II) s. under i-Bu₂AlH ←

Dichloro[1,1'-bis(diphenylphosphino)ferrocene]palladium(II)/9-borabicyclo- ←
[3.3.1]nonane/sodium hydroxide
Regiospecific hydroboration-Suzuki coupling with ethylene derivs. C=C → CHC(R)
C-β-benzyl glycosides from exocyclic glycals cf. *52*, 419s55; *49*, 836s67; 1-alkyl- from 1-iodoglycals s. J.S. Potuzak, D.S. Tan, Tetrahedron Lett. *45*, 1797-801 (2004).

Aquo[N,N'-bis(2,6-diisopropylphenyl)imidazol-2-ylidene]palladium(II) ←
trifluoroacetate/trifluoroacetic acid
Styrenes from acetylene derivs. and arenes ArH → ArC=CH
cis-styrenes with Pd(OAc)₂/CF₃COOH cf. *59*, 311, and under Rh-catalysis cf. *18*, 762s46; *trans*-styrenes with aquo[N,N'-bis(2,6-diisopropylphenyl)imidazol-2-ylidene]palladium(II) trifluoroacetate in trifluoroacetic acid s. M.S. Viciu, S.P. Nolan et al., Organometallics *23*, 3752-5 (2004).

(1,3-Dimesitylimidazol-2-ylidene)(η²,η²-1,1,3,3-tetramethyl-1,3- ←
divinyldisiloxane)palladium(0)/sodium methoxide
Palladium-catalyzed telomerization of 1,3-dienes ←
with amines using Pd(acac)₂/Ph₃P cf. *27*, 724; with alcohols or phenols using *0.001 mol%* (1,3-dimesitylimidazol-2-ylidene)palladium(0)(η²,η²-1,1,3,3-tetramethyl-1,3-divinyldisiloxane) and 1 mol% NaOMe s. R. Jackstell, S.P. Nolan, M. Beller et al., Chem. Eur. J. *10*, 3891-900 (2004).

Chloro(1,5-cyclooctadiene)iridium(I) dimer/(R)-2,2'-bis[bis(p- ←
methoxyphenyl)phosphino]-1,1'-binaphthyl
Iridium-catalyzed intramolecular Pauson-Khand reaction of dienynes ○
with desymmetrization

332.

A soln. of 30 mol% (R)-2,2'-bis[bis(*p*-methoxyphenyl)phosphino]-1,1'-binaphthyl and 15 mol% [Ir(cod)Cl]₂ in anhydrous toluene warmed to 40° under 1 atm. CO for 15 min, the startg. dienyne in toluene added, and refluxed at 130° for 24 h → product. Y 75% (e.e. 96%; d.r. 75:1). The method provides optically active bicyclic cyclopent-2-enones with high diastereoselectivity and enantioselectivity, both oxygen and nitrogen being tolerated in the tether. The corresponding chiral β-vinyl derivs. were obtained predominantly with [Rh(CO)₂Cl]₂. F.e.s. N. Jeong, D.H. Kim, J.H. Choi, Chem. Commun. *2004*, 1134-5.

Rearrangement ∩

Hydrogen/Oxygen Type   CC ∩ HO

Without additional reagents   w.a.r.
Oxy-Cope rearrangement
s. *21*, 744s25; (Z)-4,4-difluorocyclodec-5-en-1-ones s. G. DiMartino, J.M. Percy et al., Org. Biomol. Chem. *1*, 4423-34 (2003).

Hydrogen/Carbon Type   CC ∩ HC

Irradiation s. under HCl

Lithium diisopropylamide   i-Pr_2NLi
Base-catalyzed cycloisomerization of 1,3-dienes
with KH cf. *22*, 730; fused 1,4-cycloheptadienes with LDA s. M. Matsumoto, Y. Watanabe, N. Watanabe et al., Tetrahedron Lett. *45*, 3895-8 (2004).

Cesium carbonate s. under Me₃P Cs_2CO_3

Trimethylaluminum/2,6-di-tert-butyl-4-methylphenol/triethylamine
2-Cyclohexenones from cross-conjugated dienones
Stereospecific cycloisomerization via (E)-1,3,5-trien-3-olates under mild conditions

333.

6-Sulfonyl-2-cyclohexenones. A 2 M soln. of 2 eqs. Me₃Al in heptane added to a soln. of 4 eqs. 2,6-di-*tert*-butyl-4-methylphenol in anhydrous toluene at room temp. under N₂, stirred for 1 h, cooled to 0°, 1.1 eqs. Et₃N added, followed immediately by a soln. of the startg. divinyl ketone in anhydrous toluene, stirred for 15 min at 0°, warmed to room temp. over 2.5 h, then quenched with satd. aq. NH₄Cl → product. Y 86%. The sterically demanding Lewis acid and amine are critical in generating the intermediate trienolate, further stabilized by the sulfonyl group, so that Nazarov cycloisomerization is prevented. F.e. **and 4-sulfonyl-1,3,5-cyclooctatrien-3-ols** by vinylogous cyclization s. N.A. Magomedov, P.L. Ruggiero, Y. Tang, Org. Lett. *6*, 3373-5 (2004).

Ethylaluminum dichloride $EtAlCl_2$
Bicyclo[3.n.1]alk-3-en-2-ones from cyclic α'-allyl-α,β-ethyleneketones

334.

A soln. of 1 eq. startg. cyclic ketone in toluene treated dropwise below 10° with 1.5 eqs. neat EtAlCl₂, stirred at room temp. for 15 h, then quenched with satd. aq. NH₄Cl at 0° → product. Y

90% (d.r. 1.6:1). Reaction involves initial generation of a bridged zwitterionic species, which undergoes 1,2-hydrogen (or alkyl) shift prior to skeletal rearrangement. γ-Substituted substrates, however, afforded a mixture of products formed by intramolecular [2+2]-cycloaddition and cylopropanation. F.e.s. A. Goeke, D. Mertl, G. Brunner, Angew. Chem. Int. Ed. Engl. 44, 99-1 (2005).

Europium(III) chloride s. under [PtCl$_2$(ethylene)]$_2$	*EuCl$_3$*
Imidazolium ionic liquids s. under Hf(OTf)$_4$ and [IrCl(cod)]$_2$	←
Chiral N-condensed 1,2,4-triazol-5-ylidenes	←
Catalytic asym. intramolecular Stetter reaction	○

335.

Chiral quaternary centres can be generated with high enantioselectivity by intramolecular Stetter reaction with new, tunable, electron-deficient chiral bicyclic 1,2,4-triazol-5-ylidenes as catalyst. E: A soln. of 0.2 eq. condensed 1,2,4-triazolium salt in anhydrous toluene treated with 0.2 eq. K-bis(trimethylsilyl)amide (0.5 M in toluene) under argon, stirred at room temp. for 5 min, a soln. of 1 eq. of the startg. δ,ε-ethylenealdehyde in the same solvent added to the generated carbene soln., and stirred at room temp. for 24 h → product. Y 90% (e.e. 84%). This method is applicable to both ar. and aliphatic aldehydes, but yields and enantioselectivities were lower with substrates possessing a (Z)-alkene residue. F.e. and comparison of carbenes, also chiral 2,2-disubst. 3(2H)-benzofuranones, S-analogs and 1-indanones, s. M.S. Kerr, T. Rovis, J. Am. Chem. Soc. 126, 8876-7 (2004).

2,6-Di-tert-butyl-4-methylphenol s. under Me$_3$Al	*ArOH*
Stannic chloride	*SnCl$_4$*
Regiospecific cycloisomerization of α,β-ethylenecarboxylic acid anilides	

3,4-dihydrocarbostyrils with PPA cf. 19, 787; oxindoles with SnCl$_4$, also 2(3H)-benzofuranones from aryl esters, and comparison of Lewis acids, s. S. Yamazaki, K. Kuramoto et al., Org. Biomol. Chem. 2, 3134-8 (2004).

Hafnium(IV) triflate/1-n-butyl-3-methylimidazolium hexafluoroantimonate	←
Intramolecular Friedel-Crafts vinylation with acetylene derivs. s. 68, 299	

Trimethylphosphine/cesium carbonate	*Me$_3$P/Cs$_2$CO$_3$*
Decalin-2,8-diones from 2,8-diene-1,7-diones	
via stereospecific Rauhut-Currier reaction-intramolecular Michael addition	

336.

1 eq. Trimethylphosphine and 4 eqs. Cs$_2$CO$_3$ added to a soln. of the startg. bis(enone) in acetonitrile under N$_2$, and the resulting suspension stirred under reflux for 16 h → product. Y 75% (after purification; d.r. 4:3:2:1). Reaction generates two carbon-carbon bonds and up to five contiguous stereocenters in one step, and serves as a useful **alternative to the Lewis acid-catalyzed Diels-Alder reaction**. The phosphine is effective as catalyst for both steps of the cycloisomerization, the geometry of the terminal enone being of no consequence. A bicyclo[5.4.0]-undecane analog was also prepared by the same procedure. F.e. and in protic media (without base) s. M. Couturier et al., Org. Lett. 6, 1857-60 (2004).

Tri-n-butylphosphine Bu_3P
Rauhut-Currier reaction
with bis(α,β-ethylenecarbonyl compds.) cf. *63*, 326; with α,β-ethylenesulfones as Michael acceptor s. A.L. Luis, M.J. Krische, Synthesis *2004*, 2579-85.

Triphenylphosphine Ph_3P
Intramolecular Baylis-Hillman reaction
with piperidine cf. *54*, 338; 5-, 6- and 7-membered 2-acylcycloalk-2-enols with Ph_3P s. J.E. Yeo, S. Koo et al., Chem. Commun. *2004*, 236-7.

Triflimide/ethyldiisopropylamine $Tf_2NH/i\text{-}Pr_2NEt$
Cycloisomerization of acetylene derivs.
with CF_3SO_3H cf. *51*, 339s*67*; 4-siloxy-1,2-dihydronaphthalenes with $Tf_2NH/i\text{-}Pr_2NEt$ s. L.-M. Zhang, S.A. Kozmin, J. Am. Chem. Soc. *126*, 10204-5 (2004).

Sulfuric acid H_2SO_4
Cycloisomerization of ethylene derivs.
fused indenes with BF_3 cf. *25*, 527s*66*; 5,6-dihydro-11*H*-dibenz[*b,e*]azepines (cf. *20*, 542; *5*, 518) s. A. Palma, J. Amaro-Luis et al., Synlett *2004*, 2721-4.

Pentacarbonyl(tetrahydrofuran)tungsten $W(CO)_5(THF)$
9-Oxatricyclo[3.3.1.0^{1,3}]nonanes from 1,7-enyn-4-ols
via stereospecific tungsten-catalyzed cycloisomerization-intramolecular cyclopropanation

337.

A soln. of 25 *mol%* $W(CO)_5$-THF complex in anhyd. THF treated at room temp. under argon with 1 eq. startg. 1,7-enyn-4-ol, the resulting soln. concentrated to one fifth of the initial volume and freeze-pump-thaw degassed (three cycles), and the resulting soln. stirred at room temp. in the absence of light for 24 h → (-)-product. Y 91%. This is a rare example of a *catalytic* reaction involving a heteroatom-stabilized Fischer carbene complex. F.e. and [more conveniently] with 10 mol% [$W(CO)_6$] and 2 *mol%* Et_3N, also acid-catalyzed conversion to **1,5-oxidocyclooctanols**, s. J. Barluenga et al., Angew. Chem. Int. Ed. Engl. *44*, 126-8 (2005).

Hydrogen chloride/irradiation $HCl/⚡$
Photochemical migration of carbon-carbon double bonds ←
with 1,4-dicyanobenzene as sensitizer cf. *20*, 533s*60*; 3-[hetero]arylmethylindenes with HCl in acetonitrile s. T.-I. Ho, T.-C. Li, Tetrahedron Lett. *45*, 5665-7 (2004).

Bis(acetonitrile)[hydridotris(pyrazolyl)borato](triphenylphosphine)ruthenium(II) ←
   hexafluorophosphate
2-Vinylindenes from *o*-ethynylstyrenes
via ruthenium-catalyzed skeletal rearrangement

338.

A mixture of 10 mol% predried bis(acetonitrile)[hydridotris(pyrazolyl)borato](triphenylphosphine)ruthenium(II) hexafluorophosphate and 1 eq. startg. enyne in anhydrous benzene heated at 80° under N_2 for 18 h → product. Y 91% (5:1 mixture of regioisomers). The ring closure involves complete cleavage of the carbon-carbon double bond with insertion of the alkyne residue, reaction involving 5-*endo-dig* cyclization of an intermediate ruthenium vinylidene complex and a methylenecyclopropane-trimethylenemethane rearrangement. However, a *trisubst.* styryl residue appears essential to eliminate the possibility of naphthalene ring closure. F.e., also 1-vinylindenes from allyl(*o*-ethynyl)arenes by ring-closing metathesis, s. R.J. Madhushaw, R.-S. Liu et al., J. Am. Chem. Soc. *126*, 15560-5 (2004).

Alkylidene(dichloro)ruthenium imidazolidin-2-ylidene complex/trimethylsilyl vinyl ether ←
Ruthenium carbene-catalyzed cycloisomerization of dienes ○

339.

An atom-economical *non-metathetical* cycloisomerization of dienes has been effected with a ruthenium carbene complex. **E:** A soln. of 1 eq. of the startg. 1,6-diene and 1 eq. trimethylsilyl vinyl ether in methylene chloride treated with 5 mol% dichloro(1,3-dimesitylimidazolidin-2-ylidene)(tricyclohexylphosphine)(benzylidene)ruthenium(II) under argon, and refluxed for 2 h → product. Y 87%. The enol ether is thought to react with the ruthenium catalyst to generate a metal hydride complex, which hydridometalates one of the unsaturations prior to intramolecular insertion of the free alkene residue into the Ru-C bond and *syn*-β-hydride elimination. The procedure is applicable to the preparation of methylenecyclopentanes, N-protected 3-methylene-pyrrolidines, 3-methylene-2,3-dihydrobenzofurans and N-protected 3-methyleneindolines. F.e.s. Y. Terada, M. Arisawa, A. Nishida, Angew. Chem. Int. Ed. Engl. *43*, 4063-7 (2004).

[(2S,4S)-2,4-Bis(diphenylphosphino)pentane]rhodium(I) hexafluoroantimonate ←
Asym. intramolecular Alder-ene reaction of 1,6-enynes
with (S)-BINAP as ligand cf. *60*, 307s*65*; chiral spirocyclics with [(2S,4S)-2,4-bis(diphenyl-phosphino)pentane]rhodium(I) hexafluoroantimonate s. K. Mikami et al., Chem. Commun. *2004*, 98-9.

Dicarbonyl(chloro)rhodium(I) dimer $[Rh(CO)_2Cl]_2$
Rhodium-catalyzed cycloisomerization of 1,2,7-trienes
with [RhCl(cod)]$_2$/(ArO)$_3$P cf. *64*, 302s*66*; 4-alkylidene-2,3,4,5-tetrahydro-1*H*-azepines and oxepine analogs with [Ru(CO)$_2$Cl]$_2$ s. K.M. Brummond, A.D. Casarez et al., Org. Lett. *6*, 2161-3 (2004); N-protected 3-alkylidene-4-vinyl-1,2,3,6-tetrahydropyridines s. ibid. 2245-8.

Rhodium-catalyzed cycloisomerization of 1,2-dien-n-ynes
intramolecular Alder-ene reaction of 1,2-dien-7-ynes cf. *65*, 314; double ring closure of 1,2-dien-8-ynes to 2-alkylidenebicyclo[5.2.0]non-9-enes (in xylene) and cyclic cross-conjugated trienes (in toluene) s. C. Mukai, T. Yoshida, S. Kitagaki et al., Tetrahedron Lett. *45*, 4117-21 (2004).

Palladous acetate/1,3-bis(diphenylphosphino)propane $Pd(OAc)_2/dppp$
1,3-Dienes from allenes CHC=C=C → C=C-CH=C
with xanthione cf. *28*, 521; 2-vinylfurans from 2-vinylidene-2,3-dihydrofurans with Pd(OAc)$_2$/dppp (cf. *12*, 931s*60*) s. L. Wavrin, J. Rodriguez et al., Synlett *2004*, 1820-2.

Cationic carbonyl(methyl)iridium(III) di(phosphine) complexes
Stereospecific iridium(III)-catalyzed Nazarov cyclization under mild conditions

340.

2 Mol% Cationic carbonyl(methyl)iridium(III) di(phosphine) complex and the startg. 1,4-dien-3-one sealed in a dry NMR tube under N_2, cooled to -78°, methylene chloride-d_2 added, the tube quickly transferred to a precooled NMR spectrometer, and warmed to room temp. during 20 min → product. Y 100%. The catalytic activity is considerably higher than that of $Cu(OTf)_2$, the intermediate oxyallyl cation being stabilized by coordination of *two* oxygen atoms to iridium. The procedure is high-yielding and generally applicable to both divinyl ketones and aryl vinyl ketones. F.e.s. M. Janka, A.J. Frontier, R. Eisenberg et al., J. Am. Chem. Soc. *126*, 6864-5 (2004).

Chloro(cyclooctadiene)iridium(I) dimer/1-n-butyl-3-methylimidazolium fluoroborate
Iridium-catalyzed cycloisomerization of 1,6-enynes
s. *61*, 312; intramolecular ene-type reaction **in ionic liquids,** e.g. 1-*n*-butyl-3-methylimidazolium fluoroborate, s. T. Shibata, M. Yamasaki, K. Takagi et al., Synlett *2004*, 2812-4.

Dichloro(ethylene)platinum(II) dimer/europium(III) chloride/hydrogen chloride
Regiospecific intramolecular addition of ketones to unactivated ethylene derivs.
of β-ketocarbonyl compds. with $PdCl_2(MeCN)_2/Ln(OTf)_3$ cf. *62*, 318s66; of cyclohexanone derivs. with $[PtCl_2(ethylene)]_2/EuCl_3/HCl$ s. C. Liu, R.A. Widenhoefer, Tetrahedron Lett. *46*, 285-7 (2005).

Platinum chloride
**Bicyclo[3.1.0]hexan-3-ones from 1,5-enyn-4-ols
by stereospecific platinum-catalyzed cycloisomerization**

341.

A suspension of the startg. enynol and 6 mol% $PtCl_2$ in benzene stirred at 60° for 40 h → product. Y 78%. Reaction proceeds through a platinum carbene complex which triggers an irreversible 1,2-hydrogen shift to procure the keto group. Interestingly, the corresponding 1,5-enyn-4-ol acetate affords **bicyclo[3.1.0]hexan-2-ones** with 2 mol% each of $(Ph_3P)AuCl$ and $AgSbF_6$ (cf. *68*, 351). F.e. and stereoselectivity, also one-pot procedure from α,β-acetylenealdehydes, s. V. Mamane, A. Fürstner et al., J. Am. Chem. Soc. *126*, 8654-5 (2004).

Oxygen/Carbon Type   CC ∩ OC

Without additional reagents   w.a.r.
Claisen rearrangement of allyl enolethers
s. *27*, 738s55; diastereoselective synthesis of δ,ε-ethylene-α-ketophosphonic acid esters and amide esters s. K. Afarinkia, A.J. Twist, H.-W. Yu, J. Org. Chem. *69*, 6500-3 (2004).

Intramolecular hetero-Diels-Alder reaction
s. *47*, 698s65; 3a,7a-dihydro-3*H*,4*H*-furo[3,4-*c*]pyran-1-ones s. C. Fuhrer, R. Messer, R. Haner, Tetrahedron Lett. *45*, 4297-300 (2004); intramolecular cycloaddition of formyl-subst. 1,2,4-

trienes with BF$_3$ s. D. Regás, J.A. Palenzuela et al., ibid. *44*, 8471-4 (2003); of imino-subst. 1,2,4-trienes s. Synthesis *2004*, 757-60.

Microwaves s. under Zn and SiO$_2$ [\\\\]

n-*Butyllithium*   *BuLi*
α**-Alleneketones from terminal 3-acetyleneepoxides via dilithium 1,3-enyn-1-olates**   ⊂

342.

A soln. of 1 eq. startg. epoxide in anhydrous THF treated under N$_2$ at -80° with 2.2 eqs. BuLi (2.2 *M* in hexanes), the resulting mixture stirred at the same temp. for 10 min, allowed to warm to -20°, stirring continued until reaction complete, then quenched with 0.5 *M* aq. HCl → product. Y 64%. Ring opening is presumed to proceed via 1,2-hydrogen shift to give an intermediate dilithium enynolate, rather than by an electrocyclic process. Reaction also takes place with *trans*-isomers and with trisubst. epoxides via 1,2-aryl or [less efficiently] 1,2-alkyl shift. F.e.s. A. Denichoux, F. Ferreira, F. Chemla, Org. Lett. *6*, 3509-12 (2004).

sec-Butyllithium/N,N,N',N'-tetramethylethylenediamine   *s-BuLi/tmeda*
Anionic O→C-carbamyl group migration   ←
s. *56*, 313; for preparing (*o*-hydroxyarylthio)acetamides s. C. Mukherjee, S. Kamila, A. De, Synlett *2003*, 1474-8; f. details and conversion to 1,4-benzoxathiin-2-ones s. Tetrahedron *60*, 5215-24 (2004); α-carbamyl-*o*-hydroxystilbenes with LDA s. M.A. Reed, M.T. Chang, V. Snieckus, Org. Lett. *6*, 2297-300 (2004).

Potassium cyanide/potassium hydrogen carbonate   *KCN/KHCO$_3$*
α**-Acyl-β-diketones from β-acoxy-α,β-ethyleneketones**   ←
with AlCl$_3$ cf. *35*, 592; with KCN/KHCO$_3$ in the absence of solvent s. H. Lehmann, German patent DE-10113137 (Bayer Crop Science GmbH).

Tris(triphenylphosphinegold)oxonium fluoroborate/sodium tetrahydridoborate   ←
Gold(I)-catalyzed Claisen rearrangement of vinyloxy-2-acetylenes   ←

343.

Chiral 3-allenealcohols. A soln. of 1 eq. of the startg. propargyl vinyl ether in methylene chloride treated with 1 mol% [(Ph$_3$PAu)$_3$O]BF$_4$, stirred at room temp. for 50 min, then diluted with methanol, treated with 1 eq. NaBH$_4$, and stirring continued at the same temp. for 1 h → product. Y 81% (e.e. 94%; d.r. >20:1). This is the first example of a general catalytic Claisen rearrangement of propargyl vinyl ethers, being tolerant of electron-withdrawing or -donating groups in the aromatic ring, applicable to both terminal and internal acetylene derivs., and proceeding with complete central→axial **transfer of chirality**. Reaction is thought to take place via 6-*endo-dig* addition of the enol ether onto an intermediate gold(I)-alkyne complex, terminating with a Grob-type fragmentation. Conditions are mild, and the catalyst is air- and moisture-resistant. F.e. and with retention of O-silyl and O-pivaloyl groups s. B.D. Sherry, F.D. Toste, J. Am. Chem. Soc. *126*, 15978-9 (2004).

Aurous chloride   AuCl
**1-Siloxy-1,4-cyclohexadienes from 6-siloxy-1,5-enynes
via gold(I)-catalyzed cycloisomerization**

344.

under mild conditions. 1 *Mol%* AuCl added to a soln. of startg. siloxyenyne in anhydrous methylene chloride under N_2, stirred at 20° for 30 min, a drop of triethylamine added, and the mixture worked up → product. Y 99%. After coordination of the π-acidic AuCl with the alkyne residue, reaction is thought to proceed through a gold cyclopropylcarbenoid, followed by two 1,2-alkyl shifts and a fragmentation-type ring closure. 4-Subst. 6-siloxy-1,5-enynes afforded the corresponding **2-siloxy-1,3-cyclohexadienes** possessing a quaternary centre at the 5-position. There was no reaction, however, with substrates possessing a terminal monosubst. alkene residue. F.e. and with $PtCl_2$ (at 80°) s. L. Zhang, S.A. Kozmin, J. Am. Chem. Soc. *126*, 11806-7 (2004).

Auric chloride/silver triflate $AuCl_3$ /AgOTf
3-Chromanols from 3-aryloxyepoxides

345.

Startg. epoxide (0.5 mmol) added with stirring to a suspension of 2.5 mol% $AuCl_3$ and 7.5 mol% Ag(I)-triflate in anhydrous dichloroethane, and heated at 50° under N_2 for 3 h → product. Y 82%. Reaction possibly involves initial auration to give an arylgold(III) complex, followed by regiospecific S_N2 attack on the appended oxirane ring **with inversion of configuration.** Reaction is also more facile with electron-rich substrates, leaves aromatic halogen unaffected, and is stereospecific with formation of 3,4-*trans*-products from *trans*-epoxides. F.e. and intramolecular process s. Z. Shi, C. He, J. Am. Chem. Soc. *126*, 5964-5 (2004).

Zinc/dimethylformamide/microwaves   Zn/DMF/[\\\\]
Fries rearrangement under microwave irradiation in the absence of solvent s. *1*, 537s68 ←

Sodium tetrahydridoborate s. under $[(Ph_3PAu)_3O]BF_4$ $NaBH_4$

Trimethylaluminum Me_3Al
Cyclic alcohols from 2-methylene-O-heterocyclics ←
with *i*-Bu_3Al cf. *51*, 345s61; rearrangement of O-benzyl-protected 5,6-unsatd. glycosides with Me_3Al s. C. Jia, P. Sinay et al., Tetrahedron:Asym. *15*, 699-703 (2004).

Boron fluoride BF_3
Intramolecular hetero-Diels-Alder reaction with 1,2,4-trienes s. *47*, 698s68

Erbium(III) triflate $Er(OTf)_3$
Oxo compds. from epoxides with rearrangement
with $EtAlCl_2$ cf. *45*, 436s66; from aliphatic and aromatic oxo compds. with *0.1 mol%* $Er(OTf)_3$ s. A. Procopio, R. Dalpozzo, A. Tagarelli et al., Synlett *2004*, 2633-5.

Silica gel/microwaves SiO_2/[\\\\]
Claisen rearrangement of allyl phenolethers ←
s. 2, 621; rapid procedure under microwave irradiation in the absence of solvent with silica gel s. S. Kotha, S. Banerjee et al., Tetrahedron Lett. *45*, 9603-5 (2004); catalyzed conversion with 5 mol% Bi(OTf)$_3$, also Fries rearrangement (cf. *1*, 537s68), s. B. Sreedhar, V. Swapna, C. Sridhar, Synth. Commun. *34*, 1433-40 (2004).

Bismuth(III) triflate Bi(OTf)$_3$
Catalytic Claisen rearrangement of allyl phenolethers s. 2, 621s68 ←

Fries rearrangement ←
with Y(OTf)$_3$ cf. *1*, 537s67 and with Bi(OTf)$_3$ s. above; with Bi(OTf)$_3$ s.a. T. Ollevier, M.C. Brochu et al., Synlett *2004*, 2794-6; with Zn/DMF under microwave irradiation in the absence of solvent s. S. Paul, M. Gupta, Synthesis *2004*, 1789-92.

5,10,15,20-Tetraphenylporphyrinatochromium(III) triflate ←
Aldehydes from epoxides under mild conditions C.
Regio- and stereo-specific chromium(III)-catalyzed rearrangement

346.

Chiral β-siloxyaldehydes. A soln. of 1 eq. of the startg. chiral epoxide in freshly distilled 1,2-dichloroethane treated under argon with 1 mol% freshly dried 5,10,15,20-tetraphenylporphyrinatochromium(III) triflate, and refluxed under argon for 1 h → product. Y 97% (e.e. >99%). Contrasting with iron(III)-catalyzed rearrangement, the aldehyde rather than ketone is obtained exclusively, reaction taking place with no erosion of chirality. F.e. incl. rearrangement of trialkyl-subst. spirocyclic and bicyclic epoxides s. K. Suda et al., J. Am. Chem. Soc. *126*, 9554-5 (2004).

Bis(acetonitrile)[hydridotris(pyrazolyl)borato](triphenylphosphine)ruthenium(II) ←
 hexafluorophosphate
Electrocyclization of *o*-acetyleneepoxides via ruthenium π-ketene complexes ←

347.

2-Naphthols. 10 Mol% bis(acetonitrile)[hydridotris(pyrazolyl)borato](triphenylphosphine)-ruthenium(II) hexafluorophosphate and the startg. *o*-ethynylphenyloxiranc (1.2 *M*) in anhydrous toluene heated in a long, dry tube under N$_2$ at 100° for 3 h → product. Y 95%. Reaction of 1,2-disubst. epoxides takes place by initial generation of a highly electrophilic ruthenium vinylidenium species to which oxygen is transferred intramolecularly to give a key ruthenium π-ketene complex prior to 6-*endo-dig* cyclization. 1,2,2-Trisubst. epoxides, however, were converted to **1-alkylidene-2-indanones** via 5-*endo-dig* cyclization. F.e.s. R.J. Madhushaw, R.-S. Liu et al., J. Am. Chem. Soc. *126*, 6895-9 (2004).

Nitrogen/Carbon Type   CC ↻ NC

Without additional reagents   w.a.r.
2,4-Enynenitriles from (Z)-N-(alk-1-ynyl)-α,β-ethyleneketimines   ←
via aza-Bergman cyclization-retro-aza-Bergman cleavage

348.

1.1 eqs. 1 *M* Tetrabutylammonium fluoride in dry THF added slowly to a soln. of 1,4-diphenyl-6-(triisopropylsilyl)-3-azahex-3-ene-1,5-diyne in the same solvent at -78°, stirred for 5-10 min, and poured into ice-water → (Z)-2,5-diphenylpent-2-en-4-ynenitrile. Y 89%. The intermediate desilylated azaenediyne was characterizable, but attempts to trap the intermediate 2,5-didehydropyridine failed. F.e.s. L. Feng, D. Kumar, S.M. Kerwin, J. Org. Chem. *68*, 2234-42 (2003).

Lithium diisopropylamide   i-Pr_2NLi
Aniline ring from *o*-acetylenealdimines   ○
N-Alkylative ring closure through a carbanionic rearrangement cascade

349.

7-*sec*-Aminobenzofurans. A soln. of 1.12 eqs. diisopropylamine in anhydrous THF treated at -50° with 1.12 eqs. *n*-BuLi (1.6 *M* in hexane), the mixture warmed to 0°, stirred for 30 min, cooled to -78°, treated dropwise over 30 min with a soln. of the startg. *o*-acetylenealdimine in anhydrous THF, allowed to warm to room temp. over 16 h, 2 eqs. methyl iodide added, and quenched with water → product. Y 82%. After initial deprotonation, reaction is thought to involve a series of isomerizations via the 2*H*-azepine ring, terminating with N-alkylation of the generated N-lithioaniline. F.e. incl. 7-*sec*-aminobenzo[*b*]thiophenes and 1-*sec*-aminonaphthalenes s. P. Sagar, R. Fröhlich, E.-U. Würthwein, Angew. Chem. Int. Ed. Engl. *43*, 5694-7 (2004).

Boron fluoride BF_3
Intramolecular hetero-Diels-Alder reaction with 1,2,4-trienes s. *47*, 698s68
5-Iminocycloheptene ring   ←
via Lewis acid-catalyzed intramolecular [4+3]-cycloaddition with 2-alkylideneaziridines

350.

55 : 45

A stirred soln. of the startg. 2-alkylideneaziridine in methylene chloride treated at -30° with 1.5 eqs. BF_3-etherate, stirred at the same temp. for 1 h, allowed to warm to room temp., and stirring continued for 16 h → product. Y 72% (d.r. 55:45). Reaction is thought to involve generation of a highly strained aziridinium ion, which undergoes fragmentation to a planar Lewis acid-complexed 2-aminoallyl cation. Simple 1,3-dienes also participate in the cycloaddition. F.e. and with $Sc(OTf)_3$ s. G. Prié, M. Shipman et al., Angew. Chem. Int. Ed. Engl. *43*, 6517-9 (2004).

Titanium tetrachloride/triethylamine $TiCl_4/Et_3N$
Cyclic β-aminocarbonyl from (alkylideneamino)carbonyl compds.
cyclic β-aminoketones with 3-bromopropanol cf. *36*, 715; *cis*-2,3-disubst. pyrrolidine-3-carboxylic from γ-(alkylideneamino)carboxylic acid esters with $TiCl_4/Et_3N$ s. S. Suresh, M. Periasamy, Tetrahedron Lett. *45*, 6291-3 (2004).

Halogen/Carbon Type   CC ∩ HalC

Irradiation
Polymeric distannanes
Ring closures with iodine atom transfer
with In/I_2 cf. *40*, 493s67, and with $BF_3/Bu_3SnSnBu_3$ under irradiation cf. *42*, 695s65; with polymeric distannanes s. A.G. Hernán, J.D. Kilburn, Tetrahedron Lett. *45*, 831-4 (2004); ring closure of cyclic α-(ω-allene)-α-iodoketones under irradiation s. H.-H. Lin, C.-K. Sha, Org. Lett. *6*, 3289-92 (2004).

Remaining Elements/Carbon Type   CC ∩ RemC

Irradiation s. under Et_2AlCl
Microwaves
Regiospecific radical ring closures of ethylenetellurides with aryltelluro group migration
with $Bu_3SnSnBu_3$ under irradiation cf. *51*, 355; rapid procedure under microwave irradiation **in ethylene glycol or water** s. C. Ericsson, L. Engman, J. Org. Chem. *69*, 5143-6 (2004).

Diethylaluminum chloride/irradiation $Et_2AlCl/$
Regiospecific radical ring closures of ethyleneselenides with arylseleno group migration
with 1,5-dimethoxynaphthalene/ascorbic acid cf. *49*, 718; chiral cyclic γ-(arylseleno)carboxylic acid esters with Et_2AlCl s. D. Yang, N.-Y. Zhu, J. Org. Chem. *69*, 8821-8 (2004).

Carbon/Carbon Type   CC ∩ CC

Chloro(triphenylphosphine)gold(I)/silver fluoroborate $Au(PPh_3)Cl/AgBF_4$
Regiospecific gold(I)-catalyzed cycloisomerization of 1,6-enynes under mild conditions

351.

1-Vinylcyclopentenes. A mixture of the startg. enyne, 2 mol% $Au(PPh_3)Cl$, and 2 mol% $AgBF_4$ in methylene chloride stirred at 23° for 15 min → product. Y 100% (E/Z 4:1). *in situ*-Generated (triphenylphosphine)gold fluoroborate forms an active (η^2-alkyne) complex which evolves to a cyclopropylcarbene complex by 5-*exo-dig* cyclization prior to skeletal rearrangement. 4-Aza-

1,6-enynes, however, favour the unprecedented 6-*endo-dig* cyclization to give the corresponding **3-alkylidene-1,2,3,6-tetrahydropyridines** (in one instance as the unique product). F.e. and with AgSbF$_6$, also intramolecular cyclopropanation of dienynes, and trapping of the intermediate carbocations with O-nucleophiles (*68*, 290), s. C. Nieto-Oberhuber, A.M. Echavarren et al., Angew. Chem. Int. Ed. Engl. *43*, 2402-6 (2004).

Imidazolium ionic liquids s. under PtCl$_2$ ←

Titanium tetrachloride   *TiCl$_4$*
Cyclopentene ring from acetylenecyclopropanes
3-Acyl-5-(silylmethyl)cyclopentene ring s. *68,* 308

Alkylidene(dichloro)ruthenium imidazolidin-2-ylidene complex ←
Ring closing ene-yne metathesis
with methylene group transfer s. *50*, 443s*64*; 1,2-oxasilacycloalk-3-enes s. R.L. Miller, S.V. Maifeld, D. Lee, Org. Lett. *6*, 2773-6 (2004).

Dichlorobis(tricyclohexylphosphine)benzylideneruthenium(II)   *RuCl$_2$(PCy$_3$)$_2$=CHPh*
2,3-Fused 4-alkylidenecyclopentenes
via ruthenium carbene-catalyzed intramolecular [3+2]-cycloaddition
with alkylidenecyclopropanes

352.

A mixture of 1 eq. startg. alkylidenecyclopropane and 15 mol% Grubb's complex in anhydrous toluene refluxed under argon for 205 min → product. Y 62%. This is the first example of such a *non-metathetical* ruthenium-catalyzed [3+2]-cycloaddition, which is applicable to both terminal and internal alkyne derivs. (excepting silylacetylenes). Carboxylic acid esters, silyl ethers and alcohols tolerate these conditions. F.e.s. F. Lopez, J.L. Mascareñas et al., J. Am. Chem. Soc. *126*, 10262-3 (2004).

(1,5-Cyclooctadiene)(η^6-naphthalene)rhodium(I) hexafluoroantimonate ←
Regio- and stereo-specific rhodium-catalyzed intramolecular [4+2+2]-cycloaddition of silyl-tethered 1,3,n-trien-m-ynes

353.

Cycloocta-1,4-diene ring. A mixture of 1 eq. of the startg. trienyne and 20 mol% (1,5-Cyclooctadiene)(η^6-naphthalene)rhodium(I) hexafluoroantimonate in acetonitrile stirred in a sealed tube under N$_2$ at 110° for 16 h → product. Y 88% (d.r. >19:1). The enyne functions can be tethered by carbon-, nitrogen- or oxygen-residues (not sulfonyl), and the 1,3-diene residue can be substituted at the 2-position (thereby circumventing the regiochemical problems associated with the intermolecular version). Furthermore, (E)- and (Z)-olefins participate stereospecifically. F.e.s. P.A. Evans, E.W. Baum, J. Am. Chem. Soc. *126*, 11150-1 (2004).

Platinum chloride/1-n-*butyl-3-methylimidazolium hexafluorophosphate*   *PtCl$_2$/[bmim]PF$_6$*
Platinum tetrachloride   *PtCl$_4$*
Ring-closing ene-yne metathesis
1-vinylcycloalkenes with [Pt(dppp)(PhCN)$_2$][BF$_4$]$_2$ cf. *56*, 326s*62*; **under mild conditions** with PtCl$_2$ **in ionic liquids**, e.g. 1-*n*-butyl-3-methylimidazolium hexafluorophosphate, as readily recyclable media s. Y. Miyanohana, H. Inoue, N. Chatani, J. Org. Chem. *69*, 8541-3 (2004); ring-closing metathesis of 1,6- and 1,7-enynes with PtCl$_4$ s. C.H. Oh, S.Y. Bang, C.Y. Rhim, Bull. Korean Chem. Soc. *24*, 887-8 (2003).

Exchange ⇅
Hydrogen ↑   CC ⇅ H

Microwaves s. under PhI(OAc)$_2$ [\\\\]
Cupric acetate s. under Pd(OAc)$_2$ Cu(OAc)$_2$
Cuprous bromide/tert-butyl hydroperoxide   CuBr/t-BuOOH
Tert. 2-nitramines from aliphatic nitro compds. and tert. amines   CH(N<) → C(N<)C(NO$_2$)
via copper(I)-catalyzed dehydrogenative cross-coupling

354.

A mixture of 5 mol% CuBr and 1 eq. 2-phenyl-1,2,3,4-tetrahydroisoquinoline treated at room temp. under N$_2$ with excess of nitroethane, followed dropwise by 1-1.2 eqs. *t*-BuOOH, the reaction flask sealed, and the soln. stirred for 6 h → product. Y 53% (1.7:1 mixture of diastereoisomers). This is the first example of a highly efficient C-C bond formation by dehydrogenative coupling *of two sp^3 C-H bonds*. It is possible that reaction involves an aza-Henry-type addition of the nitro compd. to an intermediate imine coordinated to copper(II). F.e. and with nitromethane, also comparison of copper salts, s. Z. Li, C.-J. Li, J. Am. Chem. Soc. *127*, 3672-3 (2005).

Aluminum chloride   AlCl$_3$
Ar. formylation with tetraformylhydrazine   H → CHO

355.

4 eqs. AlCl$_3$ added at -12° to a suspension of 1 eq. tetraformylhydrazine in toluene, the mixture allowed to warm to 18°, stirred for 66 h, then hydrolyzed with ice water → product. Y 98%. Azines were obtained as by-products, notably from arenes possessing electron-donating substituents. F.e.s. W. Kantlehner et al., Z. Naturforsch. B: Anorg. Chem. Org. Chem. *59*, 357-65 (2004).

Ytterbium(III) triflate   Yb(OTf)$_3$
Sym. diaryl ketones from arenes   2 ArH → Ar$_2$CO
with triphosgene/AlCl$_3$ cf. *59*, 333s*64*; also di(hetaryl) ketones with Yb(OTf)$_3$ in place of AlCl$_3$ s. W.K. Su, C. Jin, Synth. Commun. *34*, 4249-56 (2004).

Benzoquinone s. under Pd(OCOCF$_3$)$_2$ ←
Iodosobenzene s. under Chiral rhodium(II) α-imidocarboxylates   PhIO

Phenyl iodosoacetate   PhI(OAc)$_2$
Phenyl iodosoacetate/microwaves   PhI(OAc)$_2$/[\\\\]
N-Chlorosuccinimide/triethylamine   NCS/Et$_3$N
1,3-Dipolar cycloaddition with *in situ*-generated nitrile oxides   ○
soluble polymer-based synthesis of isoxazoles s. *58*, 314s*63*; also of Δ^2-isoxazolines s. Y.J. Shang, L.L. Yuan, Y.G. Wang, J. Chem. Res. Synop 2004, 336-8; soln.-phase method s. R. Braun et al., German patent DE-10114597 (Bayer Crop Science GmbH); from Baylis-Hillman adducts with PhI(OAc)$_2$ cf. B. Das, M.R. Reddy et al., Tetrahedron Lett. *45*, 7347-50 (2004); polymer-based synthesis of Δ^2-pyrazolines from *in situ*-generated nitrilimines with PhI(OAc)$_2$ under microwave irradiation in the absence of solvent s. M. Xia, X.-J. Pan, Synth. Commun. *34*, 3521-8 (2004).

Zirconium or tin dioxide/oxygen ZrO_2 *or* SnO_2/O_2
Aerobic dimerization of phenols   2 ArH → Ar-Ar
with $CuCl_2$/tmeda cf. *31*, 719s65; of naphthols with SnO_2, ZrO_2 or activated carbon (cf. *27*, 761s65) s. T. Otsuka, T. Takeya et al., Tetrahedron Lett. *45*, 2643-7 (2004); with $Rh(acac)_3$ s. M. Mizuno, Japanese patent JP-2002338509 (Sumitomo Chem. Co. Ltd.).

Tetrakis(pyridine)cobalt(II) dichromate/ethyldiisopropylamine $Co(C_5H_5N)_4(HCrO_4)_2$/i-Pr_2NEt
Indolizines from pyridinium bromides and electron-deficient ethylene derivs. ○
polymer-based synthesis with an insoluble pyridinium bromide cf. *58*, 315; library synthesis with a soluble (PEG-based) pyridinium bromide, **also from acetylene derivs.** without the cobalt complex, s. Z. Chen et al., Synthesis *2004*, 1231-4.

1,8-Bis(diphenylmethylium)naphthalenediyl bis(perchlorate)   ←
Oxidative ar. dimerization   2 ArH → Ar-Ar
with $PhI(OCOCF_3)_2/BF_3$ cf. *29*, 910s67; of N,N-dialkylanilines with 1,8-bis(diphenylmethylium)-Naphthalenediyl bis(perchlorate) s. T. Saitoh, S. Yoshida, J. Ichikawa, Org. Lett. *6*, 4563-5 (2004).

Rhodium(III) acetoacetonate/oxygen $Rh(acac)_3/O_2$
Aerobic dimerization of phenols s. *31*, 719s68

Chiral rhodium(II) α-imidocarboxylates/iodosobenzene/magnesium oxide   ←
Asym. synthesis of cyclopropanes from ethylene derivs. and active methylene groups ▽
with added $PhI(OAc)_2/Al_2O_3$ cf. *49*, 936s67; with PhIO/MgO s. P. Müller, A. Ghanem, Org. Lett. *6*, 4347-50 (2004).

Palladous acetate/cupric acetate/air $Pd(OAc)_2/Cu(OAc)_2/O_2$
Benzolactams from ω-aryl-*sec*-amines via oxidative carbonylation ○

356.

3,4-Dihydroisocarbostyrils. A stirred suspension of the startg. phenethylamine, 5 mol% $Pd(OAc)_2$ and 50 mol% $Cu(OAc)_2$ in toluene refluxed at 120° under a balloon of CO (1 atm.) containing air for 2 h → product. Y 86%. Reaction is thought to involve initial *o*-palladation, followed by insertion of CO and intramolecular nucleophilic substitution to close the ring and release palladium(0). Cupric acetate serves to re-oxidize the latter to palladium(II), as well as function as a ligand in the *absence* of a phosphine residue. Reaction is strongly accelerated by the methylenedioxy substituent, which probably stabilizes the intermediate palladacyclic. F.e., regioselectivity and substituent effects, **also phthalimidines from benzylamines,** s. K. Orito et al., J. Am. Chem. Soc. *126*, 14342-3 (2004).

Oxygen ↑   CC ↓↑ O

Without additional reagents   w.a.r.
α-Aminomethylation   H → $CH_2N\leqslant$
of ketones s. *3*, 654; of α-acyl-γ-lactones s. H. Tanaka, L. Pan, K. Ikura, European patent EP-1249448 (Daicel Chem. Ind. Ltd.).

***o*-Aminomethylation of phenols**
s. *3*, 661; in the absence of solvent s. A.D. d'Hardemare, O. Jarjayes, F. Mortini, Synth. Commun. *34*, 3975-88 (2004); in ethanol, rapid procedure under microwave irradiation, s. R. Mahesh, R.V. Perumal, Indian J. Chem. *43B*, 1012-4 (2004).

α,β-Ethylenenitriles from aldehydes   CHO → CH=C-CN
with methanolic NaOMe cf. *11*, 821; in methanol *without* base s. S. Theodoropolus, United States patent US-2002078857.

Ugi 4-component condensation   ←
s. *17*, 809s67; with chiral β-amino-α,α-difluorocarboxylic acids *en route* to difluoropseudopeptides s. V. Gouge, P. Jubault, J.-C. Quirion, Tetrahedron Lett. *45*, 773-6 (2004); with α,β-

ethylenecarboxylic acids and subsequent intramolecular Heck arylation s. V. Gracias, J.D. Moore, S.W. Djuric, ibid. 417-20; **intramolecular Ugi condensation** with N-alkyl-3-*exo*-amino-7-oxabicyclo[2.2.1]heptane-2-*endo*-carboxylic acids, also 3-component condensation-esterification, s. A. Basso, G. Guanti et al., ibid. 587-90; rapid, *fluorous* condensation under microwave irradiation for a simplified extraction s. W. Zhang, P. Tempest, ibid. 6757-60.

Chromans from ethylene derivs. ○
and *o*-hydroxybenzyl alcohols with LiClO$_4$/montmorillonite cf. *57*, 316; and *o*-hydroxybenzyl acetates, thermal procedure, s. R. Rodriguez, J.E. Baldwin et al., Org. Lett. *6*, 3617-9 (2004).

4-Component synthesis of carbostyril-1-acetic acid amides from *o*-aminoketones by Ugi-Knoevenagel condensation

357.

A soln. of 1 eq. cyclohexyl isocyanide in methanol added to an equimolar soln. of 2-aminobenzophenone, cinnamaldehyde and cyanoacetic acid in the same solvent, and stirred for 48 h → product. Y 78%. In this process, the reactants undergo an Ugi multicomponent condensation followed by an intramolecular Knoevenagel condensation. With sulfonylacetic acids the Ugi adduct was first isolated by filtration and subsequently converted to the carbostyril on treatment with methanolic NaH. F.e.s. S. Marcaccini, T. Torroba et al., Tetrahedron Lett. *45*, 3999-4001 (2004).

2,3-Condensed 1,2,3,4-tetrahydroquinolines from ethylenealdehydes
with ZnCl$_2$/SiO$_2$ under microwave irradiation cf. *63*, 364s66; 1,2,3,4,4a,9,9a,10-octahydroacridines without reagent s. N.V. Mayekar, S.K. Nayak, S. Chattopadhyay, Synth. Commun. *34*, 3111-9 (2004).

Microwaves (s.a. under NaBr, Et$_3$N, i-Pr$_2$NEt, Piperidine, CuCl$_2$, CaCl$_2$, Zn-L-prolinate, [\\\\]
Diethylene glycol, NH$_4$OAc, Ac$_2$O, NBS and FeCl$_3$)
o-**Aminomethylation of phenols under microwave irradiation** s. *3*, 661s68   H → CH$_2$N⊄
Hantzsch-type synthesis of 1-hydroxy-1,4-dihydropyridines s. *47*, 727s68   ○

Sodium methoxide or tert-butoxide   NaOMe or NaOBu-t
α,γ-Diketocarboxylic acid esters from ketones   H → COCOOR
and *tert*-butyl methyl oxalate cf. *13*, 730; and dimethyl oxalate in ether for isolation of products as sodium enolates s. C. Maurin, F. Bailly, P. Cotelle, Tetrahedron *60*, 6479-86 (2004); with NaOBu-*t* cf. X.-H. Jiang, Y.-Q. Long, Chinese J. Chem. *22*, 978-83 (2004).

Organolithium compds.   RLi
β-Amino-α,β-ethylene-ketones from -carboxylic acid esters   COOR → COR

358.

2.5 eqs. Phenyllithium added to a soln. of the startg. enamino-ester in dry toluene under N$_2$ at 0°, stirred until reaction complete, and quenched with satd. aq. NH$_4$Cl → product. Y 84%. Excess of the organolithium compd. is required for generation of the intermediate dilithio derivs. but yields were lower with >2.5 eqs. Subsequent addition of the organolithium compd. to the keto group is thought to be prevented by complexation of lithium with the enamine nitrogen. The method is simple, inexpensive, regiospecific, complementary with existing procedures, and generally applicable to alkyl- and aryl-lithiums. F.e.s. C. Cimarelli, G. Palmieri, E. Volpini, Tetrahedron Lett. *45*, 6629-31 (2004).

sec-*Butyllithium/(-)-sparteine* ←
Chelation-controlled asym. *o*-α-alkylation H → R
of N,N-disubst. *o*-alkylbenzamides cf. *50*, 495; of *o*-benzylphenyl 2-methoxyethyl ethers with alkyl tosylates s. J.A. Wilkinson, N. Hussain et al., Tetrahedron Lett. *45*, 5481-3 (2004).

Potassium carbonate/polyethylene glycol-400 K_2CO_3/PEG
Knoevenagel condensation under phase transfer catalysis CO → C=C
in the absence of solvent
with K_2CO_3/Aliquat 336 under microwave irradiation cf. *46*, 713s*50*; with K_2CO_3/PEG-400 s. Y.-Q. Cao, B.-H. Chen et al., Synth. Commun. *34*, 2965-71 (2004).

Potassium cyanide/magnesium sulfate $KCN/MgSO_4$
α-Aminonitriles from oxo compds. CO → C(N⩽)CN
from aldehydes with $NaCN/NaHSO_3$ cf. *7*, 777s*42*; also from ketones, large-scale procedure with $KCN/MgSO_4$, s. A. Alcade, A. Anne, D. Capraro, French patent FR-2827282 (Sanofi Synthelabo SA); from aldehydes with $BiCl_3/Me_3SiCN$ s. S.K. De, R.A. Gibbs, Tetrahedron Lett. *45*, 7407-8 (2004).

Potassium fluoride/alumina (s.a. under NH_4OAc) KF/Al_2O_3
Rubidium fluoride RbF
Sodium bromide [or Piperidine or Diethylene glycol]/microwaves ←
3-Component synthesis of 2-amino-4*H*-pyran ring from aldehydes ○
update s. *61*, 340s*67*; condensation with 5,5-dimethyl-1,3-cyclohexanedione using KF/Al_2O_3 under ultrasonication s. J.-T. Li, T.-S. Li et al., Synth. Commun. *34*, 4565-71 (2004); with 4-hydroxycarbostyril s. X.-S. Wang, Z.-M. Zong et al., ibid. 3021-7; condensation with β-ketocarboxylic acid esters using RbF s. B.P.V. Lingaiah, P.S. Rao et al., ibid 4431-7; with NaBr, rapid procedure under microwave irradiation in the absence of solvent, s. I. Devi, P.J. Bhuyan, Tetrahedron Lett. *45*, 8625-7 (2004); condensation with 4-hydroxycoumarin as enol component using piperidine in ethanol under microwave irradiation cf. S.-J. Tu, D.-Q. Shi et al., J. Chem. Res. Synop *2004*, 396-8; with di(ethylene glycol) s. Y.-J. Feng, D.-Q. Shi et al., Chinese J. Chem. *22*, 622-6 (2004).

Lithium chloride s. under $CuCl_2$ LiCl
Sodium iodide s. under $CeCl_3$ NaI

Sodium salt Na⁺
Fulvenes from ketones CO → C=C
and cyclopentadienes with KF/Al_2O_3 cf. *14*, 806s*52*; rapid procedure from Na-cyclopentadienide s. K. Chajara, H. Ottosson, Tetrahedron Lett. *45*, 6741-4 (2004).

Choline hydroxide/magnesium oxide [$Me_3NCH_2CH_2OH$]OH/MgO
α,β-Ethyleneoxo compds. via heterogeneous aldol condensation
Supported ionic liquids as Brønsted-type basic catalysts

359.

Choline hydroxide-on-MgO (1.11 mmol OH⁻ per 1 g of support) added to a stirred soln. of citral (E/Z mixture) and 4.4 eqs. acetone, and stirring continued at 60° under argon for 1 h → product. Y 94.2% (E/Z mixture; selectivity 95.5%). Selectivity and turnover numbers were higher than with basic hydrotalcites or NaOH, and yields comparable. F.e.s. S. Abello, F. Medina et al., Chem. Commun. *2004*, 1096-7.

Triethylamine/silica gel/microwaves Et_3N/SiO_2/[\\\\]
Pyrroles from aldehydes, two acetylene deriv. molecules and prim. amines ○
Regiospecific synthesis in one pot via vinyloxy-2-acetylenes and 4-alkylideneoxazolidines

360.

1,2,3,4-Tetrasubst. pyrroles. A mixture of 1.82 eqs. startg. acetylene deriv. and 1 eq. startg. aldehyde in anhydrous methylene chloride cooled to 0°, treated with 6.5 eqs. redistilled Et_3N, stirred at the same temp. for 30 min, solvent and excess reagents removed under reduced pressure, the residue mixed with 1.2 eqs. benzylamine and silica gel, and microwave irradiated (900 W) *for 8 min* → product. Y 49%. The metal-free synthesis combines two key steps: base-catalyzed generation of vinyloxy-2-acetylenes, and the subsequent reaction with the amine via spontaneous rearrangement of the intermediate 4-alkylideneoxazolidines under microwave irradiation in a solvent-less environment. The procedure is simple, modular, direct, and based on readily available substrates (incl. ar. amines and functionalized aldehydes). F.e. and with isolation of the intermediate vinyloxy-2-acetylenes s. D. Tejedor, F. Garcia-Tellado et al., J. Am. Chem. Soc. *126*, 8390-1 (2004).

Ethyldiisopropylamine/microwaves i-Pr_2NEt/[\\\\]
Gewald 2-aminothiophene synthesis under microwave irradiation
in the absence of solvent s. *43*, 765s68

Piperidine/microwaves (s.a. under NaBr) $(CH_2)_5NH$/[\\\\]
Stilbenes from ar. aldehydes and methylarenes CHO → CH=C
under microwave irradiation in the absence of solvent
with pyrrolidine cf. *7*, 782s62; with piperidine s. K. Moth-Poulsen, J.B. Christensen et al., Synth. Commun. *34*, 2215-21 (2004).

1,8-Diazabicyclo[5.4.0]undec-7-ene dbu
3-Chromenes from phenols and α,β-ethylenealdehydes ○
with pyridine cf. *27*, 785; with dbu, regiospecific conversion with 4,6-dihydroxyphthalide, s. M. Mondal, N.P. Argade, Synlett *2004*, 1243-6.

4-Dimethylaminopyridine DMAP
Knoevenagel condensation CO → C=C
with piperidine cf. *3*, 632; with 10 mol% DMAP in the absence of solvent, (E)-selectivity, s. A.V. Narsaiah, K. Nagaiah et al., Synth. Commun. *34*, 2893-901 (2004).

Copper(II)-exchanged hydroxyapatite ←
3-Component synthesis of 2-acetyleneamines CHO → CH(N<)C≡C
with $RuCl_3$/CuBr cf. *63*, 356; heterogeneous conversion with copper(II)-exchanged hydroxyapatite s. B.M. Choudary, B. Sreedhar et al., Tetrahedron Lett. *45*, 7319-21 (2004).

Cuprous triflate s. under R_2Zn CuOTf
Cuprous iodide s.a. under $RhCl(PPh_3)_3$ and Iridium complexes CuI

Cuprous iodide/L-proline CuI/Pro-OH
Asym. Kinugasa reaction L_N
chiral 2-azetidinones with CuCl/dicyclohexylcarbodiimide/chiral azaferrocenes cf. *63*, 277; chiral 3-methylene-2-azetidinones by dehydrative conversion with CuI/L-proline (e.e. 15%) s. A. Basak, S.C. Ghosh, Synlett *2004*, 1637-9.

Cupric chloride/lithium chloride or Cupric chloride/cupric sulfate/microwaves [or Calcium chloride/microwaves or N-Bromosuccinimide/microwaves or Trimethylsilyl chloride or Stannous chloride or Polyaniline bismuth oxide chloride or Niobium pentachloride or Potassium hydrogen sulfate or Trimethylsilyl triflate or p-Toluenesulfonic acid or Phosphotungstic acid or Iodine or Ferric chloride/trimethylsilyl chloride]
Catalytic Biginelli synthesis
update s. 55, 337s67; 3,4-dihydro-2(1H)-pyrimid-inones and -inethiones with $CuCl_2/LiCl$ s. A. Manjula, B.V. Rao, P. Neelakantan, Synth. Commun. *34*, 2665-71 (2004); with $CuCl_2/CuSO_4$ under microwave irradiation in the absence of solvent s. M. Gohain, D. Prajapati, J.S. Sandhu, Synlett *2004*, 235-8; with $CaCl_2$ under microwave irradiation in the absence of solvent s. A.K. Misra, G. Agnihotri, S.K. Madhusudan, Indian J. Chem. *43B*, 2018-20 (2004); with 0.2 eq. NBS under microwave irradiation in N,N-dimethylacetamide s. H. Hazarkhani, B. Karimi, Synthesis *2004*, 1239-42; with Me_3SiCl s. Y.-L. Zhu, Y.-J. Pan, S.-L. Huang, Synth. Commun. *34*, 3167-74 (2004); with $SnCl_2$ s. S. Kumar, A. Saini, J.S. Sandhu, Indian J. Chem. *43B*, 1485-6 (2004); with readily retrievable polyaniline bismuth oxide chloride complex s. B. Gangadasu, S. Palaniappan, V.J. Rao, Synlett *2004*, 1285-7; with $NbCl_5$ s. J.S. Yadav et al., Chem. Lett. *33*, 926-7 (2004); with $KHSO_4$ in glycol s. S. Tu et al., Synlett *2004*, 537-9; with 1 mol% trimethylsilyl triflate s. D.S. Bose, R.K. Kumar, L. Fatima, ibid. 279-82; with 5 mol% TsOH in the absence of solvent s. A.K. Bose, M.S. Manhas et al., Tetrahedron Lett. *45*, 8351-3 (2004); with phosphotungstic acid s. T.-S. Jin, T.-S. Li et al., J. Chem. Res. Synop *2004*, 190-1; with 5 mol% I_2 s. R.S. Bhosale, P.K. Zubaidha et al., Tetrahedron Lett. *45*, 9111-3 (2004); with $FeCl_3/Me_3SiCl$ s. Z.-T. Wang, H.-Q. Wang et al., ibid. 7951-3.

Silver phosphotungstate $Ag_3PW_{12}O_{40}$
Heterogeneous catalytic Friedländer quinoline synthesis s. *65*, 334s68

Triphenylphosphinegold(III) chloride $AuCl_3(PPh_3)$
Stereospecific transition metal-catalyzed 3-component Mannich reaction CH(NHR)C-CO

361.

N-Protected β-aminoketones. 1.5 eqs. Ethyl carbamate, 1 eq. *p*-chlorobenzaldehyde, and 5 eq. 1-tetralone added successively to a soln. of 5 mol% $AuCl_3(PPh_3)$ in acetonitrile at room temp., stirred for 24 h, then quenched with satd. aq. $NaHCO_3$ and brine → product. Y 78% (*syn/anti* 99:1). The procedure is simple, atom-economical, highly diastereoselective, and generally applicable to electron-rich or -poor ar. aldehydes and aryl ketones at catalyst loadings as low as 1 mol%. F.e. and catalysts ($FeCl_3/Me_3SiCl$, $RuCl_3$) s. L.-W. Xu, C.-G. Xia, L. Li, J. Org. Chem. *69*, 8482-4 (2004).

Auric bromide $AuBr_3$
1-Acylnaphthalenes from *o*-acetylenealdehydes and oxo compds.
via gold(III)-catalyzed [4+2]-benzannulation

362.

1 eq. Startg. *o*-alkynylbenzaldehyde and 1.2 eqs. heptanal added under argon at room temp. to a suspension of 10 mol% $AuBr_3$ in dioxane, and stirred at 100° for 3 h → product. Y 81%. Reaction is thought to involve initial activation of the alkyne residue by gold(III), followed by generation of a zwitterionic isobenzopyrylium ate complex prior to reverse electron-demand Diels-Alder reaction with the enolic form of the oxo compd.; dehydration and ring opening

complete the sequence with liberation of the catalyst. The method is applicable to benzaldehydes, α,β-unsatd. aldehydes, α-alkoxyaldehydes, paraldehyde, and cyclohexanone, as well as acetals. F.e.s. N. Asao, H. Aikawa, Y. Yamamoto, J. Am. Chem. Soc. *126*, 7458-9 (2004).

Calcium oxide   *CaO*
Knoevenagel condensation   CO → C=C
with CaO under microwave irradiation in ethanol cf. *46*, 713s*65*; α-cyanocinnamic acid esters with CaO, **solid-state procedure** on grinding, s. Y.-Y. Lu, M.-F. Gao et al., Synth. Commun. *34*, 2047-51 (2004).

Calcium chloride/microwaves s. under *CuCl₂*   *CaCl₂/[\\\\]*
Zinc s. under *TiCl₄*   *Zn*
Magnesium oxide s. under *Choline chloride*   *MgO*

Dialkylzinc/cuprous triflate/chiral N-(2-hydroxy-1-naphthylmethylene)dipeptide amides   ←
Dialkylzinc/cupric chloride/chiral [1-(2-oxy-1,1′-binaphthyl-2-yl)-3-mesitylimidazolidin-2-   ←
ylidene]silver(I) dimer
Regiospecific copper-catalyzed asym. synthesis of terminal ethylene derivs.   C(R)CH=CH₂
from allyl phosphates

363.

A mixture of 5 mol% (CuOTf)₂·(benzene) and 10 mol% chiral N-(2-hydroxy-1-naphthyl-methylene)dipeptide amide in anhydrous THF cooled to -15°, stirred at the same temp. for 5 min, treated successively with 3 eqs. diethylzinc and 1 eq. of the startg. allyl phosphate in the same solvent, stirring continued for 24 h, and quenched with satd. aq. NH₄Cl → product. Y 76% (e.e. 96%; 82% selectivity for S$_N$2′ displacement). The procedure is generally applicable to both aromatic and aliphatic allyl phosphates bearing either a di- or tri-subst. alkene residue so that both tertiary and **quaternary carbon centres** can be generated with high regio- and enantio-selectivity. This is facilitated by binding of copper(I) to the olefinic centre with coordination of the dialkylzinc through phosphoryl oxygen and the amide carbonyl of the ligand. F.e. and comparison of dipeptide ligands s. M.A. Kacprzynski, A.H. Hoveyda, J. Am. Chem. Soc. *126*, 10676-81 (2004); exclusive S$_N$2′-displacement with CuCl₂ and chiral [1-(2-oxy-1,1′-binaphthyl-2-yl)-3-mesityl-imidazolidin-2-ylidene]silver(I) dimer cf. A.O. Larsen, A.H. Hoveyda et al., ibid. 11130-1.

Diethylzinc s. under *TiCl₄*   *Et₂Zn*

Lithium trialkylzincates/trimethylsilyl chloride/zinc chloride   ←
Regiospecific synthesis of 2-acetylenehydroperoxides   R-C≡C-C-OOH
from 2-acetylenemesylates s. *67*, 428

Zinc L-prolinate/alumina/microwaves   *(Pro-O)₂Zn/Al₂O₃/[\\\\]*
2,3-Dihydro-1H-1,5-benzodiazepines from o-diamines and two ketone molecules   ○
under microwave irradiation in the absence of solvent s. *50*, 471s*68*

Magnesium iodide   *MgI₂*
Tetrahydro-1,2-oxazines from cyclopropanes and aldehydes s. *66*, 314s*68*   ○

Trialkylalanes R_3Al
3-Component Mannich-type synthesis of hydrazones $CHO \rightarrow CH(R)N(R')N=CHAr$

364.

A soln. of the startg. hydrazone in 1,2-dichloroethane treated at -30° with 2 eqs. Me$_3$Al (2 M in hexane), the cold bath removed, the mixture stirred at room temp. under inert atmosphere for 5 min, re-cooled to -30°, treated with 1.1 eqs. cinnamaldehyde, refluxed for 4 h, then quenched with satd. aq. dipotassium L-tartrate → product. Y 94%. This is the first such Mannich-type reaction with trialkylalanes, facilitated by alkyl transfer from an intermediate aluminacyclic. Reaction is applicable to the coupling of aliphatic, aromatic or α,β-ethylenic aldehydes and ketones with N-monoalkyl- or N-monoaryl-hydrazones. F.e.s. L. El Kaim et al., J. Org. Chem. *68*, 8733-5 (2003).

Trimethylaluminum Me_3Al
Erythrina and B-homoerythrina skeleton from 2-aryl-*prim*-amines
by aluminum-mediated double ring closure

365.

B-Homoerythrina skeleton. A soln. of 1 eq. startg. amine in benzene (0.14 M) treated with a soln. of 2 eqs. AlMe$_3$ in the same solvent (1.36 M) at 0°, stirred at room temp. for 1 h, a soln. of 1 eq. startg. enol acetate in the same solvent (0.14 M) added, heated at 80° for 5 h, quenched with 2 N aq. HCl at 0°, and stirred for a further 30 min → product. Y 89%. Three bonds are formed in a domino ring closure, the rate-limiting step being the ultimate intramolecular 1,2-addition of the arene ring on an intermediate cyclimmonium ion. F.e. and erythrina ring s. S.A.A. El Bialy, H. Braun, L.F. Tietze, Angew. Chem. Int. Ed. Engl. *43*, 5391-3 (2004).

Triorganoindium compds./tris(dibenzylideneacetone)dipalladium/triphenylphosphine   ←
Regio- and stereo-specific synthesis of ethylene derivs.
from acoxy-2-ethylenes and triorganoindium compds. s. *68*, 468

Alumina (s.a. under KF and Zn-L-prolinate) Al_2O_3
Sym. 1,3-dinitro compds. from aldehydes $CHO \rightarrow CH(C-NO_2)_2$
with Et$_2$NH cf. *11*, 829; in nitromethane with basic alumina s. R. Ballini, A. Palmieri et al., Synthesis *2004*, 1938-40.

Potassium aluminum sulfate $KAl(SO_4)_2$
3,4-Dihydroisocarbostyril-4-carboxylic acids from azomethines   ←
and homophthalic anhydride with BF$_3$/Na$_2$SO$_4$ for preparing *trans*-isomers cf. *32*, 617s55; *cis*-isomers with KAl(SO$_4$)$_2$·12H$_2$O s. J. Azizian, M. Koohshari et al., Heterocycles *63*, 2013-7 (2004).

Potassium aluminum sulfate/microwaves s. under Montmorillonite $KAl(SO_4)_2/[\backslash\backslash\backslash\backslash]$
Hydrotalcite s.a. under Ru(IV) and RuCl_3   ←

Hydrotalcite/1-n-butyl-3-methylimidazolium fluoroborate   ←
Knoevenagel condensation in ionic liquids   CO → C=C
with ethylenediammonium diacetate cf. *27*, 198s65 with Mg-Al hydrotalcite in 1-*n*-butyl-3-methylimidazolium fluoroborate (cf. *57*, 310s60) s. F.A. Khan et al., Tetrahedron Lett. *45*, 3055-8 (2004).

Hydroxyapatite s. under Copper(II)-exchanged hydroxyapatite   ←
Montmorillonite s.a. under Iron(III)-exchanged montmorillonite   ←

Montmorillonite [or Amberlyst 15 or Cyanuric chloride or Potassium aluminum sulfate/   ←
microwaves or Ferric chloride/silica gel/microwaves]
Sym. 1,1-bis(indol-3-yl)alkanes from oxo compds.   CO → CAr$_2$
carbohydrate derivs. with montmorillonite s. *5*, 549s67; under heterogeneous conditions with Amberlyst 15 s. Farhanullah, V.J. Ram et al., Tetrahedron Lett. *45*, 5099-102 (2004); f. ion exchange resins s. X.-L. Feng, C.-J. Guan, C.-X. Zhao, Synth. Commun. *34*, 487-92 (2004); with 10 mol% cyanuric chloride s. G.V.M. Sharma, P.R. Krishna et al., Tetrahedron Lett. *45*, 7729-3 (2004); with potassium aluminum sulfate under microwave irradiation in aq. medium s. J. Azizian, M.R. Mohammadizadeh et al., J. Chem. Res. Synop *2004*, 424-6; with FeCl$_3$/SiO$_2$ under microwave irradiation in the absence of solvent s. M. Xia, S.-H. Wang, W.-B. Yuan, Synth. Commun. *34*, 3175-82 (2004); **from acetals** with montmorillonite s. M. Chakrabarty et al., Synth. Commun. *34*, 421-34 (2004); sym. 1,1,1-tris(indol-3-yl)alkenes with acid-treated montmorillonite in the absence of solvent (cf. *5*, 549s66) s. ibid. 1801-10; 1,1,3-tris(indol-3-yl)alkanes from α,β-ethyleneoxo compds. with Zr(OTf)$_4$ s. M. Shi, S.-C. Cui, Q.-J. Li, Tetrahedron *60*, 6679-84 (2004); sym. 1,1-bis(imidazo[1,2-*a*]pyridin-2-yl)methanes s. R. Zhang, Y.-Z. Ho, Synth. Commun. *34*, 3955-62 (2004); sym. 1,1-bis(2-pyrrolyl)alkanes [dipyrromethanes] with aq. HCl s. V. Kral, P. Vasek, B. Dolensky, Collect. Czech. Chem. Commun. *69*, 1126-36 (2004).

Zeolite [or Trifluoroacetic acid or Methanesulfonic acid]   ←
Pictet-Spengler ring closure   O
with CF$_3$COOH s. *8*, 823s48; 1,2,3,4-tetrahydro-9*H*-pyrid[3,4-*b*]indoles with asym. induction s. L. Alberch, R.G. Pritchard et al., Eur. J. Org. Chem. *2004*, 1887-90; from oxo compds. with Ersorb-E4a zeolite s. A. Hegedus, Z. Hell, Tetrahedron Lett. *45*, 8553-5 (2004); N-phosphoryl-1,2,3,4-tetrahydroisoquinolines with MeSO$_3$H s. S.I. Al, H.S. Yoon, C.-H. Lee et al., J. Korean Chem. Soc. *48*, 542-8 (2004).

Boron chloride or bromide/n-butyllithium BCl_3 or BBr_3/BuLi
(Z)-1-Halogen-1,4-enynes   C(Hal)=C-C-C≡C
from 2-acetylenealcohols and acetylene derivs.

366.

A mixture of 1 eq. phenylacetylene and a soln. of 1 eq. BBr$_3$ in anhydrous methylene chloride (1 M) stirred at room temp. under argon for 30 min, a soln. of 1 eq. of the startg. Li-propargyloxide (prepared by treatment of the parent propargyl alcohol in anhydrous methylene chloride with 1.02 eqs. 1.6 M *n*-BuLi in hexane at 0°) added at room temp., stirred at room temp. for 2 h, then hydrolyzed with water → product. Y 45% (Z/E 99:1). The procedure is mild, regiospecific, stereospecific in favour of the (Z)-isomers, and applicable to both aromatic and aliphatic propargyl alcohols. There was no reaction, however, with primary propargyl alcohols and aliphatic alkynes. Reaction appears to involve migration of the halogenovinyl group from an intermediate halogenovinyl(propargyloxy)boron halide. F.e. and chloro derivs. (with BCl$_3$) s. G.W. Kabalka, Z. Wu, Y. Ju, Org. Lett. *6*, 3929-31 (2004).

Gallium(III) bromide or iodide $GaBr_3$ or GaI_3
4-Halogenotetrahydropyrans from 3-ethylenealcohols and aldehydes s. *56*, 347s*68*

Indium(I) iodide s. under $Ni(acac)_2$ *InI*

Scandium(III) triflate (s.a. under $Bi(OTf)_3$) $Sc(OTf)_3$
Catalytic ar. chloromethylation in a 2-phase aq. organic medium H → CH_2Cl

367.

A mixture of *m*-xylene, 0.5 eq. paraformaldehyde, 5 eqs. concd. HCl and *1 mol%* $Sc(OTf)_3$ stirred at 70° for 5 h, extracted with cyclohexane, and subjected to silica gel column chromatography → chloromethyl-2,4-dimethylbenzene (Y 73%) and 1,3-bis(chloromethyl)-2,4-dimethylbenzene (Y 20%). This is the first instance of a *catalytic* ar. chloromethylation, the catalyst being environmentally friendly, active at very low concentrations, water soluble, and readily recovered (in 94% yield) from the aq. phase for reuse without significant loss of activity. F.e. and with $Yb(OTf)_3$ and $Sm(OTf)_3$ s. T. Kishida, Y. Sugi et al., Green Chem. *6*, 57-62 (2004).

Ytterbium(III) triflate $Yb(OTf)_3$
α,α'-Bis(alkylidenation) of cyclic ketones with aldehydes CO → C=C
with Me_3SiCl/NaI cf. *49*, 766s*67*; α,α'-bis(benzylidenation) with $Yb(OTf)_3$ **in the absence of solvent** s. L.-M. Wang, C.-T. Qian et al., Synthesis *2004*, 3060-4.

Cerium(III) sulfate $Ce_2(SO_4)_3$
Friedel-Crafts benzylation H → Bn
with $La(OTf)_3$ cf. *49*, 763s*66*; with $Ce_2(SO_4)_3$, also ar. allylation with 2-ethylenealcohols, s. J.-H. Li, W.-J. Liu, D.-L. Yin, Synth. Commun. *34*, 3161-5 (2004).

Samarium(III) nitrate $Sm(NO_3)_3$
Pechmann-Duisberg coumarin synthesis in the absence of solvent
with $Yb(OTf)_3$ cf. *1*, 591s*66*; with $Sm(NO_3)_3$ s. S.S. Bahekar, D.B. Shinde, Tetrahedron Lett. *45*, 7999-8001 (2004); with sulfamic acid s. P.R. Singh, D.U. Singh, S.D. Samant, Synlett *2004*, 1909-12; with $ZrCl_4$, **also from α,β-acetylenecarboxylic acids** (cf. *54*, 367s*55*), s. B. Gangadasu, V.J. Rao et al., J. Chem. Res. Synop *2004*, 480-1.

Cerium(III) chloride/sodium iodide/silica gel $CeCl_3/NaI/SiO_2$
2,3-Dihydro-1*H*-1,5-benzodiazepines from *o*-diamines and two ketone molecules
in the absence of solvent with $Ag_3PW_{12}O_{40}$ cf. *50*, 471s*67*; with $CeCl_3/NaI$ on silica gel in acetonitrile s. G. Sabitha, J.S. Yadav et al., Adv. Synth. Catal. *346*, 921-3 (2004); with I_2 under mild conditions cf. B.P. Bandgar, S.V. Bettigeri, N.S. Joshi, Synth. Commun. *34*, 1447-53 (2004); with zinc L-prolinate on neutral Al_2O_3, rapid procedure under microwave irradiation, s. V. Sivamurugan, V. Murugesan et al., ibid. 3833-46.

Samarium diiodide SmI_2
Sym. 1,5-dienes from 2-ethylenealcohols 2 ROH → R-R
with $TiCl_3/MeLi$ cf. *23*, 793; with SmI_2, regio- and stereo-selectivity, also deoxygenation, s. J. Li, W.-X. Qian, Y.-M. Zhang, Tetrahedron *60*, 5793-8 (2004).

Graphite/methanesulfonic acid $C_8/MeSO_3H$
Aryl ketones from arenes and carboxylic acids H → COR
Acylation of phenolethers s. *4*, 729s*68*

Ammonium acetate (s.a. under 1-Hexyl-3-methylimidazolium fluoroborate) NH_4OAc
Pyridines from α,β-acetyleneketones
3-carbalkoxy derivs. with $NH_4OAc/AcOH$ cf. *13*, 526s*64*; improved procedure without acid s. X. Xiong, M.C. Bagley, K. Chapaneri, Tetrahedron Lett. *45*, 6121-4 (2004).

Pyridine ring from enamines
s. *34*, 706 and *32*, 764 (with HCl); with NH_4OAc in the absence of solvent s. C. Tanyeli, I.M. Akhmedov, M. Isik, Tetrahedron Lett. *45*, 5799-801 (2004).

Ammonium acetate/potassium fluoride-alumina $NH_4OAc/KF/Al_2O_3$
*Ammonium acetate/tetra-*n-*butylammonium bromide/microwaves* ←
Hantzsch 1,4-dihydropyridine synthesis ○
with NH_4OAc in the absence of solvent cf. *47*, 727s*67* and with NH_3 cf. *1*, 542; with added KF/Al_2O_3 in acetonitrile s. F. Aydin, R. Ozen, J. Chem. Res. Synop *2004*, 486-7; with added Bu_4NBr **in water,** rapid procedure under microwave irradiation, s. H. Salehi, Q.X. Guo, Synth. Commun. *34*, 4349-57 (2004); N-aryl-derivs. from prim. ar. amines with 4-dodecylbenzenesulfonic acid in water s. T.-S. Jin, T.-S. Li et al., Synthesis *2004*, 2001-5; N-hydroxy-derivs. with hydroxylamine under microwave irradiation in ethylene glycol s. S.-J. Tu, Q.-Y. Zhuang et al., J. Heterocycl. Chem. *41*, 767-70 (2004).

*Ethylenediammonium diacetate [or 1-*n-*Butyl-3-methylimidazolium fluoroborate]* ←
Knoevenagel condensation-intramolecular hetero-Diels-Alder reaction
with NaOAc cf. *54*, 357s*67*; with ethylenediammonium diacetate, asym. induction, s. G. Sabitha, J.S. Yadav et al., Synthesis *2004*, 1150-4; **in ionic liquids,** e.g. 1-*n*-butyl-3-methylimidazolium fluoroborate, s. J.S. Yadav, K. Nagaiah et al., ibid. 1783-8.

*Ethylenediammonium diacetate/1-*n-*butyl-3-methylimidazolium fluoroborate* ←
Gewald 2-aminothiophene synthesis
with calcined Mg-Al hydrotalcite cf. *43*, 765s*62*; with readily recyclable ethylenediammonium diacetate **in ionic liquids,** e.g. 1-*n*-butyl-3-methylimidazolium fluoroborate, s. Y. Hu, Q.-G. Zheng et al., Synth. Commun. *34*, 3801-6 (2004); polymer-based synthesis using a *soluble* PEG-based nitrile, rapid procedure under microwave irradiation in the absence of solvent with *i*-Pr_2NEt as base, s. H.-Q. Zhang, Z.-X. Chen et al., J. Chem. Res. Synop *2004*, 360-1.

Imidazolium ionic liquids s.a. under Hydrotalcite, Ethylenediammonium diacetate and ←
  HC(OMe)₃

1-Hexyl-3-methylimidazolium fluoroborate/ammonium acetate *[hexmim]BF_4/NH_4OAc*
*Tetra-*n-*butylammonium hydrogen sulfate* Bu_4NHSO_4
Ionic liquid-catalyzed 4-component synthesis of 1,4-dihydropyridines in the absence of solvent

368.

A mixture of benzaldehyde, 1.5 eqs. ammonium acetate, 1 eq. ethyl acetoacetate, 1 eq. dimedone and 12 mol% 1-hexyl-3-methylimidazolium fluoroborate stirred with heating at 90° for 10 min, and the resulting solid recrystallized → product. Y 95%. The procedure is environmentally friendly, simple, short, high-yielding and generally applicable to aliphatic and aromatic aldehydes. F.e. and comparison of ionic liquids s. S.-J. Ji, T.-P. Loh et al., Synlett *2004*, 831-5; **3-component synthesis** from enamines in diethylene glycol with Bu_4NHSO_4 **under phase transfer catalysis,** glycosyl derivs., s. N. Tewari, N. Dwivedi, R.P. Tripathi, Tetrahedron Lett. *45*, 9011-4 (2004).

1-Methylimidazolium trifluoroacetate *[Hmim]$OCOCF_3$*
Mannich reaction in Brønsted acidic ionic liquids CHO → CH(NHR)C-CO

369.

Equimolar amounts of benzaldehyde, aniline and acetophenone in 1-methylimidazolium trifluoroacetate allowed to react at 25° for 12 h, the mixture washed with distilled water, filtered, and the solid recrystallized → product. Y 85%. The ionic liquid was simply recovered from the filtrate and reused at least four times without significant loss of activity. Yields are higher and reaction faster than in conventional media. However, there was no reaction with aliphatic amines and carbonyl compds. F.e. and comparison of ionic liquids s. G. Zhao, T. Jiang, B. Han et al., Green Chem. *6*, 75-7 (2004).

Dicyclohexylcarbodiimide/1-hydroxybenzotriazole/sodium hydride   ←
4-Hydroxycarbostyrils from *o*-aminocarboxylic acid esters   ○
and malonic acid monoesters cf. *47*, 793; from *o*-aminocarboxylic acids and carboxylic acid esters with DCC/1-hydroxybenzotriazole/NaH s. L. Zikou, O. Igglessi-Markopoulou, Bull. Chem. Soc. Jpn. *77*, 1505-8 (2004).

Methyl orthoformate/1-n-butyl-3-methylimidazolium fluoroborate $HC(OMe)_3/[bmim]BF_4$
3,4,4a,5-Tetrahydro-2*H*,10b*H*-pyrano[3,2-*c*]benzopyrans from *o*-hydroxyaldehydes via intramolecular hetero-Diels-Alder reaction with *in situ*-generated *o*-quinone methids
with $HC(OMe)_3/I_2$ cf. *63*, 359s*65*; **in ionic liquids**, e.g. 1-*n*-butyl-3-methylimidazolium fluoroborate, s. J.S. Yadav, B. Padmavani et al., Adv. Synth. Catal. *346*, 607-10 (2004).

Acetic [or Trifluoroacetic] anhydride $Ac_2O\ [or\ (CF_3CO)_2O]$
Ar. acylation with carboxylic acids   H → Ac
s. *7*, 798; 2-acylation of N-tosylpyrroles with $(CF_3CO)_2O$ s. C.J. Song, D.W. Knight, M.A. Whatton, Tetrahedron Lett. *45*, 9573-6 (2004); regiospecific C-cyanoacetylation of pyrroles and indoles (with Ac_2O), also N-cyanoacetylation (of anilines), s. J. Slatt, I. Romero, J. Bergman, Synthesis *2004*, 2760-5.

Acetic anhydride/microwaves $Ac_2O/[\backslash\backslash\backslash\backslash]$
Styrylheterocyclics   CHO → CH=C
s. *6*, 135; 2-(β-styryl)benzimidazoles under microwave irradiation in the absence of solvent s. L.-Y. Wang, Z.-X. Zhang et al., Synth. Commun. *34*, 2245-52 (2004); with Ac_2O/AcOH s. B. Hayter et al., World Intellectual Property Organisation patent WO-2003000262 (Astra Zeneca UK Ltd.).

Perfluorocarboxylic acid anhydrides s.a. under Bi(III)-triflate $(RfCO)_2O$
Trifluoroacetic anhydride s. under Ac_2O $(CF_3CO)_2O$

Anion exchanger   ←
Heterogeneous Knoevenagel condensation   CO → C=C
with Amberlite IRA-401 or IRC-50 cf. *38*, 756s*49*; with a strongly basic anion exchange resin **in water** (cf. *7*, 764s*64*) s. T.-S. Jin, T.-S. Li et al., Synth. Commun. *34*, 2611-6 (2004).

Amberlyst 15 s. under Montmorillonite   ←

L-*Proline (s.a. under CuI)*   *Pro-OH*
α-Aminomethylation of ketones   H → CH_2NHR
3-Component organocatalyzed asym. Mannich reaction

370.   cyclohexanone + [CH_2O] + $ArNH_2$ → 2-(NHAr)-cyclohexanone   Ar = p-$MeOC_6H_4$

with prim. amines. A mixture of 1 eq. formaldehyde (36% aq.), 1.1 eqs. *p*-methoxyaniline, and 10 mol% (S)-proline in DMSO treated at room temp. with 2 eqs. cyclohexanone, stirred vigorously for 20 h, then quenched with aq. NH_4Cl → product. Y 90% (e.e. >99%). The procedure is highly chemo- and enantio-selective with cyclic and acyclic ketones; it can also be scaled up to the 10 g level, and is insensitive to water and air. With unsym. ketones reaction takes place *regioselectively* at the least substituted position. F.e., chiral amines, and solvents s. I. Ibrahem, J. Casas, A. Cordova, Angew. Chem. Int. Ed. Engl. *34*, 6528-31 (2004).

Organocatalyzed Biginelli synthesis in the absence of solvent

371.

3,4-Dihydro-2(1H)-pyrimidinethiones. A mixture of *p*-chlorobenzaldehyde, 1 eq. startg. β-dicarbonyl compd., and 1.5 eqs. thiourea treated with 10 mol% L-proline at 25° for 1 h → product. Y 93%. The procedure is simple, environmentally friendly, requires no additive or protic/Lewis acid, and is generally applicable to the condensation of β-diketones and β-ketocarboxylic acid esters with a variety of aliphatic, aromatic and heterocyclic aldehydes, incl. acid-sensitive and volatile ones. The amino function of the catalyst serves to generate an intermediate enamine (as in aldol condensation), while the carboxyl residue serves as a Brønsted acid co-catalyst. Carboxylic acid esters, furans, ar. halides, ar. nitro groups, phenols, phenolethers and styrenes were unaffected. F.e. and 3,4-dihydro-2(1H)-pyrimidinones with urea s. J.S. Yadav, K. Nagaiah et al., Chem. Lett. *33*, 1168-9 (2004).

2,3-Dichloro-5,6-dicyanoquinone s. under Ph_2PCl	*DDQ*
N-Bromosuccinimide/microwaves s. under $CuCl_2$	*NBS/[\\\\]*
Cyanuric chloride s. under Montmorillonite	←
Acetyl chloride s.a. under BiOCl	*AcCl*

Acetyl chloride/ethyldiisopropylamine/sodium salt $AcCl/i\text{-}Pr_2NEt/Na^+$
Chromones from *o*-hydroxyketones
with alkyl formates cf. *2*, 642; isoflavones with NaOCHO and AcCl/*i*-Pr$_2$NEt, large-scale procedure, s. C. Burdick, World Intellectual Property Organisation patent WO-200285881 (Roche Vitamins AG).

Trimethylsilyl cyanide s. under $Bi(OTf)_3$ and $BiCl_3$	Me_3SiCN
Trimethylsilyl chloride s. under $CuCl_2$, $LiZnR_3$ and $FeCl_3$	Me_3SiCl

Titanium tetrachloride/triethylamine/dimethylzinc $TiCl_4/Et_3N/Me_2Zn$
Stereospecific synthesis of α-alkoxy-β-aminocarboxylic acid esters   C(NH)C(OR)COOR'
via chlorotitanium(IV) enolates
from aldimines cf. *60*, 252; 3-component synthesis from *in situ*-generated aldimines with Et$_3$N as the base and added Me$_2$Zn (for enolizable aldehydes) s. A.L. Joffe, T.M. Thomas, J.C. Adrian, Jr., Tetrahedron Lett. *45*, 5087-90 (2004).

Titanium tetrachloride/zinc $TiCl_4/Zn$
Pyrroles from β-diketones and oximes
with Zn/NaOAc cf. *11*, 452; with TiCl$_4$/Zn, **also from azomethines**, s. D. Shi et al., Synlett *2004*, 2239-41.

Zirconium tetrachloride $ZrCl_4$
Pechmann-Duisberg coumarin synthesis in the absence of solvent
Also from α,β-acetylenecarboxylic acids s. *1*, 591s68

1,2,3,4-Tetrahydroquinolines from prim. ar. amines, aldehydes and ethylene derivs.
with cyclic enolethers as the ene component using KHSO$_4$ cf. *52*, 363s67; using ZrCl$_4$ s. B. Das, R. Ramu et al., Chem. Lett. *33*, 1526-7 (2004); using readily recyclable Fe(III)-exchanged montmorillonite K10 s. K.V.N.S. Srinivas, B. Das, Synlett *2004*, 1715-8; 4-aminochroman ring from *o*-hydroxyaldehydes (cf. *52*, 363s67) with Bi(OTf)$_3$ **in ionic liquids,** e.g. 1-*n*-butyl-3-methylimidazolium hexafluorophosphate, s. J.S. Yadav, B.V.S. Reddy, P.N. Reddy, Chem. Lett. *33*, 1436-7 (2004).

Stannous chloride s. under $CuCl_2$ and $[Rh(cod)Cl]_2$ $SnCl_2$

Chlorodiphenylphosphine/n-butyllithium/2,3-dichloro-5,6-dicyanoquinone/diethyl ←
  phosphorocyanidate
Nitriles from prim. alcohols OH → CN
with Ph$_3$P/DDQ/Bu$_4$NCN cf. *27*, 782s*67*; with Ph$_2$PCl/*n*-BuLi/DDQ/(EtO)$_2$P(O)CN s. T. Mukaiyama, K. Masutani, Y. Hagiwara, Chem. Lett. *33*, 1192-3 (2004).

Bismuth(III) triflate Bi(OTf)$_3$
2,4-Dialkoxychromans from *o*-hydroxyaldehydes ○
with FeCl$_3$ cf. *60*, 341s*63*; with 0.1 mol% Bi(OTf)$_3$ s. M.P. Nguyen, R.S. Mohan et al., Tetrahedron Lett. *45*, 9369-71 (2004).

Bismuth(III) [or Scandium(III)] triflate Bi(OTf)$_3$ [or Sc(OTf)$_3$]
Catalytic Friedländer quinoline synthesis
with NaAuCl$_4$ cf. *65*, 334; with 5 mol% Bi(OTf)$_3$ or Sc(OTf)$_3$ s. J.S. Yadav, B.V.S. Reddy et al., Synlett *2004*, 963-6; **heterogeneous conversion** with silver phosphotungstate cf. Synthesis *2004*, 2381-5.

Bismuth(III) [or Scandium(III)] triflate/perfluorocarboxylic acid anhydrides ←
Aryl ketones from arenes and carboxylic acids H → COR
with P$_2$O$_5$ cf. *4*, 729s*67*; with Bi(OTf)$_3$ or Sc(OTf)$_3$ and a perfluorocarboxylic acid anhydride, e.g. (CF$_3$CO)$_2$O or heptafluorobutyric anhydride, **in the absence of solvent** (cf. *49*, 763) s. Y. Matsushita, K. Sugamoto, T. Matsui, Tetrahedron Lett. *45*, 4723-7 (2004); regiospecific acylation of phenolethers with graphite powder and MeSO$_3$H (H$_2$SO$_4$ or PPA) cf. M.H. Sarvari, H. Sharhi, Synthesis *2004*, 2165-8.

Bismuth(III) triflate/1-n-butyl-3-methylimidazolium hexafluorophosphate Bi(OTf)$_3$/[bmim]PF$_6$
4-Aminochromans from *o*-hydroxyaldehydes, prim. amines and ethylene derivs. ○
with cyclic enolethers as ene component in ionic liquids s. *52*, 363s*68*

Bismuth(III) triflate/trimethylsilyl cyanide Bi(OTf)$_3$/Me$_3$SiCN
2,3-Unsatd. α-glycosyl cyanides from O^3-acylglycals ←
s.*38*, 759s*68*

Bismuth oxide chloride s.a. under CuCl$_2$ BiOCl

Bismuth oxide chloride/acetyl chloride BiOCl/AcCl
β-Acylaminoketones from nitriles CH(NHAc)C-CO
and two ketone molecules with concd. H$_2$SO$_4$ cf. *16*, 827; from aldehydes and ketones with BiOCl/AcCl s. R. Ghosh, S. Maiti, A. Chakraborty, Synlett *2005*, 115-8.

Bismuth trichloride/trimethylsilyl cyanide BiCl$_3$/Me$_3$SiCN
α-Aminonitriles from aldehydes s. *7*, 777s*68* CHO → CH(N≤)CN

Niobium pentachloride (s.a. under CuCl$_2$) NbCl$_5$
4-Chlorotetrahydropyrans from 3-ethylenealcohols and aldehydes ○
in Lewis acidic ionic liquids cf. *56*, 347s*66*; with NbCl$_5$, also 4-bromo- and 4-iodo-derivs. with GaBr$_3$ or GaI$_3$, s. J.S. Yadav, S.K. Biswas et al., Synthesis *2004*, 2711-5.

Thionyl chloride/ethanol SOCl$_2$/EtOH
Chalcones from ar. aldehydes and methyl ketones CHO → CH=CHCO
with SmI$_3$/Me$_3$SiCl cf. *47*, 710s*63*; with SOCl$_2$/EtOH under mild conditions s. Z.-G. Hu, P.-L. Zeng et al., J. Chem. Res. Synop *2004*, 158-9.

Potassium hydrogen sulfate s. under CuCl$_2$ KHSO$_4$
Trimethylsilyl triflate s. under CuCl$_2$ Me$_3$SiOTf

Trifluoromethanesulfonic acid/manganese(III) acetate/acetic acid ←
Quinolines from N-arylaldimines and enoxysilanes via hetero-Diels-Alder reaction ○

372.

One-pot procedure. A soln. of benzylideneaniline and 2 eqs. α-(trimethylsiloxy)styrene in *acetonitrile* treated with a soln. of 10 mol% trifluoromethanesulfonic acid in the same solvent at room temp., stirred for 3 h, 2 eqs. Mn(OAc)$_3$·2H$_2$O in acetic acid added, and stirring continued at the same temp. for 24 h → product. Y 100%. The initially formed Diels-Alder adduct, generated via Mannich-type reaction under Brønsted acid catalysis, is dehydrogenated to the quinoline with Mn(OAc)$_3$. F.e. and comparison of Brønsted acids, oxidants and solvents s. T. Akiyama et al., Chem. Lett. *33*, 922-3 (2004).

Methanesulfonic acid s. under Zeolite or Graphite	MeSO$_3$H
p-Toluenesulfonic acid s. under CuCl$_2$	TsOH
4-Dodecylbenzenesulfonic acid	ArSO$_3$H
Hantzsch-type synthesis of 1-aryl-1,4-dihydropyridines in water s. *47*, 727s68	
Sulfamic acid	H$_2$NSO$_3$H
Pechmann-Duisberg coumarin synthesis in the absence of solvent s. *1*, 591s68	
Phosphotungstate s. under Silver phosphotungstate	←
Phosphotungstic acid s. under CuCl$_2$	H$_3$PW$_{12}$O$_{40}$
Iodine (s.a. under CuCl$_2$)	I$_2$
2,3-Dihydro-1H-1,5-benzodiazepines from o-diamines and two ketone molecules s. *50*, 471s68	
Diethylamine hydrochloride	Et$_2$NH·HCl
α-Methylenealdehydes from aldehydes	CH$_2$ → C═CH$_2$

s. *4*, 737; f. method, also bis(methylenation) of dialdehydes, s. K. Basu, J. Richards, L.A. Paquette, Synthesis *2004*, 2841-4.

2-Chloropyridine methiodide/triethylamine ←
Coumarins from o-hydroxyoxo compds. and carboxylic acids ○
from *o*-hydroxyaldehydes with montmorillonite cf. *57*, 315; 3-arylcoumarins with 2-chloropyridine methiodide/Et$_3$N s. S.H. Mashraqui, D. Vashi, H.D. Mistry, Synth. Commun. *34*, 3129-34 (2004).

2-Chloropyridine methiodide/ethyldiisopropylamine ←
Polymer-based 2-iodo-5-(N-methylcarbamyl)pyridine methiodide/triethylamine ←
2-Azetidinones from carboxylic acids and azomethines ⌐N
with 2-chloropyridine methiodide/Pr$_3$N cf. *21*, 445s46; *trans*-1-*tert*-amino-2-azetidinones from chiral hydrazones **with asym. induction**, also chiral N-unsubst. 2-azetidinones, with *i*-Pr$_2$NEt as base s. E. Diez, J.M. Lassaletta et al., Org. Lett. *6*, 2749-52 (2004); **heterogeneous conversion** with polymer-based 2-iodo-5-(N-methylcarbamyl)pyridine methiodide/Et$_3$N as a supported Mukaiyama reagent s. D. Donati, M. Taddei et al., J. Org. Chem. *69*, 9316-8 (2004).

Manganese(III) acetate s. under CF$_3$SO$_3$H   Mn(OAc)$_3$

Iron(III)-exchanged montmorillonite ←
1,2,3,4-Tetrahydroquinolines from prim. ar. amines, aldehydes and ethylene derivs. ○
with cyclic enolethers as ene component s. *52*, 363s68

Ferric chloride (s.a. under CuCl$_2$)   FeCl$_3$
Alkoxy-3-ethylenes from acetals and ethylene derivs.   C(OR)C-C═C
via carbonyl ene-type reaction
2-allyl-O-heterocyclics from lactolides with MeAlCl$_2$ cf. *49*, 762; alkoxy-3-ethylenes from ar. or aliphatic acetals with FeCl$_3$ s. A. Ladepeche, U. Ghosez et al., Synthesis *2004*, 1375-80.

Ferric chloride/silica/microwaves s. under Montmorillonite $FeCl_3/SiO_2/[\backslash\backslash\backslash\backslash]$
Ferric chloride/trimethylsilyl chloride s. under CuCl$_2$ $FeCl_3/Me_3SiCl$
Nickel(II) acetoacetonate/triphenylphosphine/indium(I) iodide $Ni(acac)_2/Ph_3P/InI$
Regiospecific synthesis of 3-ethylenealcohols CO → C(OH)C-C=C
from 2-ethylenealcohols and oxo compds.
with PdCl$_2$(PhCN)$_2$/SnCl$_2$ cf. *43*, 725; with Ni(acac)$_2$/Ph$_3$P/InI s. T. Hirashita, S. Araki et al., J. Org. Chem. *69*, 5054-9 (2004); with [Rh(cod)Cl]$_2$/SnCl$_2$ s. Y. Masuyama, Y. Kaneko, Y. Kurusu, Tetrahedron Lett. *45*, 8969-71 (2004).

Ruthenium(IV)-grafted hydrotalcite ←
Heterogeneous C-α-alkylation with prim. alcohols H → R

373.

of nitriles. A mixture of phenylacetonitrile, excess of ethanol and ruthenium(IV)-grafted hydrotalcite (0.75 mol% Ru) heated under argon in an autoclave at 180° for 20 h, filtered, and worked up → product. Y 94%. The multifunctional catalyst facilitates initial oxidative dehydrogenation of the alcohol to an aldehyde, the subsequent Knoevenagel condensation with the nitrile (courtesy of the basic hydrotalcite), and the ultimate hydrogenation with the liberated ruthenium hydride. The catalyst is more active than other supported ruthenium catalysts and can be simply recycled with no significant loss of activity. The procedure is simple, environmentally friendly (no byproducts other than water or dialkylated products) and applicable to a wide range of aryl- and heteroaryl-acetonitriles, incl. hindered substrates. F.e. and C-α-alkylation **of ketones,** also C-α-alkylation-Michael addition, s. K. Motokura, K. Kaneda et al., J. Am. Chem. Soc. *126*, 5662-3 (2004).

Thiolate-bridged diruthenium complex/ammonium fluoroborate ←
4H-Pyrans from 2-acetylenealcohols O
2-chromenes from phenols cf. *64*, 338; 4H-pyran-3-carbonyl compds. from β-ketocarbonyl compds. s. Y. Nishibayashi, S. Uemura et al., J. Org. Chem. *69*, 3408-12 (2004).

Ruthenium trichloride/hydrotalcite/oxygen ←
Quinolines from *o*-aminobenzylalcohols and oxo compds.
from ketones with RuCl$_2$(PPh$_3$)$_3$/1-dodecene/KOH cf. *62*, 355s66; also from aldehydes and nitriles, heterogeneous procedure with RuCl$_3$-on-hydrotalcite under oxygen, s. K. Motokura, K. Kaneda et al., Tetrahedron Lett. *45*, 6029-32 (2004).

Chloro(cyclooctadiene)rhodium(I) dimer/stannous chloride $[Rh(cod)Cl]_2/SnCl_2$
Regiospecific synthesis of 3-ethylenealcohols CO → C(OH)C-C=C
from 2-ethylenealcohols and oxo compds. s. *43*, 725s68

Chlorotris(triphenylphosphine)rhodium(I)/trimethyl phosphite/lithium
bis(trimethylsilyl)amide/cuprous iodide
Regiospecific C-α-allylation of α-alkoxyketones H → C-C=C
via (Z)-copper(I) enolates

374.

with asym. induction. 45 Mol% trimethyl phosphite added directly to a red suspension of 10 mol% Wilkinson's catalyst in anhydrous THF, stirred under argon at room temp. for 10 min, cooled to 0°, added via Teflon cannula to a soln. of the startg. copper(I) enolate [prepared in a separate flask by adding dropwise 1.7 eqs. 1 *M* Li-bis(trimethylsilyl)amide in THF to a suspension of 1.7 eqs. CuI and 1.7 eqs. startg. ketone in the same solvent at room temp., leaving for 5 min, then cooling to 0°], the startg. allyl carbonate (e.e. 97%) added via a syringe, allowed to warm to room temp. over ca. 4 h (with TLC control), then quenched with satd. aq. NH$_4$Cl → product. Y

94% (regiospecificity >99%, d.r. 24:1, e.e. 99%). With racemic secondary allylic carbonates, the regiospecificity was tolerant of a wide range of substituents, and the diastereoselectivity dependent on their relative size. Diastereoselectivity was low, however, with unprotected allyl alcohols and O-silyl derivs. F.e.s. P.A. Evans, M.J. Lawler, J. Am. Chem. Soc. *126*, 8642-3 (2004).

Palladous acetate/chiral 3,3'-disubst. 6,6'-dimethoxy-2,2'-bis(diphenylphosphino)- ←
biphenyl/ethyldiisopropylamine
Asym. Heck arylation H → Ar
chiral 2-aryl-2,3-dihydrofurans s. *46*, 738s67; improved enantioselectivity with chiral 3,3'-disubst. 6,6'-dimethoxy-2,2'-bis(diphenylphosphino)biphenyl as ligand s. E. Gorobets, B.A. Keay et al., Tetrahedron Lett. *45*, 3597-601 (2004).

Tris(dibenzylideneacetone)dipalladium s. under R_3In $Pd_2(dba)_3$

(η^3-Allyl)(η^5-cyclopentadienyl)palladium(II)/1,1'-bis(diphenylphosphino)ferrocene ←
C-α-Benzylation via η^3-benzylpalladium complexes H → Bn
with (η^3-allyl)(cod)palladium(II) fluoroborate/dppf and added KOAc/N,O-bis(trimethylsilyl)-acetamide cf. *66*, 366; with (η^3-allyl)(η^5-cyclopentadienyl)palladium(II)/dppf in the *absence* of base with added 1,5-cyclooctadiene to prevent aggregation s. R. Kuwano, Y. Kondo, Org. Lett. *6*, 3545-7 (2004).

Tetrakis(triphenylphosphine)palladium(0) $Pd(PPh_3)_4$
Pyrroles from 2-methyleneaziridines and methyl ketones

375.

2-(N-Hetaryl)pyrroles. A mixture of 30 mol% $Pd(PPh_3)_4$ and 2 eqs. startg. methyl ketone treated under argon with 1 eq. startg. methyleneaziridine, and stirred at 120° for 72 h → product. Y 96%. The procedure, which is a useful alternative to hetar. cross-coupling, is also applicable to 2-, 3- and 4-acetylpyridines, as well as acetophenone, indicating that chelation control by the substrate is not a significant factor. Reaction apparently involves initial oxidative addition of Pd(0) to the active C-H bond of the ketone, followed by hydropalladation of the methyleneaziridine prior to elimination of the catalyst and ring expansion. F.e.s. A.I. Siriwardana, Y. Yamamoto et al., J. Am. Chem. Soc. *126*, 13898-9 (2004).

Tetrakis(triphenylphosphine)palladium(0)/sodium hydride $Pd(PPh_3)_4/NaH$
C-α-Allylation with acoxy-2-ethylenes H → C-C=C
s. *26*, 827s44; with trifluoroacetoxy-2-ethylenes for the regiospecific synthesis of alkoxy-2-ethylenes with asym. induction s. N. Maezaki, Y. Hirose, T. Tanaka, Org. Lett. *6*, 2177-80 (2004).

Tetrakis(triphenylphosphine)palladium(0)/triethylamine $Pd(PPh_3)_4/Et_3N$
α,β-Ethylenecarboxylic acid esters from enol triflates by carbonylation OTf → COOR
with $Pd(OAc)_2/Ph_3P/Et_3N$ cf. *40*, 521; polymer-based synthesis of 2-acylaminotropone-5-carboxylic acid esters with $Pd(PPh_3)_4/Et_3N$ s. M. Hashimoto, A. Mori et al., Tetrahedron Lett. *44*, 1251-4 (2003).

Tetrakis(triphenylphosphine)palladium(0)/carboxylic acids $Pd(PPh_3)_4/RCOOH$
Regiospecific palladium-catalyzed C-α-allylation with 2-ethylenealcohols   H → C-C=C
with $Pd(OAc)_2/Ph_3P/Et_3B$ cf. *48*, 771s*61*; with $Pd(PPh_3)_4$/carboxylic acids **in the absence of solvent** (cf. *66*, 367) s. N.T. Patil, Y. Yamamoto, Tetrahedron Lett. *45*, 3101-3 (2004); α,α-diallylation with $Pd(PPh_3)_4$ in toluene s. Y. Kayaki, T. Koda, T. Ikariya, J. Org. Chem. *69*, 2595-7 (2004).

Bis(η³-allylpalladium chloride)/triphenylphosphine/lithium carbonate/N,O-   ←
  bis(trimethylsilyl)acetamide
Palladium-catalyzed allylation of indoles with 2-ethylenecarbonic acid esters
Effect of base and solvent on regioselectivity

C₃-Allylation under thermodynamic control. A soln. of 5 mol% [(η³-allyl)PdCl]₂ and 0.22 eq. triphenylphosphine in anhydrous methylene chloride stirred at room temp. under N₂ for 30 min, treated with 2 eqs. startg. allyl carbonate for 30 min, indole added, followed by 2 eqs. Li₂CO₃ and 2 eqs. N,O-bis(trimethylsilyl)acetamide, the mixture refluxed for 8 h, then quenched with water → product. Y 80%. In highly coordinating solvents, e.g. THF, with K₂CO₃ as base and dppe as ligand, **N-allylation** predominates **under kinetic control.** The procedure is applicable to indoles possessing electron-withdrawing and -donating groups, as well as hindered compds., and appears to be limited to *N-unsubst.* indoles. There was no reaction with allyl acetates. F.e. with cyclic and acyclic allyl carbonates s. M. Bandini, A. Melloni, A. Umani-Ronchi, Org. Lett. *6*, 3199-202 (2004); 3-allylation of indoles with allyl acetates in the presence of $Pd(OAc)_2/2,2'$-bipyridyl cf. S.M. Ma, S.-C. Yu, Tetrahedron Lett. *45*, 8419-22 (2004).

Bis(η³-allylpalladium chloride)/1,2-bis(diphenylphosphino)ethane/cesium carbonate   ←
C-α-Allylation with 2-ethylenecarbonic acid esters
s. *38*, 772s*44*; of α-isocyanocarboxylic acid esters with [(η³-allyl)PdCl]₂/dppe/Cs₂CO₃, regioselectivity, s. U. Kazmaier, S. Ackermann, Synlett *2004*, 2576-8.

Chloro(cyclooctadiene)iridium(I) dimer/1,2-bis(diphenylphosphino)-   [Ir(cod)Cl]₂/dppe/NaH
  ethane/sodium hydride
Regiospecific synthesis of allenes from acoxy-2-allenes

Generation of quaternary carbon centres. Startg. allenyl acetate added with stirring to 2 mol% [Ir(cod)Cl]₂ and 4 mol% 1,2-bis(diphenylphosphino)ethane in THF under argon, treated dropwise via syringe with a soln. of diethyl sodiomalonate (prepared from 2 eqs. diethyl malonate and 2 eqs. NaH in THF), and stirring continued at reflux for 1 h → product. Y 85%. Reaction is presumed to involve nucleophilic attack on an intermediate iridium π-(1-methylene)allyl complex, and proceeds without rearrangement of the allene bonds and without attack on any of the allenyl carbon atoms. F.e. and comparison of iridium catalysts and ligands s. S. Kezuka, K. Kanemoto, R. Takeuchi, Tetrahedron Lett. *45*, 6403-6 (2004).

Chloro(cyclooctadiene)iridium(I) dimer/chiral cyclic phosphoromonoamidites/ cuprous iodide/thiolane/1,5,7-triazabicyclo[4.4.0]dec-5-ene
Regiospecific asym. iridium-catalyzed C-α-allylation   H→C-C≡C
s. *62*, 39s67; with allyl carbonates, f. chiral ligands and with LiCl as additive, s. A. Alexakis, D. Polet, Org. Lett. *6*, 3529-32 (2004); with added CuI/thiolane/1,5,7-triazabicyclo[4.4.0]dec-5-ene cf. G. Lipowsky, N. Miller, G. Helmchen, Angew. Chem. Int. Ed. Engl. *43*, 4595-7 (2004).

Nitrogen ↑   CC ↓↑ N

Without additional reagents   w.a.r.
α,β-Acetylenealdehydes from terminal acetylene derivs.   C≡CH→C≡C-CHO
with DMF/BuLi cf. *55*, 361; with dimethylformamide dimethyl acetal, also α,β-acetyleneketones from higher amide acetals, s. K.Y. Lee, J.N. Kim et al., Tetrahedron Lett. *45*, 5043-6 (2004).

3-Amino-4,5-dihydroazocines from 1,2,4-triazines, cyclobutanones and sec. amines via regiospecific Diels-Alder reaction-retrodiene scission

Powdered 4 Å molecular sieves and 3 eqs. each of pyrrolidine and cyclobutanone added sequentially to a soln. of the startg. 1,2,4-triazine in chloroform, heated to reflux for 2.5 h, cooled to room temp., and worked up → product. Y 56%. Reaction is thought to involve initial enamine formation, inverse electron demand Diels-Alder reaction, retrodiene scission, and electrocyclic ring opening of a strained dihydropyridine. F.e.s. S.A. Raw, R.J.K. Taylor, Tetrahedron Lett. *45*, 8607-10 (2004).

Microwaves s. under Piperidine and POCl₃   [\\\\]

Potassium hydroxide   KOH
5-Vinyl-2(5H)-furanones from 2-pyrones

Ar = p-Tol

A mixture of the startg. 2-pyrone, 1 eq. nitromethane and 1.5 eqs. powdered KOH in dry DMF stirred at room temp. for 24 h, poured into ice water, neutralized with 10% aq. HCl, and filtered → product. Y 75%. Reaction appears to involve attack of deprotonated nitromethane on C_6 of the pyrone ring, followed by ring opening, re-lactonization, and elimination of the nitro group. The procedure is mild, work-up is simple, and a catalyst is not required. F.e.s. D. Sil, V.J. Ram et al., Tetrahedron Lett. *45*, 6273-6 (2004).

Organolithium compds.   *RLi*
Ketones from hydroxamic acid esters $CON(OR) \rightarrow COR'$
α,β-acetyleneketones s. *37*, 806s*51*; s.a. O. Labeeuw, P. Phansavath, J.P. Genêt, Tetrahedron Lett. *45*, 7107-10 (2004).

sec-Butyllithium/trimethyl borate/trifluoroacetic acid $s\text{-}BuLi/(MeO)_3B/CF_3COOH$
3,4-Dihydroisocoumarins
from 2-(*o*-tolyl)-Δ²-oxazolines and oxo compds.
via *o*-α-lithiation with *n*-BuLi/HCl cf. *41*, 744; with *s*-BuLi via *o*,(*o'*-α)-dilithium compds., also conversion to 8-hydroxy-3,4-dihydroisocoumarins with $(MeO)_3B/H_2O_2/AcOH$ in one pot, s. N. Tahara, T. Fukuda, M. Iwao, Tetrahedron Lett. *45*, 5117-20 (2004).

Potassium carbonate K_2CO_3
Cyclopropanes from ethylene derivs.
and pyridinium salts with Et_3N cf. *45*, 459; cyclopropyl ketones from quaternary 2-ketoammonium salts with K_2CO_3 s. L. Shi, Y.-M. Liang et al., Synthesis *2004*, 2342-6.

Piperidine/microwaves $(CH_2)_5NH/[\backslash\backslash\backslash\backslash]$
Ring closures with dimethylformamide dimethyl acetal
s. *33*, 753s*65*; 3-component synthesis of the 2-pyridone ring from cyclic ketones and malononitrile with piperidine, rapid procedure under microwave irradiation, s. N.Y. Gorobets, C.O. Kappe et al., Tetrahedron *60*, 8633-44 (2004).

Cupric hexafluoroacetoacetonate $Cu(CF_3COCHCOCF_3)_2$
γ-Keto- from α-diazo-carboxylic acid esters and enamines $C(N<)=C \rightarrow CO\text{-}C\text{-}CHCOOR$

380.

A mixture of the startg. α-diazo ester, 1.5 eqs. of the startg. enamine and 3 mol% Cu(II)-hexa-fluoroacetonate in methylene chloride refluxed until reaction complete, and the mixture hydrolyzed over silica gel → product. Y 85%. Coupling is thought to involve nucleophilic addition of the enamine to a metal carbenoid, followed by hydrogen transfer through a zwitterionic azomethinium species. F.e. and with $Rh(OAc)_2$ and other copper salts s. M. Yan, W.-J. Zhao et al., Tetrahedron Lett. *45*, 6365-7 (2004).

Cupric triflate $Cu(OTf)_2$
Pyridine ring expansion with α-diazocarbonyl compds.

381.

1*H*-1-Benzazepine-1,2-dicarboxylic acid esters. A mixture of 1 eq. 3-methylquinoline, 1.1 eqs. ethyl chloroformate, 1.2 eqs. startg. diazocarbonyl compd., and 5 mol% $Cu(OTf)_2$ in 1,2-dichloroethane stirred at 75° for 0.5 h → product. Y 85%. No such reaction took place with other metal triflates. F.e. and with α-diazoketones, also 3*H*-3-benzazepine analogs from isoquinolines, s. J.S. Yadav, B.V. Subba Reddy et al., Chem. Commun. *2004*, 2124-5.

Cupric triflate/chiral 4,5-diphenyl-2-spiroimidazolidines or bis(Δ²-oxazolines)
Asym. cyclopropanation with diazo compds.
with chiral bis(Δ²-oxazolines) as ligand s. *23*, 819s*67*; improved enantioselectivity on reaction

with diazomethyltrimethylsilane s. M.B. France et al., Tetrahedron Lett. *44*, 9287-90 (2003); with chiral 4,5-diphenyl-2-spiroimidazolidines cf. D. Tepfenhart, P.I. Dalko, J. Cossy et al., ibid. 1781-3.

Cupric chloride $CuCl_2$
Meerwein reaction   C=C → C(Ar)C(Cl)
s. *33*, 768s*36*; β-aryl-α-chloraldehydes s. N.D. Obushak, Y.V. Ostapyuk et al., Russ. J. Org. Chem. *40*, 383-9 (2004).

[N,N'-Bis(2,6-diisopropylphenyl)imidazol-2-ylidene]copper(I) chloride   ←
Catalytic diazo transfer with suppression of diazo coupling   ←

382.

Cyclopropanation of ethylene derivs. A mixture of 4 mol% [N,N'-bis(2,6-diisopropylphenyl)-imidazol-2-ylidene]copper(I) chloride and 10 eqs. styrene in anhydrous methylene chloride stirred under N_2 at room temp. for 5 min, treated with 1 eq. ethyl diazoacetate in one portion, and stirring continued for 6 h → product. Y 99% (*trans/cis* 68:32). There was no diazo coupling even in the absence of the olefin, suggesting that a substrate-containing complex is the active species rather than the copper(I) carbene itself. Diazo insertion into H-O and N-H bonds was also effected with the same catalyst with no complicating homocoupling. F.e.s. M.R. Fructos, M.M. Diaz-Requejo, P.J. Pérez et al., J. Am. Chem. Soc. *126*, 10846-7 (2004).

Trimethyl borate s. under s-BuLi $(MeO)_3B$

Aluminum chloride (s.a. under $COCl_2$) $AlCl_3$
Ar. formylation with tetraformylhydrazine s. *68*, 355   H → CHO

Indium(III) chloride $InCl_3$
2,3,6-Trisubst. tetrahydro-4-pyrones
from N-(3'-hydroxy)eneurethans and oxo compds.
Stereospecific Prins cyclization under mild conditions

383.

A soln. of 1 eq. of the startg. N-Boc-protected enamine in methylene chloride treated at 0° with 2 eqs. startg. aldehyde and 0.5 eq. $InCl_3$, stirred at the same temp. for 4 h, allowed to warm to room temp. over 25 min, and quenched with satd. aq. NH_4Cl → product. Y 91%. The protocol affords *all-cis*-2,3,6-trisubst. tetrahydro-4-pyrones from aliphatic, aromatic and α,β-ethylenic aldehydes, but yields were only modest from ketones. The diastereoselectivity is explained by the intermediate generation of an oxocarbenium ion in a diequatorial chair-conformation. F.e.s. K.N. Cossey, R.L. Funk, J. Am. Chem. Soc. *126*, 12216-7 (2004).

Imidazolium ionic liquids s. under Iron(III) complexes   ←
Trifluoroacetic acid s. under s-BuLi CF_3COOH

Cyanuric chloride   ←
4-Formylpyrazoles from hydrazones by Vilsmeier-type reaction s. *22*, 826s*68*

Phosgene/aluminum chloride $COCl_2/AlCl_3$
Vilsmeier-type formylation s. *9*, 871s*68*   H → CHO

Trimethylphosphine Me_3P
Ring closures via aza-Wittig synthesis-Ugi condensation with asym. induction

Chiral 1-acylpipecolic acid amides. A soln. of the masked azidoaldehyde in methanol treated dropwise under argon at 0° with a soln. of 2 eqs. trimethylphosphine (1 M in toluene), stirring continued until evolution of N_2 ceased, the mixture cooled to -78°, 2 eqs. formic acid and 2 eqs. *tert*-butyl isonitrile added, and stirred at room temp. for a further 12 h → product. Y 78%. F.e. incl. oxido-bridged derivs. s. M.S.M. Timmer, J.H. van Boom et al., Tetrahedron:Asym. *16*, 177-85 (2005).

Phosphorus oxide chloride/microwaves $POCl_3/[\backslash\backslash\backslash\backslash]$
Vilsmeier formylation H → CHO
s. *9*, 871; rapid procedure under microwave irradiation s. R. Nagarajan, P.T. Perumal, Synth. Commun. *34*, 2127-33 (2004); with $COCl_2/AlCl_3$ (cf. *13*, 786) s. G. Vergne, O. Dabard, F. Cornile, French patent, FR-2824555 (SNPE Soc. Nat. Poudres & Explosifs SA).

Phosphorus oxide chloride/microwaves $POCl_3/[\backslash\backslash\backslash\backslash]$
Phosphorus oxide chloride/silica gel/microwaves $POCl_3/SiO_2/[\backslash\backslash\backslash\backslash]$
Pyrazoles from hydrazones
s. *22*, 826s65; improved procedure in the absence of solvent without support s. R. Sridhar, G. Sivaprasad, P.T. Perumal, J. Heterocycl. Chem. *41*, 405-8 (2004); pyrazole-4-carboxaldehydes with added silica gel s. K. Mogilaiah, C.S. Reddy, Indian J. Chem. *43B*, 2010-3 (2004); with cyanuric chloride s. L. De Luca, A. Porcheddu et al., Synlett *2004*, 2299-302.

Cyclooctenechromium pentacarbonyl $Cr(coe)(CO)_5$
Regio- and stereo-specific synthesis of 2,4-dienecarbonyl compds. from electron-rich furans and diazo compds.

(1E,3Z)-1,3-Diene-1,4-dicarboxylic acid esters. A soln. of the startg. diazocarbonyl compd. in methylene chloride added over 2 h at 4° to a stirred soln. of 2 eqs. 2-methoxyfuran and 2 mol% $Cr(CO)_5$(cyclooctene) in the same solvent, and stirring continued for 8 h → product. Y 99%. The diazo compd. preferentially attacks the least substituted double bond of the furan to give an intermediate cyclopropane, which undergoes stereospecific double ring opening. F.e. and with 2-alkylfurans to give the corresponding dienones s. N.D. Hahn, M. Nieger, K.H. Dötz et al., J. Organomet. Chem. *689*, 2662-73 (2004).

Hydrogen chloride HCl
1,4-Dihydropyridines from two enamine molecules
and aldehydes with Me_3SiCl/NaI cf. *40*, 592s67; with HCl s. S. Youssif, J. Chem. Res. Synop *2004*, 341-3.

*5,10,15,20-Tetraphenylporphyrinatoiron(III) chloride/triphenylphosphine/
1-n-butyl-3-methylimidazolium hexafluorophosphate*
(E)-α,β-Ethylenecarboxylic acid esters from oxo compds.   CO → C=CHCOOR
with 5,10,15,20-tetraphenylporphyrinatoiron(III) chloride/triphenylphosphine cf. *54*, 388s66;
in ionic liquids, e.g. 1-*n*-butyl-3-methylimidazolium hexafluorophosphate, s. W. Sun, F.E. Kuhn,
Tetrahedron Lett. *45*, 7415-8 (2004).

Bis(1,5-cyclooctadiene)nickel(0) $Ni(cod)_2$
**2,3-Fused 1,4-cycloheptadienes from 1,3-dien-8-ynes and diazo compds.
via regio- and stereo-specific nickel-catalyzed [4+2+1]-cycloaddition**

386. E = CO_2Me

A premixed soln. of the startg. dienyne and 2 eqs. diazomethyltrimethylsilane in anhydrous THF
treated at 60° with a soln. of 10 mol% $Ni(cod)_2$ in the same solvent, and stirred at the same temp.
for 10-30 min → product. Y 78% (d.r. 95:5). The alkyne residue may be terminal or internal, the
diene may be substituted terminally or internally, and the tether may be all-carbon or contain a
nitrogen or oxygen atom. A metathesis cascade is invoked with intermediate formation of a
metallacyclobutane. F.e.s. Y. Ni, J. Montgomery, J. Am. Chem. Soc. *126*, 11162-3 (2004).

Chiral carbonylruthenium(II) porphyrin complexes
*Dichloro(p-cymene)ruthenium(II) dimer/chiral bis(Δ^2-oxazolines) or
bis(Δ^2-thiazolines)*
Asym. cyclopropanation with diazo compds.
with chiral ruthenium(II) salen complexes cf. *23*, 819s67; chiral 2-arylcyclopropanephosphonic
acid esters with carbonyl[5,10,15,20-tetrakis((1S,4R,5R,8S)-1,2,3,4,5,6,7,8-octahydro-1,4:5,8-
dimethanoanthracen-9-yl)porphyrinato]ruthenium(II) s. Y. Ferrand, P. Le Maux, G. Simonneaux,
Org. Lett. *6*, 3211-4 (2004); with [$RuCl_2$(*p*-cymene)]$_2$ and chiral bis(Δ^2-oxazolin-2-yl)thiophenes
s. M.Z. Gao, R.A. Zingaro et al., Tetrahedron Lett. *45*, 5649-52 (2004); with chiral bis(Δ^2-thiazolines) cf. P. Le Maux, G. Simonneaux et al., Tetrahedron:Asym. *15*, 2569-73 (2004).

Dichloro(p-cymene)ruthenium(II) dimer/2,6-bis(4(S)-isopropyl-Δ^2-oxazolin-2-yl)pyridine
2-Alkoxy-2,3-dihydrofurans from enolethers s. *29*, 787s68

Rhodium(II) acetate $Rh_2(OAc)_4$
β-Aryl-α-arylamino-β-hydroxycarboxylic acid esters   ArCH(OH)C(NHAr)COOR
from α-diazocarboxylic acid esters, ar. amines and ar. aldehydes

387.

A refluxing mixture of 1.1 eqs. *p*-nitrobenzaldehyde, 1.1 eqs. startg. ar. amine and 1 mol%
$Rh_2(OAc)_4$ in anhydrous methylene chloride treated slowly via syringe pump over 1 h under
argon with a soln. of 1 eq. methyl phenyldiazoacetate in the same solvent → product. Y 52%
(*threo/erythro* 67:33). The method is presumed to involve aldol condensation with an *in situ*-

generated ammonium ylid. Reaction is facilitated by electron-withdrawing groups in the ar. aldehyde and electron-donating groups in the phenyldiazoacetate. F.e.s. Y. Wang, W. Hu et al., Chem. Commun. *2004*, 2486-7.

Cyclopropanation with diazo compds.
s. *23*, 819s*67*; 2-fluorocyclopropanecarboxylic acid esters by cyclopropanation with ethyl diazoacetate, also with Pd(acac)$_2$ for cyclopropanation with diazomethane (cf. *23*, 819s*43*), s. E.V. Guseva, O.M. Nefedov, Eur. J. Org. Chem. *2004*, 3136-44.

2,3-Dihydrofurans from α-diazoketones
s. *29*, 787s*63*; 2-alkoxy-2,3-dihydrofuran-4-phosphonic acid esters s. D.-G. Gong, L. Zhang, C.-Y. Yuan, Synth. Commun. *34*, 3251-8 (2004); with [RuCl$_2$(*p*-cymene)]$_2$ and chiral bis(Δ^2-oxazolines), e.g. 2,6-bis(4(S)-isopropyl-Δ^2-oxazolin-2-yl)pyridine, s. S. Chappellet, P. Muller, Synlett *2004*, 2573-5.

Tetrahydrofurans from ethylene derivs., aldehydes and diazo compds.
s. *64*, 353s*67*; with maleimide as ene component s. C.-D. Lu, M.P. Doyle et al., J. Org. Chem. *69*, 4856-9 (2004); tetrahydro-2-spirofurans, **also 2,5-dihydrofuran ring from acetylene derivs.**, s. S. Muthusamy, C. Gunanathan, M. Nethaji, ibid. 5631-7.

**2,4,5-Triaryl-1,3-dioxolane-4-carboxylic acid esters
from two different ar. aldehyde molecules
via regio- and stereo-specific 1,3-dipolar cycloaddition with carbonyl ylids**

388.

A soln. of 2 eqs. piperonal, 1 eq. 2,4-dinitrobenzaldehyde and 1 mol% Rh$_2$(OAc)$_4$ in anhydrous methylene chloride treated at reflux with a soln. of 1.5 eqs. methyl phenyldiazoacetate in the same solvent over 1 h → product. Y 94% (d.r. 81:19). The combination of an electron-rich and an electron-deficient ar. aldehyde is essential, the former reacting initially with the diazo compd., while the latter serves as the dipolarophile for cycloaddition to the generated carbonyl ylid. F.e.s. C.-D. Lu, W.-H. Hu et al., Org. Lett. *6*, 3071-4 (2004).

**1,2,3,3a,6,6a-Hexahydrocyclopenta[*b*]pyrroles
from aldimines and two α,β-ethylenediazo compd. molecules**

389.

A refluxing soln. of the startg. aldimine and 1 mol% Rh$_2$(OAc)$_4$ in anhydrous methylene chloride treated slowly under N$_2$ via syringe pump over 1 h with a soln. of 2 eqs. methyl styryldiazoacetate in the same solvent, and refluxing continued for 1 h → product. Y 71% (*cis/trans* 52:48). Reaction involves initial generation of an azomethinium ylid, followed by coupling with a second molecule of the diazo compd. prior to ring closure, rather than via an intermediate dihydropyrrole. F.e.s. M. Yan, M.P. Doyle et al., Angew. Chem. Int. Ed. Engl. *43*, 6713-6 (2004).

Regiospecific 1,3-dipolar cycloaddition with cyclic carbonyl ylids ○
s. *43*, 943s*63*; with cyclopropenes as ene component s. A.P. Molchanov, R.R. Kostikov et al., Russ. J. Org. Chem. *40*, 431-3 (2004).

Dirhodium(II) tetrakis[(S)-N-(1,8-naphthoyl)-tert-leucinate] ←
Asym. cyclopropanation with diazo compds. ▽
with chiral cationic chlororhodium(II) bis(Δ^2-oxazoline) complexes cf. *23*, 819s*67*; chiral 1-(α-siloxyvinyl)cyclopropanecarboxylic acid esters with dirhodium(II) tetrakis[(S)-N-(1,8-naphthoyl)-*tert*-leucinate] s. P. Müller, H.D. Flack et al., Org. Lett. *6*, 1725-8 (2004).

Chiral bridged dirhodium(II) tetrakis(N-sulfonylprolinates) ←
Asym. cyclopropanation with diazo compds. at low catalyst loading
s. *65*, 372; chiral cyclopropanephosphonic acid esters s. H.M.L. Davies, G.H. Lee, Org. Lett. *6*, 2117-20 (2004).

Tetrakis((R,R)-1,3-diphenyl-1-triflyl-2-imidazolidonato)dirhodium(II) ←
Asym. cyclopropenation with diazo compds.
with dirhodium tetrakis[(S)-N-(4-dodecylbenzenesulfonyl)prolinate] cf. *47*, 770s*67*; with tetrakis-((R,R)-1,3-diphenyl-1-triflyl-2-imidazolidonato)dirhodium(II) (e.e. 92-5%), also asym. cyclopropanation and intramolecular carbene insertion into C-H bonds, s. Y. Lou, E.J. Corey et al., J. Am. Chem. Soc. *126*, 8916-8 (2004).

Palladous acetoacetonate $Pd(acac)_2$
Cyclopropanation with diazo compds.
2-Fluorocyclopropanecarboxylic acid esters s. *23*, 819s*68*

Halogen ↑   CC ↕ Hal

Without additional reagents w.a.r.
4-Hydroxy-2-pyrones from α-ketoketenes ○
and ketones cf. *50*, 387; from α-chlorocarbonylketenes and activated ketones s. H. Sheibani, K. Saidi et al., Tetrahedron *60*, 5931-4 (2004).

Irradiation s. under Co(acac)₂

Electrolysis
Cathodic coupling of halides   2 RHal → R-R
s. *35*, 549s*67*; of α-bromohydrazones, also subsequent conversion to 1-acylaminopyrroles, s. B. Batanero, M.N. Elinson, F. Barba, Tetrahedron *60*, 10787-92 (2004).

Electrolysis/cuprous bromide   ⚡/CuBr
Epoxides from oxo compds. and 1,1-dihalides
from aldehydes and methylene halides with Li cf. *26*, 852s*52*; indirect electrochemical procedure from oxo compds. and 1,1-dichlorides with added CuBr/Bu₄NBr at an iron rod anode and nickel foam cathode s. S. Oudeyer, J.P. Paugam, J.-Y. Nédélec et al., Synthesis *2004*, 389-400.

Microwaves s. under NaCN, Ni, Pd-C, Pd(OAc)₂ and ArPdCl [\\\\]

Lithium   Li
Aryl ketones from nitriles   CN → COAr
from aryllithiums s. *1*, 522; large-scale procedure from ar. chlorides with Li s. A. Meudt, M. Erbes, K. Forstinger, European patent EP-1270535 (Clariant GMBH).

Lithium/naphthalene/bis(2-methoxyethyl)amine/chiral 2-oxazolidones ←
N-Protected 2-carbalkoxy-Δ^3-pyrrolines from 2-carbalkoxypyrroles ←
s. *47*, 773s*58*; **asym. synthesis** with chiral 2-oxazolidones as proton source s. D.R. Carbery, T.J. Donohoe, Chem. Commun. *2004*, 722-3.

Sodium/n-octyl chloride $Na/C_8H_{17}Cl$
Diaryls from ar. halides   Ar-Ar'
and aryllithium compds. with added piperidine cf. *14*, 852; *o*-(Δ^2-oxazolin-2-yl)diaryls without additive s. D. Astley, S.T. Astley et al., Tetrahedron Lett. *45*, 7315-7 (2004); **and arylsodium**

compds. generated by metalation of arenes with micronized sodium/n-octyl chloride s. J.-M. Becht, A. Wagner, C. Mioskowski et al., ibid. 9331-3; from ar. bromides and arenes via metalation with n-BuLi s. Tetrahedron 60, 6853-7 (2004).

Sodium hydride/peroxyacetic acid/malononitrile $NaH/AcOOH/CH_2(CN)_2$
Hetarylcarboxylic acid amides from hetar. chlorides and amines   Hal → CON<
Synthesis with addition of one C-atom using malononitrile as carbon monoxide equivalent

390.

A mixture of 6 eqs. NaH (60% in oil) and 3 eqs. malononitrile in dry THF stirred at room temp. under N_2 for 10 min, 2-chloro-4,6-dimethoxy-1,3,5-triazine added, stirring continued for 12 h at the same temp., treated with 2 eqs. n-propylamine, followed after 5 min by 2 eqs. peroxyacetic acid (32 wt.% in acetic acid), stirred for an additional 15 min, and quenched with $NaHSO_3$ → product. Y 65%. Reaction involves S_NAr substitution of the halide by sodiomalononitrile, followed by oxidation to the corresponding acyl cyanide which then undergoes nucleophilic substitution with the amine. The protocol is simple, convenient, and based on a readily available carbonyl synthon. F.e.s. J. Zhu, T. Wang et al., Tetrahedron Lett. 45, 5909-11 (2004); with 4,5-dichloro-imidazol-1-ylacetonitrile in place of malononitrile for substitution by prim. or sec. amines cf. Z. Zhang, T. Wang et al., Synlett 2004, 2323-6.

Potassium hydroxide/tetra-n-butylammonium bromide KOH/Bu_4NBr
C-α-Alkylation of α-(alkylideneamino)carboxylic acid esters   H → R
under phase transfer catalysis with K_2CO_3/Bu_4NBr cf. 27, 843s64; polymer-based C-α-alkylation of α-(benzylideneamino)carboxylic acid esters with KOH/Bu_4NBr s. H. Park, S. Jew et al., Tetrahedron Lett. 46, 93-5 (2005).

Potassium hydroxide/chiral 1,1'-binaphthyl-based spirocyclic quaternary ammonium salts   ←
Asym. C-α-alkylation
of α-(alkylideneamino)carboxylic acid esters s. 58, 353s67; with 3,3'-bis(3,4,5-trifluorophenyl)-1,1'-binaphthyl-derived salts s. T. Ooi, Y. Uematsu, K. Maruoka, Tetrahedron Lett. 45, 1675-8 (2004); asym. 4-alkylation of Δ^2-oxazoline-4-carboxylic acid esters s. S. Jew, H. Park et al., Angew. Chem. Int. Ed. Engl. 43, 2382-5 (2004).

Potassium hydroxide/cinchonidinium salts or clay-supported variants   ←
Asym. C-α-alkylation
of α-(alkylideneamino)carboxylic acid esters s. 54, 394s67; of ethyl, tert-butyl, benzhydryl or benzyl esters s. B. Lygo, B. Allbutt, Synlett 2004, 326-8; with N-anthracenylmethylcinchonidinium chloride-on-kaolin or -montmorillonite K10 s. H. Yu, H. Koshima, Tetrahedron Lett. 44, 9209-11 (2003); asym. C-α-alkylation **of β-ketocarboxylic acid esters** s. E.J. Park, M.H. Kim, D.Y. Kim, J. Org. Chem. 69, 6897-9 (2004); of α-benzyloxyketones with N-(2,3,4-trifluorobenzyl)-O-allyldihydrocinchonidinium bromide s. M.B. Andrus, H.J. Hicken, J.C. Stephens, Org. Lett. 6, 2289-92 (2004).

Potassium hydroxide/polymer-based cinchonidinium salts   ←
Phase transfer-catalyzed Darzens-Claisen condensation
with KOH/tetra-n-hexylammonium bromide cf. 28, 795s67; glycidic acid esters with polymer-based cinchonidinium salts, diastereoselectivity, s. Z.-T. Wang, L.-W. Xu, C.-G. Xia, H.-Q. Wang, Helv. Chim. Acta 87, 1958-62 (2004).

Sodium methoxide/magnesium oxide s. under Ph_3P NaOMe/MgO

Potassium tert-butoxide   KOBu-t
α-Arylation of ketones   H → Ar
with KOBu-t in liq. NH_3 cf. 40, 540; of β-ketocarboxylic acid esters with KOBu-t in N-methyl-2-pyrrolidone *en route* to indole-3-carboxylic acid esters s. F. Gallou et al., Synlett 2004, 883-5.

Butyllithium s.a. under Lithium 2,2,6,6-tetramethylpiperidide BuLi
n-*Butyllithium* BuLi
Asym. synthesis of α-aminocarboxylic acid esters H → R
via 2-alkylation of 3,6-dialkoxy-2,5-dihydropyrazines
s. *38*, 802s*60*; generation of chiral quaternary centres from 3-subst. derivs., also conversion to chiral N-sulfonyl-2-azetidinone-4-carboxylic acid esters, s. S. Vassiliou, C. Dimitropoulos, P.A. Magriotis, Synlett *2003*, 2398-400.

Diaryls from ar. bromides and arenes s. *14*, 852s*68* Ar-Ar'
n-*Butyllithium/sodium iodide* BuLi/NaI
Diynes from triflyloxybromides and two different terminal acetylene deriv. molecules ←

391.

One-pot procedure. 1 eq. *n*-BuLi (1.6 *M* in hexane) added at -78° to a stirred soln. of 3-butyn-1-ol tetrahydropyran-2-yl ether in THF, stirred at 0° for 15 min, cooled to -78°, treated slowly with 1 eq. startg. triflyloxybromide in the same solvent, the mixture stirred at 0° for 1 h, 2 eqs. of a soln. of dec-1-ynyllithium (freshly prepared by treatment of dec-1-yne with 2 eqs. *n*-BuLi at -78 to 0° over 15 min) and *10-20 mol% NaI* added, the mixture refluxed for 16-30 h, cooled to room temp., and treated with aq. NH$_4$Cl → 1-tetrahydropyranyloxy-3,13-docosadiyne. Y 78%. The procedure takes advantage of the vastly different reactivities of the alkyl triflates and alkyl bromides, and the fact that displacement of bromine is facilitated by iodide ion. F.e. and 2-step procedure with isolation of the intermediate acetylenebromides s. R.J. Armstrong-Chong, K. Matthews, J.M. Chong, Tetrahedron *60*, 10239-44 (2004).

sec-*Butyllithium* s-*BuLi*
Regiospecific synthesis of 1-alkoxyallenes from alkoxy-2-acetylenes ←
3-subst. 1-alkoxyallenes with *n*-BuLi s. *27*, 835s*38*; 1-alkoxyallenesilanes with *s*-BuLi s. B.K. Tokeshi, M.A. Tius, Synthesis *2004*, 786-90.

sec-*Butyllithium/N,N,N',N'-tetramethylethylenediamine* s-*BuLi/tmeda*
Metalation of epoxides with retention of configuration ←
with *n*-BuLi cf. *33*, 786; chiral trisubst. epoxides with *s*-BuLi/tmeda s. V. Capriati, I. Nuzzo et al., J. Org. Chem. *69*, 3330-5 (2004).

sec-*Butyllithium/chiral 7,11-diazatricyclo[7.3.1.0^{2,7}]tridecanes* ←
Asym. 2-lithiation of N-carbalkoxypyrrolidines ←
with *s*-BuLi/(-)-sparteine cf. *62*, 379; with chiral 7,11-diazatricyclo[7.3.1.0^{2,7}]tridecanes as *simplified* sparteine-type diamines s. J.-P.R. Hermet, P. O'Brien et al., Org. Biomol. Chem. *1*, 3977-88 (2003).

sec-*Butyllithium/(-)-sparteine* ←
Asym. benzylic metalation ←
of 2-arylacylamines cf. *52*, 398s*64*; of 2-oxydiarylmethanes, regioselectivity, s. J.A. Wilkinson et al., Tetrahedron Lett. *45*, 1191-3 (2004).

tert-Butyllithium/hexamethylphosphoramide   t-BuLi/HMPA
α,β-Ethylenecarboxylic acid esters   CO → C=C(R)COOR
from lithium ynolates and ketones
with Li/naphthalene cf. 62, 468; tetrasubst. (E)-enoates with t-BuLi/HMPA s. M. Shindo, K. Shishido et al., J. Org. Chem. 69, 3912-6 (2004).

Lithium acetylides/tris(dibenzylideneacetone)dipalladium/triphenylphosphine   ←
Kumada coupling of acetylides and alkyl halides   Hal → C≡C

392.   Ph—≡—Li + Br(CH₂)₄Br ⟶ Ph—≡—(CH₂)₄Br

A soln. of the startg. Li-acetylide in THF added dropwise to a soln. of 15 mol% tris(dibenzylideneacetone)dipalladium, 60 mol% triphenylphosphine and 1.2 eqs. 1,4-dibromobutane in the same solvent at 65° under argon, refluxed 8-24 h, cooled to room temp., and quenched with satd. aq. NH₄Cl → product. Y 86%. Reaction is generally applicable to the coupling of lithium aryl-, alkyl- and silyl-acetylides with unactivated alkyl iodides and bromides, and appears to proceed by an elimination-reduction process. F.e. and comparison of catalysts, also coupling with magnesium phenyl- and trimethylsilyl-acetylide s. L.-M. Yang, L.-F. Huang, T.-Y. Luh, Org. Lett. 6, 1461-3 (2004).

Lithium diisopropylamide   i-Pr₂NLi
Asym. C-α-alkylation of hydrazones   H → R
s. 31, 812s60; polymer-based asym. C-α-alkylation with a resin-supported hydrazone s. R. Lazny, A. Nodzewska, K. Wolosewicz, Synthesis 2003, 2858-64.

Asym. C-α-alkylation of 3-acyl-2-oxazolidones
s. 44, 776s67; polymer-based asym. C-α-alkylation with a resin-supported substrate s. T. Kotake, Y. Kiso et al., Tetrahedron Lett. 45, 3651-4 (2004).

Synthesis of 4,5-dihydro-3H-2-benzazepines from o-ethylenealdimines
via anionic 1,7-electrocyclization

393. [reaction scheme: o-ethylenealdimine with LDA → lithiated intermediate → bicyclic azapentadienyl anion with Li⁺ → (with CH₂=CHCH₂Br) → 4,5-dihydro-3H-2-benzazepine with allyl and Ph substituents]

A soln. of the startg. imine in THF added dropwise over 30 min to a soln. of 1.1 eqs. freshly-prepared Li-diisopropylamide in the same solvent at -78°, stirrred for 1 h at the same temp., warmed to 0°, 2 eqs. allyl bromide added after 30 min, and quenched with water → 5-allyl-4-methyl-3-phenyl-4,5-dihydro-3H-benz[c]azepine. Y 72%. The driving force for the reaction is the generation of an energetically favourable bicyclic 1-azapentadienyl anion, the diastereoselectivity being dependent on the geometric configuration of the startg. ethylenealdimine. F.e. and electrophiles s. K. Gerdes, E.-U. Würthwein et al., Eur. J. Org. Chem. 2004, 3465-76.

Ring closures with oxaldiimidoyl dichlorides
review s. 46, 346s62; 3-amino-5-(carbalkoxyene)-Δ³-2-pyrrolones from β-ketocarboxylic acid esters s. J.T. Anders, H. Gorls, P. Langer, Eur. J. Org. Chem. 2004, 1897-910.

Lithium 2,2,6,6-tetramethylpiperidide   LiNR₂
Indazole ring from benzynes via 1,3-dipolar cycloaddition
2,3-dihydroindazoles from alkylidene-N-ylids cf. 47, 622; 3-silylindazoles from ar. halides and diazomethyltrimethylsilane with Li-2,2,6,6-tetramethylpiperidide s. Y. Shoji, Y. Hari, T. Aoyama, Tetrahedron Lett. 45, 1769-71 (2004).

Lithium 2,2,6,6-tetramethylpiperidide/lithium bis(trimethylsilyl)amide/sec-butyllithium/ ←
n-butyllithium
Kowalski homologization $COOR \rightarrow CH_2COOR$
of N-protected α-aminocarboxylic acid esters
with retention of configuration

394.

A stirred soln. of (2S,4R)-N-benzyl-4-hydroxy-L-proline methyl ester and 4.5 eqs. methylene bromide in THF treated dropwise at -78° with a freshly prepared soln. of Li-tetramethylpiperidide (from 4.5 eqs. *n*-BuLi and 4.9 eqs. 2,2,6,6-tetramethylpiperidine in THF), after 15 min 4 eqs. Li-bis(trimethylsilyl)amide in THF added dropwise, allowed to warm to -20°, re-cooled to -78°, treated dropwise with a soln. of 4 eqs. *s*-BuLi in hexanes, warmed to -20°, 4 eqs. *n*-BuLi in hexanes added, stirred at room temp. for 1 h, and quenched over 20 min into acidic methanol (prepared from acetyl chloride and methanol) at 0° → product. Y 57% (d.e. 98%). Method s. *37*, 796. Yields were low with N-Boc-protected derivs. F.e.s. D. Gray, C. Concellon, T. Gallagher, J. Org. Chem. *69*, 4849-51 (2004).

Sodium bis(trimethylsilyl)amide $NaN(SiMe_3)_2$
Asym. synthesis of α-aminocarboxylic acids via C-α-alkylation $H \rightarrow R$
of chiral condensed 5-imino-2-piperazinones cf. *54*, 395s*63*; of chiral N-carbobenzoxy-N-(6-methyltetrahydropyran-2-yl)glycine N,N-dimethylamide as a chiral glycine equivalent s. D.J. Dixon, R.A.J. Horan, N.J.T. Monck, Tetrahedron:Asym. *15*, 913-6 (2004).

Asym. 3-alkylation of phthalimidines
s. *10*, 617s*64*; asym. induction with a chiral N-carbalkoxyphthalimidine s. D.L. Comins, S. Schilling, Y.C. Zhang, Org. Lett. *7*, 95-8 (2005).

Asym. deconjugative C-α-alkylation ←
of chiral N-(α,β-ethyleneacyl)-2-oxazolidones s. *47*, 786s*59*; generation of chiral quaternary carbon centres s. T. Abe, S. Kobayashi et al., Tetrahedron Lett. *44*. 9303-5 (2003).

Potassium carbonate K_2CO_3
Thiophenes from α,β-dihalogenoketones

395.

Startg. dihalogenoketone added over 4 h to a mixture of 211.5 g K_2CO_3 and 54.1 g methyl thioglycolate in methanol at 40°, and stirred for an additional 2 h → product. Y 75%. The use of this protocol allows the rapid synthesis of thiophenes simply and inexpensively on a large scale. F.e.s. Y. Iida et al., Japanese patent JP-2001247563 (Sumitomo Seika Chem. Co. Ltd.).

2-Aminothiophenes from carboxylic acid thioamides and α-bromooxo compds.
from α-bromoketones without reagent cf. *64*, 355; also from α-bromaldehydes with K_2CO_3 s. F.M. Moghaddam, H.Z. Boinee, Tetrahedron *60*, 6085-9 (2004).

Potassium carbonate/oligo(ethylene glycol)-derived telluronium bromide/ ←
sodium hydrogen sulfite
(E)-α,β-Ethylenecarboxylic acid esters $CHO \rightarrow CH=C-COOR$
from α-bromocarboxylic acid esters and aldehydes
Tellurium-catalyzed Wittig-type synthesis
from *tert*-butyl bromoacetate with α,ω-bis(*n*-butyltelluro)polyethylene glycol as catalyst cf. *62*, 378; more general procedure with an oligo(ethylene glycol)-derived telluronium bromide as catalyst s. K. Li, Y. Tang et al., J. Org. Chem. *69*, 3986-9 (2004).

Cesium carbonate/quin[id]ine derivs.
2-Acylcyclopropanecarboxylic acid derivs.
from α,β-ethyleneketones and α-bromocarboxylic acid derivs.
Organocatalyzed asym. cyclopropanation with stabilized quaternary ammonium ylids

The first example of a general organocatalyzed asym. cyclopropanation is reported. **E:** 0.1 eq. quinidine deriv., the startg. α-bromocarboxylic acid deriv., and 1.2 eqs. startg. α,β-ethyleneketone added successively under N_2 to a soln. of 1.2 eqs. Cs_2CO_3 in anhydrous acetonitrile, stirred at 80° for 24 h, and quenched with aq. 1 M HCl → product. Y 74% (e.e. 97%). Reaction is applicable to both alkyl and aryl α,β-ethyleneketones, and involves 1,4-addition of an *in situ*-generated ammonium ylid to the enone, followed by *3-exo-tet* cyclization. Enantio- and diastereo-selectivity are very high, and face selectivity can be simply reversed by appropriate choice of quinidine or quinine deriv. F.e. incl. chiral cyclopropane-1,2-dicarboxylic acid esters, and comparison of *cinchona* alkaloid derivs. s. C.D. Papageorgiou, S.V. Ley, M.J. Gaunt et al., Angew. Chem. Int. Ed. Engl. *43*, 4641-4 (2004).

Cesium acetate s. under Pd(OAc)$_2$	*CsOAc*
Sodium cyanide/silver nitrate/montmorillonite/microwaves	←
Heterogeneous nucleophilic substitution	

ar. nitriles from halides under ultrasonication with KCN/Al_2O_3 cf. *39*, 759; with $NaCN/AgNO_3$/montmorillonite under microwave irradiation in the absence of solvent s. M.M. Hashemi, M. Akhbari, Synth. Commun. *34*, 2783-7 (2004).

Potassium cyanide s.a. under Pd$_2$(dba)$_3$	*KCN*
Potassium cyanide/polyethylene glycol-400/zinc iodide	*KCN/PEG/ZnI$_2$*
Acyl cyanides from carboxylic acid chlorides	COCl → COCN

with CuCN cf. *3*, 689; *6*, 898; aroyl cyanides with KCN/ZnI_2/polyethylene glycol-400 s. Y.-Q. Cao, J.-T. Li et al., Synth. Commun. *34*, 2951-7 (2004).

Sodium hydrogen sulfite s. under K$_2$CO$_3$	*NaHSO$_3$*
Potassium fluoride-alumina s. under Ni	*KF-Al$_2$O$_3$*
Lithium bromide s. under In	*LiBr*
Lithium iodide s. under CrCl$_3$	*LiI*
Sodium iodide s. under BuLi	*NaI*
Ethylenediamine s. under GaCl$_3$	*H$_2$NCH$_2$CH$_2$NH$_2$*
N,N,N',N'-Tetramethylethylenediamine s. under s-BuLi and CrCl$_2$	*tmeda*
7,11-Diazatricyclo[7.3.1.0^{2,7}]tridecanes s. under s-BuLi	←
(-)-Sparteine s. under s-BuLi	←
Quin[id]ine derivs. s. under Cs$_2$CO$_3$	←
Cuprous tert-butoxide	*CuOBu-t*
Syntheses via C→O-silyl group migration	←

3-subst. 2-ethylenealcohols from 3-hydroxyenesilanes cf. *67*, 397; 2-α-siloxy-1,4-dienes from 2'-hydroxyenesilanes and β,γ-ethylenehalides s. A. Tsubouchi, M. Itoh, T. Takeda et al., Synthesis *2004*, 1504-8.

Lithium bis(2-methyl-2-phenylpropyl)cuprate   *LiCuR₂*
Allylarenes from ar. iodides and acoxy-2-ethylenes   C=C-C(OAc) → C=C-C(Ar)
Nucleophilic substitution with lithium aryl(2-methyl-2-phenylpropyl)cuprates with inversion of configuration

1.2 eqs. *p*-Bromoiodobenzene in THF treated with 1.2 eqs. Li-bis(2-methyl-2-phenylpropyl)-cuprate at 0° under argon, stirred for 0.5 h, cooled to -40°, 1 eq. (R)-2-iodo-2-cyclohexen-1-yl acetate (e.e. 98%) added, the mixture warmed to -20°, stirred for 12 h, then quenched with satd. aq. NH₄Cl → product. Y 89% (e.e. 96%). Reaction takes place with exclusive inversion of configuration, leaving esters, nitriles, ketones and phenolethers unaffected. Coupling with 2-methyl-2-cyclohexenyl acetate, however, was sluggish with loss of stereospecificity. F.e.s. M.I. Calaza, P. Knochel et al., Org. Lett. **6**, 529-31 (2004); *trans*-4-arylcyclopent-2-enols from *cis*-cyclopent-4-ene-1,3-diol 1-monoacetate with PhMgCl/CuCN or Ph₂Cu(CN)(MgCl)₂ s. T. Ainai, M. Ito, Y. Kobayashi, Tetrahedron Lett. **44**, 3983-6 (2003).

Aryl ketones from ar. iodides and carboxylic acid chlorides   COCl → COAr
2- and 3-acylindoles cf. *64*, 365s*67*; 3-acyl-1*H*-indazoles s. X.Y. Yang, P. Knochel, Synlett *2004*, 2303-6.

Dilithium diorgano(cyano)cuprates   *Li₂Cu(CN)R₂*
N,N-Disubst. carboxylic acid amides from carbamyl chlorides   ClCON< → RCON<
and Grignard compds. with NiCl₂(PPh₃)₂ cf. *60*, 376; and dilithium diorgano(cyano)cuprates s. L. Lemoucheux, J. Rouden et al., Org. Lett. **6**, 3703-6 (2004).

Silver carbonate s. under Pd₂(dba)₃   *Ag₂CO₃*

Cuprous cyanide (s.a. under i-PrMgCl)   *CuCN*
Ar. nitriles from halides   Hal → CN
with CuCN/pyridine cf. *29*, 821s*67*; large-scale procedure from ar. bromides without added base s. Y. Hamied, R. Kankan, D. Rao, Great Britain patent GB-2376945 (Cipla Ltd.).

Cupric triflate s.a. under R₂Zn   *Cu(OTf)₂*

Cupric triflate/2,2-bis(4(S)-phenyl-Δ²-oxazolin-2-yl)propane/potassium   ←
   carbonate/tetrakis(triphenylphosphine)palladium(0)
Asym. 3-component synthesis of 3-vinylpyrazolidine-1,2-dicarboxylic acid esters   ○

under dual catalysis. A soln. of 10 mol% Cu(OTf)₂ and 1.1 eqs. 2,2-bis(4(S)-phenyl-2-oxazolin-2-yl)propane in dry methylene chloride stirred at room temp. for 1 h, the startg. allene and 1.2 eqs. startg. azodicarboxylate added, allowed to react for 3 h, diluted with dioxane under N₂, treated with 2 eqs. K_2CO_3, 5 mol% $Pd(PPh_3)_4$ and 1.2 eqs. β-styryl iodide, heated at 100° for 4 h, and the resulting mixture of diastereomers separated by flash chromatography on silica gel → (R,S)-product (Y 54%; e.e. 99%) and (R,R)-product (Y 32%; e.e. 99%). Reaction involves initial copper(II)-catalyzed asym. α-hydrazination with the azodicarboxylate, followed by regiospecific carbopalladation of the allene residue with the *in situ*-generated *trans*-vinylpalladium iodide prior to intramolecular nucleophilic substitution of the intermediate π-allyl complex. The abs. configuration depends on that of the chiral auxiliary, and the stereochemistry of the vinyl iodide is retained. F.e. and solvent effect s. S. Ma et al., Org. Lett. 6, 2193-6 (2004).

Cuprous chloride s. under Mg and $PdCl_2(PPh_3)_2$ *CuCl*
Cuprous bromide s. under Electrolysis and Cp_2ZrBu_2   *CuBr*
Cuprous iodide s.a. under Ni, Pd-C, and Palladium complexes   *CuI*

Cuprous iodide/N,N-dimethylglycine hydrochloride/potassium carbonate   ←
Palladium- and ligand-free Sonogashira coupling   C≡CH → C≡CAr
with CuI/Cs_2CO_3 under microwave irradiation cf. 66, 384s67; with CuI/N,N-dimethylglycine hydrochloride/K_2CO_3 **in aq. medium** s. D.W. Ma, F. Liu, Chem. Commun. *2004*, 1934-5.

Silver nitrate s. under NaCN   *$AgNO_3$*

Magnesium (s.a. under $TiCl_4$)   *Mg*
Cross-coupling of Grignard compds. with phenolethers   OR → R'
s. 24, 839s61; 2-(*o*-alkylphenyl)-Δ²-oxazolines s. J.A. Seijas, M.P. Vázquez-Tato et al., Tetrahedron Lett. 45, 1937-9 (2004).

Magnesium/cuprous chloride   *Mg/CuCl*
***cis*-1-Halogenocyclopropane-1,2-dicarboxylic acid esters via double 1,4-addition** ▽

399.

0.5 eq. CuCl added to a soln. of *2 eqs.* of the startg. bromoacrylate in ether, the mixture cooled to -78°, treated with 1 eq. *n*-BuMgBr (1 M in THF) for 30 min, and the resulting slurry quenched with 3 M aq. HCl → product. Y 59%. 1,4-Addition of the Grignard compd. to the 2-halogenoacrylate generates an enolate, which then adds to a second molecule of the 2-halogenoacrylate prior to intramolecular alkylation. Various Grignard compds., incl. alkynyl derivs., as well as methyllithium participated in the reaction. F.e. and chloro derivs. s. C. Chen, C. Xi et al., Tetrahedron Lett. 45, 6067-9 (2004).

Zinc/1-n-butyl-3-methylimidazolium hexafluorophosphate   *$Zn/[bmim]PF_6$*
Methylene from oxo compds.   CO → C=CH_2
from aldehydes with Zn/CH_2I_2 under ultrasonication cf. 40, 568; from ketones with bis(iodozincio)-methane **in ionic liquids**, e.g. 1-*n*-butyl-3-methylimidazolium hexafluorophosphate, s. H. Yoshino, S. Matsubara et al., Chem. Lett. 33, 1224-5 (2004).

Zinc/iodine   *Zn/I_2*
Sym. γ-diketones from α-bromoketones   2 COC(Br) → CO-C-C-CO
with $Ni(CO)_4$ cf. 23, 863; with Zn/I_2 s. M. Ceylan, H. Secen et al., Synthesis *2004*, 1750-4.

Zinc/ammonium chloride   *Zn/NH_4Cl*
Regio- and stereo-specific synthesis   C(OAc)C=C → C=C-C(R)
of trisubst. electron-deficient ethylene derivs. in water

400.

α-Subst. (Z)-α,β-ethylenenitriles from β-acoxy-α-methylenenitriles. A suspension of the startg. Baylis-Hillman acetate, 4 eqs. isopropyl iodide, and 3 eqs. zinc powder in satd. aq. NH_4Cl

stirred for 12 h at room temp. → product. Y 77% (Z/E 95:5). Reaction is presumed to involve initial 1,4-addition of a generated alkylzinc iodide, followed by β-elimination of the acetoxy group. α-Subst. (E)-α,β-ethylenecarboxylic acid esters were obtained similarly **from β-acoxy-α-methylenecarboxylic acid esters**. The role of water is significant as there was no reaction in other solvents, e.g. dioxane or methanol, in the presence of NH_4Cl. Furthermore, there was no reaction with samarium or indium, and unactivated alkyl bromides gave much lower yields. F.e.s. B. Das et al., Org. Lett. *6*, 3349-52 (2004).

Zinc/bis(dibenzylideneacetone)palladium(0)/tri-2-furylphosphine $Zn/Pd(dba)_2/Fu_3P$
Zinc/tris(dibenzylideneacetone)dipalladium/dicyclohexyl- $Zn/Pd_2(dba)_3/Cy_2PAr$
[2-(2,6-diisopropoxyphenyl)phenyl]phosphine
Negishi diaryl synthesis   Ar-Ar'
with $PdCl_2(PPh_3)_2$ cf. *38*, 836s*60*, *64*; nitrodiaryls with $Pd(dba)_2$/tri-2-furylphosphine (cf. *61*, 375) s. I. Sapountzis, H. Dube, P. Knochel, Adv. Synth. Catal. *346*, 709-12 (2004); general procedure, incl. synthesis of tri- and tetra-*o*-subst. diaryls with $Pd_2(dba)_3$/dicyclohexyl[2-(2,6-diisopropoxyphenyl)phenyl]phosphine s. J.E. Milne, S.L. Buchwald, J. Am. Chem. Soc. *126*, 13028-32 (2004); cobalt-catalyzed preparation of arylzinc halides from ar. halides and Zn dust s. I. Kazmierski, C. Gosmini et al., Tetrahedron Lett. *44*, 6417-20 (2003).

Zinc oxide   ZnO
Heterogeneous Friedel-Crafts acylation under mild conditions   H → Ac
in the absence of solvent

401.

Anisole added to a mixture of 0.5 eqs. ZnO powder and 1 eq. 2-chlorobenzoyl chloride *at room temp.*, stirred intermittently at the same temp. for 10 min with TLC monitoring, and the resulting solid mass extracted with methylene chloride → product. Y 95%. The procedure is simple, economical, rapid, devoid of toxic waste, does not require acid or base nor aqueous work-up or chromatographic purification, can be scaled up, and the catalyst can be simply recovered and reused at least three times with no loss of activity. F.e. and with alkanoyl chlorides s. M.H. Sarvari, H. Sharghi, J. Org. Chem. *69*, 6953-6 (2004).

Isopropylmagnesium chloride   i-PrMgCl
Mild generation of functionalized arynes via *o*-sulfonyloxyarylmagnesium chlorides   ←

402.

Diels-Alder reaction with furan. A soln. of the startg. iodoaryl sulfonate in anhydrous THF treated dropwise with ca. 1 eq. isopropylmagnesium chloride (1.1 *M* in THF) under argon at -78° in a Schlenk tube, stirred at the same temp. for 30 min, 5 eqs. furan added slowly at the same temp., warmed to room temp., stirring continued for 2 h, then quenched with satd. aq. NH_4Cl → product. Y 93%. The procedure leaves a variety of functional groups in the aromatic ring unaffected, e.g. nitriles, esters, trifluoromethyl and nitro groups, and ketones, and the intermediate *o*-sulfonyloxyarylmagnesium chlorides can be trapped at low temperature with electrophiles. Other sulfonate groups, incl. mesylates and tosylates, were less effective. F.e. incl. generation of functionalized 7,8-dehydroquinolines s. I. Sapountzis, P. Knochel et al., Angew. Chem. Int. Ed. Engl. *43*, 4364-6 (2004).

Isopropylmagnesium chloride/lithium chloride/cuprous cyanide-lithium chloride ←
Cross-coupling with [het]arylmagnesium halides ←
s. 55, 391s58; improved procedure with added LiCl s. A. Krasovskiy, P. Knochel, Angew. Chem. Int. Ed. Engl. 43, 3333-6 (2004).

Dialkylzinc/cupric triflate/chiral cyclic phosphites or phosphoromonoamidites ←
Regiospecific asym. synthesis of ethylene derivs. $C(Hal)C=C \rightarrow C=C-C(R)$
from β,γ-ethylenehalides
with $[Cu(MeCN)_4]BF_4$/(S)-3,3'-bis(methylthio)-1,1'-bi-2-naphthol cf. 60, 379; with $Cu(OTf)_2$ and chiral spirocyclic phosphites or phosphoromonoamidites (cf. 57, 363; 62, 381) for ca. 100% S_N2' regioselectivity (e.e. up to 74%) s. W.-J. Shi, Q.-L. Zhou et al., Tetrahedron:Asym. 14, 3867-72 (2003).

Dialkylzinc/bis(tri-tert-butylphosphine)palladium(0) $R_2Zn/Pd(t-Bu_3P)_2$
Negishi cross-coupling with 2-bromo-1,3-dienes $Br \rightarrow R$
with inversion of configuration using dichloro[bis[2-(diphenylphosphino)ethyl] ether]-palladium(II) cf. 66, 399; with retention of configuration using $Pd(t-Bu_3P)_2$, chiral 2-alkyl-1,3-dienes, s. X. Zeng, E. Negishi et al., Angew. Chem. Int. Ed. Engl. 43, 2259-63 (2004).

Diethylzinc/triphenylphosphine Et_2Zn/Ph_3P
Mixed dihalogenomethylene compds. from oxo compds. ←
1,2-ethylene-1,1-bromochlorides from ketones via mixed 2,2,2-trihalogenalcohols cf. 17, 884s58; 1,2-ethylene-1,1-bromofluorides from tribromo(fluoro)methane with Et_2Zn/Ph_3P s. X.S. Lei, J.C. Quirion et al., Org. Lett. 6, 2101-4 (2004).

Zinc cyanide s. under Pd(OAc)₂ $Zn(CN)_2$

Magnesium sulfate $MgSO_4$
4-Component synthesis of 2-α-(acylamino)thiazole-4-carboxylic acid esters ○

403.
R = $CH_2CH_2=CH_2$

2,4,5-Trisubst. thiazoles. A mixture of benzaldehyde, allylamine and $MgSO_4$ in dry methanol stirred at 0° under a dry, inert atmosphere for 2 h, cooled to -10°, 1 eq. thioacetic acid and 1 eq. startg. isonitrile added, further solvent added, the mixture allowed to warm to room temp., and stirred for 24 h → product. Y 57%. Reaction proceeds by Ugi condensation, followed by intramolecular Michael addition and dehydrobromination, products being obtained with 4-5 points of molecular diversity. F.e.s. M. Umkehrer et al., Synlett 2005, 79-82.

Magnesium iodide/chiral bis(Δ²-oxazolines) ←
1,3-Dipolar cycloaddition with nitrile oxides
with asym. induction using $MgBr_2/Et_3N$ cf. 47, 640s66; **asym. conversion** on cycloaddition to 2-(α,β-ethyleneacyl)-3-pyrazolidones using MgI_2/chiral bis(Δ²-oxazolines) s. M.P. Sibi, K. Itoh, C.P. Jasperse, J. Am. Chem. Soc. 126, 5366-7 (2004).

Zinc chloride s. under Pd(OAc)₂ $ZnCl_2$
Zinc iodide s. under KCN ZnI_2

Indium In
Indium-mediated Simmons-Smith-type cyclopropanation under mild conditions ▽

404.

1.2 eqs. Methylene iodide added *dropwise* to a stirred mixture of cyclohexene and 1 eq. indium in acetonitrile at room temp. under N_2, stirring continued for 1.75 h at the same temp., then filtered and concentrated → product. Y 92%. Reaction is generally applicable to cyclic and alicyclic alkenes, as well as styrenes possessing electron-donating groups. There was no cyclopropanation with methylene chloride. F.e.s. Virender, S.L. Jain, B. Sain, Tetrahedron Lett. *46*, 37-8 (2005).

α-Methylene-γ-lactones from aldehydes in aq. medium
with ethyl α-(bromomethyl)acrylate cf. *40*, 576s*55*; with α-(bromomethyl)acrylic acid s. H.-Y. Kang et al., Bull. Korean Chem. Soc. *24*, 1819-26 (2003).

Indium/palladous acetoacetonate/lithium bromide/bromine
Synthesis of 3-alkylideneoxindoles
via intramolecular carbopalladation-Stille coupling cf. *60*, 455; from α,β-acetylenecarboxylic acid N-(*o*-iodoaryl)amides via intramolecular carboindation-Heck arylation with In/Pd(acac)$_2$/LiBr/Br$_2$, stereoselectivity, s. R. Yanada, Y. Takemoto et al., Org. Lett. *6*, 2825-8 (2004).

Montmorillonite s. under NaCN   ←
Zeolites s. under Palladium(II)-exchanged zeolite   ←

Gallium chloride/n-butyllithium/ethylenediamine $GaCl_3/BuLi/H_2NCH_2CH_2NH_2$
Catalytic *o*-silylethynylation   H → C≡CSi≼
of phenols with GaCl$_3$/BuLi/2,6-di-*tert*-butyl-4-methylpyridine cf. *64*, 378; of N-benzylanilines with added ethylenediamine s. R. Amemiya, A. Fujii, M. Yamaguchi, Tetrahedron Lett. *45*, 4333-5 (2004).

Indium(I) bromide   InBr
Sym. γ-diketones from α,α-dichloroketones   2 COCCl$_2$ → CO-C-C-CO

405.

Sym. 1,4-diarylbutanediones. A soln. of α,α-dichloroacetophenone in dry THF treated with 2 eqs. InBr at 20° in a Schlenk tube, stirred for 24 h, and quenched with 0.05 *M* aq. HCl → product. Y 90%. Reaction is presumed to involve initial oxidative insertion of InBr into one of the C-Cl bonds, followed by coupling and 1,2-aryl shift. The method was insensitive to the electronic character of ring substituents, but substrates possessing *acidic* hydroxyl or amino groups failed to react. Unsym. γ-diketones were also obtained by **cross-coupling,** while the intermediate organoindium(III) species could be trapped by oxo compds. to provide **α-chloro-β-hydroxyketones** in a Darzens-type condensation. F.e.s. C. Peppe, R.P. das Chagas, Synlett *2004*, 1187-90.

Indium(III) chloride s. under Co(acac)$_2$ InCl$_3$

Ytterbium(III) triflate   Yb(OTf)$_3$
Friedel-Crafts acylation   H → Ac
with simultaneous O-demethylation s. *54*, 413s*68*

Samarium diiodide/samarium   SmI$_2$/Sm
Cyclopropane- via α,β-ethylene-carboxylic acid amides   ▽
from α-chloro-β-hydroxycarboxylic acid amides cf. *65*, 399; stereospecific synthesis of di-, tri- and tetra-subst. derivs. from glycidic acid amides, also reduction to 2,3-dideuteriocarboxylic acid amides, s. J.M. Concellón, M. Huerta, E. Bardales, Tetrahedron *60*, 10059-65 (2004).

Ammonium hydrogen carbonate NH_4HCO_3
Friedel-Crafts benzylation in aq. medium under neutral conditions   H → Bn

406.

A stirred soln. of 5 eqs. 2-methylfuran and 2 eqs. NH_4HCO_3 in 90% *aq. acetonitrile* (v/v) treated dropwise at 20° with 1 eq. 4-methoxybenzyl bromide, and stirring continued for 24 h → product. Y 73%. Reaction was also effected **in fluorinated alcohols** (with added NH_4HCO_3 or 2,6-lutidine) where, as in aq. medium, the nucleophilicity of the arene is significantly enhanced. F.e. and **Friedel-Crafts allylation** s. M. Hofmann, H. Mayr et al., Angew. Chem. Int. Ed. Engl. *43*, 5402-5 (2004).

Imidazolium ionic liquids s. under Zn, Pd-C, Pd(OAc)$_2$, PdCl$_2$ and Palladium complexes	←
Tetrakis(dimethylamino)ethylene s. under PdCl$_2$	$(Me_2N)_2C{=}C(NMe_2)_2$
Nitriles s. under NaH and NaN(SiMe$_3$)$_2$	*RCN*
Peroxyacetic acid s. under NaH and NaN(SiMe$_3$)$_2$	$MeCOO_2H$
Telluronium bromides s. under K$_2$CO$_3$	$[R_3Te]Br$
Trimethylsilyl chloride s. under CrCl$_3$	Me_3SiCl
Di-n-butylzirconocene/cuprous bromide-dimethyl sulfide	$Cp_2ZrBu_2/CuBr{\cdot}Me_2S$
α-Arylketones from benzyl ethers and carboxylic acid chlorides	COCl → COCH$_2$Ar

407.

α-(*o*-Vinylaryl)ketones. A soln. of dibutylzirconocene (prepared from 1 eq. Cp_2ZrCl_2 and 2 eqs. *n*-BuLi in THF at -78°) and 1 eq. *o*-(benzyloxymethyl)styrene gradually warmed to room temp., stirred for 3 h, chilled to 0°, a soln. of 3 eqs. acetyl chloride in the same solvent and 20 mol% CuBr·Me$_2$S added, refluxed 5 h, cooled to room temp., and quenched with satd. aq. NaHCO$_3$ → product. Y 93%. Reaction involves generation of intermediate benzylzirconocene ethers, which undergo Zr→Cu-transmetalation prior to coupling with the acyl chloride. The method was successfully applied to aromatic, aliphatic and α,β-ethylenic acid chlorides, but α,β-acetylene- carboxylic acid chlorides failed to react. F.e. and comparison of copper salts s. Y. Ikeuchi, T. Taguchi, Y. Hanzawa, Tetrahedron Lett. *45*, 4495-8 (2004).

Titanium tetrachloride/magnesium $TiCl_4/Mg$
Enolethers from carboxylic acid esters and 1,1-dichlorides   COOR → C(OR)=C
with $Cp_2TiCl_2/Mg/(EtO)_3P$ cf. *56*, 393; methylene compds. with $TiCl_4/Mg$, preferential conversion, s. T.-H. Yan, Y.-H. Wu et al., Org. Lett. *6*, 4965-7 (2004).

Tri-n-butyltin chloride s. under Pd$_2$(dba)$_3$ Bu_3SnCl

Triphenylphosphine/sodium methoxide-magnesium oxide $Ph_3P/NaOMe{-}MgO$
Coumarins from *o*-hydroxyaldehydes via Wittig synthesis   ○
with ethyl triphenylphosphoranylideneacetate cf. *33*, 851; direct procedure from ethyl chloroacetate with Ph$_3$P/NaOMe-on-MgO s. A. Shockravi, H. Valizadeh, M.M. Heravi, Phosphorus, Sulfur Silicon Relat. Elem. *178*, 501-4 (2003).

Antimony pentachloride/benzyltriethylammonium chloride $SbCl_5/BnEt_3NCl$
Friedel-Crafts acylation   H → Ac
with Bi(OTf)$_3$ in ionic liquids cf. *54*, 413s*66*; with readily recyclable 2:1 SbCl$_5$·benzyltriethyl-ammonium chloride complex, also sulfonylation, s. A.-P. Huang, Y.-M. Liang et al., Adv. Synth. Catal. *346*, 599-602 (2004); Friedel-Crafts acylation of phenolethers using Yb(OTf)$_3$ with simultaneous O-demethylation, s. W.K. Su, C. Jin, Synth. Commun. *34*, 4199-205 (2004).

Chromium(II) chloride $CrCl_2$
(Z)-α,β-Ethylene-α-halogenocarbonyl compds.   CO → C=C(Cl)CO
from oxo compds.
ester derivs. cf. *65*, 404; ketone, amide, and cyano derivs., also catalytic procedure with 0.5 eq. $CrCl_2$ and excess of Mn/Me_3SiCl, s. J.R. Falck et al., Tetrahedron Lett. *45*, 3039-42 (2004).

Chromium(II) chloride $CrCl_2$
Chromium(III) chloride/manganese/lithium iodide/trimethylsilyl chloride   ←
Functionalized ethylene derivs. from 1,1-dihalides and aldehydes   CHO → CH=C
enesilanes with $CrCl_2$ cf. *42*, 829; (E)-α,β-ethylenecarboxylic acid esters s. D.K. Barma, J.R. Falck et al., Tetrahedron Lett. *45*, 5917-20 (2004); (E)-enesilanes and (E)-α,β-ethyleneboronic acid esters with $CrCl_3(THF)_3/Mn/LiI/Me_3SiCl$ s. K. Takai, E. Nakatani et al., Bull. Chem. Soc. Jpn. *77*, 1581-6 (2004); (E)-2-vinylcyclopropanecarboxylic acid esters with $CH_2I_2/CrCl_2$ s. K. Ujihara, Japanese patent JP-2002212138 (Sumitomo Chem. Co. Ltd.).

Chromium(II) chloride/N,N,N′,N′-tetramethylethylenediamine $CrCl_2$/tmeda
Cyclopropanes from ethylene derivs.   ▽
trans-cyclopropyl iodides from terminal ethylene derivs. and iodoform cf. *66*, 406; *trans*-cyclopropylsilanes with (diiodomethyl)trimethylsilane s. K. Takai, M. Hirano, S. Toshikawa, Synlett *2004*, 1347-50.

Molybdenum hexacarbonyl s. under Pd(OAc)$_2$ $Mo(CO)_6$
N,N-Dimethylglycine hydrochloride s. under CuI $Me_2NCH_2COOH·HCl$
Tetra-n-butylammonium bromide s. under KOH and Pd(PPh$_3$*)*$_4$ Bu_4NBr
Manganese s. under CrCl$_3$ Mn

Cobalt(II) acetoacetonate/indium(III) chloride/irradiation $Co(acac)_2/InCl_3$/💡
Carboxylic acid esters from halides by carbonylation   Hal → COOR
with $Co_2(CO)_8$ and KOMe-on-alumina cf. *12*, 867s39; from *prim-* or *sec-*alkyl or aryl bromides with $Co(acac)_2$ under irradiation, enhanced procedure with $InCl_3$ as Lewis acid, s. D. Cash, A. Combs, V. Dragojlovic, Tetrahedron Lett. *45*, 1143-5 (2004).

Nickel/cuprous iodide/triphenylphosphine/potassium fluoride-alumina/microwaves   ←
Ni-Catalyzed Sonogashira coupling   C≡CH → C≡CAr
with $Ni/CuI/Ph_3P/KOH$ cf. *54*, 414s67; rapid procedure under microwave irradiation in the absence of solvent on $KF-Al_2O_3$ s. M. Wang, P.-H. Li, L. Wang, Synth. Commun. *34*, 2803-12 (2004).

Carbonyl(chloro)bis(tri-2-furylphosphine)rhodium(I)/3,3-dimethylbutene/cesium carbonate   ←
Dehydrogenative α-arylation of cyclic sec. amines   CHNH → C(Ar)=N

6-Aryl-2,3,4,5-tetrahydropyridines. A mixture of 1.2 eqs. anhydrous Cs_2CO_3 and 5 mol% carbonyl(chloro)bis(tri-2-furylphosphine)rhodium(I) in deoxygenated anhydrous dioxane stirred under argon for 0.5 min, treated successively with 2 eqs. 3,3-dimethylbutene (to prevent dehalogenation), 1.2 eqs. (S)-ethyl nipecotate (distilled) and 1 eq. iodobenzene, and stirring continued under argon at 150° for ca. 16 h in a sealed pressure vessel → product. Y 52% (e.e. 99%). In this interesting departure from classical transition metal-catalyzed N-arylation, the initial N-metalation is followed by β-hydride elimination, carbometalation and a second β-hydride elimination, the choice of a robust triarylphosphine being critical. The procedure is applicable to the coupling of aryl and hetaryl halides with 5- to 8-membered cyclic sec. amines, incl. chiral substrates. F.e.s. B. Sezen, D. Sames, J. Am. Chem. Soc. *126*, 13244-6 (2004).

Palladium-carbon/sodium acetate/4-methoxyphenol   Pd-C/NaOAc/ArOH
Palladium/mesoporous silica/triethylamine   ←
Heterogeneous Heck arylation s. *27*, 871s68   H → Ar

Palladium-carbon/cuprous iodide/triphenylphosphine/2-aminoethanol   ←
Indoles from *o*-halogenamines and acetylene derivs.   ◯
from N-protected *o*-iodoamines and terminal acetylene derivs. with Pd(II)-exchanged zeolite/Cs_2CO_3 cf. *27*, 851s67; from N-sulfonyl derivs. with Pd-C/CuI/Ph_3P/2-aminoethanol **in water** s. M. Pal, I. Dager et al., Synlett *2004*, 1965-9; **pyrrole ring** from internal silylacetylenes with $Pd(OAc)_2$/LiCl/LiOAc s. M.B. Gee, W.J. Lee, E.K. Yum, Bull. Korean Chem. Soc. *24*, 1193-6 (2003); **from *o*-chlorosulfonylamines** with simultaneous N-desulfonylation using $PdCl_2(dppf)$/LiCl/Na_2CO_3 s. C.R. Hopkins, N. Collar, Tetrahedron Lett. *45*, 8087-90, 8631-3 (2004).

Palladium-carbon/1-octyl-3-methylimidazolium fluoroborate/microwaves   ←
Heck arylation in ionic liquids under microwave irradiation s. *27*, 871s68   H → Ar

Palladium(II)-exchanged zeolite   ←
Heterogeneous copper-free Sonogashira coupling s. *63*, 411s68   C≡CH → C≡CAr

Pallodous acetoacetonate s. under In $Pd(acac)_2$

Pallodous acetate/sodium hydrogen carbonate/tetra-n-butylammonium chloride   ←
ω-Arylketones from ethylenealcohols and ar. halides   ←
β-arylketones from 2-ethylenealcohols cf. *31*, 847; γ-arylketones from 3-ethylenealcohols with $Pd(OAc)_2$/$NaHCO_3$/Bu_4NCl s. M. Qadir, K.K. Hii et al., Tetrahedron Lett. *44*, 3675-8 (2003).

Pallodous acetate/tetra-n-butylammonium acetate $PdOAc)_2$/Bu_4NOAc
Copper-free Sonogashira coupling   C≡CH → C≡CAr
update s. *63*, 411s67; **copper-, ligand- and amine-free Sonogashira coupling** with $Pd(OAc)_2$/Bu_4NOAc for reactions with electron-rich and -deficient ar. iodides or bromides s. S. Urgaonkar, J.G. Verkade, J. Org. Chem. *69*, 5752-5 (2004); copper- and amine-free procedure with *N,N-diisopropyl-N-(diphenylphosphino)amine* as ligand and K_2CO_3 as base s. J. Cheng, Z.-G. Zhang et al., ibid. 5428-32; with a ferrocene-based dichloro(diphenylphosphinomethylphosphine enimine)palladium(II) complex s. A. Arques, D. Aunon, P. Molina, Tetrahedron Lett. *45*, 4337-40 (2004); copper- and phosphine-free procedure with *chlorobis(N-methylimidazol-2-yl)methylpalladium(II)* **in ionic liquids**, e.g. 1-*n*-butyl-3-methylimidazolium hexafluorophosphate, for coupling ar. iodides (with piperidine as base) s. S.B. Park, H. Alper, Chem. Commun. *2004*, 1306-7; **heterogeneous copper-free Sonogashira coupling** with $Pd^{II}(NH_3)_4$-exchanged zeolite NaY s. L. Djakovitch, P. Rollet, Tetrahedron Lett. *45*, 1367-70 (2004).

Pallodous acetate/1-n-butyl-3-methylimidazolium hexafluorophosphate/silica gel/   ←
tri-n-butylamine
Immobilization of catalysts in ionic liquids within amorphous silica pores   ←

409.

Heck arylation. Iodobenzene, 1.2 eqs. cyclohexyl acrylate and 2 eqs. *n*-Bu_3N added under N_2 to a suspension of 0.1 eq. $Pd(OAc)_2$ (immobilized in 1-*n*-butyl-3-methylimidazolium hexafluorophosphate within amorphous silica pores) in *n*-dodecane, the mixture heated at 150° for 15 h, cooled to room temp., and the organic layer worked up → product. Y 96%. The procedure is environmentally friendly, economical, does not require a ligand or a large amount of ionic liquid, and the air- and moisture-resistant catalyst can be readily recycled at least 6 times without significant loss of activity with TONs up to 68, 400. Furthermore, there was minimal leaching of the metal into the medium, and the catalyst can be stored without precautions. Both electron-withdrawing and -donating groups in the aryl halides were tolerated. F.e., also prepn. of the catalyst s. H. Hagiwara et al., Org. Lett. 6, 2325-8 (2004).

Palladous acetate/triphenylphosphine/cesium carbonate
Intramolecular carbopalladation-carbonylation ← ○
phthalimidine-3-acetamides s. 49, 829s59; also acetic acid derivs. with Cs_2CO_3 as base s. X.J. Gai, R. Grigg et al., Tetrahedron Lett. 44, 7441-3 (2003).

Palladous acetate/triphenylphosphine/cesium acetate $Pd(OAc)_2/Ph_3P/CsOAc$
Palladous acetate/2-(dicyclohexylphosphino)biphenyl/zinc chloride/N-sodio compd. ←
Regiospecific Heck-type arylation of 5-membered heteroarenes H → Ar
s. 57, 376s67; 2-arylation of N-alkyl- and N-aryl-indoles s. B.S. Lane, D. Sames, Org. Lett. 6, 2897-900 (2004); of N-sodiopyrroles with 2-(dicyclohexylphosphino)biphenyl as ligand and added $ZnCl_2$ s. R.D. Rieth, J.P. Sadighi et al., ibid. 3981-3.

Palladous acetate/triphenylphosphine/triethylamine $Pd(OAc)_2/Ph_3P/Et_3N$
3-Vinyl-2-azetidinones from aldimines
via carbonylation of palladium π-allyl complexes
with allyl phosphates as electrophile cf. 49, 781; with β,γ-ethylenehalides using $Pd(OAc)_2/Ph_3P/Et_3N$, asym. induction, s. L. Troisi, E. Pindinelli et al., Tetrahedron 60, 6895-900 (2004).

Palladous acetate/polymer-based triphenylphosphine/zinc cyanide/microwaves ←
Ar. nitriles from halides under microwave irradiation s. 29, 845s68 Hal → CN

Palladous acetate/(4-hydroxyphenyl)diphenylphosphine/tetra-n-butylammonium bromide/ ← sodium hydroxide
Heck arylation H → Ar
update s. 27, 871s67; **in aq. medium** (cf. 27, 871s64, 67) with (4-hydroxyphenyl)diphenylphosphine as ligand s. E. Shirakawa, K. Ishii, T. Tsuchimoto, Chem. Commun. 2004, 2752-3; **at low catalyst loading** with Tedicyp as ligand (cf. 62, 403) for the synthesis of 2-[het]arylmethyl-1,3-dioxolanes s. I. Kondolff, H. Doucet, M. Santelli, Synlett 2004, 1561-4; with *0.002 mol%* dichlorobis(η^1-2-ethyl-Δ^2-oxazoline)palladium(II)/NaOAc s. R.A. Gossage, H.A. Jenkins, P.N. Yadav, Tetrahedron Lett. 45, 7689-91 (2004); with 10^{-4} *mol%* O,N,S-tridentate chloro(salicylaldehyde N^4-ethylthiosemicarbazone)palladium(II) s. D. Kovala-Demertzi et al., ibid. 2923-6; with 0.01 mol% *palladacyclic* chloro[2-(N,N-dicyclohexylaminothiocarbonyl)furan-3-yl]palladium(II) dimer (cf. 51, 416s61, 67) under atmospheric conditions s. Z.-C. Xiong, Z. Yang et al., Org. Lett. 6, 3337-40 (2004); with air-stable, readily recoverable *fluorous palladacyclics*, e.g. 2,6-bis[(4-tridecafluorohexylphenyl)thiomethyl]phenylpalladium(II) chloride, in DMAc under microwave irradiation s. D.P. Curran, K. Fischer, G. Moura-Letts, Synlett 2004, 1379-82; **heterogeneous Heck arylation** with 0.02 mol% palladium-on-mesoporous silica s. L. Li, J.L. Shi, J.N. Yan, Chem. Commun. 2004, 1990-1; with Pd-C/4-methoxyphenol/NaOAc cf. S.W. Krska, T.S. Rosner, Y. Sun, United States patent US-2002128478; with $Pd(OAc)_2$ **in phosphonium ionic liquids** (cf. 27, 871s64, 67), e.g. tetradecyl(trihexyl)phosphonium chloride, s. D.A. Gerritsma, A. Capretta et al., Tetrahedron Lett. 45, 7629-31 (2004); with Pd-C in imidazolium ionic liquids, e.g. 1-octyl-3-methylimidazolium fluoroborate, under microwave irradiation without a phosphine ligand s. X. Xie, X. She, X. Pan et al., ibid. 809-11.

Palladous acetate/tri-2-furylphosphine/potassium carbonate/norbornene ←
3,4-Fused carbostyrils from ar. halides and *o*-bromocarboxylic acid amides ○

410.

A mixture of 5 mol% $Pd(OAc)_2$, 10 mol% tri-2-furylphosphine, 2 eqs. K_2CO_3, 1 eq. of the startg. amide, 1.1 eqs. norbornene and 1 eq. *o*-iodotoluene in anhydrous DMF stirred at 85° under N_2

for 24 h → product. Y 82%. Reaction is presumed to involve initial *o*-palladation of the aryl iodide via insertion of norbornene, followed by Heck-type arylation with the *o*-bromoamide, elimination of norbornene, and intramolecular N-arylation. The method is applicable to the coupling of aryl iodides possessing electron-releasing groups with aromatic and electron-poor or -rich heteroaromatic *o*-bromoamides. F.e.s. R. Ferraccioli, M. Catellani et al., Org. Lett. *6*, 4759-62 (2004); **1-subst. 2-carbalkoxy-1,2,3,4-tetrahydroisoquinolines** and [in lower yield] benzazepine analogs via *o*-alkylation-Heck-type vinylation-intramolecular Michael addition with Cs_2CO_3 as base s. Tetrahedron Lett. *45*, 6903-7 (2004).

Palladous acetate/1,1′-bis(diphenylphosphino)ferrocene/4-dimethylaminopyridine/ ←
   ethyldiisopropylamine/molybdenum hexacarbonyl
Phthalides from *o*-bromobenzyl alcohols   ○
with $Pd(OAc)_2/Ph_3P$ under carbonylation cf. *34*, 832s*49*; with $Pd(OAc)_2$/dppf/DMAP/*i*-Pr_2NEt, rapid procedure under microwave irradiation with $Mo(CO)_6$ as source of CO, also f. cyclocarbonylations, s. X.-Y. Wu, M. Alterman et al., Tetrahedron Lett. *45*, 4635-8 (2004).

Palladous acetate/N,N-diisopropyl-N-(diphenylphosphino)amine/potassium carbonate ←
Copper- and amine-free Sonogashira coupling s. *63*, 411s*68*   C≡CH → C≡CAr

Palladous acetate/tetradecyl(trihexyl)phosphonium chloride/sodium acetate ←
Heck arylation in ionic liquids s. *27*, 871s*68*   H → Ar

*Bis(tri-*tert*-butylphosphine)palladium(0) s.a. under R_2Zn* $Pd(t$-$Bu_3P)_2$

*Bis(tri-*tert*-butylphosphine)palladium(0)/acetic acid/magnesium sulfate/* ←
   potassium phosphate
Indoles from *o*-halogenamines and ketones under mild conditions   ○

411.

A suspension of 1 eq. 2-chloroaniline, 3 eqs. of the startg. ketone, *1.5 eqs. acetic acid*, and 0.5 eq. $MgSO_4$ in DMAc degassed with argon for 10 min in a test-tube, treated with 1.3 eqs. K_3PO_4 and 10 mol% $Pd(t$-$Bu_3P)_2$, the mixture further degassed with argon for 5 min, and heated at 90° under argon for 2 h → product. Y 96%. The inclusion of acetic acid is critical to moderate the basicity of potassium phosphate. The procedure is simple, efficient, and generally applicable to the coupling of electron-poor and -rich *o*-chloro- or *o*-bromo-amines, incl. N-alkyl derivs., with cyclic and acyclic ketones. Acid-labile 1,3-dioxolane groups, carboxylic acids, amides, methyl and methoxy remained unaffected. An enamine-Heck mechanism is invoked. F.e., also 4- and 7-azaindoles, s. M. Nazaré et al., Angew. Chem. Int. Ed. Engl. *43*, 4526-8 (2004).

Bis(dibenzylideneacetone)palladium(0) s. under Zn $Pd(dba)_2$
Tris(dibenzylideneacetone)dipalladium s.a. under Lithium acetylides $Pd_2(dba)_3$

*Tris(dibenzylideneacetone)dipalladium/tri-*tert*-butylphosphine/potassium carbonate* ←
Benzofurans from *o*-iodophenols and acetylene derivs.
from terminal acetylene derivs. with $PdCl_2(PPh_3)_2$/CuI/Et_3N cf. *47*, 839s*65*; from *internal* acetylene derivs. with $Pd_2(dba)_3$/*t*-Bu_3P/K_2CO_3, regioselectivity, s. T. Konno, H. Yamanaka et al., Tetrahedron *60*, 11695-700 (2004).

*Tris(dibenzylideneacetone)dipalladium/tri-*tert*-butylphosphine/potassium cyanide/* ←
   tri-n-butyltin chloride
Ar. nitriles from halides   Hal → CN
with $Pd_2(dba)_3$/dppf/Zn/Zn(CN)$_2$/Zn(OAc)$_2$ cf. *29*, 845s*67*; thienyl cyanides (without Zn(OAc)$_2$) s. T. Erker, S. Nemec, Synthesis *2004*, 23-5; ar. and hetar. nitriles with $Pd_2(dba)_3$/*t*-Bu_3P/KCN/ Bu_3SnCl (or from hetar. bromides with Xanthphos) s. C.H. Yang, J.M. Williams, Org. Lett. *6*, 2837-40 (2004); general procedure with $Pd(OAc)_2$/Zn(CN)$_2$ and polymer-based triphenyl-

phosphine under microwave irradiation in DMF s. R.R. Srivastava, S.E. Collibee, Tetrahedron Lett. 45, 8895-7 (2004).

Tris(dibenzylideneacetone)dipalladium/tri-o-tolylphosphine/silver carbonate
**2-(3-Arylprop-1(Z)-enyl)cyclopentanones
from 1-(1(Z),3-butadienyl)cyclobutanols and ar. iodides**

412.

A mixture of the startg. cyclobutanol, 1.5 eqs. iodobenzene, 5 mol% $Pd_2(dba)_3$, 20 mol% $(o\text{-Tol})_3P$ and 2 eqs. Ag_2CO_3 in dry toluene heated at 45° under argon for 3-6 h → product. Y 89%. The procedure is applicable to ar. iodides possessing electron-withdrawing or -releasing groups, incl. naphthalene derivs., and is thought to involve a concerted rearrangement of a zwitterionic *anti*-configured palladium π-allyl complex. The corresponding (E)-substrates, however, were unreactive as the necessary chelation control is not possible. Incorporation of a monodentate phosphine, rather than a bidentate one, is critical for high yields. F.e. and palladium-catalyzed α-arylation of the products s. M. Yoshida, K. Sugimoto, M. Ihara, Org. Lett. 6, 1979-82 (2004).

Tris(dibenzylideneacetone)dipalladium/1,2-bis(diphenylphosphino)ethane/sodium tert-butoxide
2-Benzylheterocyclics from 5-functionalized ethylene derivs. and ar. bromides
2-benzyltetrahydrofurans from 4-ethylenealcohols cf. 66, 413; 2-benzylpyrrolidines from 4-ethyleneamines with dppe as ligand, stereoselectivity, s. J.E. Ney, J.P. Wolfe, Angew. Chem. Int. Ed. Engl. 43, 3605-8 (2004).

Tris(dibenzylideneacetone)dipalladium/9,9-dimethyl-4,5-bis(diphenylphosphino)-xanthene/cesium carbonate
Carbostyrils from *o*-halogenocarbonyl compds. and acetamides

413.

A mixture of *o*-bromobenzaldehyde, 1.2 eqs. 2-phenylacetamide, 1.4 eqs. Cs_2CO_3, 0.9 mol% $Pd_2(dba)_3$ and 2.9 mol% Xantphos in dry toluene refluxed under N_2 for 2 h, then cooled and diluted with water → product. Y 94%. This is a useful alternative to the Friedländer synthesis, apparently involving initial Pd-catalyzed N-arylation and subsequent intramolecular Knoevenagel condensation. 4-Hydroxy- and 4-amino-derivs. were also obtained from *o*-bromocarboxylic acid esters and *o*-bromonitriles, while propionamides and methoxyacetamides (with NaOBu-*t* as base) gave 3-methyl and 3-methoxy derivs., respectively. F.e. incl. naphthyridinones and 3-hetaryl derivs., also with N-subst. acetamides, s. P.J. Manley, M.T. Bilodeau, Org. Lett. 6, 2433-5 (2004).

*Tris(dibenzylideneacetone)dipalladium/2-di-tert-butylphosphinobiphenyl/bis[2-
(diphenylphosphino)phenyl] ether/sodium tert-butoxide*
N-Aryl-2-benzylindolines from *o*-allylamines and two different ar. bromide molecules
Sequential coupling in one pot with *in situ* modification of the catalyst by ligand exchange

414.

1 eq. *p*-Chlorobromobenzene added to a cooled mixture of 0.5 mol% $Pd_2(dba)_3$, 2 mol% *2-di-tert-butylphosphinobiphenyl* and 2.1 eqs. *t*-BuONa under N_2, stirred for 10 min, treated with the startg. *o*-allylamine in toluene, heated at 80° until the startg. m. was consumed, 2 mol% *bis[2-(diphenylphosphino)phenyl] ether* in toluene added, stirred at the same temp. for 10 min, 1 eq. *tert*-butyl *p*-bromobenzoate added, heated with GC monitoring, cooled to room temp., and quenched with satd. aq. NH_4Cl → product. Y 88%. The bulky, electron-rich biphenylylphosphine facilitates the N-arylation with the first ar. bromide, and is then exchanged *in situ* by the *chelating* bis[2-(diphenylphosphino)phenyl] ether which promotes olefin insertion and subsequent C-arylation with the second ar. bromide rather than a second N-arylation. F.e.s. R. Lira, J.P. Wolfe, J. Am. Chem. Soc. *126*, 13906-7 (2004).

Tetrakis(triphenylphosphine)palladium(0) s.a. under $Cu(OTf)_2$ $Pd(PPh_3)_4$

*Tetrakis(triphenylphosphine)palladium(0)/potassium carbonate/tetra-n-butylammonium
 bromide*
Synthesis of vinylcyclopropanes from allenes
2-cyclopropyl-1,3-dienes with $Pd_2(dba)_3$/dppe/Na^+ cf. *43*, 806; *trans*-products with $Pd(PPh_3)_4$/K_2CO_3/Bu_4NBr, also α-cyclopropylstyrenes with ar. halides, s. S.-M. Ma, Z.-L. Zheng et al., J. Org. Chem. *69*, 6463-6 (2004).

Tetrakis(triphenylphosphine)palladium(0)/lithium tetraorganoindates
Ketones from reactive halides and lithium tetraorganoindates   Hal → COR
Carbonylative cross-coupling s. *58*, 462s68

[(o-(tert-Butylselenomethyl)phenyl]palladium(II) acetate dimer/sodium acetate
Heck arylation with highly active selenium-ligated palladium complexes   H → Ar

415.

A mixture of *p*-bromobenzonitrile, 1.2 eqs. styrene, *0.0033 mol%* [(*o*-(*tert*-butylselenomethyl)-phenyl]palladium(II) acetate dimer and 1.12 eqs. NaOAc in DMAc heated at 140° under argon for 20 h → product. Y 99% (TON 30, 000). Such air- and moisture-stable Se-ligated complexes, incl. SeCSe *pincer-type* catalysts, not only rival but vastly outperform the corresponding phosphorus and sulfur analogs at very low catalyst loadings. The protocol does not require the use of any additives, and is generally applicable to activated and deactivated ar. and hetar. bromides (not chlorides). F.e. and prepn. of the catalysts s. Q. Yao, E.P. Kinney, C. Zheng, Org. Lett. *6*, 2997-9 (2004).

Palladous chloride/tetrakis(dimethylamino)ethylene/1-n-butyl-3-methylimidazolium ←
 hexafluorophosphate
Sym. diaryls from ar. halides 2 ArHal → Ar-Ar
with Pd-C/HCOONa/Na$_2$CO$_3$/Bu$_4$NBr cf. *34*, 825s*64*; from ar. iodides with PdCl$_2$/tetrakis(dimethylamino)ethylene **in ionic liquids,** e.g. 1-*n*-butyl-3-methylimidazolium hexafluorophosphate, s. S.B. Park, H. Alper, Tetrahedron Lett. *45*, 5515-7 (2004); with bis(2-chloropallada-4,4'-dichlorobenzophenone oxime) cf. D.A. Alonso, M.C. Pacheco, C. Najera, J. Org. Chem. *67*, 5588-94 (2002).

Palladous chloride/1,1'-bis(diphenylphosphino)ferrocene/sodium tert-*butoxide* ←
3-Component synthesis of α-iminoiminoesters Br → C(=NR)C(=NR)OR'

416.

A mixture of 1 eq. *p*-bromobenzonitrile, 5 eqs. ethanol, 3 eqs. cyclohexyl isocyanide, 1.2 eqs. *t*-BuONa, 5 mol% PdCl$_2$, and 10 mol% dppf in dioxane heated at 98° for 4 h → product. Y 73%. Reaction involves double insertion of the isonitrile, followed by trapping of the alkoxide, the mono-insertion product being <5% under these conditions. F.e. and comparison of ligands and bases s. R.J. Whitby, C.G. Saluste, M. Furber, Org. Biomol. Chem. *2*, 1974-6 (2004).

*Bis(η^3-allylpalladium(II) chloride)/4-*tert*-butyl-1,2-bis(diphenylphosphino)-1'-* ←
 (diisopropylphosphino)ferrocene/cuprous iodide/potassium carbonate
Sonogashira coupling at low catalyst loading C≡CH → C≡CAr

417.

A mixture of 1 eq. iodobenzene, 2 eqs. phenylacetylene, 2 eqs. K$_2$CO$_3$, 5 mol% CuI, and 0.001 mol% [(η^3-allyl)PdCl]$_2$/4-*tert*-butyl-1,2-bis(diphenylphosphino)-1'-(diisopropylphosphino)-

ferrocene in DMF heated under argon at 100° for 20 h → product. Y 95%. The new *multidentate mixed ferrocenyl aryl/alkyl phosphine* is thermally stable, insensitive to air and moisture, and is efficient at catalyst loadings ranging from 10^{-4} mol% for ar. bromides and iodides to 10^{-1} mol% for activated ar. chlorides (without CuI) with TONs up to 250, 000. F.e.s. J.-C. Hierso, H. Doucet et al., Org. Lett. *6*, 3473-6 (2004).

Chlorobis(η^1-2-ethyl-Δ^2-oxazoline)palladium(II)/potassium carbonate ←
Chloro[2-(N,N-dicyclohexylaminothiocarbonyl)furan-3-yl]palladium(II) dimer/ ←
  triethylamine
Ligand-free Heck arylation at low catalyst loading s. *51*, 416s68   H → Ar

Dichlorobis(triphenylphosphine)palladium(II)/triethylamine $PdCl_2(PPh_3)_2/Et_3N$
Stereospecific synthesis of cyclic δ-aryl-γ,δ-ethylenealdehydes   ○
from (Z)-2,n-enynols and ar. halides via intramolecular carbopalladation

418.

A soln. of 2 mol% $PdCl_2(PPh_3)_2$ in degassed triethylamine treated sequentially at room temp. with 1 eq. startg. enynol and 1.1 eqs. *p*-iodotoluene, the resulting mixture refluxed for 2.5 h, cooled to room temp., and ether added to effect precipitation → product. Y 85%. **Syntheses via intramolecular carbopalladation-Wittig reaction and carbopalladation-reductive N-alkylation** were also effected by trapping of the generated aldehyde *in situ*. F.e.s. C.J. Kressierer, T.J.J. Müller, Angew. Chem. Int. Ed. Engl. *43*, 5997-6000 (2004).

Dichlorobis(triphenylphosphine)palladium(II)/cuprous chloride/tetra-n-butylammonium   ←
  chloride/triethylamine
(E)-1,2-Dibenzyl-1,3-enynes   BnC≡C(Bn)C≡C
from two terminal acetylene deriv. molecules and two benzyl halide molecules s. *68, 469*

Dichlorobis(triphenylphosphine)palladium(II)/cuprous iodide/base   ←
Sonogashira coupling   C≡CH → C≡CAr
update s. *27*, 851s*67*; with ethyne *in DMF* s. S.F. Vasilevsky, S.V. Klyatskaya, J. Elguero, Tetrahedron *60*, 6685-8 (2004); with ynamides by delaying the addition of CuI to avoid homocoupling s. M.R. Tracey, R.P. Hsung et al., Org. Lett. *6*, 2209-12 (2004); coupling with bridgehead bromocyclimmonium salts s. D. Garcia, J.J. Vaquero et al., ibid. 4175-8; synthesis of 1,3,5-trisethynylbenzenes s. G. Hennrich, A.M. Echavarren, Tetrahedron Lett. *45*, 1147-9 (2004);

4-(alk-1-ynyl)-2-pyrones s. I.J.S. Fairlamb, F.J. Lu, J.P. Schmidt, Synthesis *2003*, 2564-70; Sonogashira coupling **in water** (cf. *53*, 473s*59*) with Pd(PPh$_3$)$_4$/CuI/*i*-Pr$_2$NEt s. S. Bhattacharya, S. Sengupta, Tetrahedron Lett. *45*, 8733-6 (2004); **in aq. ammonia** s. M.S.M. Ahmed, A. Mori, Tetrahedron *60*, 9977-82 (2004); **polymer-based Sonogashira coupling in water** with dichlorobis(di-*tert*-butylphosphinous acid)palladium(II)/CuI/pyrrolidine/tetra-*n*-butylammonium bromide s. C. Wolf, R. Lerebours, Org. Biomol. Chem. *2*, 2161-4 (2004); in DMF cf. Y. Kashiwagi, J.I. Anzai et al., Synlett *2004*, 2513-6; **at low catalyst loading** with Tedicyp as ligand (cf. *62*, 403s*66*) for coupling ar. bromides with alkynols s. M. Feuerstein, H. Doucet, M. Santelli, Tetrahedron Lett. *45*, 1603-6 (2004); under continuous flow with a polymer-tagged complex s. J. Hillerich, H. Plenio, Chem. Commun. *2003*, 3024-5.

Dichlorobis(triphenylphosphine)palladium(II)/cuprous iodide/potassium carbonate/ sodium lauryl sulfate
α,β-Acetyleneketones H → COR
from terminal acetylene derivs. and carboxylic acid chlorides
s. *33*, 830s*62*; **in water** with Na-lauryl sulfate as surfactant and K_2CO_3 as base s. L. Chen, C.-J. Li, Org. Lett. *6*, 3151-3 (2004); ferrocenylethynyl ketones s. J. Yin, B. Chen et al., Synthesis *2004*, 331-3.

Dichlorobis(triphenylphosphine)palladium(II)/cuprous iodide/triethylamine
Cyclic sulfoximines by palladium-catalyzed ring closure
2,1-S(VI)-benzothiazine S-oxides cf. *57*, 377; 1,2-S(VI)-benzothiazine S-oxides from terminal acetylene derivs. and *o*-halogenosulfoximines with PdCl$_2$(PPh$_3$)$_2$/CuI/Et$_3$N s. M. Harmata et al., Org. Lett. *7*, 143-5 (2005).

Palladium-catalyzed ring closures of ω-(*o*-iodoaryl)acetylenes with subsequent Sonogashira coupling-intramolecular Diels-Alder reaction

419.

A mixture of 1 eq. startg. α,β-acetylenecarboxylic acid N-(*o*-iodoaryl)amide, 1.1 eqs. startg. 1,6-enyne, 5.3 mol% PdCl$_2$(PPh$_3$)$_2$ and 4.7 mol% CuI in 1:1 degassed butyronitrile/triethylamine stirred at room temp. for 2.5 h, and refluxed for 48 h → product. Y 86%. Critical steps are the intermediate generation of configurationally stable (E)-vinylpalladium complexes, and base-catalyzed acetylene-allene isomerization to set up the inverse electron-demand intramolecular Diels-Alder reaction. F.e.s. D.M. D'Souza, F. Rominger, T.J.J. Müller, Angew. Chem. Int. Ed. Engl. *44*, 153-8 (2005).

Dichlorobis(triphenylphosphine)palladium(II)/cuprous iodide/triethylamine ←
Stereospecific 4-component synthesis
of N³-condensed 1,2,3,4-tetrahydropyrid[3,4-b]indoles
via Sonogashira acylation-Michael addition-Pictet-Spengler cyclization

A mixture of 2 mol% PdCl$_2$(PPh$_3$)$_2$ and 4 mol% CuI in degassed THF treated successively in a screw-capped pressure vessel with 1 eq. Et$_3$N, 1 eq. *p*-methoxybenzoyl chloride and 1.05 eqs. hex-1-yne, stirred under N$_2$ at room temp. for 1 h, 2 eqs. tryptamine added, heated at 70° under N$_2$ for 10 h, treated with 5 eqs. acryloyl chloride, stirred under N$_2$ for 3 h at the same temp., diluted with methanol, and stirring continued for 3 h → product. Y 59%. F.e.s. A.S. Karpov, T. Oeser, T.J.J. Müller, Chem. Commun. *2004*, 1502-3.

Dichlorobis(triphenylphosphine)palladium(II)/cuprous iodide/tri-n-propylamine ←
1-Azafluorenones via intramolecular Diels-Alder reaction
s. *40*, 669s63; one-pot procedure from terminal acetylene derivs. **via Sonogashira coupling-intramolecular Diels-Alder reaction** with PdCl$_2$(PPh$_3$)$_2$/CuI/Pr$_3$N s. T. Hundsdorf, E.V. Blyumin, H. Neunhoeffer, Synthesis *2002*, 2532-6.

*Dichlorobis(di-*tert*-butylphosphinous acid)palladium(II)/cuprous iodide/piperidine/* ←
tetra-n-butylammonium bromide
Sonogashira coupling in aq. medium s. *27*, 851s68   C≡CH → C≡CAr

Ferrocene-based dichloro(diphenylphosphinomethylphosphine enimine)palladium(II) ←
complexes/tetra-n-butylammonium acetate
Copper-free Sonogashira coupling s. *63*, 411s68

Chlorobis(N-methylimidazol-2-yl)methylpalladium(II)/1-n-butyl-3-methylimidazolium ←
hexafluorophosphate/piperidine
Copper- and phosphine-free Sonogashira coupling in ionic liquids s. *63*, 411s68

2,6-Bis[(4-tridecafluorohexylphenyl)thiomethyl]phenylpalladium(II) chloride/tri-n- ←
butylamine/microwaves
Heck arylation under microwave irradiation s. *51*, 416s68   H → Ar

Chloro(pentamethylcyclopentadienyl)hydridoiridium(III) dimer/   [Cp*Ir(H)Cl]$_2$/KOBu-t
potassium tert-butoxide
Diaryls from ar. iodides and arenes   Ar-Ar'
via iridium(III)-catalyzed radical arylation under mild conditions

A mixture of 40 eqs. benzene, 1 eq. *p*-iodoanisole, [Cp*IrHCl]$_2$ (5 mol% Ir), and 3.3 eqs. *t*-BuOK heated under argon at 80° for 30 h → product. Y 66%. A radical mechanism is invoked, this being the first example of a transition metal-catalyzed arylation of unreactive aromatic C-H bonds requiring no directing group. F.e. and arylation of toluene and anisole s. K. Fujita, M. Nonogawa, R. Yamaguchi, Chem. Commun. *2004*, 1926-7.

Via intermediates v.i.
Dihalogenomethylene compds. from iodides CHI → C=CHal$_2$
dichloromethylene compds. via α,α-dichlorosulfoxides cf. *38*, 813; **difluoromethylene compds.** via α,α-difluorosulfones with KOBu-*t* as base s. G.K.S. Prakash, G.A. Olah et al., Angew. Chem. Int. Ed. Engl. *43*, 5203-6 (2004).

Sulfur ↑   CC ↓↑ S

Microwaves s. under PdCl$_2$(dppf) [\\\\]

Sodium hydride NaH
3-Hydroxytetrahydrofurans from 2,3-epoxyalcohols ○
Regio- and stereo-specific ring expansion via Payne rearrangement

422.

Chiral 2-subst. 3-hydroxytetrahydrofurans. A soln. of 10 eqs. NaH in freshly dried DMSO treated portionwise at room temp. with 10 eqs. trimethylsulfoxonium iodide over 20-30 min, stirred at the same temp. for 30 min until bubbling ceased, a soln. of 1 eq. of the startg. chiral epoxyalcohol (0.1 *M*) in the same solvent added dropwise, stirring continued in the dark at 80-85° for 36 h, and quenched sequentially with water and satd. aq. NH$_4$Cl → product. Y 91%. Reaction proceeds with full translation of the stereochemistry, *cis*-epoxides yielding *cis*-disubst. products, and *trans*-epoxides yielding *trans*-disubst. products. F.e.s. J.M. Schomaker, V.R. Pulgam, B. Borhan, J. Am. Chem. Soc. *126*, 13600-1 (2004).

Lithium tert-butoxide t-BuOLi
Asym. synthesis of N-sulfinylaziridines from N-sulfinylimines and sulfonium salts ▽
with NaH cf. *53*, 435s67; general procedure with *t*-BuOLi s. D. Morton, R.A. Stockman et al., Org. Lett. *6*, 2377-80 (2004).

tert-Butyllithium t-BuLi
Iminocyclopentadienes ○
from zirconacyclopentadienes and isonitriles cf. *44*, 621s67; from 1,4-diiodo-1,3-dienes and isothiocyanates via 1,4-dilithio-1,3-dienes (with *t*-BuLi) s. C.-Y. Wang, Q.-L. Song, Z.-F. Xi, Tetrahedron *60*, 5207-14 (2004).

Lithium acetylides/magnesium/methyl triflate LiC≡CR/Mg/MeOTf
3-Component synthesis of 1,1-disubst. 2-acetyleneamines ←
from carboxylic acid thioamides
via sequential incorporation of lithium acetylides and Grignard compds.

423.

1 eq. Methyl triflate added to a soln. of 1 eq. startg. thioamide in anhydrous ether at room temp., the mixture stirred at the same temp. for 0.5 min, a soln. of 1.5 eqs. of the startg. alkynyllithium

in the same solvent added at 0°, stirring continued at room temp. for 0.5 h, treated with 10 eqs. allylmagnesium bromide in the same solvent, heated at 70° for 6 h, then quenched with satd. aq. NH$_4$Cl → product. Y 70%. Reaction involves preferential addition of the acetylide on the intermediate thioiminium salt, followed by preferential coupling of the resulting S,N-acetal with the Grignard compd. A wide range of alkyl-, alkynyl- and aryl-magnesium halides participated in the conversion. F.e.s. T. Murai et al., J. Am. Chem. Soc. *126*, 5968-9 (2004).

Sodium cyanide/ytterbium(III) triflate   NaCN/Yb(OTf)$_3$
Regio- and stereo-specific synthesis of alcohols
from cyclic glycol sulfates s. *49*, 843s65; **from carbohydrate cyclic glycol sulfites** for preparing *trans*-glycosyl cyanides with NaCN/Yb(OTf)$_3$ s. A. Benksim, D. Beaupere, A. Wadouachi, Org. Lett. *6*, 3913-5 (2004).

Potassium cyanide/tetra-n-butylammonium hydrogen sulfate   KCN/Bu$_4$NHSO$_4$
Synthesis of urethans from 1,1-sulfonylurethans   SO$_2$R → R'
syn-β-(carbalkoxyamino)nitriles from nitriles with *n*-BuLi cf. *60*, 408s62; α-(carbalkoxyamino)-nitriles with KCN/Bu$_4$NHSO$_4$ under phase transfer catalysis s. V. Banphavichit, T. Vilaivan et al., Synth. Commun. *34*, 3147-60 (2004).

1,8-Diazabicyclo[5.4.0]undec-7-ene   dbu
3-Alkylthio-4-nitro-2-cyclohexenones
from β,γ-ethylene-α-ketoketene mercaptals and aliphatic nitro compds.

A mixture of the startg. ketene mercaptal and 3 eqs. nitroethane in anhydrous DMF treated *at room temp.* with a soln. of *1 eq.* 1,8-diazabicyclo[5.4.0]undec-7-ene in anhydrous THF over 5 min, and stirred for 30 min. → product. Y 93%. Reaction involves initial Michael addition of the nitro compd., followed by displacement of an alkylthio group by an S$_N$V [addition-elimination] mechanism. Aromatization of the products takes place on heating with 1.5 eqs. of the base at ca. 70° over 1-1.5 h to give the corresponding **m-hydroxythioethers**. F.e. incl. biaryl derivs. s. X. Bi, D. Dong, Q. Liu et al., J. Am. Chem. Soc. *127*, 4578-9 (2005).

Magnesium s.a. under Lithium acetylides   Mg

Magnesium/dichloro[1,3-bis(diphenylphosphino)propane]nickel(II)   Mg/NiCl$_2$(dppp)
Cross-coupling of *o*-alkylthio-N-heterocyclics   SR → R'
with benzylzinc bromides using Pd(PPh$_3$)$_4$ cf. *60*, 412; 2-alkyl-Δ^1-pyrrolines by cross-coupling with Grignard compds. using NiCl$_2$(dppp), 5-stannyl-derivs., s. D.M. Mans, W.H. Pearson, J. Org. Chem. *69*, 6419-26 (2004).

Dialkylzinc/zinc/bromine/palladium-carbon/dimethylformamide   ←
Ketones from thiolic acid esters   COSR → COR'
with organozinc halides/Pd(OH)$_2$-C/Me$_3$SiCl/BrCH$_2$CH$_2$Br cf. *29*, 853s67; with alkylzinc bromides (generated *in situ* from dialkylzinc/Zn/Br$_2$) in the presence of Pd-C/DMF s. Y. Mori, M. Seki, Tetrahedron Lett. *45*, 7343-5 (2004).

Ytterbium(III) triflate s. under NaCN   Yb(OTf)$_3$

Tetra-n-*butylammonium hydrogen sulfate s. under KCN* Bu_4NHSO_4

Azodi(cyclohexanecarbonitrile) $RN\!=\!NR$
Radical syntheses with O-benzyl-1-sulfonyloximes ←
ketoximes from halides cf. *51*, 424s*64*; O-benzyl-aldoximes and -ketoximes from allyl sulfones as source of alkyl radicals (cf. *65*, 450) in the presence of azodi(cyclohexanecarbonitrile) s. S. Kim, C.J. Lim, Bull. Korean Chem. Soc. *24*, 1219-22 (2003).

tert-*Butyl isocyanide/azodiisobutyronitrile* t-*BuNC/AIBN*
Generation of alkyl radicals from mercaptans via thioimidoyl radicals ←

425.

1,2-Addition to electron-rich ethylene derivs. A soln. of 1.1 eqs. *tert*-butyl isocyanide and 10 eqs. startg. electron-rich alkene in toluene treated at 80° under N_2 with a soln. of 1 eq. α-mercaptobutyrolactone and 0.1 eq. AIBN over 1 h, and stirred at the same temp. for 1 h → product. Y 92%. In this environmentally friendly (*tin-free*!) procedure from readily accessible substrates, the catalytic cycle features C-S β-scission of intermediate thioimidoyl radicals as the key step. Work-up and purification are both straightforward. F.e. and radical ring closure of ethylenemercaptans, **also replacement of sulfhydryl groups by hydrogen,** s. L. Benati, M. Minozzi, D. Nanni et al., Angew. Chem. Int. Ed. Engl. *43*, 3598-601 (2004).

Chiral thiolanes s. under Et₂Zn ←

Titanium tetrachloride/triphenylphosphine $TiCl_4/Ph_3P$
Lewis acid-mediated reductive Claisen-type condensation CHCO-C-COSR
of α-bromothiolic acid esters

426.

(50%)

β-Ketothiolic acid esters. 1.48 eqs. Triphenylphosphine in 1 part methylene chloride added to a mixture of the startg. α-bromothiolic acid ester and 1.52 eqs. $TiCl_4$ in 3 parts dichloroethane at room temp. under argon, the mixture stirred for 1 h, then quenched with water → product. Y 76%. This is the first example of a *reductive* Claisen ester condensation, significantly avoiding the use of a strong base so that base-labile functions can be incorporated. **Crossed Claisen-type condensation** of *hindered* α-bromothiolic acid esters with thiolic acid esters was also effected under the same conditions (self-condensation being sterically inhibited). F.e. and comparison of Lewis acids, solvents and phosphines s. Y. Hashimoto, H. Konishi, S. Kikuchi, Synlett *2004*, 1264-6.

Hexabutyldistannane/di-tert-*butylhyponitrite/3-pyridylsulfonyl azide* ←
γ-Azidocarboxylic acid esters from ethylene derivs. $C\!=\!C \to C(N_3)C(R)$
Regiospecific radical synthesis with addition of two C-atoms
by addition of ethyl iodoacetate with $PhSO_2N_3$ cf. *64*, 383; by addition of S-carbethoxymethyl O-ethyl xanthate, also with 3-pyridylsulfonyl azide for a simpler work-up, s. P. Panchaud, P. Renaud, Adv. Synth. Catal. *346*, 925-8 (2004).

Triphenylphosphine s. under TiCl$_4$ Ph_3P

Phosphazene base (P4-t-Bu)   ←
Ethylene derivs. from oxo compds. and sulfones   CO→C=C
Modified Julia olefination
from 2-sulfonylpyridines cf. *38*, 861s62; (E)-ethylene derivs. from 3,5-bis(trifluoromethyl)phenyl sulfones with phosphazene base P4-*t*-Bu s. D.A. Alonso, C. Nájera, M. Varea, Tetrahedron Lett. *45*, 573-7 (2004).

Phosphorus oxide chloride/ammonium acetate $POCl_3/NH_4OAc$
Functionalized pyridines from α-ketoketene mercaptals   ○
4-alkylthiopyridines from ketones cf. *37*, 833; 2-alkylthio-4-chloropyridines with the Vilsmeier reagent (DMF/POCl$_3$) and NH$_4$OAc s. S. Sun, Q. Liu, D. Dong et al., Synlett *2004*, 1731-4.

3-Pyridylsulfonyl azide s. under Bu$_3$SnSnBu$_3$ RSO_2N_3
Dichloro[1,3-bis(diphenylphosphino)propane]nickel(II) s. under Mg $NiCl_2(dppp)$
Palladium-carbon s. under R$_2$Zn   Pd-C

Dichloro[1,1'-bis(diphenylphosphino)ferrocene]pal- $PdCl_2(dppf)/LiCl/Na_2CO_3/$[\\\\]
ladium(II)/lithium chloride/sodium carbonate/microwaves
Pyrrole ring from *o*-chlorosulfonylamines and acetylene derivs.
with simultaneous N-desulfonylation s. *27*, 851s68

Remaining Elements ↑   CC ↓↑ Rem

Without additional reagents   w.a.r.
Uncatalyzed asym. synthesis of 3-ethylenealcohols from aldehydes CHO→CH(OH)C-C=C
and chiral Si-allyl-Si-chloro-1,3,2-diazasilacyclopentanes s. *64*, 406; regiospecific, diastereoselective and asym. nucleophilic crotylation s. B.M. Hackman, P.J. Lombardi, J.L. Leighton, Org. Lett. *6*, 4375-7 (2004).

3-Ethylene-*prim*-amines   CH(NH$_2$)C-C=C
from aldehydes and β,γ-ethyleneboronic acid esters

427.

with asym. induction. 1.2 eqs. Startg. allylboronate in anhydrous ethanol added to a mixture of ca. 40 eqs. liq. ammonia in the same solvent at -78°, stirred at 0° for 30 min, treated with 1 eq. startg. chiral α-oxyaldehyde (e.e. 94%) in the same solvent, and stirring continued at 0° for 12 h → product. Y 67% (e.e. 95%; *syn/anti* 85:15). This is the first example of such an incorporation of ammonia, the procedure being environmentally friendly and generally applicable to a range of aliphatic (incl. enolizable derivs.), aromatic (possessing electron-withdrawing or -donating substituents), heteroaromatic and α,β-ethylenic aldehydes. Furthermore, high *syn*-selectivity was recorded with chiral α-oxyaldehydes, while substituted β,γ-ethyleneboronic acid esters reacted regiospecifically **with double bond shift.** There was no reaction, however, with benzylamine or isopropylamine. F.e. and procedure with aq. ammonia s. M. Sugiura, K. Hirano, S. Kobayashi, J. Am. Chem. Soc. *126*, 7182-3 (2004).

α-Ketocarboxylic acid amides from carboxylic acid chlorides   COCl→CO-CON<
Synthesis with addition of one C-atom

428.

A soln. of acetyl chloride in benzene treated dropwise under argon with 1.4 eqs. trimethyl(N,N-dimethylcarbamyl)silane, and the mixture stirred in a sealed vial at room temp. for 12 h →

product. Y 81%. Reaction avoids the use of carbon monoxide and tin-containing reagents, and is thought to involve an intermediate O-acylisoimidium salt which undergoes 1,2-acyl migration. In certain instances the product reacts with a second molecule of the silane, but this can be minimized at lower temperature (-78°). F.e. and with retention of ester groups and chlorine s. J. Chen, R.F. Cunico, J. Org. Chem. *69*, 5509-11 (2004).

Phenols from 1,3-disiloxy-1,3-dienes ○
o-hydroxyketones s. *36*, 885; phenols from electron-deficient acetylene derivs. via Diels-Alder reaction (cf. *34*, 625) s. A. Barbero, F.J. Pulido, Synthesis *2004*, 401-4.

Microwaves (s.a. under KOBu-t, 1,8-Diazabicyclo[5.4.0]undec-7-ene and [\\\\]
Palladium complexes)
Methylene from carbonyl compds. $CO \rightarrow C{=}CH_2$
with Tebbe's reagent cf. *35*, 622; α-alkoxyacrylic from unsym. oxalic acid esters with Cp_2TiMe_2 under microwaves s. M.J. Cook, D.W. Fleming, T. Gallagher, Tetrahedron Lett. *46*, 297-300 (2005).

Lithium hydroxide s. under AgOTf LiOH

Lithium tert-butoxide/hydrogen peroxide/sodium hydroxide $LiOBu\text{-}t/H_2O_2/NaOH$
Carboxylic acids from cyclic bor(o,i)nic acid derivs. $B(OR)R' \rightarrow COOH$
Synthesis with addition of one C-atom
from B-alkyl-1,3,2-dithiaborolanes with $HCCl_3/n$-BuLi cf. *39*, 844; from B-alkyl-9-oxa-10-borabicyclo[3.3.2]decanes with dichloromethyl methyl ether/LiOBu-*t*, with retention of configuration, s. J.A. Soderquist et al., Tetrahedron Lett. *45*, 5541-3 (2004).

Potassium tert-butoxide/microwaves KOBu-t/[\\\\]
3-Alkylideneoxindoles ○
from α-aminooxy-α-phosphonylacetic acid anilides and aldehydes via radical ring closure-Horner synthesis

429.

A soln. of 1 eq. startg. TEMPO-substituted phosphonate in anhydrous DMF irradiated with microwaves in an MLS high-pressure reaction vessel (up to 15 bar) at 180° for 2 min under argon (after three 10 second pulses of irradiation between 25 and 180°), the resulting mixture allowed to cool to room temp., treated with 1.2 eqs. *t*-BuOK and 10 eqs. startg. aldehyde, irradiation continued at 180° for another 6 min, then quenched with satd. aq. Na_2SO_3 → product. Y 87%. In this one-pot coupling of a radical and an ionic process, the key step is *microwave-assisted homolytic cleavage* of the aminooxy residue (mediated by a *persistent* radical effect), followed by intramolecular radical addition to the benzene ring. F.e. and with the N-benzylanilide s. A. Teichert, A. Studer et al., Org. Lett. *6*, 3477-80 (2004).

n-*Butyllithium* BuLi
1-Alkoxycycloheptene ring from transition metal alkoxycarbene complexes
3-alkoxy-2-cycloheptenones cf. *59*, 411; 3-alkoxy-3,5-cycloheptadienols from tungsten 2,4-diene(alkoxy)carbene complexes and enoxysilanes, stereoselectivity, s. J. Barluenga et al., Angew.

Chem. Int. Ed. Engl. *43*, 5510-3 (2004); **3,4-di(alkylidene)cycloheptanones** from chromium α,β-ethylene(alkoxy)carbene complexes and two allene molecules with Ni(cod)$_2$, also 2,4-di-(alkylidene)-derivs. under rhodium catalysis, s. J. Am. Chem. Soc. *126*, 14354-5 (2004).

n-*Butyllithium/dichloro[1,2-bis(diphenylphosphino)ethane]nickel(II)*   *BuLi/NiCl$_2$(dppe)*
1,3-Enynes from enetellurides and terminal acetylene derivs.   C≡C-C≡C
with PdCl$_2$/CuI/Et$_3$N cf. *57*, 442s*62*, *67*; (Z)-1,3-enynes from Li-acetylides with *n*-BuLi/NiCl$_2$(dppe) s. C. Raminelli, J.V. Comasseto et al., Tetrahedron Lett. *45*, 4927-30 (2004).

sec-*Butyllithium/hexamethylphosphoramide*   s-*BuLi/HMPA*
Peterson olefination   CO → C=C
(E)-α,β-ethylenecarboxylic acid selenoamides s. *28*, 856s*66*; α,β-ethylene-α-(silylmethyl)-carboxylic acid esters with *s*-BuLi/HMPA s. H. Suzuki, S. Ohta, C. Kuroda, Synth. Commun. *34*, 1383-92 (2004); (Z)-α,β-ethylenenitriles with KN(SiMe$_3$)$_2$ or *n*-BuLi s. S. Kojima, Y. Murai et al., Org. Lett. *6*, 3197-20 (2004).

tert-*Butyllithium/hexamethylphosphoramide*   t-*BuLi/HMPA*
3-Component synthesis of 2-ethylenealcohols from aldehydes   ←
with insertion of three C-atoms

430.

via Brook rearrangement. A soln. of 2-bromoallyltrimethylsilane in dry THF treated under argon at -78° with 2 eqs. *t*-BuLi (1.7 *M* in hexanes), stirred for 1 h, 1 eq. benzaldehyde added, stirring continued for 3 h, treated with 4 eqs. HMPA and 3 eqs. allyl bromide, warmed to 0° in an ice bath, gradually warmed to room temp. with stirring overnight, and quenched with 1 *M* aq. HCl → product. Y 69%. Initial bromine-lithium exchange affords 2-lithioallyltrimethylsilane, which adds to the aldehyde prior to HMPA-mediated Brook rearrangement and quenching of the generated, highly active allyl anion with the second electrophile. Reaction is applicable to aryl, aliphatic and α,β-ethylenic aldehydes as startg. m. F.e. and electrophiles s. A.B. Smith III, M.O. Duffey, Synlett *2004*, 1363-6.

Sodium bis(trimethylsilyl)amide   NaN(SiMe$_3$)$_2$
(Z)-1-Chloro-3,1-enynes from aldehydes   CHO → CH=C-C≡CCl
Synthesis with addition of three C-atoms

431.

A mixture of 1.6 eqs. 3,3,3-trichloropropyl(triphenyl)phosphonium chloride in anhydrous THF cooled to -45°, treated dropwise with a suspension of 1.4 eqs. NaN(SiMe$_3$)$_2$ in the same solvent, stirred for 20 min while the temp. increased to -35°, chilled to -78°, a soln. of 1 eq. startg. aldehyde in the same solvent added dropwise, treated dropwise with a further 2.5 eqs. of the base in the same solvent while the temp. was allowed to rise to -50°, and quenched at the same temp. with satd. aq. NH$_4$Cl → product. Y 95% (Z/E 92:8). With 1.4 eqs. NaN(SiMe$_3$)$_2$ *in toluene* the corresponding **(Z)-3-ethylene-1,1,1-trichlorides** were formed, these being converted to **(Z,Z)-1-chloro-1,3-dienes** (with CrCl$_2$) and **1,1-dichloro-1,3-dienes** (with dbu). F.e. and conversion of the products to **terminal 1,3-diynes** (with *t*-BuLi/KOBu-*t*) s. M.S. Karatholuvhu, P.L. Fuchs, J. Am. Chem. Soc. *126*, 14314-5 (2004).

Sodium bis(trimethylsilyl)amide/tetra-n-butylammonium fluoride   *NaN(SiMe$_3$)$_2$/Bu$_4$NF*
(E)-α,β-Ethylenealdehydes from halides under mild conditions   Hal → CH=CHCHO
Metalated *trans*-3-(*tert*-butyldimethylsilyl)-2,3-epoxypropyl *p*-tolyl sulfone
as acrolein β-carbanion equivalent

432.

A soln. of 1 eq. NaN(SiMe$_3$)$_2$ in THF added to a mixture of *trans*-3-(*tert*-butyldimethylsilyl)-2,3-epoxypropyl *p*-tolyl sulfone and 1 eq. benzyl bromide in the same solvent at -80°, allowed to warm to -60° over 30 min, recooled to -85° before successive addition of 3 eqs. ethanol (to aid solubility) in THF and 1 eq. Bu$_4$NF in the same solvent, allowed to warm to -70° over 15 min, and diluted with water → product. Y 85%. Reaction involves base-promoted cleavage of the epoxide ring, followed by Brook rearrangement and terminates by displacement of the sulfonyl group. Silyl ethers and esters were left intact. F.e. and comparison of leaving groups, **also (E)-α,β-ethylene-γ-hydroxyaldehydes from aldehydes**, s. M. Sasaki, K. Takeda, Org. Lett. *6*, 4849-51 (2004).

Lithium acetate   *LiOAc*
Base-catalyzed Mannich-type reaction in aq. media s *63*, 424s*68*   C(=N-) → C(NH-)C-CO

Potassium carbonate/tetra-n-butylammonium bromide   *K$_2$CO$_3$/Bu$_4$NBr*
Wittig synthesis of α,β-ethylenehalides   CO → C=C(Hal)
(Z)-α-bromo-α,β-ethyleneketones s. *35*, 607s*65*; **(Z)-α,β-ethylene-α-iodocarboxylic acid esters** with K$_2$CO$_3$/Bu$_4$NBr s. X.-G. Zhang, P. Zhong, F. Chen, Synth. Commun. *34*, 1729-36 (2004).

Potassium cyanide   *KCN*
(E)-α-Alkylideneadipic   C(OAc)C=CH$_2$ → C=C-CH$_2$CH$_2$COOR
from β-acoxy-α-methylenecarboxylic acid esters
Synthesis with addition of two C-atoms under mild conditions

433.

(E)-α-Arylideneadipic acid esters. A stirred soln. of the startg. Baylis-Hillman acetate and 1 eq. (carbethoxymethylene)triphenylphosphorane in THF heated to reflux for 15 h, 1 eq. aq. KCN added, and stirred at 60° for 10 h → product. Y 90%. Reaction involves a novel S$_N$2′ displacement with the phosphorane, followed by elimination. Nitrile analogs were obtained similarly as mixtures of E/Z isomers. F.e.s. Y.J. Im, J.E. Na, J.N. Kim, Bull. Korean Chem. Soc. *24*, 511-3 (2003).

Potassium fluoride (s.a. under CuI and [Rh(MeCN)$_2$(cod)]BF$_4$)   *KF*
Cyclopropanes from ethylene derivs.   ▽
and phosphonium salts cf. *29*, 872; **cyclopropyl ketones from 2-ketoarsonium salts** with KF·2H$_2$O s. Z.J. Ren, L.-L. Wang et al., Synth. Commun. *34*, 3785-92 (2004).

Potassium fluoride-alumina s. under PdCl$_2$(PPh$_3$)$_2$ KF-Al$_2$O$_3$
Cesium fluoride s.a. under CuI, NiBr$_2$ and Palladium complexes   CsF

Cesium fluoride/4-[2-(2-ethoxyethoxy)ethyl]-4-methylmorpholinium triflimide   ←
2,2,2-Trifluoroalcohols from oxo compds.   CO → C(OH)CF$_3$
and trifluoromethyl(trimethyl)silane with Bu$_4$NF/HCl cf. *44*, 577; with CsF (10 mol%) in 4-[2-(2-ethoxyethoxy)ethyl]-4-methylmorpholinium triflimide **as ionic liquid**, also with Ph$_3$P in place of CsF, and synthesis of 1,1,1-trifluorides from halides with CuI/KF, s. J. Kim, J.M. Shreeve, Org. Biomol. Chem. 2, 2728-34 (2004).

Lithium salt   Li$^+$
Lewis base-catalyzed aldol-type condensation   CHO → CH(OH)C-COOR
with LiNPh$_2$ cf. *63*, 424, and with LiOAc cf. *63*, 424s66; *self-promoted* aldol-type condensation with aldehydes possessing Lewis basic sites, e.g. COOLi, COONBu$_4$ or N-sodio derivs., s. T. Nakagawa, H. Fujisawa, T. Mukaiyama, Chem. Lett. *33*, 92-3 (2004); **base-catalyzed Mannich-type reaction** in aq. media with LiOAc s. E. Takahashi, H. Fujisawa, T. Mukaiyama, ibid. 936-7.

Tetra-n-butylammonium phenoxide   [Bu$_4$N]OPh
3,4-Dihydro-2-pyrones
from α,β-ethyleneketones and O-silyl O-aryl keteneacetals
via Lewis base-catalyzed Michael addition-lactonization

434.

A soln. of chalcone in THF and a soln. of 1.6 eqs. startg. O-silyl O-phenyl keteneacetal in the same solvent added to 5 mol% tetra-*n*-butylammonium phenoxide in THF (0.1 *M*) in THF at -78°, stirred at the same temp. for 0.5 h, then quenched with 1 *M* aq. HCl → product. Y 99%. The catalyzed cycle is facilitated by elimination of phenoxide at the lactonization phase. There was no such reaction with O-silyl O-methyl keteneacetals, but O-silyl S-*tert*-butyl ketene-O,S-acetals gave moderate yields. Alkyl and aryl substitution of the enone was tolerated. F.e. and comparison of bases s. T. Tozawa, H. Fujisawa, T. Mukaiyama, Chem. Lett. *33*, 1454-5 (2004).

Dibenzylamine/1-n-butyl-3-methylimidazolium fluoroborate   Bn$_2$NH/[bmim]BF$_4$
3-Chromenes from *o*-hydroxyaldehydes and α,β-ethyleneboronic acids
with poly[4-(N-benzylaminomethyl)styrene] cf. *60*, 427; with dibenzylamine **in ionic liquids**, e.g. 1-*n*-butyl-3-methylimidazolium fluoroborate, s. G.W. Kabalka, B. Venkataiah, B.C. Das, Synlett *2004*, 2194-6.

Chiral 1,2-diamines s. under Cu(OTf)$_2$ and ZnF$_2$ ←

1,8-Diazabicyclo[5.4.0]undec-7-ene   dbu
Horner synthesis   CO → C=C
s. *39*, 854s66; α-carbalkoxyamino-α,β-ethylenecarboxylic acid esters s. G. Su et al., Synth. Commun. *34*, 665-71 (2004).

1,8-Diazabicyclo[5.4.0]undec-7-ene/microwaves   dbu/[\\\\]
Wittig synthesis
s. *39*, 854s67; with cyclohexanones under microwave irradiation in DMF, effect of temperature on *exo/endo*-selectivity, s. J.-L. Wu, W.-M. Dai et al., Tetrahedron Lett. *45*, 4401-4 (2004).

Pyridine   C$_5$H$_5$N
α-Arylation with aryllead tricarboxylates   H → Ar
s. *45*, 542; *36*, 877s64; in pyridine (cf. *36*, 877), also N-arylation, s. A.Y. Fedorov, J.P. Finet, Eur. J. Org. Chem. *2004*, 2040-5.

Chiral 2,2'-bipyridyls s. under Sc(OTf)$_3$ ←

Chiral 2,2'-bipyridine N,N'-dioxides or (R)-2-(1-naphthyl)-3-methylquinoline ←
N-oxide or chiral 2,2':6',2''-terpyridyl tri-N-oxides/ethyldiisopropylamine
Asym. synthesis of 3-ethylenealcohols from aldehydes   CHO → CH(OH)C-C=C
and 2-ethylene(trichloro)silanes with chiral N-oxides s. *55*, 433s*64*, *66*; with (R)-3,3'-bis(hydroxymethyl)-6,6'-bis(4-methoxy-3,5-dimethylphenyl)-2,2'-bipyridine N,N'-dioxide s. A. Kina, T. Shimada, T. Hayashi, Adv. Synth. Catal. *346*, 1169-74 (2004); enhanced enantioselectivity with *monodentate* (R)-2-(1-naphthyl)-3-methylquinoline N-oxide s. M. Nakajima et al., Tetrahedron Lett. *45*, 61-4 (2004); with chiral 2,2':6',2''-terpyridyl tri-N-oxides s. W.-L. Wong, H.-L. Kwong et al., Org. Biomol. Chem. *2*, 1967-9 (2004).

Chiral copper(II) bis(Δ^2-oxazolines) ←
Vinylogous asym. aldol-type condensation ←
using CuF$_2$/(S)-2,2'-bis(di-*p*-tolylphosphino)-1,1'-binaphthyl cf. *55*, 434; with α-ketocarboxylic acid esters using chiral copper(II) bis(Δ^2-oxazolines), e.g. [2,2-bis[(4(S)-2-methoxy-5-*tert*-butylphenyl)-2-oxazolin-2-yl]propane]copper(II) chloride, s. J.C.D. Le, B.L. Pagenkopf, Org. Lett. *6*, 4097-9 (2004).

Cuprous thiophene-2-carboxylate s. under Pd(PPh$_3$)$_4$ RCOOCu
Cupric fluoroborate s. under Palladium complexes   Cu(BF$_4$)$_2$

Cupric triflate   Cu(OTf)$_2$
β-Functionalized sec. amines   C=N → C(NH)R
from aldimines and α-functionalized stannanes
O-protected 2-aminoalcohols from 1,1-hydroxystannanes cf. *58*, 447s*66*; 2-aminothioethers from 1,1-stannylthioethers s. H. Kagoshima, N. Takahashi, Chem. Lett. *33*, 962-3 (2004).

Cupric triflate/chiral diamines/hexafluoroisopropanol ←
Asym. Mannich-type reaction   C=N- → C(NH-)C-CO
chiral β-acylaminoketones s. *63*, 427s*66*; chiral α-(carbalkoxyamino)-γ-ketophosphonic acid esters with (1R,2R)-N,N'-bis(1-naphthylmethyl)-1,2-diphenylethylenediamine/hexafluoroisopropanol s. S. Kobayashi, Y. Nakamura, R. Matsubara et al., J. Am. Chem. Soc. *126*, 6558-9 (2004).

Cupric triflate/(S)-N-[2-(2,4,6-triisopropylbenzylamino)phenyl]-S-methyl-S- ←
phenylsulfoximine/2,2,2-trifluoroethanol
Asym. aldol-type condensation   CO → C(OH)C-CO
with Cu(OTf)$_2$/chiral bis(Δ^2-oxazolines) in aq. media cf. *56*, 422s*58*; chiral α-hydroxy-γ-ketocarboxylic acid esters with chiral aminosulfoximes as ligand, e.g. (S)-N-[2-(2,4,6-triisopropylbenzylamino)phenyl]-S-methyl-S-phenylsulfoximine/CF$_3$CH$_2$OH s. M. Langner, C. Bolm, Angew. Chem. Int. Ed. Engl. *43*, 5984-7 (2004).

Cuprous chloride s.a. under Bis(η^3-allylpalladium chloride)   CuCl

Cuprous chloride/2,2'-bipyridyl or Cuprous iodide/cesium fluoride ←
Sym. 1,3-dienes from enestannanes   2 C=C(Sn≤) → C=C-C=C
with Cu(NO$_3$)$_2$ cf. *43*, 847; sym. (E,E)-1,3-dienes with CuCl/2,2'-bipyridyl, polyfluoro-derivs., s. Y.-C. Shen, G.-P. Wang, Chinese J. Chem. *22*, 894-5 (2004); **from enesilanes** (Si-2-pyridyl derivs.) with CuI/CsF s. K. Itami, J.I. Yoshida et al., Org. Lett. *6*, 3695-8 (2004).

Cuprous chloride/benzaldehyde   CuCl/PhCHO
Copper(I)-mediated coupling of zirconacyclics with halides ←
s. *54*, 444s.*59*; 1,7-dienes from [bicyclic] 2-methylzirconacyclopentanes and allyl halides, also further electrophiles, s. Z.-F. Xi, T. Takahashi et al., Chem. Lett. *33*, 1110-1 (2004).

Cuprous bromide/microwaves   CuBr/\\\\]
Cuprous bromide/trimethylaluminum/aluminum bromide   CuBr/Me$_3$Al/AlBr$_3$
Alkoxy-3-ethylenes from acetals and 2-ethylenesilanes   C(OR)$_2$ → C(OR)C-C=C
with TiCl$_4$ cf. *33*, 874; with CuBr (1 eq.) under microwave irradiation s. M.E. Jung, A. Maderna,

J. Org. Chem. *69*, 7755-7 (2004); with CuBr (0.1 eq.) in the presence of Me$_3$Al (1 mol%) and AlBr$_3$ (0.1 eq.) s. Tetrahedron Lett. *45*, 5301-4 (2004).

Cuprous bromide/(R)-1-[2-(diphenylphosphino)-1-naphthyl]isoquinoline CuBr/Quinap
3-Component asym. synthesis of propargylamines from aldehydes CHO → CH(N<)C≡CH

435.

A mixture of 5 mol% CuBr and 5.5 mol% (R)-Quinap in anhydrous toluene stirred at room temp. for 30 min, treated successively with 4 Å molecular sieves, 1 eq. trimethylsilylacetylene, 1 eq. butanal, and 1 eq. dibenzylamine, and stirring continued at the same temp. for 120 h → product. Y 88% (e.e. 90%). Although reaction times are long, both yields and enantioselectivities are very high, and the chiral reagent can be simply recycled up to three times with no significant loss of activity. Hindered dibenzylamine facilitated the high enantioselectivity and the benzyl groups can be readily removed by hydrogenation. F.e. with aryl, aliphatic and α,β-ethylenic aldehydes, also with retention of ester groups and bromine, s. N. Gommermann, P. Knochel, Chem. Commun. *2004*, 2324-5.

Cuprous iodide s.a. under CuCl, Zn and Palladium complexes CuI

Cuprous iodide/potassium fluoride/4-[2-(2-ethoxyethoxy)ethyl]-4-methylmorpholinium ←
triflimide
1,1,1-Trifluorides from halides in ionic liquids s. *44*, 577s68 Hal → CF$_3$

Cupric fluoride/1,2-bis((R,R)-2,5-diisopropylphospholan-1-yl)benzene/lanthanum ←
triisopropoxide
Asym. allylboration of ketones CO → C(OH)C-C=C

436.

A mixture of 3 mol% CuF$_2$·2H$_2$O and 6 mol% (R,R)-*i*-Pr-DuPHOS refluxed in anhydrous methanol for 2 h, the solvent removed, the resulting amorphous residue coevaporated with anhydrous toluene twice, treated with 4.5 mol% La(OPr-*i*)$_3$ (0.2 M in THF), the solvent removed under vacuum, the resulting yellow solid dissolved in anhydrous DMF, cooled to -40°, treated sequentially with 1.2 eqs. startg. crotylboronate and a soln. of 1 eq. acetophenone in anhydrous DMF, stirred at the same temp. for 1 h, and quenched with 10% aq. citric acid → product. Y 94% (*syn/anti* 84:16; e.e. *syn*-isomer 87%; e.e. *anti*-isomer 74%). Reaction proceeds with high enantio- and regio-selectivity, and is the first instance of an asym. allylation of ketones with a crotylboronate. The copper salt activates the boronate, presumably by intermediate formation of an active allylcopper species, while La(OPr-*i*)$_3$ serves a dual role: as Lewis acid to activate the ketone, and to facilitate the dynamic B→Cu transmetalation. The protocol is applicable to ar., hetar., aliphatic, cyclic and α,β-unsatd. ketones. F.e.s. R. Wada, M. Kanai, M. Shibasaki et al., J. Am. Chem. Soc. *126*, 8910-1 (2004).

Silver triflate/lithium hydroxide/triethylamine   *AgOTf/LiOH/Et$_3$N*
trans-α,β-Epoxyketones
from aldehydes and α,β-acetyleneselenonium salts

437.

6 eqs. Anhydrous LiOH and 4 eqs. Et$_3$N added sequentially to a mixture of the startg. aldehyde, 4 eqs. of the startg. alkynylselenonium salt and 4 eqs. AgOTf in 4:1 methylene chloride/acetonitrile, stirred for 2 h at room temp., and quenched with water → *trans*-product. Y 92%. Reaction involves intermediate formation of a 2-ketoselenonium ylid, which is trapped with the aldehyde prior to ring closure. F.e. with ar. or aliphatic aldehydes, **also 2-acyl-1-tosylaziridines** with N-sodio-*p*-toluenesulfonamide, s. S. Watanabe, S. Asaka, T. Kataoka, Tetrahedron Lett. *45*, 7459-63 (2004).

Zinc/palladous chloride/cuprous iodide   *Zn/PdCl$_2$/CuI*
Palladium-catalyzed cross-coupling with enetellurides   C=C(TeR) → C=C(R')
review s. *27*, 851s*65*; coupling with hetarylzinc halides in the presence of PdCl$_2$/CuI with retention of configuration, also cross-coupling with ar. tellurides, s. G. Zeni, C.W. Nogueira et al., Tetrahedron Lett. *45*, 4823-6 (2004).

Diethylzinc/(S)-1,1'-bi-2-naphthol   *Et$_2$Zn/(S)-BINOL*
2,3-Dihydro-4-pyridones by Lewis acid-catalyzed asym. hetero-Diels-Alder reaction   ○
with AgOAc/chiral α-[*o*-(diphenylphosphino)benzylideneamino]carboxylic acid amides cf. *65*, 434; with Et$_2$Zn/(S)-BINOL s. S. Guillarme, A. Whiting, Synlett *2004*, 711-3; chiral N-phosphoryl derivs. s. L. Di Bari, S. Guillarme et al., ibid. 708-10.

Diethylzinc/1-[diphenyl(hydroxy)methyl]-2-(4(S)-tert-butyl-Δ^2-oxazolin-2-yl)ferrocene   ←
Asym. synthesis of sec. benzylalcohols from aldehydes   CHO → CH(OH)Ar

438.

A soln. of 3 eqs. diethylzinc in heptane (1 *M*) added via syringe to a sealed vial containing a soln. of 1 eq. triphenylborane in freshly-distilled toluene under argon, stirred for 45 min at room temp., 10 mol% 1-[diphenyl(hydroxy)methyl]-2-(4(S)-*tert*-butyl-Δ^2-oxazolin-2-yl)ferrocene in the same solvent added via syringe, stirring continued for 30 min at the same temp., chilled to 10° and stirred again for 10 min, a pre-chilled (10°), argon-flushed soln. of 4-chlorobenzaldehyde in toluene added via syringe, stirred at the same temp. for 12 h, then quenched with water and diluted with 20% aq. acetic acid → product. Y 98% (e.e. 97%). The procedure is less expensive than the classical route with diphenylzinc, and was performed on ar. and aliphatic aldehydes with higher enantioselectivities. Furthermore, the chiral reagent was readily recovered and reused. F.e. and large-scale procedure s. J. Rudolph, F. Schmidt, C. Bolm, Adv. Synth. Catal. *346*, 867-72 (2004).

Zinc fluoride/chiral diamines/hexadecyltrimethylammonium bromide ←
Zinc chloride $ZnCl_2$
Asym. Mannich-type reaction with N-acylhydrazones in aq. medium CH(NHNHAc)C-CO
in aq. THF with added CF_3SO_3H cf. *63*, 430; **in water** with added hexadecyltrimethylammonium bromide (2 mol%) s. T. Hamada, K. Manabe, S. Kobayashi, J. Am. Chem. Soc. *126*, 7768-9 (2004); Mannich-type reaction with chiral N-(2-oxazolidon-3-yl)imines using $ZnCl_2$ **with asym. induction** s. M.F. Jacobsen, L. Ionita, T. Skrydsrup, J. Org. Chem. *69*, 4792-6 (2004).

Diisobutylaluminum hydride/potassium carbonate $i\text{-}Bu_2AlH/K_2CO_3$
Terminal acetylene derivs. from aldehydes CHO → C≡CH
with dimethyl 2-oxopropylphosphonate/TsN_3/K_2CO_3 cf. *36*, 864s*67*; **from carboxylic acid esters** or hydroxamic acid esters via *in situ*-generated aldehydes with i-Bu_2AlH/dimethyl 1-diazo-2-oxopropylphosphonate/K_2CO_3, retention of chirality, s. H.D. Dickson, S.C. Smith, K.W. Hinkle, Tetrahedron Lett. *45*, 5597-9 (2004).

Trialkylboranes R_3B
Radical ring closures of ethylenealkoximes ○
s. *54*, 299s*61*; synthesis of 5-alkoxyamino-5,6-dihydro-2*H*-1,2-oxazin-3(4*H*)-ones with trialkylboranes as source of alkyl radicals, stereoselectivity, and f. conversion to β-*prim*-amino-γ-lactones or 1-alkoxy-4-α-oxy-2-azetidinones s. O. Miyata, M. Ueda, T. Naito et al., Org. Biomol. Chem. *2*, 1274-6 (2004).

Tris(pentafluorophenyl)borane $(C_6F_5)_3B$
1,5-Enynes from acoxy-2-acetylenes and 2-ethylenesilanes OAc → C-C≡C

439.

5 Mol% Tris(pentafluorophenyl)borane in anhydrous methylene chloride added to a stirred mixture of the startg. acoxy-2-acetylene and 1.5 eqs. allyltrimethylsilane in the same solvent, stirred at room temp. for 1 h, filtered, and concentrated → product. Y 95%. No allenic side-products are detected during the course of the reaction. Bis-propargylic acetates provided enediyne products. Reaction with allyl acetates and pivalates required days for completion, while allyl trichloro- and trifluoro-acetates afforded lower yields. It is, however, applicable to a wide range of substituted acetylene derivs., and notably accelerated by electron-withdrawing groups in the aromatic ring. F.e. and with allyl carbonates s. T. Schwier, M. Rubin, V. Gevorgyan, Org. Lett. *6*, 1999-2001 (2004).

Trimethylaluminum s. under CuBr Me_3Al

Cyclic aminoboranes/2-piperidone ←
3-Component Mannich-type reaction with asym. induction CHO → CH(N<)C-COOR
via aminoborane-mediated generation of azomethinium salts under mild conditions

440.

Chiral β-aminocarboxylic acid esters. A soln. of 1 eq. (4*H*-benzo[1,3,2]-dioxaborinin-2-yl)-diisopropylamine in N-methyl-2-pyrrolidone treated with 20 mol% 2-piperidone, 1.52 eqs.

benzaldehyde and 1 eq. startg. chiral sec. amine, followed by 1.04 eqs. of the startg. O-silyl O-alkyl keteneacetal, stirred at room temp. for 1-3 h, treated with ice water and *tert*-butyl methyl ether with stirring, the organic phase extracted with 0.5 M aq. HCl, the acidic phase washed with *tert*-butyl methyl ether at -10°, concd. ammonia added to pH 8, then extracted with *tert*-butyl methyl ether → product. Y 88% (d.r. 91:9). The procedure is applicable to ar. and aliphatic aldehydes, incl. enolizable derivs., and leaves acetals, urethans, phenolethers, and ethers unaffected. F.e. and comparison of aminoboranes in achiral conversions, also with β,β-disubst. O-silyl O-alkyl keteneacetals, s. M. Suginome, L. Uehlin, M. Murakami, J. Am. Chem. Soc. *126*, 13196-7 (2004).

Chiral 1-(2-phenyl-3-tosyl-1,3,2-oxazaborolidin-5-on-4-yl)ethyl carboxylates/ ←
*2,6-diisopropylphenol/*tert-*butyl methyl ether*
Asym. Michael-type addition to α,β-ethyleneketones C=C → CHC(R)
chiral δ-ketothiolic acid esters s. *62*, 429; enhancement of enantioselectivity by addition of S-*tert*-butyl O-dimethyl(hydrido)silyl ketene O,S-acetal to acyclic enones with *t*-BuOMe as additive s. T. Harada, S. Adachi, X. Wang, Org. Lett. *6*, 4877-9 (2004).

Indium(III) triflate/2,6-bis(4(S)-isopropyl-5,5-diphenyl-Δ²-oxazolin-2-yl)pyridine/ ←
trimethylsilyl chloride
3-Ethylenealcohols from aldehydes CHO → CH(OH)CH$_2$CH=CH$_2$
Asym. synthesis with addition of three C-atoms

441.

0.22 eqs. 2,6-Bis(4(S)-isopropyl-5,5-diphenyl-2-oxazolin-2-yl)pyridine added to a mixture of 0.2 eqs. In(OTf)$_3$ and 4 Å molecular sieves in methylene chloride at room temp. under N$_2$, stirred for 2 h, the startg. aldehyde and 1.2 eqs. trimethylsilyl chloride in methylene chloride added to the suspension, cooled to -60° for 15 min, treated with 1.2 eqs. allyltributylstannane, stirred at the same temp. for 30 h, warmed to room temp., and quenched with satd. NaHCO$_3$ → product. Y 81% (e.e. 94%). The protocol is applicable to aromatic, aliphatic and α,β-ethylenic aldehydes with high enantioselectivity, and the chiral auxiliary can be easily recovered without racemization. F.e. and comparison of indium(III) salts and silyl chlorides s. J. Lu, S.-J. Ji, T.-P. Loh et al., Org. Lett. *7*, 159-61 (2005).

Boron fluoride/potassium salt BF_3
Stereospecific synthesis of 3-ethylenetosylamines C=NTs → C(NHTs)C-C=C
from N-tosylimines

442.

and potassium allyl(trifluoro)borates. A mixture of 2 eqs. K-(Z)-crotyltrifluoroborate, startg. N-tosylimine, and 10 mol% BF$_3$-etherate in methylene chloride stirred for 48 h → product. Y 99% (*anti/syn* >98:2). Air- and water-resistant potassium allyl- and crotyl-trifluoroborates offer advantages over classical allylboron reagents, notably in affording high yields and excellent levels of diastereoselectivity with the latter on reaction with aliphatic (incl. enolizable), aromatic and heteroaromatic N-tosylimines. Allylboron difluorides are invoked as intermediates. F.e. and stereospecificity, also 3-ethylenesulfinylamines from S-chiral N-sulfinylimines with asym. induction, s. S.-W. Li, R.A. Batey, Chem. Commun. *2004*, 1382-3.

**1-Aryl-3-hydroxymethyl-2-vinyltetralins
from 6-benzyl-1,2-oxasilacyclohept-4-enes and ar. aldehydes**

Stereospecific conversion. A soln. of 1 eq. of the startg. cyclic allylsiloxane in methylene chloride treated at -78° with 3 eqs. BF_3-etherate, after 5 min a soln. of 1 eq. of the startg. aldehyde in the same solvent added dropwise, stirring continued for 8 h, warmed slowly to room temp. with stirring over 14 h, and quenched with brine → product. Y 60% (single stereoisomer). Reaction involves generation of a stable benzylic cation, which undergoes intramolecular Friedel-Crafts alkylation. However, it is limited to electron-rich ar. aldehydes. F.e. and with trimethylsilyl triflate s. S.M. Miles, S.P. Marsden et al., Chem. Commun. *2004*, 2292-3.

Aluminum bromide s. under CuBr $AlBr_3$

Gallium triiodide GaI_3
Synthesis of 3-ethylenealcohols from aldehydes $CH(OH)C-C{=}C$
and 2-ethylenesilanes s. *36*, 884s68

Indium(III) chloride $InCl_3$
4-Chlorotetrahydropyrans from two aldehyde molecules
Stereospecific Prins-type ring closure
with allyltributylstannane cf. *58*, 432; from two different aldehyde molecules, incl. α,β-ethylenealdehydes, and allyl(chloro)dimethylsilane s. K.-P. Chan, T.-P. Loh, Tetrahedron Lett. *45*, 8387-90 (2004).

Indium(III) bromide $InBr_3$
Indium(III)-catalyzed coupling of activated alcohols with 2-ethylenesilanes ←
coupling of benzyl alcohols using $InCl_3$ cf. *67*, 439; also coupling of allyl alcohols and the corresponding acetates using $InBr_3$, regioselectivity, s. S.-H. Kim, Y.-S. Cho et al., Synthesis *2004*, 1581-4.

Indium(III) chloride/ 1-hexyl-3-methylimidazolium chloride $InCl_3/[hexmim]Cl$
Scandium(III) triflate $Sc(OTf)_3$
Synthesis of 3-ethylenealcohols from aldehydes $CHO \rightarrow CH(OH)C-C{=}C$
and 2-ethylenestannanes with $Sc(OTf)_3$ in ionic liquids cf. *58*, 238s63; **in polyethylene glycol**, also 3-ethyleneamines (cf. *54*, 459s63), and 4-ethylenealcohols from epoxides [cf. *54*, 465 (incorrectly under *54*, 564 in Vol. 63)], s. B.M. Choudary et al., Synlett *2004*, 231-4; with $InCl_3$ in ionic liquids, e.g. 1-hexyl-3-methylimidazolium chloride, s. J. Lu, S.-J. Ji, T.-P. Loh et al., ibid. 534-6; stereospecific synthesis of 2-deuterio-3-ethylenealcohols with BF_3 (cf. *36*, 879) s. Y. Nishigaichi, A. Takuwa, Tetrahedron Lett. *43*, 3045-7 (2002); syn-α-alkoxy-γ,δ-ethylene-carboxylic acid esters with $TiCl_4$ s. D. Basavaiah, B. Sreenivasulu, ibid. 2987-90; **from 2-ethylenesilanes** with GaI_3 (cf. *36*, 884) s. P.-P. Sun, Y.-F. Man, Y.-P. Xiao, J. Chem. Res. Synop *2004*, 216-7.

Scandium(III) triflate/(R,R)-6,6'-bis(1-hydroxy-2,2-dimethylpropyl)-2,2'-bipyridyl ←
Asym. aldol-type condensation with formaldehyde in aq. media $C(CH_2OH)CO$
chiral α-(hydroxymethyl)carbonyl compds. with $Pr(OTf)_3$ cf. *61*, 431s67; chiral α-(hydroxymethyl)ketones with $Sc(OTf)_3$ and (R,R)-6,6'-bis(1-hydroxy-2,2-dimethylpropyl)-2,2'-bipyridyl s. S. Ishikawa, S. Kobayashi et al., J. Am. Chem. Soc. *126*, 12236-7 (2004).

Polymer-based scandium(III) sulfate bis(triflate) ←
Aldol-type condensation in water $CHO \rightarrow CH(OH)C-CO$
with scandium(III) dodecyl sulfate cf. *57*, 421; with readily recoverable polymer-based

scandium(III) sulfate bis(triflate), β-hydroxythiolic acid esters, s. S. Iimura, K. Manabe, S. Kobayashi, Tetrahedron 60, 7673-8 (2004).

Lanthanum triisopropoxide s. under CuF$_2$ La(OPr-i)$_3$
Samarium(III) triisopropoxide/5,5',6,6',7,7',8,8'-octahydro-1,1'-bi-2-naphthol/ cumene hydroperoxide ←
***trans*-N-(α,β-Epoxyacyl)pyrroles from aldehydes**
Asym. synthesis with addition of two C-atoms via Wittig synthesis-epoxidation

444.

One-pot procedure. 1 eq. *p*-Chlorobenzaldehyde added to a stirred suspension of 1.3 eqs. pyrrol-1-ylcarbonylmethylenetriphenylphosphorane in toluene at 25°, stirred at 100° for 36 h, cooled to 25°, treated with a suspension of chiral Sm(III)-octahydro-1,1'-bi-2-naphthoxide (prepared *in situ* from 5 mol% Sm(OPr-i)$_3$ and 5 mol% (R)-H$_8$-BINOL), 1.5 eqs. cumene hydroperoxide, and 4 Å molecular sieves, stirred for 30 min at the same temp., and quenched with 2.5% aq. citric acid → product. Y 100% (e.e. 99%). The incorporation of the *robust* N-acylpyrrole residue imparts high reactivity and enantioselectivity, and can be readily manipulated as an **ester equivalent** on reaction with nucleophiles. F.e.s. S. Matsunaga, M. Shibasaki et al., J. Am. Chem. Soc. *126*, 7559-70 (2004).

Imidazolium ionic liquids s. under Bn$_2$NH ←
4-[2-(2-Ethoxyethoxy)ethyl]-4-methylmorpholinium triflimide s. under CsF, CuI and Ph$_3$P ←
Azodiisobutyronitrile AIBN
Carbonylative 4-component radical synthesis of β-functionalized ketones ←
δ,ε-ethyleneketones with allyltributylstannane as electron-rich alkene component s. *48*, 893s57; 3-functionalized 1,5-diketones with enoxystannanes, also carbonylative 3-component radical synthesis of β-diketones with halides (cf. *48*, 892), s. K. Miura, A. Hosomi, R. Ryu et al., Angew. Chem. Int. Ed. Engl. *43*, 2423-5 (2004).

2,2'-Azobis(4-methoxy-2,4-dimethylvaleronitrile) RN=NR
Radical synthesis of γ-subst. N-protected (E)-α,β-ethylenecarboxylic acid amides ←
from N-protected 1-siloxylamino-1-siloxy-1,3-dienes

445.

A soln. of 1 eq. startg. O,N-acetal, 1.5 eqs. α-iodoacetophenone, and 20 mol% V-70 initiator in anhydrous methylene chloride degassed with N$_2$ for 10 min, and stirred under N$_2$ at 30° for 10 h → product. Y 86%. The procedure is environmentally friendly (notably *tin-free*), applicable to a range of activated bromides and iodides, and is not complicated by α-alkylation. F.e.s. S. Kim, C.J. Lim, Angew. Chem. Int. Ed. Engl. *43*, 5378-80 (2004).

1,1,3,3-Tetramethylguanidine (Me$_2$N)$_2$C=NH
α-Vinylation of ketones with vinylbismuth compds. ←
with triaryl(vinyl)bismuth(V) fluorides for α-vinylation via enoxysilanes cf. *66*, 424; direct α-vinylation of β-ketocarbonyl compds. with triaryl(vinyl)bismuthonium salts in the presence of tetramethylguanidine, with retention of configuration, s. Y. Matano, H. Imahori, J. Org. Chem. *69*, 5505-8 (2004).

Chiral 1,1'-bi-2-naphthols s.a. under Et$_2$Zn, Sm(OPr-i)$_3$, Ti(OPr-i)$_4$ and Zr(OBu-t)$_4$ BINOLs
(R)-3,3'-Bis(trifluoromethyl)-1,1'-bi-2-naphthol   *(R)-3,3'-(CF$_3$)$_2$-BINOL*
Asym. allylboration of oxo compds.   CO → C(OH)CH$_2$CH=CH$_2$

446.

1.8 eqs. 3,3'-bis(trifluoromethyl)-1,1'-bi-2-naphthol added to a soln. of 1.5 eqs. triallylborane in dry THF under argon at room temp., stirred for 2 h at the same temp., refluxed 1 h, chilled to -78°, a soln. of 4-nitrobenzaldehyde in the same solvent (dry) added dropwise, stirring continued for 1 h, quenched with cold aq. 1 M NaOH, warmed to room temp., and extracted with methylene chloride → product. Y 96% (R/S 94:6). The nucleophilicity of the intermediate allylboronate is significantly enhanced by the electron-withdrawing trifluoromethyl groups, which are sufficiently large to effect high selectivities for the asym. allylboration of aliphatic, ar. and α,β-ethylenic aldehydes *and ketones* (the latter requiring a more elevated temp. (-40°) in toluene and much longer reaction times). Although stoichiometric amounts of the BINOL are necessary, the robust reagent can be readily recovered in quantitative yield. F.e. and comparison of chiral 3,3'-disubst. 1,1'-bi-2-naphthols s. T.R. Wu, L. Shen, J.M. Chong, Org. Lett. **6**, 2701-4 (2004).

(R)-3,3'-Dibromo-1,1'-bi-2-naphthol/n-butyllithium   *(R)-3,3'-Br$_2$-BINOL/BuLi*
Brønsted base-catalyzed asym. aldol-type condensation   CHO → CH(OH)C-CO

447.

A stirred soln. of 10 mol% (R)-3,3'-dibromo-1,1'-bi-2-naphthol in THF treated under argon at -23° with *1.5 eqs. water* in THF and 20 mol% *n*-BuLi (0.16 M in hexane), stirred at the same temp. for a few min, the resulting mixture treated with a soln. of 1 eq. benzaldehyde in THF and 1.5 eqs. cyclohexanone trimethylsilyl enol ether, stirring continued for 0.5 h, quenched with aq. 15% KF and 10% KH$_2$PO$_4$, and worked up by column chromatography on SiO$_2$ → product. Y 94% (*syn/anti* 3.1:1; e.e. *syn*-product 80%; e.e. *anti*-product 50%). This is the first instance of a Brønsted base-catalyzed asym. aldol-type condensation, coordination of water to silicon increasing the nucleophilicity of the intermediate silicate complex and favouring the *syn*-adduct via an acyclic transition state with high enantioselectivity. Results were poor, however, with (Z)-enoxysilanes. F.e.s. M. Nakajima et al., Org. Lett. **6**, 3763-5 (2004).

Sodium dodecyl sulfate s. under [Rh(cod)Cl]$_2$ $NaOSO_2OC_{12}H_{25}$
Chiral sulfoximines s. under Cu(OTf)$_2$ ←
Oxalyl chloride   (COCl)$_2$
Furans from N-unsubst. carboxylic acid amides
via hetero-Diels-Alder reaction of 4-siloxyoxazoles with acetylene derivs.

448.

One-pot conversion. 1.2 eqs. Oxalyl chloride added to a soln. of 4-chlorobenzamide in 1,2-dichloroethane, stirred under reflux for 24 h, the solvent replaced by acetonitrile, the intermediate acylisocyanate treated with a soln. of 1.2 eqs. trimethylsilyldiazomethane in hexane (1.67 M) at 0°, stirred for 30 min, 2 eqs. dimethyl acetylenedicarboxylate added, and refluxed for a further 11 h → product. Y 75%. There was no reaction with phenylacetylene. F.e. **and from the intermediate acylisocyanates, also regiospecific synthesis** of 2,3-disubst. furans with ethyl propiolate, s. Y. Hari, T. Iguchi, T. Aoyama, Synthesis 2004, 1359-62.

Trimethylsilyl cyanide s. under FeCl$_3$ Me$_3$SiCN

Titanium tetraisopropoxide/(S)-1,1'-bi-2-naphthol/4-(trifluoromethyl)phenylboroxin   ←
Asym. synthesis of 3-ethylenealcohols from aldehydes   CHO → CH(OH)C-C≡C
and 2-ethylenestannanes with TiCl$_2$(OPr-i)$_2$/(S)-1,1'-bi-2-naphthol cf. 49, 898; acceleration and enhancement of enantioselectivity with Ti(OPr-i)$_4$/(S)-1,1'-bi-2-naphthol and added 4-(trifluoromethyl)phenylboroxin (5 mol%) s. G.Y. Xia, K. Shibatomi, H. Yamamoto, Synlett 2004, 2437-9.

Titanium tetraisopropoxide/(1R,2S)-N-(3,5-di-tert-butylsalicylidene)-2-amino-1,2-   ←
    diphenylethanol
5,6-Dihydro-2-pyrones from aldehydes via asym. hetero-Diels-Alder reaction
with Cu(OTf)$_2$/(S)-Tol-BINAP/Bu$_4$N[Ph$_3$SiF$_2$] cf. 62, 423; with Ti(OPr-i)$_4$/(1R,2S)-N-(3,5-di-tert-butylsalicylidene)-2-amino-1,2-diphenylethanol s. Q. Fan, G.-L. Zhang et al., Org. Lett. 6, 2185-8 (2004).

Zirconium tetra-tert-butoxide/chiral 3,3'-diiodo-1,1'-bi-2-naphthols/n-propanol   ←
2,3-Dihydro-4-pyrones from aldehydes via asym. hetero-Diels-Alder reaction
with Ti(OPr-i)$_4$/(R)-5,5',6,6',7,7',8,8'-octahydro-1,1'-bi-2-naphthol cf. 61, 434; with Zr(OBu-t)$_4$/chiral 3,3'-diiodo-1,1'-bi-2-naphthol/n-PrOH s. O. Kobayashi, H. Ishitani, Japanese patent JP-2002356454 (Japan Science & Technology Corp).

Zirconium tetra-tert-butoxide/(R)-3,3',6,6'-tetraiodo-1,1'-bi-2-   ←
    naphthol/n-propanol
Asym. aldol-type condensation   CHO → CH(OH)C-CO
with Zr(OPr-n)$_4$/(R)-3,3'-diiodo-1,1'-bi-2-naphthol/n-PrOH cf. 59, 431s66; chiral anti-α-(trifluoroacetylamino)-β-hydroxycarboxylic acid esters with Zr(OBu-t)$_4$/(R)-3,3',6,6'-tetraiodo-1,1'-bi-2-naphthol/PrOH s. J. Kobayashi, S. Kobayashi et al., J. Am. Chem. Soc. 126, 9192-3 (2004).

Trimethylsilyl chloride s. under In(OTf)$_3$ and FeCl$_3$ Me$_3$SiCl

Tetra-n-butylammonium difluorotriphenylsilicate/tert-butanol   Bu$_4$N[Ph$_3$SiF$_2$]/t-BuOH
N'-Acyl-3-ethylenehydrazones   CH(NHNHAc)C-C≡C
from acylhydrazones and 2-ethylenesilanes
from 2-ethylene(trichloro)silanes with 1,3-bis(diphenylphosphino)propane dioxide cf. 58, 406s67;

from less corrosive 2-ethylene(trialkoxy)silanes with $Bu_4N[Ph_3SiF_2]$/t-BuOH or under copper catalysis s. H. Ding, G.K. Friestad, Synthesis *2004*, 2216-21.

Zirconocene dichloride/n-butyllithium/diphenyl(methyl)phosphine ←
Synthesis of indenes ○
reviews s. *29*, 932s60; *42*, 915s59; 1,2,3-trisubst. indenes from silylethynylarenes and acetylene derivs. with Cp_2ZrBu_2/Ph_2PMe, also from aryl ketones and acetylene derivs., s. Z.-F. Xi, T. Takahashi et al., J. Org. Chem. *68*, 1252-7 (2003).

Titanium tetrachloride $TiCl_4$
Vinylogous asym. aldol-type condensation ←
using $Ti(OPr-i)_4$/chiral 1,1'-bi-2-naphthol/i-PrOH cf. *64*, 432; chiral N-(α,β-ethylene-δ-hydroxy-acyl)-2-oxazolidones from chiral 1-(2-oxazolidon-3-yl)-1-siloxy-1,3-dienes using $TiCl_4$ **with asym. induction** s. S.I. Shirokawa, S. Kobayashi et al., J. Am. Chem. Soc. *126*, 13604-5 (2004).

Tri-n-butylphosphine/ethyldiisopropylamine Bu_3P/i-Pr_2NEt
C-α-Arylation of α,β-ethyleneoxo compds. with triarylbismuth dichlorides H → Ar
via regiospecific generation of bismuth(V) 3-phosphonioenolates

449.

under nucleophilic catalysis. A mixture of 2-cyclohexenone, 1 eq. triphenylbismuth dichloride, 20 mol% tri-n-butylphosphine and 1 eq. ethyldiisopropylamine in 9:1 methylene chloride/tert-butanol stirred at room temp. for 2-12 h → product. Y 93%. The method is applicable to the arylation of cyclic (not acyclic) enones and to enals. Yields were low with arylbismuth substrates possessing strong electron-donating substituents in the *para*-position. Ar. halogen was unaffected. F.e.s. P.K. Koech, M.J. Krische, J. Am. Chem. Soc. *126*, 5350-1 (2004).

Triphenylphosphine Ph_3P
Regio- and stereo-specific synthesis of 5-allyl-2(5H)-furanones ←
from 2-siloxyfurans and acoxy-2-ethylenes

450.

$Ar = p\text{-}NO_2C_6H_4$

with asym. induction. A soln. of 1 eq. startg. Baylis-Hillman acetate, 2 eqs. 2-(trimethylsiloxy)furan and 20 mol% triphenylphosphine in anhydrous THF stirred at 25° until complete consumption of the startg. m. → product. Y 87% (d.r. >98:2). This is the first example of the coupling between an acoxy-2-ethylene as electrophile and a siloxyfuran as nucleophile. Reaction involves initial Michael addition of the phosphine, followed by regiospecific elimination of the acetoxy group with formation of a carbonyl-stabilized phosphonium acetate which completely suppresses direct addition of the nucleophile to the less substitutued carbon atom of the enone residue. The conversion of racemic substrates proceeds with high diastereoselectivity, leading to **β-(2(5H)-furanon-5-yl)-α-methylenecarbonyl compds.** substituted at the 5-position by aryl, alkyl, vinyl or alkynyl groups. F.e.s. C.-W. Cho, M.J. Krische, Angew. Chem. Int. Ed. Engl. *43*, 6689-91 (2004).

Triphenylphosphine/4-[2-(2-ethoxyethoxy)ethyl]-4-methylmorpholinium triflimide ←
2,2,2-Trifluoroalcohols from oxo compds. s. *44*, 577s68   CO → C(OH)CF$_3$
Tris(2,4,6-trimethoxyphenyl)phosphine   Ar$_3$P
2-Azetidinones from O-silyl O-alkyl keteneacetals   ⌐$_N$
and N-silylimines with ZnI$_2$/t-BuOH/MeMgBr cf. *40*, 619; **from azomethines** (cf. *33*, 879) with tris(2,4,6-trimethoxyphenyl)phosphine s. S. Matsukawa, K. Obu, Chem. Lett. *33*, 1626-7 (2004).

Chiral 2,2'-bis(diarylphosphino)-1,1'-binaphthyl dioxides ←
N'-Acyl-3-ethylenehydrazines   CH(NHNHAc)C-C≡C
from N-acylhydrazones and 2-ethylene(trichloro)silanes
Asym. synthesis under neutral organocatalysis
with (R)-methyl *p*-tolyl sulfoxide cf. *66*, 442; with 2 eqs of a chiral 2,2'-bis(diarylphosphino)-1,1'-binaphthyl dioxide (cf. *58*, 406s67) s. C. Ogawa, M. Sugiura, S. Kobayashi, Angew. Chem. Int. Ed. Engl. *43*, 6491-3 (2004).

Polymer-based phosphoric acid amides ←
Organocatalyzed aldol-type condensation   CHO → CH(OH)C-CO
asym. conversion with chiral phosphoric acid amides s. *52*, 459; heterogeneous conversion with a resin-supported phosphoric acid amide, *syn*-selectivity, s. R.A. Flowers, C. Timmons et al., Eur. J. Org. Chem. *2004*, 2988-90.

Phosphoric acid/silica gel   H$_3$PO$_4$/SiO$_2$
Heterogeneous 3-component Mannich-type reaction   CHO → CH(NHR)C-CO
with polymer-based sulfonic acids in water cf. *66*, 451; with H$_3$PO$_4$-on-silica gel **in the absence of solvent** s. S. Lock, N. Miyoshi, M. Wada, Chem. Lett. *33*, 1308-9 (2004).

Bismuth(III) triflate   Bi(OTf)$_3$
3-Component Mannich-type reaction
with aq. HBF$_4$ in isopropanol cf. *61*, 427; with Bi(OTf)$_3$·4H$_2$O in acetonitrile s. T. Ollevier, E. Nadeau, J. Org. Chem. *69*, 9292-5 (2004).

2,3-Unsatd. α-glycosides from O^3-acylglycals and Si-nucleophiles ←
unsatd. C-α-allyl glycosides and α-glycosyl cyanides with In(OTf)$_3$ cf. *38*, 759s65; with Bi(OTf)$_3$ s. J.S. Yadav et al., Synthesis *2004*, 2523-6.

Hydrogen peroxide s. under LiOBu-t   H$_2$O$_2$
Triflimide s. under Pd(OAc)$_2$ Tf$_2$NH

Trimethylsilyl triflate   Me$_3$SiOTf
3-Hydroxymaleic anhydrides from ketene disilyl acetals   O

451.

0.5 eq. Trimethylsilyl triflate in methylene chloride added at -78° to a soln. of the startg. ketene disilyl acetal and 1.3 eqs. oxalyl chloride in the same solvent, allowed to warm to 20° over 12 h, stirred for 3 h, then treated with 10% aq. HCl → product. Y 70%. Attempts to secure the same anhydrides by direct addition of phenylacetic acid dianion gave a complex mixture of products. F.e. incl. 4-aryl-, 4-alkyl- and 4-alkoxy-derivs. s. E. Ullah, P. Langer, Synlett *2004*, 2782-4.

1-Aryl-3-hydroxymethyl-2-vinyltetralins   O
from 6-benzyl-1,2-oxasilacyclohept-4-enes and ar. aldehydes s. *68*, 443

*[(S,S)-N,N'-Bis(3,5-di-*tert*-butylsalicylidenato)cyclohexane-1,2-diamine]-* ←
chromium(III) chloride
Transition metal-catalyzed regiospecific asym. synthesis $C(OSn≤)=C → COC(R)$
of cyclic ketones from cyclic enoxystannanes and alkyl halides

452.

The first example of a transition metal-catalyzed asym. α-alkylation of an enolate with an *alkyl* halide is reported. **E: Chiral α,α-disubst. cyclic ketones.** A soln. of 2.5 mol% [(S,S)-N,N'-bis(3,5-di-*tert*-butylsalicylidenato)cyclohexane-1,2-diamine]chromium(III) chloride and 4 eqs. propargyl bromide in benzene cooled to 0°, treated dropwise under N_2 with a soln. of the startg. tin(IV) enolate in the same solvent (pre-chilled to 0°), stirred at the same temp. for 2 h, satd. aq. NaCl and solid KF added sequentially, and worked up when reaction complete → (-)-product. Y 81% (e.e. 96%). Products possessing **chiral quaternary hydrocarbon groups** were obtained cleanly and with high enantioselectivity (even with methyl iodide as electrophile) from 5-, 6- and 7-membered enolates, with no evidence of S_N2' substitution. F.e. and comparison of transition metal salen complexes, and solvent and temperature effects, s. A.G. Doyle, E.N. Jacobsen, J. Am. Chem. Soc. *127*, 62-3 (2005).

Pyridinium chlorochromate/sodium acetate $[C_5H_5NH][CrO_3Cl]/NaOAc$
Wittig synthesis with *in situ*-generated aldehydes $CH_2OH → CH=C$
(E)-α,β-ethylenecarboxylic acid esters with pyridinium chlorochromate/Celite cf. *55*, 451s67; (E)-α,β-ethylenecarbonyl compds. with pyridinium chlorochromate/NaOH s. J. Shet, V. Desai, S. Tilve, Synthesis *2004*, 1859-63.

Iodine I_2
Iodine-catalyzed reactions of oxo compds. with Si-nucleophiles ←
3-ethylenealcohols from aldehydes cf. *63*, 449; 3-component synthesis of N-protected 3-ethylene-amines from aldehydes, allyltrimethylsilane and benzyl carbamate s. P. Phukan, J. Org. Chem. *69*, 4005-6 (2004); **synthesis of cyclic ethylene derivs. from cyclic acoxy-2-ethylenes** with silylacetylenes or allyltrimethylsilane as nucleophile s. J.S. Yadav et al., Tetrahedron Lett. *45*, 6505-7 (2004).

Tetra-n-butylammonium fluoride s. under $NaN(SiMe_3)_2$ and Palladium complexes Bu_4NF
Tetra-n-butylammonium bromide s. under K_2CO_3 Bu_4NBr
Hexadecyltrimethylammonium bromide s. under ZnF_2 $[C_{16}H_{33}NMe_3]Br$

Ferric chloride/trimethylsilyl chloride/trimethylsilyl cyanide $FeCl_3/Me_3SiCl/Me_3SiCN$
3-Component syntheses with aldehydes, alkoxysilanes and Si-nucleophiles ←
alkoxy-2-allenes from 2-acetylenesilanes with triphenylcarbonium perchlorate cf. *61*, 441; α-alkoxynitriles with $Me_3SiCN/FeCl_3$ in the absence of solvent s. K. Iwanami, T. Oriyama, Chem. Lett. *33*, 1324-5 (2004).

Chiral [N,N'-bis(2-quinolylmethylene)-1,1'-binaphthyl-2,2'-diamine]- ←
nickel(II) complexes/hexafluoroisopropanol
Asym. vinylgous Michael-type addition with 2-siloxyfurans ←
with $Sc(OTf)_3/(R)$-3,3'-bis(diethylaminomethyl)-1,1'-bi-2-naphthol cf. *53*, 453; with chiral [N,N'-bis(2-quinolylmethylene)-1,1'-binaphthyl-2,2'-diamine]nickel(II) complexes/hexafluoroiso-propanol for highly enantioselective addition to N-(α,β-ethyleneacyl)-2-oxazolidones s. H. Suga et al., Chem. Commun. *2004*, 1414-5.

Dichloro[1,2-bis(diphenylphosphino)ethane]nickel(II) s. under BuLi $NiCl_2(dppe)$

Nickel(II) bromide/4,7-diphenyl-1,10-phenanthroline/cesium fluoride
Cross-coupling of arylsilanes with alkyl halides ArSi≤ → ArR
using PdBr$_2$/t-Bu$_2$PMe/Bu$_4$NF cf. 65, 465; coupling of aryl(trifluoro)silanes with *prim*- and *sec*-alkyl halides using NiBr$_2$·diglyme/4,7-diphenyl-1,10-phenanthroline/CsF s. D.A. Powell, G.C. Fu, J. Am. Chem. Soc. *126*, 7788-9 (2004).

Dodecacarbonyltriruthenium $Ru_3(CO)_{12}$
Aryl ketones from carboxylic acid 2-pyridylmethyl esters B(OR)$_2$ → COR′
and arylboronic acid esters s. *68*, 465

Carbonyl(hydrido)tris(triphenylphosphine)rhodium(I) $RhH(CO)(PPh_3)_3$
Aryl γ-diketones C═C → CHC-COAr
from arylboronic acids and α,β-ethyleneketones
via rhodium-catalyzed carbonylative 1,4-addition

453.

A stainless steel autoclave containing a mixture of 5 eqs. phenylboronic acid and 5 mol% RhH(CO)(PPh$_3$)$_3$ charged (via cannula) with a soln. of methyl vinyl ketone in methanol under N$_2$, stirred for 2 min, CO introduced to a pressure of 20 bar, and stirred at 80° for 18 h → product. Y 72%. Reaction is presumed to involve 1,4-addition of an intermediate aroylrhodium species, and is facilitated by electron-donating groups in the *para*-position of the arylboronic acid. 1,4-Addition of the initially formed arylboronic acid was minimal, and the presence of water was not required. Ar. halogen was left intact. F.e. and solvent effects s. M. Sauthier, Y. Castanet, A. Mortreux, Chem. Commun. *2004*, 1520-1.

Dirhodium(II) tetrakis[3(S)-(2,3-naphthalenedicarboximido)-2-piperidonate]/
  trifluoroacetic acid
2,3-Dihydro-4-pyrones from 1-alkoxy-3-siloxy-1,3-dienes and aldehydes
Rhodium-catalyzed *endo*-selective asym. hetero-Diels-Alder reaction
under neutral conditions

454.

1 Mol% dirhodium(II) tetrakis[3(S)-(2,3-naphthalenedicarboximido)-2-piperidonate] and 1 eq. *p*-nitrobenzaldehyde in anhydrous methylene chloride added to a soln. of 1.5 eqs. startg. diene *at 23°*, stirred at the same temp. under argon for 2 h, 10% trifluoroacetic acid in the same solvent added, and stirring continued for 0.5 h → product. Y 92% (e.e. 97%). The catalyst is robust, air-stable and highly active for the enantio- and diastereo-selective hetero-Diels-Alder reactions with

a wide range of aromatic, aliphatic, α,β-unsatd. and α-alkoxylated aldehydes at catalyst loadings *as low as 0.002 mol%* with turnover numbers as high as 48, 000. F.e.s. M. Anada et al., Angew. Chem. Int. Ed. Engl. *43*, 2665-8 (2004).

1,5-Cyclooctadiene(hydroxy)rhodium(I) dimer/phenol   [Rh(cod)(OH)]$_2$/PhOH
Arylcarboxylic acid amides from arylstannanes and isocyanates   Sn≤ → CONHR

455.

$$\text{Ar-SnBu}_3 \xrightarrow{[Rh]OPh} [\text{Ar-[Rh]}] \xrightarrow{O=C=NAr} [\text{Ar-C(=O)-NAr-[Rh]}] \xrightarrow[-[Rh]OPh]{PhOH} \text{Ar-C(=O)-NHAr}$$

Ar = o-NO$_2$C$_6$H$_4$

under mild conditions. A mixture of 2 eqs. 2-nitrophenyl isocyanate, 1 eq. phenol, 5 mol% [Rh(cod)(OH)]$_2$ and the startg. arylstannane in THF heated for 24 h at 70° → product. Y 99%. The active species is thought to be a phenoxyrhodium species, yields being low without the added phenol. F.e. and comparison of phenolic additives, **also α,β-ethylenecarboxylic acid amides from enestannanes**, s. T. Koike, A. Mori et al., Chem. Lett. *33*, 1364-5 (2004).

1,5-Cyclooctadiene(hydroxy)rhodium(I) dimer/water-soluble   [Rh(cod)OH]$_2$/Ar$_3$P
triarylphosphines
Styrenes from acetylene derivs. and arylboronic acids   C≡C → CH=C(Ar)
by Pd-catalyzed hydroarylation cf. **56**, 464; regiospecific hydroarylation of acetylenealcohols, also hydrovinylation with α,β-ethyleneboronic acid esters, s. N. Kim, C.H. Oh et al., Chem. Commun. *2004*, 618-9; by Rh-catalyzed hydroarylation of aryl- and alkyl-acetylenes **in a 2-phase aq. organic medium** with [Rh(cod)OH]$_2$ and water-soluble triarylphosphine, e.g. tris(*m*-carboxyphenyl)phosphine trilithium salt, s. E. Genin, V. Michelet, J.P. Genêt, Tetrahedron Lett. *45*, 4157-61 (2004).

Bis(cyclooctadiene)rhodium(I) hexafluorophosphate/(R)-2,2'-bis(diphenylphosphino)-   ←
1,1'-binaphthyl
Acetoacetonato- or chloro-bis(ethylene)rhodium(I)/chiral norbornadienes or   ←
bicyclo[2.2.2]octa-2,5-dienes or chiral di(phosphines) or cyclic phosphoromonoamidites
Asym. 1,4-addition of arylboronic acids   C=C → CHC(Ar)
update s. **55**, 452s*67*; asym. addition to 2-ene-1,4-dicarbonyl compds. using (R,R)-2,5-bis(2,4,6-trimethylbenzyl)norbornadiene as ligand with KOH in aq. dioxane s. R. Shintani, T. Hayashi et al., Org. Lett. *6*, 3425-7 (2004); with (1R,4R,8S)-5-allyl-2-isobutoxy-8-methoxy-1,8-dimethyl-bicyclo[2.2.2]octa-2,5-diene s. C. Defieber, E.M. Carreira et al., ibid. 3873-6; asym. addition to 2-pyridyl α,β-ethylenesulfones with (S,S)-2,3-bis(diphenylphosphino)butane as ligand s. P. Mauleón, J.C. Carretero, ibid. 3195-8; **polymer-based synthesis in water** with polystyrene-based PEG-supported 2,2'-bis(diphenylphosphino)-1,1'-binaphthyl-6-ylcarboxamide s. Y. Otomaru, T. Senda, T. Hayashi, ibid. 3357-9; asym. addition of K-aryl(trifluoro)borates to α,β-ethylenecarboxylic acid amides with (R)-2,2'-bis(diphenylphosphino)-1,1'-binaphthyl in aq. medium s. M. Pucheault, V. Michaut, J.P. Genêt et al., Tetrahedron Lett. *45*, 4729-32 (2004); chiral α-benzylsuccinic acid esters from dimethyl itaconate s. R.J. Moss, K.J. Wadsworth, C.J. Chapman et al., Chem. Commun. *2004*, 1984-5; asym. addition of K-aryl-, -vinyl- or -hetaryl-(trifluoro)borates *in ethanol* with chiral 5,5',6,6',7,7',8,8'-octahydro-1,1'-binaphthyl-2,2'-diyl N,N-diethylphosphoramidite as ligand s. A. Duursma, B.L. Feringa et al., J. Org. Chem. *69*, 8045-52 (2004); asym. addition of triarylbismuthines to enones with bis(benzonitrile)[(S,S)-1,2-bis[2-methoxyphenyl(phenyl)phosphino]ethane]palladium(II) bis(hexafluoroantimonate)/ Cu(II)-fluoroborate *in aq. methanol* s. T. Nishikata, Y. Yamamoto, N. Miyaura, Chem. Commun. *2004*, 1822-3.

(1,5-Cyclooctadiene)(naphthalene)rhodium(I) hexafluoroantimonate
2-Alkoxy-3-methylenecyclopentenes
**from chromium α,β-ethylene(alkoxy)carbene complexes and allenes
via regio- and stereo-specific rhodium-catalyzed [3+2]-cycloaddition**

456.

10 Mol% [Rh(cod)(naphthalene)]SbF$_6$ added to a soln. of the startg. chromium carbene complex and 1.5 eqs. of the startg. allene in anhydrous methylene chloride, and the mixture stirred at room temp. until reaction complete (18-24 h) → product. Y 93%. Reaction is presumed to involve initial Cr→Rh exchange, the formation of *trans*-4,5-disubst. products from monosubst. allenes providing evidence for an *exo*-selective non-concerted [4+2]-cycloaddition prior to elimination of the catalyst. F.e.s. J. Barluenga et al., J. Am. Chem. Soc. *126*, 5974-5 (2004); **2-alkoxy-3,5-di(alkylidene)cycloheptenes from two allene molecules** with the same catalyst s. ibid. 14354-5.

Bis(acetonitrile)(1,5-cyclooctadiene)rhodium(I) fluoroborate/potassium fluoride
N-Protected benzylamines from imines
and arylstannanes with [Rh(cod)Cl]$_2$ cf. *58*, 447s67; N-sulfonylbenzylamines **from arylsilanes** with [Rh(MeCN)$_2$(cod)]BF$_4$/KF s. S. Oi, Y. Inoue et al., Tetrahedron Lett. *45*, 4855-7 (2004).

Chlorobis(ethylene)rhodium(I) dimer/(1S,4S)-2,5-dibenzylbicyclo[2.2.2]octa-2,5-diene/potassium hydroxide
**Cyclic 2-arylidenealcohols from acetyleneoxo compds. and arylboronic acids
via catalytic asym. arylative ring closure**

457.

Chiral 2-arylidenecyclopentanols. A soln. of 6.7 mol% [RhCl(C$_2$H$_4$)$_2$]$_2$ and 7.5 mol% (1S,4S)-2,5-dibenzylbicyclo[2.2.2]octa-2,5-diene in dioxane treated under N$_2$ with 30 mol% aq. KOH (0.3 M), stirred at room temp. for 5 min, 3.5 eqs. startg. arylboronic acid and 1 eq. startg. alkynal added, and stirring continued at 60° for 4 h → product. Y 71% (e.e. 96%). The relatively simple and inexpensive chiral ligands are a considerable improvement on classical phosphorus-based reagents, such as (S)-BINAP. Ethers, esters and sulfonamides remained unaffected. F.e. and achiral process with cyclooctadiene as ligand for preparing 5- and 6-membered cyclic 2-arylidene-alcohols s. R. Shintani, T. Hayashi et al., J. Am. Chem. Soc. *127*, 54-5 (2005).

*Chlorobis(ethylene)rhodium(I) dimer/(1R,4R)-2,5-diphenylbicyclo[2.2.2]octa-2,5-diene/ ←
potassium hydroxide*
Asym. synthesis of N-sulfonyldiarylmethylamines $CH{=}NSO_2R \rightarrow CH(NHSO_2R)Ar$
from ar. N-sulfonylaldimines and arylboroxines

458.

A soln. of 1.5 mol% [RhCl(C$_2$H$_4$)$_2$]$_2$ and 3.3 mol% (1R,4R)-2,5-diphenylbicyclo[2.2.2]octa-2,5-diene in anhydrous dioxane treated at room temp. with 20 mol% aq. KOH over 5 min, the mixture added under N$_2$ to a soln. of 1 eq. of the startg. sulfonylimine and 1.2 eqs. startg. arylboroxine in the same solvent at the same temp., and stirred at 60° for 6 h → product. Y 99% (e.e. 99%). Enantioselectivity and catalytic activity werer lower with conventional chiral phosphorus ligands, e.g. (R)-BINAP and SEGPHOS. The (S)-configuration of the product is rationalized by coordination of the imine to rhodium with its *Si*-face. Although limited to ar. sulfonylimines, the conversion is tolerant of a variety of functional groups. F.e. and N-desulfonylation with SmI$_2$ s. N. Tokunaga, T. Hayashi et al., J. Am. Chem. Soc. *126*, 13584-5 (2004); with [Rh(acac)(C$_2$H$_4$)$_2$] and *N-Boc*-L-*valine (S)-2-(diphenylphosphinomethyl)pyrrolidide* as ligand cf. M. Kuriyama, K. Tomioka et al., ibid. 8128-9.

*Chlorobis(ethylene)rhodium(I) dimer/tri-*tert*-butylphosphine/acetone/potassium salt* ←
Diaryl ketones from ar. aldehydes and potassium aryl(trifluoro)borates $CHO \rightarrow COAr$
Rhodium-catalyzed Heck-type arylation under mild conditions

459.

A mixture of 2 eqs. K-phenyl(trifluoro)borate, 1 eq. *p*-hydroxybenzaldehyde, and 1.5 mol% [RhCl(C$_2$H$_4$)$_2$]$_2$ in degassed, anhydrous dioxane treated under argon at room temp. with a soln. of 3 mol% tri-*tert*-butylphosphine in degassed, anhydrous toluene (3 *M*), stirred under argon for 5 min, degassed, anhydrous acetone added, and stirring continued at 80° until reaction complete → product. Y 97%. This is the first example of such a catalytic Heck-type arylation of aldehydes, reaction apparently involving 1,2-addition of an intermediate arylrhodium(I) species to the C=O bond, followed by β-hydride elimination from a diarylalkoxyrhodium(I) complex with liberation of a rhodium(I) hydride. Conversion of the latter to the arylrhodium(I) species is mediated by acetone which is an essential additive. There was no reaction with aliphatic aldehydes, but aryl-stannanes or -boronic acids could be used in place of the aryl(trifluoro)borates. F.e. incl. *o*-subst. derivs., and from heteroaryl aldehydes, s. M. Pucheault, S. Darses, J.P. Genêt, J. Am. Chem. Soc. *126*, 15356-7 (2004).

Chloro(1,5-cyclooctadiene)rhodium(I) dimer
**Regiospecific synthesis of (E)-allylarenes
from arylboronic acids and 2-ethylenealcohols**

[Rh(cod)Cl]$_2$
C(Ar)C=C

460.

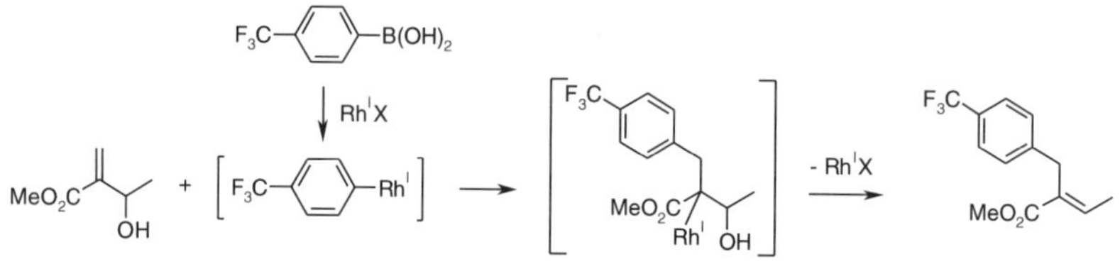

α-Benzyl-α,β-ethylenecarboxylic acid esters. A mixture of the startg. Baylis-Hillman adduct, 2 eqs. startg. arylboronic acid, and *0.5 mol%* [Rh(cod)Cl]$_2$ in methanol stirred at 50-55° *in an open vessel* until reaction complete (GC monitoring) → product. Y 86% (E/Z 99:1). The process appears to involve 1,4-addition of an arylrhodium(I) species, followed by *syn*-β-hydroxy elimination, rather than an intermediate rhodium π-allyl complex. Reaction is applicable to aliphatic and ar. aldehydes at low catalyst loadings, and there was no loss of catalytic activity under aerobic conditions. F.e.s. L. Navarre, S. Darses, J.P. Genet, Chem. Commun. *2004*, 1108-9; less efficiently from simple 2-ethylenealcohols with Pd(PPh$_3$)$_4$, also 1,3-dienes from α,β-ethyleneboronic acids, s. H. Tsukamoto, H. Sato, Y. Kondo, ibid. 1200-1; **(E)-2-aryl-1,3-dienes from 2-allenealcohols** with the same Pd-catalyst via π-allylpalladium hydroxides s. M. Yoshida, T. Gotou, M. Ihara, ibid. 1124-5.

Chloro(1,5-cyclooctadiene)rhodium(I) dimer/sodium dodecyl sulfate/sodium carbonate
1,4-Addition of arylboronic acids in water
to enones cf. *62*, 449; to enoates with added Na-lauryl sulfate/Na$_2$CO$_3$ s. K.J. Wadsworth, C.G. Frost et al., Synlett *2004*, 2022-4.

←
C=C → CHC(Ar)

*Chloro(1,5-cyclooctadiene)rhodium(I) dimer/tri-*tert-*butylphosphonium fluoroborate/ sodium carbonate*
**Indenes
from electron-deficient *o*-ethyleneboronic acid esters and activated acetylene derivs.**

←
○

461.

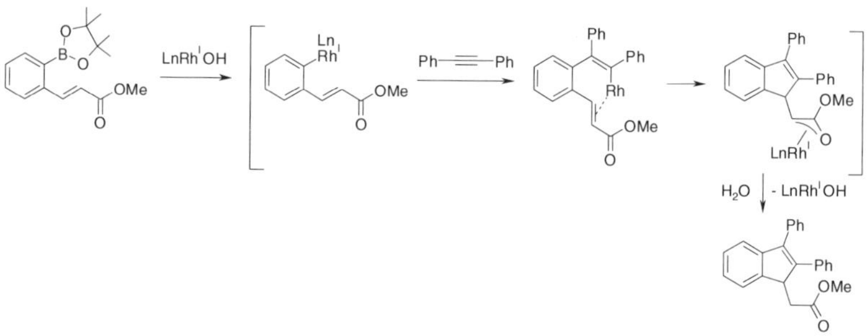

in aq. medium. 3 Mol% [Rh(cod)Cl]$_2$, 6.6 mol% tri-*tert*-butylphosphonium fluoroborate and 2 eqs. Na$_2$CO$_3$ in degassed 10:1 dioxane/water stirred vigorously under N$_2$ at room temp. for 0.5 h, 1.3 eqs. diphenylacetylene and 1 eq. startg. boronate ester added, stirred at 80° for 3 h, cooled to room temp., and worked up → product. Y 100%. Reaction is thought to involve regiospecific carborhodation of the acetylene deriv. with a generated arylrhodium(I) species, followed by 5-*exo-trig* cyclization to give an oxa-π-allylrhodium complex prior to protodemetalation with water. The bulky, electron-rich ligand stabilizes the arylrhodium species and reduces protodeboronation. F.e.s. M. Lautens, T. Marquardt, J. Org. Chem. *69*, 4607-14 (2004).

Chloro(1,5-cyclooctadiene)rhodium(I) dimer/2-(di-tert-butylphosphino)ethyl- ←
trimethylammonium chloride/sodium carbonate/sodium dodecyl sulfate
Heck-type arylation with arylboronic acids s. *61*, 446s68   H → Ar

Chlorotris(triphenylphosphine)rhodium(I) s. *under Palladium imidazol-2-ylidene* RhCl(PPh$_3$)$_3$
complexes

Rhodium trichloride/triphenylphosphine/potassium carbonate   RhCl$_3$/Ph$_3$P/K$_2$CO$_3$
Aryl ketones from arylboronic acids and α,β-ethylenealdehydes ArB(OH)$_2$ → ArCOCHCH
via rhodium-catalyzed self-conjugate reduction-cross-coupling

462.

Cinnamaldehyde added to a suspension of 2 eqs. phenylboronic acid, 0.06 eq. RhCl$_3$(H$_2$O)$_x$, 0.25 eq. triphenylphosphine, and 3 eqs. K$_2$CO$_3$ in 3:1 toluene/water, and stirred at 100° under N$_2$ for 24-30 h → product. Y 65%. This unprecedented reductive arylation is thought to involve an intermediate rhodacyclopropanone, which undergoes reductive elimination to give an α-rhodio-acylophenone prior to hydrolysis via oxidative addition of water. F.e.s. Z. Wang, G. Zou, J. Tang, Chem. Commun. *2004*, 1192-3.

Poly(N,N-dialkylcarbodiimide)-stabilized palladium nanoparticles/potassium carbonate/ ←
microwaves or Dodecanethiolate-stabilized palladium nanoparticles/sodium hydroxide or
Silica gel-entrapped palladium nanoparticles
Suzuki diaryl coupling s. *37*, 902s68   Ar-Ar'

Palladous acetate   Pd(OAc)$_2$
3,4-Benzocoumarins from 10-hydroxy-10,9-boroxarophenanthrenes   ←
by carbonylation s. *68*, 247

Palladous acetate/sodium carbonate/oxygen   Pd(OAc)$_2$/Na$_2$CO$_3$/O$_2$
Palladous acetate/2,9-dimethyl-1,10-phenanthroline/N-methylmorpholine/oxygen   ←
Heck-type arylation with arylboronic acids   H → Ar
s. *61*, 446s66; (E)-selective β-arylation of α,β-ethylenephosphonic acid esters, also Heck-type vinylation, s. G.W. Kabalka et al., Tetrahedron Lett. *45*, 4685-7 (2004); of α,β-ethylenesulfones s. ibid. 4021-2; 1-arylation of enacylamines with added 2,9-dimethyl-1,10-phenanthroline/N-methylmorpholine (cf. *61*, 446s67) s. M.M.S. Andappan, M. Larhed et al., J. Org. Chem. *69*, 5212-8 (2004); **in aq. emulsions** with [Rh(cod)Cl]$_2$/2-(di-*tert*-butylphosphino)ethyl(trimethyl)-ammonium chloride/Na$_2$CO$_3$/Na-dodecyl sulfate (cf. *61*, 446s64) s. M. Lautens, J. Mancuso, H. Grover, Synthesis *2004*, 2006-14.

Palladous acetate/triethylenediamine/potassium carbonate   ←
Suzuki diaryl coupling   Ar-Ar'
update s. *37*, 902s67; **under aerobic conditions** with triethylenediamine as ligand (cf. *61*, 446s67) s. J.-H. Li, W.-J. Liu, Org. Lett. *6*, 2809-11 (2004); with 0.2-0.3 mol% PdCl$_2$ and K$_2$CO$_3$ in pyridine **without ligand** s. X. Tao, Y. Zhao, D. Shen, Synlett *2004*, 359-61; coupling with

halogenopyridines **at low catalyst loading** (0.025 mol%) with dichlorobis(di-*tert*-butylphosphinous acid)palladium(II)/Cs_2CO_3 (cf. *67,* 461) s. S. P. Khanapure, D.S. Garvey, Tetrahedron Lett. *45,* 5283-6 (2004); **under microwave irradiation in water** (cf. *61,* 463s*64*) with $PdCl_2(PPh_3)_2$/K_2CO_3/Bu_4NBr s. L. Bai, J.X. Wang, Chin. Chem. Lett. *15,* 286-7 (2004); under heterogeneous conditions with dichloro(pyridine-4-aldoxime)palladium(II)/K_2CO_3/Bu_4NBr (*in a 'teabag'*) cf. W. Solodenko, A. Kirschning et al., Synlett *2004,* 1699-702; under microwave irradiation with robust poly(N,N-dialkylcarbodiimide)-stabilized palladium nanoparticles and K_2CO_3 in dioxane (cf. *64,* 448) s. Y. Liu, C. Khemtong, J. Hu, Chem. Commun. *2004,* 398-9; with dodecanethiolate-stabilized palladium nanoparticles and NaOH in aq. medium s. F. Lu, J. Ruiz, D. Astruc, Tetrahedron Lett. *45,* 9443-5 (2004); with silica gel-entrapped palladium nanoparticles, also application as a hydrogenation catalyst, s. N. Kim, J. Park et al., ibid. 7057-9 (2004); **in aq. media** under homogeneous or heterogeneous conditions with [1,2-bis(2-pyrazinylethynyl)benzene]palladium(II) dichloride s. N. Schultheiss, C.L. Barnes, E. Bosch, Synth. Commun. *34,* 1499-505 (2004); with a polymer-based palladium(II) imidazol-2-ylidene complex/ Na_2CO_3 cf. J.-W. Byun, Y.-S. Lee, Tetrahedron Lett. *45,* 1837-40 (2004); **polymer-based synthesis** with a supported ar. halide in aq. medium (cf. *37,* 902s*64*) using $Pd_2(dba)_3$/1,3,5,7-tetramethyl-6-phenyl-2,4,8-trioxa-6-phosphaadamantane/K_3PO_4 s. S.A. Ohnmacht, J. McNulty et al., ibid. 5661-3; with supported hetaryl halides (using $PdCl_2(PPh_3)_2$/Ph_3P/CuI/CsF s. P. Gros, A. Doudouh, Y. Fort, ibid. 6239-41; diaryl coupling **with ar. chlorides at low catalyst loadings** (cf. *67,* 461) with $Pd_2(dba)_3$/K_3PO_4 and 2-(di-*tert*-butylphosphino)-N,N-diethylbenzamide as ligand s. F.Y. Kwong, A.S.C. Chan et al., Chem. Commun. *2004,* 1922-3; with 1-(N-phenylimino)methyl-1'-(di-*tert*-butylphosphino)ferrocene as ligand cf. Z.Q. Weng, T.S.A. Hor et al., Organometallics *23,* 4342-5 (2004); with [(2,6-dimesitylphenyl)dimethylphosphine]palladium(II) chloride dimer/ CsF cf. R.C. Smith et al., Tetrahedron Lett. *45,* 8327-30 (2004); with 2-(diphenylphosphino)phenylferrocene as ligand s. F.Y. Kwong, A.S.C. Chan et al., Chem. Commun. *2004,* 2336-7; coupling with unactivated and hindered ar. chlorides with [1,1'-bis(di-*tert*-butylphosphino)ferrocene]palladium(II) chloride s. T.J. Colacot, H.A. Shea, Org. Lett. *6,* 3731-4 (2004); **with sterically demanding, electron-rich bis(Δ^2-oxazoline)-condensed palladium(II) imidazol-2-ylidene complexes** for preparing **tetra-*o*-subst. biphenyls** s. G. Altenhoff, F. Glorious et al., J. Am. Chem. Soc. *126,* 15195-201 (2004); with palladium(II) 1,3-diarylimidazol-2-ylidene complexes s. K. Arentsen, S. Caddick et al., Tetrahedron Lett. *45,* 3511-5 (2004); with a palladium(II) 1-(2,6-diisopropylphenyl)-3-[2-(diphenylphosphino)benzyl]imidazol-2-ylidene complex s. A.E. Wang, Q.-L. Zhou et al., Adv. Synth. Catal. *346,* 595-8 (2004); with 1,1'-ethylenebis(benzimidazolium bromides) as ligand in aq. medium cf. I. Ozdemir, B. Cetinkaya et al., Synth. Commun. *34,* 4135-44 (2004); with ferrocenylpalladacyclics (cf. *56,* 445s*64*) s. F.X. Roca, C.J. Richards, Chem. Commun. *2003,* 3002-3; with unsym. *NCP-pincer-type* palladacyclics s. G.R. Rosa, A.L. Monteiro et al., Synthesis *2003,* 2894-7.

*Pallodous acetate/tri-*tert*-butylphosphine/acetic acid* $Pd(OAc)_2$/*t-Bu_3P*/AcOH
Synthesis of 2(5*H*)-furanones
from α,β-acetylene-γ-hydroxycarboxylic acid esters and unsatd. boronic acids

463.

3-Aryl-2(5*H*)-furanones. A mixture of the startg. 4-hydroxyacetylenecarboxylic acid ester, 1 eq. *p*-methoxyphenylboronic acid, 3 mol% $Pd(OAc)_2$, 6 mol% tri-*tert*-butylphosphine and 10 mol% acetic acid in *THF* heated at 60° for 4 h → product. Y 98%. Reaction involves initial regiospecific hydroarylation of the acetylene bond, followed by lactonization, the regioselectivity being largely dependent on the bulk of the γ-substituent(s), the solvent, and the choice of ligand [1,2-bis(diphenylphosphino)ethane favouring the 4-aryl-derivs.]. F.e., also vinyl derivs. with α,β-ethyleneboronic acids, s. C.H. Oh et al., Tetrahedron Lett. *45,* 7039-42 (2004).

Palladous acetate/tricyclohexylphosphine/cesium fluoride $Pd(OAc)_2/Cy_3P/CsF$
Carbazoles from *o*-iodoamines and *o*-silyltriflates
Benzynes as intermediates

464.

A soln. of 1 eq. startg. *o*-iodoaniline in acetonitrile treated with 1.1 eqs. *o*-(trimethylsilyl)phenyl triflate and 3 eqs. CsF, stirred at room temp. under air for 10 h, flushed with argon, treated with 5 mol% Pd(OAc)$_2$ and 10 mol% tricyclohexylphosphine, and heated under argon at 100° for 24 h → product. Y 87%. This simple, mild and economical protocol involves initial fluoride ion-mediated N-phenylation with benzyne, followed by intramolecular Heck arylation. F.e., regioselectivity, and comparison of Pd-catalysts, **also dibenzofurans from *o*-iodophenols**, s. Z. Liu, R.C. Larock, Org. Lett. *6*, 3739-41 (2004).

Palladous acetate/triphenylphosphine $Pd(OAc)_2/Ph_3P$
Aryl ketones from carboxylic acid 2-pyridyl esters and arylboronic acids $B(OH)_2 \rightarrow COR$

465.

$Ar = p\text{-}NO_2C_6H_4$

Diaryl ketones. A mixture of 1 eq. startg. 2-pyridyl ester, 2 eqs. phenylboronic acid, 3 mol% Pd(OAc)$_2$, and 9 mol% triphenylphosphine in anhydrous dioxane stirred at 50° under N$_2$ for 10 h → product. Y 94%. The 2-pyridyloxy residue serves a dual role: as an efficient leaving group, and in facilitating the condensation by initial coordination to palladium as the key step. The procedure is mild, tolerant of a range of functional groups, and applicable to both aliphatic and aromatic 2-pyridyl esters. Coupling with 9-benzyl-9-borabicyclo[3.3.1]nonane was also effected in the presence of tricyclohexylphosphine. F.e. and comparison of catalysts s. H. Tatamidani, F. Kakiuchi, N. Chatani, Org. Lett. *6*, 3597-9 (2004); **from 2-pyridylmethyl esters and arylboronic acid esters** with Ru$_3$(CO)$_{12}$ cf. J. Org. Chem. *69*, 5615-21 (2004).

Palladous acetate/triphenylphosphine/sodium hydroxide $Pd(OAc)_2/Ph_3P/NaOH$
Intramolecular carbopalladation-Suzuki coupling
4-benzyl-3-methylene-1-tosylpyrrolidines with Pd(PPh$_3$)$_4$/Na$_2$CO$_3$ cf. *55*, 454s60; (E)-3-aryl-idenephthalimidines with Pd(OAc)$_2$/Ph$_3$P/NaOH in aq. medium s. S. Couty, J. Cossy et al., Org. Lett. *6*, 2511-4 (2004).

Palladous acetate/triphenylphosphine/potassium carbonate/isopropanol/triflimide/   ←
   sulfur dioxide
Synthesis of benzyloxy-3-ethylenes   ←
from benzyl (1,3-dien)olethers and Si-nucleophiles
Asym. induction via δ-benzyloxy-β,γ-ethylenesulfonic acid silyl esters
with allyl(trimethyl)silane as nucleophile cf. *67*, 448; chiral (E)-β-benzyloxy-δ,ε-ethyleneketones from enoxysilanes under Pd-catalysis with Pd(OAc)$_2$/Ph$_3$P/K$_2$CO$_3$/*i*-PrOH s. X.G. Huang, C. Craita, P. Vogel, J. Org. Chem. *69*, 4272-5 (2004).

Palladous acetate/triphenylphosphine/potassium phosphate $Pd(OAc)_2/Ph_3P/K_3PO_4$
Diarylmethanes from arylboronic acids and benzyl halides   ArCH$_2$Ar'
with Pd(PPh$_3$)$_4$/Na$_2$CO$_3$ cf. *64*, 453s67 (Vol 67, p. 293); from benzyl bromides or chlorides with

Pd(OAc)$_2$/Ph$_3$P/K$_3$PO$_4$ s. S.M. Nobre, A.L. Monteiro, Tetrahedron Lett. *45*, 8225-8 (2004); ligand-less procedure from benzyl bromides or iodides **in aq. medium** with PdCl$_2$/K$_2$CO$_3$ s. B.P. Bandgar, S.V. Bettigeri, J. Phophase, ibid. 8225-8.

Palladous acetate/dicyclohexyl(2,6-dimethoxybiphenyl-2-yl)phosphine/potassium salt ←
Diaryls from potassium aryl(trifluoro)borates Ar-Ar'
and diaryliodonium salts cf. *57*, 438; **and ar. or hetar. chlorides** with dicyclohexyl(2,6-dimethoxybiphenyl-2-yl)phosphine as ligand s. T.E. Barder, S.L. Buchwald, Org. Lett. *6*, 2649-52 (2004).

Palladous acetate/bis[2-(diphenylphosphino)phenyl] ether/cuprous iodide/lithium salt ←
Sym. 1,3-diynes from lithium alk-1-ynyl(trialkoxy)borates RC≡C-C≡CR
s. *53*, 471s68

Palladous acetate/1,3,5,7-tetramethyl-6-(2,4-dimethoxyphenyl)-2,4,8-trioxa-6- ←
phosphaadamantane
Suzuki coupling of alkyl halides with 9-alkyl-9-borabicyclo[3.3.1]nonanes >BR → R-R'
using Pd$_2$(dba)$_3$/tri-2-furylphosphine/CsOH cf. *62*, 451s63; coupling of alkyl chlorides, bromides or tosylates using Pd(OAc)$_2$ and 1,3,5,7-tetramethyl-6-(2,4-dimethoxyphenyl)-2,4,8-trioxa-6-phosphaadamantane as ligand, also coupling with arylboronic acids (cf. *64*, 453), s. T. Brenstrum, J. McNulty, A. Capretta et al., J. Org. Chem. *69*, 7635-9 (2004); α-arylsulfoxides from arylboronic acids and α-bromosulfoxides with Pd(PPh$_3$)$_4$/CsF s. N. Rodriguez, G. Asensio et al., ibid. 8070-6.

Bis(dibenzylideneacetone)palladium(0)/3-iodo-2-methyl-2-cyclohexenone ←
Stereospecific synthesis of 3'-hydroxyenesilanes from allenes and aldehydes ←
via regiospecific palladium-catalyzed silaboration
One-pot conversion via (E)-β,γ-ethylene-β-silylboronic acid esters

466.

Ethyl acetate (as solvent), phenylallene and 1 eq. *p*-chlorobenzaldehyde added to 5 mol% 3-iodo-2-methyl-2-cyclohexenone, 2.5 mol% Pd(dba)$_2$, and 0.5 eq. 2-(dimethylphenylsilanyl)-4,4,5,5-tetramethyl[1,3,2]dioxaborolane, and stirred under N$_2$ at 80° for 5 h → product. Y 92% (*syn/anti* >99:1). This mild procedure is generally applicable to monoaryl- and monoalkylallenes, as well as 1,1-dimethylallene, affording *syn*-products predominantly with tolerance towards a variety of functional groups in both the allene and aldehyde. Interestingly, reaction is equally facile without the organic iodide as additive, but the regioselectivity of the silaboration is completely reversed. F.e. and isolation of the intermediates s. K.-J. Chang, C.-H. Cheng et al., J. Am. Chem. Soc. *127*, 126-31 (2005).

Bis(dibenzylideneacetone)palladium(0)/2-(dicyclohexylphosphino)biphenyl/tetra-n- ←
butylammonium fluoride/microwaves
Diaryls from triethylammonium arylsilicates and ar. bromides Ar-Ar'
under microwave irradiation s. *44*, 889s68

Bis(dibenzylideneacetone)palladium(0)/1,2-bis(diphenylphosphino)- Pd(dba)$_2$/dppe/CsF
ethane/cesium fluoride
***o*-Disubst. arenes from benzynes** ←
o-(arylthio)stannanes cf. *67*, 255; *o*-allylarylacetylenes from β,γ-ethylenechlorides and acetylenestannanes via carbopalladation-Stille coupling with Pd(dba)$_2$/dppe/CsF s. M. Jeganmohan, C.H. Cheng, Org. Lett. *6*, 2821-4 (2004).

Tris(dibenzylideneacetone)dipalladium/cuprous iodide/sodium tert-*butoxide* ←
Diaryls from arylsilanols and ar. halides Si(OH)< → Ar
with Pd(PPh$_3$)$_4$/Ag$_2$O cf. *45*, 555s58; 2-arylindoles from indol-2-yl(dimethyl)silanols with Pd$_2$(dba)$_3$/CuI/NaOBu-*t* s. S.E. Denmark, J.D. Baird, Org. Lett. *6*, 3649-52 (2004).

*Tris(dibenzylideneacetone)dipalladium/N-aryl-2-(1-pyrazolyl)benzaldimines/
cesium fluoride*
Suzuki diaryl coupling with N-aryl-2-(1-pyrazolyl)benzaldimines as ligand Ar-Ar'

467.

under mild conditions. 4-Bromoacetophenone and dioxane added via syringe to 1.5 eqs. phenylboronic acid, 1 mol% $Pd_2(dba)_3 \cdot CHCl_3$, 2 mol% N-(2,6-diisopropylphenyl)-2-(3,5-dimethyl-1-pyrazolyl)benzaldimine and 3 eqs. CsF, and heated with stirring at 45-55° under argon for 1 h → 4-acetylbiphenyl. Y 93%. The new *non-phosphorus* σ-donor ligands facilitate oxidative addition, while the steric congestion around the electron-rich metal centre accelerates the reductive elimination. Reaction is generally applicable to ar. bromides (incl. *o*-subst. derivs.) as well as activated and neutral ar. chlorides. F.e. and comparison of ligands s. A. Mukherjee, A. Sarkar, Tetrahedron Lett. **46**, 15-8 (2005).

Tris(dibenzylideneacetone)dipalladium/triphenylphosphine $Pd_2(dba)_3/Ph_3P$
Regio- and stereo-specific synthesis of ethylene derivs. $C=C-C(OAc) \rightarrow C=C-C(R)$
from acoxy-2-ethylenes and triorganoindium compds.

468.

under mild conditions. Atom-economical and environmentally friendly triorganoindium compds. are useful alternatives to the corresponding toxic organotin compds. and Grignard reagents in the classical synthesis of ethylene derivs. via palladium π-allyl complexes. **E:** A stirred soln. of the startg. cyclohex-2-enyl acetate, 1 mol% $Pd_2(dba)_3$, and 4 mol% triphenylphosphine in anhydrous THF treated with 0.5 eq. *in situ*-generated tris(*p*-methoxyphenyl)indium in the same solvent (0.06 *M*), and refluxed under argon for 3 h → product. Y 98%. The protocol is generally applicable to electron-rich and -poor triarylindiums and trivinylindiums, but trialkynyl- and trialkyl-indiums were not reactive. Substitution of a chiral cyclohex-2-enyl benzoate was shown to proceed **with inversion of configuration**. F.e.s. L. Baker, T. Minehan, J. Org. Chem. **69**, 3957-60 (2004).

Tris(dibenzylideneacetone)dipalladium/tri-2-furylphosphine $Pd_2(dba)_3/Ar_3P$
Regio- and stereo-specific synthesis of 1,2-dibenzyl-1,3-enynes $C(Bn)=C(Bn)C\equiv C$
from two acetylenestannane and two benzyl halide molecules

469.

2 eqs. Freshly-prepared startg. acetylenestannane added to a soln. of 5 mol% $Pd_2(dba)_3$, 10 mol% tri-2-furylphosphine and 2-bromobenzyl bromide in dioxane under N_2, warmed to 50° with TLC

monitoring until the benzyl halide was consumed (3-5 h), cooled to room temp., treated with aq. KF, stirred for 2 h at the same temp., tributyltin fluoride filtered off, and the filtrate worked up → product. Y 42%. Reaction is presumed to involve initial Stille coupling, followed by regiospecific carbopalladation and a second Stille coupling. F.e. and with benzyl chlorides s. L.R. Pottier, M. Alami et al., Tetrahedron Lett. *45*, 4035-8 (2004); **from two terminal acetylene deriv.** and two benzyl halide molecules with $PdCl_2(PPh_3)_2$/CuI/Bu_4NCl/Et_3N cf. Synlett *2004*, 1503-8.

Tris(dibenzylideneacetone)dipalladium/tetra-n-*butylammonium fluoride/sec-butyllithium/* ←
acetic acid
Regio- and stereo-specific 3-component synthesis CHO → CH(OH)CH$_2$CH=CH(Ar)
of (E)-4-aryl-3-ethylenealcohols
from oxo compds. and ar. halides with insertion of three C-atoms

470.

via (E)-4-hydroxyenesilanes. A soln. of 1 eq. allyl(isopropoxy)dimethylsilane in anhydrous THF treated dropwise with 1.1 eqs. *s*-BuLi in cyclohexane at -78° under N_2, stirred at the same temp. for 1 h, treated dropwise with 1.1 eqs. benzaldehyde, stirring continued at the same temp. for 0.5 h, warmed to 0°, 1.1 eqs. acetic acid added dropwise, followed by 0.7 eq. *p*-iodoacetophenone and 5 mol% $Pd_2(dba)_3$, the resulting mixture degassed with N_2, treated with 2.4 eqs. Bu_4NF (1 *M* in THF), stirred at room temp. under N_2 overnight, then quenched with water → (E)-product. Y 91%. Reaction involves initial regiospecific γ-lithiation of the allylsilane, followed by 1,2-addition to the oxo compds. and cross-coupling with the aryl halides with retention of configuration. F.e., scope and catalysts, **also 3,5-dienols** from α,β-ethylenebromides, s. L. Li, N. Navasero, Org. Lett. *6*, 3091-4 (2004).

[2,6-Bis(diphenylphosphinoxy)phenyl]palladium(II) trifluoroacetate ←
3-Ethylenealcohols from aldehydes and 2-ethylenestannanes CH(OH)C-C=C
via nucleophilic pincer-type palladium η^1-allyl complexes

471.

1.2 eqs. Allyltributylstannane added to a mixture of *p*-nitrobenzaldehyde and 5 mol% [2,6-bis-(diphenylphosphinoxy)phenyl]palladium(II) trifluoroacetate in anhydrous THF under argon, and stirred at 25° for 3 h → product. Y 95%. The key intermediate is a *mono*-allylpalladium species formed by displacement of the weakly coordinated trifluoroacetoxy ligand with the allylstannane, reaction being a significant improvement over syntheses via palladium bis-allyl complexes in that by-products are negligible and the scope is broader. The catalyst is also highly active and robust. F.e., also regio- and stereo-selectivity, s. N. Solin, J. Kjellgren, K.J. Szabo, J. Am. Chem. Soc. *126*, 7026-33 (2004).

Bis(benzonitrile)[(S,S)-1,2-[phenyl(2-methoxyphenyl)phosphino]ethane]palladium(II) ←
bis(hexafluoroantimonate)/cupric fluoroborate
Asym. 1,4-addition of triarylbismuthines to α,β-ethyleneketones C=C → CHC(Ar)
in aq. methanol s. *55*, 452s68

*Aquo[1,3-bis(2,6-diisopropylphenyl)imidazol-2-ylidene]palladium(II) acetate/tetra-*n- ←
butylammonium acetate/chlorotris(triphenylphosphine)rhodium(I)/triphenylphosphine/
potassium peroxymonosulfate/isopropanol/oxygen
Methylene compds. from alcohols via oxo compds. CHOH → C=CH$_2$
One-pot conversion under tandem catalysis

472.

The startg. alcohol added to a mixture of 2.5 mol% aquo[1,3-bis(2,6-diisopropylphenyl)imidazol-2-ylidene]palladium(II) acetate, 5 mol% Bu$_4$NOAc, and activated powdered 3 Å molecular sieves in toluene under argon, stirred under O$_2$ (1 atm.) at 60° for 12 h, cooled to room temp., treated under argon with a soln. of 2.5 mol% RhCl(PPh$_3$)$_3$, 10 eqs. isopropanol, and 1.1 eqs. triphenylphosphine in dioxane, 1.6 eqs. trimethylsilyldiazomethane added under argon, stirring continued at 50° until GC or TLC indicated completion of reaction, treated with 1 eq. Oxone, and stirred at the same temp. under argon for 2 h → product. Y 92%. The combination of catalysts is compatible with both aliphatic and benzylic alcohols, and yields are higher than by the stepwise approach. F.e. and dienes s H. Lebel, V. Paquet, J. Am. Chem. Soc. *126*, 11152-3 (2004).

Palladium(II) imidazol-2-ylidene complexes or polymer-based or bis(Δ^2- ←
oxazoline)-condensed variants
Suzuki diaryl coupling s. *37*, 902s68   Ar-Ar′

Tetrakis(triphenylphosphine)palladium(0)   *Pd(PPh$_3$)$_4$*
(E)-2-Aryl-1,3-dienes from arylboronic acids and 2-allenealcohols   C=C-C(Ar)=C
s. *68*, 460

Regiospecific palladium-catalyzed cross-coupling of 2-acetylenealcohols ←
with arylboronic acids

473.

Arylallenes. 2 eqs. 2-Methylphenylboronic acid and 10 mol% Pd(PPh$_3$)$_4$ added to a stirred soln. of 2-phenyl-3-butyn-2-ol in 1,4-dioxane at room temp., and stirred for 30 min at 100° → product. Y 99%. Reaction is tolerant of electron-withdrawing and -donating groups in the aryl residue, but 2-acetylene-*prim*-alcohols gave the corresponding **propargylarenes** predominantly. An allenylpalladium hydroxide is invoked as the key intermediate. F.e.s. M. Yoshida, T. Gotou, M. Ihara, Tetrahedron Lett. *45*, 5573-5 (2004).

Cross-coupling with tetraorganoindates   ←
with bromomagnesium tetraorganoindates cf. *58*, 462s67; **ketones by carbonylative cross-coupling** of Li-tetraorganoindates (alkyl and aryl derivs.) with reactive halides s. S.W. Lee, D. Seomoon, P.H. Lee, J. Org. Chem. *69*, 4852-5 (2004).

**Regiospecific synthesis of 1,7-enynes
from electron-deficient ethylene derivs., β,γ-ethylenechlorides and allenestannanes**

474.

Ar = C₆H₄OMe-p

A soln. of 2-(4-methoxybenzylidene)-1,3-indanedione and 5 mol% Pd(PPh₃)₄ in THF treated under N₂ with 1.2 eqs. methallyl chloride and 1.2 eqs. tri-*n*-butylstannyllallene, stirred at room temp. for 8 h, satd. aq. KF added, stirring continued at the same temp. for 30 min, then filtered through Celite → product. Y 81%. Reaction is presumed to involve a completely regioselective 1,2-allylpropargylation of the electron-deficient ethylene deriv. with an intermediate η¹-allenyl-palladium π-allyl complex. Other allyl derivs. and allyl alcohol itself were less effective. F.e.s. M. Jeganmohan, M. Shanmugasundaram, C.-H. Cheng, J. Org. Chem. *69*, 4053-62 (2004).

Tetrakis(triphenylphosphine)palladium(0)/potassium phosphate   Pd(PPh₃)₄/K₃PO₄
**Cyclic 2-aryl-1,5-dienes from 9-chloro-1,2,7-trienes and arylboronic acids
via regio- and stereo-specific intramolecular carbopalladation-Suzuki coupling**

475.

E = CO₂Me

A mixture of 1 eq. of the startg. 9-chloro-1,2,7-triene, 2 eqs. startg. arylboronic acid, 2 eqs. K₃PO₄·3H₂O and 5 mol% Pd(PPh₃)₄ in anhydrous toluene heated with stirring under argon at 50° for 4 h → product. Y 95% (*cis/trans* 85:15). *cis*-Selectivity was 100% from O- and N-tethered substrates. The ring closure affords *cis*-disubst. 5-membered rings, and reaction is tolerant of electron-withdrawing or -donating groups in the aryl ring. However, yields were lower from substrates possessing a terminal allene group. F.e. and with allylic bromides or carbonates as substrate s. G. Zhu, Z. Zhang, Org. Lett. *6*, 4041-4 (2004).

Tetrakis(triphenylphosphine)palladium(0)/cesium fluoride   Pd(PPh₃)₄/CsF
α-Arylsulfoxides from arylboronic acids and α-bromosulfoxides s. *64*, 453s68   Ar-R

Tetrakis(triphenylphosphine)palladium(0)/cuprous 2-carboxylate/microwaves   ←
Cross-coupling of unsatd. boronic acids with organothio-N-heterocyclics   SR → R'
s. *63*, 406s65; with 2-alkylthio-Δ²-imidazol-5-ones, rapid procedure under microwave irradiation in DMF, also coupling with arylstannanes, s. S. Oumouch, J.J. Bourguignon et al., Synthesis *2005*, 25-7.

[(S)-2,2'-Bis(dicyclohexylphosphino)-1,1'-binaphthyl]palladium(II) hexafluoro-   ←
antimonate/(S)-2,2'-bis(dicyclohexylphosphino)-1,1'-binaphthyl/barium hydroxide
Asym. Suzuki diaryl coupling   Ar-Ar'
with PdCl₂/chiral ferrocenyl(amino)phosphines/CsF cf. *59*, 447; rapid procedure with [(S)-2,2'-bis(dicyclohexylphosphino)-1,1'-binaphthyl]palladium(II) hexafluoroantimonate/(S)-2,2'-bis-(dicyclohexylphosphino)-1,1'-binaphthyl/Ba(OH)₂ and related cationic palladium(II) complexes s. K. Mikami, T. Miyamoto, M. Hatano, Chem. Commun. *2004*, 2082-3.

Palladous chloride s.a. under Zn   PdCl₂

Palladous chloride/potassium carbonate   PdCl₂/K₂CO₃
Diarylmethanes from arylboronic acids and benzyl halides s. *64*, 453s68   ArCH₂Ar'

Bis(η^3-allylpalladium chloride)/cuprous chloride/tetra-n-*butylammonium fluoride* ←
Styrenes from ar. iodides and enesilanes C=C(Si≤) → C=C(Ar)
from enesilanols with Pd(PPh$_3$)$_4$/Ag$_2$O cf. *45*, 555s*59*; from sym. divinyldisiloxanes with [(η^3-allyl)PdCl]$_2$/CuCl/Bu$_4$NF s. S.K. Gjosh, R. Singh, G.C. Singh, Eur. J. Org. Chem. *2004*, 4141-7.

Bis(η^3-allylpalladium chloride)/2-(dicyclohexylphosphino)- ←
2′,4′,6′-triisopropylbiphenyl/tetra-n-*butylammonium fluoride*
Diaryls from arylsilanes and ar. halides Ar-Ar′
from aryl(triallyl)silanes and ar. bromides in aq. medium with PdCl$_2$/Cy$_3$P/Bu$_4$NF cf. *52*, 467s*67*; **from ar. chlorides** with [(η^3-allyl)PdCl]$_2$/2-(dicyclohexylphosphino)-2′,4′,6′-triisopropylbiphenyl/Bu$_4$NF s. A.K. Sahoo, Y. Nakao, T. Hiyama, Chem. Lett. *33*, 632-3 (2004); from triethylammonium arylsilicates with Pd(dba)$_2$/2-(dicyclohexylphosphino)biphenyl/Bu$_4$NF in THF, rapid procedure under microwave irradiation (cf. *44*, 889s*67*), s. W.M. Seganish, P. DeShong, Org. Lett. *6*, 4379-8 (2004).

Dichlorobis(triphenylphosphine)palladium(II) $PdCl_2(PPh_3)_2$
Intramolecular carbopalladation-Wittig synthesis s. *68*, 418 ○

Dichlorobis(triphenylphosphine)palladium(II)/microwaves $PdCl_2(PPh_3)_2$/[\\\\]
Aryl ketones from carboxylic acid anhydrides (RCO)$_2$O → RCOAr
and arylboronic acids with [RhCl(CH$_2$=CH$_2$)]$_2$ cf. *62*, 452; acetophenones from sodium tetraphenylborate with PdCl$_2$(PPh$_3$)$_2$ under microwave irradiation s. J.X. Wang, Y.Q. Zhang, Chin. Chem. Lett. *15*, 641-2 (2004).

Dichlorobis(triphenylphosphine)palladium(II)/potassium $PdCl_2(PPh_3)_2/KF\text{-}Al_2O_3$/[\\\\]
fluoride-alumina/)/microwaves
Diaryls from tetraarylborates under microwave irradiation Ar-Ar′
with Pd(OAc)$_2$/Na$_2$CO$_3$ s. *46*, 906s*61*; with PdCl$_2$(PPh$_3$)$_2$/KF-Al$_2$O$_3$ in the absence of solvent s. J.-X. Wang, Y.-H. Yang, B.-G. Wei, Synth. Commun. *34*, 2063-9 (2004).

Dichlorobis(triphenylphosphine)palladium(II)/cuprous iodide $PdCl_2(PPh_3)_2$/CuI
α,β-Acetyleneketones C≡C-CO
from lithium alk-1-ynyl(trialkoxy)borates and carboxylic acid chlorides s. *64*, 449s*68*

Dichlorobis(triphenylphosphine)palladium(II)/tetra-n-*butylammonium fluoride/oxygen* ←
Homocoupling of organoboron compds. R-R
sym. diaryls from arylboronic acids cf. *53*, 471; with PdCl$_2$(PPh$_3$)$_2$/Bu$_4$NF/O$_2$ **in aq. medium**, also from arylboronic acid esters, s. S. Punna, D.D. Diaz, M.G. Finn, Synlett *2004*, 2351-4; sym. 1,3-diynes from lithium alk-1-ynyl(trialkoxy)borates with Pd(OAc)$_2$/bis[2-(diphenylphosphino)-phenyl] ether/CuI s. C.H. Oh, V.R. Reddy, Tetrahedron Lett. *45*, 5221-4 (2004).

Dichloro[1,1′-bis(diphenylphosphino)ferrocene]palladium(II) $PdCl_2$(dppf)
Tetrakis(triphenylphosphine)platinum(0)/cuprous iodide $Pt(PPh_3)_4$/CuI
Cross-coupling with alkali metal alk-1-ynylborates ←
arylacetylenes from potassium alk-1-ynyl(trifluoro)borates s. *64*, 449s*65*; 4-alk-1-ynyl-2(5*H*)-furanones and -coumarins with PdCl$_2$(dppf)·CH$_2$Cl$_2$ s. G.W. Kabalka, G. Dong, B. Venkataiah, Tetrahedron Lett. *45*, 5139-41 (2004); **α,β-acetyleneketones** from lithium alk-1-ynyl(trialkoxy)borates and carboxylic acid chlorides with PdCl$_2$(PPh$_3$)$_2$/CuI s. C.H. Oh, V.R. Reddy, ibid. 8545-8; **arylacetylenes** from ar. iodides with Pt(PPh$_3$)$_4$/CuI s. Synlett *2004*, 2091-4.

Carbon ↑ CC ↓↑ C

Microwaves (s.a. under AcOH) [\\\\]
Decarboxylative 1,3-dipolar cycloaddition via non-stabilized azomethinium ylids ○
s. *43*, 897s*67*; rapid procedure under microwave irradiation in the absence of solvent, 2,3-dispiropyrrolidines, s. J. Jayashankaran, R.D.R.S. Manian, R. Raghunathan, Tetrahedron Lett. *45*, 7303-5 (2004); 2-spiropyrrolidines in DMSO s. J. Azizian, M.R. Mohammadizedeh et al., J. Chem. Res. Synop *2004*, 347-9.

Sodium hydride/sulfuric acid   NaH/H$_2$SO$_4$
Synthesis of ketones from α-aminonitriles   CH(N⊂)CN → COR
with KNH$_2$/HCl cf. *18*, 881; large-scale procedure with NaH/H$_2$SO$_4$ in one pot s. T. Ohshima, S. Nishimura, T. Ando et al., World Intellectual Property Organisation patent WO-2003014051 (Ishihara Sangyo Kaisha Ltd.).

Potassium hydroxide   KOH
Benzene ring from 2-pyrones and ketones   ←
s. *22*, 877s59; with methylglyoxal dimethyl acetal as ketone component s. R. Pratap, D. Sil, V.J. Ram, Tetrahedron Lett. *45*, 5743-5 (2004); **benzocyclobutenes** from cyclobutanones s. D. Sil, V.J. Ram et al., Synlett *2004*, 2163-4; 4,5-dihydronaphtho[2,1-*b*]furans s. A. Geol, M. Dixit, Tetrahedron Lett. *45*, 8819-21 (2004).

Sodium fluoride   NaF
1,1-Difluorocyclopropanes from ethylene derivs.   ▽
using Me$_3$SiOCOCF$_2$SO$_2$F as the carbene precursor s. *21*, 879s65; 2,2-difluorocyclopropyl difluoromethyl ethers from electron-rich and α,β-unsatd. ketones s. X.-H. Cai, W.R. Dolbier et al., J. Org. Chem. *69*, 4210-5 (2004).

Cupric triflate/chiral 1,2-bis(benzyloxy)-1,2-bis(1-benzylimidazol-2-yl)ethane   ←
β-Hydroxythiolic acid esters   CHO → CH(OH)C-C(O)SR
from aldehydes and monothiolmalonic acid S-monoesters
with Cu(II)-2-ethylhexanoate and 5-methoxybenzimidazole cf. *65*, 477; **asym. decarboxylative aldol condensation** with Cu(OTf)$_2$ and chiral 1,2-bis(benzyloxy)-1,2-bis(1-benzylimidazol-2-yl)ethane s. S. Orlandi, M. Benaglia, F. Cozzi, Tetrahedron Lett. *45*, 1747-9 (2004).

Cuprous iodide/triphenylphosphine/potassium carbonate   CuI/Ph$_3$P/K$_2$CO$_3$
Pyrrole ring from *o*-halogenacylamines and acetylene derivs. s. *47*, 819s68   ◯

Cupric chloride s. under PdBr$_2$ CuCl$_2$

Magnesium/ferric acetoacetonate   Mg/Fe(acac)$_3$
Diaryl ketones from aroylcyanides and ar. halides   COCN → COAr

476.

A soln. of 1.2 eqs. 4-iodobenzonitrile in anhydrous THF treated slowly under argon at -20° with 1.3 eqs. isopropylmagnesium chloride (1.4 *M* in THF), stirred for 30 min, the resulting Grignard soln. added dropwise via cannula over 25 min to a stirred soln. of 1 eq. of the startg. aroyl cyanide and 5 mol% Fe(acac)$_3$ in anhydrous THF at -10°, and quenched with aq. NH$_4$Cl soln. → product. Y 71%. Yields were considerably lower with aroyl chlorides. The method is efficient and high yielding for the coupling of functionalized aroyl cyanides (incl. *p*-methoxy-, *p*-carbethoxy- and *p*-chloro-derivs.) with functionalized Grignards (incl. *o*-subst. and heteroaryl derivs.). F.e.s. C. Duplais, P. Knochel et al., Angew. Chem. Int. Ed. Engl. *43*, 2968-70 (2004).

Indium s. under TiCl$_4$ In

Trimethylaluminum/chiral 2'-aryl-2-hydroxy-3-(o-hydroxyphenyl)-1,1'-binaphthyls   ←
Meerwein-Ponndorf-Verley synthesis of 2-acetylenealcohols from aldehydes   CH(OH)C≡C
with (*o,o'*-biphenylenedioxy)methylaluminum s. *56*, 454; **asym. synthesis** with Me$_3$Al and chiral 2'-aryl-2-hydroxy-3-(*o*-hydroxyphenyl)-1,1'-binaphthyls s. T. Ooi, T. Miura, K. Maruoka et al., Org. Biomol. Chem. *2*, 3312-9 (2004).

Trimethylaluminum/(R)-2,2'-bis(trifluoromethanesulfonylamino)-1,1'-binaphthyl ←
β-Hydroxyketones from aldehydes and enolethers CHO → CH(OH)C-CO
Asym. carbonyl-ene reaction under mild conditions

477.

A soln. of 5 mol% trimethylaluminum in hexane (1 *M*) added to a soln. of 5 mol% (R)-2,2'-bis-(trifluoromethanesulfonylamino)-1,1'-binaphthyl in freshly-distilled methylene chloride at room temp. under argon, refluxed 1 h, chilled to -78°, 3-phenyl-1-propanal added, followed dropwise by 2.1 eqs. 2-methoxypropene, stirred at the same temp. for 30 min, poured into 1 *N* aq. HCl at 0°, and stirring continued at the same temp. for 30 min → product. Y 95% (e.e. 86%). Reaction is applicable to aliphatic and ar. aldehydes, but enantioselectivity was lower with α-branched derivs. F.e., also **chiral 4-hydroxy-2-methylenesilanes** by asym. carbonyl-ene reaction with methallylsilanes, s. T. Ooi, K. Maruoka et al., Tetrahedron Lett. *45*, 4481-4 (2004).

Indium(III) triflate $In(OTf)_3$
4-Hydroxy-1-silylacetylenes from aldehydes CHO → CH(OH)CH$_2$C≡CSi≤
Synthesis with addition of three C-atoms via 2-oxonia-[3.3]-sigmatropic rearrangement

478.

under mild conditions. A soln. of 1 mol% In(OTf)$_3$ in anhydrous methylene chloride treated at room temp. under N$_2$ with a mixture of 4 eqs. cyclohexanecarboxaldehyde and 1 eq. of the startg. 2-allenealcohol (0.03 *M*), stirred at the same temp. for 1 h, and quenched with satd. aq. NaHCO$_3$ → product. Y 98%. Interestingly, reaction with chiral silylallenealcohols proceeds **with asym. induction** to give products with opposite hydroxyl group configuration. The silyl group, which stabilizes the developing carbocation by the β-effect, appears to be essential. F.e. with a variety of different aldehydes s. K.-C. Lee, M.-J. Lin, T.-P. Loh, Chem. Commun. *2004*, 2456-7.

Ytterbium(III) triflate s. under Pd$_2$(dba)$_3$ $Yb(OTf)_3$

Samarium Sm
C-Transacylation of β-ketocarboxylic acid esters COR → COR'
with carboxylic acid chlorides
with NaOH/NH$_4$Cl cf. *13*, 838; with *1 mol%* Sm in toluene s. Y.-D. Zhang, Y.-M. Zhang, J. Chem. Res. Synop *2004*, 510-2.

Δ^2-Imidazolinium salts s. under Pd(OAc)$_2$ ←

Benzoyl peroxide (PhCOO)$_2$
Radical synthesis of (E)-ethylene derivs. from (E)-1,1-nitroethylene derivs. NO$_2$ → R
and alkyl iodides with Et$_3$Al/(PhCOO)$_2$ cf. *61*, 382; and branched aldehydes with (PhCOO)$_2$ s. Y.-J. Jang, C.-F. Yao et al., J. Org. Chem. *69*, 3961-3 (2004).

Acetic acid/piperidine/microwaves $AcOH/(CH_2)_5NH/[\backslash\backslash\backslash\backslash]$
Doebner synthesis of α,β-ethylenecarboxylic acids $CHO \rightarrow CH=CHCOOH$
under microwave irradiation
in pyridine cf. *1*, 569s67; cinnamic acids in acetic acid with piperidine (cf. *1*, 569s60) and subsequent reduction to 3-phenylpropionic acids s. A. Sharma, B.P. Joshi, A.K. Sinha, Chem. Lett. *32*, 1186-7 (2003).

Titanium tetrachloride/indium $TiCl_4/In$
Sym. α-diketones from acyl cyanides $2\ RCOCN \rightarrow RCOCOR$
with SmI_2 cf. *54*, 475; coupling of aroyl cyanides with $TiCl_4/In$ s. B.W. Yoo et al., Bull. Korean Chem. Soc. *24*, 263-4 (2003).

Di-n-butyltin dimethoxide/methanol $Bu_2Sn(OMe)_2/MeOH$
(E)-α,β-Ethyleneketones $C(OCOR)=CH \rightarrow COC=CH$
from aldehydes and enol trichloroacetates

479.

A soln. of 5 mol% dibutyltin dimethoxide in dry THF added to a soln. of 2 eqs. of the startg. enol trichloroacetate and cinnamaldehyde in the same solvent at 30° under argon, 20 eqs. methanol added dropwise, stirring continued for 24 h at the same temp., methanol, brine and solid KF added, and stirred again for 30 min at room temp. → product. Y 89% (purity 98%). The method is milder and superior to the classical Claisen-Schmidt condensation which requires a strong base and is often complicated by aldol condensation. It is also generally applicable on a substantial scale to aliphatic, aromatic and α,β-ethylenic aldehydes. F.e.s. A. Yanagisawa, R. Goudu, T. Arai, Org. Lett. *6*, 4281-3 (2004).

Camphorsulfonic acid RSO_3H
3-Ethylenealcohols from aldehydes via asym. C-allyl transfer $CHO \rightarrow CH(OH)C-C=C$
with TfOH cf. *62*, 264s65; with camphorsulfonic acid at 0° to minimize racemization s. C.H.A. Lee, T.-P. Loh, Tetrahedron Lett. *45*, 5819-22 (2004).

p-Toluenesulfonic acid $TsOH$
Indoles from N-protected N-arylhydrazines and ketones
from N-aryl-N-benzylhydrazine hydrochlorides cf. *14*, 836; from N-aryl-N-carbo-*tert*-butoxyhydrazines and enolizable ketones **with simultaneous N-decarbo-*tert*-butoxylation** using TsOH s. Y.-K. Lim, C.-G. Cho, Tetrahedron Lett. *45*, 1857-9 (2004).

Molybdenum hexacarbonyl/3-hexyne/1,2-diphenoxyethane/o-fluorophenol   ←
Cross-metathesis of acetylene derivs. $C≡C$
with tris[3,5-xylyl(*tert*-butyl)amino]molybdenum(III) and methylene chloride as activator cf. *30*, 467s61; with $Mo(CO)_6$/3-hexyne/1,2-diphenoxyethane and *o*-fluorophenol as activator for cross-metathesis of internal alkynes s. V. Sashuk, J. Ignatowska, K. Grela, J. Org. Chem. *69*, 7748-51 (2004).

Ferric acetoacetonate s. under Mg $Fe(acac)_3$

Bis(1,5-cyclooctadiene)nickel(0) $Ni(cod)_2$
3,4-Di(alkylidene)cycloheptanones
from chromium α,β-ethylene(alkoxy)carbene complexes and two allene molecules s. *59*, 411s68

Alkylidene(dichloro)ruthenium(II) imidazolidin-2-ylidene complex (s.a. under $RhCl(PPh_3)_3$) ←
Cross-metathesis of ethylene derivs. ←
s. *49*, 932s67; trisubst. (Z)-α,β-ethyleneboronic acid esters s. C. Morrill, T.W. Funk, R.H. Grubbs, Tetrahedron Lett. *45*, 7733-6 (2004); (Z)-1,3-enynes s. E.C. Hansen, D. Lee, Org. Lett. *6*, 2035-8 (2004); (E)-vinyl-chlorins and -porphyrins s. X. Liu, E. Sternberg, D. Dolphin, Chem. Commun. *2004*, 852-3.

**1,3-Cyclohexadienes from terminal acetylene derivs.
via cross-metathesis with 1,5-cyclooctadiene**

480.

R = CH$_2$CH$_2$COOEt

A soln. of 1 eq. of the startg. alkyne and 2 eqs. 1,5-cyclooctadiene in anhydrous methylene chloride added *over 4 h* to a refluxing mixture of 2 eqs. 1,5-cyclooctadiene and 5 mol% Grubbs' second generation catalyst in the same solvent, and stirring continued at the same temp. for 45 min → product. Y 68%. Significantly, reaction proceeds without the participation of a terminal alkene residue so that a 'methylene-free' cross-metathesis ensues with the intermediacy of a key ruthenium (Z)-α,β-ethylenecarbene species. Both propargylic and homopropargylic functionality is tolerated, and remote ester groups are left intact. F.e.s. A.A. Kulkarni, S.T. Diver, J. Am. Chem. Soc. *126*, 8110-1 (2004).

Soluble polymer-based dichloro(o-isopropoxybenzylidene)ruthenium(II) imidazolidin-2-ylidene complexes ←
Cross-metathesis of ethylene derivs. ←
Also ring opening-cross metathesis s *60*, 498s68

Dichloro(tricyclohexylphosphine)[o-isopropoxy(nitro)benzylidene]ruthenium(II) complexes ←
Cross-metathesis of ethylene derivs. ←
with the Grubbs'-Hoveyda complex cf. *59*, 467s62; enhancement of catalytic activity with nitro analogs, also details of ring-closing metathesis (cf. *64*, 497) s. A. Michrowska, K. Grela et al., J. Am. Chem. Soc. *126*, 9318-25 (2004).

Chlorotris(triphenylphosphine)rhodium(I)/diphenyl[4-(carbo-2-trimethylsilylethoxy)-phenyl]phosphine/isopropanol/potassium peroxymonosulfate/dichloro-ruthenium(II) imidazol-2-ylidene complex/tetra-n-butylammonium fluoride ←
Cyclic ethylene derivs. from ethyleneoxo compds. via terminal dienes
One-pot procedure under tandem catalysis

481.

via ring-closing metathesis. A soln. of 2.5 mol% RhCl(PPh$_3$)$_3$ in dioxane treated successively with a soln. of 1.1 eqs. diphenyl[4-(carbo-2-trimethylsilylethoxy)phenyl]phosphine in the same solvent, 1 eq. isopropanol, and 1 eq. of the startg. ethylenecarbonyl compd., 1.4 eqs. trimethylsilyl-diazomethane added (with gas evolution), stirred under argon at 50° until GC or TLC indicated completion of reaction, treated with 1 eq. Oxone (to 'deactivate' the phosphine ligand), stirring continued at the same temp. for 2 h, treated with 10 mol% Grubbs' second generation catalyst, stirred at the same temp. for 16 h, cooled to 0°, 5 eqs. Bu$_4$NF in THF added, warmed to room temp., stirred for 12 h, diluted with methylene chloride, and washed with 10% aq. NaOH → product. Y 80%. The two transition metal complexes are mutually compatible, and yields higher than by the 2-step approach with isolation of the intermediate methylene compds. F.e. incl. 5-, 6-, and 7-membered carbo- and hetero-cyclics s. H. Lebel, V. Paquet, J. Am. Chem. Soc. *126*, 11152-3 (2004).

Palladous acetate/1-(2-methoxyethyl)-3-(2,4,6-trimethylbenzyl)-Δ²-imidazolinium chloride/cesium carbonate
Arylacetic acid esters from ar. halides   Hal → CH_2COOR
Synthesis with addition of two C-atoms under mild conditions

482.

Equimolar amounts of 4-bromobenzaldehyde and diethyl malonate, 2 eqs. Cs_2CO_3, 1.5 mol% Pd(OAc)$_2$ and 3 mol% 1-(2-methoxyethyl)-3-(2,4,6-trimethylbenzyl)-Δ²-imidazolinium chloride in dioxane heated at 80° for 24 h → product. Y 94%. With variously substituted 1,3-disubst. imidazolinium salts as ligand, reaction proceeds efficiently and rapidly **via highly active palladium(II) imidazolidin-2-ylidene complexes,** which are a distinct improvement over palladium phosphine complexes which are limited in applicability and air-sensitive. Significantly, this new variant is successful with activated and deactivated *ar. chlorides*, as well as *2,6-disubst.* ar. bromides, and can be performed in moist air. F.e.s. I. Ozdemir, B. Cetinkaya et al., Tetrahedron Lett. *45*, 5823-5 (2004).

Palladous acetate/1,1'-bis(di-tert-butylphosphino)ferrocene/potassium carbonate
Indoles from N-protected *o*-halogenamines and acetylene derivs.
with Pd(II)-exchanged zeolite NaY and Cs_2CO_3 cf. *47*, 829s67; from *o*-halogenacylamines by N-deacylative condensation with Pd(OAc)$_2$/dppf/K_2CO_3, s. M. Shen, C.H. Senanayake et al., Org. Lett. *6*, 4129-32 (2004); 1*H*-pyrrolo[2,3-*b*]quinoxalines with CuI/Ph$_3$P/K_2CO_3 s. S. Cacchi et al., Synlett *2004*, 287-90.

Tris(dibenzylideneacetone)dipalladium/ytterbium(III) chloride/O,O-isopropylidene-1,4-bis(diphenylphosphino)butane-2,3-diol
β-Hydroxyketones from aldehydes and β-ketocarboxylic acid allyl esters
Heterobimetal-catalyzed decarballyloxylative aldol condensation

483.

A soln. of 5 mol% $YbCl_3$, 2.5 mol% $Pd_2(dba)_3$, and *10 mol%* DIOP in methylene chloride stirred at room temp. for 0.5 h, 1 eq. of the startg. aldehyde and *2.5 eqs.* of the startg. allyl β-keto-ester added sequentially, and stirred under argon at the same temp. for 24 h → product. Y 84% (d.r. 1.6:1). The catalytic cycle involves Pd-catalyzed decarballyloxylation, while Yb(III) favours formation of an intermediate enolate prior to elimination of the product. The di(phosphine) ligand is thought to be associated with both metals, and an excess of the startg. keto-ester is required to serve as an allyl trapping agent. High yields were obtained with aliphatic and α,β-ethylenic aldehydes as well as *p*-nitrobenzaldehyde, but yields were lower with benzaldehyde itself. Siloxy and benzyloxy groups were left intact. F.e.s. S. Lou, J.A. Westbrook, S.E. Schaus, J. Am. Chem. Soc. *126*, 11440-1 (2004).

Palladous bromide/cupric chloride/sodium hydrogen carbonate/oxygen
Palladium-catalyzed synthesis of 4-subst. isoquinolines from *o*-acetylenealdimines
4-aryl derivs. with ar. halides using Pd(PPh$_3$)$_4$/K_2CO_3 cf. *62*, 482; 4-vinyl derivs. with terminal ethylene derivs. using $PdBr_2$/$CuCl_2$/$NaHCO_3$/O_2 s. Q.-H. Huang, R.C. Larock, J. Org. Chem. *68*, 980-8 (2003).

Palladous iodide/triphenylphosphine/potassium iodide $PdI_2/Ph_3P/KI$
α-(Benzofuran-2-yl)carboxylic acid esters from 1-(*o*-allyloxyaryl)-2-acetylenealcohols ○
Palladium-catalyzed carbonylative ring closure

A soln. of the startg. acetylenealcohol in anhydrous methanol added to a mixture of 1 mol% PdI_2, 4 mol% triphenylphosphine and 1 eq. KI in a stainless steel autoclave, 2 eqs. water added, the vessel sealed and purged repeatedly with CO (5 atm.) at room temp., pressurized to 30 atm. with CO, and heated with stirring for 15 h at 100° → product. Y 91%. The annulation is thought to involve two catalytic cycles, one featuring a palladium(0) species and the other palladium(II). F.e.s. B. Gabriele, L. Veltri et al., Chem. Commun. *2005*, 271-3.

Elimination   ⇑

Hydrogen ↑   CC ⇑ H

Irradiation s. under I_2 ///
Microwaves s. under 1,3-Dibromo-5,5-dimethylhydantoin   [\\\\]
1,8-Diazabicyclo[5.4.0]undec-7-ene s. under Trichloroisocyanuric acid   dbu

Cupric nitrate-clay $Cu(NO_3)_2$-clay
Pyrazoles from Δ^2-pyrazolines   CHCH → C=C
s. *28*, 889s*54*; rapid procedure under ultrasonication for dehydrogenation of *cis*- and *trans*-fused Δ^2-pyrazolines s. S. Mallouk, M. Soufiaoui et al., Tetrahedron Lett. *45*, 4143-8 (2004); with 1,3-dibromo-5,5-dimethylhydantoin/silica gel under microwave irradiation in the absence of solvent (cf. *28*, 889s*67*) s. D. Azarifar, M.A. Zolfigol, B. Maleki, Synthesis *2004*, 1744-6; with the same oxidant under heterogeneous conditions or in the absence of solvent, 1,3,5-trisubst. pyrazoles, s. Bull. Korean Chem. Soc. *25*, 23-4 (2004).

Carbon/acetic acid/oxygen $C/AcOH/O_2$
Pyrazoles from Δ^2-pyrazolines s. *25*, 649s*68*

o-*Iodoxybenzoic acid* $ArIO_2$
***p*-Quinones from dihydro-*p*-quinones (cyclohex-2-ene-1,4-diones)**
with $NaNO_2$ in acetic acid cf. *10*, 225; with *o*-iodoxybenzoic acid for preparing polycyclic *p*-quinones s. S. Kotha, S. Banerjee, K. Mandal, Synlett *2004*, 2043-5.

2,3-Dichloro-5,6-dicyanoquinone   DDQ
Aromatization by dehydrogenation   ←
s. *10*, 639; diaryl sulfides, sulfoxides and sulfones s. G. Hilt, S. Luers, K. Harms, J. Org. Chem. *69*, 624-30 (2004).

1,3-Dibromo-5,5-dimethylhydantoin/silica gel/microwaves   ←
Pyrazoles from Δ^2-pyrazolines under microwave irradiation   CHCH → C=C
without solvent s. *28*, 889s*68*

Trichloroisocyanuric acid/1,8-diazabicyclo[5.4.0]undec-7-ene   ←
Imidazoles from Δ^2-imidazolines s. *4*, 810s*68*

Titanium tetrachloride s. under Mo(CO)$_5$ $TiCl_4$

Lead tetraacetate $Pb(OAc)_4$
Dehydrogenative intramolecular 1,3-dipolar cycloaddition   ○
of aldoximes via nitrile oxides with NaOCl cf. *34*, 909s*58*; of N-sulfonylhydrazones via N-sulfonylnitrilimines with $Pb(OAc)_4$ s. H.A. Abd El-Nabi, J. Chem. Res. Synop *2004*, 325-7.

Molybdenum pentachloride/titanium tetrachloride $MoCl_5/TiCl_4$
Intramolecular oxidative non-phenolic coupling
with MoCl₅ cf. *29*, 910s*65*; 6,7-dihydro-5*H*-dibenzo[*a,c*]cycloheptadienes from 1,3-diarylalkanes with MoCl₅/TiCl₄ s. B. Kramer, S.R. Waldvogel, Angew. Chem. Int. Ed. Engl. *43*, 2446-9 (2004).

Iodine/irradiation $I_2/h\nu$
Aromatization by cyclodehydrogenation
s. *35*, 655s*65*; highly functionalized phenanthrenes s. S.V. Kini, M.M.V. Ramana, Tetrahedron Lett. *45*, 4171-3 (2004).

Potassium permanganate/silica gel $KMnO_4/SiO_2$
Imidazoles from Δ²-imidazolines CHCH → C=C
with DMSO cf. *4*, 810s*60*; with KMnO₄/silica gel (cf. *18*, 180s*38*), notably for rapid dehydrogenation of 2-alkyl-Δ²-imidazolines, s. I. Mohammadpoor-Baltork, M.A. Zolfigol, M. Abdollahi-Alibeik, Tetrahedron Lett. *45*, 8687-90 (2004); with trichloroisocyanuric acid/dbu cf. Synlett *2004*, 2803-5.

Ruthenium(III) hydroxide-alumina/oxygen $Ru(OH)_x/Al_2O_3/O_2$
Indoles from indolines
with Pd/calcium hydroxyapatite cf. *56*, 274s*66*; with Ru(OH)ₓ/Al₂O₃ (cf. *65*, 126) in benzotrifluoride under 1 atm. O₂ s. K. Kamata, K. Yamaguchi, N. Mizuno et al., Org. Lett. *6*, 3577-80 (2004).

Oxygen ↑   CC ↑ O

Microwaves s. under Polyphosphoric acid [\\\\]

Sodium hydroxide NaOH
Phenol ring from 2-ene-1,5-dioxo compds.
from α,β-ethylene-δ-ketoaldehydes with methanolic KOH cf. *37*, 319; from 2-ene-1,5-diones with ethanolic NaOH, 3-hydroxycarbazoles, s. E. Duval, G.D. Cuny, Tetrahedron Lett. *45*, 5411-3 (2004); from 2,4-dienecarboxylic acid amides with LDA (cf. *44*, 942), 1-hydroxycarbazole ring, s. X.W. Cai, V. Snieckus, Org. Lett. *6*, 2293-5 (2004).

Sodium/alcohol NaOR
Cyclodehydration of aldehydes
cyclic α,β-ethylenealdehydes from dialdehydes with morpholine/camphoric acid cf. *15*, 168s*37*; 2,3-dihydro-1-benzothiepin-4-carboxylic acid esters with ethanolic NaOEt/diethyl carbonate s. T. Ikemoto, T. Ito, A. Nishiguchi et al., Tetrahedron *60*, 10851-7 (2004); further **cyclic α,β-ethylenecarboxylic acid esters** s. Tetrahedron Lett. *45*, 9335-9 (2004).

Lithium diisopropylamide $i\text{-}Pr_2NLi$
3-Alkoxyquinolines from *o*-isocyanoarylacetaldehyde acetals

2-(2-Isocyanophenyl)acetaldehyde dimethyl acetal added dropwise to a stirred soln. of 4.1 eqs. LDA in diglyme at -78° under argon, stirring continued for 1 h, and quenched with satd. aq. NH₄Cl → product. Y 79%. F.e.s. K. Kobayashi et al., Tetrahedron Lett. *44*, 4733-6 (2003).

Sodium/liq. ammonia Na/NH_3
Reductive ring closures of δ,ε-ethylenecarboxylic acid esters
cyclopentanols cf. *56*, 466; cyclopentanones, incl. spirocyclic and condensed derivs., s. A. Srikrishna, S.S.V. Ramasastry, Tetrahedron Lett. *45*, 379-82 (2004).

Lithium telluride $\quad Li_2Te$
γ,δ-Ethyleneketones from 2-(tosyloxymethyl)cyclopropyl ketones

486.

A suspension of 1.1 eqs. 0.25 M Li$_2$Te in THF added at room temp. to a soln. of the startg. 2-tosyloxymethylcyclopropyl ketone in the same solvent, the mixture stirred at the same temp. for 25 min, then quenched with satd. aq. NH$_4$Cl and filtered → product. Y 90%. Reaction involves initial substitution of the tosylate group by telluride, followed by nucleophilic cyclopropane ring opening to generate a ketone enolate prior to proton quench. Significantly, a strong base is not required, and tellurium can be simply retrieved and recycled. F.e. and trapping of the enolate by stereospecific aldol condensation s. D.V. Avilov, D.C. Dittmer et al., Org. Lett. *6*, 2225-8 (2004).

Lithium iodide s. under CrCl$_2$ $\quad LiI$
(S)-N-(1-Cyclohexylethyl)pyrrolidine s. under Pd$_2$(dba)$_3$ $\quad \leftarrow$
Samarium s. under TiCl$_4$ $\quad Sm$

Acetic anhydride/pyridine $\quad Ac_2O/C_5H_5N$
Enacylamines from 1,1-acylaminoalcohols $\quad CHC(OH) \rightarrow C{=}C$
cyclic enacylamines with Ac$_2$O cf. *31*, 920; acyclic *trans*-enacylamines with Ac$_2$O/pyridine s. A. Bayer, M.E. Maier, Tetrahedron *60*, 6665-77 (2004).

Hexamethyldisiloxane s. under P$_2$O$_5$ $\quad (Me_3Si)_2O$

Titanium tetrachloride/samarium $\quad TiCl_4/Sm$
Indoles from *o*-acylaminoketones
with Sm/I$_2$ cf. *47*, 940s65; 2,3-disubst. indoles with TiCl$_4$/Sm s. X.S. Fan et al., Chin. Chem. Lett. *15*, 518-20 (2004).

Triphenylphosphine/iodine $\quad Ph_3P/I_2$
Dehydration of alcohols $\quad CHC(OH) \rightarrow C{=}C$
with [(PhO)$_3$PMe]I cf. *27*, 941s31; of tert. alcohols with Ph$_3$P/I$_2$ s. E.J. Alvarez-Manzaneda, J. Ramos et al., Tetrahedron Lett. *45*, 4453-5 (2004).

Phosphorus pentoxide/phosphorus oxide chloride/hexamethyldisiloxane $\quad \leftarrow$
3,4-Dihydroisocarbostyrils from N-2-arylurethans
with P$_2$O$_5$/POCl$_3$ cf. *33*, 694s56; traceless polymer-based synthesis with added hexamethyldisiloxane s. M.S. Chern, W.R. Li, Tetrahedron Lett. *45*, 8323-6 (2004).

Polyphosphoric acid/microwaves $\quad PPA/[\backslash\backslash\backslash\backslash]$
Cyclic ketones from carboxylic acids
s. *6*, 854; *8*, 899; *9*, 947; thiochroman-4-ones under microwave irradiation s. J.-T. Li, L.-W. Xiao et al., J. Chem. Res. Synop *2004*, 394-5.

Chromous chloride/lithium iodide $\quad CrCl_2/LiI$
Regio- and stereo-specific intramolecular Nozaki-Hiyama reaction with allyl phosphates

487.

3-Methylenecyclooctanol ring. 6 eqs. CrCl$_2$ and 1 eq. LiI added to a soln. of the startg. allyl phosphate in THF, and stirred at room temp. for 1 h → product. Y 91%. This is the first example of a Nozaki-Hiyama reaction with an allyl phosphate, there being no conversion with the customary allyl chlorides, nor in such solvents as DMF, DMSO and DMPU. F.e. incl. isolated **2-vinylcycloheptanols and -octanols** s. M. Iwamoto, M. Nakada et al., Tetrahedron Lett. 45, 8653-7 (2004).

Iodine s. under Ph_3P I_2

[Hydridotris(3,5-dimethylpyrazolyl)borato]rhenium(VII) oxide/triphenylphosphine
Ethylene derivs. from epoxides
Rhenium(VII)-catalyzed oxygen transfer

488.

A mixture of 1-dodecene oxide, 1.2 eqs. triphenylphosphine, and 5.3 mol% [hydridotris(3,5-dimethylpyrazolyl)borato]rhenium(VII) oxide in benzene heated to reflux under argon for 86 h with exclusion of atmospheric oxygen → product. Y 94%. Mono- and 1,1-di-subst. epoxides reacted fastest, while *cis*-1,2-disubst. epoxides reacted faster than *trans*-1,2-disubst. epoxides; trisubst. epoxides were more reactive than the latter, but tetrasubst. derivs. were not reduced. A range of functional groups remained unaffected: ketones, esters, nitriles, ethers, silyl ethers and phthalimides. F.e.s. K.P. Gable, E.C. Brown, Synlett *2003*, 2243-5.

Dodecacarbonyltriruthenium/carbon monoxide/triethylamine $Ru_3(CO)_{12}/CO/Et_3N$
Catalytic regio- and stereo-specific intramolecular nucleophilic allylation
with acoxy-2-ethylenes via ruthenium π-allyl complexes

489.

Cyclic 2-vinylalcohols. A mixture of 1 mol% $Ru_3(CO)_{12}$, 3 eqs. triethylamine (as hydride source) and the startg. ketone in THF flushed with 15 atm. CO three times in a stainless steel autoclave, the latter pressurized to 15 atm. with CO, stirred at 90° for 16 h, cooled to room temp., vented carefully, and quenched with 1 *N* aq. HCl → product. Y 89%. In this *non-reductive* umpolung, advantage is taken of the facility of generating nucleophilic ruthenium π-allyl complexes under catalytic conditions. Other ruthenium complexes and transition metal catalysts were ineffective. F.e., incl. *cis*-disubst. carbo- and hetero-cyclic 2-vinylalcohols by intramolecular allylation of both aldehydes and ketones, s. C.-M. Yu et al., Tetrahedron Lett. 45, 6557-61 (2004).

Thiolate-bridged diruthenium complex/platinum(II) chloride/ammonium fluoroborate
Bicyclo[3.1.0]hex-2-ene ring from 1,n-enyn-(n-1)-ols
Stereospecific triple ring closure under tandem catalysis

490.

1-[2-(3-Methyl-2-butenyloxy)phenyl]prop-2-yn-1-ol added with stiring to a mixture of 5 mol% thiolate-bridged ruthenium complex, 10 mol% NH_4BF_4, and 10 mol% $PtCl_2$ in dry dichloroethane at room temp. under N_2, and heated at 60° for 24 h → product. Y 75% (*syn/anti* 92:8). The two transition metal catalysts are mutually compatible, the ruthenium complex promoting the initial propargylic substitution via a ruthenium allenylidene species, while $PtCl_2$ effects cycloisomerization of the intermediate cyclic enyne. F.e. and intermolecular process s. Y. Nishibayashi, S. Uemura et al., J. Am. Chem. Soc. *126*, 16066-72 (2004).

Tris(dibenzylideneacetone)dipalladium/chiral 2-[o-(diarylphosphino)phenyl]-Δ^2- ←
imidazolines/(S)-N-(1-cyclohexylethyl)pyrrolidine
Intramolecular asym. Heck arylation
with $Pd(OAc)_2$/(R)-BINAP/1,2,2,6,6-pentamethylpiperidine cf. *48*, 952s65; chiral 3-spiro-oxindoles with chiral 2-[*o*-(diarylphosphino)phenyl]-Δ^2-imidazolines/(S)-N-(1-cyclohexylethyl)-pyrrolidine, optimization of ligand, s. C.A. Busacca et al., J. Org. Chem. *69*, 5187-95 (2004).

Platinum(II) chloride s. under Thiolate-bridged diruthenium complexes $PtCl_2$

Nitrogen ↑   CC ⇑ N

Microwaves s. under $Rh_2(OCOR)_4$ [\\\\]

Lithium diisopropylamide $i\text{-}Pr_2NLi$
Phenol ring from 2,4-dienecarboxylic acid amides   ○
1-Hydroxycarbazole ring s. *44*, 942s68

Chiral copper(I) bis(Δ^2-oxazoline) complexes   ←
Asym. intramolecular cyclopropanation   ▽
s. *46*, 954s53; with α-diazo-β-ketosulfones s. M. Honma, M. Nakada, Tetrahedron Lett. *44*, 9007-11 (2003).

Trifluoroacetyl triflate/4-dimethylaminopyridine $CF_3COOTf/DMAP$
Benzofurans from O-aryloximes   ○
s. *65*, 316; with added DMAP s. O. Miyata, N. Takeda, T. Naito, Org. Lett. *6*, 1761-3 (2004).

Rhodium(II) acetate $Rh_2(OAc)_4$
Intramolecular carbene insertion into carbon-hydrogen bonds
s. *34*, 954s67; 3,4-fused 2,3,4,5-tetrahydrothiophenes from 3-diazothioethers s. P.S. Skerry, R.C.D. Brown et al., Chem. Commun. *2004*, 1772-3.

Rhodium(II) pivalate/microwaves $Rh_2(OCOR)_4$/[\\\\]
Carbonyl(5,10,15,20-tetraarylporphyrinato)ruthenium(II) complexes
Stereospecific triple ring closure via cyclic carbonyl ylids
with $Rh_2(OAc)_4$ s. *43*, 943s48, 49; pentacyclics with heteroarenes as dipolarophile using Rh(II)-pivalate under microwave irradiation s. J.M. Mejia-Oneto, A. Padwa, Org. Lett. *6*, 3241-4 (2004); with carbonyl(5,10,15,20-tetraarylporphyrinato)ruthenium(II) complexes, effect of substitution on diastereoselectivity, s. C.-Y. Zhou, C.-M. Che et al., Synthesis *2003*, 1403-12.

Chiral rhodium(II) α-imidocarboxylates $Rh_2(OCOR)_4$
Asym. intramolecular carbene insertion into carbon-hydrogen bonds
s. *47*, 955s67; desymmetrization of *meso*-oxabicyclics with chiral Rh(II)-α-imidocarboxylates s. P. Chiu, X. Zhang, R.Y.Y. Ko, Tetrahedron Lett. *45*, 1531-4 (2004).

Chiral tetrakis(1,1'-bi-2-naphthol phosphate)dirhodium(II) complexes   ←
Asym. triple ring closure
via intramolecular 1,3-dipolar cycloaddition with cyclic carbonyl ylids
s. *54*, 484s65; with chiral 4,4',6,6'-tetrasubst. complexes s. D.M. Hodgson, D.A. Selden, A.G. Dossetter, Tetrahedron:Asym. *14*, 3841-9 (2003).

Halogen ↑   CC ⇑ Hal

Electrolysis/nickel(II) cyclamin complexes   ←
Electrocatalytic double ring closure   ○
of 2-halogeno-1,6-dienes s. *41*, 942s52; fused 5-methylenebicyclo[2.2.1]heptanes s. M. Toyota, M. Ihara et al., Org. Lett. *6*, 3629-32 (2004).

Microwaves s. under Bu_3SnH [\\\\]

tert-*Butyllithium* t-*BuLi*
Cyclic alcohols from halogenoketones ○
s. *41*, 946; siloxy-tethered, bridgehead tert. alcohols s. M. Iwamoto, M. Nakada et al., Tetrahedron Lett. *45*, 8647-51 (2004).

tert-*Butyllithium/N,N,N',N'-tetramethylethylenediamine* t-*BuLi/tmeda*
Ring closures via intramolecular carbolithiation
1,2-di(alkylidene)cycloalkanes from 2-bromo-1,n-enynes cf. *52*, 485; functionalized 3-methylenepyrrolidines from 2-bromo-4-aza-1,6-dienes with added tmeda s. J. Barluenga et al., Compt. Rend. Chim. *7*, 855-64 (2004).

Sodium acetate or pivalate *NaOAc or NaOCOBu*-t
(Z)-α,β-Ethylenebromides from 1,2-dibromides C(Br)CH(Br) → C=C(Br)
s. *19*, 972s68

Cesium pivalate s. under $Pd(OAc)_2$ *CsOCOBu*-t
Ethylenediamine s. under $NaBH_3CN$ $H_2NCH_2CH_2NH_2$

Triethylenediamine/sodium carbonate *dabco/Na_2CO_3*
Stereospecific organocatalyzed intramolecular cyclopropanation ▽○
of electron-deficient ethylene derivs. with α-chlorocarbonyl compds.

491.

R = CH_2CH_2Ph R_3N = dabco

20 Mol% anhydrous dabco in anhydrous acetonitrile and 1.3 eqs. anhydrous Na_2CO_3 added to a soln. of the startg. α-chloroketone in the same solvent, the mixture stirred at 80° under argon for 18 h, diluted with ether, and quenched with aq. NH_4Cl → product. Y 91%. This is the first example of an organocatalyzed intramolecular cyclopropanation which avoids handling the customary α-diazocarbonyl compds. Reaction involves catalytic generation of quaternary ammonium ylids, which undergo intramolecular Michael addition to the alkene residue prior to cyclopropane ring closure with elimination of the amine. The alkene residue may be an enone, an enal, an enoate, or an α,β-ethylenesulfone. F.e. and with quinuclidine, also **asym. conversion** with quin(id)ine derivs., s. N. Bremeyer, S.V. Ley, M.J. Gaunt et al., Angew. Chem. Int. Ed. Engl. *43*, 2681-4 (2004).

1,8-Diazabicyclo[5.4.0]undec-7-ene *dbu*
α,β-Ethylenebromides from 1,2-dibromides C(Br)CH(Br) → C=C(Br)
with Et_2NH cf. *19*, 972; (Z)-products with dbu, NaOAc or NaOCOBu-*t* in DMF, regioselectivity, s. T. Ohgiya, S. Nishiyama, Chem. Lett. *33*, 1084-5 (2004).

Zinc *Zn*
Intramolecular 1,4-addition ○
s. *49*, 953; α-cyclopropyl-carboxylic acid derivs., -ketones and -sulfones s. D. Sakuma, H. Togo, Synlett *2004*, 2501-4.

Sodium tetrahydridoborate/indium(III) chloride $NaBH_4/InCl_3$
2-Ethylenealcohols from 2,3-epoxyhalides ↶
with Zn cf. *29*, 968; general procedure with $NaBH_4$ and a catalytic amount of $InCl_3$ s. B.C. Ranu, S. Banerjee, A. Das, Tetrahedron Lett. *45*, 8579-81 (2004).

Sodium trihydridocyanoborate/acetic acid/ethylenediamine ←
Cyclic alkoxylamines from halogenoximes ○
electrocatalytic reduction cf. *50*, 382s61; *cis*-1-alkoxy-2-vinylpyrrolidines from (Z)-ε-bromo-γ,δ-ethylenealkoximes with $NaBH_3CN/AcOH$/ethylenediamine via S_N2' displacement s. S.Q. Wang, K. Zhao et al., Chin. Chem. Lett. *15*, 1-4 (2004).

Dichloroindium hydride Cl_2InH
Reductions with *in situ*-generated dichloroindium hydride ←
from $InCl_3/NaBH_4$ cf. *65*, 489; *23*, 543s66; *64*, 34; improved procedure from $InCl_3/Et_3SiH/Et_3B$ for [among others] ring closures of enynes and ethylenehalides, and Michael addition s. N. Hayashi, I. Shibata, A. Baba, Org. Lett. *6*, 4981-3 (2004); (E)-ethylene derivs. from 1,2-dibromides with $InCl_3/Sm$ **in aq. medium** s. M. Wang, J.-C. Yan et al., Chinese J. Chem. *22*, 863-6 (2004).

Indium(III) chloride s. under $NaBH_4$ and Cl_2InH $InCl_3$
Ammonium formate s. under $PdCl_2$ $HCOONH_4$
Imidazolium ionic liquids s. under $PdCl_2$ ←

Dicumyl peroxide ROOR
Intramolecular radical C-alkylation with iodides
of the pyridinium ring with $Bu_3SnH/AIBN$ cf. *46*, 968; ring closures of N-(ω-iodoalkyl)hetarenes with dicumyl peroxide s. M. Menes-Arzate, L.D. Miranda et al., J. Org. Chem. *69*, 4001-4 (2004).

Tris(trimethylsilyl)silane/azodiisobutyronitrile $(Me_3Si)_3SiH/AIBN$
Radical ring closures of ethylenebromides
s. *58*, 482; N-protected piperidines with asym. induction s. L.A. Gandon, A.G. Russell, J.S. Snaith, Org. Biomol. Chem. *2*, 2270-1 (2004).

Tri-n-butyltin hydride/azodiisobutyronitrile $Bu_3SnH/AIBN$
N-Protected 1,2,3,6-tetrahydropyridines from 2-iodomethyl-Δ^3-pyrrolines
Radical ring expansion by one C-atom

A soln. of the startg. pyrroline in deoxygenated benzene heated at reflux under argon for 1 h, 1.2 eqs. tri-*n*-butyltin hydride and 0.2 eq. AIBN in the same solvent added over 12 h via syringe pump, and heating continued for a further 12 h → product. Y 78%. Reaction is thought to involve initial formation of the α-methyl radical, followed by a 3-*exo-trig* attack on the double bond, then a retro-3-*exo-trig* ring opening of the strained cyclopropane ring prior to hydride abstraction by the generated tetrahydropyridyl radical. F.e. and N-protected 5,6-dihydro-2-pyridones s. P.G. Turner, T.J. Donohoe, R.P.C. Cousins, Chem. Commun. *2004*, 1422-3.

Tri-n-butyltin hydride/azodiisobutyronitrile/microwaves $Bu_3SnH/AIBN/[\backslash\backslash\backslash\backslash]$
Oxindoles by radical ring closure
s. *43*, 957s48; combinatorial polymer-based synthesis under microwave irradiation s. H. Akamatsu, K. Fukase, S. Kusumoto, Synlett *2004*, 1049-53.

Nickel(II) cyclamin complexes s. under ⇁ ←

Palladous acetate/2-(dimethylamino)-2'-(diphenylphosphino)biphenyl/cesium pivalate ←
Intramolecular Heck-type diaryl coupling
with $Pd(OAc)_2/Bu_3P/Ag_2CO_3$ cf. *53*, 496s65; with 2-(dimethylamino)-2'-(diphenylphosphino)-biphenyl as ligand and K_2CO_3 as base s. L.-C. Campeau, K. Fagnou et al., J. Am. Chem. Soc. *126*, 9186-7 (2004).

Palladous acetate/bis(diphenylphosphino)methane/cesium pivalate
**Benzo-condensed polycyclics
via sequential palladium-catalyzed activation of carbon-hydrogen bonds**

493.

Polycyclic indene ring. A mixture of 1 eq. of the startg. ar. halide, 5 mol% Pd(OAc)$_2$, 5 mol% bis-(diphenylphosphino)methane, and 2 eqs. Cs-pivalate in anhydrous DMF stirred at 100° under argon for 4 h, and quenched with satd. aq. NaHCO$_3$ → product. Y 76%. Reaction involves initial intramolecular carbopalladation, followed by the novel, *through-space* alkyl→aryl **1,4-palladium shift** (possibly via a hydridopallada(IV)cyclic) prior to intramolecular Heck arylation. Migration is most efficient with electron-rich aromatics. F.e. incl. polycyclic benzofurans (incl. dibenzofurans) and carbazoles s. Q. Huang, R.C. Larock et al., J. Am. Chem. Soc. *126*, 7460-1 (2004).

Tris(dibenzylideneacetone)dipalladium/tri-o-tolylphosphine/n-butyl(dimethyl)amine
**Stereospecific palladium-catalyzed intramolecular cross-coupling
of ar. iodides with acoxy-2-ethylenes**

494.

4-Vinyl-1,2,3,4-tetrahydroquinolines. A mixture of 1 eq. of the startg. ar. iodide, 22 mol% tri-o-tolylphosphine, and 2 eqs. n-butyl(dimethyl)amine in 10:1 acetonitrile/water treated under argon with 5 mol% Pd$_2$(dba)$_3$·CHCl$_3$, the resulting mixture degassed with argon, refluxed under N$_2$ for 6 h, then quenched with water → product. Y 88%. In this rare intramolecular coupling where the allyl acetate residue effectively serves *as a nucleophile*, the tertiary amine regenerates palladium(0) from palladium(II) after each catalytic cycle. The nature of the phosphine ligand, however, appears critical. F.e. incl. 5-, 6- and 7-membered benzo-condensed hetero- and carbo-cyclics, also under microwave enhancement, s. M. Lautens, E. Tayama, C. Herse, J. Am. Chem. Soc. *127*, 72-3 (2005).

Tetrakis(triphenylphosphine)palladium(0)/triethylamine or potassium phenoxide
Intramolecular Heck arylation
s. *36*, 957s*66*; *43*, 962s*47*; 2a,3,4,8b-tetrahydrocyclobuta[*a*]naphthalenes with Pd(PPh$_3$)$_4$/Et$_3$N s. A. Rivkin, D.P. Curran et al., J. Org. Chem. *69*, 3719-25 (2004); intramolecular arylation of cyclic 1,2-nitroethylene derivs. with KOPh as base, also intramolecular Heck vinylation, s. D. Solé, X. Urbaneja, J. Bonjoch, Tetrahedron Lett. *45*, 3131-5 (2004); fused indoles s. T. Watanabe, S. Arai, A. Nishida, Synlett *2004*, 907-9.

*Palladous chloride/tri-n-butylamine/ammonium formate/1-n-butyl-3-methylimidazolium
fluoroborate*
Benzofurans from *o*-allyloxyhalides
with Pd(OAc)$_2$/Na$_2$CO$_3$/HCOONa/Bu$_4$NCl cf. *36*, 957s*44*; with PdCl$_2$/Bu$_3$N/HCOONH$_4$ **in ionic liquids**, e.g. 1-*n*-butyl-3-methylimidazolium fluoroborate, for improved recovery of the catalyst s. X.-G. Xie, X.-F. Pan et al., Tetrahedron Lett. *45*, 6235-7 (2004).

Sulfur ↑   CC ⇑ S

Potassium tert-butoxide   KOBu-t
Difluoromethylene compds. from α,α-difluorosulfones s. *38*, 813s68   C=CF$_2$

1,8-Diazabicyclo[5.4.0]undec-7-ene   dbu
1,3-Dienes from α-cyclopropylsulfones   C
alkylative ring opening with LDA cf. *37*, 834; polyenes by direct elimination of sulfinic acid with dbu s. H.S. Jeon, S. Koo, Tetrahedron Lett. *45*, 7023-6 (2004).

Lauroyl peroxide   (RCOO)$_2$
Radical ring closures of xanthates   O
s. *52*, 491s65; pyridine-fused N-acyl-N-heterocyclics or lactams with lauroyl peroxide s. E. Bacque, M. El Qacemi, S.Z. Zard, Org. Lett. *6*, 3671-4 (2004).

Acetic acid   AcOH
Pyrazole from 1,3,4-thiadiazine ring   O
with NaOEt cf. *33*, 962; 5-aminopyrazoles with acetic acid s. W.-D. Pfeiffer, P. Langer et al., Synlett *2003*, 2392-4.

Dibromodifluoromethane/potassium hydroxide-alumina   CBr$_2$F$_2$/KOH-Al$_2$O$_3$
Ethylene derivs. from sulfones   CHSO$_2$CH → C=C
s. *29*, 973s67; (E)-α,β-ethylenecarboxylic acid amides s. Y. Li et al., Can. J. Chem. *82*, 622-30 (2004); also (E,E)-2,4-dienecarboxylic acid amides s. Chin. Chem. Lett. *15*, 631-4 (2004).

Remaining Elements ↑   CC ⇑ Rem

Titanocene dichloride/manganese   Cp$_2$TiCl$_2$/Mn
Titanium(III)-mediated regio- and stereo-specific radical ring closures   O
of α,β-ethylene(epoxy)phosphine oxides
via β-elimination of phosphinoyl radicals

N-Protected 4-alkylidene-3-pyrrolidinylcarbinols. A degassed soln. of 1 eq. startg. epoxyphosphine oxide in anhydrous THF treated dropwise with 2.5 eqs. Cp$_2$TiCl$_2$ and 10 eqs. manganese at room temp. under argon, the resulting mixture stirred at the same temp. for 2-3 h, and quenched with aq. 10% H$_2$SO$_4$ → product. Y 71%. Phosphine oxides have been used for the first time in such a radical β-elimination, and offer characteristics which are different to the more familiar sulfoxides. Reaction proceeds with retention of olefinic configuration. F.e.s. D. Leca, L. Fensterbank, M. Malacria et al., Angew. Chem. Int. Ed. Engl. *43*, 4220-2 (2004).

Hydrogen peroxide   H$_2$O$_2$
Ethylene derivs. from selenides   C(SeR)CH → C=C
polymer-based synthesis of acrylamides cf. *29*, 912s67; of aryl vinyl ethers s. S.-R. Sheng, C.-S. Song et al., Synthesis *2004*, 2833-6; of (E)-α,β-ethylenesulfones s. W.-M. Xu, E. Tang, X. Huang, ibid. 2094-8.

Trifluoromethanesulfonic anhydride/2,6-lutidine   ←
Ring closures of sulfinylenoxysilanes via Pummerer rearrangement   O
with (CF$_3$CO)$_2$O/2,6-di-*tert*-butyl-4-methylpyridine cf. *46*, 983; 2-arylthio-3-spiroindolenines with Tf$_2$O/2,6-lutidine via *vinylogous* Pummerer rearrangement s. K.S. Feldman, D.B. Vidulova, Org. Lett. *6*, 1869-71 (2004).

Methanesulfonic acid $MeSO_3H$
2-Cyclohexenones from 6-siloxy-1,5-enynes

Startg. siloxyenyne added dropwise (neat) to a soln. of 4 eqs. methanesulfonic acid in anhydrous methylene chloride under N_2, stirred at 20° for 2 h, then quenched with satd. aq. $NaHCO_3$ → product. Y 91%. Protonation initially affords an intermediate O-silylketenium ion which undergoes nucleophilic attack by the appended unsaturation. F.e. and with triflimide (preferably for 1,1-disubst. ethylenic derivs.), **also 4-siloxy-1,2-dihydronaphthalenes from 4-aryl-1-siloxyacetylenes**, s. L. Zhang, S.A. Kozmin, J. Am. Chem. Soc. *126*, 10204-5 (2004).

Manganese s. under Cp_2TiCl_2 Mn

Carbon ↑ CC ↑ C

Without additional reagents w.a.r.
Ring contraction of cyclic ketones by decarbonylation
under photolysis cf. *30*, 691s*62*; of cyclic α-cyanoketones under flash vacuum pyrolysis s. G. Ruedi, M.A. Oberli, H.J. Hansen, Tetrahedron Lett. *45*, 7887-9 (2004).

Microwaves s. under AgOAc [\\\\]

Lithium diisopropylamide $i\text{-}Pr_2NLi$
Carroll rearrangement ←
with $Al(OPr-i)_3$ cf. *3*, 758s*32*; δ-subst. γ,δ-ethyleneketones with LDA, stereoselectivity, s. M.E. Jung, B.A. Duclos, Tetrahedron Lett. *45*, 107-9 (2004); with [Cp*RuCl]/bipy cf. E.C. Burger, J.A. Tunge, Org. Lett. *6*, 2603-5 (2004).

Silver acetate/microwaves $AgOAc/$[\\\\]
α,β-Ethylenebromides from α,β-dibromocarboxylic acids C(Br)C(Br)COOH → C=C(Br)
under microwave irradiation with Et_3N cf. *6*, 880s*61*; (E)-products from *anti*-substrates with AgOAc in acetic acid s. C.X. Kuang, H. Senboku, M. Tokuda, Tetrahedron *61*, 637-42 (2005).

Imidazolium ionic liquids s. under Ruthenium complexes ←

Phosphorus oxide chloride $POCl_3$
Bischler-Napieralski ring closure
with $POCl_3$ s. *17*, 942; with simultaneous cleavage of chiral N-alkyl groups s. H.M. Ma, Z.Z. Liu, S.Z. Chen, Chin. Chem. Lett. *15*, 253-6 (2004).

Molybdenum hexacarbonyl/p-(trifluoromethyl)phenol $Mo(CO)_6/ArOH$
Macrocyclic acetylene derivs. from diynes by ring-closing metathesis
with *o*-fluorophenol as additive cf. *55*, 497s*64*; with *p*-(trifluoromethyl)phenol s. B. Hellbach, R. Gleiter, F. Rominger, Synlett *2003*, 2535-41.

Bis(acetonitrile)[hydridotris(pyrazolyl)borato](triphenylphosphine)ruthenium(II)
  hexafluorophosphate
1-Arylindenes from *o*-(acetylene)stilbene oxides
Decarbonylative ring closure with 1,2-aryl migration

A mixture of 10 mol% bis(acetonitrile)[hydridotris(pyrazolyl)borato](triphenylphosphine)-ruthenium(II) hexafluorophosphate and the startg. *o*-(acetylene)stilbene oxide in toluene heated in a long tube for 12 h at 100° → product. Y 80%. Reaction is thought to involve intermediate formation of a cyclic ruthenium acyl species. Non-aromatic analogs, however, gave the corresponding **phenols or 2,4-cyclohexadienones,** depending on the nature of the substitution and epoxide stereochemistry. Here, a cationic ruthenium-complexed ketene is the presumed intermediate. F.e.s. L. Min-Yuan, R.J. Madhushaw, R.-S. Liu, J. Org. Chem. *69*, 7700-4 (2004).

(η⁵-Pentamethylcyclopentadienyl)ruthenium(II) chloride tetramer/   *[Cp*RuCl]₄/bipy*
  2,2'-bipyridyl
Ruthenium-catalyzed Carroll rearrangement s. *3*, 758s68

Alkylidene(dichloro)ruthenium(II) imidazolidin-2-ylidene complex
Ring-closing metathesis
with Grubbs' second generation catalyst, update, s. *56*, 495s65; 2,5-dihydrofurans and Δ³-pyrrolines s. J.M. Kim, J.N. Kim et al., Tetrahedron Lett. *45*, 2805-8 (2004); chiral polyoxy-1,2,5,6,7,8-hexahydroazocine ring s. G. Godin, O.R. Martin et al., ibid. 579-81; 2*H*-1,5-benzo-dioxepins and 2,5-dihydro-1,6-benzodioxocins s. R. Mamouni, G. Guillaumet et al., ibid. 2631-3; chiral 1-azabicyclo[3.n.0]alkenones s. L. Manzoni, M. Colombo, C. Scolastico, ibid. 2623-5; α,β-ethylene-α-fluorolactams s. M. Marhold, G. Haufe et al., ibid. 57-60; huperzine B ring s. I.Y.C. Lee et al., ibid. 285-7; synthesis of iso-β-bisabolol s. J.M. Morgenthaler, D. Spitzner, ibid. 1171-2; macrocyclic peptidylureas s. X.-Z. Wang, T.R. Burke Jr., Synlett *2004*, 469-72; 3,4-dihydroquinolizinium salts s. A. Nunez, J.J. Vaquero et al., Org. Lett. *6*, 4125-7 (2004); phenanthrenes from *o,o'*-divinylbiphenyls by **aromatizing ring-closing metathesis** s. A. Iuliano, P. Piccioli, D. Fabbri, ibid. 3711-4; bicyclo[4.2.1]non-3-enes s. A. Michaut, J. Rodriguez et al., ibid. 3075-8.

Two-directional double ring-closing metathesis
of tetraenes with Grubbs' complex cf. *59*, 496; of trienynes with simultaneous elimination of ethene and methylene group transfer with Grubbs' 2ⁿᵈ generation complex for preparing bicyclic N-condensed vinyl-N-heterocyclics s. S.-M. Ma, B.-K. Ni, Z.-Q. Liang, J. Org. Chem. *69*, 6305-9 (2004).

**Tricyclic vinylcyclopropanes from dienynes
via intramolecular cyclopropanation-ring-closing metathesis
Bicyclic ruthenium cyclopropylcarbenes as intermediates**

2,3,3a,4,5,7a-Hexahydro-3a,7a-methano-1H-indenes. A soln. of 1 eq. of the startg. dienyne in anhydrous benzene (0.1 M) treated under reflux with 5 mol% Grubbs' second generation complex, and stirred under argon for 24 h → product. Y 83%. F.e. and comparison of transition metal catalysts s. B.P. Peppers, S.T. Diver, J. Am. Chem. Soc. *126*, 9524-5 (2004).

Dichloro(2-isopropoxy-3-methoxybenzylidene)ruthenium(II) imidazolidin-2-ylidene complex
Ring-closing metathesis with highly active catalysts under mild conditions
s. *64*, 497s68

Soluble polymer-based dichloro(2-isopropoxybenzylidene)ruthenium(II) imidazolidin-2-ylidene complexes
Ring-closing metathesis using a soluble polymer-based catalyst
s. *60*, 498s65; with a soluble polymer-based dichloro(*o*-isopropoxybenzylidene)ruthenium(II) imidazolidin-2-ylidene complex s. Q. Yao, A.R. Motta, Tetrahedron Lett. *45*, 2447-51 (2004).

Imidazolium-tagged alkylidene(dichloro)ruthenium(II) imidazolidin-2-ylidene complex/ 1-n-butyl-3-methylimidazolium hexafluorophosphate
Ring-closing metathesis in ionic liquids
in 9:1 methylene chloride/1-*n*-butyl-3-methylimidazolium hexafluorophosphate with an imidazolium-tagged dichloro(*o*-isopropoxybenzylidene)ruthenium(II) phosphine complex cf. *67*, 499; in toluene/1-*n*-butyl-3-methylimidazolium hexafluorophosphate with an imidazolium-tagged alkylidene(dichloro)ruthenium imidazolidin-2-ylidene complex s. H. Clavier, N. Audic, J.-C. Guillemin et al., Chem. Commun. *2004*, 2282-3.

Grubbs' ruthenium carbene complex $\quad RuCl_2(PCy_3)_2=CHPh$
Ring-closing metathesis
with Grubbs' catalyst, update, s. *49*, 985s65; improved work-up by scavenging the catalyst with a polymer-based aminodi(phosphine) s. M. Westus, R. Breinbauer, Tetrahedron Lett. *45*, 3141-2 (2004).

Dichlorobis(tricyclohexylphosphine)[o-isopropoxy(nitro)benzylidene]- $\quad RuCl_2(PCy_3)_2=CHAr$ ruthenium(II) complexes
Ring-closing metathesis with highly active catalysts
with dichloro(tricyclohexylphosphine)[*o*-isopropoxy(nitro)benzylidene]ruthenium(II) complexes s. *64*, 497s68; with a dichloro(2-isopropoxy-3-methoxybenzylidene)ruthenium imidazolidin-2-ylidene complex under mild conditions, also ring opening-cross-metathesis, s. N. Buschmann, H. Wakamatsu, S. Bleshert, Synlett *2004*, 667-70.

Tris(dibenzylideneacetone)dipalladium/(1R,2R)-N,N'-bis[2-(diphenylphosphino)-
benzoyl]-1,2-diaminocyclohexane
**γ,δ-Ethyleneketones from β-ketocarboxylic acid allyl esters
via asym. decarboxylative Claisen rearrangement**

CO-C-C-C=C

A mixture of the startg. β-ketocarboxylic acid ester, 5 mol% Pd$_2$(dba)$_3$ and 10 mol% (R,R)-N,N'-bis[2-(diphenylphosphino)benzoyl]-1,2-diaminocyclohexane in benzene stirred at room temp. under argon for 15 h, the soln. concentrated, and the residue chromatographed → product. Y 85% (e.e. 86%). The intermediate enolates are generated regioselectively **via palladium π-allyl complexes,** offering the advantages of atom-economy, high enantioselectivities, and mild, base-free reaction conditions. F.e.s. E.C. Burger, J.A. Tunge, Org. Lett. *6*, 4113-5 (2004).

Tris(dibenzylideneacetone)dipalladium/(S)-2-[2-(diphenylphosphino)phenyl]-4-tert-butyl-
Δ^2-oxazoline or chiral N,N'-bis[2-(diphenylphosphino)benzoyl]-1,2-diaminoalkanes
**Decarboxylative intramolecular asym. C-α-allylation of allyl enol carbonates
under neutral conditions**

Chiral cyclic α-allylketones. A 0.1 M soln. of the startg. allyl enol carbonate (readily prepared from 1-tetralone) in dioxane treated with 2.5 mol% Pd$_2$(dba)$_3$·CHCl$_3$ and 5.5 mol% chiral Trost-type ligand at 23° for 20 h → product. Y 81% (e.e. 97%). Significantly, the procedure is racemization-free, regiospecific, and obviates the handling of a base, as required to generate enolates in the traditional bimolecular asym. C-α-allylation of ketones. **Chiral quaternary carbon centres** can also be generated by this method (in toluene), affording [by an inner-sphere allylation] the *opposite* enantiomer to that obtained by the conventional [outer-sphere] bimolecular approach. F.e. incl. 5-, 6- and 7-membered products s. B.M. Trost, J. Xu, J. Am. Chem. Soc. *127*, 2846-7 (2005); with (S)-2-[*o*-(diphenylphosphino)phenyl]-4-*tert*-butyl-Δ^2-oxazoline as ligand cf. D.C. Behenna, B.M. Stoltz, ibid. *126*, 15044-5 (2004).

Formation of Electron Pair on Nitrogen

Elimination ⇑

Oxygen↑   EIN ⇑ O

Gallium   *Ga*
Hexamethylenetetramine   *(CH$_2$)$_6$N$_4$*
Deoxygenation of cyclic N-oxides   ≡NO → ≡N
with InCl$_3$ cf. *59*, 498s*63*; with Ga in water s. J.H. Han, B.W. Yoo et al., Synth. Commun. *34*, 3197-201 (2004); Δ^2-imidazoline 1-oxyls from the corresponding 3-oxides with hexamethylenetetramine s. E. Yu, V.I. Ovcharenko et al., Tetrahedron Lett. *44*, 6397-9 (2003).

Carbon ↑   EIN ↑ C

Polymer-based amines   ←
Tert. amines by Hofmann elimination   ≧N⁺R → ≧N
with polymer-based bicyclic guanidines cf. *8,* 917s*63*; with a weakly basic polymer-based amine for Hofmann elimination of soluble PEG-based quaternary ammonium salts s. Z. Chen, G. Yang, Z. Zhang, Synth. Commun. *33,* 729-34 (2003).

Lithium hydridotriethylborate   *Li[BHEt₃]*
Tert. amines from quaternary ammonium salts
s. *29,* 992s*30*; stereospecific dealkylation of N-chiral quaternary N-alkylgalanthaminium halides, also with L-Selectride, s. M. Hirnschall, U. Jordis et al., Tetrahedron:Asym. *14,* 675-81 (2003).

Formation of Electron Pair on Sulfur

Elimination   ↑

Oxygen ↑   EIS ↑ O

2,4-Bis(p-methoxyphenyl)-1,3,2,4-dithiadiphosphetane 2,4-disulfide   ←
S-Deoxygenation   >SO → >S
thioethers from sulfoxides cf. *25,* 701s*41*; dithiiranes from their mono-S-oxides s. A. Ishii, J. Nakayama et al., J. Org. Chem. *68,* 1555-8 (2003).

Dichlorodioxobis(dimethylformamide)molybdenum(VI)/triphenyl phosphite   ←
Chlorotris(triphenylphosphine)rhodium(I)/catecholborane   ←
Thioethers from sulfoxides
catalytic transfer deoxygenation with ReOCl₃(PPh₃)₂/Ph₃P cf. *52,* 495; with MoO₂Cl₂(DMF)₂/(PhO)₃P s. R. Sanz, F.J. Anaiz et al., Synthesis *2004,* 1629-32; catalytic deoxygenation with RhCl(PPh₃)₃/catecholborane s. Tetrahedron Lett. *45,* 8493-6 (2004).

Formation of Electron Pair on Remaining Elements

Elimination   ↑

Oxygen ↑   ElRem ↑ O

Trichlorosilane/triphenylphosphine   *Cl₃SiH/Ph₃P*
Phosphines from phosphine oxides   ≧PO → ≧P
with trichlorosilane cf. *21,* 988; transfer-deoxygenation with added triphenylphosphine with retention of P-chirality s. H.C. Wu, J.Q. Yu, J.B. Spencer, Org. Lett. *6,* 4675-8 (2004).

Remaining Elements ↑   ElRem ↑ Rem

Triethylsilane/trifluoroacetic acid   *Et₃SiH/CF₃COOH*
Cleavage of borane complexes   ←
of borane-amine complexes with Pd-C cf. *20,* 71s*63*; protection of dinucleoside H-phosphonates as borane complexes and decomplexation with Et₃SiH/CF₃COOH s. M. Shimizu, T. Wada et al., Tetrahedron Lett. *45,* 371-4 (2004).

Heteropolar Bond

Uptake ⇓

Addition to Nitrogen Het ⇓ N

Without additional reagents w.a.r.
Quaternization of 6-membered N-hetarenes N⋜ → RN⁺⋜
of pyridines cf. *10*, 79s*59*; of pyrazine, pyridazine and pyrimidine with alkyl and polyfluoroalkyl halides s. Y. Gao, J.M. Schreeve, Synthesis *2004*, 1072-82.

1-n-Butyl-3-methylimidazolium hexafluorophosphate [bmim]PF$_6$
Quaternization of imidazoles
for the preparation of ionic liquids s. *30*, 701s*67*; environmentally friendly procedure with KPF$_6$ in an ionic liquid as solvent, e.g. 1-*n*-butyl-3-methylimidazolium hexafluorophosphate, s. D.-Q. Xu et al., Synthesis *2003*, 2626-8.

Resolutions Res

(s.a. Subject Index under Resolution)

Lithium amides/lithium diisopropylamide LiNHR/i-Pr$_2$NLi
Catalyzed Haller-Bauer reaction with kinetic resolution s. *68*, 149 ←

Dicyclohexylcarbodiimide/4-dimethylaminopyridine RN=C=NR/DMAP
Resolution of 1,1′-bi-2-naphthols via chiral derivatization
as cyclic 1,1′-bi-2-naphthol boric acid esters cf. *60*, 500; as N$^\alpha$-Boc-tryptophan esters (with DCC/DMAP) s. B.M. Panchal, C. Einhorn, J. Einhorn, Tetrahedron Lett. *43*, 9245-8 (2003); via menthyl carbonates (with NaOH/Bu$_4$NBr), also resolution of 4,4′-dibromo-1,1′-spirobiindane-7,7′-diol, s. Z. Li, B. Wan et al., Tetrahedron:Asym. *15*, 665-9 (2004); resolution of 2-diarylphosphino-2′-hydroxy-1,1′-binaphthyls as (1S)-10-camphorsulfonates s. Y. Luo, Z. Zhang et al., ibid. 17-9.

Hydrolase ←
Glycols from epoxides with kinetic resolution s. *48*, 108s*68* ←

Lipase/sodium tetrahydridoborate/alumina ←
Sec. alcohols from ketones ←
with subsequent kinetic resolution by asym. enzymatic O-acylation – Chiral 2-azidoalcohols s. *66*, 128s*68*

Lipase/1-n-butyl-3-methylimidazolium hexafluorophosphate ←
Kinetic resolution of alcohols by asym. enzymatic O-acylation s. *44*, 214s*68* ←
in ionic liquids

Lipase/ruthenium hydride complex ←
Dynamic kinetic resolution of sec. alcohols ←
via enzymatic O-acylation-catalytic racemization
s. *53*, 500s*67*; of 1,2-halogenhydrins s. O. Pamies, J.-E. Backvall, J. Org. Chem. *67*, 9006-10 (2002).

Resin-supported lipase ←
Aminocarboxylic acids from lactams with enzymatic kinetic resolution s. *68*, 64 ←

Dehydrocholic acid ←
Optical resolution via complexation ←
s. *5*, 666s*65*; of lactams via inclusion complexation in dehydrocholic acid s. O. Bartolini, G. Fantin et al., Chem. Lett. *32*, 206-7 (2003).

6-(1,2:3,4-Di-O-isopropylidene-α-D-galactopyranosyl) hydrogen pththalate ←
Optical resolution via salt formation ←
s. *5*, 666s*67*; of 1-arylalkylamines with 6-(1,2:3,4-di-O-isopropylidene-α-D-galactopyranosyl) hydrogen pththalate s. H.B. Mereyala, L. Fatima, P. Pola, Tetrahedron:Asym. *15*, 585-7 (2004); of 2-subst. 1,4-benzodioxanes with (+)-dehydroabietylamine s. C. Bolchi, E. Valoti et al., ibid. *14*, 3779-85 (2003).

Chiral di-n-butyl[3-(2-phenyl-1-naphthyl)pyrid-4-yl]amine or 2-phenyl-6- ←
(trifluoromethyl)-2,3-dihydroimidazo[1,2-a]pyridine/trialkylamine
Kinetic resolution of sec. alcohols by asym. O-acylation ←
with chiral N-(4-pyridyl)prolinamide cf. *52*, 497s*66*; with chiral di-*n*-butyl[3-(2-phenyl-1-naphthyl)pyrid-4-yl]amine and other chiral 4-dimethylaminopyridine derivs. s. A.C. Spivey et al., Tetrahedron *60*, 4513-25 (2004); with chiral 2-phenyl-6-(trifluoromethyl)-2,3-dihydro-imidazo[1,2-*a*]pyridine cf. V.B. Birman, C.J. Kilbane et al., J. Am. Chem. Soc. *126*, 12226-7 (2004).

*[(R,R)-N,N′-Bis(3,5-di-*tert-*butylsalicylidenato)-1,2-cyclohexanediamine]-* ←
chromium(III) chloride
*[(R,R)-N,N′-Bis(3,5-di-*tert-*butylsalicylidenato)-1,2-cyclohexanediamine]cobalt(II)/* ←
p-nitrobenzoic anhydride
2-Arylaminoalcohols from epoxides ←
Regiospecific ring opening with kinetic resolution s. *68*, 141

*Chlorobis(cyclooctene)iridium(I) dimer/(1S,4R,8R)-2-(4-*tert-*butylphenyl)-8-methoxy-* ←
1,8-dimethylbicyclo[2.2.2]octa-2,5-diene
Kinetic resolution of 2-ethylenecarbonic acid esters
by asym. O-allylation of phenols s. *68*, 124

Reviews

This is a collection of reviews in the field of synthetic organic chemistry published largely from January to September 2005. The layout is designed for rapid scanning and to facilitate retrieval of information via the Subject Index. Supplementary data, such as reviews, are indexed in the latter in the following format:

Willgerodt-Kindler reaction
–, review **2**, 180s**68**

The s68 suffix indicates that the reader should refer to the Supplementary References section to locate the page in this volume on which the information is given.

2, 180   Some aspects of the **Willgerodt-Kindler reaction** and connected reactions, G. Purrello, Heterocycles 65, 411-49 (2005).

12, 455   Overview of **fluorous technologies**, M. Freemantle, Chem. Eng. News 83, No.33, 39-42 (2005).

13, 837   **Ketones from carboxylic acids** by decarboxylation: mechanism and scope, M. Renz, Eur. J. Org. Chem. 2005, 979-88.

16, 180   Synthesis of **fluorine-containing compounds** under operationally convenient conditions, V.A. Soloshonok, D.O. Berbasov, J. Fluorine Chem. 125, 1757-63 (2004); **elemental fluorine** and HOF·CH$_3$CN in service of general organic chemistry, S. Rozen, Eur. J. Org. Chem. 2005, 2433-47; the chemistry of trifluoromethyl imines and related acetals derived from fluoral, J.P. Bégué, D. Bonnet-Delpon, B. Crousse, J. Legros, Chem. Soc. Rev. 34, 562-72 (2005); recent applications of trifluoroacetaldehyde ethyl hemiacetal for the synthesis of **trifluoromethylated compounds**, Y. Gong, K. Kato, Curr. Org. Chem. 8, 1659-75 (2004); synthesis of fluoro analogues of unsaturated fatty acids and corresponding acyclic metabolites, M. Prakesch, D. Grée, S. Chandrasekhar, R. Grée, Eur. J. Org. Chem. 2005, 1221-32; modified natural substances: fluorinated and fluoroalkylated monosaccharides and inositols, R. Miethchen, J. Fluorine Chem. 125, 895-901 (2004); molecular rearrangements of 1-oxa-2-azoles as an expedient route to fluorinated heterocyclic compounds, A. Pace, I. Pibiri, S. Buscemi, N. Vivona, Heterocycles 63, 2627-48 (2004).

16, 820   The **fulvalenes**, B. Halton, Eur. J. Org. Chem. 2005, 3391-414.

17, 169   **Nucleosides and oligonucleotides** containing 2'-reactive groups: synthesis and applications, T.S. Zatsepin, E.A. Romanova, T.S. Oretskaya, Russ. Chem. Rev. 73, 701-33 (2004).

18, 699   Stable **phosphinous acids**, B. Hoge, S. Neufeind, S. Hettel, W. Weibe, C. Thoesen, J. Organomet. Chem. 690, 2382-7 (2005); recent advances in phosphorus-carbon bond formation: synthesis of **H-phosphinic acid derivatives** from hypophosphorous compounds, J.-L. Montchamp, ibid. 690, 2388-406 (2005).

19, 33   Conformationally rigid **cyclic α-aminocarboxylic acids** in the design of peptidomimetics, **peptide models** and biologically active compounds, I.V. Komarov, A.O. Grigorenko, A.V. Turov, V.P. Khilya, Russ. Chem. Rev. 73, 785-810 (2004); modelling and synthesis of conformationally restricted amino acids, R. Galeazzi, G. Mobbili, M. Orena, Curr. Org. Chem. 8, 1799-829 (2004); **α,β-diaminocarboxylic acids**: biological significance and synthetic approaches, A. Viso, R. Fernández de la Pradilla, A. García, A. Flores, Chem. Rev. 105, 3167-96 (2005); the trifluoromethyl group: an effective xenobiotic function for **peptide backbone modification**, M. Zanda, New J. Chem. 28, 1401-11 (2004); N- and Cα-methylation in biologically active peptides: synthesis, structural and functional aspects, S. Sagan, P. Karoyan, O. Lequin, G. Chassaing, S. Levielle, Curr. Med. Chem. *11*, 2799-822 (2004); stereoselective synthesis of aza- and diaza-bicyclo[x.y.0]alkane dipeptide mimetics, W. Maison, A.H.G.P. Prenzel, Synthesis *2005*, 1031-48; peptide- and amide bond-containing **dendrimers**, L. Crespo, G. Sanclimens, M. Pons, E. Giralt, M. Royo, F. Albericio, Chem. Rev. *105*, 1663-82 (2005); overview of applications of dendrimers, B. Halford, Chem. Eng. News *83*, No.24, 30-6 (2005); **β-phosphono- and -phosphino-peptides** derived from β-aminophosphonic and -phosphinic acids, F. Palacios, C. Alonso, J.M. de los Santos, Curr. Org. Chem. *8*, 1481-96 (2004); recent advances in design, synthesis and biological activity of aminoalkylsulfonates and **sulfonamidopeptides**, A. Obreza, S. Gobec, Curr. Med. Chem. *11*, 3263-78 (2004).

20, 501 **Niobium pentachloride** in organic synthesis: applications and perspectives, C.K.Z. Andrade, Curr. Org. Synth. *1*, 333-53 (2004).

23, 739 Recent advances in charge-accelerated **aza-Claisen rearrangement**, U. Nubbemeyer, Topics Curr. Chem. *244*, (Natural Products Synthesis II), 149-213 (2005).

24, 118 **Photochemistry** of aromatic compounds, A. Gilbert, Photochemistry *35*, 79-115 (2004).

27, 57 Overview of **asymmetric catalysis**, A.M. Thayer, Chem. Eng. News *83*, No.36, 40-8 (2005); overview of **separation of enantiomers** by supercritical fluid chromatography, ibid. 49-53; overview of **removal of impurities** with metal scavengers and by immobilization, ibid. 55-8; **asymmetric organocatalysis**, J. Seayad, B. List, Org. Biomol. Chem. *3*, 719-24 (2005); the power of **cooperativity**: Lewis acid-Lewis base bifunctional asymmetric catalysis, M. Kanai, N. Kato, E. Ichikawa, M. Shibasaki, Synlett *2005*, 1491-508; **asymmetric catalysis** of carbon-carbon bond-forming reactions **using metal salen complexes**, T.R.J. Achard, L.A. Clutterbuck, M. North, ibid. 1828-47; the central chirality of the metal atom and configuration relations in asymmetric reactions catalyzed by metal complexes, V.A. Pavlov, Russ. Chem. Rev. *73*, 1173-209 (2004); **enzymatic asymmetric synthesis** of the C-C bond, J. Sukumaran, U. Hanefeld, Chem. Soc. Rev. *34*, 530-42 (2005); **modified BINAP**: the how and the why, M. Berthod, G. Mignani, G. Woodward, M. Lemaire, Chem. Rev. *105*, 1801-36 (2005); atroposelective synthesis of **axially chiral biaryls**, G. Bringmann, A.J. Price Mortimer, P.A. Keller, M.J. Gresser, J. Garner, M. Breuning, Angew. Chem. Int. Ed. Engl. *44*, 5384-427 (2005); recent advances in **biaryl-type di(phosphine) ligands**, H. Shimizu, I. Nagasaki, T. Saito, Tetrahedron *61*, 5405-32 (2005); acyclic and cyclic **chiral aminophosphonic acids**: asymmetric syntheses mediated by chiral sulfinyl auxiliary, M. Mikolajczyk, J. Organomet. Chem. *690*, 2488-96 (2005); **chiral phosphites as ligands** in asymmetric metal complex catalysis and synthesis of coordination compounds, K.N. Gavrilov, O.G. Bondarev, A.I. Polosukhin, Russ. Chem. Rev. *73*, 671-99 (2004); progress in stereoselective catalysis by metal complexes with **chiral ferrocenylphosphines**, P. Barbaro, C. Bianchini, G. Giambastiani, S.L. Parisel, Coord. Chem. Rev. *248*, 2131-50 (2004); **chiral 1,3,2-oxazaborolidines** in asymmetric synthesis: recent advances, V.A. Glushkov, A.G. Tolstikov, Russ. Chem. Rev. *73*, 581-608 (2004); synthetic utility of **chiral 5-membered heterocyclics**, H. Matsunaga, T. Ishizuka, T. Kunieda, Tetrahedron *61*, 8073-94 (2005); the development and application of **chiral tris(Δ^2-oxazolines)** in asymmetric catalysis and molecular recognition, J. Zhou, Y. Tang, Chem. Soc. Rev. *34*, 664-76 (2005); **carbohydrate-derived ligands** in asymmetric catalysis, M. Dieguez, O. Pamies, A. Ruiz, Y. Diaz, S. Castillon, C. Claver, Coord. Chem. Rev. *248*, 2165-92 (2004); aminosugars and glycosylamines as tools in stereoselective synthesis, S. Knauer, B. Kranke, L. Krause, H. Kunz, Curr. Org. Chem. *8*, 1739-61 (2004); C_1- and C_2-symmetric carbohydrate-based P-ligands in asymmetric catalysis, S. Castillon, C. Claver, Y. Díaz, Chem. Soc. Rev. *34*, 702-13 (2005); **chiral ionic liquids**: synthesis and applications, J. Ding, D.W. Armstrong, Chirality *17*, 281-92 (2005); **asymmetric fluorous catalysis**: the particular case of nitrogen-containing chiral auxiliaries, F. Fache, New J. Chem. *28*, 1277-83 (2004); **resolution of enantiomers** by non-conventional methods, E. Fogassy, M. Nógrádi, E. Pálovics, J. Schindler, Synthesis *2005*, 1555-68; design of resolving agents based on crystal engineering, K.

Kinbara, Synlett *2005*, 732-43; application of lipase in **kinetic resolution** of racemates, A. Ghanem, H.Y. Aboul-Enein, Chirality *17*, 1-15 (2004); efficiency in non-enzymatic kinetic resolution, E. Vedejs, M. Jure, Angew. Chem. Int. Ed. Engl. *44*, 3974-4001 (2005); stereolabile chiral compounds: analysis by dynamic chromatography and stopped-flow methods, C. Wolf, Chem. Soc. Rev. *34*, 595-608 (2005); applications of catalytic **asymmetric oxidation of thioethers** to the synthesis of biologically active sulfoxides, J. Legros, J.R. Dehli, C. Bolm, Adv. Synth. Catal. *347*, 19-31 (2005); transition metal-catalyzed **asymmetric hydroamination** of alkenes, K.C. Hultzsch, ibid. 367-91 (2005); catalytic asymmetric hydroamination of non-activated olefins, K.C. Hultzsch, Org. Biomol. Chem. *3*, 1819-24 (2005); catalytic **asymmetric vinylogous aldol condensation**, S.E. Denmark, J.R. Heemstra Jr., G.L. Beutner, Angew. Chem. Int. Ed. Engl. *44*, 4682-98 (2005); recent advances in catalytic **asymmetric α-amination and -oxygenation** of carbonyl compounds, J.M. Janey, ibid. 4292-300; chiral auxiliary-controlled **asymmetric epoxidation**, W. Adam, A. Zhang, Synlett *2005*, 1047-72; advances in homogeneous and heterogeneous catalytic asymmetric epoxidation, Q.-H. Xia, H.-Q. Ge, C.-P. Ye, Z.-M. Liu, K.-X. Su, Chem. Rev. *105*, 1603-62 (2005); asymmetric epoxidation of olefins with chiral metalloporphyrin catalysts, E. Rose, B. Andrioletti, S. Zrig, M. Quelquejeu-Ethève, Chem. Soc. Rev. *34*, 573-83 (2005); **asymmetric ring opening of epoxides**, I.M. Pastor, M. Yus, Curr. Org. Chem. *9*, 1-29 (2005); palladium catalyzed **aerobic dehydrogenation**: from alcohols to indoles and asymmetric catalysis, B.M. Stolz, Chem. Lett. *33*, 362-7 (2004); **chiral N-acylhydrazones**: versatile imino acceptors for asymmetric amine synthesis, G.K. Friestad, Eur. J. Org. Chem. *2005*, 3157-72; the development of rhodium-catalyzed **asymmetric hydroboration** of olefins, A.-M. Carroll, T.P. O'Sullivan, P.J. Guiry, Adv. Synth. Catal. *347*, 609-31 (2005).

27, 729 ***gem*-Disubstituent effect**: theoretical basis and synthetic applications, M.E. Jung, G. Piizzi, Chem. Rev. *105*, 1735-66 (2005).

27, 851 **Commercial catalysts**, J. Black, M. North, Chem. Ind. *2005*, No.12, 22-3; applications of catalysis in academia and industry, Tetrahedron Symposium-in-Print Number 112, Tetrahedron *61*, 6165-471 (2005) (29 Papers); some highlights from the development and use of **bulky monodentate ligands**, P.P. Power, J. Organomet. Chem. *689*, 3904-19 (2004); **functional ligands** and complexes for new structures, homogeneous catalysts and nanomaterials, P. Braunstein, ibid. 3953-67; stability and reactivity of **N-heterocyclic carbene complexes**, C.M. Crudden, D.P. Allen, Coord. Chem. Rev. *248*, 2247-73 (2004); recent homogeneous catalytic applications of chelate- and pincer-type N-heterocyclic carbenes, E. Peris, R.H. Crabtree, ibid. 2239-46; **NCN-pincer palladium complexes** with multiple anchoring points for functional groups, M.Q. Slagt, D.A.P. van Zwieten, A.J.C.M. Moerkerk, R.J.M.K. Gebbink, G. van Koten, ibid. 2275-82; **palladacyclics** in catalysis – a critical survey, I.P. Beletskaya, A.V. Cheprakov, J. Organomet. Chem. *689*, 4055-82 (2004); the potential of palladacyclics: more than just pre-catalysts, J. Dupont, C.S. Consorti, J. Spencer, Chem. Rev. *105*, 2527-72 (2005); non-covalently **supported catalysts** for organic synthesis, J. Horn, F. Michalek, C.C. Tzschucke, W. Bannwarth, Topics Curr. Chem. *242*, 43-75 (2004); recent progress in **polymeric palladium catalysts** for organic synthesis, Y. Uozumi, ibid. 77-112; polyurea-**encapsulated palladium catalysts**: the development and application in homogeneous catalysis, D.A. Pears, S.C. Smith, Aldrichimica Acta *38*, 24-34 (2005); catalysis by **sol-gels**: an advanced technology for organic chemistry, R. Ciriminna, M. Pagharo, Curr. Org. Chem. *8*, 1851-62 (2004); **metallodendritic catalysis** for redox reactions and carbon-carbon bond formation: a step towards green chemistry, D. Astuc et al., Adv. Synth. Catal. *347*, 329-38 (2005); organometallic chemistry of **15-membered macrocyclic trienes**: catalysis by palladium(0) complexes for carbon-carbon bond formation, M. Moreni-Manas, R. Pleixats, R.M. Sebastian, A. Vallribera, A. Roglans, J. Organomet. Chem. *689*, 3669-84 (2004); *green* **Suzuki coupling in aqueous media**, R. Franzen, Y. Xu, Can. J. Chem. *83*, 266-72 (2005); *green* **Suzuki diaryl coupling**, L. Bai, J.X. Wang, Curr. Org. Chem. *9*, 535-53 (2005); fast, easy, and clean **chemistry in**

water under microwave heating: Suzuki coupling as an illustration, N.E. Leadbeater, Chem. Commun. *2005*, 2881-902; the development of efficient catalysts for **palladium-catalyzed coupling** of aryl halides, A. Zapf, M. Beller, ibid. 431-40; palladium-catalyzed cross-coupling reactions **in total synthesis**, K.C. Nicolaou, P.G. Bulger, D. Sarlah, Angew. Chem. Int. Ed. Engl. *44*, 4442-89 (2005); palladium-catalyzed cross-coupling **in aqueous media**: recent progress and current applications, K.H. Shaughnessy, R.B. DeVasher, Curr. Org. Chem. *9*, 585-604 (2005); **metathesis** in total synthesis, K.C. Nicolaou, P.G. Bulger, D. Sarlah, Angew. Chem. Int. Ed. Engl. *44*, 4490-527 (2005); metathesis strategy **in nucleoside chemistry**, F. Amblard, S.P. Nolan, L.A. Agrofoglio, Tetrahedron *61*, 7067-80 (2005); metathesis: from a historical perspective to recent developments, D. Astruc, New J. Chem. *29*, 42-56 (2005); olefin metathesis: catalyst development, microwave catalysis, and domino applications, S.G. Aitken, A.D. Abell, Australian J. Chem. *58*, 3-13 (2005); **olefin metathesis** and related reactions initiated by carbene derivatives of metals in low oxidation states, T.J. Katz, Angew. Chem. Int. Ed. Engl. *44*, 3010-19 (2005); **alkyne metathesis**, A. Furstner, P.W. Davies, Chem. Commun. *2005*, 2307-20; regio- and stereo-controlled **palladium- or iridium-catalyzed allylation**, H. Miyabe, Y. Takemoto, Synlett *2005*, 1641-55; palladium-catalyzed **electrophilic allylation** via bis(allylpalladium) complexes and related intermediates, K.J. Szabo, Chem. Eur. J. *10*, 5269-75 (2004); applications of non-stabilized enolates as nucleophiles in palladium catalyzed allylation, U. Kazmaier, J. Indian Chem. Soc. *80*, 957-67 (2003); **palladium-catalyzed activation of allyl alcohols** as allyl cations, allyl anions, or amphiphilic allylic species, Y. Tamaru, Eur. J. Org. Chem. *2005*, 2647-56; developments in catalytic aromatic **C-H transformations:** promising tools for organic synthesis, L.A. Goj, T.B. Gunnoe, Curr. Org. Chem. *9*, 671-85 (2005); organometallic **C-H-activation of hydrocarbons**, R.H. Crabtree, J. Organomet. Chem. *689*, 4083-91 (2004); selective molecular recognition, C-H bond activation, and catalysis in nanoscale reaction vessels, D. Fiedler, D.H. Leung, R.G. Bergman. K.N. Raymond, Acc. Chem. Res. *38*, 349-58 (2005); recent advances in **transition metal-catalyzed oxidation with molecular oxygen**, T. Punniyamurthy, S. Velusamy, J. Iqbal, Chem. Rev. *105*, 2329-64 (2005); **palladium-catalyzed allylic oxidation** of alkenes, I.I. Moiseev, M.N. Vargaftik, Coord. Chem. Rev. *248*, 2381-91 (2004); branch-selective **hydroformylation:** a useful tool for organic synthesis, M.L. Clarke, Curr. Org. Chem. *9*, 701-18 (2005); transition metal-mediated routes to **cyclopentenones**, S.E. Gibson, S.E. Lewis, N. Mainolfi, J. Organomet. Chem. *689*, 3873-90 (2004); the intermolecular **Pauson-Khand reaction**, S.E. Gibson, N. Mainolfi, Angew. Chem. Int. Ed. Engl. *44*, 3022-37 (2005); transition metal-catalyzed **decarboxylative addition of enolates**, J.A. Tunge, E.C. Burger, Eur. J. Org. Chem. *2005*, 1715-26; palladium-catalyzed reactions of alcohols. Part C: **ether formation**, J. Muzart, Tetrahedron *61*, 5955-6008 (2005); Part D: rearrangements, carbonylations, carboxylations and miscellaneous reactions, ibid. 9415-46; the virtue of palladium-catalyzed **domino reactions** – diverse oligocyclizations of acyclic 2-bromoenynes and bromoenediynes, A. de Meijere, P. von Zezschwitz, S. Bräse, Acc. Chem. Res. *38*, 413-22 (2005); **the golden age to catalysis**, A. Hoffmann-Roder, N. Krause, Org. Biomol. Chem. *3*, 387-91 (2005); **methylrhenium oxide** and its application in olefinic oxidation, metathesis and in aldehyde olefination, F.E. Kuehn, A. Scherbaum, W.A. Herrmann, J. Organomet. Chem. *689*, 4149-64 (2004); synthesis of **polyoxygenated steroids** with transition metal-based oxidants: methylrhenium oxide-hydrogen peroxide, ruthenium tetroxide, osmium tetroxide and potassium permanganate, D. Musumeci, D. Sica, F. Zollo, Curr. Org. Synth. *2*, 1-20 (2005); advances in **iron-catalyzed cross-coupling**, A. Furstner, R. Martin, Chem. Lett. *34*, 624-9 (2005); **vinylideneruthenium complexes** in catalysis, H. Katayama, F. Ozawa, Coord. Chem. Rev. *248*, 1703-15 (2004); **vinylidenerhodium complexes** as promising tools for C-C coupling, H. Werner, ibid. 1693-702; chromium- and manganese-salen promoted **epoxidation**, E.M. McGarrigle, D.G. Gilheany, Chem. Rev. *105*, 1563-602 (2005); Group 6 **Fisher carbene complexes**: "chemical multitalents" for multi-component reactions, J. Barluenga, M.A. Fernandez-Rodriguez, E. Aguilar, J. Organomet. Chem. *690*, 539-87 (2005); **zirconate complexes**: multifaceted reagents,

J.-P. Majoral, M. Zablocka, New J. Chem. *29*, 32-41 (2005); high oxidation state transition metal **alkylidene and alkylidyne complexes**, R.R. Schrock, Chem. Commun. *2005*, 2773-7; stable **1-titana- and 1-zircona-cyclopenta-2,3,4-trienes**, U. Rosenthal, V.V. Burlakov, P. Arndt, W. Baumann, A. Sparmenberg, Organometallics *24*, 456-71 (2005); cyclic π-systems with anellated rings – highly selective oxy-anion driven reactions at chromium complexes, H. Butenschon, J. Chem. Soc. Pak. *26*, 322-7 (2004); the decomposition of **metal alkyls** revisited: surprising wellspring of novel reagents for organic synthesis, J.J. Eisch, A.A. Adeosun, S. Dutta, P.O. Fregene, Eur. J. Org. Chem. *2005*, 2657-70; transition metal-catalyzed **reactions of carbon dioxide and other heterocumulenes**, J. Louie, Curr. Org. Chem. *9*, 605-23 (2005); metal-mediated and -catalyzed **nucleophilic addition to cyclopropenes**, J.M. Fox, N. Yan, ibid. 719-32; **single electron transfer** in the synthetic organometallic chemistry of first-row transition metals, K.M. Smith, Organometallics *24*, 778-84 (2005).

27, 899   **Cyclopropene pyrolysis**, R. Walsh, Chem. Soc. Rev. *34*, 714-32 (2005).

28, 13   Research inspired by the chemistry of **nitrogenase** – novel metal complexes and their reactivity toward dinitrogen, nitriles, and alkynes, M. Hidai, Y. Mizobe, Can. J. Chem. *83*, 358-74 (2005).

29, 746   **Copper in cross-coupling**, I.P. Beletskaya, A.V. Cheprakov, Coord. Chem. Rev. *248*, 2337-64 (2004).

30, 321   **Tartaric acid** and its O-acyl derivatives. Part 1: synthesis of tartaric acids and anhydrides, L. Synoradzki, P. Ruskowski, U. Bernas, Org. Prep. Proced. Int. *37*, 37-63 (2005).

31, 101   **Synthesis of allyl alcohols** from alkenes and their derivatives, A.K. Banerjee, P.S. Poon, M.S. Laya, W.J. Vera, Russ. Chem. Rev. *73*, 621-36 (2004).

32, 11   Methods for the **cleavage of allylic and propargylic C-N bonds** in amines and amides – selected alternative applications of the 1,3-hydrogen shift, S. Escoubet, S. Gastaldi, M. Bertrand, Eur. J. Org. Chem. *2005*, 3855-73.

32, 279   Synthesis and chemical transformations of mono- and di-substituted **cyanamides**, D.D. Nekrasov, Russ. J. Org. Chem. *40*, 1387-402 (2004).

32, 604   **Silicon-mercury derivatives** in organic synthesis, V.D. Romanenko, V.L. Rudzevich, Tetrahedron *61*, 4509-30 (2005).

33, 370   Acyclic α-**nitroketones**: a versatile class of α-functionalized ketones in organic synthesis, R. Ballini, G. Bosica, D. Fiorini, A. Palmieri, Tetrahedron *61*, 8971-93 (2005).

33, 786   α-**Lithiated styrene oxides**: useful reactive intermediates, V. Capriati, S. Florio, R. Luisi, Synlett *2005*, 1359-69.

34, 693   **Boron compounds in Diels-Alder reactions** and other cycloadditions, G. Hilt, P. Bolze, Synthesis *2005*, 2091-115.

35, 141   Hydrogen bonding and protonation as modifying factors of **quinone reactivity**, M. Aguilar-Martinez, N.A. Marcias-Ruvalcaba, J.A. Bautista-Martinez, M. Gomez, F.J. Gonzalez, I. Gonzalez, Curr. Org. Chem. *8*, 1721-38 (2004); enone cycloadditions and rearrangements: **photoreactions of dienones and quinones**, W.M. Horspool, Photochemistry *34*, 29-67 (2003).

35, 661   Planar **dehydro[8]annulenes** and their ramifications: substituted tribenzo[*a,c,e*]cyclooctenes and tetrabenzo[*a,c,e,g*]cyclooc..., X.-L. Hou, H. Huang, H.N.C. Wong, Synlett *2005*, 1073-89.

37, 120   **Oxidation of thioethers** to sulfoxides. Part 2: Oxidation by hydrogen peroxide, K. Kaczorowska, Z. Kolarska, K. Mitka, P. Kowalski, Tetrahedron *61*, 8315-27 (2005).

37, 626   Past, present, and future of **cyclodextrin research**, J. Szejtli, Pure Applied Chem. *76*, 1825-45 (2004).

37, 933   A facile approach to **bicyclo[n.2.0]alkan-1-ols**: an overview, W.A. Loughlin, Australian J. Chem. *57*, 335-8 (2004).

38, 1	Recent advances in **cleavage of ethers**, S.A. Weissman, D. Zewge, Tetrahedron *61*, 7833-63 (2005).
38, 723	Chemistry of **pyramidalized alkenes**, S. Vázquez, P. Camps, Tetrahedron *61*, 5147-208 (2005); CH/π **hydrogen bonds** in organic reactions, M. Nishio, ibid. 6923-50.
39, 363	A journey across recent advances in catalytic and stereoselective **alkylation of indoles**, M. Bandini, A. Melloni, S. Tommasi, A. Umani-Ronchi, Synlett *2005*, 1199-222.
41, 48	**Magnesium in methanol** in organic syntheses, G.H. Lee, I.K. Youn, E.B. Choi, H.K. Lee, G.H. Yon, H.C. Yang, C.S. Pak, Curr. Org. Chem. *8*, 1263-87 (2004).
41, 134	Advances in **singlet oxygen** chemistry, E.L. Clennan, A. Pace, Tetrahedron *61*, 6665-91 (2005).
41, 173	Enzymes in preparative **carbohydrate and oligosaccharide synthesis**, C.J. Hamilton, Nat. Prod. Res. *21*, 365-85 (2004); overview of advances in carbohydrate chemistry: arrays, functional analysis and synthetic techniques, S. Borman, Chem. Eng. News *83*, No.32, 41-50 (2005); thioglycosides in sequential glycosylation strategies, J.D.C. Codée, R.E.J.N. Lijens, L.J. van den Bos, H.S. Overkleeft, G.A. van der Marel, Chem. Soc. Rev. *34*, 769-82 (2005); **protein glycosylation** – new challenges and opportunities, C.H. Wong, J. Org. Chem. *70*, 4219-25 (2005); recent advances in the chemistry of aza-pyranose sugars, K. Afarinkia, A. Bahar, Tetrahedron:Asym. *16*, 1239-87 (2005); recent advances in the total synthesis of piperidine **azasugars**, M.S.M. Pearson, M. Mathé-Allainmat, V. Fargeas, J. Lebreton, Eur. J. Org. Chem. *2005*, 2159-91; synthesis of aza-C-disaccharides (dideoxyimino-alditols C-linked to monosaccharides) and analogues, I. Robina, P. Vogel, Synthesis *2005*, 675-702; synthesis of stable **carbohydrate mimetics** as potential glycotherapeutics, M.H.D. Postema, J.L. Piper, R.L. Betts, Synlett *2005*, 1345-58; **sugar allyltin compounds**: preparation and application in organic synthesis, S. Jarosz, A. Gawel, Eur. J. Org. Chem. *2005*, 3415-32; carbohydrates: from 'chirons' to new glycosubstances, G.V.M. Sharma, P.R. Krishna, Curr. Org. Chem. *8*, 1187-209 (2004).
41, 644	Applications of **ultrasound** irradiation in organic synthesis, J.-T. Li, S.-X. Wang, G.-F. Chen, T.-S. Li, Curr. Org. Synth. *2*, 415-36 (2005).
41, 696	**Hypervalent iodine chemistry** in synthesis: scope and new directions, T. Wirth, Angew. Chem. Int. Ed. Engl. *44*, 3656-65 (2005); benziodoxole-based hypervalent iodine reagents, V.V. Zhdankin, Curr. Org. Synth. *2*, 121-45 (2005).
42, 45	Recent progress in the total synthesis of **dolabellane and dolastane diterpenes**, M. Hiersemann, H. Helmboldt, Topics Curr. Chem. *243*, (Natural Product Synthesis I), 73-136 (2005).
42, 676	Recent advances in **intramolecular alkyne cyclotrimerization** and its applications, Y. Yamamoto, Curr. Org. Chem. *9*, 503-19 (2005).
42, 725	**Olefination of carbonyl compounds**: modern and classical methods, V.N. Korotchenko, V.G. Nenajdenko, E.S. Balenkova, A.V. Shastin, Russ. Chem. Rev. *73*, 957-89 (2004).
42, 853	Recent advances in microwave-assisted **synthesis of heterocyclic compounds**, V. Molteni, D.A. Ellis, Curr. Org. Synth. *2*, 333-75 (2005); recent developments in palladium-catalyzed synthesis of heterocyclics and functionalization, J.P. Wolfe, J.S. Thomas, Curr. Org. Chem. *9*, 625-55 (2005); reductive cyclization in the synthesis of **5-membered N-heterocyclics**, P.G. Tsoungas, A.I. Diplas, ibid. *8*, 1579-606 (2004); reductive cyclization in the synthesis of **6-membered N-heterocyclics**, ibid. 1607-28; the utility of diaryl sulfides and diaryl sulfones in heterocyclic synthesis, M.M. Kandeel, M.S.K. Youssef, Phosphorus, Sulfur Silicon Relat. Elem. *180*, 217-82 (2005); cyclic 1,3-diones and their derivatives as versatile reactive intermediates in the synthesis of **condensed heterocyclics**, B.C. Sekhar, J. Heterocycl. Chem. *41*, 807-55 (2004); 4-alkoxy-1,1,1-trichloro-3-alken-2-ones: preparation and applications in heterocyclic synthesis, M.A.P. Martins, W. Cunico, C.M.P. Pereira, A.P. Sinhorin, A.F.C. Flores, H.G. Bonacorso, N. Zanatta, Curr. Org. Synth. *1*, 391-403 (2004); **lithiated α-chloroalkylheterocyclics**:

utility in synthetic organic chemistry, S. Florio, V. Capriati, R. Luisi, Curr. Org. Chem. *8*, 1529-45 (2004); tandem methodology for heterocyclic synthesis, A. Padwa, Pure Applied Chem. *76*, 1933-52 (2004); conformation-directed **macrocyclization,** J. Blankenstein, J. Zhu, Eur. J. Org. Chem. *2005*, 1949-64; **intramolecular dipolar cycloaddition** of azomethinium ylids, I. Coldham, R. Hufton, Chem. Rev. *105*, 2765-810 (2005); azomethinium ylids from carbenes and carbenoids: generation and synthetic applications, A.F. Khlebnikov, M.S. Novikov, R.R. Kostikov, Russ. Chem. Rev. *74*, 171-92 (2005); centennial methodology for the preparation of **O-heterocyclics** by iodocyclization of functionalized alkenes, F. Martins da silva, J. Jones Jr., M. de Mattos, Curr. Org. Synth. *2*, 393-414 (2005); synthetic strategies of marine **polycyclic ethers** via intramolecular allylations, I. Kadoto, Y. Yamamoto, Acc. Chem. Res. *38*, 423-32 (2005); transformation of epoxides into O-heterocyclics, L.I. Kas'yan, I.N. Tarabara, A.O. Kas'yan, Russ. J. Org. Chem. *40*, 1227-57 (2004); **β-lactones**: intermediates for natural product total synthesis and new transformations, Y. Wang, R.L. Tennyson, D. Romo, Heterocycles *64*, 605-58 (2004); the recent impact of solid-phase synthesis on medicinally relevant **benzo-condensed O-heterocyclics**, R.E. Ziegert, J. Toraeng, K. Knepper, S. Braese, J. Comb. Chem. *7*, 147-69 (2005); photochemical **transformations of chromones**, S.C. Gupta, R.C. Kamboj, J. Indian Chem. Soc. *80*, 1007-14 (2003); synthesis, reactions and biological activity of phosphorus-containing derivatives of chromone and coumarin, E. Budzisz, Phosphorus, Sulfur Silicon Relat. Elem. *179*, 2131-47 (2004); heterocyclics directly linked to the 3-position of chromones, C.K. Ghosh, Heterocycles *63*, 2875-98 (2004); synthesis of **2-ene-2,3-dihydro-1,4-benzodioxins**, D. Sinou, Curr. Org. Chem. *9*, 377-87 (2005); synthesis of dimethyl O-heterocyclic-dicarboxylates using dimethyl acetylenedicarboxylate, Y. Tominaga, K. Ueda, J. Heterocycl. Chem. *42*, 337-52 (2005); hexamethyldisilthiane-based thionation of carbonyl compounds: a versatile approach to **S-heterocyclics**, A. Degl'Innocenti, A. Capperucci, G. Castagnoli, Synlett *2005*, 1965-83; synthesis and reactivity of **thioaurones** over the past one hundred years, M.T. Konieczny, W. Konieczny, Heterocycles *65*, 451-64 (2005); the latest achievements in **thienothiophene chemistry**, V.P. Litvinov, Russ. Chem. Rev. *74*, 217-48 (2005); **2(3H)-oxazolone** – a simple heterocycle with manifold potential, S.P. Fearnley, Curr. Org. Chem. *8*, 1289-337 (2004); recent advances on the synthesis and reactivity of **isoxazoles**, T.M.V.D. Pinho e Melo, ibid. *9*, 925-58 (2005); **supported 1,3-dipolar cycloaddition**: nitrone approach towards isoxazolidines and isoxazolines, and subsequent transformations, K. Rück-Braun, T.H.E. Freysoldt, F. Wierschem, Chem. Soc. Rev. *34*, 507-16 (2005); directly linked **polyazoles**: important moieties in natural products, E. Riego, D. Hernández, F. Albericio, M. Álvarez, Synthesis *2005*, 1907-22; the development of novel **ninhydrin** analogues, D.B. Hansen, M.M. Joullié, Chem. Soc. Rev. *34*, 408-17 (2005); **nitropyridines**, their synthesis and reactions, J.M. Bakke, J. Heterocycl. Chem. *42*, 463-74 (2005); synthesis of functionalized compounds containing **pyridazine** and related moieties, J. Svete, ibid. 361-73; functionalization and synthetic application of 3(2H)-**pyridazinones**, S.-K. Kim, D.-H. Kweon, S.D. Cho, Y.-J. Kang, K.-H. Park, S.-G. Lee, Y.-J. Yoon, ibid. 353-9; s.a. Curr. Org. Chem. *8*, 1463-80 (2004); exploiting synthetic chemistry with mesoionic rings: improvements achieved with **thioisomunchnones**, M. Ávalos, R. Babiano, P. Cintas, L. Jiménez, J.C. Palacios, Acc. Chem. Res. *38*, 460-8 (2005); **1,3,5-triazine**: a versatile heterocycle in organic chemistry, G. Giacomelli, A. Porcheddu, L. de Luca, Curr. Org. Chem. *8*, 1497-519 (2004); synthesis and functionalization of **indoles** through palladium-catalyzed reactions, S. Cacchi, G. Fabrizi, Chem. Rev. *105*, 2873-920 (2005); **spiroquinolines** annulated at the heterocyclic fragment – synthesis and properties, V.V. Kouznetsov, J. Heterocycl. Chem. *42*, 39-59 (2005); recent advances in the synthesis of **2H-1,4-benzoxazin-3(4H)-ones and 3,4-dihydro-2H-1,4-benzoxazines**, J. Ilaš, P.Š. Anderluh, M.S. Dolenc, D. Kikelj, Tetrahedron *61*, 7325-48 (2005); synthetic approaches to **1,2,5-benzothiadiazepine 1,1-dioxides** – sulfonamide analogues of the 1,4-benzodiazepines, K. Hemming, C. Loukou, J. Chem. Res. Synop *2005*, 1-2; **2-azabicyclo[2.2.0]hex-5-enes and 2-azabicyclo[2.2.0]hexanes**, G.R. Krow, K.C. Cannon, Heterocycles *64*, 577-603 (2004); synthesis and **heterocyclization of 3-alkynyl-6,8-**

dimethylpyrimido[4,5-c]pyridazine-5,7(6H,8H)-diones and their lumazine analogues, A.V. Gulevskaya, S. Van Dang, A.F. Pozharskii, J. Heterocycl. Chem. *42*, 413-9 (2005); pyrimido[4,5-c]pyridazine-5,7(6H,8H)-diones: marvellous substrates for the study of nucleophilic substitution of hydrogen, A.F. Pozharskii, A.V. Gulevskaya, ibid. 375-85; cyclization to new **azolopyridazines** and related ring systems, G. Hajos, Z. Riedl, P. Matyus, B.U.W. Maes, ibid. 421-6; synthesis of biologically active **pyridazinoquinoxalines**, Y. Kurasawa, H.S. Kim, ibid. 387-93; recent synthetic approaches to **azoloquinolines**, M. Abass, Heterocycles *65*, 901-65 (2005); **benziporphyrins**: exploring arene chemistry in a macrocyclic environment, M. Stepien, L. Latos-Grazynski, Acc. Chem. Res. *38*, 88-98 (2005); **fullerene-porphyrin constructs**, P.D.W. Boyd, C.A. Reed, ibid. 88-98; synthesis, reactivity and stereochemistry of new **P-heterocyclics** with 5- or 6-membered rings, H.-J. Cristau, J.-L. Pirat, D. Virieux, J. Monbrun, C. Ciptadi, Y.-A. Bekro, J. Organomet. Chem. *690*, 2472-81 (2005); "ESHC (Sopron) Plenary Lecture": exciting fields in P-heterocyclic chemistry, G. Keglevich, J. Heterocycl. Chem. *42*, 451-62 (2005); **domino reactions** in the synthesis of heterocyclic natural products and analogs, L.F. Tietze, N. Rackelmann, Pure Applied Chem. *76*, 1967-83 (2004); **[3+3]-cycloaddition** and related strategies **in alkaloid natural product synthesis**, J.P.A. Harrity, O. Provoost, Org. Biomol. Chem. *3*, 1349-58 (2005); development of a novel synthetic method for ring construction using organometallic complexes and its application to the **total synthesis of natural products**, M. Mori, Chem. Pharm. Bull. *53*, 457-70 (2005); on the remarkable antitumor properties of **fludelone**: how we got there, A. Rivkin, T.-C. Chou, S.J. Danishefsky, Angew. Chem. Int. Ed. Engl. *44*, 2838-50 (2005); synthesis of **benzo[c]phenanthridine alkaloids** based on palladium-catalyzed aryl-aryl coupling, T. Harayama, Heterocycles *65*, 697-713 (2005); advances in the synthesis of analogues of the **delphinium alkaloid, methyllycaconitine**, K.J. Goodall, D. Barker, M.A. Brimble, Synlett *2005*, 1809-27; chemistry of **domoic acid**, isodomoic acids, and their analogues, J. Clayden, B. Read, K.R. Hebditch, Tetrahedron *61*, 5713-24 (2005); occurance, biological activity, and convergent organometallic synthesis of **carbazole alkaloids**, H.-J. Knoelker, Topics Curr. Chem. *244*, (Natural Products Synthesis), 115-48 (2005); **methanophenazine** and other natural biologically active phenazines, U. Beifuss, M. Tietze, ibid. 77-113; **calixarenes** as platforms for the construction of multimetallic complexes, A.J. Petrella, C.L. Raston, J. Organomet. Chem. *689*, 4125-36 (2005); homooxacalixarenes. Part I. Structure, synthesis, and chemical reactions, E.A. Shokova, V.V. Kovalev, Russ. J. Org. Chem. *40*, 607-43 (2004); the **cucurbit[n]uril family**, J. Lagona, P. Mukhopadhyay, S. Chakrabarti, L. Isaacs, Angew. Chem. Int. Ed. Engl. *44*, 4844-70 (2005); synthesis of the **hamigerans**, D.L.J. Clive, J. Wang, Org. Prep. Proced. Int. *37*, 1-35 (2005).

42, 887   **Hypervalent silicon** as a reactive site in selective bond-forming processes, S. Rendler, M. Oestreich, Synthesis *2005*, 1727-47.

42, 970   Catalytic methods for the synthesis of **stilbenes** with an emphasis on phytoalexins, K. Ferre-Filmon, L. Delaude, A. Demonceau, A.F. Noels, Coord. Chem. Rev. *248*, 2323-36 (2004).

43, 40   Diastereoselective Lewis acid mediated **reductions of β-functionalized α-alkylated carbonyl compounds**, G. Bartoli, M. Bartolacci, A. Giuliani, E. Marcantoni, M. Massaccesi, Eur. J. Org. Chem. *2005*, 2867-78.

43, 520   Addition of metalloid hydrides to alkynes: hydrometallation with boron, silicon, and tin, B.M. Trost, Z.T. Ball, Synthesis *2005*, 853-87.

43, 980   Recent developments in **Nazarov cyclization**, H. Pellissier, Tetrahedron *61*, 6479-517 (2005); s.a. A.J. Frontier, C. Collison, ibid. 7577-606; some new Nazarov chemistry, M.A. Tius, Eur. J. Org. Chem. *2005*, 2193-205; substituent effects, catalysis and asymmetric catalysis in the Nazarov cyclization, M. Harmota, CHEMTRACTS: Org. Chem. *17*, 416-35 (2004).

44, 496   Generation of **cycloalkynes** by hydroiodonio-elimination of vinyl iodonium salts, T. Okuyama, M. Fujita, Acc. Chem. Res. *38*, 679-86 (2005).

44, 533 Synthesis and reactions of **selenothioic acid *S*-esters and diselenocarboxylic acid esters**, T. Murai, Synlett *2005*, 1509-20.

44, 602 Recent approaches towards synthesis of *cis*-**decalins**, V. Singh, S.R. Iyer, S. Pal, Tetrahedron *61*, 9197-231 (2005).

45, 486 **Activation of nitrogen** for organic synthesis, M. Mori, J. Organomet. Chem. *689*, 4210-27 (2004).

47, 48 Organic reactions in **aqueous media** with a focus on carbon-carbon bond formation: a decade update, C.-J. Li, Chem. Rev. *105*, 3095-166 (2005); overview of reactions in plain water, E.K. Wilson, Chem. Eng. News *83,* No.30, 49-51 (2005).

48, 625 **N-Phosphinylimines**: an emerging class of reactive intermediates for stereoselective organic synthesis, S.M. Weinreb, R.K. Orr, Synthesis *2005*, 1205-27.

48, 640 **Open-cage fullerenes**: synthesis, structure, and molecular encapsulation, S. Iwamatsu, S. Murata, Synlett *2005*, 2117-29.

50, 555 Comprehensive survey of **combinatorial library synthesis**, R.E. Dolle, J. Comb. Chem. *6*, 623-79 (2004); application of combinatorial and parallel synthesis to antiparisitic drug discovery, C.C. Musonda, K. Chibale, Curr. Med. Chem. *11*, 2519-33 (2004).

54, 266 **Cyanohydrins from ketones,** F.-X. Chen, X. Feng, Synlett *2005,* 892-9.

55, 159 Recent advances in metal-mediated carbon-nitrogen bond formation reactions: **aziridination and amidation**, J.A. Halfen, Curr. Org. Chem. *9*, 657-69 (2005).

57, 230 Recent advances in **vinylogous aldol condensation** and applications in the synthesis of natural products, M. Kalesse, Topics Curr. Chem. *244*, (Natural Products Synthesis II), 43-76 (2005).

57, 418 **Solid-phase synthesis** using organometallic reagents, H. Graden, N. Kann, Curr. Org. Chem. *9*, 733-63 (2005); organic solid-state reactions with 100% yield, G. Kaupp, Topics Curr. Chem. *254,* (Organic Solid State Reactions), 95-183 (2005).

60, 153 Towards rapid, green, predictable **microwave-assisted synthesis**, B.A. Roberts, C.R. Strauss, Acc. Chem. Res. *38*, 653-61 (2005).

61, 74 Room-temperature **ionic liquids**: different classes and physical properties, S.T. Handy, Curr. Org. Chem. *9*, 959-88 (2005); overview of industrial interest in ionic liquids, M. Freemantle, Chem. Eng. News *83,* No.31, 33-8 (2005); supported ionic liquid phases, C.P. Mehnert, Chem. Eur. J. *11,* 50-6 (2005); biodegradable ionic liquids. Part II. Effect of the anion and toxicology, M.T. Garcia, N. Gathergood, P.J. Scammells, Green Chem. *7*, 3-6 (2005); **green chemical pathways**: a need of the day, S.C. Ameta, S. Mehta, A. Sancheti, J. Vardia, J. Indian Chem. Soc. *81*, 1127-40 (2004); overview of green technologies, S.K. Ritter, Chem. Eng. News *83,* No.26, 40-3 (2005); **green solvents** for sustainable organic synthesis: state of the art, R.A. Sheldon, Green Chem. *7*, 243-52 (2005); **polyethylene glycol** and solutions of the latter as green media, ibid. 64-82.

65, 88 **Alkyl carbonates** as 'green reactants' – Preparation and perspectives, J. Kijenski, E. Smigiera, J. Polaczek, Przem. Chem. *83*, 493-7 (2004).

65, 369 The use of **tosylhydrazone salts as safe alternatives for diazo compounds** and their applications in organic synthesis, J.R. Fulton, V.K. Aggarwal, J. de Vicente, Eur. J. Org. Chem. *2005*, 1479-92.

65, 377 Overview of harnessing microreactors, A.M. Thayer, Chem. Eng. News *83,* No.22, 43-52 (2005).

65, 447 Catalytic significance of **organometallic compounds immobilized on mesoporous silica**: economically and environmentally important examples, J.M. Thomas, R. Raja, J. Organomet. Chem. *689*, 4110-24 (2004).

65, 461 Recent advances in the use of **tri-2-furylgermane, triphenylgermane** and their derivatives in organic synthesis, H. Yorimitsu, K. Oshima, Inorg. Chem. Commun. *8*, 131-42 (2005).

66, 135 **Oxidative cleavage of the carbon-carbon triple bond**, T.S.S. Rao, S. Awasthi, J. Indian Chem. Soc. *80*, 1129-41 (2003).

66, 204 Recent advances in the chemistry of **lithium aminoborohydrides**, L. Pasumansky, B. Singaram, Aldrichimica Acta *38*, 62-6 (2005).

66, 287 Chemistry of hydroxyhydrazines and their heterocyclic derivatives. Part 1. Synthesis of **hydroxyhydrazines**, Z. Zalan, L. Lazar, F. Fülöp, Curr. Org. Chem. *9*, 357-76 (2005).

66, 356 Regioselective control of **electrophilic aromatic substitution**, K. Smith, G.A. El-Hiti, Curr. Org. Synth. *1*, 253-74 (2004).

66, 442 Neutral coordinate-organocatalysts in organic synthesis: **nucleophilic allylation of acylhydrazones** with allyltrichlorosilanes, S. Kobayashi, M. Sugiura, C. Ogawa, Adv. Synth. Catal. *346*, 1023-34 (2004); acylhydrazones as versatile electrophiles for the synthesis of nitrogen-containing compounds, M. Sugiura, S. Kobayashi, Angew. Chem. Int. Ed. Engl. *44*, 5176-86 (2005).

66, 495 **Mercaptals** as zwitterion synthons, T.-Y. Luh, C.-F. Lee, Eur. J. Org. Chem. *2005*, 3875-85.

67, 69 Some typical advances in the synthetic applications of **allenes**, S. Ma, Chem. Rev. *105*, 2829-72 (2005).

67, 188 **Azides**: an exploding diversity of a unique class of compounds, S. Bräse, C. Gil, K. Knepper, V. Zimmermann, Angew. Chem. Int. Ed. Engl. *44*, 5188-240 (2005).

67, 189 Rich chemistry of **nitroso compounds**, H. Yamamoto, N. Momiyama, Chem. Commun. *2005*, 3514-25; dinitroso and polynitroso compounds, B.G. Gowenlock, G.B. Richter-Addo, Chem. Soc. Rev. *34*, 797-809 (2005).

67, 222 **Organo(trifluoro)borates**: expanding organoboron chemistry, G.A. Molender, R. Figueroa, Aldrichimica Acta *38*, 49-56 (2005).

67, 224 Recent advances in the chemistry of **trichloromethyl chloroformate and bis(trichloromethyl) carbonate**, W. Su, W. Zhong, G. Bian, X. Shi, J. Zhang, Org. Prep. Proced. Int. *36*, 499-547 (2004).

67, 365 A decade of advances in **3-component reactions**, M. Syamala, Org. Prep. Proced. Int. *37*, 103-71 (2005).

67, 371 Synthesis of **enamines, enolethers** and related compounds by cross-coupling, I.R. Dehli, J. Legros, C. Bolm, Chem. Commun. *2005*, 973-86.

67, 386 Reactions of organic nitrogen compounds with **carbenoids and diarylketenes** from diazoalkanes and diazocarbonyls, G.S. Singh, Curr. Org. Synth. *2*, 377-91 (2005).

67, 413 **Coupling of zirconocene complexes** with heterosubstituted alkenes, J. Barluenga, F. Rodríguez, L. Álvarez-Rodrigo, F.J. Fañanás, Chem. Soc. Rev. *34*, 762-8 (2005).

68, 226 **N-Acylbenzotriazoles** as advantageous N-, C-, S-, and O-acylating agents, A.R. Katritzky, K. Suzuki, Z. Wang, Synlett *2005*, 1656-65.

Index to Volume 68

As in previous volumes, reactions are indexed from both the starting material and product aspects, e.g. '**Azides** startg. m.f. amines' and '**Amines** from azides'. Nomenclature for complex functions can be located under the 'special s.' sub-entry, e.g. '**Carboxylic acids** special s. aminocarboxylic acids' or by consulting the Formula Index of Complex Functional Groups (Volume *48*, p. 471).

Hydrogenated and functionalized ring systems are indexed by the conventional reversal, e.g. '**Pyridines, aryl-**', the only important exception to the rule being alkylideneisocyclics which are indexed as such, e.g. '**Alkylidenecyclopentanes**'.

As from Volume *51*, '**Epoxides**' has been used in place of 'Oxido compds.'; '**Thiiranes**' in place of 'Sulfido compds.'; '**Diels-Alder reaction**' in place of 'Diene synthesis'; and '**Benzo[*b*]thiophenes**' in place of 'Thianaphthenes'.

References to abstracts in this volume are in the format **68,** 234. An entry such as '**Peptide *p*-nitroanilides**, synthesis, polymer-based **26,** 398s**68**' refers to the indexing of a supplementary reference, which must be followed up via the Supplementary References section (p. 387).

Abs. configuration s. Configuration, abs.
Acetalation 68, 98
– in ionic liquids 68, 96
–, cobalt- or ruthenium-catalyzed
– of aldehydes 68, 99
Acetals (s.a. Ketals)
–, cleavage 56, 9s68
–, –, selective 68, 9
– special s.
    arylacetaldehyde acetals
    dioxo compd. monoacetals
    formals
    hydroxyacetals
– startg. m. f.
    1,2,4,5-tetroxanes 66, 52s68
–, cyclic
–, cleavage, preferential 56, 9s68
– special s.
    O,O-alkylidene derivs.
– startg. m. f.
    alcohols 68, 48
    mercaptals, cyclic 46, 162s68
Acetamide
–, N-acetylation with – 10, 296s68
Acetamides
– startg. m. f.
    carbostyrils 68, 413
Acetone
– as H-acceptor 68, 198
Acetonyltriphenylphosphonium bromide
– as reagent 68, 2
Acetoxy... s.a. Acoxy...
Acetyl... s.a. Acyl...
N-Acetylation
– with acetamide 10, 296s68
O-Acetylation, heterogeneous,
    preferential and selective 68, 122
–, partial 54, 79s68
–, selective and preferential 68, 92
Acetyl chloride
– as reagent 2, 642s68
2-Acetyleneacylamines
– startg. m. f.
    oxazoles 68, 80
2-Acetylenealcohols
– from
    aldehydes, asym. synthesis 56, 454s68
– special s.
    1-aryl-2-acetylenealcohols
    1,5-enyn-4-ols
    ethynylcarbinols
– startg. m. f.
    arylallenes 68, 473
    (Z)-1-halogen-1,4-enynes 68, 366
    1,3-oxaselenolanes, 4-alkylidene-2-
        imino- 68, 235
    oxazoles 68, 175
    4H-pyrans 64, 338s68
2-Acetylene-prim-alcohols
– startg. m. f.
    propargylarenes 68, 473
3-Acetylenealcohols
– special s.
    4-hydroxy-1-silylacetylenes
4-Acetylenealcohols
– special s.
    1,7-enyn-4-ols
α,β-Acetylenealdehydes
– startg. m. f.
    bicyclo[3.1.0]hexan-3-ones 68, 341
o-Acetylenealdehydes
– startg. m. f.

naphthalenes, 1-acyl- 68, 362
α,β-Acetylenealdimines
– from
    acetylene derivs., terminal and
        isonitriles 68, 279
o-Acetylenealdimines
– startg. m. f.
    aniline ring, with N-alkylation 68, 349
2-Acetyleneamines
– from
    acetylene derivs., terminal and
        azomethines 68, 278
– special s.
    propargylamin...
–, 1,1-disubst.
– from
    carboxylic acid thioamides,
        3-component synthesis 68, 423
β,γ-Acetylene-α-aminocarboxylic acid
    esters
– from
    acetylene derivs., terminal, with 2 extra
        C-atoms 68, 354
Acetyleneazomethines
–, ring closures via 1,2-azazircona-
    cyclopentenes, condensed
    51, 315s68
α,β-Acetyleneazomethines
– special s.
    α,β-acetylenealdimines
    N-(alk-1-ynyl)-α,β-acetyleneketimines
o-Acetyleneazomethines
– special s.
    o-acetylenealdimines
α,β-Acetylene-ω-benzyloxy-
    ω'-hydroxyketones
– startg. m. f.
    spiroketals 68, 138
α,β-Acetylenecarboxylic acid esters
–, anti-Michael addition of ketones to –
    68, 310
– special s.
    ethyl propiolate
    methyl –
Acetylene derivs.
–, C-cleavage, oxidative of the triple
    bond, review 66, 135s68
–, cross-metathesis 30, 467s68
–, cyclotrimerization, intramolecular,
    review 42, 676s68
–, Friedel-Crafts vinylation with – in ionic
    liquids 68, 299
–, hydro-boration, -silylation and
    -stannylation, review 43, 520s68
–, metathesis, review 27, 851s68
–, nitrogenase-like reactivity towards –,
    review 28, 13s68
–, radical ring closures, thiiyl-mediated,
    regiospecific via 1,5-hydrogen
    transfer 68, 302
– special s.
    acoxy-2-acetylenes
    alkoxy-2-acetylenes
    arylacetylenes
    diynes
    enyn...
    siloxyacetylenes
    silylacetylenes
– startg. m. f.
    (Z)-cinnamonitriles, tetrasubst. 68, 316
    1,3-cycloheptadienes, 5-carbalkoxy-
        methylene- 68, 317

enephosphines, regiospecific
    conversion 68, 239
enesilanes 68, 240
1,4-enynes, synthesis 68, 305
(E,E)-α,β-ethyleneketimines 68, 307
furans 68, 448
(E)-2-halogenenol tosylates, polymer-
    based synthesis 68, 203
(Z)-1-halogen-1,4-enynes 68, 366
indenes 29, 932s68; 68, 461
phenols 68, 293
4(3H)-pyrimidinones, 1,2-dihydro-,
    N-condensed 68, 281
pyrroles (from 2 molecules) 68, 360
2-stannyl-1,4,6-dienynes, regio-
    stereospecific synthesis 68, 318
Acetylene derivs., cyclic
– from
    α,β-ethyleneiodonium salts, exocyclic,
        review 44, 496s68
– –, electron-deficient
– startg. m. f.
    phenols 36, 885s68
– –, terminal (s.a. Acetylides)
–, coupling with alkyl halides 68, 392
– from
    carboxylic acid esters 36, 864s68
– startg. m. f.
    α,β-acetylenealdimines 68, 279
    2-acetyleneamines 68, 278
    β,γ-acetylene-α-aminocarboxylic acid
        esters, with 2 extra C-atoms 68, 354
    γ,δ-acetyleneketones, via 1,4-addition
        68, 328
    3-acetylenesulfonylamines,
        regiostereospecific synthesis
        49, 610s68
    aldehydes 68, 118
    amines, sec. 58, 126s68
    1,3-cyclohexadienes 68, 480
    cyclopent-2-enyl ketones, 4-(silyl-
        methyl)- 68, 308
    1,2-dibenzyl-1,3-enynes (from 2
        molecules) 68, 469
    diynes (from 2 different molecules)
        68, 391
    enesilanes, regiospecific conversion
        68, 237
    enolesters, 2-subst. 68, 72
    (E)-α,β-ethyleneboronic acid esters
        68, 236
    α,β-ethyleneketones, regiospecific
        dimerization 68, 326
    (E,E)-1-halogeno-1,3-dienes, with 2
        extra C-atoms 68, 294
    methyl N-arylketimines 64, 143s68
    N'-sulfonylamidines 68, 181
    1,2,3-triazoles 68, 184
Acetylenedicarboxylic acid esters
– special s.
    dimethyl acetylenedicarboxylate
– startg. m. f.
    O-heterocyclics, review 42, 853s68
    pyrrole-3,4-dicarboxylic acid esters,
        2-amino-5-imido-, N-subst. 68, 280
α,β-Acetylene-ω-diketones
–, aldol condensation, intramolecular,
    reductive, stereospecific 68, 287
3-Acetyleneepoxides, terminal
– startg. m. f.
    α-allenketones 68, 342
o-Acetyleneepoxides

- startg. m. f.
  2-indanones, 1-alkylidene- **68**, 347
  2-naphthols **68**, 347
2-Acetyleneethers
- special s.
  alkoxy-2-acetylenes
  vinyloxy-2-acetylenes
α,β-Acetylenehalides
-, [2+2]-cycloaddition with – **60**, 288s68
- special s.
  α,β-acetyleneiodides
  1-halogen-3,1-enynes
α,β-Acetylene-γ-hydroxycarboxylic acid esters
- from
  oxo compds., with 3 extra C-atoms **68**, 254
- startg. m. f.
  2(5H)-furanones, synthesis **68**, 463
α,β-Acetyleneiodides
- startg. m. f.
  2-silyl-1(Z),3-enynes **66**, 318s68
α,β-Acetyleneketones
- from
  acetylene derivs., terminal **55**, 361s68
  lithium alk-1-ynyl(trialkoxy)borates and carboxylic acid chlorides **64**, 449s68
- special s.
  α,β-acetylene-ω-diketones
γ,δ-Acetyleneketones
- from
  α,β-ethyleneketones and erminal acetylene derivs. **68**, 328
Acetyleneoxo compds.
- startg. m. f.
  2-arylidenealcohols, cyclic, asym. conversion **68**, 457
α,β-Acetyleneoxo compds.
- startg. m. f.
  β-dioxo compd. monoacetals **68**, 66
o-Acetylenephosphonic acid esters
- startg. m. f.
  1H-2,1-benzoxaphosphorin P-oxides, 1-alkoxy-4-iodo- **62**, 203s68
1-Acetylene-1-selenides, ar.
- startg. m. f.
  selenolic acid aryl esters **2**, 818s68
α,β-Acetyleneselenonium salts
- startg. m. f.
  aziridines, 2-acyl-1-tosyl- **68**, 437
  trans-α,β-epoxyketones **68**, 437
1-Acetylenesilanes s. Silylacetylenes
Acetylenestannanes
- startg. m. f.
  1,2-dibenzyl-1,3-enynes (from 2 molecules) **68**, 469
  1-halogenenestannanes **43**, 625s68
  2-stannyl-1,4,6-dienynes, regiostereospecific synthesis **68**, 318
  vinylstannanes, α-subst. **68**, 32
o-Acetylenestilbene oxides
- startg. m. f.
  indenes, 1-aryl- **68**, 497
o-Acetylenestyrenes
- special s.
  o-ethynylstyrenes
3-Acetylenesulfonylamines
- from
  acetylene derivs., terminal, regiostereospecific synthesis **49**, 610s68

2'-Acetylene-2,2,2-trihalogenalcohols, chiral 58, 236s68
Acetylides
- special s.
  lithium acetylides
  zinc –
Acoxy-2-acetylenes
- startg. m. f.
  α-acoxy-α,β-ethyleneoxo compds. **68**, 78
  1,5-enynes **68**, 439
Acoxy-2-allenes
- startg. m. f.
  allenes, synthesis, regiospecific **68**, 377
N-Acoxyamines s. Acoxylamines
α-Acoxycarboxylic acid amides s.a. Passerini...
β-Acoxycarboxylic acid amides
- from
  epoxides, isonitriles, and carboxylic acids **68**, 275
Acoxy compds. (s.a. Carboxylic acid esters)
- from
  ethylene derivs. **68**, 74
α-Acoxy-α,β-ethyleneoxo compds.
- from
  acoxy-2-acetylenes **68**, 78
Acoxy-2-ethylenes (s.a. Carboxylic acid allyl esters)
-, allylation, nucleophilic, intramolecular, regiostereospecific with – **68**, 489
-, cross-coupling, intramolecular, Pd-catalyzed, stereospecific with ar. halides **68**, 494
- special s.
  β-acoxy-α-methylene...
- startg. m. f.
  allylarenes, with inversion of configuration **68**, 397
  ethylene derivs., regiostereospecific synthesis with triorganoindiums **68**, 468
  2(5H)-furanones, 5-allyl-, regiostereospecific synthesis with asym. induction **68**, 450
Acoxy-2-ethylenes, cyclic
- startg. m. f.
  ethylene derivs., cyclic, synthesis **63**, 449s68
1,2-Acoxyhalides
- special s.
  1,2-acoxyiodides
1,2-Acoxyiodides
- from
  ethylene derivs. **68**, 205
α-Acoxy-β-ketocarboxylic acid amides
- startg. m. f.
  β-ketocarboxylic acid amides **68**, 42
Acoxylamines
- special s.
  N-(tert-butyl)acoxylamines
α-Acoxylation
- of aldehydes with N-(tert-butyl)acoxylamines **68**, 105
β-Acoxy-α-methylenecarboxylic acid esters
- startg. m. f.
  (E)-α-alkylideneadipic acid esters, with 2 extra C-atoms **68**, 433
  (E)-α,β-ethylenecarboxylic acid esters, α-subst. **68**, 400

β-Acoxy-α-methylenenitriles
- startg. m. f.
  (Z)-α,β-ethylenenitriles, α-subst. **68**, 400
Acrolein β-carbanion equivalent
-, trans-3-(tert-butyldimethylsilyl)-2,3-epoxypropyl p-tolyl sulfone, metalated as – **68**, 432
Activation
- of
  α-aminocarboxylic acids as 1,3,2-oxaza-borolidin-5-ones, 2,2-difluoro- **68**, 163
  hydrocarbons with organometallics, review **27**, 851s68
-, catalyzed, nanoscale
- of C-H bonds, review **27**, 851s68
-, sequential, Pd-catalyzed
- of C-H bonds **68**, 493
O-Acylamidoximes
- special s.
  N-allyl-O-acylamidoximes
Acylamines (s.a. Carboxylic acid amides)
- from
  carboxylic acid esters **48**, 346s68
-, Michael addition, Pd-catalyzed with – **61**, 143s68
- special s.
  acetyleneacylamines
  halogenacylamines
-, cyclic
- startg. m. f.
  acylaminocarboxylic acids **68**, 65
1,1-Acylaminoalcohols
- startg. m. f.
  enacylamines **31**, 920s68
α-Acylaminocarboxylic acid amides
- special s.
  N-(3,5-xylyl)-2-(N-formylamido)-3-methylbutyramide
β-Acylaminocarboxylic acid amides
- from
  aziridines, isonitriles and carboxylic acids **68**, 275
α-Acylaminocarboxylic acid esters
- from
  Δ²-5-oxazolones, dynamic kinetic resolution **68**, 60
-, 4-alkylidene- **28**, 288s68
Acylaminocarboxylic acids
- from
  acylamines, cyclic **68**, 65
anti-β-Acylamino-α-hydroxycarboxylic acid amides 23, 348s68
α-Acylaminoketenimines
-, 3-component synthesis **59**, 279s68
α-Acylaminoketones
- from
  aldehydes and in situ-generated N-acylimines, asym. synthesis, organocatalyzed **68**, 273
γ-Acylaminoketones
- from
  Δ¹-pyrrolines **13**, 487s68
o-Acylaminomercaptans
- startg. m. f.
  benzothiazoles, soluble polymer-based synthesis **21**, 543s68
α-Acylaminonitriles
- startg. m. f.
  imidazoles, 5-chloro- **68**, 213

Acy – Alc

o-Acylaminophenols
– startg. m. f.
  benzoxazoles, soluble polymer-based synthesis 21, 543s68
Acylation
– under carbene catalysis, nucleophilic 68, 109
– with
  benzotriazoles, N-acyl-, review 68, 226s68
  α-halogenaldehydes 68, 109
Acylation, Bi-catalyzed 68, 110
–, Ru-catalyzed 68, 99
–, Zr-catalyzed 68, 110
C-Acylation s.a. Sonogashira acylation
N-Acylation
– of indoles 41, 339s68
– special s.
  N-acetylation
–, partial 50, 185s68
–, preferential
– with N-acylsulfonamides 56, 154s68
–, selective 10, 296s68
O-Acylation
– special s.
  O-acetylation
  per-O-acylation
–, preferential 42, 164s68
S-Acylation
– with benzotriazoles, N-acyl- 68, 226
N-Acylcarboxylic acid amides
– from
  carboxylic acid amides, N-subst. 68, 88
– special s.
  N-acyl-α,β-ethylenecarboxylic acid amides
  N-acyl-β-hydroxycarboxylic – –
Acylcyanides
– special s.
  aroylcyanides
N¹-Acyl-N²-α-cyanosemicarbazides
– startg. m. f.
  hydantoins, 1-acylamino- 68, 153
4-Acyl-1,7-dicarboxylic acid esters 29, 668s68
2-Acyl-1,3-enynes
– startg. m. f.
  furans, 3-α-functionalized 68, 67
N-Acyl-α,β-ethylenecarboxylic acid amides
– startg. m. f.
  N-acyl-β-hydroxycarboxylic acid amides, asym. conversion 68, 68
N-Acyl-3-ethylenehydrazines
– from
  N-acylhydrazones and 2-ethylene-(trichloro)silanes under organo-catalysis, review 66, 442s68
Acyl glycosides
– from
  aldoses 55, 79s68
Acyl halides s. Carboxylic acid halides
N-Acyl-N-heterocyclics, pyridine-fused 52, 491s68
N-Acylhydrazines
– special s.
  tetraformylhydrazine
– startg. m. f.
  N¹,N⁴-diacylthiosemicarbazides 22, 470s68
N-Acylhydrazones
– in synthesis, review 66, 442s68

– startg. m. f.
  N-acyl-3-ethylenehydrazines under organocatalysis, review 66, 442s68
  pyrazolidines, 1-acyl-, asym. conversion 68, 306
–, synthesis, asym. with –, review 27, 57s68
N-Acyl-β-hydroxycarboxylic acid amides
– from
  N-acyl-α,β-ethylenecarboxylic acid amides, asym. conversion 68, 68
N-Acylimines, *in situ*-generated
– startg. m. f.
  α-acylaminoketones, asym. synthesis, organocatalyzed 68, 273
Acylisocyanates
– startg. m. f.
  furans 68, 448
Acylophenones (s.a. Aryl ketones)
– special s.
  4-hydroxy-α,α,α-trifluoroaceto-phenone
Acyl phosphites, cyclic, chiral
– as ligand 60, 34s68
Acylphosphonic acid esters 25, 185s68
N-Acylsulfonic acid amides
–, N-acylation with – 56, 154s68
O-Acyltartaric acids
–, synthesis, review 30, 321s68
N-Acylthiosemicarbazides
– special s.
  N¹,N⁴-diacylthiosemicarbazides
Acylthioureas 68, 225
1,4-Addition (s.a. CC∜CC, Michael addition, Radical 1,4-addition)
–, asym.
– of
  arylboronic acids, update 55, 452s68
  dialkylzincs, update 52, 297s68
  Grignards to α,β-ethyleneketones, acyclic 68, 291
  potassium organo(trifluoro)borates 55, 452s68
  triarylbismuthines 55, 452s68
–, –, polymer-based
– with arylboronic acids 55, 452s68
–, –, Rh-catalyzed 68, 453
–, carbonylative, Pd-catalyzed 68, 329
–, Pd-catalyzed
– of acetylene derivs., terminal in water 68, 328
–, double
–, cyclopropane-1,2-dicarboxylic acid esters, *cis*-1-halogeno- via – 68, 399
1,4-Addition-intramolecular aldol condensation, stereospecific
– via zinc enolates 68, 292
1,4-Addition-intramolecular Blaise reaction, – 68, 292
1,4-Addition-Dieckmann condensation, – 68, 292
Adipic acid esters
– special s.
  α-alkylideneadipic acid esters
Adiponitriles s. 1,3-Dinitriles
L-Alanine
– as reagent 68, 55
Albumin
– as reagent 48, 686s68
Alcohols

–, deoxygenation via phosphorous acid esters 68, 46
– from
  acetals, cyclic 68, 48
  glycol sulfites, cyclic, synthesis 49, 843s68
  oxo compds., reduction (s.a. HC∜OC) 68, 21, 27
  – –, – (prim. alcohols) 68, 19, 22
  – – (sec. –), reduction, asym. 68, 23
–, reactions, Pd-catalyzed, review 27, 851s68
–, resolution, kinetic by oxidation, review 27, 57s68
–, ring closures, dehydrogenative, aerobic, asym., Pd-catalyzed, review 27, 57s68
– special s.
  acetylenealcohols
  acylaminoalcohols
  (alkylideneamino)alcohols
  allenealcohols
  aminoalcohols
  aminooxyalcohols
  arylalcohols
  azidoalcohols
  benzylalcohols
  bridgehead alcohols
  diols
  epoxyalcohols
  ethylenealcohols
  glycol...
  halogenhydrins
  hydroxy...
  hydroxylaminoalcohols
  sulfonylaminoalcohols
– startg. m. f.
  ethers s.a. O-Alkylation and OCl↑
  iodides, partial conversion 68, 212
  methylene compds. 68, 472
  monoselenoiminocarbonic acid esters 68, 235
  nitrous acid esters 68, 51
  oxo compds., oxidation (s.a. OCft H) 68, 130 (without solvent)
  – –, –, heterogeneous 55, 113s68 (in water); 68, 130
  – – (aldehydes) 41, 240s68; 65, 128s68
  – – (ketones) 68, 128, 129 (in aq. medium)
  phosphorous acid monoesters 68, 54
  urethans, N-subst. 68, 158
Alcohols, prim. (s.a. Hydroxy-methylation)
–, C-α-alkylation with – 68, 373
– from
  carboxylic acid chlorides 27, 65s68
  – – esters 27, 65s68; 68, 44
  ethylene derivs., terminal, C-cleavage 68, 121
– startg. m. f.
  benzimidazoles 68, 174
  carboxylic acid esters (from 2 molecules) 44, 149s68
  – acids 66, 100s68
Alcohols, sec.
–, deoxygenation via
  oxalic or phosphorous acid esters 31, 49s68
– startg. m. f.
  α-iodoketones 68, 210
Alcohols, tert.

Ald – Alk

– special s.
trityl alcohols
Aldehyde homoenolate equivalents
68, 301
Aldehydes (s.a. Carbonyl compds.,
Hydroformylation, Oxo compds.)
–, α-acoxylation with N-(tert-butyl)-
acoxylamines **68**, 105
–, C-α-allylation with acetylene derivs.
67, 335s68
–, cyclodehydration **15**, 168s68
–, decarbonylation **68**, 49
– from
acetylene derivs., terminal **68**, 118
alcohols, prim. s. OCñH and under
Alcohols startg. m. f. oxo compds.
carboxylic acid anhydrides **68**, 134
– – halides **68**, 134
enamines, synthesis **68**, 160
epoxides, regiostereospecific
conversion **68**, 346
α,β-ethylenealdehydes, asym. transfer-
hydrogenation, organocatalyzed
68, 28
ethylene derivs., terminal **68**, 75
2-oxazolidones, 3-acyl- **49**, 638s68
piperidines, 1-acoxy-2,2,6,6-
tetramethyl- **68**, 134
–, α-selenylation, organocatalyzed
68, 245
– special s.
acetylenealdehydes
aminoaldehydes
dialdehydes
ethylenealdehydes
halogenaldehydes
ketoaldehydes
nitroaldehydes
siloxyaldehydes
– startg. m. f.
2-acetylenealcohols, asym. synthesis
56, 454s68
α-acylaminoketones, asym. synthesis,
organocatalyzed **68**, 273
alcohols, prim. s. HCⱵOC and under
Alcohols from oxo compds.
α-alkoxynitriles **61**, 441s68
β'-amino-β-hydroxyketones,
N-protected **68**, 270
β-aryl-α-amino-β-hydroxycarboxylic
acid esters, N,O-protected, asym.
conversion **68**, 262
benzylalcohols, sec., asym. synthesis
68, 438
carboxylic acid amides **68**, 149
– – esters **68**, 85
cyanohydrins, asym. conversion
68, 256
α,α'-dihydroxyphosphinic acids, sym.
68, 234
trans-α,β-epoxyketones **68**, 437
2-ethylenealcohols, 3-component
synthesis with 3 extra C-atoms
68, 430
3-ethylenealcohols **66**, 272s68; **68**, 471
–, asym. synthesis with 3 extra C-atoms
68, 441
3-ethylene-prim-amines, regiospecific
synthesis with asym. induction
68, 427
ethylene derivs., under Rh-catalysis,
review **27**, 851s68

(E)-α,β-ethylene-γ-hydroxyaldehydes
68, 432
(E)-α,β-ethyleneketones **68**, 479
(Z)-3-ethylene-1,1,1-trihalides, with 3
extra C-atoms **68**, 431
furan-3-carboxylic acid amides,
tetrahydro-, asym. induction **68**, 298
furans, 2-amino- **68**, 300
glycol monoethers **68**, 63
(Z)-1-halogen-3,1-enynes, with 3 extra
C-atoms **68**, 431
hexoses (from 3 molecules), asym.
synthesis **68**, 258
3'-hydroxyenesilanes, stereospecific
synthesis **68**, 466
β-hydroxyketones (s.a. Aldol...)
68, 483
–, asym. conversion **68**, 477
β-hydroxymercaptals **68**, 296
β-hydroxynitriles **68**, 276
4-hydroxy-1-silylacetylenes, with 3
extra C-atoms **68**, 478
β-lactones, asym. conversion **68**, 313
γ-lactones **68**, 301
2-oxazolidones, 3-(carbalkoxyamino)-,
asym. conversion **68**, 170
oxindoles, 3-alkylidene- **68**, 429
propargylamines, asym. 3-component
synthesis **68**, 435
pyrans, tetrahydro-, 4-chloro- (from 2
different molecules) **58**, 432s68
4-pyrones, 2,3-dihydro-, asym.
conversion **68**, 454
pyrroles **68**, 360
–, trans-N-(α,β-epoxyacyl)-, asym.
synthesis with 2 extra C-atoms
68, 444
4-quinazolones **68**, 173
N-tosylimines **68**, 196
–, transfer-hydrogenation, heterogeneous
17, 65s68
Aldehydes, ar.
– startg. m. f.
α-aryl-α-arylamino-β-hydroxy-
carboxylic acid esters **68**, 387
diaryl ketones **68**, 459
1,3-dioxolane-4-carboxylic acid esters,
2,4,5-triaryl- (from 2 different
molecules) **68**, 388
tetralins, 1-aryl-3-hydroxymethyl-2-
vinyl- **68**, 443
**γ-Aldehydo-α-aminocarboxylic acid
esters, chiral 67**, 275s68
Aldimines (s.a. Azomethines)
– special s.
N-arylaldimines
– startg. m. f.
cyclopenta[b]pyrroles, 1,2,3,3a,6,6a-
hexahydro- **68**, 389
(E,E)-α,β-ethyleneketimines **68**, 307
–, ar.
– startg. m. f.
benzylamines, sec. **68**, 268
Aldol condensation (s.a. 1,4-Addition-
intramolecular aldol condensation)
– –, asym.
– with glycine equivalents **68**, 262
– –, –, organocatalyzed
– in ionic liquids **68**, 259
– in polyethylene glycol **68**, 259
– –, decarballyloxylative, heterobimetal-catalyzed **68**, 483

– –, decarboxylative, asym. **65**, 477s68
– –, intramolecular (s.a. Hydroformylation-intramolecular aldol
condensation)
– –, –, reductive, stereospecific
– of α,β-acetylene-ω-diketones **68**, 287
– –, organocatalyzed, iterative **68**, 258
– –, vinylogous
–, review **52**, 230s68
– –, –, asym., catalyzed
–, review **27**, 57s68
**Aldol-Tishchenko reaction, asym.,
catalytic 68**, 257
**Aldol-type condensation, asym.,
Bronsted base-catalyzed 68**, 447
– –, self-promoted
– with aldehydes **63**, 424s68
Aldonolactones
– from
aldoses **68**, 131
– special s.
dideoxyaldonolactones
Aldoses
– special s.
hexoses
– startg. m. f.
acyl glycosides **55**, 79s68
aldonolactones **68**, 131
Aldoximes (s.a. Oximes)
– from
nitro compds., prim. **68**, 199
–, chiral **68**, 199
Alkaloids
– by [3+3]-cycloaddition, review
42, 853s68
– special s.
benzo[c]phenanthridine alkaloids
carbazole –
erythrina...
homoerythrina...
methyllycaconitine...
pyrrolidine alkaloids
Alkanes s. Hydrocarbons
Alkenes s. Ethylene derivs.
Alkoximes
– special s.
O-benzyloximes
hydroxyalkoximes
– startg. m. f.
ketones **68**, 101
Alkoxy-2-acetylenes s.a. 2-Acetylene-
ethers and O-Depropargylation
α-**Alkoxyacrylic acid esters 35**, 622s68
1-Alkoxyallenesilanes 27, 835s68
α-**Alkoxy-β-aminocarboxylic acid
esters**
–, 3-component synthesis **60**, 252s68
(Z)-α-**Alkoxy-ω-amino-α,β-
ethylenecarboxylic acid esters**
– from
2-azetidinones, 3-alkoxy-4-ω-
halogeno- **68**, 107
p-**Alkoxybenzyl ethers**
– from
2-cyclohexenones, 4-alkylidene- **68**, 89
α-**Alkoxy-α,β-ethylenecarboxylic acid
esters**
– special s.
α-alkoxyacrylic acid esters
syn-α-**Alkoxy-γ,δ-ethylenecarboxylic acid**
– – **58**, 238s68

β-Alkoxy-α,β-ethyleneketones
– special s.
  trichloromethyl β-alkoxy-α,β-
  ethyleneketones
Alkoxy-2-ethylenes
– special s.
  methallyl ethers
Alkoxy-3-ethylenes
– from
  aldehydes 49, 762s68
–, exocyclic
– from
  enynes 68, 290
1,2-Alkoxyhalides
– special s.
  1,2-alkoxyiodides
Alkoxy(hydroxy)ketones
– special s.
  α,β-acetylene-ω-benzyloxy-ω'-
  hydroxyketones
1,2-Alkoxyiodides
– from
  ethylene derivs. 46, 432s68
α-Alkoxyketones
–, C-α-allylation, regiospecific, asym.
  induction 68, 374
– special s.
  α-benzyloxyketones
β-Alkoxyketones
– from
  α,β-ethyleneketones 68, 77
Alkoxylamines
–, radical cleavage under microwaves
  68, 429
– special s.
  aminooxy...
  O-methylhydroxylamine
N-Alkoxymethylation
– special s.
  N-methoxymethylation
– with formals 68, 172
N-Alkoxymethyl groups
– startg. m. f.
  N-methyl groups 68, 43
α-Alkoxynitriles
– from
  aldehydes 61, 441s68
β-Alkoxyphosphonic acid esters
  53, 240s8
Alkoxysilanes s.a. Siloxy..., O-Silylation,
  Silyl ethers
1-Alkoxy-3-siloxy-1,3-dienes
– startg. m. f.
  4-pyrones, 2,3-dihydro-, asym.
  conversion 68, 454
Alkylarenes
– special s.
  allylarenes
  propargylarenes
– startg. m. f.
  aryl ketones 68, 86, 90
Alkylation, stereospecific, catalyzed
– of indoles, review 39, 363s68
C-Alkylation
– special s.
  C-allylation
Alkylation, ar.
– special s.
  allylation, ar.
  benzylation, ar.
C-α-Alkylation
– of peptides, review 19, 33s68

– special s.
  C-α-methylation
C-α-Alkylation, asym., polymer-based
– of
  hydrazones 31, 812s68
  2-oxazolidones, 3-acyl- 44, 776s68
–, heterogeneous
– of
  ketones 68, 373
  nitriles 68, 373
– with prim. alcohols 68, 373
–, polymer-based 27, 843s68
C-α-Alkylation-Michael addition
  68, 373
N-Alkylation
– of
  dicarboxylic acid imides 56, 159s68
  pyrroles 56, 159s68
– special s.
  N-benzylation
  N,N-dialkylation
  N-methylation
  mono-N-alkylation
–, heterogeneous 68, 169
–, reductive (s.a. Carbopalladation,
  intramolecular-reductive N-alkylation)
– with oxo compds. (without solvent or in
  water) 68, 162
O-Alkylation (s.a. Williamson...)
– special s.
  O-allylation
– with
  diazo compds., in situ-generated 68, 94
  glycol monocarbamates 68, 104
(E)-α-Alkylideneadipic acid esters
– from
  β-acoxy-α-methylenecarboxylic acid
  esters, with 2 extra C-atoms 68, 433
2-(Alkylideneamino)alcohols
– special s.
  N-(3,5-diiodosalicylidene)-tert-leucinol
  3,3-dimethyl-2-[(2-hydroxy-2'-
  pivaloyloxy-1,1'-binaphthyl-3-yl)-
  methyleneamino]butanol
–, chiral
– as reagent 62, 423s68
α-(Alkylideneamino)carboxylic acid
  esters
– special s.
  N-arylideneglycinates
Alkylidenecyclopentanes
– from
  1,6-enynes 68, 320
– special s.
  cyclopentanes, di(alkylidene)-
  methylenecyclopentanes
Alkylidenecyclopropanes
–, [3+2]-cycloaddition, intramolecular,
  Ru-carbene-catalyzed with – 68, 352
O,O-Alkylidene derivs.
– special s.
  O,O-benzylidene derivs.
  O,O-p-methoxybenzylidene –
2-Alkylidene-1,5-diketones
– from
  α,β-ethyleneketones, asym.
  dimerization 68, 283
α-Alkylidene-γ-lactones
– special s.
  α-(aminomethylene)-γ-lactones
Alkylidenephosphines
– special s.

  bis(alkylidenephosphines)
Alkylidenephosphoranes
– special s.
  (carbethoxymethylene)triphenyl-
  phosphorane
Alkyl radicals
– from
  allyl sulfones 51, 424s68
  mercaptans via thioimidoyl radicals
  68, 425
Alkynes s. Acetylene derivs.
(Z)-N-(Alk-1-ynyl)-α,β-acetylene-
  ketimines
– startg. m. f.
  2,4-enynenitriles 68, 348
2-Allenealcohols
– special s.
  2,3-dienol...
– startg. m. f.
  (E)-2-aryl-1,3-dienes 68, 460
  2-ethylene-4-hydroxystannanes 68, 238
  4-hydroxy-1-silylacetylenes 68, 478
3-Allenealcohols, chiral 68, 343
Alleneamines, N-protected
–, Pauson-Khand reaction with –
  53, 318s68
α-Allenecarboxylic acids
– startg. m. f.
  2(5H)-furanones, 4-halogeno-
  5-hydroxy- 68, 207
α-Alleneketones
– from
  3-acetyleneepoxides, terminal 68, 342
Allenoxo compds.
– startg. m. f.
  α-methylene-γ-lactones, cis-fused
  68, 311
Allenes
–, C-α-allylation, stereospecific with –
  68, 331
– from
  acoxy-2-allenes, regiospecific
  synthesis 68, 377
– in synthesis, review 67, 69s68
– special s.
  acoxyallenes
  arylallenes
  1,2-dien...
  1,2,6-dienynes
  1,2,7-trienes
– startg. m. f.
  cycloheptanones, 3,4-di(alkylidene)-
  (from 2 molecules) 59, 411s68
  cyclopentenes, 1-alkoxy-5-methylene-
  68, 456
  2,6-enynols 68, 264
  β,γ-ethylene-β-silylboronic acid esters
  68, 241
  3'-hydroxyenesilanes, stereospecific
  synthesis 68, 466
  pyrazolidine-1,2-dicarboxylic acid
  esters, 3-vinyl-, asym. synthesis
  68, 398
  2-stannyl-1,4,6-dienynes, regiostereospecific synthesis 68, 318
Allenes, 1-functionalized
– startg. m. f.
  1,4-enynes, synthesis 68, 305
Allenes, terminal
– startg. m. f.
  1-methylene-1,2-di(boronic acid
  esters), asym. conversion 68, 242

Allenesilanes
– special s.
  alkoxyallenesilanes
Allenestannanes
– startg. m. f.
  1,7-enynes, regiospecific synthesis
  68, 474
Alloxazine, 5,10-dihydro-, 1,3-dimethyl-5-ethyl-
– as reagent **64**, 81s68
N-Allyl-O-acylamidoximes
– startg. m. f.
  imidazoles **68**, 201
Allyl alcohols s. 2-Ethylenealcohols
Allylamines s. 2-Ethyleneamines
o-**Allylamines**
– startg. m. f.
  indolines, N-aryl-2-benzyl- **68**, 414
Allylarenes (s.a. Allylation, ar.)
– from
  iodides, ar. and acoxy-2-ethylenes, with inversion of configuration **68**, 397
(E)-**Allylarenes**
– from
  arylboronic acids and 2-ethylenealcohols, regiospecific synthesis **68**, 460
o-**Allylarylacetylenes**
– from
  benzynes **67**, 255s68
Allylation
– with acetylene derivs. **67**, 335s68
Allylation, Pd- and Ir-catalyzed, regiostereospecific
–, review **27**, 851s68
Allylation, ar. (s.a. Friedel-Crafts allylation)
– with 2-ethylenealcohols **49**, 763s68
–, **Ir-catalyzed 68**, 123
–, **Pd-catalyzed**
– via bis(π-allylpalladium) complexes, review **27**, 851s68
–, –, **regiospecific**
– of indoles **68**, 376
–, **electrophilic and nucleophilic, Pd-catalyzed**
– with 2-ethylenealcohols, review **27**, 851s68
–, **intramolecular**
–, ethers, polycyclic via –, review **42**, 853s68
C-Allylation, nucleophilic, intramolecular, regiostereospecific, catalytic
– with acoxy-2-ethylenes **68**, 489
C-α-Allylation (s.a. α,α-Diallylation)
– of α-isocyanocarboxylic acid esters **38**, 772s68
– with
  acetylene derivs. **68**, 330
  allenes **68**, 331
  1,3-dienes **48**, 691s68
–, asym.
– with 1,3-dienes **48**, 691s68
–, **Pd-catalyzed**
– of enolates, non-stabilized, review **27**, 851s68
–, **intramolecular, asym., decarboxylative**
– of allyl enol carbonates **68**, 500
–, **regiospecific**

– of α-alkoxyketones with asym. induction **68**, 374
N-Allylation, asym., Ir-catalyzed, regiospecific
– of amines, ar. **68**, 178
N-Allylation, Pd-catalyzed
– with desymmetrization **68**, 177
O-Allylation, asym.
– of phenols **68**, 124
–, –, **Ir-catalyzed, regiospecific**
– of copper(I) alkoxides **68**, 93
–, **Pd-catalyzed**
–, review **27**, 851s68
Allylboration, asym.
– of
  ketones **68**, 436
  oxo compds. **68**, 446
Allyl cations
– special s.
  2-aminoallyl cations
Allyl(chloro)dimethylsilane
– as reactant **58**, 432s68
Allyl enol carbonates
–, C-α-allylation, intramolecular, asym., decarboxylative **68**, 500
α′-Allyl-α,β-ethyleneketones, cyclic
– startg. m. f.
  bicyclo[3.n.1]alk-1-en-2-ones **68**, 334
Allyl glycosides
–, cycloaddition, 1,3-dipolar to –
  16, 888s68
Allyl halides s. β,γ-Ethylenehalides
Allyl(isopropoxy)dimethylsilane
– as reactant **68**, 470
α-Allylketones, cyclic, chiral 68, 500
1-(*o*-Allyloxyaryl)-2-acetylenealcohols
– startg. m. f.
  α-(benzofuran-2-yl)carboxylic acid esters **68**, 484
o′-**Allyloxychalcones**
– startg. m. f.
  flavones **68**, 137
Allyl phenolethers
– startg. m. f.
  chromans, 3-iodo- **68**, 211
Allyl phosphates
–, Nozaki-Hiyama reaction, intramolecular, regiostereospecific with –
  68, 487
– startg. m. f.
  ethylene derivs., terminal, regiospecific asym. synthesis **68**, 363
1,2-Allylpropargylation 68, 474
Allylsilanes s. 2-Ethylenesilanes
Allylstannanes s. 2-Ethylenestannanes
Allyl sulfones
– as source of alkyl radicals **51**, 424s68
Allyltributylstannane
– as reactant **68**, 441
π-Allyltricarbonyliron lactone complexes
–, decomplexation, reductive **68**, 41
o-**Alumination 68**, 209
Aluminum chloride 9, 871s68;
  53, 230s68; **68**, 247, 355
– –/silica gel **60**, 195s68
– –/sodium iodide **29**, 186s68
– **complexes**
  chloroaluminum tetra-*tert*-butylphthalocyanine complexes
  33, 593s68
– –, chiral

bis[(R,R)-N,N′-bis(3,5-di-*tert*-butylsalicylidenato)cyclohexane-1,2-diamine](μ-oxo)aluminum **68**, 68
– **compds., organo-** (s.a. Hydroalumination...)
  trimethylaluminum **33**, 874s68;
  56, 454s68; **68**, 365
  –/1,1′-binaphthyls, 2′-aryl-2-hydroxy-3-(*o*-hydroxyphenyl)-, chiral
  56, 454s68
  –/2,6-di-*tert*-butyl-4-methylphenol
  68, 333
– as reactant **68**, 268, 364
– **halides, organo-**
  diethylaluminum chloride **49**, 718s68;
  68, 269
  – iodide **68**, 298
  ethylaluminum dichloride **68**, 334
– **hydrides, organo-**
  diisobutylaluminum hydride **36**, 864s68;
  58, 58s68; **68**, 95, 134, 294
– **triflate 49**, 254s68
Amberlite IR-120 21, 270s68
Amberlyst 15 5, 549s68; **11**, 770s68;
  62, 195s68; **66**, 178s68; **67**, 276s68
Amberlyst A-26 diazidoiodate
  43, 264s68
Amidines
– special s.
  sulfonylamidines
Amidoximes
– special s.
  hydroxyamidoximes
– **O-acyl-** s. O-Acylamidoximes
Amination, intramolecular, asym.
– with sulfonamides **64**, 183s68
C-α-Amination, asym., organocatalyzed
– with azodicarboxylic acid esters
  68, 143, 170
C-α-Amination, asym.-carbopalladation
68, 398
Amines (s.a. Hydroamination, Oxyamination)
–, N-chlorination **68**, 139
– from
  azides via phosphine imines **12**, 42s68
– special s.
  acetyleneamines
  acoxylamines
  acylamines
  alleneamines
  ω-arylamines
  benzylamines
  diamines
  enamines
  ethyleneamines
  halogenamines
  polyamines
– startg. m. f.
  ureas, sym. **66**, 169s68
Amines, ar. (s.a. *o*-Amino..., Anilines)
–, N-allylation, asym., Ir-catalyzed, regiospecific **68**, 178
– from
  azo compds., ar. **53**, 9s68
  halides, ar. **68**, 187
  nitro compds., ar. **51**, 163s68; **68**, 13
– startg. m. f.
  4(3*H*)-quinazolones **28**, 418s68

Amines, ar., prim.
- from
  halides, ar. **59**, 173s68
-, -, **tert.**
- special s.
  diarylamines, tert.
Amines, cyclic
- from
  lactams **68**, 43
Amines, polymer-based
- as reagent **8**, 917s68
Amines, prim.
- from
  carboxylic acid amides, N-unsubst. **27**, 65s68
  nitriles **27**, 65s68
- startg. m. f.
  amines, sec. **68**, 183
  -, tert., cyclic **68**, 179
  N,N-dihalogenamines **68**, 139
  indoles **68**, 192
  pyrroles **68**, 151, 360
  urethans, N-subst. **68**, 158
Amines, sec.
- from
  acetylene derivs., terminal **58**, 126s68
  amines, prim. and nitriles **68**, 183
  nitro compds. **68**, 183
-, -, **cyclic**
-, α-arylation, dehydrogenative **68**, 408
Amines, tert.
- special s.
  butyl(dimethyl)amine
  ethyldiisopropylamine
-, -, **cyclic**
- from
  diols and amines, tert., cyclic **68**, 179
2-Aminoalcohols
- special s.
  γ-amino-β-hydroxy...
  2-(arylamino)alcohols
  α-arylamino-β-hydroxy...
  2-(prolylamino)alcohols
- startg. m. f.
  2-oxazolidones **66**, 169s68
-, **chiral**
- as reagent **49**, 41s68; **66**, 290s68
- special s.
  N-(o-hydroxybenzyl)-2-aminoalcohols, chiral
-, **β-cyclodextrin-anchored, chiral**
- as reagent **68**, 23
-, **fiber-supported, chiral**
- as reagent **58**, 236s68
-, **N-protected**
- from
  epoxides, asym. conversion **68**, 141
2-tert-Aminoalcohols
- startg. m. f.
  1,2-di-tert-amines **68**, 171
4-Aminoalcohols 62, 42s68
α-Aminoaldehydes, cyclic
- from
  α,β-ethylene-α-halogenosulfoxides, cyclic **68**, 136
  2-spiroaziridines, 3-sulfinyl- **68**, 136
2-Aminoallyl cations
- as intermediates **68**, 350
ω-(o-Aminoaryl)alcohols
- startg. m. f.
  benzolactams **68**, 198
o-(Aminoaryl)ethynylcarbinols

- startg. m. f.
  quinolines **13**, 526s68
(Aminoaryl)phosphine oxides
- from
  (sulfonyloxyaryl)phosphines and azides **68**, 180
Aminoboranes, cyclic
- as reagent **68**, 440
α-Aminocarboxylic acid amides 68, 163
α-prim-Aminocarboxylic - -, chiral 26, 55s68
o-Aminocarboxylic - -
- startg. m. f.
  4-quinazolones **68**, 173
α-Aminocarboxylic acid esters
- special s.
  acetylene-α-aminocarboxylic acid esters
  aldehydo-α-aminocarboxylic - -
- - - -, **N-protected**
-, Kowalski homologization, with retention of configuration **68**, 394
β-Aminocarboxylic acid esters
- special s.
  alkoxy-β-aminocarboxylic acid esters
- - - -, **chiral 68**, 440
α-Aminocarboxylic acid 2-phosphinopyrrolidides, N-protected, chiral
- as reagent **68**, 458
Aminocarboxylic acids
- from
  lactams, kinetic resolution **68**, 64
prim-Aminocarboxylic acids
-, N,N-dialkylation **46**, 317s68
α-Aminocarboxylic acids 13, 27s68
- as reagent **33**, 43s68
- special s.
  alanine
  α,β-diaminocarboxylic acids
  glycine
  proline
- -, **conformationally restricted**
-, synthesis, review **19**, 33s68
- - -, **cyclic, conformationally rigid**
-, use in design of peptide models, review **19**, 33s68
α-prim-Aminocarboxylic acids
- startg. m. f.
  nitriles **68**, 139, 202
2-Amino-2-deoxy-β-glycosides 34, 209s68
- from
  glycals **68**, 148
Aminodi(phosphines), polymer-based
- as Ru scavenger in metathesis **49**, 985s68
1-Amino-1,4-enynes
- startg. m. f.
  pyrroles **68**, 155
1,1-Aminoethers (s.a. N-Alkoxymethyl...)
syn-2-Aminoethers, ar., N-protected
- from
  aziridines, N-protected **68**, 114
(Z)-β-Amino-α,β-ethylenecarbonyl compds.
- from
  β-ketocarbonyl compds. (in ionic liquids or without solvent) **68**, 164
β-Amino-α,β-ethylenecarboxylic acid derivs., N-unsubst.
-, hydrogenation, asym., homogeneous **68**, 38

β-Amino-α,β-ethylenecarboxylic acid esters
- startg. m. f.
  β-amino-α,β-ethyleneketones **68**, 358
  pyrroles **68**, 155
ω-Amino-α,β-ethylenecarboxylic - -
- special s.
  α-alkoxy-ω-amino-α,β-ethylenecarboxylic acid esters
β-Amino-α,β-ethyleneketones
- from
  β-amino-α,β-ethylenecarboxylic acid esters **68**, 358
  isoxazoles **39**, 418s68
1-Amino-4-halogeno-1,4-dienes
- startg. m. f.
  pyrroles **11**, 573s68
o-Amino-N-heterocyclics
- startg. m. f.
  imidazole ring **68**, 191
β-Amino-α-hydroxycarboxylic acid derivs., chiral 68, 265
α-Amino-β-hydroxycarboxylic acid esters
- special s.
  β-aryl-α-amino-β-hydroxycarboxylic acid esters
- - -, **chiral 55**, 26s68
β'-Amino-β-hydroxyketones, N-protected
- from
  aziridines, 2-acyl-, N-protected and aldehydes **68**, 270
syn- and anti-γ-Amino-β-hydroxyphosphonic acid esters, N-protected 23, 85s68
α-Amino-γ-ketocarboxylic acid esters, chiral 67, 275s68
syn-β-Aminoketones
- by 3-component Mannich reaction **68**, 361
o-Aminoketones
- startg. m. f.
  carbostyril-1-acetic acid amides, 4-component synthesis **68**, 357
β-prim-Amino-γ-lactones 54, 299s68
α-Aminomethylation s.a. Mannich reaction
o-Aminomethylation
- under microwaves **3**, 661s68
α-(Aminomethylene)-γ-lactones 30, 463s68
α-Aminonitriles
- startg. m. f.
  2-imidazolidones, 3-amino-4-imino- **68**, 157
β-Aminonitriles, N-protected
- from
  imines, N-protected, with 2 extra C-atoms **68**, 276
2-(Aminooxy)alcohols, chiral 40, 57s68
α-(Aminooxy)ketones
- from
  enamines and nitroso compds., asym. conversion **68**, 103
Aminooxy(phosphonyl)acetic acid anilides
- startg. m. f.
  oxindoles, 3-alkylidene- **68**, 429
β-Aminophosphinic acids
- startg. m. f.
  β-phosphinopeptides, review **19**, 33s68

α-*prim*-Aminophosphonic acid esters
  59, 234s68
Aminophosphonic acids
– , synthesis, asym. using chiral sulfinyl
  auxiliaries, review 27, 57s68
β-Aminophosphonic acids
– startg. m. f.
  β-phosphonopeptides, review 19, 33s68
Aminosugars
– in synthesis, stereospecific, review
  27, 57s68
α-Aminosulfonic acid esters
– , synthesis, review 19, 33s68
2-Aminothioethers
– from
  1,1-stannylthioethers 58, 447s68
– special s.
  2-*tert*-butylthioethylamine
–, N-protected
– from
  aziridines, N-protected and mercaptans
  68, 220
2-Aminothioureas
– from
  isothiocyanates, with retention of
  configuration 68, 145
2-Aminoureas, chiral
– as reagent 68, 59
Ammonia
– as reactant 35, 348s68; 68, 427
Ammonium acetate 68, 205
– –/alumina 17, 165s68
– bromide 44, 420s68
– carbonate 64, 151s68
– cerium(IV) nitrate 33, 593s68;
  45, 70s68; 47, 106s68; 68, 95
– chloride 44, 420s68
– formate
– as reactant 68, 161
– as reagent 13, 442s68, 539s68;
  36, 957s68
– hydroxides, quaternary
– special s.
  hydroxyammonium hydroxides
– nitrate 68, 195
– salts, quaternary, polymeric
– special s.
  poly(diallyldimethylammonium
  chloride)
– –, –, spirocyclic, chiral
– as reagent 18, 193s68
– sulfide 19, 378s68
– ylids, quaternary, stabilized
– , cyclopropanation, asym., organocatalyzed with – 68, 396
Aniline ring
– from
  o-acetylenealdimines with N-alkylation
  68, 349
Anilines s.a. Amines, ar.
Anilinium hypophosphite
– as reactant 38, 584s68
[8]Annulenes, dehydro-, planar
– , review 35, 661s68
Anthracene, (S,S)-1,8-bis(4-isopropyl-
  Δ²-oxazolin-2-yl)-
– as reagent 68, 186
Anti-Michael addition
– of ketones to α,β-acetylenecarboxylic
  acid esters 68, 310
Antimony pentachloride/benzyltriethyl-
  ammonium chloride 54, 413s68

Antimony trichloride 57, 207s68
Arenes (s.a. Benzene ring)
– , epoxidation 39, 124s68
– from
  o-benzenedisulfonimides 33, 71s68
– , functionalization, oxidative, catalyzed,
  review 27, 851s68
– , Michael-type addition, organocatalyzed 11, 770s68
– , photochemistry, review 24, 118s68
– special s.
  alkylarenes
  allylarenes
  propargylarenes
– startg. m. f.
  diaryls 68, 421
  quinones 42, 235s68
Aroylcyanides
– startg. m. f.
  diaryl ketones 68, 476
Arsonium salts
– special s.
  2-ketoarsonium salts
Arylacetaldehyde acetals
– special s.
  o-isocyanoarylacetaldehyde acetals
Arylacetic... s.a. α-Arylcarboxylic...
Arylacetic acid esters
– from
  halides, ar. 68, 482
1-Aryl-2-acetylenealcohols
– special s.
  1-(*o*-allyloxyaryl)-2-acetylenealcohols
Arylacetylenes
– from
  iodides, ar. 64, 449s68
– special s.
  o-allylarylacetylenes
  silylethynylarenes
2-Arylalcohols 11, 59s68
ω-Arylalcohols
– special s.
  ω-(*o*-aminoaryl)alcohols
N-Arylaldimines
– startg. m. f.
  quinolines 68, 372
Arylallenes
– from
  2-acetylenealcohols and arylboronic
  acids 68, 473
2-Arylallyl
– as protective group 68, 3
ω-Aryl-*sec*-amines
– startg. m. f.
  benzolactams, carbonylation, oxidative
  68, 356
2-(Arylamino)alcohols
– from
  epoxides, desymmetrization 68, 58
– , kinetic resolution and desymmetrization 68, 141
α-Arylamino-β-hydroxycarboxylic acid
  esters
– special s.
  α-aryl-α-arylamino-β-hydroxy-
  carboxylic acid esters
β-Aryl-α-amino-β-hydroxycarboxylic
  acid esters, N,O-protected
– from
  aldehydes, asym. conversion 68, 262
α-Aryl-α-arylamino-β-hydroxy-
  carboxylic acid esters

– by 3-component synthesis 68, 387
Arylation (s.a. Hydroarylation, Radical
  arylation)
–, heterogeneous
– with arylboronic acids 68, 193
C-Arylation (s.a. Heck arylation)
C-α-Arylation
– of α,β-ethyleneoxo compds. with
  triarylbismuth dichlorides 68, 449
–, dehydrogenative
– of amines, sec., cyclic 68, 408
N-Arylation (s.a. High-pressure
  N-arylation)
– of
  carboxylic acid amides 62, 171s68
  2-pyridones 62, 171s68
  sulfamides 59, 173s68
  sulfoximines 62, 171s68; 65, 178s68
– with aryllead tricarboxylates
  45, 542s68
–, Cu(I)-catalyzed
– without solvent 68, 187
–, fluorous 59, 173s68
–, heterogeneous, selective 68, 193
–, sequential (intermolecular-
  intramolecular) 68, 191
–, – (intramolecular-intermolecular),
  Pd-catalyzed 68, 190
O-Arylation, heterogeneous
– of phenols 68, 193
1-Aryl-1,1-azidoethers
– from
  benzyl ethers 43, 264s68
1-Arylbiguanides
– from
  dicyanodiamide 16, 395s68
Arylbis[2-(carbomethoxy)ethyl]-
  sulfonium triflates
– as reagent 31, 522s68
Arylboronic acid esters
– by [2+2+2]-cycloaddition 33, 658s68
Arylboronic acids (s.a. under Suzuki)
– , arylation, heterogeneous with – 68, 193
– startg. m. f.
  (E)-allylarenes, regiospecific synthesis
  68, 460
  arylallenes 68, 473
  (E)-2-aryl-1,3-dienes 68, 460
  2-aryl-1,5-dienes, cyclic 68, 475
  aryl γ-diketones 68, 453
  2-arylidenealcohols, cyclic, asym.
  conversion 68, 457
  aryl ketones 68, 462, 465
  nitro compds., ar. 68, 195
  propargylarenes 68, 473
  sulfones, ar. 68, 232
Arylboroxines
– startg. m. f.
  N-sulfonyldiarylmethylamines, asym.
  conversion 68, 458
N-Aryl-N''-carbalkoxyguanidines
  54, 100s68
N-Arylcarbazic acid esters
– startg. m. f.
  indoles 14, 836s68
Arylcarboxylic acid amides
– from
  arylstannanes and isocyanates 68, 455
ω-Arylcarboxylic acid amides
– from
  ketones, cyclic 68, 149

Arylcarboxylic acid anhydrides
– special s.
  2-methyl-6-nitrobenzoic anhydride
Arylcarboxylic acids
– from
  benzyl halides **68**, 111
1,2-Arylcyanation, Ni-catalyzed 68, 316
(E)-2-Aryl-1,3-dienes
– from
  2-allenealcohols and arylboronic acids
  68, 460
2-Aryl-1,5-dienes, cyclic
– from
  9-halogeno-1,2,7-trienes and
  arylboronic acids **68**, 475
Aryl γ-diketones
– from
  arylboronic acids and α,β-ethylene-
  ketones **68**, 453
δ-Aryl-γ-diketones 68, 329
(E)-4-Aryl-3-ethylenealcohols
–, 3-component synthesis, regiospecific
  with insertion of 3 C-atoms **68**, 470
δ-Aryl-γ,δ-ethylenealdehydes, cyclic
– from
  (Z)-2,n-enynols and ar. halides,
  stereospecific conversion **68**, 418
N-Aryl-2-ethylenesulfonylamines
– startg. m. f.
  quinolines, 1,2,3,4-tetrahydro-, 3-iodo-
  1-sulfonyl- **68**, 211
β-Aryl-α-halogenaldehydes 33, 768s68
**N-Aryl-N-heterocyclics, benzo-
condensed**
– from
  halides, ar. and ω-(o-halogenoaryl)-
  amines **68**, 190
N-Arylhydrazonoesters 18, 416s68
2-Arylidenealcohols, cyclic
– from
  acetyleneoxo compds. and arylboronic
  acids, asym. conversion **68**, 457
**N-Arylideneglycinates, Ni(II)-
complexed**
–, Michael addition of – **36**, 668s68
Aryl ketones
– from
  alkylarenes **68**, 86, 90
  arylboronic acids and carboxylic acid
  2-pyridyl or 2-pyridylmethyl esters
  68, 465
  – – and α,β-ethylenealdehydes **68**, 462
  halides, ar. **1**, 522s68
–, hydrogenation, homogeneous, asym.
  (s.a. HC⇓OC) **68**, 25 (in alcoholic
  media)
– special s.
  acylophenones
  diaryl ketones
–, transfer-hydrogenation, asym. in water
  68, 24
α-Arylketones
– from
  benzyl ethers and carboxylic acid
  chlorides **68**, 407
–, transfer-hydrogenation, asym.
  46, 42s68
γ-Arylketones
– from
  3-ethylenealcohols **31**, 847s68
Aryllead tricarboxylates
–, N-arylation with – **45**, 542s68

Aryloxo compds.
– startg. m. f.
  benzylalcohols s. HC⇓OC
**α-Aryloxycarboxylic acids, chiral
42**, 45s68
3-Aryloxyepoxides
– startg. m. f.
  3-chromanols, with inversion of
  configuration **68**, 345
H-Arylphosphonates 38, 584s68
Arylsilanes
– startg. m. f.
  N-sulfonylbenzylamines **58**, 447s68
4-Aryl-1-siloxyacetylenes
– startg. m. f.
  naphthalenes, 1,2-dihydro-, 4-siloxy-
  68, 496
Arylsodium compds.
– startg. m. f.
  diaryls **14**, 852s68
Arylstannanes
– startg. m. f.
  arylcarboxylic acid amides **68**, 455
**α-Aryl-α-sulfonylaminocarboxylic acid
esters 68**, 267
α-Arylsulfoxides
– from
  arylboronic acids **62**, 451s68
1-(Arylthio)enolethers, cyclic
– startg. m. f.
  spiroorthocarboxylic acid esters
  68, 112
N-(Arylthio)lactams
– special s.
  N-(phenylthio)caprolactam
Aryl tosylates
– startg. m. f.
  thioethers, ar. **53**, 230s68
Aryl triflates
– startg. m. f.
  phenols **68**, 1
Arylzinc halides
–, preparation **38**, 836s68
– startg. m. f.
  (E)-β-styryl halides, synthesis **68**, 294
Arynes (s.a. Benzynes)
–, functionalized
– via o-sulfonyloxyarylmagnesium
  chlorides **68**, 402
**4-Aza-1-azoniabicyclo[2.2.2]octane
dichromate, 1-butyl-**
– as reagent **4**, 274s68
– **tribromide, 1-benzyl-**
– as reagent **48**, 447s68
**Aza-Baylis-Hillman reaction, asym.,
organocatalyzed 68**, 272
**Aza-Bergman cyclization-aza-Bergman
cleavage 68**, 348
Azabicyclo[x.y.0]alkanes
–, synthesis, stereospecific, review
  19, 33s68
**1-Azabicyclo[3.n.0]alkenones, chiral
56**, 495s68
**3-Azabicyclo[4.4.0]decan-8-one ketals,
N-carbalkoxy-1-α-hydroxy-, chiral
9**, 741s68
2-Azabicyclo[2.2.0]hexanes
–, synthesis, review **42**, 853s68
2-Azabicyclo[2.2.0]hex-5-enes
–, synthesis, review **42**, 853s68
2-Azabicyclo[3.3.0]octenes s.a.
  Cyclopenta[b]pyrroles, hexahydro-

**Aza-Claisen rearrangement, charge-
accelerated**
–, review **23**, 739s68
2-Aza-1,3-dienes s. Enazomethines
Aza-C-disaccharides
–, synthesis, review **41**, 173s68
Azaindoles 68, 411
Azasugars, 6-membered
–, total synthesis, review **41**, 173s68
Aza-Wittig synthesis-Ugi condensation
–, ring closure by – with asym. induction
  68, 384
**1,2-Azazirconacyclopentenes,
condensed**
– as intermediates **51**, 315s68
**1H-Azepines, 2,3,4,5-tetrahydro-,
4-alkylidene- 64**, 302s68
Azetidines, N-tosyl-
– startg. m. f.
  pyrimidines, 1,4,5,6-tetrahydro-,
  1-tosyl- **68**, 146
**2-Azetidinone-4-carboxylic acid esters,
N-sulfonyl-, chiral 38**, 802s68
2-Azetidinones
– from
  azomethines **40**, 619s68
–, **3-alkoxy-4-ω-halogeno-**
– startg. m. f.
  (Z)-α-alkoxy-ω-amino-α,β-
  ethylenecarboxylic acid esters
  68, 107
–, **trans-1-tert-amino-, chiral 21**, 445s68
–, **3-methylene-, chiral 63**, 277s68
Azides
–, review **67**, 188s68
– special s.
  glycosyl azides
– startg. m. f.
  amines via phosphine imines **12**, 42s68
  (aminoaryl)phosphine oxides **68**, 180
  2-amino-2-deoxy-β-glycosides **68**, 148
  2-ethylenephosphorylamines **68**, 185
  N'-sulfonylamidines **68**, 181
–, **in situ-generated**
–, cycloaddition, 1,3-dipolar,
  regiospecific with – **68**, 184
Azides, ar.
– startg. m. f.
  formanilides **68**, 161
2-Azidoalcohols, chiral 66, 128s68
**1,2-cis-2-Azido-2-deoxyselenoglycosides
65**, 223s68
1,1-Azidoethers
– special s.
  1-aryl-1,1-azidoethers
α-Azidoketones 36, 266s68
Aziridines
– by C-N bond formation, metal-
  mediated, review **55**, 159s68
– startg. m. f.
  β-acylaminocarboxylic acid amides
  68, 275
  2-oxazolidones **23**, 139s68; **68**, 147
–, **2-acyl-, N-protected**
– startg. m. f.
  β'-amino-β-hydroxyketones,
  N-protected **68**, 270
–, **N-(N-acyliminosulfinyl)- 62**, 159s68
–, **2-acyl-1-tosyl-**
– from
  α,β-acetyleneselenonium salts **68**, 437
–, **2-alkylidene-**

–, [4+3]-cycloaddition, intramolecular, Lewis acid-catalyzed with – **68**, 350
–, **2-methylene-**
– startg. m. f.
pyrroles **68**, 375
–, **N-protected**
– startg. m. f.
syn-2-aminoethers, ar., N-protected **68**, 114
2-aminothioethers, N-protected **68**, 220
–, **N-sulfonyl-**
– from
epoxides, asym. conversion **68**, 142
ethylene derivs., – – **68**, 186
–, **N-tosyl-**
– from
ethylene derivs. **68**, 189 (aq. medium)
– startg. m. f.
N-tosylimines **68**, 154
Aziridinium triflates
–, ring opening, regiospecific **68**, 171
4,4′-Azobis(4-cyanovaleric acid)
– as water-soluble initiator **46**, 451s68
2,2′-Azobis(4-methoxy-2,4-dimethylvaleronitrile)
– as initiator **68**, 445
Azocine ring, 1,2,5,6,7,8-hexahydro-, polyoxy-, chiral 56, 495s68
Azocines, 4,5-dihydro-, 3-amino-
– by 3-component synthesis **68**, 378
Azodicarboxylic acid esters
–, α-amination, asym., organocatalyzed with – **68**, 143, 170
–, hydroacylation **68**, 144
– startg. m. f.
pyrazolidine-1,2-dicarboxylic acid esters, 3-vinyl-. asym. synthesis **68**, 398
– – –, **polymeric**
– as reagent **68**, 169
Azoles
– special s.
biazolyls
Azolopyridazines
–, synthesis, review **42**, 853s68
Azoloquinolines
–, synthesis, review **42**, 853s68
Azomethines (s.a. Imin…)
– special s.
acetyleneazomethines
aldimines
di(azomethines)
ethyleneazomethines
ketimines
trifluoroacetaldimines
– startg. m. f.
2-acetyleneamines **68**, 278
2-azetidinones **40**, 619s68
3-ethyleneamines **40**, 567s68; **66**, 272s68
Azomethinium salts
–, generation, aminoborane-mediated **68**, 440
– **ylids**
–, cycloaddition, 1,3-dipolar, intramolecular with –, review **42**, 853s68
–, generation from carbenoids and syntheses with –, review **42**, 853s68

Barbier-type synthesis, Ti(III)-catalyzed 68, 260
Barbituric acids, 5-amino-
– startg. m. f.
hydantoins, 5-carbamyl- **68**, 153
Barium dichromate 41, 240s68
Barium hydroxide 59, 449s68
Baylis-Hillman reaction (s.a. Aza-Baylis-Hillman reaction)
– in aqueous media **39**, 593s68
– in ionic liquids **39**, 593s68
– in polyethylene glycol **39**, 593s68
–, update **39**, 593s68
– with 1,1-nitroethylene derivs. **39**, 593s68
– with asym. induction, double **39**, 593s68
– – –, asym. **39**, 593s68
– –, co-catalyzed
– – without solvent **68**, 252
– –, intramolecular, reductive
– with α,β-acetylene-ω-diketones **68**, 287
– reaction-Michael addition **68**, 286
Baylis-Hillman-type reaction, stereospecific
– with 2,3-dienol 2-monocarbamates **68**, 251
Bentonite 41, 199s68
1H-1-Benzazepine-1,2-dicarboxylic acid esters
– from
quinolines **68**, 381
3H-3-Benzazapine-2,3-dicarboxylic – –
– from
isoquinolines **68**, 381
3H-2-Benzazepines, 4,5-dihydro-
– from
o-ethynylaldimines, synthesis **68**, 393
Benzene ring (s.a. Arenes)
– special s.
aniline ring
Benzenes, 1,2,3-trisubst. 68, 209
Benzhydrylamines... s. Diarylmethyl-amines
Benzimidazole, 1-methyl-2-(2-pyridyl)-4,6-bis(perfluorooctyl)-
– as reagent **68**, 76
Benzimidazoles
– from
N-acyl-*o*-diamines, soluble polymer-based synthesis **21**, 543s68
o-diamines and alcohols, prim., activated **68**, 174
– and carboxylic acid halides **68**, 188
– special s.
bis(benzimidazoles)
–, synthesis, polymer-based **43**, 316s68
–, **2-amino-**
–, synthesis, polymer-based **43**, 316s68
–, **-(β-styryl)- 6**, 135s68
1,2-Benziodoxole derivs.
– as reagent **41**, 696s68 (review)
Benziporphyrins
–, review **42**, 853s68
3,4-Benzocoumarins
– from
o-hydroxydiaryls **68**, 247
Benzocyclobutenes
– from
cyclobutanones **22**, 877s68
1H-1,4-Benzodiazepine-2,5-diones, 3,4-dihydro- 48, 346s68

1H-1,5-Benzodiazepines
– from
o-diamines **13**, 896s68
1,3,2-Benzodioxaphospholes
– special s.
2,2′-spirobi(1,3,2-benzodioxaphospholes)
–, **2-amino-, chiral**
– as reagent **60**, 34s68
2H-1,5-Benzodioxepines 56, 495s68
1,4-Benzodioxins, 2,3-dihydro-, 2-alkylidene-
–, review **42**, 853s68
1,6-Benzodioxocins, 2,5-dihydro- 56, 495s68
2(3H)-Benzofuranones
– by cycloisomerization **19**, 787s68
3(2H)-Benzofuranones, 2,2-disubst., chiral 68, 335
Benzofuran ring, 2,3-dihydro-, 4-alkoxy-2,3-dihydroxy- 68, 89
Benzofurans, 7-*sec*-amino- 68, 349
–, **2,3-dihydro-, 3-methylene- 68**, 339
–, **polycyclic 68**, 493
α-**(Benzofuran-2-yl)carboxylic acid esters**
– from
1-(*o*-allyloxyaryl)-2-acetylenealcohols **68**, 484
Benzo-O-heterocyclics
–, synthesis, polymer-based, review **42**, 853s68
Benzoic acid
– as reagent **68**, 326, 331
Benzolactams
– from
ω-(*o*-aminoaryl)alcohols **68**, 198
ω-aryl-*sec*-amines, carbonylation, oxidative **68**, 356
Benzo[*c*]phenanthridine alkaloids
–, synthesis, review **42**, 853s68
Benzophenones s.a. Diaryl ketones
1,2,5-Benzothiadiazepine 1,1-dioxides
–, synthesis, review **42**, 853s68
1,2-S(VI)-Benzothiazine S-oxides 57, 377s68
Benzothiazoles
– from
o-acylaminomercaptans, soluble polymer-based synthesis **21**, 543s68
–, synthesis, polymer-based **43**, 316s68
Benzothiazoles, 2-amino-
– from
o-halogenothioureas **68**, 233
Benzo[*b*]thiophenes (s. Thianaphthenes in Vol. **1-50**)
–, **7-*sec*-amino- 68**, 349
Benzo[*b*]thiophen-3(2H)-ones, 2,2-disubst., chiral 68, 335
Benzotriazoles, N-acyl-
–, acylation with –, review **68**, 226s68
–, S-acylation with – **68**, 226
–, **N-amidinyl-**
– startg. m. f.
thioureas **68**, 225
1-(Benzotriazol-1-yl)-2-hydroxy-thioethers 29, 262s68
Benzotriazol-1-yloxytris(dimethyl-amino)phosphonium hexafluoro-phosphate
– as reagent **50**, 182s68

2-(Benzotriazol-1-yl)-1,1,3,3-tetra-
methyluronium −
– as reagent 9, 672s68
3,1,5-Benzoxadiazepines
– from
  o-diamines and carboxylic acid halides
  (2 molecules) 68, 188
1H-2,1-Benzoxaphosphorin P-oxides,
1-alkoxy-4-iodo- 62, 203s68
Benz[e][1,4]oxathiepin-5-ones
– from
  o-mercaptocarboxylic acids and
  epoxides 68, 223
1,4-Benzoxathiin-2-ones 56, 313s68
2H-1,4-Benzoxazines, 3,4-dihydro-
–, synthesis, review 42, 853s68
2H-1,4-Benzoxazin-3(4H)-ones
19, 561s68
–, synthesis, review 42, 853s68
Benzoxazoles
– from
  o-acylaminophenols, soluble polymer-
  based synthesis 21, 543s68
Benzylalcohols
– from
  aryloxo compds. s. HC⇓OC
– special s.
  α-deuteriobenzylalcohols
–, sec.
– from
  aldehydes and triarylboranes, asym.
  synthesis 68, 438
Benzylamines
–, resolution, optical by salt formation
  5, 666s68
– special s.
  o-nitrobenzylamines
– startg. m. f.
  phthalimidines, carbonylation, oxidative
  68, 356
Benzylamines, sec.
– from
  aldimines, ar. 68, 268
–, –, chiral 50, 379s68
Benzylation, ar. s.a. Friedel-Crafts
  benzylation
N-Benzylation
– special s.
  N,N-dibenzylation
Benzyl bromide
– as reagent 68, 199
Benzyl ethers (s.a. O-Debenzylation)
– special s.
  p-alkoxybenzyl ethers
– startg. m. f.
  1-aryl-1,1-azidoethers 43, 264s68
  α-arylketones 68, 407
α-Benzyl-α,β-ethylenecarboxylic acid
esters 68, 460
Benzyl halides (s.a. Chloromethylation,
  ar.)
– special s.
  benzyl iodides
– startg. m. f.
  arylcarboxylic acids 68, 111
  1,2-dibenzyl-1,3-enynes (from 2
  molecules) 68, 469
Benzyl iodides 62, 195s68
O-Benzyloximes
– from
  O-benzyl-1-sulfonyloximes, synthesis
  51, 424s68

(E)-β-Benzyloxy-δ,ε-ethyleneketones,
chiral 67, 448s68
α-Benzyloxyketones
–, C-α-alkylation, asym. 54, 394s68
Benzyl thioethers
– from
  mercaptans 54, 83s68
Benzyltriethylammonium chloride
– as reagent 30, 154s68
Benzyltrimethylammonium
dichloroiodate
– as reagent 43, 421s68
Benzyltriphenylphosphonium
peroxymonosulfate
– as reagent 47, 431s68
Benzynes (s.a. Arynes)
– startg. m. f.
  o-allylarylacetylenes 67, 255s68
  carbazoles 68, 464
  o-di(stannanes) 67, 255s68
Bergman cyclization s.a. Aza-
  Bergman…
Biaryls (s.a. Diaryls)
–, di(phosphino)- (s.a. Bis(diarylphosphino)diaryls)
– as reagent 27, 57s68 (review)
Biazolyls
–, review 42, 853s68
Bicyclo[n.2.0]alkan-1-ols
–, review 37, 933s68
Bicyclo[3.n.1]alk-3-en-2-ones
– from
  α′-allyl-α,β-ethyleneketones, cyclic
  68, 334
Bicyclo[2.2.1]heptane, 2-hydroperoxy-
2-(2-furyl)-
– as reagent 42, 115s68
Bicyclo[2.2.1]heptanes, 5-methylene-,
fused 41, 942s68
Bicyclo[3.1.0]hexan-2-ones 68, 341
Bicyclo[3.1.0]hexan-3-ones
– from
  1,5-enyn-4-ols 68, 341
Bicyclo[3.1.0]hex-2-ene ring
– from
  1,n-enyn-(n-1)-ols 68, 490
Bicyclo[4.2.1]non-3-enes 56, 495s68
Bicyclo[5.2.0]non-9-enes, 2-alkylidene-
65, 314s68
Bicyclo[2.2.2]octa-2,5-dienes, chiral
– as reagent 55, 452s68; 68, 124, 457,
  458
Bicyclo[3.3.0]oct-1-en-2-ones 40, 475s68
1,1″-Biferrocenes, di(phosphino)-,
chiral
– as reagent 68, 36
Biginelli synthesis
– under microwaves 55, 337s68
–, update 55, 337s68
– –, 1–, organocatalyzed, solventless
  68, 371
Biguanides
– special s.
  1-arylbiguanides
(R)-1,1′-Bi-2-naphthol
– as reagent 52, 68s68; 68, 257
(S)-1,1′-Bi-2-naphthol
– as reagent 49, 898s68; 65, 434s68;
  66, 275s68
1,1′-Bi-2-naphthol, (R_S,S_S)-3,3′-
bis(benzenesulfinylmethyl)-
– as reagent 68, 269

–, (R)-3,3′-bis(trifluoromethyl)-
– as reagent 68, 446
–, (R)-3,3′-dibromo-
– as reagent 68, 447
–, (R)-3,3′-diiodo-
– as reagent 61, 434s68; 68, 306
–, (R)-3,3′-diphenyl-
– as reagent 50, 61s68
–, (S)-3-[N-isopropyl-N-(3-pyridyl)-
aminomethyl]-
– as reagent 68, 272
–, (R)-5,5′,6,6′,7,7′,8,8′-octahydro-
– as reagent 68, 444
–, –, (S)-3,3′-bis(morpholinomethyl)-
– as reagent 58, 236s68
–, (R)-3,3′,6,6′-tetraiodo-
– as reagent 59, 431s68
1,1′-Bi-2-naphthols
–, resolution, optical by chiral
  derivatization 60, 500s68
1,1′-Binaphthyl, (R)-2,2′-bis(trifluoromethanesulfonylamino)-
– as reagent 68, 477
1,1′-Binaphthyl-2,2′-diyl hydrogen
phosphate, (R)-3,3′-bis(3,5-dimesityl-
phenyl)-
– as reagent 68, 274
1,1′-Binaphthyl-2-phosphine oxides,
2′-diamino-, chiral
– as reagent 68, 180
1,1′-Binaphthyls, 2′-aryl-2-hydroxy-3-
(o-hydroxyphenyl)-, chiral
– as reagent 56, 454s68
–, 2,2′-bis(4,5-polymethylene-2-
pyridyl)-, chiral
– as reagent 37, 674s68
Binaphthyls, phosphino- and di-
(phosphino)-
– special s.
  2,2′-bis[bis(p-methoxyphenyl)-
  phosphino]-1,1′-binaphthyl
  2,2′-bis(dicyclohexylphosphino)-1,1′-
  binaphthyl
  2,2′-bis(diphenylphosphino)-1,1′-
  binaphthyl
  2,2′-bis(diphenylphosphinomethyl)-
  1,1′-binaphthyl
  2,2′-bis(diphenylphosphino)-2-(p-
  toluenesulfonylamino)-1,1′-bi-
  naphthyl
  2,2′-bis(di-p-tolylphosphino)-1,1′-bi-
  naphthyl
Biocatalysis s. under Enzymes
Biphenyls (s.a. Diaryls)
Biphenyls, phosphino- and di(phosphino)-
(s.a. Biaryls, di(phosphino)-)
– special s.
  bis(diarylphosphino)diaryls
  2,3:2′,3′-bis(methylenedioxy)-6,6′-
  bis[bis(3,5-di-tert-butyl-4-methoxy-
  phenyl)phosphino]biphenyl
  2-(di-tert-butylphosphino)biphenyl
  2-(dicyclohexylphosphino)biphenyl
  2-(dicyclohexylphosphino)-2′,6′-
  dimethoxybiphenyl
  2-(dicyclohexylphosphino)-2′-
  (dimethylamino)biphenyl
  2-(dicyclohexylphosphino)-2′,4′,6′-
  triisopropylbiphenyl
  6,6′-dimethoxy-2,2′-bis(diphenylphosphino)biphenyls, 3,3′-disubst.

2-(dimethylamino)-2′-(diphenylphosphino)biphenyl
–, tetra-*o*-subst. 37, 902s68
2,2′-Bipyridyl
– as reagent 43, 847s68; 68, 158, 376
–, (R,R)-6,6′-bis(1-hydroxy-2,2-
dimethylpropyl)-
– as reagent 61, 431s68; 68, 58
3,3′-Bipyridyl, 2,2′,6,6′-tetramethoxy-
4,4′-bis(dicyclohexylphosphino)-,
chiral
– as reagent 66, 42s68
2,2′-Bipyridyl N,N-dioxides, chiral
– as reagent 55, 433s68
Birch reduction, alkylative
– with asym. induction 47, 773s68
α-Bis(alkylidenephosphines)
– as ligand 68, 187
Bis(benzimidazoles)
–, synthesis, polymer-based 43, 316s68
1,2-Bis(benzyloxy)-1,2-bis(1-benzyl-
imidazol-2-yl)ethane, chiral
– as reagent 65, 477s68
(R)-2,2′-Bis[bis(*p*-methoxyphenyl)-
phosphino]-1,1′-binaphthyl
– as reagent 68, 322
(R,R)-N,N′-Bis[N-[3,5-bis(trifluoromethyl)phenylthiocarbamyl]]-
cyclohexane-1,2-diamine
– as reagent 58, 233s68
N,N′-Bis[3,5-bis(trifluoromethyl)-
phenyl]thiourea
– as reagent 11, 770s68
(1R,2R)-N,N′-Bis(4-bromobenzyl-
idene)cyclohexane-1,2-diamine
– as reagent 68, 253
1,2-Bis(*tert*-butyldimethylsilyl)hydrazine
– as reagent 68, 45, 94
2,2′-Bis(diarylphosphino)-1,1′-bi-
naphthyl dioxides, chiral
– as reagent 66, 442s68
Bis(diarylphosphino)diaryls (s.a.
Biphenyls, di(phosphino)-)
– as ligand, review 27, 57s68
4,5-Bis(diarylphosphino)xanthenes
– as reagent 4, 667s68
4,4′-Bis(dichloroiodo)biphenyl
– as reagent 46, 432s68
(S)-2,2′-Bis(dicyclohexylphosphino)-
1,1′-binaphthyl
– as reagent 59, 447s68
1,3-Bis(dicyclohexylphosphino)propane
– as reagent 48, 691s68
1,4-Bis(9-O-dihydroquinidine)-
phthalazine
– as reagent 68, 79
–, polyethylene glycol-linked
– as reagent 51, 132s68
1,1′-Bis(diisopropylphosphino)ferrocene
– as reagent 36, 561s68
1,2-Bis((R,R)-2,5-diisopropyl-
phospholan-1-yl)benzene
– as reagent 68, 436
1,8-Bis(diphenylmethylium)-
naphthalenediyl bis(perchlorate)
– as reagent 29, 910s68
N,N′-Bis[2-(diphenylphosphino)-
benzoyl]-1,2-diamines, chiral
– as reagent 68, 500
–, polymer-based, chiral
– as reagent 51, 188s68
(1R,2R)-N,N′-Bis[2-(diphenylphosphino)benzoyl]-1,2-diamino-
cyclohexane
– as reagent 68, 177, 499
2,2′-Bis(diphenylphosphino)-1,1′-
binaphthyl
– as reagent 37, 49s68; 65, 178s68
(R)-2,2′-Bis(diphenylphosphino)-1,1′-
binaphthyl
– as reagent 55, 452s68; 68, 194
(S)-2,2′-Bis(diphenylphosphino)-1,1′-
binaphthyl
– as reagent 62, 18s68; 66, 155s68
2,2′-Bis(diphenylphosphino)-1,1′-
binaphthyls, 4,4′-disubst., chiral
– as reagent 67, 22s68
–, modified, chiral
–, review 27, 57s68
2,2′-Bis(diphenylphosphino)biphenyl
– as reagent 68, 320
1,4-Bis(diphenylphosphino)butane
– as reagent 68, 74
1,2-Bis(diphenylphosphino)ethane
– as reagent 66, 413s68; 68, 377
(R,R)-2,2′′-Bis[(S)-1-(diphenylphosphino)ethyl]-1,1′′-biferrocene
– as reagent 68, 36
1,1′-Bis(diphenylphosphino)ferrocene
– as reagent 34, 832s68; 66, 366s68;
68, 416
Bis(diphenylphosphino)methane
– as reagent 68, 493
2,2′-Bis(diphenylphosphinomethyl)-1,1′-
binaphthyl
– as reagent 68, 321
Bis[2-(diphenylphosphino)phenyl] ether
– as reagent 51, 171s68; 53, 471s68;
54, 244s68; 68, 29, 192, 414
1,3-Bis(diphenylphosphino)propane
– as reagent 28, 521s68; 38, 584s68;
68, 264
4,5-Bis(diphenylphosphino)xanthene,
9,9-dimethyl-
– as reagent 4, 667s68; 56, 211s68;
59, 173s68; 61, 344s68; 68, 29, 191,
192, 322, 413
(S)-2,2′-Bis(di-*p*-tolylphosphino)-1,1′-
binaphthyl
– as reagent 68, 325
(R,R)-1,2-Bis(*o*-hydroxybenzylamino)-
cyclohexane
– as reagent 51, 46s68
Bis(Δ²-imidazolines)
– as reagent 45, 397s68
1,1-Bis(indol-3-yl)alkanes
– from
acetals 5, 549s68
Bis(iodozincio)methane
– as reactant 40, 568s68
Bismuth 40, 567s68; 49, 591s68
bismuth nanoparticles 40, 567s68
Bismuth(V) dichlorides, organo-
– special s.
triarylbismuth dichlorides
Bismuthines
– special s.
triarylbimuthines
Bismuth(III) nitrate/montmorillonite
41, 261s68
–(III) –/phosphotungstic acid 39, 171s68
–(III) –/silica 39, 171s68
Bismuthonium salts
– special s.
triaryl(vinyl)bismuthonium salts
Bismuth oxide chloride 16, 827s68;
25, 396s68; 68, 110
– – –/polyaniline 55, 337s68
–(V) 3-phosphonioenolates
– as intermediates 68, 449
– trichloride 7, 777s68; 49, 8s68;
57, 207s68
–, generation *in situ* 68, 110
–(III) triflate 2, 621s68; 4, 729s68;
8, 165s68; 38, 759s68; 49, 254s68;
52, 363s68; 60, 341s68; 61, 427s68;
65, 334s68; 67, 159s68; 68, 220
Bis[(1S,2R)-2-(1-naphthyl)cyclohexyl]
dichloromalonate
– as reagent 68, 217
Bis(Δ²-oxazolines), chiral
– as reagent 23, 819s68; 29, 787s68;
47, 646s68; 60, 247s68; 64, 244s68;
68, 150, 186, 208, 262, 266, 398, 441
Bis(π-allylpalladium) complexes
–, allylation via –, review 27, 851s68
Bis(phosphine oxides)
– special s.
2,2′-bis(diarylphosphino)-1,1′-bi-
naphthyl dioxides
1,2-Bis(phosphine oxides)
– special s.
1-methylene-1,2-bis(phosphine oxides)
Bis(pinacolato)diboron
– as reactant 68, 242
Bis(pyridine)iodine(I) fluoroborate
– as reagent 68, 211
(1S,2S)-N,N′-Bis(2-pyridylmethylene)-
1,2-diphenylethylenediamine
– as reagent 66, 280s68
1,4-Bis(9-O-quinine)phthalazinium
bromide, N-benzyl-
– as reagent 64, 81s68
Bis(Δ²-thiazolines)
– as reagent 23, 819s68
Bis(trichloromethyl) carbonate
– as reagent 33, 491s68; 51, 133s68;
67, 207s68, 224s68 (review)
(R,R)-N-[3,5-Bis(trifluoromethyl)-
phenyl]-N′-[2-(dimethylamino)cyclo-
hexyl]thiourea
– as reagent 68, 303, 304
Bis(2,4,6-triisopropylphenyl) telluroxide
– as reagent 37, 86s68
N,O-Bis(trimethylsilyl)acetamide
– as reagent 68, 376
Bis(triphenylphosphoranylidene)iminium
chloride
– as reagent 62, 306s68
Blaise reaction, intramolecular (s.a.
1,4-Addition-intramolecular Blaise
reaction)
Borane-amine complexes
–, cleavage 20, 71s68
–, protection of dinucleoside
H-phosphonates as – 20, 71s68
Borane-α-picoline 68, 162
Borane-tetrahydrofuran 68, 20, 43
Borane-triethylamine 10, 50s68
Boranes (s.a. Hydroboration)
Boranes, cyclic
– special s.
aminoboranes, cyclic
Boranes, sec.
– special s.
dicyclohexylborane

Boranes, tert.
– special s.
  triarylboranes
  triethylborane
  tris(pentafluorophenyl)borane
Boranes, unsatd.
–, Diels-Alder reaction with –, review **34**, 693s68
Borates, organo-
– special s.
  potassium organo(trifluoro)borates
Borates, organo(trifluoro)-
–, review **67**, 222s68
Boric acid
– as reagent **39**, 157s68
Boric acid aryl esters
– startg. m. f.
  syn-2-aminoethers, ar., N-protected **68**, 114
  glycol monoaryl ethers, unsatd. **68**, 114
Borinic acid esters
– special s.
  B-cyclohexyloxydiisopinocampheylborane
  enol borinates
– – –, cyclic
– special s.
  9-oxa-10-borabicyclo[3.3.2]decanes, B-alkyl-
Boron enolates s. Enoxyboranes
Boron bromide 68, 366
Boron chloride 19, 471s68; **68**, 247, 366
Boron fluoride 24, 582s68; **28**, 641s68; **40**, 493s68; **66**, 52s68; **68**, 163, 188, 296, 297, 350, 442, 443
Boronic acid esters (s.a. 1,2-Diboration, 1,2-Silylboration)
– special s.
  arylboronic acid esters
  di(boronic – –)
  ethyleneboronic – –
  hydrazonoboronic – –
  indolylboronic – –
  silylboronic – –
– startg. m. f.
  2(5*H*)-furanones, synthesis **68**, 463
Boronic acids (s.a. under Suzuki)
– special s.
  arylboronic acids
  ethyleneboronic acids
– – –, polymer-based
– special s.
  phenylboronic acid, polymer-based
Boroxa... s.a. Oxabora...
10,9-Boroxarophenanthrenes, 10-hydroxy-
– as intermediates **68**, 247
Boroxine, 4-(trifluoromethyl)phenyl-
– as reagent **49**, 898s68
Boroxines
– special s.
  arylboroxines
  α,β-ethyleneboroxines
Bridgehead alcohols, siloxy-tethered 41, 946s68
– **halides** s.a. Cyclimmonium salts, bridgehead-bromo-
Bromamine-T
– as reagent **55**, 159s68; **63**, 55s68
Bromate ion s. Tetraalkylammonium bromate, Tetrapropylammonium –
Bromination, benzylic 68, 215s68

Bromine (s.a. Hexamethylenetetraminebromine) **56**, 223s68
2-Bromoallyltrimethylsilane
– as reactant **68**, 430
Bromobenzene
– as reagent **68**, 131
N-Bromobis(*p*-toluenesulfonyl)amine
– as reagent **62**, 102s68
Bromodimethylsulfonium bromide
– as reagent **46**, 162s68
(E)-1-Bromo-2-iodoethylene
– as reactant **68**, 294
N-Bromosuccinimide
– as reagent **43**, 625s68; **55**, 337s68; **57**, 120s68; **65**, 197s68; **68**, 69, 203, 206
Bronsted acids, chiral
– special s.
  phosphoric acid monoesters, cyclic, chiral
Bronsted-type bases, heterogeneous
–, ionic liquids, supported as – **68**, 359
Brook rearrangement
–, 3-component synthesis of 2-ethylenealcohols via – **68**, 430
***tert*-Butoxyformic anhydride**
– as reactant **68**, 168
N-(*tert*-Butyl)acoxylamines
–, α-acoxylation with – **68**, 105
4-*tert*-Butyl-1,2-bis(diphenylphosphino)-1′-(diisopropylphosphino)ferrocene
– as reagent **68**, 417
***n*-Butyl(dimethyl)amine**
– as reagent **68**, 494
***trans*-3-(*tert*-Butyldimethylsilyl)-2,3-epoxypropyl *p*-tolyl sulfone, metalated**
– as acrolein β-carbanion equivalent **68**, 432
***tert*-Butyl hydroperoxide**
– as reagent **68**, 90, 91
***tert*-Butyl isocyanide**
– as reagent **68**, 425
***tert*-Butyl methyl ether**
– as reagent **62**, 429s68
***tert*-Butyl nitrite**
– as reagent **68**, 104
2-(4(S)-*tert*-Butyl-Δ²-oxazolin-2-yl)-ferrocene, 1-[diphenyl(hydroxy)methyl]-
– as reagent **68**, 438
2-*tert*-Butylthioethylamine
– as reagent **68**, 25
***n*-Butyltriphenylphosphonium dichromate**
– as reagent **68**, 113

Cadmium acetate 68, 205
Calcium chloride 60, 194s68
Calcium complexes
  (β-diketiminato)calcium bis(trimethylsilyl)amide complexes **68**, 156
– **hypochlorite 19**, 356s68
– **oxide 56**, 137s68
Calixarenes
– special s.

homooxacalixarenes
–, synthesis with –, review **42**, 853s68
Camphorsulfonic acid
– as reagent **68**, 112
CAN s. Ammonium cerium(IV) nitrate
Cannizzaro reaction 68, 149
Carbalkoxyamines s. N-Carbalkoxylation, O-Carbamyl..., Carbobenzoxyamines, Carbo-*tert*-butoxyamines, Carbopropargyloxyamines, N-Decarbalkoxylation, Urethans
α-(Carbalkoxyamino)-α,β-ethylenecarboxylic acid esters
– by Horner synthesis **39**, 854s68
α-(Carbalkoxyamino)-γ-ketophosphonic acid esters, cyclic 63, 427s68
β-(Carbalkoxyamino)-α-methylenecarboxylic acid esters 67, 187s68
α-(Carbalkoxyamino)nitriles
– from
  1,1-sulfonylurethans **60**, 408s68
N-Carbalkoxyguanidines
– special s.
  N-aryl-N″-carbalkoxyguanidines
N-Carbalkoxyhydrazones
–, N-alkylation **33**, 412s68
γ-(N-Carbalkoxyimino)-α-hydroxycarboxylic acid esters, chiral
– as intermediates **68**, 253
N-Carbalkoxylation
– special s.
  N-carbo-*tert*-butoxylation
N-Carbalkoxythioureas
– from
  halogenoformic acid esters **22**, 470s68
Carbamic acid esters s. Carbalkoxyamin..., Urethans
1,4-O-Carbamyl group migration 68, 251
Carbamylsilanes
– special s.
  trimethyl(N,N-dimethylcarbamyl)silane
Carbazic acid esters
– special s.
  N-arylcarbazic acid esters
Carbazole alkaloids
–, synthesis, review **42**, 853s68
Carbazole ring, 1-hydroxy- 37, 319s68
Carbazoles
– from
  o-silyltriflates and *o*-iodoamines **68**, 464
–, polycyclic **68**, 493
Carbene catalysis, nucleophilic
–, acylation under – **68**, 109
–, γ-lactones from α,β-ethylenealdehydes under – **68**, 301
–, Stetter reaction under – **68**, 335
Carbene complexes (s.a. Fischer carbene complexes)
– –, N-heterocyclic
–, stability and reactivity, review **27**, 851s68
Carbenes
–, reactions with nitrogen compds., review **67**, 386s68
–, N-heterocyclic, chelate and pincertype
– in catalysis, homogeneous, review **27**, 851s68
Carbenoids
– startg. m. f.

azomethinium ylids, review **42**, 853s68
**(Carbethoxymethylene)triphenyl-
phosphorane**
– as reactant **68**, 433
Carboamination, Zr-catalyzed 68, 307
Carbobenzoxyamines
– from
  trichloroacetylamines **68**, 15
Carbo-*tert*-butoxyamines
– from
  trichloroacetylamines **68**, 15
**N-Carbo-*tert*-butoxylation, selective
68**, 168
**N-Carbo-*tert*-butoxy-2-(trimethylsilyl)-
ethanesulfonamide**
– as reactant **68**, 142
**Carbocyclization, hydrogenative,
stereospecific 68**, 320
**Carbohydrate O^4,O^6-benzylidene
derivs.**
–, ring opening, Lewis acid-catalyzed,
  regiospecific **68**, 20
Carbohydrate chemistry
–, overview of advances **41**, 173s68
– O,O-*p*-methoxybenzylidene derivs.
–, ring opening, reductive, regiospecific
  39, 33s68
– Δ^2-oxazolines **68**, 135
Carbohydrates
– as ligand, review **27**, 57s68
– special s.
  aldonolactones
  aldoses
  aminosugars
  azasugars
  disaccharides
  2-ethylenestannanes, carbohydrate-
    derived
  glycals
  glycos...
  oligosaccharides
  selenoglycosides
  thioglycosides
–, synthesis, enzymatic, review
  41, 173s68
–, **fluorinated and fluoroalkylated**
–, review **16**, 180s68
–, **phosphorus-containing**
– as ligand, review **27**, 57s68
Carbometalation
– special s.
  carbopalladation
Carbon, activated 25, 649s68; **68**, 86
Carbon dioxide
– as promoter **42**, 676s68
–, reactions, transition metal-catalyzed,
  review **27**, 851s68
– startg. m. f.
  2-oxazolidones **23**, 139s68; **68**, 147
  urethans, N-subst. **68**, 158
Carbon dioxide, supercritical
–, cycloaddition, 1,3-dipolar,
  regiospecific of nitrile oxides in –
  68, 282
–, quinazoline-2,4-diones from *o*-amino-
  nitriles in – **24**, 601s68
Carbonic acid aryl esters
– from
  trityl alcohols **68**, 120
Carbonic acid esters
– as green reactants, review **65**, 88s68
– special s.

bis(trichloromethyl) carbonate
carbonic acid diaryl esters
dimethyl carbonate
di-2-thienyl carbonate
2-ene-1,4-diol monocarbonates
enol carbonates
– – imides s. Imidodicarbonates
Carbonium ions and salts
– special s.
  allyl cations
  1,8-bis(diphenylmethylium)-
    naphthalenediyl bis(perchlorate)
Carbon monoxide
– startg. m. f.
  1,3-oxathiolan-2-ones **68**, 218
– –/selenium **68**, 182
Carbon monoxide equivalent
–, formaldehyde as – **68**, 325
–, imidazol-1-ylacetonitrile, 4,5-dichloro-
  as – **68**, 390
–, malononitrile as – **68**, 390
Carbon monoxide source
–, molybdenum hexacarbonyl as –
  34, 832s68
Carbon tetrachloride (s.a. Triphenyl-
  phosphine/carbon tetrachloride)
Carbonylation (s.a. 1,4-Addition,
  carbonylative, Cyclocarbonylation,
  Ring closure, carbonylative, Ring
  expansion, –)
–, 3,4-benzocoumarins via – **68**, 247
–, **Pd-catalyzed**
– of alcohols, review **27**, 851s68
–, **oxidative**
–, benzolactams via – **68**, 356
–, phthalimidines via – **68**, 356
–, **polymer-based 40**, 521s68
Carbonyl compds. (s.a. Aldehydes,
  Carboxylic acid..., Ketones, Oxo
  compds.)
– special s.
  diazocarbonyl compds.
  ethylenecarbonyl compds.
  halogenocarbonyl compds.
  ketocarbonyl compds.
– startg. m. f.
  ethylene derivs., review **42**, 725s68
  S-heterocyclics via thionation, review
    42, 853s68
N,N'-Carbonyldiimidazole
– as reagent **26**, 417s68
Carbonyl-ene reaction, asym.
– with enolethers **68**, 477
– – –, **intramolecular** (s.a. Diels-Alder
  reaction-intramolecular carbonyl-ene
  reaction)
Carbopalladation (s.a. α-Amination,
  asym.-carbopalladation)
–, δ-aryl-γ,δ-ethylenealdehydes, cyclic
  via – **68**, 418
–, **intramolecular-reductive alkylation
  68**, 418
–, **intramolecular-Sonogashira coupling-
  intramolecular Diels-Alder reaction
  68**, 419
–, **intramolecular-Suzuki coupling,
  regiospecific 68**, 475
–, **intramolecular-Wittig synthesis
  68**, 418
**Carbopalladation-Stille coupling
67**, 255s68

Carbopropargyloxyamines
– as intermediates **23**, 479s68
Carbostyril-1-acetic acid amides
– from
  o-aminoketones, 4-component synthesis
    68, 357
Carbostyrils
– from
  o-halogenocarbonyl compds. and
    acetamides **68**, 413
–, **3,4-fused**
– from
  halides, ar. and *o*-halogenocarboxylic
    acid amides **68**, 410
–, **4-hydroxy-**
– from
  o-aminocarboxylic acids and
    carboxylic acid esters **47**, 793s68
Carboxylation, Pd-catalyzed
– of alcohols, review **27**, 851s68
Carboxylic acid allyl esters (s.a. Acoxy-
  2-ethylenes)
–, cleavage under microwaves **16**, 201s68
Carboxylic acid amide enolates
–, Michael addition of – **36**, 652s68
Carboxylic acid amides (s.a.
  Acylamines)
–, N-alkoxymethylation **68**, 172
–, N-arylation **62**, 171s68
– from
  aldehydes **68**, 149
  carboxylic acids **32**, 148s68
– special s.
  acetamides
  acoxycarboxylic acid amides
  acylaminocarboxylic – –
  N-alkylcarboxylic – –
  aminocarboxylic – –
  arylcarboxylic – –
  ω-arylcarboxylic – –
  carboxylic acid anilides
  deuteriocarboxylic acid amides
  ethylenecarboxylic – –
  formamides
  halogenocarboxylic acid amides
  heteroarylcarboxylic – –
  hydroxycarboxylic – –
  ketocarboxylic – –
  phosphonylcarboxylic – –
  N-silylcarboxylic – –
  sulfonylaminocarboxylic – –
–, synthesis by C-N bond formation,
  review **55**, 159s68
– – –, **N-subst.**
– startg. m. f.
  N-acylcarboxylic acid amides **68**, 88
– – –, **N-unsubst.**
– startg. m. f.
  amines, prim. **27**, 65s68
  carboxylic acid anilides **68**, 182
  furans **68**, 448
  nitriles **4**, 457s68; **68**, 200
  oxazoles **68**, 175
Carboxylic acid anhydrides
– special s.
  arylcarboxylic acid anhydrides
– startg. m. f.
  aldehydes **68**, 134
Carboxylic acid anilides
– from
  nitro compds., ar. and carboxylic acid
    amides, N-unsubst. **68**, 182

(Carboxylic acid anilides
- from)
  nitro compds., ar. and carboxylic acid esters **68,** 165
- special s.
  formanilides
Carboxylic acid azides
- special s.
  ethylenecarboxylic acid azides
  nicotinoyl azide
Carboxylic acid benzyl esters
-, cleavage, selective and preferential **16,** 201s68
Carboxylic acid derivs. (s.a. Carbonyl compds.)
- special s.
  ethylenecarboxylic acid derivs.
  halogenocarboxylic – –
  hydroxycarboxylic – –
Carboxylic acid esters (s.a. Acoxy..., O-Acylation, Carbalkoxy...)
- from
  alcohols, prim. (2 molecules) **44,** 149s68
  aldehydes **68,** 85
  carboxylic acids (with alcohols) **7,** 246s68 (in ionic liquids); **39,** 162s68; **61,** 85s68 (in fluorous media)
  – – (with oxo compds.) **68,** 94
  α,β-ethylenecarboxylic acid esters, asym. reduction **68,** 33
- special s.
  acetylenecarboxylic acid esters
  acylaminocarboxylic – –
  (alkylideneamino)carboxylic – –
  aminocarboxylic – –
  carboxylic acid allyl esters
  – – benzyl –
  – – ethyl –
  – – 2-pyridyl or 2-pyridylmethyl –
  – – 2,2,2-trifluoroethyl –
  cyanocarboxylic acid esters
  diazocarboxylic – –
  dicarboxylic – –
  ethylenecarboxylic – –
  halogenocarboxylic – –
  hydroxycarboxylic – –.
  iminocarboxylic – –
  isocyanocarboxylic – –
  ketocarboxylic – –
  phosphonylcarboxylic – –
  sulfonylaminocarboxylic – –
- startg. m. f.
  acetylene derivs., terminal **36,** 864s**68**
  acylamines **48,** 346s**68**
  alcohols, prim. **27,** 65s**68; 68,** 44
  carboxylic acid anilides **68,** 165
  – acids, selective and preferential cleavage **68,** 7
  nitriles, gas-phase conversion **35,** 348s**68**
Carboxylic acid ethyl esters
- from
  carboxylic acids **68,** 104
Carboxylic acid halides
- special s.
  acetyl chloride
- startg. m. f.
  alcohols, prim. **27,** 65s**68**
  aldehydes **68,** 134
  α-arylketones **68,** 407

benzimidazoles **68,** 188
3,1,5-benzoxadiazepines (from 2 molecules) **68,** 188
α-ketocarboxylic acid amides, with 1 extra C-atom **68,** 428
thiolic acid aryl esters **53,** 230s**68**
Carboxylic acid 2-pyridyl or 2-pyridylmethyl esters
- startg. m. f.
  aryl ketones **68,** 465
Carboxylic acids (s.a. Decarboxylation)
- from
  alcohols, prim. **66,** 100s**68**
  carboxylic acid esters, selective and preferential cleavage **68,** 7
  9-oxa-10-borabicyclo[3.3.2]decanes, B-alkyl-, with 1 extra C-atom **39,** 844s**68**
  2-oxazolidones, 3-acyl- **68,** 7
- special s.
  allenecarboxylic acids
  aminocarboxylic acids
  arylcarboxylic acids
  aryloxycarboxylic acids
  ethylenecarboxylic acids
  halogenocarboxylic acids
  mercaptocarboxylic acids
- startg. m. f.
  β-acoxycarboxylic acid amides **68,** 275
  β-acylaminocarboxylic acid amides **68,** 275
  carboxylic acid amides **32,** 148s**68**
  – – esters (with alcohols) **7,** 246s**68** (in ionic liquids); **39,** 162s**68; 61,** 85s**68** (in fluorous media)
  – – – (with oxo compds.) **68,** 94
  – – ethyl esters **68,** 104
  ketones, decarboxylative syntheses, review **13,** 837s**68**
  thiolic acid esters **39,** 162s**68**
Carboxylic acid silyl esters
- special s.
  dicarboxylic acid amide silyl esters
Carboxylic acid thioamides
- startg. m. f.
  2-acetyleneamines, 1,1-disubst., 3-component synthesis **68,** 423
Carboxylic acid 2,2,2-trifluoroethyl esters 68, 89
Catalysis
- by sol-gels, review **27,** 851s**68**
- special s.
  carbene catalysis
Catalysis, asym. (s.a. Fluorous catalysis, asym.)
-, overview **27,** 57s**68**
- with (as ligand)
  carbohydrate derivs., review **27,** 57s**68**
  carbohydrates, phosphorus-containing, review **27,** 57s**68**
  ferrocenylphosphines, review **27,** 57s**68**
  1,3,2-oxazaborolidines, review **27,** 57s**68**
  phosphorous acid esters, cyclic, review **27,** 57s**68**
  tris(Δ²-oxazolines), review **27,** 57s**68**
- with metal salen complexes, review **27,** 57s**68**
-, -, cooperative
- with Lewis acid-Lewis base combinations, review **27,** 57s**68**

-, -, organo-
-, review **27,** 57s**68**
-, heterogeneous
- with mesoporous silica as support, review **65,** 447s**68**
-, metallodendritic
-, review **27,** 851s**68**
Catalysis, tandem 68, 175, 481, 490
Catalysts, commercial
-, review **27,** 851s**68**
-, supported non-covalently
-, review **27,** 851s**68**
Cerium(IV) ammonium nitrate s. Ammonium cerium(IV) nitrate
Cerium(III) chloride 36, 266s**68; 66,** 155s**68; 68,** 164
–**(III)** –/sodium iodide **50,** 471s**68; 54,** 307s**68**
–**(III)** sulfate **49,** 763s**68**
–**(III)** triflate **58,** 7s**68**
–**(IV)** triflate **33,** 593s**68; 36,** 266s**68**
Cesium acetate 62, 171s**68**
Cesium carbonate 43, 187s**68; 68,** 336, 396
– fluoride **44,** 577s**68; 65,** 253s**68; 68,** 464
– hydroxide **17,** 490s**68; 68,** 299
– pivalate **68,** 493
Chalcones
- special s.
  o′-allyloxychalcones
Chloramine-T
- as reagent **44,** 301s**68; 68,** 189
Chlorides, ar. s. Halides, ar.
Chlorination, ar. 44, 420s**68**
N-Chlorination
- of amines **68,** 139
Chlorochromate ion s. Chromate, chloro-
Chlorodiphenylphosphine
- as reagent **27,** 782s**68**
Chloromethylation, ar., catalyzed
- in a 2-phase medium **68,** 367
m-**Chloroperoxybenzoic acid**
- as reagent **68,** 134
2-Chloropyridine methiodide
- as reagent **4,** 457s**68; 57,** 315s**68**
2-Chloropyridinium salts, polymer-based
- as reagent **32,** 148s**68; 48,** 367s**68**
N-Chlorosuccinimide
- as reagent **68,** 208
Choline chloride
- as reagent **68,** 359
3-Chromanols
- from
  3-aryloxyepoxides, with inversion of configuration **68,** 345
Chromans, 3-iodo-
- from
  allyl phenolethers **68,** 211
Chromate s.a. Dichromate
-, chloro- s. 2,2′-Dipyridinium chlorochromate, γ-Picolinium –, Pyridinium –
-, fluoro- s. Hexamethylenetetrammonium fluorochromate, Quinolinium –
Chromium(III) acetate hydroxide 68, 18
Chromium(II) chloride/lithium iodide 68, 487
Chromium complexes

[1,1'-binaphthyl-2,2'-diyl-bis(7-*tert*-butyl-8-N,N'-bis(3,5-di-*tert*-butylsalicylidenato)-1,2-cyclohexanediamine]chromium(III) chloride **68**, 147
cyclooctenechromium pentacarbonyl **68**, 385
5,10,15,20-tetraphenylporphyrinatochromium(III) triflate **68**, 346
–, reactions, oxyanion-driven, selective with –, review **27**, 851s68
– – –, chiral
[1,1'-binaphthyl-2,2'-diylbis(7-*tert*-butyl-8-quinolinolato)]chromium(III) chloride, chiral **68**, 261
[(R,R)- or (S,S)-bis(3,5-di-*tert*-butylsalicylidenato)-1,2-cyclohexanediamine]chromium(III) chloride **68**, 141, 452
– α,β-ethylene(alkoxy)carbene complexes
– startg. m. f.
cycloheptanones, 3,4-di(alkylidene)- **59**, 411s68
cyclopentenes, 1-alkoxy-5-methylene-, asym. conversion **68**, 456
Chromium trioxide
– as catalyst **68**, 88
– – –/zeolite **39**, 231s68; **41**, 261s68
4-Chromones
–, phototransformations, review **42**, 853s68
– special s.
flavones
–, 3-heterocyclyl-
–, review **42**, 853s68
–, phosphorus-containing
–, review **42**, 853s68
Cinchonan, (3R,4S,8R,9S)-10,11-dihydro-, 3,9-epoxy-6'-hydroxy-
– as reagent **68**, 143
Cinchonidinium bromide, N-(9-anthracenylmethyl)-
– as reagent **68**, 283
– **salts, clay-supported**
– as reagent **54**, 394s68
– –, polymer-based
– as reagent **28**, 795s68
(Z)-**Cinnamonitriles, tetrasubst.**
– from
acetylene derivs. and ar. nitriles **68**, 316
Claisen rearrangement (s.a. Aza-Claisen rearrangement)
– –, asym., decarboxylative **68**, 499
– –, Au(I)-catalyzed
– of vinyloxy-2-acetylenes, asym. induction **68**, 343
Claisen-type condensation, reductive, Lewis acid-mediated
– of α-halogenothiolic acid esters **68**, 426
Cobalt(II) acetoacetonate 12, 867s68
Cobalt(II) chloride 68, 99
Cobalt complexes
diiodobis(triphenylphosphine)cobalt(II) **33**, 658s68; **63**, 304s68
5,10,15,20-tetrakis(4-hydroxyphenyl)porphyrinatocobalt(II) **59**, 203s68
Cobalt complexes, chiral
[(R,R)-N,N'-bis(3,5-di-*tert*-butylsalicylidenato)-1,2-cyclohexanediamine]cobalt(II) **68**, 141

[(S,S)-N,N'-bis(3,5-di-*tert*-butylsalicylidenato)-1,2-cyclohexanediamine]cobalt(III) acetate **68**, 142
[(R,R)-N,N'-bis(3,5-di-*tert*-butylsalicylidenato)-1,2-cyclohexanediamine]cobalt(III) chloride **23**, 139s68
bis(β-ketoiminato)cobalt(III) complexes, cationic, chiral **56**, 294s68
(S,S)-N,N'-[1,2-bis(3,5-xylyl)-ethylene]bis[3-oxo-2-(2,4,6-trimethylbenzoyl)butaniminato]cobalt(II) **68**, 263
(1,5-cyclooctadiene)(1-neomenthylindenyl)cobalt(I) **68**, 314
Cobaltotungstate s. Potassium cobaltotungstate
Cobalt(II) salen complexes, chiral 68, 263
2,4,6-Collidine
– as reagent **46**, 40s68; **68**, 260
Combinatorial libraries s.a. under Libraries
Combinatorial and parallel synthesis
– in drug discovery, review **50**, 555s68
3-Component Mannich reaction, asym., organocatalyzed 68, 370
– – – –, transition metal-catalyzed, stereospecific **68**, 361
– **Mannich-type reaction**
– of hydrazones **68**, 364
– via azomethinium salts, asym. induction **68**, 440
3-Component synthesis (s.a. Multicomponent..., Passerini..., Ugi...)
– of
2-acetyleneamines, 1,1-disubst. **68**, 423
α-acylaminoketenimines **59**, 279s68
α-alkoxy-β-aminocarboxylic acid esters **60**, 252s68
α-aryl-α-arylamino-β-hydroxy-carboxylic acid esters **68**, 387
(E)-4-aryl-3-ethyleneaIcohols **68**, 470
azocines, 4,5-dihydro-, 3-amino- **68**, 378
3-ethyleneamines, N-protected **63**, 449s68
furans, 2-amino- **68**, 300
δ-hydrazonoboronic acid esters **68**, 284
α-iminoiminoesters **68**, 416
phosphines, tert. **68**, 239
2-pyridone ring **33**, 753s68
4(3H)-pyrimidinones, 1,2-dihydro-, N-condensed **68**, 281
pyrrole-3,4-dicarboxylic acid esters, 2-amino-5-imido-, N-subst. **68**, 280
4-quinazolones, 2,3-disubst. **68**, 173
–, review **67**, 365s68
3-Component synthesis, asym.
– of
propargylamines **68**, 435
pyrazolidine-1,2-dicarboxylic acid esters, 3-vinyl- **68**, 398
3-Component synthesis, phase transfer-catalyzed
– of pyridines, 1,4-dihydro- **68**, 368
4-Component synthesis (s.a. Ugi...)
– of
pyrid[3,4-b]indoles, 1,2,3,4-tetrahydro-, N-condensed **68**, 420

thiazole-4-carboxylic acid esters, 2-α-acylamino- **68**, 403
– –, ionic liquid-catalyzed, solventless
– of pyridines, 1,4-dihydro- **68**, 368
Copper 68, 184
Copper-bronze 46, 186s68
Copper(II) acetate 62, 18s68; **68**, 29, 232, 356
Copper(II) acetoacetonate 55, 159s68
–(I) alkoxides
–, O-allylation, asym., Ir-catalyzed, regiospecific **68**, 93
Copper are complexes, organo- s. Cuprates, organo-
–(II) bis(Δ²-oxazoline) complexes, chiral **55**, 434s68
–(II) – –, polymer-based, chiral **56**, 242s68
–(II) – –, silica-supported, chiral **46**, 662s68
–(II) carboxylates, polymer-based **68**, 193
Copper catalysis
– of cross-coupling, review **29**, 746s68
Copper complexes
bis(triphenylphosphine)(1,10-phenanthroline)copper(I) nitrate **68**, 230
tetrakis(acetonitrile)copper(I) hexafluorophosphate **47**, 337s68
– perchlorate **68**, 253
–(II) α-di(azomethine) complexes, chiral **54**, 296s68
–(I) (Z)-enolates
– as intermediates **68**, 374
Copper(II)-exchanged hydroxyapatite 63, 356s68
Copper(II) fluoroborate 55, 452s68
–(I) halides
–(I) bromide **26**, 852s68; **33**, 874s68; **68**, 435
–(I) –/dimethyl sulfide **68**, 291, 407
–(I) chloride **29**, 476s68; **42**, 127s68; **43**, 847s68; **68**, 249, 284, 399, 420
–(I) –/kieselgel **4**, 254s68
–(I) iodide **23**, 693s68; **27**, 851s68; **43**, 847s68; **44**, 577s68; **45**, 555s68; **53**, 230s68; **62**, 39s68; **63**, 80s68; **68**, 181, 187, 233, 374, 417, 419, 469
–(II) halides
–(II) bromide **68**, 207
–(II) chloride **42**, 676s68; **68**, 122, 207, 363
–(II) –/copper(II) sulfate **55**, 337s68
–(II) –/lithium chloride **55**, 337s68
–(II) fluoride **66**, 34s68; **68**, 436
–(II) hexafluoroacetonate **68**, 380
–(I) hydride complexes
triphenylphosphinecopper(I) hydride hexamer **58**, 32s68; **68**, 287
–(I) imidazol-2-ylidene complexes
[N,N'-bis(2,6-diisopropylphenyl)-imidazol-2-ylidene]copper(I) chloride **68**, 382
–(I) oxide **53**, 230s68
–(II) sulfate **56**, 73s68; **68**, 184
–(I) triflate **49**, 610s68; **55**, 159s68; **68**, 204
–(II) triflate **60**, 379s68; **62**, 159s68; **68**, 20, 150, 186, 208, 266, 292, 363, 381, 398
–(II) trifluoroacetoacetonate **62**, 189s68

Coumarins
- from
  α,β-acetylenecarboxylic acids 54, 367s68
-, 4-alk-1-ynyl- 64, 449s68
-, phosphorus-containing
-, review 42, 853s68
Coupling, sequential, Pd-catalyzed
- with ar. halides 68, 414
Criegee rearrangement, consecutive 68, 120
Cross-coupling, Cu-catalyzed
-, review 29, 746s68
-, Fe-catalyzed
-, review 27, 851s68
-, Pd-catalyzed
- in aq. medium, review 27, 851s68
- in total synthesis, review 27, 851s68
- with ar. halides, review 27, 851s68
Cross-coupling, intramolecular, Pd-catalyzed, stereospecific
- of ar. iodides with acoxy-2-ethylenes 68, 494
Cross-metathesis (s.a. Metathesis, Ring opening metathesis-cross-metathesis)
- of acetylene derivs. 30, 467s68
Cucurbit[n]urils
-, review 42, 853s68
Cumene hydroperoxide
- as reagent 52, 68s68; 68, 444
Cuprates, organo-
- special s.
  lithium cuprates, organo-
Cyanamides
-, review 32, 279s68
Cyanides s. Acylcyanides, Nitriles
Cyanoacetylation, ar. 7, 798s68
N-Cyanoacetylation 7, 798s68
α-Cyanocarboxylic acid esters
-, α-amination, asym. 68, 143
Cyanohydrins
- from
  aldehydes, asym. conversion 68, 256
  ketones, review 54, 266s68
- startg. m. f.
  2-oxazolidones, 3-alkoxy-4-imino- 68, 157
α-Cyanoketones, cyclic
-, ring contraction by decarbonylation 30, 691s68
Cyanosemicarbazides
- special s.
  N^1-acyl-N^2-α-cyanosemicarbazides
Cyanuric chloride
- as reagent 5, 549s68; 22, 826s68
Cyclimmonium salts, bridgehead-bromo-
-, Sonogashira coupling with – 27, 851s68
Cycloaddition, 1,3-dipolar
- with nitrilimines, in situ-generated 58, 314s68
-, -, asym., Mg-catalyzed 47, 640s68
-, -, intramolecular
- with azomethinium ylids, review 42, 853s68
-, -, dehydrogenative
- with sulfonylhydrazones 34, 909s68
-, -, regiospecific
- with
  azides, in situ-generated 68, 184
  nitrile oxides in supercritical CO_2 68, 282

-, -, regiostereospecific
- with carbonyl ylids 68, 388
-, -, exo-specific
-, -, Δ^1-pyrroline-5-carboxylic acid esters via – 68, 288
-, -, solid-supported
- with nitrones, review 42, 853s68
[2+2]-Cycloaddition, stereospecific
- with siloxyacetylenes 68, 289
-, asym., Fe(II)-catalyzed 68, 313
-, polymer-based 22, 705s68
-, solid-state, regiospecific
- with diaryl ketones 19, 764s68
[3+2]-Cycloaddition, asym.
-, pyrazolidines, 1-acyl- by – 68, 306
-, Rh-catalyzed, regiostereospecific 68, 456
-, intramolecular, Ru-carbene-catalyzed
- with alkylidenecyclopropanes 68, 352
[3+3]-Cycloaddition
-, alkaloids by –, review 42, 853s68
[4+3]-Cycloaddition, intramolecular, Lewis acid-catalyzed
- with aziridines, 2-alkylidene- 68, 350
[2+2+2]-Cycloaddition, asym., Co(I)-catalyzed
-, pyridines, 2-aryl-, atropoisomeric by – 68, 314
-, Ni-catalyzed 68, 315
[3+2+2]-Cycloaddition, – 68, 317
[4+2+1]-Cycloaddition, –, regiostereospecific 68, 386
[4+2+2]-Cycloaddition, intramolecular, Rh-catalyzed, regiostereospecific
- of 1,3,n-trien-m-ynes, silyl-tethered 68, 353
Cycloalkenes s. Ethylene derivs., cyclic and under specific rings
Cycloalk-2-enols, 2-acyl- 54, 338
Cyclobuta[a]naphthalenes, 2a,3,4,8b-tetrahydro- 36, 957s68
Cyclobutanols, 1-(1(Z),3-butadienyl)-
- startg. m. f.
  cyclopentanones, 2-(3-arylprop-1(Z)-enyl)- 68, 412
Cyclobutanones
- startg. m. f.
  azocines, 4,5-dihydro-, 3-amino- 68, 378
  benzocyclobutenes 22, 877s68
Cyclobutene, 1,2-diphenyl-3,4-bis[(2,4,6-tri-tert-butylphenyl)phosphinidene]-
- as reagent 68, 187
Cyclobut-2-enecarbonyl compds., 2-siloxy-
- from
  siloxyacetylenes and α,β-ethylene-carbonyl compds. 68, 289
Cyclobutenones
- startg. m. f.
  2-pyrones, 6-vinyl- 68, 323
3-(Cyclobutyl)alcohols
- from
  2H-pyrans, 3,4-dihydro-, synthesis 68, 250
Cyclocarbonylation
-, 2,4-cycloheptadienones via – 68, 324
**(Z)-Cyclodec-5-en-1-ones, 4,4-difluoro-21, 744s68
β-Cyclodextrin (s.a. 2-Aminoalcohols, β-cyclodextrin-anchored)

- as reagent 31, 185s68; 55, 205s68; 57, 120s68; 67, 207s68
Cyclodextrins
-, review 37, 626s68
1,3-Cycloheptadienes, 5-carbalkoxy-methylene-
- from
  cyclopropylideneacetic acid esters and acetylene derivs. 68, 317
1,4-Cycloheptadienes, fused 22, 730s68
- from
  1,3-dien-8-ynes and diazo compds. 68, 386
3,5-Cycloheptaenols, 3-alkoxy- 59, 411s68
2,4-Cycloheptadienones, tricyclic
- from
  enediynes 68, 324
Cycloheptanols, 2-vinyl- 68, 487
Cycloheptanones, 2,4-di(alkylidene)- 59, 411s68
-, 3,4-di(alkylidene)-
- from
  chromium α,β-ethylene(alkoxy)-carbene complexes and allenes (2 molecules) 59, 411s68
Cycloheptene ring, 5-imino- 68, 350
Cycloheptenes, 2-alkoxy-3,5-di(alkylidene)- 68, 456
1,3-Cyclohexadienes
- from
  acetylene derivs., terminal and 1,5-cyclooctadiene 68, 480
-, 2-siloxy- 68, 345
1,4-Cyclohexadienes, 1-siloxy-
- from
  6-siloxy-1,5-enynes 68, 344
2,4-Cyclohexadienones 68, 497
1,2-Cyclohexanediamine, (R,R)-N,N,N',N'-tetramethyl-
- as reagent 50, 379s68
Cyclohexanone-2-carboxylic acid esters, 4-nitro-, chiral 68, 304
Cyclohexanones, 4-nitro-
- from
  α,β-ethyleneketones and 1,1-nitroethylene derivs., asym. synthesis 68, 304
Cyclohex-2-ene-1,4-diones
- startg. m. f.
  p-quinones 10, 225s68
Cyclohexene ring, 1-chloro- 68, 215
2-Cyclohexenone, 3-iodo-2-methyl-
- as reagent 68, 241, 466
2-Cyclohexenones
- from
  dienones, cross-conjugated 68, 333
  6-siloxy-1,5-enynes 68, 496
-, 4-alkylidene-
- startg. m. f.
  p-alkoxybenzyl ethers 68, 89
-, 3-alkylthio-4-nitro-
- from
  β,γ-ethylene-α-ketoketene mercaptals and aliphatic nitro compds. 68, 424
-, 6-sulfonyl- 68, 333
B-Cyclohexyloxydiisopinocampheylborane
- as reagent 68, 22
Cycloisomerization, acid-catalyzed, regiospecific
- of 4-ethylenealcohols 68, 81

–, Au(I)-catalyzed 68, 344
–, –, regiospecific
– of 1,6-enynes 68, 351
–, Pt-catalyzed, regiostereospecific
– of ethylenealcohols 68, 83
–, Ru-catalyzed
– of dienes 68, 339
Cycloisomerization-intramolecular cyclopropanation, stereospecific 68, 337
1,5-Cyclooctadiene
– startg. m. f.
1,3-cyclohexadienes 68, 480
Cycloocta-1,4-diene ring 68, 353
Cyclooctanol ring, 3-methylene- 68, 487
Cyclooctanols, 1,5-oxido- 68, 337
–, 2-vinyl- 68, 487
1,3,5-Cyclooctatrien-3-ols, 4-sulfonyl- 68, 333
Cyclopentadienes, imino-
– from
1,4-diiodo-1,3-dienes and isothiocyanates 44, 621s68
Cyclopentadienylium triflates, sulfoalkyl-
– as ionic liquids 59, 293s68
Cyclopentanes
– special s.
alkylidenecyclopentanes
–, 1,2-di(alkylidene)-
– from
1,2,6-dienynes 68, 330
Cyclopentanols, 2-arylidene-, chiral 68, 457
Cyclopentanones
– from
δ,ε-ethylenecarboxylic acid esters 56, 466s68
–, 2-(3-arylprop-1(Z)-enyl)-
– from
cyclobutanols, 1-(1(Z),3-butadienyl)- and ar. iodides 68, 412
–, 2-vinyl-, fused 67, 330s68
Cyclopenta[b]pyrroles, 1,2,3,3a,6,6a-hexahydro- 68, 389
Cyclopentenes, 1-alkoxy-5-methylene-
– from
chromium α,β-ethylene(alkoxy)carbene complexes and allenes, asym. conversion 68, 456
–, 4-alkylidene-, 2,3-fused
– via [3+2]-cycloaddition, intramolecular 68, 352
–, 1-vinyl- 68, 351
Cyclopent-2-enones s.a. Pauson-Khand reaction
Cyclopent-2-enyl ketones, 2-aryl-4-(silylmethyl)- 68, 308
– –, 4-(silylmethyl)-
– from
cyclopropyl ketones, 2-(silylmethyl)- and terminal acetylene derivs. 68, 308
Cyclopropanation (s.a. Simmons-Smith...)
– with diazo compds., improved procedure 68, 382
–, asym., organocatalyzed
– with ammonium ylids, quaternary, stabilized 68, 396
–, intramolecular (s.a. Cycloisomerization-intramolecular

cyclopropanation)
– of dienynes 68, 351
–, –, asym., organocatalyzed
– of ethylene derivs., electron-deficient 68, 491
– with α-halogenocarbonyl compds. 68, 491
–, intramolecular-ring-closing metathesis 68, 498
Cyclopropanecarboxylic acid amides
– from
glycidic acid amides 65, 399s68
– startg. m. f.
furan-3-carboxylic acid amides, tetrahydro-, asym. induction 68, 298
– – derivs., 2-acyl-
– from
α,β-ethyleneketones and α-halogenocarboxylic acid derivs., asym. conversion 68, 396
– – esters, 1-(α-siloxyvinyl)-, chiral 23, 819s68
Cyclopropane-1,2-dicarboxylic acid esters, cis-1-halogeno-
– via 1,4-addition, double 68, 399
Cyclopropanephosphonic acid esters, chiral 65, 372s68
– – –, 2-aryl-, chiral 23, 819s68
Cyclopropanes
– special s.
alkylidenecyclopropanes
vinylcyclopropanes
Cyclopropenes
–, addition, nucleophilic, catalyzed to –, review 27, 851s68
–, pyrolysis, review 27, 899s68
α-Cyclopropylcarbonyl compds. 49, 953s68
Cyclopropyl difluoromethyl ethers, 2,2-difluoro- 21, 879s68
– fluorides 23, 819s68
Cyclopropylideneacetic acid esters
– startg. m. f.
1,3-cycloheptadienes, 5-carbalkoxymethylene- 68, 317
α-Cyclopropylideneketones
– startg. m. f.
furans, fused 64, 85s68
Cyclopropyl ketones 45, 459s68
– from
2-ketoarsonium salts 29, 872s68
– startg. m. f.
Δ¹-pyrrolines 68, 167
– –, 2-(silylmethyl)-
– startg. m. f.
cyclopent-2-enyl ketones, 4-(silylmethyl)- 68, 308
– –, 2-α-tosyloxy-
– startg. m. f.
γ,δ-ethyleneketones 68, 486
trans-Cyclopropylsilanes 66, 406s68
α-Cyclopropylstyrenes 43, 806s68

Dabco s. Triethylenediamine
O-Deacetylation, partial 54, 79s68
N-Deacylation (s.a. HNⅡC) 68, 17

– special s.
N-detrichloroacetylation
O-Deacylation (s.a. High-pressure O-deacylation and HOⅡC)
– special s.
O-deacetylation
N-Dealkylation (s.a. HNⅡC)
– special s.
N-deallylation
N-debenzylation
N-depropargylation
N-detritylation
–, oxidative
– of sulfonamides, N-alkyl- and N,N-dialkyl- 68, 18
O-Dealkylation (s.a. HOⅡC)
– of ethers, review 38, 1s68
– special s.
O-deallylation
O-debenzylation
O-depropargylation
O-detritylation
N-Deallylation
–, review 32, 11s68
O-Deallylation, Ru-catalyzed 64, 12s68
N-Dearylation
– special s.
N-dephenylation
O-Debenzylation 31, 5s68; 68, 10
O-De-tert-butyldimethylsilylation, preferential 30, 4s68; 68, 2
–, selective 68, 2, 11
O-De-tert-butyldiphenylsilylation 68, 2
Decalin-2,8-diones
– from
2,8-diene-1,7-diones 68, 336
cis-Decalins
–, synthesis, review 44, 602s68
N-Decarbalkoxylation (s.a. HNⅡC)
– special s.
N-decarbobenzoxylation
N-decarbo-tert-butoxylation
O-Decarbalkoxylation
– special s.
O-decarballyloxylation
O-Decarballyloxylation 32, 11s68
N-Decarbobenzoxylation 19, 471s68
N-Decarbo-tert-butoxylation, selective 51, 18s68
Decarbonylation, Pd-catalyzed
– of aldehydes, 68, 49
Decarboxylation, Pd-catalyzed 68, 49
–, oxidative
– nitriles via – 68, 202
Decomplexation, reductive
– of π-allyltricarbonyliron lactone complexes 68, 41
Dehydrogenation s.a. CCⅡH
–, aerobic s.a. Ring closure, dehydrogenative, aerobic
Dendrimers
–, overview of applications 19, 33s68
Dendrimers, amide-type
–, review 19, 33s68
2-Deoxyglycosides
– special s.
2-amino-2-deoxyglycosides
2-Deoxy-β-glycosylphosphonic acid esters
– special s.
2-nitro-2-deoxy-β-glycosylphosphonic acid esters

2-Deoxyselenoglycosides
- special s.
  2-azido-2-deoxyselenoglycosides
N-Dephenylation 13, 80s68
N-Depropargylation
-, review **32**, 11s68
O-Depropargylation, selective and preferential 68, 5
O-Desilylation (s.a. HO↑Rem)
- special s.
  O-de-*tert*-butyldimethylsilylation
  O-de-*tert*-butyldiphenylsilylation
  O-detriethylsilylation
Desymmetrization
-, 2-(arylamino)alcohols from epoxides with – **68**, 141
- by carbene insertion, intramolecular **47**, 955s68
-, glycols from epoxides with – **68**, 59
- of
  1,2-di(sulfonylamines) **68**, 177
  glycols 109
-, Pauson-Khand reaction, intramolecular, Ir-catalyzed of dienynes with – **68**, 332
-, ring opening, nucleophilic of epoxides with – **68**, 58
-, ring-opening metathesis-crossmetathesis with – **68**, 319
N-Detrichloroacetylation 68, 15
N-Detritylation 68, 14
-, heterogeneous **65**, 6s68
O-Detritylation, heterogeneous 65, 6s68
-, selective **68**, 14
Deuteriation
- special s.
  perdeuteriation
α-**Deuteriobenzylalcohols, chiral 68**, 23
Deuteriocarboxylic acid amides
- special s.
  dideuteriocarboxylic acid amides
2-Deuterio-3-ethylenealcohols 58, 238s68
Diacylamines, mixed s. N-Acylcarboxylic acid amides
N¹,N⁴-Diacylthiosemicarbazides
- from
  acylhydrazines **22**, 470s68
Dialdehydes
- startg. m. f.
  α,β-ethylenealdehydes, cyclic **15**, 168s68
N,N-Dialkylation
- of *prim*-aminocarboxylic acids **46**, 317s68
N,N'-Di(alkylidene)-1,2-diamines
- special s.
  N,N'-bis(4-bromobenzylidene)-1,2-cyclohexanediamine
  N,N'-bis(2-pyridylmethylene)-1,2-diphenylethylenediamine
α,α-**Diallylation 48**, 771s68
Diamines, chiral
- as reagent **63**, 427s68
1,2-Diamines
- special s.
  N-sulfonyl-1,2-diamines
-, **chiral 68**, 271
- special s.
  (R,R)-1,2-bis(*o*-hydroxybenzylamino)cyclohexane

pyrrolidine, (S)-1-methyl-2-(1-pyrrolidinylmethyl)-
1,2-Di-*tert*-amines
- from
  2-*tert*-aminoalcohols and sec. amines **68**, 171
1,3-Diamines
- special s.
  tetramethylpropylenediamine
o-**Diamines**
- special s.
  o-phenylenediamine
- startg. m. f.
  benzimidazoles **68**, 174, 188
  1*H*-1,5-benzodiazepines **13**, 896s68
  3,1,5-benzoxadiazepines **68**, 188
  quinoxaline-2,3-diones **21**, 416s68
  quinoxalines, 1,2,3,4-tetrahydro-, 2-vinyl- **46**, 335s68
α,β-**Diaminocarboxylic acids**
-, synthesis, review **19**, 33s68
Diaminodi(phosphines), chiral
- as reagent **46**, 42s68
O,C-Dianions
- special s.
  dilithium 1,3-enyn-1-olates
Diarylalkanes, sym.
- from
  dienes, asym. hydrogenation **68**, 40
Diarylamines 51, 171s68; **65**, 178s68
-, tert. **68**, 187
1,4-Diaryl-1,4-butanediones, sym. 68, 405
Diaryl ethers (s.a. under Ullmann)
Diarylethylenes (s.a. Stilbenes)
Diarylketenes
- startg. m. f.
  nitrogen compds., review **67**, 386s68
Diaryl ketones 68, 465
- from
  aroylcyanides and ar. halides **68**, 476
  potassium aryl(trifluoro)borates and ar. aldehydes **68**, 459
Diarylmethylamines, N-protected s. N-Sulfonyldiarylmethylamines
Diaryls (s.a. Biphenyl.., Suzuki diaryl coupling)
- from
  arylsodium compds. **14**, 852s68
  chlorides, ar. **52**, 467s68; **57**, 438s68
  halides, ar. and arenes **68**, 421
  triethylammonium arylsilicates **52**, 467s68
- special s.
  hydroxydiaryls
-, axially-chiral
-, synthesis, atroposelective, review **27**, 57s68
-, tri- and tetra-*o*-subst. **38**, 836s68
Diaryl sulfides
- startg. m. f.
  heterocyclics, review **42**, 853s68
Diaryl sulfones
- special s.
  o-(dicyclohexylphosphino)diaryl sulfones
- startg. m. f.
  heterocyclics, review **42**, 853s68
3,7-Diazabicyclo[3.3.1]nonane, 3,7-di-*n*-butyl-
- as reagent **33**, 786s68
1,4-Diazabicyclo[2.2.2]octane s.

Triethylenediamine
1,4-Diazabicyclo[2.2.2]octane 1,4-dioxide bis(hydrogen peroxide)
- as reagent **4**, 274s68
1,8-Diazabicyclo[5.4.0]undec-7-ene
- as reagent **19**, 972s68; **27**, 785s68; **34**, 610s68; **41**, 325s68; **46**, 494s68; **66**, 169s68; **68**, 66, 182, 197, 235, 276, 286, 301, 424
7,11-Diazatricyclo[7,3,1,0^{2,7}]tridecanes, chiral
- as reagent **62**, 379s68
Diazene precursor 68, 30
4*H*-1,2-Diazepines
- from
  [thio]pyrylium salts **68**, 159
-, 3,5,7-triaryl- **68**, 159
α-**Diazocarbonyl compds.**
-, pyridine ring expansion with – **68**, 381
α-**Diazocarboxylic acid esters**
- startg. m. f.
  α-aryl-α-arylamino-β-hydroxycarboxylic acid esters **68**, 387
  γ-ketocarboxylic acid esters **68**, 380
Diazo compds.
-, generation from tosylhydrazone salts, review **65**, 369s68
-, – of carbenes from –, review **67**, 386s68
- special s.
  ethylenediazo compds.
  silyldiazo compds.
- startg. m. f.
  1,4-cycloheptadienes, 2,3-fused **68**, 386
  2,4-dienecarbonyl compds., regiostereospecific synthesis **68**, 385
  ketones **47**, 147s68
-, suppression of homocoupling **68**, 382
- –, *in situ*-generated
-, O-alkylation with – **68**, 94
- from
  oxo compds. **68**, 94
α-**Diazoketones**
- special s.
  dimethyl 1-diazo-2-oxopropylphosphonate
Di(azomethines)
- special s.
  N,N'-di(alkylidene)...
Diazomethyltrimethylsilane
- as reactant **23**, 819s68; **68**, 448, 472, 481
α-**Diazo-β-sulfonylaminocarboxylic acid amides**
- from
  N-sulfonylimines, asym. induction with 2 extra C-atoms **68**, 265
11*H*-Dibenz[*b,e*]azepines, 5,6-dihydro- 25, 526s68
5*H*-Dibenzo[*a,c*]cycloheptadienes, 6,7-dihydro- 29, 910s68
Dibenzo[*b,e*][1,4]diazepinones 51, 190s68
Dibenzylammonium trifluoroacetate
- as reagent **68**, 28
N,N-Dibenzylation 41, 325s68
Dibenzyldimethylammonium bromide
- as reagent **65**, 235s68
1,2-Dibenzyl-1,3-enynes
- from
  acetylene derivs., terminal **68**, 469

acetylenestannanes (2 molecules) **68**, 469
benzyl halides (2 molecules) **68**, 469
1,2-Diboration, asym., regiospecific
– of allenes, terminal **68**, 242
1,2-Di(boronic acid esters)
– special s.
   ene-1,2-di(boronic acid esters)
   1-methylene-1,2-di(boronic acid esters)
N,N-Dibromobenzenesulfonamide
– as reagent **22**, 565s68
N,N′-Dibromo-N,N′-propylenebis(p-toluenesulfonamide)
– as reagent **62**, 102s68
Di-*tert*-butyl-1-[(R)-2-[bis(4-trifluoromethylphenyl)phosphino]-ferrocenyl]ethylphosphine
– as reagent **68**, 38
Di-*tert*-butyl hyponitrite
– as reagent **65**, 107s68
2-(Di-*tert*-butylphosphino)biphenyl
– as reagent **68**, 414
2-(Di-*tert*-butylphosphino)-N,N-diethylbenzamide
– as reagent **37**, 902s68
Di-*n*-butyltin methoxide 68, 479
Dicarbonyl compds. s. Dialdehydes, Dicarboxylic..., Diketones, Dioxo compds.
α-Dicarboxylic... s. Malonic...
β-Dicarboxylic... s. Succinic...
γ-Dicarboxylic... s. Glutaric...
Dicarboxylic acid amide silyl esters
– special s.
   N-silyldicarboxylic acid amide silyl esters
Dicarboxylic acid anhydrides
– special s.
   maleic anhydrides
– startg. m. f.
   N-silyldicarboxylic acid amide silyl esters **68**, 140
Dicarboxylic acid esters
– from
   α-diketones, cyclic **68**, 87
   β-diketones, cyclic **68**, 87
   α-hydroxyketones, cyclic **68**, 87
– special s.
   dienedicarboxylic acid esters
1,7-Dicarboxylic acid esters
– special s.
   4-acyl-1,7-dicarboxylic acid esters
Dicarboxylic acid imides
–, N-alkylation **56**, 159s68
– from
   lactams **68**, 65
– startg. m. f.
   pyrrole-3,4-dicarboxylic acid esters, 2-amino-5-imido-, N-subst. **68**, 280
2,3-Dichloro-5,6-dicyanoquinone
– as reagent **50**, 182s68
-/1-hydroxybenzotriazole
– as reagent **47**, 793s68
Dichloroiodate s. Benzyltrimethylammonium dichloroiodate
Dichloromalonic acid esters, chiral
– special s.
   bis[(1S,2R)-2-(1-naphthyl)cyclohexyl] dichloromalonate
Dichloromethyl methyl ether
– as reactant **39**, 844

N,N-Dichloro-*p*-toluenesulfonamide
– as reagent **24**, 555s68; **55**, 159s68; **68**, 204
Dichromate s. 4-Aza-1-azoniabicyclo[2.2.2]octane, Dichromate, 1-butyl-, Barium dichromate, Butyltriphenylphosphonium –, Imidazolium –, Nicotinium –, Tetra-*n*-butylammonium –
Dicyanodiamide
– startg. m. f.
   1-arylbiguanides **16**, 395s68
Dicyclohexylborane
– as reagent **68**, 236
Dicyclohexylborinyl chloride
– as reagent **68**, 322
Dicyclohexyl[2-(2,6-diisopropoxyphenyl)phenyl]phosphine
– as reagent **38**, 836s68
2-(Dicyclohexylphosphino)biphenyl
– as reagent **52**, 467s68; **57**, 376s68
***o*-(Dicyclohexylphosphino)diaryl sulfones**
– as reagent **51**, 171s68
2-(Dicyclohexylphosphino)-2′,6′-dimethoxybiphenyl
– as reagent **57**, 438s68
2-(Dicyclohexylphosphino)-2′-(dimethylamino)biphenyl
– as reagent **51**, 171s68; **64**, 175s68
2-(Dicyclohexylphosphino)-2′,4′,6′-triisopropylbiphenyl
– as reagent **52**, 467s68; **65**, 178s68
2,3-Dideoxyaldonolactones, 2,3-unsatd., protected
– from
   glycals, protected **68**, 97
Dideuteriation 65, 399s68
Dieckmann condensation (s.a. 1,4-Addition-Dieckmann condensation)
Diels-Alder reaction (s.a. CC⇊CC, Hetero-Diels-Alder reaction, and under Diene synthesis in Vol. **1-50**)
– with boranes, unsatd., review **34**, 693s68
– –, W-catalyzed
– in ionic liquids under microwaves **68**, 312
– in water **68**, 312
– –, **intramolecular** (s.a. Sonogashira coupling-intramolecular Diels-Alder reaction)
– –, **Lewis acid-catalyzed**
–, alternative **43**, 336
– –, –, **polymer-based**
– with asym. induction **44**, 622s68
Diels-Alder reaction-intramolecular carbonyl-ene reaction, Lewis acid-catalyzed 68, 297
2,4-Dienecarbonyl compds.
– from
   furans, electron-rich and diazo compds., regiostereospecific synthesis **68**, 385
(E,E)-2,4-Dienecarboxylic acid amides 29, 973s68
(1E,3Z)-1,3-Diene-1,4-dicarboxylic acid esters 68, 385
2,8-Diene-1,7-diones
– startg. m. f.
   decalin-2,8-diones **68**, 336
Dienes

–, cycloisomerization, Ru carbene-catalyzed **68**, 339
–, radical ring closure-hydrophosphinylation **46**, 451s68; **53**, 240s68
– startg. m. f.
   diarylalkanes, sym., asym. hydrogenation **68**, 40
–, **bicyclic, bridged, chiral**
– special s.
   bicyclo[2.2.2]octadienes, chiral
   norbornadienes, chiral
–, **terminal**
– as intermediates **68**, 481
1,3-Dienes
–, C-α-allylation with – **48**, 691s68
– from
   α,β-ethyleneboronic acids **68**, 460
–, hydrogenation **68**, 41
– special s.
   2-aryl-1,3-dienes
   cyclobutanols, 1-(1,3-butadienyl)-
   halogeno-1,3-dienes
   siloxy-1,3-dienes
   siloxylamino-1,3-dienes
   stannyl-1,3-dienes
   1,3,n-trien-m-ynes
– startg. m. f.
   β,γ-ethylenealdehydes **68**, 75
   pyrrolidines, 3-α,3-β-dichloro-1-sulfonyl- **68**, 295
–, **chiral 66**, 399s68
–, **exocyclic**
– from
   1,6-diynes **68**, 320
– special s.
   cyclopentanes, 1,2-di(alkylidene)-
–, **sym.**
– from
   enesilanes **43**, 847s68
1,4-Dienes
– special s.
   halogeno-1,4-dienes
   siloxy-1,4-dienes
   silyl-1,4-dienes
1,5-Dienes, cyclic
– special s.
   2-aryl-1,5-dienes, cyclic
1,7-Dienes
– from
   zirconacyclopentanes, 2-methyl- **54**, 444s68
2,3-Dienol 2-monocarbamates
–, Baylis-Hillman-type reaction, stereospecific with – **68**, 251
3,5-Dienols
– from
   α,β-ethylenehalides **68**, 470
1,5-Dien-3-ols, cyclic
– special s.
   halogeno-1,5-dien-3-ols, cyclic
Dienones
–, photoreactions, review **35**, 141s68
–, **cross-conjugated**
– special s.
   β,γ-ethylene-α-ketoketene mercaptals
– startg. m. f.
   2-cyclohexenones **68**, 333
Dienynes
–, Pauson-Khand reaction, intramolecular, Ir-catalyzed with desymmetrization **68**, 332

Dienynes
– startg. m. f.
  vinylcyclopropanes, tricyclic **68**, 498
1,2-Dien-n-ynes
–, Pauson-Khand reaction, intramolecular
  55, 296s68
1,2-Dien-6-ynes
– startg. m. f.
  cyclopentanes, 1,2-di(alkylidene)-
  68, 330
1,3-Dien-8-ynes
– startg. m. f.
  1,4-cycloheptadienes, 2,3-fused
  68, 386
1,4-Dien-6-ynes
– special s.
  stannyl-1,4-dien-6-ynes
Diethoxymethylsilane
– as reagent **68**, 33
Diethyl azodicarboxylate
– as reagent **66**, 225s68
Diethyl 4-(hydrazinosulfonyl)benzyl-phosphonate
– as reagent **68**, 30
Diethyl malonate
– as reactant **68**, 482
Diethyl phosphorocyanidate
– as reagent **27**, 782s68
Difluoromethylene compds. 38, 813s68
1,1-Dihalides
– special s.
  1,1-diiodides
– startg. m. f.
  epoxides **26**, 852s68
–, cyclic **68**, 215
1,2-Dihalides
– from
  epoxides **68**, 215
– startg. m. f.
  (E)-ethylene derivs. **65**, 489s68
–, mixed
– special s.
  1,2-iodochlorides
o-**Dihalides**
– startg. m. f.
  imidazole ring **68**, 191
N,N-Dihalogenamines
– from
  amines, prim. **68**, 139
α,α-Dihalogenocarboxylic acids
  6, 170s68
1,1-Dihalogeno-1,3-dienes 68, 431
1,4-Dihalogeno-1,3-dienes
– special s.
  1,4-diiodo-1,3-dienes
α,α-Dihalogenoketones
– startg. m. f.
  γ-diketones **46**, 592s68
–, sym. **68**, 405
α,β-Dihalogenoketones
– from
  thiophenes **68**, 395
Dihalogenomethylene compds.
– special s.
  difluoromethylene compds.
  diiodomethylene –
N,N-Dihalogenosulfonic acid amides
– special s.
  N,N-dibromobenzenesulfonamide
γ-Dihydrazones 35, 549s68
1,1-Di(hydroperoxides)
– startg. m. f.

1,2,4,5-tetroxanes **66**, 52s68
2,2′-Dihydroxybiphenyl
– as reagent **68**, 237
(S,S)-1,2-Dihydroxy-1,2-diphenylethane
– as reagent **60**, 236s68
Dihydroxylation (s.a. under Glycols)
Dihydroxylation, asym.
– in ionic liquids **64**, 81s68
– in polyethylene glycol **64**, 81s68
– in *tert*-butanol/water/hexane **64**, 81s68
– with NaClO₃ as reoxidant **68**, 79
α,α′-Dihydroxyphosphinic acids, sym.
– from
  aldehydes **68**, 234
1,1-Diiodides
– from
  diiodomethylene compds. **68**, 30
1,4-Diiodo-1,3-dienes
– startg. m. f.
  cyclopentadienes, imino- **44**, 621s68
Diiodomethylene compds.
– startg. m. f.
  1,1-diiodides **68**, 30
(S)-N-(3,5-Diiodosalicylidene)-*tert*-leucinol
– as reagent **68**, 52
N,N-Diisopropyl-N-(diphenylphosphino)-amine
– as reagent **63**, 411s68
2,6-Diisopropylphenol
– as reagent **62**, 429s68
α,β-Diketocarboxylic acid esters
  68, 101
Diketones
– special s.
  acetylenediketones
α-Diketones
– from
  ketones **68**, 84
–, cyclic
– startg. m. f.
  dicarboxylic acid esters **68**, 87
β-Diketones
– from
  halides, radical carbonylation
  48, 892s68
–, cyclic
– startg. m. f.
  dicarboxylic acid esters **68**, 87
  heterocyclics, condensed, review
  42, 853s68
γ-Diketones
– from
  α,β-ethyleneketones **68**, 285
–, synthesis **68**, 329
  α,α-dihalogenoketones **46**, 592s68
– special s.
  aryl γ-diketones
  δ-aryl-γ-diketones
– startg. m. f.
  1,4-diols, asym. reduction **33**, 43s68
–, sym.
– from
  α,α-dihalogenoketones **68**, 405
– special s.
  1,4-diaryl-1,4-butanediones, sym.
1,5-Diketones
– special s.
  2-alkylidene-1,5-diketones
–, **functionalized**
– from
  enoxystannanes, radical carbonylation
  48, 492s68

1,7-Diketones
– special s.
  2,8-diene-1,7-diones
Dilithium diorgano(cyano)cuprates
– as reactant **60**, 376s68
– **1,3-enyn-1-olates**
– as intermediates **68**, 342
Dimerization, hydrative, chelation-controlled, regiospecific
– of acetylene derivs., terminal **68**, 326
6,6′-Dimethoxy-2,2′-bis(diphenyl-phosphino)biphenyl
– as reagent **46**, 738s68
Dimethyl acetylenedicarboxylate
– startg. m. f.
  furans, 2-amino- **68**, 300
  (n+4)-oxabicyclo[n.4.0]alka-
  1,3,(n+2),(n+5)-tetraene-2,3-
  dicarboxylic acid methyl esters
  68, 327
2-(Dimethylamino)-2′-(diphenyl-phosphino)biphenyl
– as reagent **53**, 496s68
[*o*-(Dimethylamino)phenyl]diphenyl-phosphine
– as reagent **68**, 318
4-Dimethylaminopyridine
– as reagent **3**, 632s68; **24**, 408s68;
  43, 162s68; **68**, 19, 142, 147
–, polymer-based
– as reagent **32**, 148s68
Dimethyl 1-diazo-2-oxopropyl-phosphonate
– as reactant **36**, 864s68
S,S-Dimethyl dithiocarbonate
– as reagent **4**, 457s68
N,N-Dimethylglycine
– as reagent **47**, 337s68; **66**, 384s68
(S)-3,3-Dimethyl-2-[(2-hydroxy-2′-pivaloyloxy-1,1′-binaphthyl-3-yl)-methyleneamino]butanol
– as reagent **51**, 46s68
N″-(1,3-Dimethylimidazolidin-2-yl)-N,N,N′,N′-tetramethylguanidinium chloride
– as reagent **4**, 513s68
Dimethyl sulfoxide
– as reagent **68**, 128, 137
1,3-Dinitriles
– startg. m. f.
  nitriles **68**, 50
2,4-Dinitrobenzenesulfonic acid
– as reagent **62**, 282s68
Diol esters
– from
  ethers, cyclic **68**, 62
1,3-Diol monoesters s.a. Aldol-Tishchenko reaction
Diols
– startg. m. f.
  amines, tert., cyclic **68**, 179
  lactones (in water) **68**, 125
  spiroorthocarboxylic acid esters
  68, 112
syn-**Diols 68**, 41
1,2-Diols s. Glycols
1,4-Diols
– by 3-component synthesis **68**, 284
– from
  γ-diketones, asym. reduction **33**, 43s68
  α,β-ethyleneketones and aliphatic nitro
  compds. **68**, 285

1,6-Diols
- special s.
  ethylene-1,6-diols
2,8-Dioxabicyclo[3.3.0]octan-3-ones,
  cis-fused **37**, 270s68
1,7-Dioxaspiro[4.4]nonanes 47, 576s68
Dioxiranes
- special s.
  dimethyldioxirane
  methyl(trifluoromethyl)dioxirane
β-Dioxo compd. monoacetals
- from
  α,β-acetyleneoxo compds. **68**, 66
1,3-Dioxolane-4-carboxylic acid esters, 2,4,5-triaryl-
- from
  aldehydes, ar. (2 different molecules) **68**, 388
1,3-Dioxolane-4,5-dimethanols, chiral
- as reagent **68**, 103
1,3-Dioxolanes
- from
  epoxides **68**, 61
  oxo compds. **58**, 78s68
-, 2-alkoxy-
- as intermediates **68**, 95
1,3-Dioxolan-2-ones
- from
  epoxides **68**, 102
-, *trans*-4-vinyl-
- from
  2-ene-1,4-diol monocarbonates **68**, 132
Dipeptide amides
- special s.
  N-(2-hydroxy-1-naphthylmethylene)-dipeptide amides
Dipeptidylthiazolium salts, chiral
- as reagent **68**, 273
1,2-Diphenoxyethane
- as reagent **30**, 467s68
Diphenyl[4-(carbo-2-trimethylsilylethoxy)phenyl]phosphine
- as reagent **68**, 481
Diphenyl diselenide
- as catalyst **33**, 477s68
Diphenyl disulfone
- as reagent **68**, 6
1-[2-(Diphenylphosphino)ferrocenyl]ethyl(dicyclohexyl)phosphine, chiral
- as reagent **66**, 34s68; **68**, 291
2-(Diphenylphosphino)phenylferrocene
- as reagent **37**, 902s68
(R,aR)-1-[2-[*o*-(Diphenylphosphino)phenyl]ferrocenyl]ethylbis[3,5-bis(trifluoromethyl)phenyl]phosphine
- as reagent **68**, 119
(R)-2-(Diphenylphosphino)-2'-(*p*-toluenesulfonylamino)-1,1'-binaphthyl
- as reagent **52**, 297s68
Diphenyl phosphorazidate
- as reagent **68**, 8
Diphenylsilane
- as reagent **62**, 18s68
Di(phosphines)
- special s.
  binaphthyls, di(phosphino)-
  biphenyls, di(phosphino)-
  3,3'-bipyridyl, 2,2',6,6'-tetramethoxy-4,4'-bis(dicyclohexylphosphino)-bis(diarylphosphino)...
  1,3-bis(dicyclohexylphosphino)propane
  1,2-bis(2,5-diisopropylphospholan-1-yl)benzene

bis(diphenylphosphino...
bis(ditolylphosphino...
diaminodi(phosphines)
ferrocenyldi(phosphines)
O,O-isopropylidene-1,4-bis(diphenylphosphino)butane-2,3-diol
phenoxazine-10-carboxamides, 4,6-bis(diphenylphosphino)-
1,1'-spirobiindane, 7,7'-bis[bis(3,5-dimethyl-4-methoxyphenyl)phosphino]-
1,2-Diphosphinylation, Pd-catalyzed 68, 244
1,1-Di(phosphonic acid esters)
- special s.
  1-hydroxy-1,1-(diphosphonic acid esters)
Dipyrid[1,2-*a*;3',2'-*d*]imidazoles 68, 191
2,2'-Dipyridinium chlorochromate
- as reagent **68**, 113
Dipyrromethanes 5, 549s68
α-Disaccharides 34, 209s68
C-Disaccharides
- special s.
  aza-C-disaccharides
Diselenocarboxylic acid esters
-, synthesis and reactions, review **44,** 533s68
1,1-Di(silanes)
- special s.
  1,2-epoxy-1,1-di(silanes)
2,3-Dispiropyrrolidines 43, 897s68
Distannanes
- special s.
  hexabutyldistannane
***o*-Di(stannanes)**
- from
  benzynes **67,** 255s68
***gem*-Disubstitution**
-, review of effects **27,** 729s68
Disulfides, sym.
- from
  mercaptans **29,** 233s68; **42,** 235s68
Disulfones
- special s.
  diphenyl disulfone
1,2-Di(sulfonylamines)
-, desymmetrization **68,** 177
1,3,2,4-Dithiadiphosphetane 2,4-disulfide, 2,4-bis(*p*-methoxyphenyl)-
- as reagent **67,** 159s68
Di-2-thienyl carbonate
- as reagent **40,** 99s68
Dithiocarbonic acid esters
- startg. m. f.
  S,S-dimethyl dithiocarbonate
Dithiocarboxylic acid esters
- startg. m. f.
  1-sulfinylthioenolethers **68,** 231
O-Dithiophosphorylation 27, 113s68
Diynes
- from
  triflyloxyhalides and terminal acetylene derivs. (2 different molecules) **68,** 391
- special s.
  enediynes
- startg. m. f.
  2-pyridone ring **68,** 315
1,3-Diynes, sym.
- from

lithium alk-1-ynyl(trialkoxy)borates **53,** 471s68
-, terminal **68,** 431
1,4(5)-Diynes
- startg. m. f.
  pyrroles **68,** 151
1,6-Diynes
- startg. m. f.
  1,3-dienes, exocyclic **68,** 320
2,(ω-1)-Diyn-1-ols
- special s.
  ω-silyl-2,(ω-1)-diyn-1-ols
4-Dodecylbenzenesulfonic acid
- as reagent **47,** 727s68
Dolabellanes and Dolastanes
-, total synthesis, review **42,** 45s68
Domino metathesis
-, review **27,** 851s68
- reactions
  in natural product synthesis, review **42,** 853s68
- –, Pd-catalyzed
-, review **27,** 851s68
Domoic acids and analogs
-, review **42,** 853s68

1,7-Electrocyclization, anionic 68, 393
Electrolysis 26, 852s68
Enacylamines
- from
  1,1-acylaminoalcohols **31,** 920s68
-, Heck-type arylation **61,** 446s68
Enamines
- by cross-coupling, review **67,** 371s68
- from
  epoxides, terminal via α-lithiation **68,** 160
  ethylene derivs. via hydroformylation **68,** 321
- special s.
  1-amino-1,4-enynes
- startg. m. f.
  aldehydes, synthesis **68,** 160
  α-(aminooxy)ketones, asym. conversion **68,** 103
  α-(hydroxylamino)ketones, – – **68,** 103
  γ-ketocarboxylic acid esters **68,** 380
Enantiomeric separation s. under Resolution and **Res** section
Encapsulation
- of palladium catalysts with polyureas, review **27,** 851s68
Ene-1,2-di(boronic acid esters)
- startg. m. f.
  glycols, asym. hydrogenation **68,** 119
2-Ene-1,4-diol monocarbonates
- startg. m. f.
  1,3-dioxolan-2-ones, *trans*-4-vinyl- **68,** 132
***anti*-3-Ene-1,2-diols, chiral 40,** 567s68
***syn*-3-Ene-1,2-diols, O-protected, chiral 68,** 132
(Z)-3-Ene-1,6-diols
- from
  oxo compds. (2 molecules) with insertion of 4 C-atoms **68,** 255

2-Ene-1,5-diones
- startg. m. f.
  phenol ring **37,** 319s**68**

Enediynes
- special s.
  halogenenediynes
- startg. m. f.
  2,4-cycloheptadienones, tricyclic
  68, 324

(Z)-Enehydrazines, zincated
–, Michael addition, stereospecific with –
  68, 284

Ene reaction s.a. Carbonyl-ene reaction, Ene-type reaction

Eneselenides
- special s.
  halogeneneselenides

Enesilanes (s.a. Silylvinylation)
- from
  acetylene derivs. **68,** 240
  – –, terminal, regiospecific conversion
  68, 237
- special s.
  α,β-ethylene-α-silyl…
  vinylsilanes
- startg. m. f.
  1,3-dienes, sym. **43,** 847s**68**
–, trisubst. **68,** 237

Enestannanes
- from
  enol phosphates and halogenostannanes
  68, 246
- special s.
  halogenenestannanes
  silylenestannanes
  2-stannyl-1,3-dienes
  2-stannyl-1,4,6-dienynes
  vinylstannanes
- startg. m. f.
  α,β-ethylenecarboxylic acid amides
  68, 455

Enetellurides
- special s.
  α,β-ethylene-β-(organotelluro)-
  sulfoxides

Ene-type reaction, intramolecular
- of 1,6-enynes in ionic liquids
  61, 312s**68**

Eneurethans
- special s.
  hydroxyeneurethans
- startg. m. f.
  α-hydroxy-γ-ketocarboxylic acid
  esters, asym. synthesis with 2 extra
  C-atoms **68,** 253

Ene-yne metathesis s.a. Ring-closing ene-yne metathesis

Enolates (s.a. Homoenolate…)
–, addition, decarboxylative, catalytic
  of –, review **27,** 851s**68**
- special s.
  bismuth(V) 3-phosphonioenolates
  carboxylic acid amide enolates
  dilithium 1,3-enyn-1-olates
  trienolates
  zinc enolates
–, non-stabilized
–, C-α-allylation, Pd-catalyzed, review
  27, 851s**68**

Enol borinates
–, hydroformylation-intramolecular aldol
  condensation, regiostereospecific
  via – **68,** 322

Enol carbamates
- special s.
  2,3-dienol 2-monocarbamates

Enol carbonates
- special s.
  allyl enol carbonates

Enolesters
- special s.
  α-acoxy-α,β-ethylene…
  enol trichloroacetates
  vinyl acetate
–, 2-subst.
- from
  acetylene derivs. terminal and
  carboxylic acids **68,** 72

Enolethers
–, cross-coupling, review **67,** 371s**68**
- special s.
  2-(trifluoromethyl)enolethers
  vinyl ethers
  vinyloxy-2-acetylenes
- startg. m. f.
  β-hydroxyketones, asym. conversion
  68, 477

(E)-Enolethers
- from
  (Z)-1-fluoroenestannanes **68,** 115

Enolethers, cyclic
–, reactions with zirconocene η²-olefin
  complexes **68,** 250
- special s.
  1-(arylthio)enolethers, cyclic
–, –, medium-ring, functionalized
  36, 148s**68**

Enol phosphates
- startg. m. f.
  enestannanes **68,** 246
  α,β-ethylenehalides **68,** 214

Enol sulfonates
- special s.
  enol triflates
  halogenenol tosylates

Enol trichloroacetates
- startg. m. f.
  (E)-α,β-ethyleneketones **68,** 479

Enol triflates
- special s.
  styryl triflates

Enones s. α,β-Ethyleneketones

Enoxysilanes (s.a. under Aldol-type…,
  Mannich-type…, Michael-type…)
- special s.
  trimethylsilyl vinyl ether
- startg. m. f.
  N-arylaldimines **68,** 372
  3,5-cycloheptadienols, 3-alkoxy-
  59, 411s**68**
  α-halogenoketones, asym. conversion
  68, 217

Enoxystannanes
- startg. m. f.
  1,5-diketones, 3-functionalized, radical
  carbonylation **48,** 492s**68**
  α-(hydroxylamino)ketones, asym.
  conversion **68,** 194
  ketones, cyclic, regiospecific asym.
  synthesis **68,** 452

2-En-4-ynaldimines
- startg. m. f.
  pyrroles, 2-α-functionalized **68,** 152

2-En-4-ynals, cyclic
- startg. m. f.

[n+4]-oxabicyclo[n.4.0]alka-
  1,3,(n+2),(n+5)-tetraene-2,3-
  dicarboxylic acid esters **68,** 327

2,4-Enynenitriles
- from
  (Z)-N-(alk-1-ynyl)-α,β-acetylene-
  ketimines **68,** 348

Enynes (s.a. Ene-yne…)
- special s.
  dienynes
  halogenenynes
  trienynes
- startg. m. f.
  alkoxy-3-ethylenes, exocyclic **68,** 290
  3-ethylenealcohols, – **68,** 290

1,3-Enynes
- special s.
  2-acyl-1,3-enynes
  1,2-dibenzyl-1,3-enynes
  1-halogen-3,1-enynes
  2-silyl-1,3-enynes
- startg. m. f.
  α,β-ethyleneketimines **58,** 126s**68**

1,4-Enynes
- from
  acetylene derivs. and allenes,
  1-functionalized, synthesis **68,** 305
- special s.
  amino-1,4-enynes
  halogen-1,4-enynes

1,5-Enynes
- from
  acoxy-2-acetylenes and 2-ethylene-
  silanes **68,** 439
- special s.
  siloxy-1,5-enynes

1,6-Enynes
–, cycloisomerization, Au(I)-catalyzed,
  regiospecific **68,** 351
–, Pauson-Khand reaction, asym. with –
  68, 325
- special s.
  1,3-dien-8-ynes
- startg. m. f.
  alkylidenecyclopentanes **68,** 320

1,7-Enynes
- by 3-component synthesis,
  regiospecific **68,** 474

1,n-Enyn-(n-1)-ols
- startg. m. f.
  bicyclo[3.1.0]hex-2-ene ring **68,** 490

1,5-Enyn-4-ols
- startg. m. f.
  bicyclo[3.1.0]hexan-3-ones **68,** 341

1,7-Enyn-4-ols
- startg. m. f.
  9-oxatricyclo[3.3.1.0¹,³]nonanes
  68, 337

(Z)-2,n-Enynols
- startg. m. f.
  δ-aryl-γ,δ-ethylenealdehydes, cyclic,
  stereospecific conversion **68,** 418

2,6-Enynols
- from
  3-ethyleneepoxides and allenes **68,** 264

1,3-Enyn-3'-ones s. 2-Acyl-1,3-enynes

Enzymes (s.a. Bio…, Microorganisms,
  Synthesis, enzymatic)
  lipases
–, use in kinetic resolution, review
  27, 57s**68**
  lipases, resin-supported **68,** 64

reductase **35**, 39s68
tyrosinase **68**, 16
– in synthesis of carbohydrates and oligosaccharides, review **41**, 173s68
–, screening from environmental libraries **68**, 59
Ephedrinium triflate, (1S,2R)-N-methyl-N-octyl-
– as ionic liquid, chiral **39**, 593s68
Epothilones, 9,10-dehydro-
–, chemistry, review **42**, 853s68
Epoxidation (s.a. Wittig synthesis-epoxidation)
– of arenes **39**, 124s68
– with Cr- and Mn-salen complexes, review **27**, 851s68
–, aerobic, Ru-catalyzed
– in a fluorous 2-phase medium **68**, 76
–, **asym.**
–, review **27**, 57s68
– with metal porphyrin complexes, chiral, review **27**, 57s68
–, –, Ru-catalyzed
– with H$_2$O$_2$ as reoxidant **68**, 73
–, –, homo- and hetero-geneous
–, review **27**, 57s68
–, **Mo(VI)-catalyzed**
– with H$_2$O$_2$ as reoxidant **68**, 70
Epoxides (s. under Oxido compds. in Vol. **1-50**)
– from
 1,1-dihalides **26**, 852s68
–, α-lithiation **68**, 160
–, ring opening, asym., review **27**, 57s68
–, – –, nucleophilic **68**, 58
–, – –, –, Lewis acid-catalyzed **68**, 61
– special s.
 acetyleneepoxides
 aryloxyepoxides
 ethyleneepox...
 stilbene oxides
 styrene oxides
– startg. m. f.
 β-acoxycarboxylic acid amides **68**, 275
 aldehydes, regiostereospecific conversion **68**, 346
 2-aminoalcohols, N-protected, asym. conversion **68**, 141
 2-(arylamino)alcohols, desymmetrization **68**, 58
 –, – and kinetic resolution **68**, 141
 aziridines, N-sulfonyl-, asym. conversion **68**, 142
 benz[e][1,4]oxathiepin-5-ones **68**, 223
 1,2-dihalides **68**, 215
 1,3-dioxolanes **68**, 61
 1,3-dioxolan-2-ones **68**, 102, 218
 ethylene derivs. **68**, 488
 glycol monoesters **68**, 61
 – monoethers **68**, 61
 – –, desymmetrization **68**, 58
 – –, with retention of configuration **68**, 63
 glycols, desymmetrization, enzymatic **68**, 59
 O-heterocyclics, review **42**, 853s68
 thiiranes **68**, 61
Epoxides, terminal
– startg. m. f.
 enamines via α-lithiation **68**, 160
–, **trisubst., chiral 33**, 786s68
–, **unsatd.**

– startg. m. f.
 glycol monoaryl ethers, unsatd. **68**, 114
Epoxyalcohols
– startg. m. f.
 epoxyketones **68**, 126
2,3-Epoxyalcohols
– startg. m. f.
 furans, tetrahydro-, 3-hydroxy-, 2-subst., regiostereospecific conversion **68**, 422
1,2-Epoxy-1,1-di(silanes) 33, 786s68
α,β-Epoxycarboxylic... s. Glycidic ...
γ,δ-Epoxy-β-hydroxy-α-methylene-carbonyl compds. 39, 593s68
Epoxyketones
– from
 epoxyalcohols **68**, 126
trans-α,β-Epoxyketones
– from
 aldehydes and α,β-acetylene-selenonium salts **68**, 437
β,γ-Epoxy-γ-silylsulfones
– special s.
 3-(*tert*-butyldimethylsilyl)-2,3-epoxypropyl *p*-tolyl sulfone
1,2-Epoxystannanes 33, 786s68
Erbium(III) triflate 45, 436s68
Erythrina skeleton 68, 365
Esterification s. Carboxylic acid esters from acids
Ethers (s.a. O-Alkylation)
–, cleavage (s.a. HOIiC), review **38**, 1s68
– from
 alcohols under Pd-catalysis, review **27**, 851s68
– special s.
 aminoethers
 azidoethers
 benzyl ethers
 tert-butyl methyl ether
 enolethers
 ethyleneethers
 glycol monoethers
 phenolethers
–, **cyclic** (s.a. O-Heterocyclics)
– from
 ethylenealcohols **68**, 83
– startg. m. f.
 diol ethers **68**, 62
–, **polycyclic**
– via allylation, intramolecular, review **42**, 853s68
Ethyl chloroacetate 33, 851s68
Ethyldiisopropylamine
– as reagent **68**, 263, 449
1-Ethyl-3-(3-dimethylaminopropyl)-carbodiimide
– as reagent **50**, 182s68
Ethyldimethylsilane
– as reagent **68**, 20
Ethylenealcohols
– startg. m. f.
 ethers, cyclic **68**, 83
2-Ethylenealcohols
–, activation, Pd-catalyzed, review **27**, 851s68
– from
 aldehydes, 3-component synthesis with 3 extra C-atoms **68**, 430
 ethylene derivs., synthesis, review **31**, 101s68
– special s.

3-ene-1,2-diols
2,6-enynols
2-ethylene-4-hydroxy...
α,β-ethylene-γ-hydroxy...
β-hydroxy-α-methylene...
– startg. m. f.
 (E)-allylarenes, regiospecific synthesis **68**, 460
 β,γ-ethylenehalides, with allyl shift **62**, 195s68
 2-ethylenephosphorylamines **68**, 185
 1,2,4-trioxanes, 6-α-arylthio- **68**, 224
–, **cyclic**
– special s.
 2-arylidenealcohols, cyclic
2-Ethylene-*tert*-alcohols, cyclic
– startg. m. f.
 α,β-ethyleneketones, cyclic **68**, 127
3-Ethylenealcohols (s.a. Allylboration, Barbier...)
– from
 aldehydes **58**, 238s68 (in PEG); **66**, 272s68; **68**, 471
 –, asym. synthesis with 3 extra C-atoms **68**, 441
– special s.
 4-aryl-3-ethylenealcohols
 2-deuterio-3-ethylenealcohols
 3-ene-1,6-diols
 1,5(7)-enyn-4-ols
 3-ethylene-1,6-halogenhydrins
 β-hydroxy-α-methylene...
 4-hydroxy-2-methylenesilanes
– startg. m. f.
 γ-arylketones **31**, 847s68
–, **exocyclic**
– from
 enynes **68**, 290
–, **hindered**
–, epoxidation **24**, 149s68
(Z)-3-Ethylenealcohols, 6-subst.
– from
 furans, 2,3-dihydro- **68**, 250
4-Ethylenealcohols
– from
 epoxides (in PEG) **58**, 238s68
– startg. m. f.
 furans, tetrahydro- **68**, 81
 pyrans, – **68**, 81
Ethylenealdehydes
– special s.
 ethylene(hydroxy)aldehydes
 vinylcyclopropanes, aldehydo-
α,β-Ethylenealdehydes (s.a. α,β-Ethyleneoxo compds.)
– special s.
 acrolein
 2-en-4-ynals
– startg. m. f.
 alcohols, asym. transfer-hydrogenation, organocatalyzed **68**, 28
 aryl ketones **68**, 462
 γ-lactones **68**, 301
(E)-α,β-Ethylenealdehydes
– from
 halides, with 3 extra C-atoms **68**, 432
α,β-Ethylenealdehydes, cyclic
– from
 dialdehydes **15**, 168s68
β,γ-Ethylenealdehydes
– from
 1,3-dienes **68**, 75

γ,δ-Ethylenealdehydes, cyclic
- special s.
  aryl-γ,δ-ethylenealdehydes, cyclic
o-Ethylenealdimines
- startg. m. f.
  3H-2-benzazepines, 4,5-dihydro-, synthesis 68, 393
2-Ethyleneamines (s.a. N-Allylation)
2-Ethylene-*tert*-amines
- startg. m. f.
  β,γ-ethylenephosphorus(V) acid esters, via N-quaternization 68, 248
3-Ethyleneamines
- from
  aldimines 40, 567s68; 66, 272s68
3-Ethyleneamines, N-protected
-, 3-component synthesis 63, 449s68
3-Ethylene-*prim*-amines
- from
  aldehydes and β,γ-ethyleneboronic acid esters, regiospecific synthesis with asym. induction 68, 427
4-Ethyleneamines
- startg. m. f.
  pyrrolidines, 2-benzyl- 66, 413s68
α,β-Ethyleneazomethines
- special s.
  2-en-4-ynaldimines
  α,β-ethyleneketimines
o-Ethyleneazomethines
- special s.
  o-ethylenealdimines
1,1'-Ethylenebis(benzimidazolium bromides)
- as reagent 37, 902s68
2-Ethylenebor... s.a. Allylboration
2-Ethyleneboranes
- special s.
  triallylboranes
α,β-Ethyleneboronic acid esters
- special s.
  α,β-ethylene-α-silylboronic acid esters
  1-methylene-1,2-di(boronic - -)
- startg. m. f.
  δ-hydrazonoboronic acid esters, 3-component synthesis, stereo-specific 68, 284
(E)-α,β-Ethyleneboronic - - 42, 829s68
- from
  acetylene derivs., terminal 68, 236
(Z)-α,β-Ethyleneboronic - -, trisubst.
- by cross-metathesis 49, 932s68
β,γ-Ethyleneboronic - -
- startg. m. f.
  3-ethylene-*prim*-amines, regiospecific synthesis with asym. induction 68, 427
o-Ethyleneboronic - -, electron-deficient
- startg. m. f.
  indenes 68, 461
α,β-Ethyleneboronic acids
-, Heck-type vinylation with - 61, 446s68
α,β-Ethyleneboroxines
-, O-vinylation with - 61, 100s68
1,2-Ethylene-1,1-bromofluorides
17, 884s68
2-Ethylenecarbonic acid esters
-, resolution, kinetic 68, 124
α,β-Ethylenecarbonyl compds.
- special s.
  amino-α,β-ethylenecarbonyl compds.

2,4-dienecarbonyl compds.
β-(2(5H)-furanon-5-yl)-α-methylenecarbonyl compds.
- startg. m. f.
  cyclobut-2-enecarbonyl compds., 2-siloxy- 68, 289
α,β-Ethylenecarboxylic acid amides
- from
  enestannanes 68, 455
- special s.
  N-acyl-α,β-ethylenecarboxylic acid amides
  2,4-dienecarboxylic - -
- startg. m. f.
  α-hydroxycarboxylic acid amides, asym. induction 68, 71
(E)-α,β-Ethylenecarboxylic - -
29, 973s68
(E)-α,β-Ethylenecarboxylic - -,
N-protected, γ-subst.
- from
  1-siloxy-1-siloxylamino-1,3-dienes, N-protected, synthesis 68, 445
γ,δ-Ethylenecarboxylic acid azides
- startg. m. f.
  2-pyrrolidones, 5-α-chloro- 68, 216
α,β-Ethylenecarboxylic acid derivs.
- special s.
  β-amino-α,β-ethylenecarboxylic acid derivs.
α,β-Ethylenecarboxylic acid ester equivalents 63, 281s68
-, syntheses with - 68, 444
α,β-Ethylenecarboxylic acid esters
-, hydrosilylation, asym. 68, 33
- special s.
  β-acoxy-α-methylenecarboxylic acid esters
  amino-α,β-ethylenecarboxylic - -
  α-benzyl-α,β-ethylenecarboxylic - -
  (carbalkoxyamino)-α,β-ethylene-carboxylic - -
  β-(carbalkoxyamino)-α-methylene-carboxylic - -
  α,β-ethylene(hydroxy)carboxylic acid esters
  α-methylenecarboxylic - -
- startg. m. f.
  carboxylic acid esters, asym. reduction 68, 33
(E)-α,β-Ethylenecarboxylic acid esters 42, 829s68
(E)-α,β-Ethylenecarboxylic - -,
α-subst.
- from
  β-acoxy-α-methylenecarboxylic acid esters 68, 400
α,β-Ethylenecarboxylic - -, cyclic 15, 168s68
γ,δ-Ethylenecarboxylic - -
- special s.
  alkoxy-γ,δ-ethylenecarboxylic acid esters
δ,ε-Ethylenecarboxylic - -
- startg. m. f.
  cyclopentanones 56, 466s68
Ethylenecarboxylic acids
- special s.
  ethylene(fluoro)carboxylic acids
γ,δ-Ethylenecarboxylic acids
- startg. m. f.

2-pyrrolidones, 5-α-chloro- (via acyl azides) 68, 216
Ethylene derivs. (s.a. C-Allylation, Horner..., Vinylation, Wittig...)
- from
  acoxy-2-ethylenes, regiostereospecific synthesis (with triorganoindiums) 68, 468
  aldehydes under Re-catalysis, review 27, 851s68
  carbonyl compds., review 42, 725s68
  epoxides 68, 488
-, hydroamination, asym., review 27, 57s68
-, hydroboration, asym., Rh-catalyzed, review 27, 851s68
-, hydrogenation, heterogeneous with asym. induction 12, 119s68
-, -, preferential 68, 31
-, hydrosilylation, Fe-catalyzed, regiospecific 68, 240
-, oxidation, allylic, Pd-catalyzed, review 27, 851s68
-, -, MeReO$_3$-catalyzed, review 27, 851s68
- special s.
  acoxyethylenes
  alkoxyethylenes
  dienes
  methylene compds.
  nitroethylene derivs.
  polyenes
  siloxyethylenes
  stilbenes
  styrenes
  tetraenes
  trienes
- startg. m. f.
  acoxy compds. 68, 74
  1,2-acoxyiodides 68, 205
  1,2-alkoxyiodides 46, 432s68
  aziridines, N-sulfonyl-, asym. conversion 68, 186
-, N-tosyl- (in aq. medium) 68, 189
  enamines, via hydroformylation 68, 321
  2-ethylenealcohols, synthesis, review 31, 101s68
  α,β-ethyleneketones 68, 90
  β,γ-ethylenesulfoxides 68, 227
  2-halogenosulfonylamines, asym. induction in ionic liquids 68, 204
  β-hydroxysulfones 68, 221
  1,2-iodohydrins 46, 432s68
  phosphines, tert., regiospecific conversion 68, 239
  pyrans, tetrahydro-, 2,6-divinyl-, desymmetrization 68, 319
  pyrazolidines, 1-acyl-, asym. conversion 68, 306
  pyrrolidines, 3-α-halogeno-1-sulfonyl- 68, 295
  Δ^1-pyrroline-5-carboxylic acid esters 68, 288
(E)-Ethylene derivs.
- from
  3,5-bis(trifluoromethyl)phenyl sulfones 38, 861s68
  1,2-dihalides 65, 489s68
(Z)-1,1-nitroethylene derivs. 24, 85s68
Ethylene derivs., cyclic
- from

acoxy-2-ethylenes, cyclic, synthesis
 63, 449s68
ethyleneoxo compds. via dienes,
 terminal 68, 481
– startg. m. f.
 α,β-ethyleneketones, cyclic 68, 91
(E)-Ethylene derivs., cyclic 62, 230s68
Ethylene derivs., electron-deficient
–, cyclopropanation, intramolecular,
 asym., organocatalyzed 68, 491
–, dimerization, reductive 63, 304s68
– startg. m. f.
 1,7-enynes, regiospecific synthesis
 68, 474
Ethylene derivs., electron-rich
–, radical 1,2-addition to – 68, 425
Ethylene derivs., functionalized
–, cross-coupling with organozirconocene
 complexes, review 67, 413s68
–, ring closures, iodinative, review
 42, 853s68
Ethylene derivs., macrocyclic
– special s.
 trienes, macrocyclic
Ethylene derivs., pyramidalized
–, review 38, 723s68
Ethylene derivs., terminal
– from
 allyl phosphates, regiospecific asym.
 synthesis 68, 363
– startg. m. f.
 alcohols, prim., C-cleavage 68, 121
 aldehydes 68, 75
Ethylenediamine
– as reagent 64, 378s68
Ethylenediaminetetraacetic acid
 disodium salt
– as reagent 68, 13
Ethylenediammonium diacetate
– as reagent 43, 765s68; 54, 357s68
α,β-Ethylenediazo compds.
– startg. m. f.
 cyclopenta[b]pyrroles, 1,2,3,3a,6,6a-
 hexahydro- (from 2 different
 molecules) 68, 389
1,2-Ethylene-1,1-dihalides s.
 Dihalogenomethylene compds.
1,2-Ethylene-1,2-dihalides
– special s.
 1-bromo-2-iodoethylene
Ethylenediols s. Enediols
3-Ethyleneepoxides
– special s.
 3,5-enyneepoxides
– startg. m. f.
 2,6-enynols 68, 264
α,β-Ethylene(epoxy)phosphine oxides
–, radical ring closure, regiostereospecific, Ti(III)-mediated 68, 495
2-Ethyleneethers s. Alkoxy-2-ethylenes
β,γ-Ethylenefluorides
–, cycloaddition, 1,3-dipolar to – with
 asym. induction 16, 735s68
Ethylene(fluoro)carboxylic acids
–, synthesis, review 16, 180s68
α,β-Ethylene-α-fluorolactams
 56, 495s68
Ethylenehalides
–, ring closures, Cl₂InH-mediated
 65, 489s68
α,β-Ethylenehalides
– from

enol phosphates 68, 214
– special s.
 dihalogenomethylene compds.
 α,β-ethyleneiodides
 halogenen...
 1-halogeno-1,3-dienes
 styryl halides
–, cyclic
– from
 ketones, cyclic 68, 215
β,γ-Ethylenehalides
– from
 2-ethylenealcohols, with allyl shift
 62, 195s68
– startg. m. f.
 1,7-enynes, regiospecific synthesis
 68, 474
 2-silyl-1(Z),4-dienes 66, 318s68
γ,δ-Ethylenehalides
– special s.
 3-ethylene-1,6-halogenhydrins
3-Ethylene-3,1-halogenhydrins, chiral
 64, 244s68
(E)-3-Ethylene-1,6-halogenhydrins,
 cyclic
– from
 vinylcyclopropanes, aldehydo- 68, 309
α,β-Ethylene-α-halogenocarboxylic
 acid esters
– special s.
 methyl α-bromoacrylate
(Z)-α,β-Ethylene-β-halogeno-β'-
 hydroxyketones 54, 307s68
α,β-Ethylene-β-halogeno-α-isocyano-
 carboxylic acid esters
– startg. m. f.
 thiazole-4-carboxylic acid esters, 2-α-
 acylamino-, 4-component synthesis
 68, 403
2-Ethylene-2-halogenosilanes
– special s.
 2-bromoallyltrimethylsilane
2-Ethylene-N-halogenosulfonylamines
– startg. m. f.
 pyrrolidines, 3-α-chloro-1-sulfonyl-
 68, 295
α,β-Ethylene-α-halogenosulfoxides,
 cyclic
– startg. m. f.
 a-aminoaldehydes, cyclic 68, 136
3-Ethylenehydrazines
– special s.
 N-acyl-3-ethylenehydrazines
(E)-α,β-Ethylene-γ-hydroxyaldehydes
– from
 aldehydes 68, 432
δ,ε-Ethylene-ξ-hydroxyaldehydes,
 O-protected
– startg. m. f.
 pyrans, tetrahydro-, 2-alkoxy-6-vinyl-
 68, 100
trans-α,β-Ethylene-γ-hydroxy-
 carboxylic acid esters 36, 45s68
α,β-Ethylene-α'-hydroxyketones
–, Michael addition, asym. of urethans
 to – 68, 150
α,β-Ethylene-β'-hydroxyketones,
 cyclic
– special s.
 cycloalk-2-enols, 2-acyl-
–, –, cis-fused 68, 287
(Z)-β,γ-Ethylene-ε-hydroxyketones

– from
 nitriles (2 molecules) 68, 255
2-Ethylene-4-hydroxystannanes
– from
 2-allenealcohols 68, 238
α,β-Ethylene-β'-hydroxysulfones
– from
 aldehydes 36, 798s68
α,β-Ethyleneiodides
– startg. m. f.
 thioenolethers 68, 230
(Z)-α,β-Ethylene-α-iodocarboxylic
 acid esters 35, 607s68
α,β-Ethyleneiodonium salts, exocyclic
– startg. m. f.
 acetylene derivs., cyclic, review
 44, 496s68
α,β-Ethyleneketimines
– from
 1,3-enynes 58, 126s68
(E,E)-α,β-Ethyleneketimines
– from
 acetylene derivs. and aldimines 68, 307
β,γ-Ethylene-α-ketoketene mercaptals
– startg. m. f.
 2-cyclohexenones, 3-alkylthio-4-nitro-
 68, 424
 m-hydroxythioethers 68, 424
α,β-Ethyleneketones (s.a. α,β-Ethylene-
 oxo compds.)
–, 1,4-addition, asym. of Grignards to –
 68, 291
– from
 acetylene derivs., terminal,
 regiospecific dimerization 68, 326
 ethylene derivs. 68, 90
 methyl ketones, heterogeneous
 conversion 68, 359s68
– special s.
 2-acyl-1,3-enynes
 alkoxy-α,β-ethyleneketones
 2-alkylidene-1,5-diketones
 amino-α,β-ethyleneketones
 chalcones
 2,8-diene-1,7-diones
 dienones, cross-conjugated
 α,β-ethylene(hydroxy)ketones
– startg. m. f.
 γ,δ-acetyleneketones via 1,4-addition
 68, 328
 β-alkoxyketones 68, 77
 2-alkylidene-1,5-diketones, asym.
 dimerization 68, 283
 aryl γ-diketones 68, 453
 cyclohexanones, 4-nitro-, asym.
 synthesis 68, 304
 cyclopropanecarboxylic acid derivs.,
 2-acyl-, asym. conversion 68, 396
 γ-diketones, synthesis 68, 329
 1,4-diols 68, 285
 2-pyrones, 3,4-dihydro- 68, 434
(E)-α,β-Ethyleneketones
– from
 aldehydes and enol trichloroacetates
 68, 479
α,β-Ethyleneketones, cyclic
– from
 2-ethylene-tert-alcohols, cyclic 68, 127
 ethylene derivs., cyclic 68, 91
– special s.
 α'-allyl-α,β-ethyleneketones, cyclic
α,β-Ethyleneketones, steroidal 68, 90

β,γ-Ethyleneketones
- from
  cyclopropyl ketones, 2-tosyloxymethyl-
    68, 486
  β-ketocarboxylic acid allyl esters,
    asym. conversion 68, 499
γ,δ-Ethyleneketones, δ-subst. 3, 758s68
-, cyclic
- special s.
  α'-allyl-α,β-ethyleneketones, cyclic
δ,ε-Ethyleneketones
- special s.
  β-benzyloxy-δ,ε-ethyleneketones
δ,ε-Ethylene-α-ketophosphonic acid
  esters 27, 738s68
α,β-Ethylenelactones
- special s.
  2,3-dideoxyaldonolactones, 2,3-unsatd.
Ethylenemercaptans
-, radical ring closures 68, 425
α,β-Ethylenenitriles
- special s.
  β-acoxy-α-methylenenitriles
  cinnamonitriles
  2,4-enynenitriles
- startg. m. f.
  nitriles 68, 29
(Z)-α,β-Ethylenenitriles
- by Peterson olefination 28, 856s68
-, α-subst.
- from
  β-acoxy-α-methylenenitriles 68, 400
Ethylenenitro... s. Nitroethylene...
Ethyleneoxo compds.
- startg. m. f.
  ethylene derivs., cyclic 68, 481
α,β-Ethyleneoxo compds.
-, C-α-arylation 68, 449
- special s.
  acoxy-α,β-ethyleneoxo compds.
α,β-Ethylenephosphine oxides
- special s.
  α,β-ethylene(epoxy)phosphine oxides
  1-methylene-1,2-bis(phosphine oxides)
α,β-Ethylenephosphonic acid esters
-, β-arylation, stereospecific 61, 446s68
- special s.
  nitro-α,β-ethylenephosphonic acid
  esters
β,γ-Ethylenephosphonic - -
- special s.
  α-methylene-β-phosphonyl...
2-Ethylenephosphoric acid esters s. Allyl
  phosphates
β,γ-Ethylenephosphorus(V) acid esters
- from
  2-ethylene-tert-amines via N-
  quaternization 68, 248
2-Ethylenephosphorylamines
- from
  2-ethylenealcohols and azides 68, 185
2-Ethylenesilanes
- special s.
  allyl(chloro)dimethylsilane
  allyl(isopropoxy)dimethylsilane
  α,β-ethylene-α-(silylmethyl)...
  4-hydroxy-2-methylenesilanes
- startg. m. f.
  1,5-enynes 68, 439
  3-ethylenealcohols, synthesis
    58, 238s68
Ethylenesiloxy... s. Siloxyethylene...

α,β-Ethylene-α-silylboronic acid esters
  68, 249
β,γ-Ethylene-β-silylboronic - -
- from
  allenes 68, 241
(E)-β,γ-Ethylene-β-silylboronic - -
- as intermediates 68, 466
α,β-Ethylene-α-(silylmethyl)carboxylic
  acid esters 28, 856s68
2-Ethylenestannanes
- special s.
  allyltributylstannane
- startg. m. f.
  3-ethylenealcohols, synthesis 68, 471
-, carbohydrate-derived
-, review 41, 173s68
3-Ethylenesulfinylamines
- from
  N-sulfinylimines, asym. induction
  68, 442
α,β-Ethylenesulfones
-, Heck-type arylation 61, 446s68
-, Rauhut-Currier reaction with - 63,
  326s68
(E)-α,β-Ethylenesulfones 29, 912s68
β,γ-Ethylenesulfones
- by desilylation 39, 74s68
- special s.
  allyl sulfones
2-Ethylenesulfonylamines
- special s.
  N-aryl-2-ethylenesulfonylamines
  N-halogeno-2-ethylenesulfonylamines
3-Ethylenesulfonylamines
- special s.
  3-ethylenetosylamines
α,β-Ethylenesulfoxides
- special s.
  α,β-ethylene-β-(organotelluro)-
  sulfoxides
β,γ-Ethylenesulfoxides
- from
  ethylene derivs. and sulfinic acid
  amides 68, 227
3-Ethylenetosylamines
- from
  N-tosylimines and potassium
  allyl(trifluoromethyl)borates,
  stereospecific synthesis 68, 442
γ,δ-Ethylene-N-tosylsulfilimines
- startg. m. f.
  δ-halogeno-γ-tosylaminosulfoxides,
  asym. induction 68, 206
(Z)-3-Ethylene-1,1,1-trihalides
- from
  aldehydes, with 3 extra C-atoms
  68, 431
2-Ethylenezirconocene complexes
- as intermediates 66, 272s68
Ethyl glyoxylate
- as reactant 68, 253
Ethyl N-(p-methoxyphenyl)imino-
  acetate
- as reactant 68, 354
Ethyl orthoformate
- as reactant 68, 98
Ethyl propiolate
- as reagent 68, 166
Ethynylcarbinols
- special s.
  o-(aminoaryl)ethynylcarbinols
- startg. m. f.

1-methylene-1,2-bis(phosphine oxides)
  68, 244
o-Ethynylstyrenes
- startg. m. f.
  indenes, 2-vinyl- 68, 338
Europium(III) chloride 62, 318s68
Europium complexes
  tris(2,2,6,6-tetramethylheptane-3,5-
    dionato)europium(III) 68, 268

Ferrocenes
- special s.
  biferrocenes
  (Δ²-oxazolin-2-yl)ferrocenes
Ferrocenyldi(phosphines)
- special s.
  1,1'-bis(diisopropylphosphino)-
    ferrocene
  1,1'-bis(diphenylphosphino)ferrocene
  di-tert-butyl-1-[2-[bis(4-trifluoro-
    methylphenyl)phosphino]-
    ferrocenyl]ethylphosphine
  1-[2-(diphenylphosphino)ferrocenyl]-
    ethyl(dicyclohexyl)phosphine
  1-[2-[o-(diphenylphosphino)phenyl]-
    ferrocenyl]ethylbis[3,5-bis(trifluoro-
    methyl)phenyl]phosphine
Ferrocenylpalladacyclics 56, 445s68
Ferrocenylphosphines
- special s.
  2-(diphenylphosphino)phenylferrocene
  1-(N-phenylimino)methyl-1'-(di-tert-
    butylphosphino)ferrocene
-, chiral
- as reagent 27, 57s68 (review);
  48, 691s68
Ferrocenyltri(phosphines)
- special s.
  4-tert-butyl-1,2-bis(diphenyl-
    phosphino)-1'-(diisopropyl-
    phosphino)ferrocene
Fischer carbene complexes (Group 6)
-, use in multicomponent reactions,
  review 27, 851s68
Flavones
- from
  o'-allyloxychalcones
Fluorapatite 25, 80s68
Fluorine
- in chemistry, review 16, 180s68
Fluorine compds.
-, reviews 16, 180s68
Fluoroboric acid 68, 290
Fluorocarboxylic acids
- special s.
  ethylene(fluoro)carboxylic acids
Fluorochromate ion s. Chromate, fluoro-
N-Fluoro-1,4-diazoniabicyclo[2.2.2]-
  octane bis(fluoroborate), N'-chloro-
  methyl-
- as reagent 38, 699s68; 60, 186s68
(E)-2-Fluoroeneselenides
- from
  acetylene derivs. 45, 290s68
(Z)-1-Fluoroenestannanes
- startg. m. f.

(E)-enolethers **68**, 115
Fluoroformamidinium salts
– special s.
   tetramethylfluoroformamidinium ...
Fluoromalonic acid esters
–, Michael addition, asym. of – **23**, 700s68
o-**Fluorophenol**
– as reagent **30**, 467s68
Fluorous catalysis, asym.
–, with nitrogen-containing chiral ligands, review **27**, 57s68
Fluorous 2-phase medium
–, epoxidation, aerobic, Ru-catalyzed in – **68**, 76
–, esterification and transesterification in – **61**, 85s68
Fluorous N-protective group
–, carbo-2-sulfonylethyl, fluorous as – **29**, 19s68
Fluorous reactions
– special s.
   N-arylation, fluorous
Fluorous reagents and functions
– special s.
   benzimidazole, 1-methyl-2-(2-pyridyl)-4,6-bis(perfluorooctyl)-
   palladacyclic complexes, fluorous
   piperidine nitroxyls, fluorous
Fluorous technologies
–, overview **12**, 455s68
Formaldehyde
– as CO substitute **68**, 325
Formals (s.a. O-Methoxymethylation)
–, N-alkoxymethylation with – **68**, 172
Formamides
– special s.
   formanilides
Formanilides
– from
   azides, ar. **68**, 161
   nitro compds., ar. **68**, 161
Formic acid
– as reagent **17**, 451s68; **68**, 330
Formylation, ar.
– with tetraformylhydrazine **68**, 355
C₂-Formylglycals
– startg. m. f.
   pyrazoles, 4-(polyoxyalkyl)-, chiral **66**, 181s68
N¹-Formylsemicarbazides
– startg. m. f.
   Δ²-1,2,4-triazolines
Friedel-Crafts... s.a. Imino-Friedel-Crafts...
Friedel-Crafts allylation and benzylation
– in aq. medium **68**, 406
– in fluoroalcohols **68**, 406
Friedel-Crafts-type acylation, heterogeneous, solventless 68, 401
Friedel-Crafts vinylation
– with acetylene derivs. in ionic liquids **68**, 299
– –, intramolecular **68**, 299
Fries rearrangement, Bi(III)-catalyzed 1, 537s68
Fullerene-porphyrins
–, review **42**, 853s68
Fullerenes, open-cage
–, review **48**, 640s68
Fulvalenes
–, review **16**, 820s68

Furan-3-carboxylic acid amides, tetrahydro-
– from
   cyclopropanecarboxylic acid amides and aldehydes, asym. induction **68**, 298
2(5*H*)-Furanones
– from
   α,β-acetylene-γ-hydroxycarboxylic acid esters and boronic acids, synthesis **68**, 463
–, radical 1,4-addition to – **35**, 474s68
–, 4-alk-1-ynyl- **64**, 449s68
–, 5-allyl-
– from
   furans, 2-siloxy- and acoxy-2-ethylenes, regiostereospecific synthesis with asym. induction **68**, 450
–, 3-aryl- **68**, 463
–, 4-halogeno-5-hydroxy-
– from
   α-allenecarboxylic acids **68**, 207
–, 5-vinyl-
– from
   2-pyrones **68**, 379
β-(2(5*H*)-Furanon-5-yl)-α-methylenecarbonyl compds., chiral 68, 450
Furan ring, 2,5-dihydro-
– from
   acetylene derivs. **64**, 353s68
Furans
– from
   acetylene derivs. **68**, 448
   acylisocyanates **68**, 448
   carboxylic acid amides, N-unsubst. **68**, 448
   γ-diketones **67**, 159s68
– startg. m. f.
   phenols **68**, 293
–, 3-α-alkoxy- **68**, 67
–, 2-amino-
– from
   aldehydes, isonitriles and dimethyl acetylenedicarboxylate **68**, 300
–, 2-α-amino-, N-protected
– from
   aldimines, N-protected, asym. synthesis **68**, 274
–, 2,3-dihydro-
– startg. m. f.
   (Z)-3-ethylenealcohols, 6-subst. **68**, 250
–, –, 2-α-arylseleno-
–, synthesis, polymer-based **29**, 180s68
–, 2,5-dihydro- **56**, 495s68
–, electron-rich
– startg. m. f.
   2,4-dienecarbonyl compds., regiostereospecific synthesis **68**, 385
–, 3-α-functionalized
– from
   2-acyl-1,3-enynes **68**, 67
–, fused
– from
   α-cyclopropylideneketones **64**, 85s68
–, 2-siloxy-
– startg. m. f.
   2(5*H*)-furanones, 5-allyl-, regiostereospecific synthesis with asym. induction **68**, 450
–, tetrahydro-

– from
   4-ethylenealcohols **68**, 81
– special s.
   2-spirofurans, tetrahydro-
–, –, 2-alkylidene-5-α-arylseleno-
–, synthesis, polymer-based **29**, 180s68
–, –, 3-hydroxy-, 2-subst.
– from
   2,3-epoxyalcohols, regiostereospecific conversion **68**, 422
–, –, –, –, chiral **68**, 422
–, –, *cis*-2-α-hydroxy-5-α-keto- **61**, 71s68
–, –, 2-α-iodo-, chiral **48**, 440s68
–, 2-vinyl- **28**, 521s68
3*H*,4*H*-Furo[3,4-*c*]pyran-1-ones, 3a,7a-dihydro- 47, 698s68
Furo[2,3-*d*]pyrimidin-2(3*H*)-ones 60, 74s68

Gallium 40, 567s68
Gallium/iodine 33, 593s68
Gallium tribromide 56, 347s68
– trichloride **66**, 311s68
– triiodide **56**, 347s68; **58**, 238s68
Germanes, tert.
– special s.
   tri-2-furylgermane
   triphenylgermane
1,4-Germylstannylation 60, 300s68
Gewald synthesis
– in ionic liquids **43**, 765s68
– under microwaves **43**, 765s68
Glucuronides
– from
   glucurono-1,6-lactones and alkoxysilanes **68**, 116
Glucurono-1,6-lactones
– startg. m. f.
   glucuronides **68**, 116
Glycals
– startg. m. f.
   2-amino-2-deoxy-β-glycosides **68**, 148
– special s.
   C₂-formylglycals
–, 1-alkyl- **52**, 419s68
–, exocyclic
–, cycloaddition, 1,3-dipolar to – **16**, 888s68
–, protected
– startg. m. f.
   2,3-dideoxyaldonolactones, 2,3-unsatd., protected **68**, 97
Glycitols s.a. 6-Thioglycitols
Glycinates
– special s.
   N-arylideneglycinates
Glycine equivalents, chiral 54, 395s68
–, aldol condensation, asym. with – **68**, 262
Glycol ethers
– special s.
   1,2-bis(benzyloxy)-1,2-bis(1-benzylimidazol-2-yl)ethane
   1,2-diphenoxyethane

Glycol monoaryl ethers, unsatd.
- from
  epoxides, unsatd. and boric acid aryl
  esters **68**, 114
Glycol monocarbamates
-, O-alkylation with - **68**, 104
- startg. m. f.
  1,3-dioxolan-2-ones **68**, 133
Glycol monoesters
- from
  epoxides **68**, 61
Glycol monoethers
- from
  epoxides **68**, 61
-, desymmetrization **68**, 58
- and aldehydes, with retention of
  configuration **68**, 63
Glycols (s.a. Dihydroxylation, Pinacol...)
-, desymmetrization **68**, 109
- from
  ene-1,2-di(boronic acid esters), asym.
  hydrogenation **68**, 119
  epoxides, desymmetrization, enzymatic
  68, 59
-, O-methoxymethylation, regiospecific
  68, 95
-, resolution, kinetic **44**, 214s68
- special s.
  1,2-dihydroxy-1,1,2-diphenylethane
  3-ene-1,2-diols
Glycol sulfites, cyclic
- startg. m. f.
  alcohols **49**, 843
Glycosidation (s.a. Glycosides from ...)
- of peptides, review **41**, 173s68
-, sequential
- with thioglycosides, review **41**, 173s68
Glycosides
- special s.
  acyl glycosides
  allyl glycosides
  deoxyglycosides
  glucuronides
  selenoglycosides
  thioglycosides
C-Glycosides
- special s.
  C-disaccharides
Glycosylamines
- from
  α-glycosyl azides **48**, 346s68
- in asym. synthesis, review **27**, 57s68
α-Glycosyl azides
- startg. m. f.
  glycosylamines **48**, 346s68
trans-Glycosyl cyanides 49, 843s68
Glycosyl iodides
- as intermediates **34**, 209s68
3-(C-Glycosyl)isoxazolidines 16, 735s68
β-Glycosylphosphonic acid esters
- special s.
  2-deoxy-β-glycosylphosphonic acid
  esters
S-Glycosylsulfenamides 28, 258s68
N-β-Glycosylureas 63, 140s68
Gold(III) bromide 68, 362
Gold catalysis
, review **27**, 851s68
Gold(I) chloride 68, 344
-(III) chloride **58**, 129s68; **63**, 88s68;
  68, 67, 175
-(III) -/alumina **68**, 85

-(III) -/silver triflate **68**, 267, 345
- complexes
  chloro(triphenylphosphine)gold(III)
  68, 361
  chloro(triphenylphosphine)gold(I)/
  silver fluoroborate **68**, 351
  -/- hexafluoroantimonate **68**, 341
  methyl(triphenylphosphine)gold(I)
  68, 290
  [tris(triphenylphosphine)gold]oxonium
  fluoroborate **68**, 343
Graphite 4, 729s68
Green chemistry
-, review **61**, 74s68
Green solvents
-, review **61**, 74s68
Grignard compds. s. Magnesium halides,
  organo-
Guanidines
- special s.
  carbalkoxyguanidines
  tetramethylguanidine
-, cyclic
- from
  isothiouronium salts, cyclic **5**, 346s68
-, N-monosubst. **60**, 147s68
Guanidinium nitrate
- as reagent **37**, 316s68
- salts
- special s.
  N″-(1,3-dimethylimidazolidin-2-yl)-
  N,N,N′,N′-tetramethylguanidinium
  chloride

**Hafnium(IV) perfluorooctane-
  sulfonimide 61**, 85s68
-(IV) salen complexes, chiral **58**, 194s68
-(IV) triflate **68**, 299
Halides
- special s.
  acoxyhalides
  alkoxyhalides
  benzyl halides
  dihalides
  ethylenehalides
  iodides
  pentahalides
  sulfonyloxyhalides
  trihalides
- startg. m. f.
  (E)-α,β-ethylenealdehydes, with 3
    extra C-atoms **68**, 432
  monoselenoiminocarbonic acid esters
    68, 235
  nitro compds., aliphatic **37**, 369s68
  oxo compds. **68**, 134
  1,1,1-trifluorides **44**, 577s68
Halides, ar.
-, cross-coupling, Pd-catalyzed, review
  27, 851s68
-, cross-coupling, intramolecular, Pd-
  catalyzed, stereospecific with
  acoxy-2-ethylenes **68**, 494
- special s.
  halogenoaryl...
- startg. m. f.

allylarenes, with inversion of
  configuration **68**, 397
amines, ar. **68**, 187
arylacetic acid esters **68**, 482
δ-aryl-γ,δ-ethylenealdehydes, cyclic,
  stereospecific conversion **68**, 418
N-aryl-N-heterocyclics, benzo-
  condensed **68**, 190
carbostyrils, 3,4-fused **68**, 410
diaryl ketones **68**, 476
diaryls (s.a. under Suzuki) **68**, 421
indolines, N-aryl-2-benzyl- (from 2
  different molecules) **68**, 414
thioethers, ar. **68**, 229
Halides, hetar.
- startg. m. f.
  hetarylcarboxylic acid amides, with 1
    extra C-atom **68**, 390
Haller-Bauer reaction, catalyzed
- with kinetic resolution **68**, 149
2-Halogenacylamines
- startg. m. f.
  Δ²-oxazolines **68**, 135
o-Halogenacylamines
- startg. m. f.
  indoles **47**, 829s68
Halogenalcohols s. Halogenhydrins
α-Halogenaldehydes
-, acylation with - **68**, 109
- special s.
  β-aryl-α-halogenaldehydes
N-Halogenamines
- special s.
  N,N-dihalogenamines
o-Halogenamines
- startg. m. f.
  carbazoles **68**, 464
  indoles **68**, 411
Halogenation
- special s.
  iodination
-, ar.
- special s.
  chlorination, ar.
α-Halogenation, asym.
- of β-ketocarboxylic acid esters **68**, 208
N-Halogenation
- special s.
  N-chlorination
Halogenenediynes
-, oligocyclization, Pd-catalyzed, review
  27, 851s68
2-Halogeneneselenides
- special s.
  2-fluoreneselenides
1-Halogenenestannanes
- from
  acetylenestannanes **43**, 625s68
- special s.
  1-fluoroenestannanes
(E)-2-Halogenenol tosylates
- from
  acetylene derivs., polymer-based
    synthesis **68**, 203
2-Halogenenynes
-, oligocyclization, Pd-catalyzed, review
  27, 851s68
(Z)-1-Halogen-1,4-enynes
- from
  2-acetylenealcohols and acetylene
    derivs. **68**, 366
(Z)-1-Halogen-3,1-enynes

– from
  aldehydes, with 3 extra C-atoms
    68, 431
1,2-Halogenhydrins
– special s.
  α-halogeno-β-hydroxy...
  1,2-iodohydrins
  2,2,2-trihalogenalcohols
1,3-Halogenhydrins
– special s.
  3-ethylene-3,1-halogenhydrins
1,4-Halogenhydrins
– special s.
  β'-hydroxy-γ-iodo...
1,6-Halogenhydrins
– special s.
  3-ethylene-1,6-halogenhydrins
N-Halogenimines
– special s.
  N-halogenoketimines
ω-(o-Halogenoaryl)amines
– startg. m. f.
  N-aryl-N-heterocyclics, benzo-
    condensed 68, 190
α-Halogenocarbonyl compds.
–, cyclopropanation, intramolecular,
  organocatalyzed, asym. with –
  68, 491
o-Halogenocarbonyl compds.
– startg. m. f.
  carbostyrils 68, 413
γ-Halogenocarboxylic acid amides
– special s.
  β'-hydroxy-γ-iodocarboxylic acid
    amides
– startg. m. f.
  2-piperidones 22, 528s68
o-Halogenocarboxylic acid amides
– startg. m. f.
  carbostyrils, 3,4-fused 68, 410
α-Halogenocarboxylic acid derivs.
– startg. m. f.
  cyclopropanecarboxylic acid derivs.,
  2-acyl-, asym. conversion 68, 396
α-Halogenocarboxylic acid esters
– special s.
  ethylene-α-halogenocarboxylic acid
    esters
  α,β-ethylene-α-iodocarboxylic – –
α-Halogenocarboxylic acids
– special s.
  α,α-dihalogenocarboxylic acids
Halogen-1,3-dienes
– special s.
  dihalogeno-1,3-dienes
(E,E)-1-Halogeno-1,3-dienes
– from
  acetylene derivs., terminal, with 2 extra
    C-atoms 68, 294
(Z,Z)-1-Halogeno-1,3-dienes 68, 431
4-Halogeno-1,4-dienes
– special s.
  amino-4-halogeno-1,4-dienes
1-Halogeno-1,5-dien-3-ols, cyclic
  40, 567s68
Halogenoformamidinium salts
– special s.
  fluoroformamidinium salts
Halogenoformic acid esters
– special s.
  trichloromethyl chloroformate
– startg. m. f.

N-carbalkoxythioureas 22, 470s68
α-Halogeno-β-hydroxyketones
  46, 592s68
β-Halogeno-β'-hydroxyketones
– special s.
  ethylene-β-halogeno-β'-hydroxy-
    ketones
α-Halogeno-β-hydroxynitriles
– from
  oxo compds., with 2 extra C-atoms
    55, 249s68
δ-Halogeno-β-hydroxy-γ-tosylamino-
  sulfoxides, chiral 68, 206
β-Halogeno-α-isocyanocarboxylic acid
  esters
– special s.
  ethylene-β-halogeno-α-isocyano-
    carboxylic acid esters
N-Halogenoketimines 68, 139
α-Halogenoketones
– from
  enoxysilanes, asym. conversion 68, 217
– special s.
  α,β-dihalogenoketones
  α-iodoketones
Halogenolactamization
– special s.
  radical halogenolactamization
α-Halogenolactams
– special s.
  α,β-ethylene-α-fluorolactams
Halogenosilanes
– special s.
  trimethylsilyl chloride
2-Halogenosilanes
– special s.
  2-ethylene-2-halogenosilanes
o-Halogeno-β-styryl triflates
– startg. m. f.
  indoles 68, 192
N-Halogenosuccinimides s. N-Bromo-,
  N-Chloro-, and N-Iodo-succinimide
N-Halogenosulfonic acid amides
– special s.
  N-bromo(p-toluenesulfonyl)amine
  N,N'-dibromo-N,N'-propylenebis(p-
    toluenesulfonamide)
  2-ethylene-N-halogenosulfonylamines
Halogenosulfonium salts
– special s.
  bromodimethylsulfonium bromide
2-Halogenosulfonylamines
– from
  ethylene derivs. in ionic liquids, asym.
    induction 68, 204
anti-β-Halogeno-α-sulfonylamino-
  carboxylic acid esters 68, 204
anti-β-Halogeno-α-sulfonylamino-
  ketones 24, 555s68
α-Halogenosulfoxides
– special s.
  ethylene-α-halogenosulfoxides
α-Halogenothiolic acid esters
–, Claisen-type condensation, reductive,
  Lewis acid-mediated with – 68, 426
o-Halogenothioureas
– startg. m. f.
  benzothiazoles, 2-amino- 68, 233
δ-Halogeno-γ-tosylaminosulfoxides
– from
  γ,δ-ethylene-N-tosylsulfilimines, asym.
    induction 68, 206

9-Halogeno-1,2,7-trienes
– startg. m. f.
  2-aryl-1,5-dienes, cyclic 68, 475
Hamigerans
–, synthesis, review 42, 853s68
Hantzsch pyridine synthesis
– in water under microwaves 47, 727s68
Heck arylation
– at low catalyst loading 27, 871s68
– in ionic liquids under microwaves
    27, 871s68
– in – – within silica pores 68, 409
– under microwaves 27, 871s68
– with Pd-complexes, Se-ligated, highly
    active 68, 415
Heck-type arylation
– of aldehydes, ar. 68, 459
– with arylboronic acids in aq. emulsions
    61, 446s68
– vinylation
– with α,β-ethyleneboronic acid esters
    61, 446s68
Heck vinylation, intramolecular
  36, 957s68
Henry reaction, asym., Co(II)-
  catalyzed 68, 263
– –, electrochemical 39, 578s68
Hetarylcarboxylic acid amides
– from
  chlorides, hetar., with 1 extra C-atom
    68, 390
Heterocumulenes
–, addition of lithium amides, chiral to –
    68, 145
–, reactions, transition metal-catalyzed,
    review 27, 851s68
Heterocyclics
–, domino synthesis, review 42, 853s68
– from
  diaryl sulfides and diaryl sulfones,
    review 42, 853s68
  trichloromethyl β-alkoxy-α,β-
    ethyleneketones, review 42, 853s68
–, functionalization, Pd-catalyzed, review
    42, 853s68
– special s.
  iodoheterocyclics
–, synthesis under microwaves, review
    42, 853s68
–, tandem synthesis, review 42, 853s68
Heterocyclics, α-chloroalkyl-, lithiated
– in synthesis, review 42, 853s68
–, fluorinated
– by rearrangement of isoxazoles,
    review 16, 180s68
–, fused
– from
  β-diketones, cyclic, review 42, 853s68
–, 5-membered, chiral
– in asym. synthesis, review 27, 57s68
N-Heterocyclics (s.a. Azoles)
– special s.
  amino-N-heterocyclics
  N-aryl-N-heterocyclics
  vinyl-N-heterocyclics
–, 5- and 6-membered
–, synthesis by reductive cyclization
    42, 853s68
O-Heterocyclics
– from
  epoxides, review 42, 853s68

O-Heterocyclics
– special s.
  benzo-O-heterocyclics
1,3-N,O-Heterocyclics, 2-arylimino-
38, 239s68
P-Heterocyclics
–, chemistry, review 42, 853s68
–, 5- and 6-membered
–, synthesis and stereochemistry, review
  42, 853s68
Hetero-Diels-Alder reaction, asym.,
  endo-selective, Rh-catalyzed 68, 454
– –, intramolecular
– in ionic liquids 63, 359s68
Hexabutyldistannane
– as reagent 40, 493s68; 45, 35s68
Hexachloroethane
– as reagent 55, 182s68
Hexadecyltrimethylammonium
  bromide
– as reagent 40, 567s68; 46, 451s68;
  63, 430s68; 68, 44
Hexamethyldisilazane
– as reagent 27, 435s68
Hexamethyldisiloxane
– as reagent 22, 594s68
Hexamethyldisilthiane
–, use in S-heterocyclic synthesis via
  thionation of carbonyl compds.,
  review 42, 853s68
Hexamethylenetetramine-bromine/
  silica gel 52, 120s68
Hexamethylenetrammonium
  fluorochromate
– as reagent 4, 274s68; 42, 235s68
Hexoses
– from
  aldehydes (3 molecules), asym.
  synthesis 68, 258
High-pressure N-arylation 8, 563s68
High-pressure O-deacylation 68, 4
Homoallyl... s. 3-Ethylene...,
  γ,δ-Ethylene...
Homoenolate equivalents
– special s.
  aldehyde homoenolate equivalents
B-Homoerythrina skeleton 68, 365
Homologization (s.a. Kowalski
  homologization)
Homooxacalixarenes
–, chemistry, review 42, 853s68
Horner synthesis (s.a. Radical ring
  closure-Horner synthesis)
Hydantoin, 1,3-dibromo-5,5-dimethyl-
– as reagent 4, 274s68; 28, 889s68
Hydantoins, 1-acylamino-
– from
  N¹-acyl-N²-α-cyanosemicarbazides
  68, 153
–, 5-carbamyl-
– from
  barbituric acids, 5-amino- 68, 153
Hydrazine hydrate
– as reagent 68, 128
Hydrazines
– special s.
  enehydrazines
  hydroxyhydrazines
  phenylhydrazine
  silylhydrazines
  sulfonylhydrazines
– startg. m. f.

2-imidazolidones, 3-amino-4-imino-
  68, 157
–, N-monosubst. 33, 412s68
Hydrazinosulfonylphosphonic acid esters
– special s.
  diethyl 4-(hydrazinosulfonyl)benzyl-
  phosphonate
Hydrazoic acid
–, generation *in situ* 13, 365s68
Hydrazones
–, C-α-alkylation, asym., polymer-based
  31, 812s68
–, 3-component Mannich-type synthesis
  68, 364
– from
  oxo compds. 50, 187s68
– special s.
  N-acylhydrazones
  di(hydrazones)
  silylhydrazones
  sulfonylhydrazones
– startg. m. f.
  oxo compds. 34, 172s68
Hydrazones, *o*-subst.
–, silylation, benzylic, chelation-
  controlled 68, 243
δ-Hydrazonoboronic acid esters
–, 3-component synthesis, stereospecific
  68, 284
Hydrazonoesters
– special s.
  N-arylhydrazonoesters
Hydroacylation
– special s.
  Stetter hydroacylation
–, Rh-catalyzed
– of nitrogen-nitrogen double bonds
  68, 144
Hydroalumination-cross-coupling
  68, 294
Hydroamination, asym., transition
  metal-catalyzed
– of ethylene derivs., review 27, 57s68
–, Ti-catalyzed, regiospecific 68, 151
–, intramolecular
– under microwaves 68, 155
– –, Ca-mediated 68, 156
Hydroaminomethylenation,
  regiostereospecific 68, 321
Hydroarylation, Rh-catalyzed
  56, 464s68
Hydroboration
– of acetylene derivs., review 43, 520s68
–, asym., Rh-catalyzed
– of ethylene derivs., review 27, 57s68
Hydrocarbon groups, quaternary
–, generation 68, 377
– –, –, chiral
–, generation 38, 802s68; 47, 786s68;
  61, 209s68; 64, 260s68; 68, 303, 335,
  363, 452, 500
Hydrocarbons
–, activation of C-H bonds, review
  27, 851s68
–, oxidation, heterogeneous in ionic
  liquids 68, 57
– special s.
  alkylarenes
  arenes
  diarylalkanes
Hydroformylation, asym.,
  heterogeneous 49, 683s68

–, selective, branched
–, review 27, 851s68
Hydroformylation-intramolecular aldol
  condensation, regiostereospecific
– via enol borinates 68, 322
Hydrogenation (s.a. HCl.., Carbocyclization, hydrogenative, Transfer-
  hydrogenation)
– in PEG-400 1, 13s68
– with 1,2-stannyl group migration 68, 32
–, asym., heterogeneous
– with metal complexes, polymeric, self-
  supported, chiral 68, 37
–, asym., homogeneous
– of
  β-amino-α,β-ethylenecarboxylic acid
  derivs., N-unsubst. 68, 38
  aryl ketones in alcoholic media 68, 25
  ene-1,2-di(boronic acid esters) 68, 119
  enolesters 60, 34s68
  indoles 68, 36
  β-ketocarboxylic acid esters 68, 26
– with (as ligand)
  acyl phosphites, cyclic, chiral 60, 34s68
  1,3,2-benzodioxaphospholenes,
  2-amino-, chiral 60, 34s68
  phosphine-cyclic phosphoramidites,
  chiral 68, 34
– with dynamic kinetic resolution
  51, 26s68; 67, 22s68
–, –, –, Ir-catalyzed
– of dienes 68, 40
–, Fe-catalyzed 68, 31, 240
–, heterogeneous
– in water 68, 39
– of ethylene derivs. with asym. induction
  12, 119s68
–, –, Ir-catalyzed
– in ionic liquids 68, 27
– of oxo compds. 68, 27
–, preferential
– of ethylene derivs. 68, 31
1,5-Hydrogen atom transfer 68, 302
Hydrogen bromide 68, 129, 189
– peroxide 8, 602s68; 44, 420s68;
  45, 150s68; 46, 106s68; 64, 81s68;
  68, 52, 70, 73, 119, 129, 189, 210, 285
– –, supported
– special s.
  1,4-diazabicyclo[2.2.2]octane 1,4-
  dioxide bis(hydrogen peroxide)
– sulfide 68, 225
Hydrolysis
– of esters s. HOIIC
Hydroperoxides
– special s.
  bicyclo[2.2.1]heptane, 2-hydro-
  peroxy...
  tert-butyl hydroperoxide
  cumene –
  di(hydroperoxides)
Hydrophosphination, regiospecific
– of ethylene and acetylene derivs. with
  silylphosphines 68, 239
Hydrosilylation
– of acetylene derivs., review 43, 520s68
–, asym. 68, 33
–, Fe-catalyzed, regiospecific 68, 240
Hydrostannylation
– of acetylene derivs., review 43, 520s68
–, Mo-catalyzed, regiospecific 68, 238
Hydrotalcite (s.a. Ruthenium(IV)-

grafted hydrotalcite)
Hydrovinylation
- with α,β-ethyleneboronic acid esters **65**, 464s68
α-Hydroxyacetals
- from
  oxo compds. **68**, 56
β-Hydroxyacetals, chiral 67, 276s68
γ-Hydroxyaldehydes
- special s.
  ethylene-γ-hydroxyaldehydes
β-Hydroxyalkoximes 57, 243s68
α-Hydroxyamidoximes 68, 157
Hydroxyamines s. Aminoalcohols
2-Hydroxyammonium hydroxides, quaternary
- special s.
  choline hydroxide
  N-(o-Hydroxybenzyl)-2-aminoalcohols, chiral
- as reagent **43**, 576s68
β-Hydroxycarbonyl compds. s.a.
  Aldol..., Reformatsky...
α-Hydroxycarboxylic acid amides
- from
  α,β-ethylenecarboxylic acid amides, asym. induction **68**, 71
- special s.
  acylamino-α-hydroxycarboxylic acid amides
β-Hydroxycarboxylic – –
- special s.
  N-acyl-β-hydroxycarboxylic acid amides
γ-Hydroxycarboxylic – –
- special s.
  γ-hydroxycarboxylic acid anilides
γ-Hydroxycarboxylic acid anilides 68, 165
α-Hydroxycarboxylic acid derivs.
- special s.
  amino-α-hydroxycarboxylic acid derivs.
α-Hydroxycarboxylic acid esters 39, 157s68
- special s.
  (N-carbalkoxyimino)-α-hydroxycarboxylic acid esters
– – –, chiral 51, 26s68
β-Hydroxycarboxylic – –
- special s.
  amino-β-hydroxycarboxylic acid esters
  arylamino-β-hydroxycarboxylic – –
– – –, chiral 68, 68
γ-Hydroxycarboxylic – –
- special s.
  acetylene-γ-hydroxycarboxylic acid esters
  ethylene-γ-hydroxycarboxylic – –
α-Hydroxycarboxylic acids
- special s.
  1-naphthylglycolic acid
o-Hydroxydiaryls
- startg. m. f.
  3,4-benzocoumarins **68**, 247
o-Hydroxy-N,N-dimethylbenzylamine N-oxide
- as reagent **65**, 235s68
1-Hydroxy-1,1-di(phosphonic acid esters)
- from
  acylphosphonic acid esters **29**, 593s68

carboxylic acid chlorides **29**, 593s68
(E)-4-Hydroxyenesilanes
- as intermediates **68**, 470
3′-Hydroxyenesilanes
- from
  allenes and aldehydes, stereospecific synthesis **68**, 466
N-(3′-Hydroxy)eneurethans
- startg. m. f.
  4-pyrones, tetrahydro-, 2,3,6-trisubst. **68**, 383
Hydroxyhydrazines
–, synthesis, review **66**, 287s68
β′-Hydroxy-γ-iodocarboxylic acid amides, chiral
- as intermediates **68**, 298
β-Hydroxy-α-ketocarboxylic acid esters 47, 147s68
α-Hydroxy-γ-ketocarboxylic – –
- from
  eneurethans, asym. synthesis with 2 extra C-atoms **68**, 253
β′-Hydroxy-β-ketocarboxylic acid esters, cyclic 68, 322
α-Hydroxy-γ-ketocarboxylic – –, chiral 56, 422s68
Hydroxyketones
- special s.
  alkoxy(hydroxy)ketones
α-Hydroxyketones (s.a. Benzoin condensation)
- special s.
  α,β-ethylene-α′-hydroxyketones
–, cyclic
- startg. m. f.
  dicarboxylic acid esters **68**, 87
β-Hydroxyketones (s.a. under Aldol..., Reformatsky...)
- by Reformatsky-type synthesis **1**, 677s68
- from
  aldehydes and enolethers, asym. conversion **68**, 477
- and β-ketocarboxylic acid allyl esters **68**, 483
- special s.
  amino-β-hydroxyketones
  ethylene-β-hydroxyketones
  halogeno-β-hydroxyketones
  β-halogeno-β′-hydroxyketones
anti-β-Hydroxyketones 63, 248s68
ε-Hydroxyketones
- special s.
  ethylene-ε-hydroxyketones
Hydroxylactones 68, 125
Hydroxylamines
- startg. m. f.
  2-oxazolidones, 3-alkoxy-4-imino- **68**, 157
–, ar.
- from
  nitro compds., ar., partial conversion **68**, 12
2-(Hydroxylamino)alcohols
- from
  nitrones and oxo compds. **68**, 271
α-(Hydroxylamino)ketones
- from
  enamines and nitroso compds., asym. conversion **68**, 103
  enoxystannanes, asym. conversion **68**, 194

2-(Hydroxylamino)sulfonylamines
- from
  nitrones and N-sulfinylimines, asym. induction **68**, 271
α-Hydroxylation, asym., organocatalyzed
- of ketones **68**, 55
3-Hydroxymaleic anhydrides
- from
  ketene disilyl acetals **68**, 451
β-Hydroxymercaptals
- from
  aldehydes and ketene mercaptals **68**, 296
α-Hydroxymethylation, asym.
- of oxo compds. **58**, 245s68
β-Hydroxy-α-methylenecarbonyl compds.
- special s.
  γ,δ-epoxy-β-hydroxy-α-methylenecarbonyl compds.
γ-Hydroxy-α-methylenecarboxylic acid esters 34, 614s68
4-Hydroxy-2-methylenesilanes, chiral 68, 477
N-(2-Hydroxy-1-naphthylmethylene)-dipeptide amides
- as reagent **68**, 363
α-Hydroxynitriles s. Cyanohydrins
β-Hydroxynitriles
- from
  aldehydes **68**, 276
  glycol sulfites, cyclic **49**, 843s68
- special s.
  halogeno-β-hydroxynitriles
o-Hydroxyoximes
- as water equivalent **68**, 68
–, Michael addition, asym. **68**, 68
(4-Hydroxyphenyl)diphenylphosphine
- as reagent **27**, 871s68
Hydroxyphosphinic acids
- special s.
  dihydroxyphosphinic acids
β-Hydroxyphosphonic acid esters
- special s.
  amino-β-hydroxyphosphonic acid esters
N-Hydroxyphthalimide, 3,4,5,6-tetraphenyl-
- as reagent **51**, 76s68
4-Hydroxy-1-silylacetylenes
- from
  aldehydes, with 3 extra C-atoms **68**, 478
2′-Hydroxy-2-silylenestannanes 41, 564s68
4-Hydroxystannanes
- special s.
  ethylene-4-hydroxystannanes
β-Hydroxysulfones
- from
  ethylene derivs. and sulfonyl halides **68**, 221
- special s.
  α,β-ethylene-β′-hydroxysulfones
β-Hydroxy-γ-sulfonylaminosulfoxides
- special s.
  halogeno-β-hydroxy-γ-sulfonylaminosulfoxides
2-Hydroxythioethers
- special s.
  1-(1-benzotriazolyl)-2-hydroxythioethers

2-Hydroxythioethers, chiral 9, 741s68; **68,** 228
***m*-Hydroxythioethers**
– from
β,γ-ethylene-α-ketoketene mercaptals and aliphatic nitro compds. **68,** 424
β-Hydroxythiolic acid esters 57, 421s68
4-Hydroxy-α,α,α-trifluoroacetophenone, soluble PEG-based
– as reagent **60,** 67s68
Hypofluorous acid/acetonitrile
– in chemistry, review **16,** 180s68
Hypophosphites s. Tetraalkylammonium hypophosphites
Hypophosphorous acid
– as reactant **68,** 234
– – derivs.
– startg. m. f.
phosphonous acid derivs., review **18,** 699s68

Imidazole, 1-acetyl-2-(diphenylphosphino)-
– as reagent **48,** 346s68
Imidazole ring
– from
o-dihalides and *o*-amino-N-heterocyclics **68,** 191
Imidazoles
– from
N-allyl-O-acylamidoximes **68,** 201
–, **5-chloro-**
– from
α-acylaminonitriles **68,** 213
Imidazolidine, (4R,5R)-4,5-diphenyl-
– as reagent **67,** 212s68
Imidazolidines
– special s.
spiroimidazolidines
Imidazolidin-2-ylidene, N,N′-bis(2,6-diisopropylphenyl)-
– as reagent **68,** 190
4-Imidazolidone, (2S,5S)-5-benzyl-2-*tert*-butyl-3-methyl-
– as reagent **67,** 276s68
2-Imidazolidones, 3-amino-4-imino-
– from
α-aminonitriles and hydrazines **68,** 157
4-Imidazolidonium salts, chiral
– as reagent **68,** 28
4-Imidazolidonium trichloromethyl peroxide, (2S,5S)-5-benzyl-2-*tert*-butyl-3-methyl-
– as reagent **68,** 28
Δ²-Imidazolines
– special s.
bis(Δ²-imidazolines)
–, **2-[*o*-(diarylphosphino)phenyl]-, chiral**
– as reagent **48,** 952s68
–, **1-tosyl- 30,** 217s68
Δ²-Imidazolinium chloride, 1-(2-methoxyethyl)-3-(2,4,6-trimethylbenzyl)-
– as reagent **68,** 482
Δ²-Imidazolinium-2-dithiocarboxylate, 1,3-dibenzyl-

– as reagent **65,** 253s68
Imidazolium chloride, 1,3-dimesityl-
– as reagent **68,** 301
– **decatungstate, 1-*n*-butyl-3-methyl-**
– as reagent **54,** 109s68
– **dichromate**
– as reagent **34,** 172s68
Imidazolium ionic liquids
– benzenesulfonate, 1-*n*-butyl-3-methyl- **42,** 127s68
– bromide, 1-methyl- **60,** 182s68
– chloride, 1-chlorosulfinyl-3-methyl- **68,** 96
– fluoroborate, 1-*n*-butyl-3-methyl- **68,** 204, 259, 300
– –, 1-ethyl-3-methyl- **34,** 610s68
– –, 1-hexyl-3-methyl- **68,** 368
– –, 1-methyl- **68,** 96
– –, 1-methyl-3-octyl- **7,** 246s68; **27,** 871s68
– hexafluoroantimonate, 1-*n*-butyl-3-methyl- **68,** 299
– hexafluorophosphate, 1-*n*-butyl-3-methyl- **68,** 409
– tribromide **67,** 215s68
– triflate, 1-ethyl-3-methyl- **35,** 476s68
– trifluoroacetate, 1-methyl- **68,** 369
Imidazolium ionic liquids, silica-supported 45, 95s68
Δ²-4-Imidazolones, 2-amino-
–, synthesis, polymer-based
Δ²-5-Imidazolones, 2-subst. 63, 406s68
Imidazol-1-ylacetonitrile, 4,5-dichloro-
– as CO equivalent **68,** 390
Imidazol-2-ylidenes, hindered
– as ligand **68,** 315
Imidazo[1,2-*b*]pyrazol-2-ones
–, synthesis, polymer-based **43,** 316s68
Imidodicarbonates
– startg. m. f.
N-sulfonylureas **68,** 197
Imines (s.a. Azomethines)
– special s.
acylimines
carbalkoxyimin…
halogenimines
phosphinylimines
sulfinylimines
sulfonylimines
–, **N-protected**
– startg. m. f.
β-aminonitriles, N-protected, with 2 extra C-atoms **68,** 276
Iminoacetic acid esters
– special s.
ethyl N-(*p*-methoxyphenyl)iminoacetate
α-Iminocarboxylic acid esters
– special s.
iminoacetic acid esters
Imino-Friedel-Crafts reaction, asym., organocatalyzed 68, 274
– –, **co-catalytic 68,** 267
α-Iminoiminoesters
–, 3-component synthesis **68,** 416
Impurities
–, removal, overview **27,** 57s68
1-Indanones, 2,2-disubst., chiral 68, 335
2-Indanones, 1-alkylidene-
– from
o-acetyleneepoxides **68,** 347
Indates, organo- s. Lithium tetraorgano-

indates
Indazoles, 3-acyl- 64, 365s68
–, **3-silyl- 47,** 622s68
–, **N-sulfonyl- 51,** 190s68
Indene ring, polycyclic 68, 493
Indenes
– from
acetylene derivs. and aryl ketones **29,** 932s68
– – and *o*-ethyleneboronic acid esters, electron-deficient **68,** 461
– – and silylethynylarenes **42,** 915s68
–, **1-aryl-**
– from
o-acetylenestilbene oxides **68,** 497
–, **2,3,3a,4,5,7a-hexahydro-, 3a,7a-methano- 68,** 498
–, **1-vinyl-**
– by ring-closing metathesis **68,** 338
–, **2-vinyl-**
– from
o-ethynylstyrenes **68,** 338
Indium 60, 249s68, 455s68; **68,** 404
Indium(0), active 40, 567s68
Indium(III) acetate 45, 417s68
–(I) bromide 68, 405
–(III) bromide 19, 630s68; **56,** 63s68; **61,** 132s68; **63,** 304s68; **67,** 439s68
–(III) –/silica gel 2, 288s68
–(III) chloride 12, 867s68; **19,** 630s68; **58,** 238s68, 432s68; **68,** 97, 294, 383
–(III) –/silica gel 2, 288s68
–(III) compds., organo-
– special s.
indates, organotrivinylindium compds.
– startg. m. f.
ethylene derivs., regiostereospecific synthesis **68,** 468
– **hydride, dichloro- 65,** 489s68
–(I) iodide 21, 719s68; **43,** 725s68; **50,** 305s68; **53,** 230s68
–(III) triflate 43, 563s68; **60,** 249s68; **68,** 441, 478
Indole, 2-(di-*tert*-butylphosphino)-1-phenyl-
– as reagent **51,** 171s68
Indole-3-carboxylic acid esters 40, 540s68
Indoles 68, 183
–, N-acylation **41,** 339s68
–, alkylation, catalytic and stereoselective, review **39,** 363s68
–, allylation, Pd-catalyzed, regiospecific **68,** 376
–, 2-arylation **57,** 376s68
– from
N-arylcarbazic acid esters **14,** 836s68
o-bromo-β-styryl triflates and prim. amines **68,** 192
o-halogenacylamines **47,** 829s68
o-halogenamines and ketones **68,** 411
–, functionalization, Pd-catalyzed, review **42,** 853s68
– special s.
bis(indolyl)…
tris(indolyl)…
– startg. m. f.
indolines, asym. reduction **68,** 36
Indoles, 2-aryl- 68, 555s68
–, **4-bromo- 37,** 49s68
–, **fused 36,** 957s68

–, 1-hydroxy-
–, synthesis, polymer-based **24**, 525s68
Indolines
– from
 indoles, asym. reduction **68**, 36
–, **N-aryl-2-benzyl-**
– from
 o-allylamines and ar. halides (2
 different molecules) **68**, 414
–, **3-methylene-, N-protected 68**, 339
–, **N-sulfonyl-, 3-subst., chiral 68**, 36
Indolizines
– from
 acetylene derivs. **58**, 315s68
2-Indolylboronic acid esters
– startg. m. f.
 oxindoles, N-carbo-*tert*-butoxy-
 15, 151s68
Iodides
– from
 alcohols, partial conversion **68**, 212
α-**Iodination, oxidative 68**, 210
Iodine
– as catalyst **55**, 337s68; **63**, 449s68
– as reactant **46**, 432s68; **68**, 207
– as reagent **40**, 99s68; **44**, 154s68;
 50, 471s68; **51**, 18s68; **64**, 86s68;
 68, 56, 128, 137, 173
Iodine chemistry, hypervalent
–, review **41**, 696s68
Iodine monochloride 37, 446s68
Iodobenzene difluoride
– as reagent **68**, 94
**Iodocarbocyclization, regiostereo-
specific**
–, iodoheterocyclics, benzo-condensed
 via – **68**, 211
1,2-Iodochlorides
– from
 ethylene derivs. **46**, 432s68
Iododifluorides
– special s.
 p-methyliodobenzene difluoride
Iododihalides
– special s.
 4,4'-bis(dichloroiodo)biphenyl
 iododifluorides
Iodoheterocyclics, benzo-condensed
– via iodocarbocyclization, regiostereospecific **68**, 211
1,2-Iodohydrins
– from
 ethylene derivs. **46**, 432s68
α-**Iodoketones**
– from
 alcohols, sec. **68**, 210
Iodonium salts
– special s.
 ethyleneiodonium salts
**2-Iodopyridine methiodide, polymer-
based**
– as reagent **21**, 445s68
Iodosobenzene
– as reagent **62**, 159s68; **68**, 52
Iodoso(hydroxy)tosylates
– special s.
 phenyl iodoso(hydroxy)tosylate
N-Iodosuccinimide
– as reagent **48**, 434s68, 440s68; **68**, 203
o-**Iodoxybenzoic acid**
– as reagent **10**, 225s68; **68**, 97, 127
Ionic liquids (s.a. under Imidazolium ionic

liquids)
–, acetalation in – **68**, 96
–, aldol condensation, asym.,
 organocatalyzed in – **68**, 259
–, amines, ar. from nitro compds., ar. in –
 39, 14s68
–, (Z)-β-amino-α,β-ethylenecarbonyl
 compds. from β-ketocarbonyl
 compds. in – **68**, 164
– as catalyst **68**, 368
–, aziridines, N-tosyl- from ethylene
 derivs. in – **55**, 159s68
–, benzofurans from *o*-allyloxyhalides
 in – **36**, 957s68
–, carboxylic acid esters from acids in –
 7, 246s68
–, 2-chlorosulfonylamines, chiral from
 ethylene derivs. in – **68**, 204
–, chroman ring, 4-amino- from
 o-hydroxyaldehydes – **52**, 363s68
–, 3-chromenes from *o*-hydroxyaldehydes
 in – **60**, 427s68
–, cycloisomerization of 1,6-enynes in –
 61, 312s68
–, diaryls, sym. from ar. halides in –
 34, 825s68
–, Diels-Alder reaction, W-catalyzed
 under microwaves in – **68**, 312
–, dihydroxylation, asym. in – **64**, 81s68
–, 1,3-dioxolan-2-ones from epoxides in –
 23, 139s68
–, –, 4-methylene-, 5,5-disubst. from
 2-acetylene-*tert*-alcohols in –
 42, 127s68
–, epoxidation of 3-ethylenealcohols,
 hindered from – **24**, 149s68
–, (E)-α,β-ethylenecarboxylic acid esters
 from oxo compds. in – **54**, 388s68
–, Friedel-Crafts vinylation in – **68**, 299
–, Gewald 2-aminothiophene synthesis
 in – **43**, 765s68
–, Heck arylation in – **27**, 871s68
–, hetero-Diels-Alder reaction,
 intramolecular in – **63**, 359s68
–, hydrogenation, heterogeneous of oxo
 compds. in – **68**, 27
–, 2-hydroxythioethers from epoxides in –
 59, 219s68
–, immobilization of catalysts in – within
 amorphous silica pores **68**, 409
–, Knoevenagel condensation-
 intramolecular hetero-Diels-Alder
 reaction in – **54**, 357s68
–, methylene from oxo compds. in –
 40, 568s68
–, oxidation, heterogeneous of
 hydrocarbons in – **68**, 57
–, oxo compds. from alcohols in –
 54, 109s68
–, resolution, kinetic of glycols in –
 44, 214s68
–, reviews **61**, 74s68
–, ring-closing ene-yne metathesis in –
 56, 326s68
–, Sonogashira coupling, Cu-free in –
 63, 411s68
– special s.
 cyclopentadienylium triflates,
 sulfoalkyl-
 imidazolium ionic liquids
 morpholinium triflimides
–, Stetter hydroacylation in – **28**, 648s68

–, sulfones from sulfinic acids in –
 58, 51s68
–, sulfonylquinols from quinones in –
 18, 638s68
–, 1,3,5-triazines, 2,4-diamino- from
 nitriles in – **5**, 247s68
–, 2,2,2-trifluoroalcohols from oxo
 compds. in – **44**, 577s68
–, O-tritylation, preferential in –
 12, 288s68
Ionic liquids, Bronsted-acidic
–, acetalation in – **68**, 96
–, Mannich reaction in – **68**, 369
– –, chiral
–, Baylis-Hillman reaction, asym. in –
 39, 593s68
–, review **27**, 57s68
– –, functionalized
– special s.
 imidazolium chloride, 1-chlorosulfinyl-
 3-methyl-
– –, supported
– as Bronsted-type basic catalysts **68**, 359
–, review **61**, 74s68
Ionic liquid tagging
– of alkylidene(dichloro)ruthenium
 imidazolidin-2-ylidene complexes
 67, 499s68
Iridium
 nanoparticles **68**, 27
Iridium complexes
 bis(acetonitrile)(η⁵-pentamethylcyclopentadienyl)(1,2,3,4-tetramethyl-
 imidazol-2-ylidene)iridium(III)
 triflate **42**, 241s68
 bis(1,5-cyclooctadiene)iridium(I)
 fluoroborate **68**, 123
 carbonyl(methyl)iridium(III)
 di(phosphine) complexes, cationic
 68, 340
 chlorobis(cyclooctene)iridium(I) dimer
 68, 124
 chloro(cyclooctadiene)iridium(I) dimer
 68, 93, 178, 278, 332, 377
 chloro(pentamethylcyclopentadienyl)-
 iridium(III) dimer **68**, 421
 dichloro(1,5-cyclooctadiene)hydrido-
 iridium(III) dimer **46**, 42s68
 dichloro(pentamethylcyclopentadienyl)iridium(III) dimer **68**, 179
 pentahydridobis(triisopropylphosphine)iridium **68**, 50
**Iridium(I) 3-(Δ²-oxazolin-2-yl)-2-
diphenylphosphino-2-azabicyclo-
[2.2.1]heptane complexes, cationic,
chiral 46**, 47s68
–**(I) 1-[2-(Δ²-oxazolin-2-yl)ethyl]-
imidazol-2-ylidene complexes, chiral
68**, 40
–**(I) phosphinoxy-Δ²-oxazoline
complexes, chiral 56**, 39s68
Iron 18, 776s68
Iron/sodium fluoride 40, 567s68
Iron(III) acetoacetonate 68, 52, 476
Iron carbonyl 55, 249s68
–**(II) chloride 68**, 216
–**(III) chloride 18**, 674s68, 776s68;
 26, 70s68; **49**, 762s68; **55**, 337s68;
 56, 129s68; **61**, 441s68; **68**, 361
–**(III) –/silica 5**, 549s68

Iron complexes
bis(dinitrogen)[2,6-bis[1-(2,6-diisopropylphenylimino)ethyl]pyridine]iron(0) **68**, 31, 240
5,10,15,20-tetrakis(pentafluorophenyl)porphyrinatoiron(II) **37**, 80s68
5,10,15,20-tetraphenylporphyrinatoiron(III) chloride **55**, 159s68
– –, chiral
[(S,S)-N,N'-bis(3,5-di-*tert*-butylsalicylidene)-2,3-diphenyl-2,3-butylenediamino]iron(III) chloride **68**, 52
(pentamethylcyclopentadienyl)[7-(pyrrolidin-1-yl)-4-azaindenyl]iron(III), chiral **68**, 313
– –, organo-
– special s.
π-allyltricarbonyliron lactone complexes
Iron(III)-exchanged montmorillonite **52**, 363s68; **54**, 79s68
Iron(II) sulfate 68, 13
Isobenzopyrylium ate complexes, zwitterionic
– as intermediates **68**, 362
Isobutyraldehyde
– as reagent **68**, 76
Isocarbostyrils, 3,4-dihydro- 68, 356
Isocoumarins, 3,4-dihydro-, 8-hydroxy- 41, 744s68
Isocyanates
– startg. m. f.
arylcarboxylic acid amides **68**, 455
α,β-ethylenecarboxylic acid amides **68**, 455
2-pyridone ring **68**, 315
4(3H)-pyrimidinones, 1,2-dihydro-, N-condensed **68**, 281
Isocyanides s. Isonitriles
*o-*Isocyanoarylacetaldehyde acetals
– startg. m. f.
quinolines, 3-alkoxy- **68**, 485
α-Isocyanocarboxylic acid esters
–, C-α-allylation **38**, 772s68
– special s.
β-halogeno-α-isocyanocarboxylic acid esters
Isodomoic acid
–, chemistry, review **42**, 853s68
Isoflavones 2, 642s68
Isonitriles (s.a. Isocyano... and under Ugi)
– special s.
1,1,3,3-tetramethylbutyl isocyanide
– startg. m. f.
α,β-acetylenealdimines **68**, 279
β-acoxycarboxylic acid amides **68**, 275
β-acylaminocarboxylic acid amides **68**, 275
furans, 2-amino- **68**, 300
α-iminoiminoesters (from 2 molecules) **68**, 416
monoselenoiminocarbonic acid esters **68**, 235
pyridine ring, 1,2-dihydro-, 1-carbalkoxy-2-carbamyl- **26**, 884s68
pyrrole-3,4-dicarboxylic acid esters, 2-amino-5-imido-, N-subst. (from 2 molecules) **68**, 280
α-Isonitrosoketones
– as intermediates **68**, 84

O,O-Isopropylidene-1,4-bis(diphenylphosphino)butane-2,3-diol
– as reagent **68**, 483
Isopropyl phenolethers
– startg. m. f.
phenol acetates **38**, 211s68
Isoquinoline, (R)-1-[2-(diphenylphosphino)-1-naphthyl]-
– as reagent **68**, 435
–, 1,2,3,4-tetrahydro-, 2-carbalkoxy-, 1-subst. **68**, 410
–, –, N-phosphoryl- **8**, 823s68
–, 4-vinyl **62**, 482s68
Isoquinolinium fluoroborate, 3,4-dihydro-, 2,3,3-trimethyl-7-nitro-
– as reagent **37**, 128s68
Isothiazolidines
– startg. m. f.
2H-1,3-thiazin-2-ones, tetrahydro- **68**, 219
Isothiocyanates
– special s.
2-oxazolidones, 3-(isothiocyanatoacetyl)-
– startg. m. f.
2-aminothioureas, with retention of configuration **68**, 145
cyclopentadienes, imino- **44**, 621s68
Isothiouronium salts, cyclic
– startg. m. f.
guanidines, cyclic **5**, 346s68
Isoxazole libraries
–, synthesis, polymer-based **16**, 888s68
Isoxazoles
– startg. m. f.
β-amino-α,β-ethyleneketones **39**, 418s68
–, synthesis and reactivity, review **42**, 853s68
Isoxazolidines
– special s.
3-(C-glycosyl)isoxazolidines
Δ²-Isoxazolines
– special s.
bis(Δ²-isoxazolines)

Kabachnick-Fields reaction 33, 593s68
Ketals (s.a. Acetals)
– special s.
spiroketals
Ketene disilyl acetals
– startg. m. f.
3-hydroxymaleic anhydrides **68**, 451
Ketene mercaptals
– startg. m. f.
β-hydroxymercaptals **68**, 296
Ketenes
– special s.
diarylketenes
– startg. m. f.
β-lactones, asym. conversion **68**, 313
Ketenimines
– special s.
acylaminoketenimines
Ketimines (s.a. Aldimines, Azomethines)
– special s.

methyl N-arylketimines
α-Ketoaldehydes
– startg. m. f.
β-ketocarboxylic acid amides **68**, 42
2-Ketoammonium salts, quaternary
– startg. m. f.
cyclopropyl ketones **45**, 459s68
2-Ketoarsonium salts
– startg. m. f.
cyclopropyl ketones **29**, 872s68
β-Ketocarbonyl compds.
–, amination, asym. **68**, 143
– startg. m. f.
(Z)-β-amino-α,β-ethylenecarbonyl compds. (in ionic liquids or without solvent) **68**, 164
β-Ketocarboxylic acid allyl esters
– startg. m. f.
γ,δ-ethyleneketones, asym. conversion **68**, 499
β-hydroxyketones **68**, 483
α-Ketocarboxylic acid amides
– from
carboxylic acid halides, with 1 extra C-atom **68**, 428
β-Ketocarboxylic acid amides
– from
α-acoxy-β-ketocarboxylic acid amides **68**, 42
α-ketoaldehydes **68**, 42
β-Ketocarboxylic acid esters
–, C-α-alkylation, asym. **54**, 394s68
–, α-halogenation, asym. **68**, 208
–, hydrogenation, asym. homogeneous **68**, 26
–, Mannich-type reaction, asym., Pd-catalyzed with – **68**, 277
– special s.
α,β-diketocarboxylic acid esters
hydroxy-β-ketocarboxylic – –
– – –, cyclic
– special s.
hydroxy-β-ketocarboxylic acid esters, cyclic
γ-Ketocarboxylic acid esters
– from
α-diazocarboxylic acid esters and enamines **68**, 380
– special s.
amino-γ-ketocarboxylic acid esters
hydroxy-γ-ketocarboxylic – –
Ketones (s.a. Acylation, Carbonyl compds., Oxo compds.)
–, C-α-alkylation, heterogeneous with prim. alcohols **68**, 373
–, allylboration, asym. **68**, 436
–, α-aminomethylation, asym. **68**, 370
–, anti-Michael addition to α,β-acetylenecarboxylic acid esters **68**, 310
–, α-chlorination **67**, 213s68
– from
alkoximes **68**, 101
carboxylic acids, decarboxylative syntheses, review **13**, 837s68
diazo compds. **47**, 147s68
lithium tetraorganoindates **58**, 462s68
–, hydrogenation, asym., homogeneous with dynamic kinetic resolution **51**, 26s68
–, α-hydroxylation, asym., organocatalyzed **68**, 55

–, reduction s. HC⇓OC and under
  Alcohols from oxo compds.
–, Reformatsky synthesis with –
  38, 624s68
– special s.
  acetyleneketones
  acoxyketo...
  acylaminoketones
  alkoxyketones
  alleneketones
  aminoketones
  aminooxyketones
  aryl ketones
  α-arylketones
  azidoketones
  cyanoketones
  cyclopropyl ketones
  diazoketones
  diketones
  epoxyketones
  ethyleneketones
  halogenoketones
  hydroxyketones
  hydroxylaminoketones
  isonitrosoketones
  methyl ketones
  sulfinylaminoketones
  sulfonylaminoketones
– startg. m. f.
  alcohols, sec. s. under HC⇓OC and
    Alcohols from oxo compds.
  cyanohydrins, review 54, 266s68
  α-diketones 68, 84
  indoles 68, 411
  1,2,4-trioxanes, 6-α-arylthio- 68, 224
–, α-vinylation 66, 424s68
Ketones, cyclic
– from
  enoxystannanes, cyclic and alkyl
    halides, regiospecific asym. synthesis
    68, 452
– special s.
  α-nitroketones, cyclic
– startg. m. f.
  ω-arylcarboxylic acid amides 68, 149
  α,β-ethylenehalides, cyclic 68, 215
–, –, α,α-disubst., chiral 68, 452
α-Ketonitriles s. Acylcyanides
β-Ketonitriles s. α-Cyanoketones
α-Ketophosphonic acid esters
– special s.
  ethylene-α-ketophosphonic acid esters
γ-Ketophosphonic acid esters
– special s.
  carbalkoxyamino-γ-ketophosphonic
    acid esters
2-Ketophosphonium salts
– special s.
  acetonyltriphenylphosphonium bromide
2-Ketoselenides, chiral 45, 383s68
β-Ketosulfonic acid derivs. 63, 219s68
2-Ketothioethers 29, 262s68
β-Ketothiolic acid esters
– by Claisen-type condensation,
    reductive 68, 426
Knoevenagel condensation (s.a. Ugi-
  Knoevenagel condensation)
– –, heterogeneous
– in water 38, 756s68
Kowalski homologization
– of α-aminocarboxylic acid esters,
    N-protected, with retention of
    configuration 68, 394

Kumada coupling
– of lithium acetylides with alkyl halides
  68, 392

Lactams
– special s.
  N-(arylthio)lactams
  benzolactams
  halogenolactams
– startg. m. f.
  amines, cyclic
  aminocarboxylic acids, kinetic
    resolution 68, 64
  dicarboxylic acid imides 68, 65
β-Lactams s. 2-Azetidinones
γ-Lactams s. 2-Pyrrolidones
γ-Lactols
– from
  α,β-ethyleneketones 68, 285
Lactones
– from
  diols in water 68, 125
– special s.
  aldonolactones
  ethylenelactones
  glucuronolactones
  hydroxylactones
β-Lactones
– as intermediates for total synthesis,
    review 42, 853s68
– from
  ketenes and aldehydes, asym.
    conversion 68, 313
–, α,α-disubst., chiral 68, 313
γ-Lactones
– from
  α,β-ethylenealdehydes and aldehydes
    68, 301
– special s.
  alkylidene-γ-lactones
  amino-γ-lactones
Lanthanum triisopropoxide 68, 436
Lanthanum(III) triflate 68, 102, 257
Lead(IV) carboxylates, organo-
– special s.
  aryllead tricarboxylates
Lewis acid
–, metalloporphyrins as – 68, 61
Libraries of compds.
–, survey and review 50, 555s68
Ligands, functional
–, review 27, 851s68
–, monodentate, bulky
–, review 27, 851s68
Lithium 1, 522s68
–/ethylenediamine 31, 5s68
–/naphthalene 68, 14, 41
Lithium acetate 68, 207
– acetylides
– as reactant 68, 423
–, Kumada coupling with alkyl halides
  68, 392
– aluminates, organo-
  – aryl(triisobutyl)aluminate 68, 209
– amides
  – anilide 68, 136

– bis(trimethylsilyl)amide 68, 374, 394
– 2,2,6,6-tetramethylpiperidide
  47, 622s68; 68, 394
– as reactant 68, 149
– –, chiral
–, addition to heterocumulenes 68, 145
– –, hindered
– as reactant 68, 160
– bromide 46, 267s68; 57, 80s68;
  60, 455s68
– *tert*-butoxide 39, 844s68; 53, 435s68
– carbonate 68, 376
– chloride 68, 200, 329
– compds., organo-
  sec-butyllithium 68, 394
  tert-butyllithium 68, 284
– cuprates, organo-
  – bis(2-methyl-2-phenylpropyl)cuprate
    60, 376s68; 68, 397
– –, –, higher order
– special s.
  dilithium diorgano(cyano)cuprates
– fluoroborate 31, 123s68; 60, 194s68
– hexafluorophosphate 56, 73s68
– hydride 48, 434s68
– hydrido(amino)borates
–, review 66, 204s68
– hydroxide 51, 132s68; 68, 437
– iodide 42, 829s68; 62, 195s68
– *p*-methoxybenzoate
– as reagent 68, 52
– perchlorate 59, 234s68
– – (etherate) 10, 50s68
– telluride 68, 486
– tetraorganoindates
– startg. m. f.
  ketones 58, 462s68
– triflate 33, 593s68; 68, 275
– triisobutyl(2,2,6,6-tetramethyl-
  piperidino)aluminate
– as reagent 68, 209
2,6-Lutidine
– as reagent 68, 9

**Macrocyclization, conformationally
  directed**
–, review 42, 853s68
Magnesium/methanol
–, review 41, 48s68
Magnesium(0), active 3, 560s68
Magnesium-aluminum hydrotalcite
  27, 198s68
Magnesium bromide 49, 398s68;
  54, 307s68
– halides, organo- (s.a. under
  Titanium(IV) alkoxides)
  3-butenylmagnesium chloride 68, 255
  tert-butylmagnesium – 68, 237
  isopropylmagnesium – 68, 402
  methylmagnesium bromide 68, 262
– special s.
  o-sulfonyloxyarylmagnesium chlorides
– iodide 63, 248s68; 64, 240s68;
  66, 314s68; 68, 278
– oxide 68, 359
– perchlorate 50, 187s68; 68, 262

Magnesium triflate 60, 55s68
Maleic anhydrides
- special s.
  hydroxymaleic anhydrides
Malonic acid esters
- special s.
  dichloromalonic acid esters
- – –, β-subst.
-, synthesis, asym., iterative 52, 297s68
Malononitrile
- as CO equivalent 68, 390
Manganese(II) acetate 53, 240s68; 68, 372
Manganese complexes
  methylmanganese(II) amides 21, 439s68
  tris(pivaloylmethanato)manganese(III) 67, 146s68; 68, 71
- porphyrin complexes, PEG-based 39, 124s68
- (III) salen – 41, 261s68
Mannich reaction (s.a. 3-Component Mannich reaction)
- in ionic liquids, Bronsted-acidic 68, 369
Mannich-type reaction (s.a. 3-Component Mannich-type reaction)
- – –, asym., Pd-catalyzed
- with β-ketocarboxylic acid esters 68, 277
- – –, Lewis base-catalyzed 63, 424s68
Mercaptals
- as zwitterionic synthons, review 66, 495s68
- special s.
  hydroxymercaptals
-, cyclic
- from
  acetals, cyclic 46, 162s68
Mercaptans (s.a. under Replacement of sulfhydryl)
-, generation of alkyl radicals from – 68, 425
-, radical reactions with – 68, 302
- special s.
  acylaminomercaptans
  arylmercaptans
  ethylenemercaptans
- startg. m. f.
  benzyl thioethers 54, 83s68
  disulfides, sym. 29, 233s68; 42, 235s68
  nitrous acid esters 68, 51
o-Mercaptocarboxylic acids
- startg. m. f.
  benz[e][1,4]oxathiepin-5-ones 68, 223
Mercury compds., organo-
- special s.
  silylmercury compds.
Mercury(II) nitrate/silica gel 12, 252s68
- (II) oxide 25, 182s68
Metalation (s.a. Deprotonation)
-, benzylic, asym.
- of 2-oxydiarylmethanes 52, 298s68
Metalloporphyrins
- as Lewis acids 68, 61
Metal salen complexes
-, catalysis, asym. of C-C bond formation with –, review 27, 57s68
Metathesis (s.a. Cross-metathesis, Ene-yne metathesis, Olefin –, Ring-closing –, and under Interchange in Vol. 1-50)
-, nucleoside synthesis via –, review 27, 851s68

- of acetylene derivs., review 27, 851s68
-, review 27, 851s68
-, total synthesis via –, review 27, 851s68
Methallyl ethers
-, radical cleavage 68, 6
Methanesulfonic acid
- as reagent 8, 823s68; 68, 496
Methanesulfonic anhydride
- as reagent 68, 142
Methanesulfonyl chloride
- as reagent 13, 441s68
Methanophenazines
-, chemistry, review 42, 853s68
O,O-p-Methoxybenzylidene derivs.
- special s.
  carbohydrate O,O-p-methoxy-benzylidene derivs.
N-Methoxymethylation 68, 172
O-Methoxymethylation, regiospecific
- of glycols 68, 95
Methyl N-arylketimines
- from
  acetylene derivs., terminal 64, 143s68
N-Methylation
- of peptides, review 19, 33s68
Methyl α-bromoacrylate
- as reactant 68, 399
Methyldiphenylphosphine
- as reagent 62, 271s68
Methylenation-ring closing metathesis 68, 481
1-Methylene-1,2-bis(phosphine oxides)
- from
  ethynylcarbinols 68, 244
(E)-α-Methylenecarboxylic acid esters 25, 59s68
Methylene compds. (s.a. Ethylene derivs., terminal)
- from
  alcohols via oxo compds. 68, 472
  1,1-dihalides 56, 393s68
Methylenecyclopentanes 68, 339
1-Methylene-1,2-di(boronic acid esters)
- from
  allenes, terminal, asym. conversion 68, 242
α-Methylene-γ-lactones 34, 614s68
-, cis-fused
- from
  alleneoxo compds. 68, 311
α-Methylene-β-phosphonylcarboxylic acid esters 68, 248
N-Methylglycine
- as reagent 31, 522s68
N-Methyl groups
- from
  N-alkoxymethyl groups 68, 43
O-Methylhydroxylamine hydrochloride
- as reagent 10, 258s68
p-Methyliodobenzene difluoride
- as reagent 45, 290s68
Methyl ketones
- startg. m. f.
  α,β-ethyleneketones, heterogeneous conversion 68, 359
  pyrroles 68, 375
Methyllycaconitines
-, synthesis, review 42, 853s68
N-Methylmorpholine
- as reagent 68, 166
2-Methyl-6-nitrobenzoic anhydride
- as reagent 24, 408s68

Methyl propiolate
- as reactant 68, 254
Methyl thioglycolate
- as reactant 68, 395
Methyl triflate
- as reagent 68, 423
Methyl(trifluoromethyl)dioxirane
- as reagent 68, 126
Michael addition (s.a. 1,4-Addition, C-α-Alkylation-Michael addition, Anti-Michael addition, Baylis-Hillman reaction-Michael addition)
- of
  N-arylideneglycinates, Ni(II)-complexed, asym. induction 36, 668s68
  carboxylic acid amide enolates 36, 652s68
  nitro compds., aliphatic (in water) 68, 285
  zinc acetylides, asym. induction 65, 266s68
- – –, amine-catalyzed 68, 66
- – –, asym.
- of
  o-hydroxyoximes as water equivalent 68, 68
  urethans (under Lewis acid catalysis) 68, 150
- – –, –, organocatalyzed
- to 1,1-nitroethylene derivs. 68, 303
- – –, Pd-catalyzed
- of acylamines 61, 143s68
- – –, Rh-catalyzed
- of alcohols 68, 77
- – –, dichloroindium hydride-mediated 65, 489s68
- – –, fluoride ion-catalyzed 63, 147s68
- – –, heterogeneous
- of amines 63, 147s68
- – –, intramolecular (s.a. Michael addition-intramolecular Michael addition, Rauhut-Currier reaction-intramolecular – –, Ugi condensation-intramolecular – –)
- addition-intramolecular Michael addition, asym., organocatalyzed 68, 304
- addition-lactonization, Lewis base-catalyzed 68, 434
- addition-Pictet-Spengler cyclization (s.a. Sonogashira acylation-Michael addition-Pictet-Spengler cyclization)
Michael-type addition, organocatalyzed
- of arenes 11, 770s68
Microorganisms s.a. Enzymes
Microreactions, nanoscale
-, C-H bond activation and catalysis in –, review 27, 851s68
Microreactors
-, Baeyer-Villiger oxidation, asym. in – 66, 77s68
-, overview 65, 377s68
Microwave irradiation
-, acetalation, heterogeneous under – 28, 141s68
-, acetylene derivs., terminal from silylacetylenes under – 23, 656s68
-, O-acylation, preferential under – 42, 164s68
-, alkoxy-2-ethylenes from 2-ethylene-alcohols under – 34, 165s68

–, alkoxy-3-ethylenes from acetals
under – 33, 874s68
–, O-alkylation, regiospecific under –
34, 187s68
–, o-aminomethylation under – 3, 661s68
–, arenes from aryl perfluorooctane-
sulfonates under – 42, 58s68
–, N-arylation with arylboronic acids
under – 55, 166s68
–, aryl ketones from carboxylic acid
anhydrides under – 62, 452s68
–, benzo[b]thiophenes from β-mercaptostyrenes under – 12, 689s68
–, 1,1-bis(indol-3-yl)alkanes from oxo
compds. under – 5, 549s68
–, carboxylic acid thioamides from nitriles
under – 19, 378s68
–, 3-component synthesis of 4-thiazolid-
ones under – 9, 672s68
–, cross-coupling of unsatd. boronic acids
with organothio-N-heterocyclics
under – 63, 406s68
–, cycloaddition, 1,3-dipolar,
decarboxylative under – 43, 897s68
–, diaryls from arylsilanes under –
52, 467s68
–, 4H-1,2-diazepines from [thio]pyrylium
salts under – 68, 159
–, Diels-Alder reaction, W-catalyzed in
ionic liquids under – 68, 312
–, fluorides, ar. from chlorides, ar.
under – 4, 513s68
–, formanilides from ar. nitro compds.
under – 68, 161
–, glycosylamines from aldoses under –
64, 151s68
–, guanidines, cyclic from isothiouronium
salts, cyclic under – 5, 346s68
–, halides from alcohols in ionic liquids
under – 60, 182s68
–, Hantzsch pyridine synthesis in water
under – 47, 727s68
–, Heck arylation under – 27, 871s68
–, heterocyclic synthesis under –, review
42, 853s68
–, hydantoins from α-ureidocarboxylic
acid esters under – 31, 452s68
–, hydroamination, intramolecular under –
68, 155
–, 2-hydroxythioethers from epoxides in
water under – 2, 532s68
–, in water, review 27, 851s68
–, ketones, cyclic from carboxylic acids
under – 6, 854s68
–, O-methylation of phenols under –
41, 325s68
–, methylene from carbonyl compds.
under – 35, 622s68
–, nitriles, ar. from halides, ar. under –
29, 845s68
–, olefin metathesis under –, review
27, 851s68
–, 1,3,4-oxadiazoles from acylhydrazones
under – 44, 301s68
–, oxo compds. from oximes under –
31, 185s68; 62, 102s68
–, phosphine-borane complexes, tert.
from ethylene derivs. under –
25, 466s68
–, phthalides by carbonylation under –
34, 832s68

–, protection of alcohols as furan-2-yl
ethers, tetrahydro- under –
42, 146s68
–, 2-pyridone ring by 3-component
synthesis under – 33, 753s68
–, 4(3H)-quinazolones from 3,1-benz-
oxazine-2,4-diones under –
28, 418s68
–, radical ring closure of ethylenetellurides under – 51, 355s68
–, radical ring closure-Horner synthesis
under – 68, 429
–, reduction, selective of aldehydes
under – 68, 19
–, replacement of carbonyl sulfur by
oxygen under – 68, 113
–, review 60, 153s68
–, ring closure, triple via carbonyl ylids,
cyclic under – 43, 943s68
–, Suzuki coupling in water under –
27, 851s68 (review); 37, 902s68
–, synthesis, polymer-based of
N-heterocyclics under – 43, 316s68
–, –, –, of oxindoles under – 43, 957s68
–, 4-thiazolidones from azomethines
under – 4, 552s68
–, α-tosyloxyketones from alcohols
under – 66, 97s68
–, 1,3,5-triazines, 2,4-diamino- from
nitriles under – 5, 247s68
–, 1,2,4-triazole ring, N-condensed from
hydrazones under – 19, 554s68
–, 1,2,3-triazoles from acetylene derivs.,
terminal under – 68, 184
–, Ugi 4-component synthesis, fluorous
under – 17, 809s68
–, ureas, cyclic from diamines under –
66, 165s68
–, urethans, cyclic from aminoalcohols
under – 66, 165s68
–, Vilsmeier formylation under –
9, 871s68
–, Wittig synthesis under – 39, 854s68
Microwave irradiation, solventless
–, N-acylation, selective under –
10, 296s68
–, aldehydes from α-hydroxysulfonic
acids under – 22, 268s68
–, C-α-allylation with acetylene derivs.
under – 67, 335s68
–, Biginelli synthesis under – 55, 337s68
–, bromides from alcohols under –
34, 371s68
–, cleavage of carboxylic acid allyl and
tert-butyl esters under – 16, 201s68
–, 3-component synthesis of 4H-pyran
ring, 2-amino- under – 61, 340s68
–, cycloaddition, 1,3-dipolar under –
58, 314s68
–, α,α'-dihydroxyphosphinic acids, sym.
from aldehydes under – 68, 234
–, dithiophosphoric acid O,O-diesters
from halides under – 17, 165s68
–, Fries rearrangement under – 1, 537s68
–, furans, fused from α-cyclopropylideneketones under – 64, 85s68
–, Gewald synthesis under – 43, 765s68
–, indoles from o-nitrostyrenes under –
40, 315s68
–, iodides from alcohols under –
62, 195s68

–, 1,3,4-oxadiazoles from acylhydrazones
under – 11, 424s68
–, oxo compds. from their N-derivs.
under – 47, 146s68
–, pyrazoles from Δ²-pyrazolines under –
28, 889s68
–, Δ²-pyrazolines from α,β-ethylene-
ketones under – 8, 927s68
–, 4(3H)-quinazolones from o-acylamino-
carboxylic acids under – 3, 341s68
–, replacement of carbonyl oxygen by
sulfur under – 34, 525s68
–, – of P-oxygen by sulfur under –
22, 594s68
–, thiiranes from epoxides under –
55, 205s68
–, thioureas, sym. from amines under –
30, 243s68
–, Williamson ether synthesis under –
68, 108
– –, –, solid-supported
–, β-amino-α,β-ethylenecarbonyl from
β-ketocarbonyl compds. under –
30, 463s68
–, arylcarboxylic acids from aldehydes,
ar. under – 54, 63s68
–, 1H-1,5-benzodiazepines from
o-diamines under – 50, 471s68
–, Claisen rearrangement of allyl
phenolethers under – 2, 621s68
–, maleimide ring from o-dicarboxylic
acid anhydrides under – 5, 341s68
–, oxo compds. from alkoxysilanes
under – 41, 261s68
–, – – from oximes under – 34, 172s68;
39, 231s68
–, – – from pyran-2-yl ethers, tetrahydro-
under – 57, 120s68
–, phenols from furans under – 68, 293
–, pyrroles from aldehydes under –
68, 360
–, Sonogashira coupling, Ni-catalyzed
under – 54, 414s68
Mitsunobu reaction
– with polymeric reagents 68, 169
Molybdenum/titanium dioxide-
zirconium dioxide 56, 63s68
Molybdenum complexes
tetraphenylphosphonium oxodiperoxy-
(salicylaldoximinato)molybdate
68, 70
tricarbonyltris(tert-butyl isocyanide)-
molybdenum 68, 238
– hexacarbonyl 30, 467s68; 51, 163s68;
68, 311
– as source of CO 34, 832s68
Molybdenyl acetoacetonate 48, 216s68
Mono-N-alkylation, reductive
– with nitriles 68, 183
Monoselenoiminocarbonic acid esters
– from
isonitriles, alcohols and halides 68, 235
O-Monothiophosphorylation 27, 113s68
Montmorillonite (s.a. Bismuth(III)
nitrate/montmorillonite, Iron(III)-
exchanged montmorillonite) 5, 549s68;
39, 759s68; 51, 226s68; 55, 146s68
Morpholinium triflimide, 4-[2-(2-
ethoxyethoxy)ethyl]-4-methyl-
– as ionic liquids 44, 577s68
Mukaiyama aldol... s. Aldol-type...

Multicomponent reactions
– with Group VI Fischer carbene
complexes, review **27**, 851s**68**

Nafion-H SAC-13 39, 214s**68**; **68**, 172
Naphthalene, 1,8-bis(dimethylamino)-
– as reagent **68**, 53
Naphthalenes, 1-acyl-
– from
  o-acetylenealdehydes and oxo compds.
  68, 362
–, **1-*sec*-amino- 68**, 349
–, **1,2-dihydro-, 4-siloxy-**
– from
  4-aryl-1-siloxyacetylenes **68**, 496
Naphtho[2,1-*b*]furans, 4,5-dihydro-
22, 877s**68**
2-Naphthols
– from
  o-acetyleneepoxides **68**, 347
1,4-Naphthoquinones 9, 254s**68**
(S)-(1-Naphthyl)glycolic acid
– as reagent **68**, 103
Nazarov cyclization
–, reviews **43**, 980s**68**
– –, Ir(III)-catalyzed, stereospecific
  68, 340
Neodymium(III) triflate 60, 194s**68**
Nickel/aluminophosphate, mesoporous
53, 9s**68**
Nickel/sulfuric acid 68, 10
Nickel(II) acetate 28, 288s**68**; **68**, 158
–(II) acetoacetonate **43**, 725s**68**
–(II) bis(Δ²-oxazoline) complexes,
  chiral **54**, 296s**68**
–(II) bromide **65**, 465s**68**
–(II) chloride **31**, 522s**68**; **58**, 194s**68**
–(II) –/ethanedithiol **68**, 11
– complexes
  bis(1,5-cyclooctadiene)nickel(0)
  45, 397s**68**; **59**, 411s**68**; **68**, 317, 318, 386
  dichloro[1,2-bis(diphenylphosphino)-
  ethane]nickel(II) **57**, 442s**68**
  dichloro[1,3-bis(diphenylphosphino)-
  propane)nickel(II) **60**, 412s**68**
– –, chiral
  [N,N'-bis(2-quinolylmethylene)-1,1'-
  binaphthyl-2,2'-diamine]nickel(II)
  complexes, chiral **53**, 453s**68**
–(0) imidazol-2-ylidene complexes
  68, 315
Nicotinium dichromate
– as reagent **25**, 185s**68**
Nicotinoyl azide
– as reagent **32**, 333s**68**
Ninhydrin analogs
–, review **42**, 853s**68**
Niobium(V) chloride 20, 501s**68**
(review); **52**, 4s**68**; **55**, 337s**68**; **56**, 347s**68**
***ipso*-Nitration**
– of arylboronic acids **68**, 195
Nitrile oxides
–, cycloaddition, 1,3-dipolar in
  supercritical CO_2 **68**, 282

Nitriles
–, C-α-alkylation, heterogeneous with
  prim. alcohols **68**, 373
– from
  α-*prim*-aminocarboxylic acids **68**, 139, 202
  carboxylic acid amides, N-unsubst.
  4, 457s**68**; **68**, 200
– – esters, gas-phase conversion
  35, 348s**68**
  γ-cyanoketones **68**, 50
  N,N-dichloramines, prim. **68**, 139
  1,3-dinitriles **68**, 50
  α,β-ethylenenitriles **68**, 29
  nitro compds., prim. **68**, 199
–, reactions with nitrogenase-like metal
  complexes, review **28**, 13s**68**
– special s.
  acylaminonitriles
  alkoxynitriles
  aminonitriles
  carbalkoxyaminonitriles
  dinitriles
  ethylenenitriles
  hydroxynitriles
– startg. m. f.
  amines, prim. **27**, 65s**68**
–, sec. **68**, 183
  (Z)-β,γ-ethylene-ε-hydroxyketones
  (from 2 molecules) **68**, 255
  pyrimidines, 1,4,5,6-tetrahydro-,
  1-tosyl- **68**, 146
  Δ¹-pyrrolines, 3-methylene- **63**, 282s**68**
  1,3,5-triazines, sym. **31**, 296s**68**
Nitriles, ar.
– startg. m. f.
  (Z)-cinnamonitriles, tetrasubst. **68**, 316
Nitrilimines, *in situ*-generated
–, cycloaddition, 1,3-dipolar with –
  58, 314s**68**
2-Nitroalcohols (s.a. Henry reaction)
4-Nitroalcohols
– as intermediates **68**, 285
γ-Nitroaldehydes, chiral 62, 282s**68**
2-Nitrobenzoic acid
– as reagent **67**, 212s**68**
***o*-Nitrobenzylamines**
– startg. m. f.
  quinazolines, 3,4-dihydro- **65**, 169s**68**
Nitro compds.
– startg. m. f.
  amines, sec. **68**, 183
Nitro compds., aliphatic
– from
  halides **37**, 369s**68**
– startg. m. f.
  2-cyclohexenones, 3-alkylthio-4-nitro-
  68, 424
  1,4-diols **68**, 285
  m-hydroxythioethers **68**, 424
Nitro compds., ar.
– from
  arylboronic acids **68**, 195
– startg. m. f.
  amines, ar. **51**, 163s**68**; **68**, 13
  carboxylic acid anilides **68**, 165, 182
  formanilides **68**, 161
  hydroxylamines, ar., partial conversion
  68, 12
– – –, prim.
– startg. m. f.
  aldoximes **68**, 199

nitriles **68**, 199
2-Nitro-2-deoxy-β-glycosylphosphonic
  acid esters 9, 719s**68**
Nitrodiaryls 38, 836s**68**
1,1-Nitroethylene derivs.
–, Baylis-Hillman reaction with –
  39, 593s**68**
–, Michael addition, asym., Ru-catalyzed
  to – **48**, 687s**68**
–, – –, –, organocatalyzed to – **68**, 303
– startg. m. f.
  cyclohexanones, 4-nitro-, asym.
  synthesis **68**, 304
(Z)-1,1-Nitroethylene derivs.
– startg. m. f.
  (E)-ethylene derivs. **24**, 85s**68**
1,2-Nitroethylene derivs., cyclic
–, Heck arylation, intramolecular
  36, 957s**68**
β-Nitro-α,β-ethylenephosphonic acid
  esters
–, Diels-Alder reaction with – **35**, 454s**68**
Nitrogen
–, activation, review **45**, 486s**68**
α-Nitroketones
–, review **33**, 370s**68**
Nitromethane
– as reactant **68**, 379
Nitrones
–, cycloaddition, 1,3-dipolar with – on
  solid supports, review **42**, 853s**68**
– startg. m. f.
  2-(hydroxyamino)alcohols **68**, 271
  2-(hydroxyamino)sulfinylamines,
  asym. induction **68**, 271
β-Nitrophosphonic acid esters
– special s.
  ethylene-β-nitrophosphonic acid esters
Nitrosamines
– startg. m. f.
  amines **53**, 9s**68**
Nitroso compds.
–, review **67**, 189s**68**
– special s.
  dinitroso compds.
  polynitroso –
– startg. m. f.
  α-(aminooxy)ketones, asym.
  conversion **68**, 103
  α-(hydroxylamino)ketones, – – **68**, 103
Nitrous acid esters
– from
  alcohols **68**, 51
  mercaptans **68**, 51
Norbornadiene
– as reagent **68**, 327
Norbornadienes, chiral
– as reagent **55**, 452s**68**
Norbornene
– as reagent **68**, 243, 410
Nozaki-Hiyama reaction, intra-
  molecular, regiostereospecific
– with allyl phosphates **68**, 487
– – –, polymer-based **34**, 614s**68**
Nucleoside H-phosphonates 68, 54
Nucleosides
– via metathesis, review **27**, 851s**68**
–, **2'-functionalized**
–, review **17**, 169s**68**
Nucleoside triphosphates
– from

nucleoside phosphoromonoamidic acid benzyl esters **10**, 125s68
Nucleotides
– special s.
  oligonucleotides

Olefin metathesis
– under microwaves, review **27**, 851s68
– with
  metal carbene complexes in low oxidation state, review **27**, 851s68
  methylrhenium oxide, review **27**, 851s68
Oligonucleoside H-phosphonates 17, 169s68
Oligonucleotides, 2′-functionalized
–, review **17**, 169s68
Oligosaccharide synthesis 45, 116s68
– –, enzymatic
–, review **41**, 173s68
Organocatalysis, asym. s. Catalysis, asym., organo- and under individual reactions
Orthocarboxylic acid esters
– special s.
  spiroorthocarboxylic acid esters
– startg. m. f.
  4(3H)-quinazolones **28**, 418s68
– – –, bicyclic **21**, 270s68
Osmate s. Potassium osmate
Osmium tetroxide, dendritic 64, 81s68
[n+4]-Oxabicyclo[n.4.0]alka-1,3,(n+2),(n+5)-tetraene-2,3-dicarboxylic acid esters 68, 327
8-Oxabicyclo[3.2.1]oct-6-enes
– startg. m. f.
  pyrans, tetrahydro-, 2,6-divinyl-, desymmetrization **68**, 319
9-Oxa-10-borabicyclo[3.3.2]decanes, B-alkyl-
– startg. m. f.
  carboxylic acids, with 1 extra C-atom **39**, 844s68
1,3,4-Oxadiazin-2-ones, tetrahydro-, 3-acyl-
–, aldol condensation, asym. with – **45**, 383s68
Oxalic acid esters
–, deoxygenation of sec. alcohols via – **31**, 49s68
– startg. m. f.
  quinoxaline-2,3-diones **21**, 416s68
Oxalyl chloride
– as reagent **67**, 207s68; **68**, 448
– startg. m. f.
  3-hydroxymaleic anhydrides **68**, 451
Oxamides, unsyn. 22, 493s68
Oxa-Pauson-Khand reaction, intramolecular 68, 311
1,3-Oxaselenolanes, 4-alkylidene-2-imino-
– from
  2-acetylenealcohols **68**, 235
1,2-Oxasilacycloalk-3-enes 50, 443s68
1,2-Oxasilacyclohept-4-enes, 6-benzyl-
– startg. m. f.

tetralins, 1-aryl-3-hydroxymethyl-2-vinyl- **68**, 443
1,3-Oxathiolan-2-ones
– from
  epoxides **68**, 218
9-Oxatricyclo[3.3.1.0^{1,3}]nonanes 68, 337
1,3,2-Oxazaborolidines, chiral
– in asym. synthesis, review **27**, 57s68
1,3,2-Oxazaborolidinium triflimides, N-condensed, chiral
– as reagent **68**, 256
1,3,2-Oxazaborolid-5-ones, 2,2-difluoro-
–, protection and activation of α-amino-carboxylic acids as – **68**, 163
2H-1,2-Oxazin-3(4H)-ones, 5,6-dihydro-, 5-alkoxylamino- 54, 299s68
Oxaziridine, trans-3-tert-butyl-3-methyl-2-(phenylsulfonyl)-
– as reagent **68**, 231
Oxazoles
– from
  2-acetyleneacylamines **68**, 80
  2-acetylenealcohols and carboxylic acid amides, N-unsubst. **68**, 175
–, 5-β-keto- **68**, 80
–, 4-siloxy-
– as intermediates **68**, 448
Oxazolidines, 4-alkylidene-
– as intermediates **68**, 360
2-Oxazolidinethiones, 3-acyl-
–, aldol condensation, asym. with – **45**, 383s68
– startg. m. f.
  thiolic acid esters **46**, 494s68
2-Oxazolidone, 3-(isothiocyanatoacetyl)-
– as reactant **68**, 262
2-Oxazolidones
– from
  2-aminoalcohols **66**, 169s68
  aziridines **23**, 139s68; **68**, 147
– special s.
  pyridines, 2-(2-oxazolidon-3-yl)-
–, 3-acyl-
–, C-α-alkylation, asym., polymer-based **44**, 776s68
–, 3-alkoxy-4-imino-
– from
  cyanohydrins and hydroxylamines **68**, 157
–, 3-(carbalkoxyamino)-
– from
  aldehydes, asym. conversion **68**, 170
  N-2-aldehydohydrazodicarboxylic acid esters **68**, 170
–, chiral
– as reagent **47**, 773s68
–, 3-diazoacetyl-, chiral
– as reactant **68**, 265
–, N-(α,β-ethylene-δ-hydroxyacyl)-, chiral **64**, 432s68
Δ^2-Oxazoline-4-carboxylic acid esters
–, 4-alkylation, asym. **58**, 353s68
Δ^2-Oxazoline N-oxides, chiral
–, cycloaddition, 1,3-dipolar to – **16**, 735s68
Δ^2-Oxazolines
– from
  2-halogenacylamines **68**, 135
– special s.
  bis(Δ^2-oxazolines)
  carbohydrate Δ^2-oxazolines

tris(Δ^2-oxazolines)
–, 2-[2-(diphenylphosphino)ferrocenyl]-, chiral
– as reagent **66**, 42s68
–, 2-(1′-α-hydroxyferrocenyl)-, chiral
– as reagent **58**, 236s68
–, 5-α-iodo- **48**, 434s68
–, 2-α-(phosphinoamino)-, chiral
– as reagent **52**, 297s68
–, 2-[o-(sulfonylamino)phenyl]-, chiral
– as reagent **64**, 244s68
(Δ^2-Oxazolin-2-yl)ferrocenes, chiral
– special s.
  2-(4(S)-tert-butyl-Δ^2-oxazolin-2-yl)-ferrocene, 1-[diphenyl(hydroxy)methyl]-
  Δ^2-oxazolines, 2-[2-(diphenylphosphino)ferrocenyl]-, chiral
–, 2-(1′-α-hydroxyferrocenyl)-, chiral
Δ^2-5-Oxazolones
– startg. m. f.
  α-acylaminocarboxylic acid esters, dynamic kinetic resolution **68**, 60
  Δ^1-pyrroline-5-carboxylic – – **68**, 288
–, 4-alkylidene-
– startg. m. f.
  α-acylaminocarboxylic acid esters **28**, 288s68
Δ^4-2-Oxazolones
– in synthesis, review **42**, 853s68
Oxepins, 2,3,4,5-tetrahydro- 31, 135s68
N-Oxide radicals
– special s.
  piperidine nitroxyls
N-Oxides
– special s.
  o-hydroxy-N,N-dimethylbenzylamine N-oxide
  triethanolamine –
–, cyclic
– special s.
  bipyridyl N,N′-dioxides
  terpyridyl tri-N-oxides
Oxido compds. s. Epoxides
Oximes (s.a. Isonitroso…)
–, cleavage **12**, 252s68; **45**, 95s68; **52**, 96s68
– special s.
  aldoximes
  hydroxyoximes
– startg. m. f.
  oxo compds. **68**, 106
– – (in the solid state) **40**, 107s68
Oximes, O-alkyl- s. Alkoximes
Oxindoles 68, 198
– special s.
  spirooxindoles
–, 3-alkylidene-
– from
  aminooxy(phosphonyl)acetic acid anilides and aldehydes **68**, 429
–, synthesis by carboindation, intramolecular-Heck arylation **60**, 455s68
–, N-carbo-tert-butoxy-
– via 2-indolylboronic acid esters **15**, 151s68
Oxo compds. (s.a. Aldehydes, Carbonyl compds., Ketones)
–, N-alkylation, reductive with – (without solvent or in water) **68**, 162
–, allylboration, asym. **68**, 446

Oxo compds.
- from
   halides **68**, 134
   alcohols, oxidation (s.a. OC⇑H and
   under Alcohols startg. m. f. oxo
   compds.)
   hydrazones **34**, 172s68
   oximes **12**, 252s68; **45**, 95s68;
   47, 146s68; **52**, 96s68; **68**, 106
   piperidines, 1-alkoxy-2,2,6,6-tetra-
   methyl- **68**, 134
   pyran-2-yl ethers, tetrahydro-
   41, 261s68
   semicarbazones **12**, 252s68;
   34, 172s68; **47**, 146s68; **52**, 96s68
-, α-hydroxymethylation, asym.
   58, 245s68
- special s.
   acetyleneoxo compds.
   alleneoxo compds.
   dioxo compds.
   ethyleneoxo compds.
- startg. m. f.
   α,β-acetylene-γ-hydroxycarboxylic
   acid esters, with 3 extra C-atoms
   68, 254
   alcohols, reduction s. HC⇓OC and
   under Alcohols from oxo compds.
   1,3-dioxolanes **58**, 78s68
   (Z)-3-ene-1,6-diols (from 2
   molecules), with insertion of 4
   C-atoms **68**, 255
   α-halogeno-β-hydroxynitriles, with 2
   extra C-atoms **55**, 249s68
   hydrazones **50**, 187s68
   α-hydroxyacetals **68**, 56
   2-(hydroxyamino)alcohols **68**, 271
   naphthalenes, 1-acyl- **68**, 362
   4-pyrones, tetrahydro-, 2,3,6-trisubst.
   68, 383
-, α-sulfenylation, asym., organocatalyzed **68**, 228
Oxo compds., β-functionalized, α-alkyl-
-, reduction, stereospecific, Lewis acid-
   mediated, review **43**, 40s68
Oxygen, molecular
-, oxidation, transition metal-catalyzed
   with –, review **27**, 851s68
-, singlet
-, cleavage of oximes with – **68**, 106
-, α-hydroxylation, asym., organocatalyzed with – **68**, 55
- in chemistry, review **41**, 134s68
α-Oxygenation, asym.
-, review **27**, 57s68
Oxyselenation, intramolecular,
   polymer-based **29**, 180s68

Palladacyclic complexes (s.a. under
   Palladium complexes for specific
   palladacyclic catalysts)
-, review **27**, 851s68
- special s.
   ferrocenylpalladacyclics
- -, fluorous **27**, 871s68
- -, NCP-pincer-type, unsym.

37, 902s68
- *sec*-phosphine complexes **51**, 171s68
Palladium
- nanoparticles, dodecanethiolate-
   stabilized **37**, 902s68
- -, polymer-supported, amphiphilic
   68, 39
- -, silica gel-entrapped **37**, 902s68
- -/hydroxyapatite **55**, 113s68
-/carbon **27**, 851s68; **65**, 237s68; **68**, 49,
   111, 138, 183
-/silica **27**, 871s68
-/-, mesoporous **53**, 9s68
Palladium(II) acetate 27, 851s68;
   37, 49s68; **41**, 564s68; **53**, 471s68;
   55, 454s68; **62**, 451s68; **63**, 411s68;
   64, 453s68; **67**, 255s68, 448s68;
   68, 131, 190, 247, 327, 328, 356, 376,
   409, 410, 463-5, 482, 493
-(II) acetoacetonate **23**, 819s68;
   60, 455s68
- η¹-allyl complexes, pincer-type,
   nucleophilic
- as intermediates **68**, 471
- π-allyl complexes
- as intermediates **68**, 460
- special s.
   bis(π-allylpalladium) complexes
-(II) bromide **62**, 482s68
- carbene complexes, N-heterocyclic
   aquo[N,N'-bis(2,6-diisopropyl-
   phenyl)imidazol-2-ylidene]-
   palladium(II) acetate **68**, 472
- trifluoroacetate **59**, 311s68
   (1,3-dimesitylimidazol-2-ylidene)-
   (η²,η²-1,1,3,3-tetramethyl-1,3-
   divinyldisiloxane)palladium(0)
   27, 724s68
   palladium(II) imidazolidin-2-ylidene
   complexes **68**, 190
- - -, highly active **68**, 482
- - -, -, polymer-based
   palladium(II) imidazol-2-ylidene
   complexes, polymer-based
   37, 902s68
- catalysts
-, *in situ*-modification by ligand exchange
   68, 414
-(II) chloride **27**, 851s68; **34**, 825s68;
   36, 957s68; **37**, 902s68; **64**, 453s68;
   68, 122, 416
-(II) -/tin(II) chloride **52**, 273s68
- complexes
   (η³-allyl)[1,2-bis(*p*-methoxyphenyl)-
   3,4-bis(2,4,6-tri-*tert*-butylphenyl-
   phosphinidene)-1-cyclobutene]-
   palladium(II) triflate **32**, 11s68
   (η³-allyl)(η⁵-cyclopentadienyl)-
   palladium(II) **48**, 691s68; **66**, 366s68
   bis(acetonitrile)dichloropalladium(II)
   46, 335s68; **61**, 143s68; **68**, 78
   bis(η³-allylpalladium chloride)
   38, 772s68; **52**, 467s68; **68**, 177, 376,
   417
   bis(benzonitrile)dichloropalladium(II)
   68, 100
   bis(2-chloropallada-4,4'-dichloro-
   benzophenone oxime) **34**, 825s68
   bis(dibenzylideneacetone)palladium(0)
   45, 555s68; **67**, 255s68; **68**, 241, 466
   [1,1'-bis(di-*tert*-butylphosphino)-
   ferrocene]palladium(II) chloride
   37, 902s68

[2,6-bis(diphenylphosphinoxy)phenyl]-
   palladium(II) trifluoroacetate
   68, 471
[1,2-bis(2-pyrazinylethynyl)benzene]-
   palladium(II) **37**, 902s68
   bis(tri-*tert*-butylphosphine)palladium(0)
   66, 399s68; **68**, 411
   bis(tricyclohexylphosphine)pal-
   ladium(0) **68**, 154
[*o*-(*tert*-butylselenomethyl)phenyl]-
   palladium(II) acetate dimer **68**, 415
   chloro[2,6-bis(2,5-diphenylphosphol-1-
   ylmethyl)pyridine]palladium(II)
   fluoroborate **54**, 244s68
   chlorobis(N-methylimidazol-2-yl)-
   methylpalladium(II) **63**, 411s68
   chloro[2-(N,N-dicyclohexylamino-
   thiocarbonyl)furan-3-yl]-
   palladium(II) dimer **27**, 871s68
   chloro(salicylaldehyde N⁴-ethyl-
   thiosemicarbazone)palladium(II)
   27, 871s68
   diacetatobis(2,3,4,5-tetraphenyl-3-
   pyridylbenzene)palladium(II)
   67, 119s68
   dichlorobis(di-*tert*-butylphosphinous
   acid)palladium(II) **27**, 851s68;
   37, 902s68
   dichloro[1,1'-bis(diphenylphosphino)-
   ferrocene]palladium(II) **27**, 851s68;
   42, 58s68; **64**, 449s68
   dichloro[bis[2-(diphenylphosphino)-
   phenyl] ether]palladium(II) **68**, 294
   dichlorobis(η¹-2-ethyl-Δ²-oxazoline)-
   palladium(II) **27**, 871s68
   dichlorobis(triphenylphosphine)-
   palladium(II) **40**, 669s68; **46**, 906s68;
   49, 836s68; **68**, 418, 419, 420, 469
   dichloro(diphenylphosphinomethylphosphine enimine)palladium(II),
   ferrocene-based **63**, 411s68
   dichloro(pyridine-4-aldoxime)-
   palladium(II) **37**, 902s68
   [(2,6-dimesitylphenyl)dimethyl-
   phosphane]palladium(II) chloride
   dimer **37**, 902s68
   (4,7-diphenyl-1,10-phenanthroline)-
   palladium(II) bis(trifluoroacetate)
   68, 176
   tetrakis(triphenylphosphine)-
   palladium(0) **43**, 806s68; **48**, 771s68;
   53, 79s68; **66**, 318s68; **68**, 132, 201,
   264, 329, 330, 331, 375, 398, 473,
   474, 475
   tris(dibenzylideneacetone)dipalladium
   38, 836s68; **41**, 564s68; **47**, 839s68;
   56, 211s68; **66**, 155s68; **68**, 192, 242,
   392, 412-4, 467-70, 483, 484, 500
- complexes, chiral
   bis(aquo)[(R)-2,2'-bis(diphenylphosphino)-1,1'-binaphthyl]-
   palladium(II) bis(triflate) **68**, 277
   bis(benzonitrile)[(S,S)-1,2-bis[2-
   methoxyphenyl(phenyl)phosphino]-
   ethane]palladium(II) bis(hexafluoroantimonate) **55**, 452s68
   [(S)-2,2'-bis(dicyclohexylphosphino)-
   1,1'-binaphthyl]palladium(II)
   hexafluoroantimonate **59**, 447s68
   [dichloro[(S)-2,3:2',3'-bis(methylenedioxy)-6,6'-bis(diphenylphosphino)]biphenyl]palladium(II)
   56, 242s68

hexafluoroacetoacetonato[η^5-(S)-2-
[(4-isopropyl-Δ^2-oxazolin-2-yl)-
cyclopentadienyl](η^4-tetraphenyl-
butadiene)cobalt]palladium(II)
54, 138s68
hydroxy[(R)-2,2'-bis(diphenylphosphino)-1,1'-binaphthyl]-
palladium(II) triflate dimer
67, 149s68
palladium(II) 2-[o-(diphenylphosphino)phenyl]pyridine
complexes, cationic, chiral 62, 80s68
– complexes, Se-ligated, highly active
68, 415
– –, organo-
– special s.
vinylpalladium complexes
– –, NCN-pincer-type
–, review 27, 851s68
– –, polymeric
–, review 27, 851s68
– –, polyurea-encapsulated
–, review 27, 851s68
Palladium(II)-exchanged zeolite
63, 411s68
Palladium(II) hydroxide 26, 55s68;
68, 47
–(II) –/carbon 34, 790s68; 68, 68
–(II) iodide 68, 484
1,4-Palladium shift 68, 493
Passerini reaction, asym., catalyzed
68, 266
Passerini-type reaction
– with epoxides or aziridines 68, 275
Pauson-Khand reaction (s.a. Oxa-
Pauson-Khand reaction)
–, review (of intermolecular conversions)
27, 851s68
– with alleneamines, N-protected
53, 318s68
– –, asym., Rh-catalyzed
– in water 68, 325
– of 1,6-enynes 68, 325
– with formaldehyde as CO source
68, 325
– –, heterogeneous
– without CO 59, 304s68
– –, intramolecular
– of 1,2-dien-n-ynes 55, 296s68
– –, –, Ir-catalyzed
– of dienynes with desymmetrization
68, 332
Payne rearrangement
–, ring expansion of 2,3-epoxyalcohols
via – 68, 422
Pentafluorobenzoic acid
– as reagent 53, 213s68
1,1,1,3,3-Pentahalides 18, 776s68
Peptide amides
– special s.
dipeptide amides
Peptide p-nitroanilides
–, synthesis, polymer-based 26, 398s68
Peptides
– as reagent 68, 53
–, glycosidation, review 41, 173s68
–, C-α- and N-methylation, review
19, 33s68
– special s.
phosphinopeptides
phosphonylpeptides
prolylpeptides

sulfonamidopeptides
–, trifluoromethylated
–, review 19, 33s68
Peptide synthesis
– using ethyl propiolate 68, 166
Peptidomimetics
– from
α-aminocarboxylic acids, conformationally rigid, review 19, 33s68
Peptidyl dendrimers
–, review 19, 33s68
Peptidylureas, macrocyclic 56, 495s68
Per-O-acylation
– of carbohydrates 55, 81s68
Perbromides s. Tribromides
Perchloric acid/silica gel 59, 76s68
Perdeuteriation, decarb(ox,on)ylative
68, 49
Perfluorooctyl bromide
– as medium 68, 76
Periodate, polymer-based
– as reagent 40, 19s68
Periodic acid 68, 18, 88
Peroxides
– special s.
hydroperoxides
Peroxyacetic acid
– as reagent 68, 390
Peroxymonosulfate ion s. Benzyltriphenylphosphonium peroxymonosulfate
Persulfate ion s. Poly(4-vinylpyridinium)
persulfate
Phenanthrenes
– by ring-closing metathesis 56, 495s68
–, highly functionalized 35, 655s68
1,10-Phenanthroline
– as reagent 62, 171s68; 68, 233
–, 2,9-dimethyl-
– as reagent 68, 158
–, 4,7-diphenyl-
– as reagent 65, 465s68
Phenol
– as reagent 68, 455
Phenol acetates
– from
isopropyl phenolethers 38, 211s68
Phenolethers (s.a. O-Arylation,
Aryloxy...)
– special s.
allyl phenolethers
isopropyl –
Phenol ring
– from
2-ene-1,5-diones 37, 319s68
Phenols
–, O-allylation 68, 123
–, –, asym. 68, 124
–, O-arylation, heterogeneous 68, 193
– from
acetylene derivs., electron-deficient
6, 885s68
aryl triflates 68, 1
3,5-enyneepoxides 68, 497
furans and acetylene derivs. 68, 293
lithium aryl(triisobutyl)aluminates
68, 209
– special s.
acylaminophenols
2,2'-dihydroxybiphenyl
2,6-diisopropylphenol
fluorophenols

hydroxydiaryls
–, O-vinylation 61, 100s68
Phenoxazine-10-carboxamide, 4,6-bis-
(diphenylphosphino)-, polymer-based
– as reagent 64, 210s68
Phenylboron dichloride
– as reagent 39, 33s68
Phenylboronic acid, polymer-based
– as reagent 54, 10s68
o-Phenylenediamine
– as reagent 55, 175s68
Phenylhydrazine
– as reagent 55, 175s68
1-(N-Phenylimino)methyl-1'-(di-tert-
butylphosphino)ferrocene
– as reagent 37, 902s68
Phenyl iodosoacetate
– as reagent 42, 146s68; 58, 314s68;
65, 223s68
Phenyl iodoso(hydroxy)tosylate
– as reagent 66, 97s68
– –, polymer-based
– as reagent 68, 203
Phenyl iodosotrifluoroacetate
– as reagent 26, 592s68
N-(Phenylseleno)phthalimide
– as reactant 68, 245
Phenylsilane
– as reagent 45, 417s68; 68, 71
N-(Phenylthio)caprolactam
– as reagent 62, 117s68
Phenyl(tosylimino)iodinane
– as reactant 68, 186
Phosgene
– as reagent 9, 871s68
P4-Phosphazene base
– as reagent 38, 861s68; 48, 129s68
Phosphine dihalides
– special s.
triphenylphosphine dihalides
Phosphine imines
– special s.
phosphine N-sulfonylimines
Phosphine oxides
– special s.
(aminoaryl)phosphine oxides
bis(phosphine oxides)
ethylenephosphine oxides
triphenylphosphine oxide
Phosphines (s.a. Hydrophosphination,
Phosphino...)
– special s.
alkylidenephosphines
di(phosphines)
enephosphines
silylphosphines
(sulfonyloxyaryl)phosphines
tri(phosphines)
Phosphines, cyclic, monodentate, robust,
chiral
– as ligand 68, 26
–, tert.
– special s.
di-tert-butylphosphino...
dicyclohexyl[2-(2,6-diisopropoxy-
phenyl)]phenylphosphine
dicyclohexylphosphino...
[o-(dimethylamino)phenyl]diphenyl-
phosphine
diphenyl[4-(carbo-2-trimethylsilyl-
ethoxy)phenyl]phosphine
diphenylphosphino...

Pho – Pla

(Phosphines, tert.
– special s.)
(4-hydroxyphenyl)diphenyl)phosphine
Δ²-imidazolines, 2-[o-(diarylphosphino)phenyl]-
indole, 2-(di-*tert*-butylphosphino)-1-
   phenyl-
isoquinoline, 1-[2-(diphenylphosphino)-
   1-naphthyl]-
methyldiphenylphosphine
triarylphosphines
tributylphosphine
tri(*p*-fluorophenyl)phosphine
tri-2-furylphosphine
tri(*p*-methoxyphenyl)phosphine
trimethylphosphine
triphenylphosphine
tritolylphosphine
–, –, β-subst.
–, 3-component synthesis **68**, 239
Phosphine N-sulfonylimines
– special s.
triphenylphosphine N-tosylimine
Phosphinic acid esters
– special s.
hydroxyphosphinic acid esters
Phosphinopeptides
–, synthesis, review **19**, 33s68
Phosphinous acid amides
– special s.
N,N-diisopropyl-N-(diphenylphosphino)amine
– – halides
– special s.
chlorodiphenylphosphine
Phosphinous acids, stable
–, review **18**, 699s68
Phosphinoyl radicals
–, ring closure via β-elimination of –
68, 495
N-Phosphinylimines
–, synthesis, stereospecific via –, review
48, 625s68
Phosphomolybdate
– special s.
tetrabutylammonium phosphomolybdate
Phosphomolybdic acid 55, 159s68
– –/silica **50**, 151s68
H-Phosphonates (s.a. Phosphorous acid
monoesters)
– special s.
H-arylphosphonates
nucleoside H-phosphonates
Phosphonic acid esters
– from
ethylene derivs. **53**, 240s68
– special s.
acetylenephosphonic acid esters
acylphosphonic – –
alkoxyphosphonic – –
aminophosphonic – –
di(phosphonic – –)
glycosylphosphonic – –
hydrazinosulfonylphosphonic – –
hydroxyphosphonic – –
ketophosphonic – –
nitrophosphonic – –
Phosphonic acids
– special s.
aminophosphonic acids
Phosphonium salts
– as ionic liquids **27**, 871s68

– special s.
ketophosphonium salts
tetrabutylphosphonium bromide
tributylethylphosphonium tosylate
3,3,3-trichloropropyl(triphenyl)-
   phosphonium chloride
Phosphonous acid derivs.
– from
hypophosphorous acid derivs., review
18, 699s68
α-Phosphonylcarboxylic acid amides
– special s.
aminooxy(phosphonyl)acetic acid
anilides
β-Phosphonylcarboxylic acid esters
– special s.
α-methylene-β-phosphonylcarboxylic
acid esters
β-Phosphonylpeptides
–, synthesis, review **19**, 33s68
Phosphoramidites s.a. Phosphoromonoamidites
Phosphoranes
– special s.
alkylidenephosphoranes
Phosphoranyl radicals, cyclic
–, deoxygenation of alcohols via – **68**, 46
Phosphorazidates
– special s.
diphenyl phosphorazidate
Phosphoric acid/silica gel 66, 451s68
Phosphoric acid amides (s.a.
Phosphorylamines)
– as reagent **68**, 274
Phosphoric acid diesters, cyclic, chiral
– as reagent **68**, 274
Phosphoric acid esters
– special s.
allyl phosphates
enol phosphates
Phosphorodihalidates
– special s.
polyethylene glycol bis(dichlorophosphate)
Phosphoromonoamidites, cyclic
– as reagent **60**, 34s68, 379s68;
64, 211s68; **68**, 93, 178, 242
–, –, polymer-based, chiral
– as reagent **52**, 297s68
–, –, C₁-symmetric
– as reagent **68**, 35
Phosphorous acid esters
–, deoxygenation of alcohols via –
31, 49s68; **68**, 46
– special s.
triphenyl phosphite
– – –, chiral
– as ligands, review **27**, 57s68
– – –, cyclic
– special s.
acyl phosphites, cyclic
– – –, –, chiral
– as reagent **52**, 297s68
– – –, spirocyclic, chiral
– as reagent **60**, 379s68
– – monoesters (s.a. H-Phosphonates)
– from
alcohols **68**, 54
Phosphorus(V) acid esters
– special s.
ethylenephosphorus(V) acid esters
**Phosphorus ligands, carbohydrate-
based, C₁ and C₂-symmetric**

– in asym. catalysis, review **27**, 57s68
Phosphorus oxide chloride 42, 420s68
– pentasulfide **55**, 205s68
– pentoxide/montmorillonite **56**, 63s68
– –/silica **28**, 141s68
– tribromide **67**, 207s68
Phosphorylamines
– special s.
ethylenephosphorylamines
Phosphotungstic acid 39, 171s68;
40, 107s68; **55**, 337s68
– –/silica **51**, 55s68
Phthalimidines
– from
benzylamines, carbonylation, oxidative
68, 356
–, (E)-3-arylidene- **55**, 454s68
–, N-carbalkoxy-
–, 3-alkylation with asym. induction
10, 617s68
3-Picoline, 2-amino-
– as reagent **68**, 326
**γ-Picolinium chlorochromate/silica gel
4**, 274s68
Pictet-Spengler cyclization s.a. Michael
addition-Pictet-Spengler cyclization
Pinacolborane
– as reactant **68**, 236
**Pinacolization, asym., Cr(III)-catalyzed
68**, 261
α-Pinene
– as reagent **6**, 461s68
**Pipecolic acid amides, 1-acyl-, chiral
68**, 384
Piperazines, N-aryl- 51, 171s68
Piperidine, 1,2,2,6,6-pentamethyl-
– as reagent **68**, 273
Piperidine azasugars
–, total synthesis, review **41**, 173s68
**Piperidine nitroxyl, 4-[4,6-bis[bis(hepta-
decafluoroundecyl)amino]-1,3,5-
triazin-2-yloxy]-2,2,6,6-tetramethyl-**
– as reagent **45**, 120s68
– –, 2,2,6,6-tetramethyl-
– as reagent **68**, 134
– nitroxyls, fluorous
– as reagent **45**, 120s68
Piperidines
– from
pyridines, 2-(2-oxazolidon-3-yl)-,
   asym. induction **68**, 47
–, 1-acoxy-2,2,6,6-tetramethyl-
– startg. m. f.
aldehydes **68**, 134
–, 1-alkoxy-2,2,6,6-tetramethyl-
– startg. m. f.
oxo compds. **68**, 134
–, N-protected **58**, 482s68
**Piperidinium fluoroborate, 1-oxo-
2,2,6,6-tetramethyl-**
– as reagent **56**, 61s68
– –, 4-acetylamino-
– as reagent **54**, 120s68
2-Piperidone
– as reagent **68**, 440
2-Piperidones
– from
γ-halogencarboxylic acid amides
22, 528s68
Pivaloyl chloride
– as reagent **4**, 457s68
Platinum(II) chloride 56, 326s68;

68, 341, 344, 490
–(IV) chloride 56, 326s68
– complexes
[bis(phenylimino)acenaphthene]-
(dimethyl fumarate)platinum(0)
49, 518s68
dichloro(ethylene)platinum(II) dimer
62, 318s68; 68, 83
terpyridylplatinum acetylide
complexes, cationic 68, 106
tetrakis(triphenylphosphine)platinum(0)
64, 449s68
Polyamines, stereodefined
–, synthesis, iterative 68, 171
Polycyclics, benzo-condensed
– via activation, Pd-catalyzed, sequential
of C-H bonds 68, 493
Poly(diallyldimethylammonium
chloride)
– as reagent 4, 513s68
Polyenes 37, 834s68
Polyethylene glycol
–, aldol condensation, asym.,
organocatalyzed in – 68, 259
– as medium, review 61, 74s68
–, dihydroxylation, asym. in – 64, 81s68
– glycol-400
– as reagent 3, 689s68; 46, 713s68
– glycol bis(dichlorophosphate)
– as reagent 44, 301
α-(Polyfluoroalkyl)styrenes 49, 836s68
Polymer-based reactions
– special s.
1,4-addition, asym., polymer-based
C-α-alkylation, –
carbonylation, –
[2+2]-cycloaddition, –
Diels-Alder reaction, Lewis acid-
catalyzed, –
Nozaki-Hiyama reaction, –
oxyselenation, intramolecular, –
Sonogashira coupling, –
Suzuki diaryl coupling, –
transesterification, –
Ullmann diaryl ether synthesis, –
– with organometallics, review
57, 418s68
– –, quantitative
–, review 57, 418s68
Polymer-based and polymeric reagents
– special s.
azodicarboxylic acid esters, polymeric
N,N′-bis[o-(diphenylphosphino)-
benzoyl]-1,2-diamines, polymer-
based
2-chloropyridinium halides, –
– triflate, –
cinchonidinium salts, –
copper(II) bis(Δ²-oxazoline)
complexes, –
– carboxylate, –
4-dimethylaminopyridine, –
2-iodopyridine methiodide, –
palladium (nanoparticles), –
palladium complexes, polymeric
–(II) imidazol-2-ylidene complex,
polymer-based
periodate, –
phenoxazine-10-carboxamide, 4,6-
bis(diphenylphosphino)-, –
phenylboronic acid, –
phenyl iodoso(hydroxy)tosylate, –

phosphoromonoamidites, cyclic, –
poly(4-vinylpyridinium) persulfate
quinines, dihydro-, polymeric
scandium(III) sulfate bis(triflate),
polymer-based
N-sulfonyl-1,2-diamines, –
tetrahydridoborate, –
thiazolium iodides, –
titanium(IV) bis(1,1′-bi-2-naphthoxide)
complexes, polymeric
– salen complexes, –
triarylphosphines, –
triphenylphosphine, polymer-based
Polymer-based synthesis (s.a. under
Combinatorial…)
– of
amidines from amidoximes 18, 48s68
α-aminocarboxylic acid esters with
dynamic kinetic resolution
65, 171s68
benzo-O-heterocyclics, review
42, 853s68
furans, 2,3-dihydro-, 2-α-arylseleno-
29, 180s68
–, tetrahydro-, 2-alkylidene-5-α-
arylseleno- 29, 180s68
2-halogenenol tosylates from acetylene
derivs. 68, 203
N-heterocyclics 43, 316s68
indoles, 1-hydroxy- 24, 525s68
isocarbostyrils, 3,4-dihydro- 33, 694s68
isoxazoles 16, 888s68
oxindoles under microwaves
43, 957s68
peptide p-nitroanilides
Δ²-pyrazolines 58, 314s68
pyridines, 1,2-dihydro-, 2-carbamyl-,
N-protected 26, 884s68
Polymer linkers, triazene-type
–, cleavage, photolytic 17, 32s68
Polymethylhydrosiloxane
– as reagent 34, 790s68; 68, 29
Polynitroso compds.
–, review 67, 189s68
Polyphosphoric acid/silica gel 51, 226s68
Polysulfates
– as reagent 68, 6
Poly(4-vinylpyridinium) persulfate
47, 431s68
Porphyrins
– special s.
benziporphyrins
fullerene-porphyrins
–, meso-acylamino- 64, 175s68
Potassium allyl(trifluoro)borates
– startg. m. f.
3-ethylenetosylamines, stereospecific
synthesis 68, 442
– aluminum sulfate 5, 549s68; 32, 617s68
– aryl(trifluoro)borates
– startg. m. f.
diaryl ketones 68, 459
– cobaltotungstate 49, 254s68
– cyanide 35, 592s68; 68, 433
– fluoride 46, 192s68; 68, 92, 135
– –/alumina 28, 418s68; 29, 668s68;
31, 395s68; 46, 906s68; 47, 727s68;
55, 166s68; 61, 340s68; 62, 171s68
– formate 17, 65s68
– hydrogen sulfate 55, 337s68
– iodide 62, 195s68; 68, 219
– organo(trifluoro)borates

–, 1,4-addition, asym. with – 55, 452s68
– special s.
potassium allyl(trifluoro)borates
– aryl(trifluoro)borates
– osmate 64, 81s68; 68, 79
– permanganate/manganese dioxide
–, oxidations with – 68, 63
– peroxymonosulfate 15, 151s68;
38, 699s68; 44, 420s68; 68, 87, 474, 481
– –/alumina 54, 63s68
– phosphate 68, 475
– thiocyanate 18, 647s68
Praseodymium(III) triflate 60, 194s68
Prins-type cyclization, intramolecular,
stereospecific 68, 309
– –, stereospecific 58, 432s68
–, 4-pyrones, tetrahydro-, 2,3,6-trisubst.
by – 68, 383
(S)-Prolinamide
– as reagent 68, 245
D-Proline
– as reagent 68, 258
L-Proline
– as reagent 35, 476s68; 63, 277s68;
67, 275s68; 68, 184, 258, 259, 370,
371
2-(Prolylamino)alcohols, chiral
– as reagent 68, 259
N-Prolylpeptides
– as reagent 58, 245s68
Propargylamines
– from
aldehydes, 3-component synthesis,
asym. 68, 435
Propargylarenes
– from
2-acetylene-prim-alcohols and
arylboronic acids 68, 473
Propargyltitanation 68, 305
Propargyl vinyl ethers s. Vinyloxy-2-
acetylenes
Propyl
– as N-protective group 68, 18
Protection
– of amino groups, prim. as
N-(3,4-dihydroxyphenethyl)ureas
68, 16
– of α-aminocarboxylic acids as
1,3,2-oxazaborolidin-5-ones, 2,2-di-
fluoro- 68, 163
– of carbonyl groups as
1,3-dioxolanes, 2-(6-bromo-7-
hydroxycoumarin-4-yl)- 30, 5s68
1,2,4-trioxepanes, acid-stable 68, 117
– of carboxyl groups as
2-(o-acetonylphenyl)alkyl esters
30, 5s68
– of glycols as
methoxymethyl ethers, partial
protection 68, 95
– of hydroxyl groups as
ethoxymethyl ethers 39, 214s68
pyran-2-yl ethers, tetrahydro- (without
solvent) 68, 69
– of phenols as
carboxymethyl phenolethers 68, 8
N-Protective group (s.a. Fluorous
N-protective group)
–, alkoxymethyl as – 68, 172
–, propyl as – 68, 18
N- and O-Protective group
–, 2-arylallyl as – 68, 3

N-Protective groups, removal (s.a. HNǁC)
– of
  2-arylallyl **68**, 3
  carbo-2-sulfonylethoxyl, fluorous **29**, 19s68
  3,4-dihydroxyphenethylaminocarbonyl **68**, 16
O-Protective groups, removal (s.a. HOǁRem, HOǁC)
– of
  2-arylallyl **68**, 3
  carballyloxyl **32**, 11s68
  carboxymethyl **68**, 8
  2,6-dimethylbenzyl **31**, 5s68
  methallyl **68**, 6
  methoxymethyl **45**, 10s68; **48**, 216s68
  pyran-2-yl, tetrahydro- s. under Pyran-2-yl ethers, tetrahydro-
  9-p-tolyl-9-xanthyl **55**, 3s68
  m-xylylmethyl **31**, 5s68
Pummerer rearrangement, vinylogous 46, 983s68
**4H-Pyran-3-carbonyl compds.
64**, 338s68
Pyran ring, 2-silyl-, condensed
– from
  ω-silyl-2,(ω-1)-diyn-1-ols **68**, 82
2H-Pyrans, 3,4-dihydro-
– startg. m. f.
  3-(cyclobutyl)alcohols, synthesis **68**, 250
–, –, 6-silyl-, condensed **68**, 82
–, 6-silyl-, condensed **68**, 82
4H-Pyrans
– from
  2-acetylenealcohols **64**, 338s68
–, 3,4-condensed
– special s.
  [n+4]-oxabicyclo[n.4.0]alka-1,3,(n+2),(n+5)-tetraene...
Pyrans, tetrahydro-
– from
  4-ethylenealcohols **68**, 81
–, –, 2-alkoxy-6-vinyl-
– from
  δ,ε-ethylene-ξ-hydroxyaldehydes, O-protected **68**, 100
–, –, 4-chloro-
– from
  aldehydes (2 molecules) **58**, 432s68
–, –, 2,6-divinyl-
– from
  8-oxabicyclo[3.2.1]oct-6-enes and ethylene derivs., desymmetrization **68**, 319
Pyran-2-yl ethers, tetrahydro-
–, cleavage **68**, 11, 69
– startg. m. f.
  oxo compds. **41**, 261s68
Pyrazole-4-carboxaldehydes 22, 826s68
Pyrazoles
– from
  Δ²-pyrazolines **25**, 649s68
–, 5-amino- **33**, 962s68
–, 4(5)-(polyoxyalkyl)-, chiral **66**, 181s68
Pyrazolidine-1,2-dicarboxylic acid esters, 3-vinyl-
–, 3-component synthesis, asym. **68**, 398
Pyrazolidines, 1-acyl-
– from

ethylene derivs. and N-acyl-hydrazones, asym. conversion **68**, 306
3-Pyrazolidones, 1-(α,β-ethyleneacyl)-
–, epoxidation with asym. induction **44**, 117s68
Δ²-Pyrazolines
–, synthesis, polymer-based **58**, 314s68
–, 1-acyl-, chiral **68**, 306
2-(1-Pyrazolyl)benzaldimines, N-aryl-
– as ligand **68**, 467
Pyridazines
– special s.
  azolopyridazines
–, functionalized
–, synthesis, review **42**, 853s68
Pyridazinoquinoxalines
–, synthesis, review **42**, 853s68
3(2H)-Pyridazones
–, chemistry, review **42**, 853s68
–, functionalization and syntheses with –, review **42**, 853s68
Pyrid[3,4-b]indoles, 1,2,3,4-tetrahydro-, N-condensed
–, 4-component synthesis, stereospecific **68**, 420
Pyridine, 2,6-di-$tert$-butyl-4-methyl-
– as reagent **44**, 154s68; **66**, 311s68
–, (S)-4-pyrrolidino-2-(pyrrolidin-2-yl-methyl)-
– as reagent **62**, 282s68
Pyridine-3-carboxylic acid derivs.
–, Reissert reaction, asym., catalyzed with – **68**, 269
Pyridine N-oxide, 2,6-dichloro-
– as reagent **68**, 65, 75
Pyridine ring
–, expansion with α-diazocarbonyl compds. **68**, 381
– –, 1,2-dihydro-, 1-carbalkoxy-2-carbamyl-
– from
  isonitriles **26**, 884s68
Pyridines
– from
  pyridines, 1,4-dihydro- **42**, 235s68
– special s.
  bipyridyls
  terpyridyls
Pyridines, 2-acoxy- s. Carboxylic acid 2-pyridyl esters
–, 2-alkylthio-4-chloro- **37**, 833s68
–, 2-amino- **24**, 955s68
–, 2-aryl-, atropoisomeric
– by [2+2+2]-cycloaddition, asym. **68**, 314
–, 1,4-dihydro-
– as reagent **68**, 28
–, 3-component synthesis under phase transfer catalysis **68**, 368
–, 4-component synthesis, ionic liquid-catalyzed, solventless **68**, 368
– startg. m. f.
  pyridines **42**, 235s68
–, –, 1-hydroxy- **47**, 727s68
–, nitro-
–, review **42**, 853s68
–, 2-(2-oxazolidon-3-yl)-
– startg. m. f.
  piperidines, asym. induction **68**, 47
–, 1,2,3,4-tetrahydro-, 2-amino-3-methylene-1-sulfonyl- **16**, 733s68

–, –, N-sulfonyl- **33**, 627s68
–, 1,2,3,6-tetrahydro-, 3-alkylidene- **68**, 351
–, –, 3-alkylidene-4-vinyl-, N-protected **64**, 302s68
–, –, N-protected
– from
  Δ³-pyrrolines, 2-iodomethyl-, N-protected **68**, 492
–, 2,3,4,5-tetrahydro- **68**, 408
–, 2-vinyl- **26**, 884s68
Pyridinium chloride, N-acetyl-
– as reagent **13**, 487s68
Pyridinium chlorochromate/Celite 55, 451s68
– –, 4-amino-/silica gel **45**, 122s68
– hydrobromide perbromide
– as reagent **44**, 149s68
– salts, 2-halogeno-
– special s.
  2-chloropyridinium...
  2-iodopyridine methiodide
– tosylate
– as reagent **39**, 214s68; **68**, 142
2-Pyridone ring
– by 3-component synthesis **33**, 753s68
– from
  diynes and isocyanates **68**, 315
2-Pyridones
–, N-arylation **62**, 171s68
–, 5,6-dihydro-
–, 1,4-addition, asym. to – **52**, 297s68
3-Pyridylsulfonyl azide
– as reagent **64**, 383s68
Pyrimidines, 2-amino- 16, 505s68
–, 1,4,5,6-tetrahydro-, 1-tosyl-
– from
  azetidines, N-tosyl- and nitriles **68**, 146
4(3H)-Pyrimidinones, 1,2-dihydro-, N-condensed
– by 3-component synthesis **68**, 281
Pyrimido[4,5-c]pyridazine-5,7(6H,8H)-diones
–, substitution, nucleophilic, review **42**, 853s68
–, 3-alkynyl-6,8-dimethyl-
–, synthesis and heterocyclization, review **42**, 853s68
2-Pyrones
– startg. m. f.
  2(5H)-furanones, 5-vinyl- **68**, 379
–, 3,4-dihydro-
– from
  α,β-ethyleneketones and O-silyl O-aryl ketenacetals **68**, 434
–, 6-vinyl-
– from
  cyclobutenones **68**, 323
3-Pyrones
–, Baylis-Hillman reaction, asym. with – **56**, 253s68
4-Pyrones, 2,3-dihydro-
– from
  1-alkoxy-3-siloxy-1,3-dienes and aldehydes, asym. conversion **68**, 454
–, –, polyoxy-, carbohydrate-based
– startg. m. f.
  pyrazoles, 5-(polyoxyalkyl)-, chiral **66**, 181s68
–, tetrahydro-, 2,3,6-trisubst.
– from

N-(3'-hydroxy)eneurethans and oxo
    compds. **68**, 383
**Pyrrole-3,4-dicarboxylic acid esters,
2-amino-5-imido-, N-subst.**
– by 3-component synthesis **68**, 280
Pyrrole ring
–, N-carbalkoxylation **9**, 507s68
– from
    o-halogenosulfonylamines and
    silylacetylenes **27**, 851s68
Pyrroles
–, N-alkylation **56**, 159s68
– from
    aldehydes, acetylene derivs. and prim.
        amines **68**, 360
    1-amino-1,4-enynes **68**, 155
    β-amino-α,β-ethylenecarboxylic acid
        esters **68**, 155
    1-amino-4-halogeno-1,4-dienes
        11, 573s68
    aziridines, 2-methylene- and methyl
        ketones **68**, 375
    azomethines **11**, 452s68
    1,4(5)-diynes and prim. amines **68**, 151
– via vinyloxy-2-acetylenes **68**, 360
–, 1-acylamino- **35**, 549s68
–, trans-N-(α,β-epoxyacyl)-
– from
    aldehydes, asym. synthesis with 2 extra
        C-atoms **68**, 444
–, N-(α,β-ethyleneacyl)-
–, Michael addition, asym. to – **63**, 281s68
–, 2-α-functionalized
– from
    2-en-4-ynaldimines **68**, 152
–, 2-(N-hetaryl)- **68**, 375
–, N-sodio-
–, 2-arylation **57**, 376s68
–, 1,2,3,4-tetrasubst. **68**, 360
–, 1-tosyl-
–, 2-acylation **7**, 798s68
–, 1,2,5-trisubst. **68**, 151
**Pyrrolidine, (S)-2-[bis[3,5-bis(trifluoro-
methyl)]phenyl](trimethylsiloxy)-
methyl-**
– as reagent **68**, 228
–, (S)-N-(1-cyclohexylethyl)-
– as reagent **48**, 952s68
–, (S)-1-methyl-2-(pyrrolidin-1-yl-
methyl)-
– as reagent **58**, 233s68
–, (S)-1-(pyrrolidin-2-ylmethyl)-
– as reagent **62**, 282s68; **67**, 275s68
–, (S)-2-(trifluoromethanesulfonylamino)-
– as reagent **67**, 275s68; **68**, 228
–, (S)-2-(trifluoromethanesulfonylmethyl)-
– as reagent **40**, 57s68
Pyrrolidine alkaloids
– special s.
    domoic acids
**Pyrrolidine-3-carboxylic acid esters,
cis-2,3-disubst. 36**, 715s68
Pyrrolidines
– special s.
    spiropyrrolidines
–, cis-1-alkoxy-2-vinyl- **50**, 382s68
–, 2-(arenesulfonylaminomethyl)-,
    chiral
– as reagent **68**, 170
–, 2-benzyl-

– from
    4-ethyleneamines **66**, 413s68
–, chiral
– as reagent **33**, 43s68
–, 3-α,β-dichloro-1-sulfonyl- **68**, 295
–, 3-α-halogeno-1-sulfonyl-
– from
    2-ethylene-N-halogenosulfonylamines
        and ethylene derivs. **68**, 295
–, 3-methylene-, functionalized
    52, 485s68
–, 3-methylene-, N-protected **68**, 339
2-Pyrrolidinylcarbinols, chiral 9, 741s68
**3-Pyrrolidinylcarbinols, 4-alkylidene-,
N-protected 68**, 495
2-Pyrrolidones, 5-α-chloro-
– from
    γ,δ-ethylenecarboxylic acids via acid
        azides **68**, 216
Δ¹-Pyrroline-5-carboxylic acid esters
– from
    Δ²-5-oxazolones and ethylene derivs.
        68, 288
Δ¹-Pyrrolines
– from
    cyclopropyl ketones **68**, 167
– startg. m. f.
    γ-acylaminoketones **13**, 487s68
–, 2-alkyl-
– by cross-coupling **60**, 412s68
–, 3-methylene-
– from
    nitriles **63**, 282s68
Δ³-Pyrrolines 56, 495s68
–, 2-iodomethyl-, N-protected
– startg. m. f.
    pyridines, 1,2,3,6-tetrahydro-,
        N-protected **68**, 492
Δ²-4-Pyrrolones, 2-amino-
–, synthesis, polymer-based **43**, 316s68
**Δ³-2-Pyrrolones, 3-amino-5-
(carbalkoxyene)- 46**, 346s68
**1H-Pyrrolo[2,3-b]quinoxalines
47**, 829s68
**5H-Pyrrolo[2,1-c][1,2,4]triazol-2-ium
chloride, 6,7-dihydro-, 2-phenyl-**
– as reagent **68**, 109
Pyrylium salts
– startg. m. f.
    4H-1,2-diazepines **68**, 159

Quinaldic acid
– as reagent **64**, 12s68
Quinazolines, 3,4-dihydro-
– from
    o-nitrobenzylamines **65**, 169s68
–, –, 2-arylamino-
–, synthesis, polymer-based **43**, 316s68
**2(1H)-Quinazolones, 3,4-dihydro-, 4-
(alk-1-ynyl)-, chiral 66**, 290s68
4(3H)-Quinazolones
– from
    o-aminocarboxylic acid amides and
        aldehydes **68**, 173
    orthocarboxylic acid esters and prim.
        amines **28**, 418s68

–, 2,3-disubst.
– by 3-component synthesis **68**, 173
–, fused **48**, 346s68
Quin[id]ine derivs.
– as reagent **68**, 396
– special s.
    bis[1-(9-O-dihydroquin...
    bis(quin[id]ine...
– –, 6'-O-demethyl-
– as reagent **64**, 260s68
Quinines, dihydro-, polymeric
– as reagent **60**, 186s68
Quinolines
– from
    o-(aminoaryl)ethynylcarbinols
        13, 526s68
    N-arylaldimines and enoxysilanes
        68, 372
    nitriles **62**, 355s68
    o-nitroaryl(vinyl)carbinols **10**, 394s68
– special s.
    spiroquinolines
– startg. m. f.
    1H-1-benzazepine-1,2-dicarboxylic
        acid esters **68**, 381
–, 3-alkoxy-
– from
    o-isocyanoarylacetaldehyde acetals
        68, 485
–, 1,2-dihydro-, 2-(alk-1-ynyl)-1-
carbalkoxy-
– from
    quinolines **68**, 278
–, 1,2,3,4-tetrahydro-, 3-iodo-1-sulfonyl-
– from
    N-aryl-2-ethylenesulfonylamines
        68, 211
–, –, N-methyl- **68**, 43
– –, 4-vinyl- **68**, 494
Quinolinium fluorochromate
– as reagent **68**, 113
**Quinolizinium salts, 3,4-dihydro-
56**, 495s68
o-Quinone imines, cyclic
– as reagent **56**, 152s68
Quinones
–, effect of hydrogen bonding and
    protonation on reactivity, review
    35, 141s68
– from
    arenes **42**, 235s68
–, photocycloaddition and rearrangement,
    review **35**, 141s68
p-Quinones
– from
    cyclohex-2-ene-1,4-diones **10**, 225s68
– special s.
    benzoquinone
    2,3-dichloro-5,6-dicyanoquinone
Quinoxaline-2,3-diones
– from
    o-diamines **21**, 416s68
**Quinoxalines, 1,2,3,4-tetrahydro-,
2-vinyl-**
– from
    o-diamines **46**, 335s68
2(1H)-Quinoxalones, 3,4-dihydro-, chiral
–, synthesis, soluble polymer-based
    19, 561s68

Radical 1,2-addition
– to ethylene derivs., electron-rich **68**, 425
Radical 1,4-addition
– to 2(5*H*)-furanones **35**, 474s68
– arylation, Ir(III)-catalyzed **68**, 421
– halogenolactamization, regiostereospecific **68**, 216
– ring closure
– in water **46**, 451s68
– of dienes with addition of phosphines **46**, 451s68
– ring closure, regiostereospecific, Ti(III)-mediated
– of α,β-ethylene(epoxy)phosphine oxides **68**, 495
– – –, thiiyl-mediated, regiospecific
– of acetylene derivs. **68**, 302
– via 1,5-hydrogen atom transfer **68**, 302
– – closure-Horner synthesis **68**, 429
Radicals
– special s.
alkyl radicals
phosphinoyl –
phosphoranyl –, cyclic
thioimidoyl –
Rauhut-Currier reaction
– with α,β-ethylenesulfones **63**, 326s68
– reaction-intramolecular Michael addition, stereospecific **68**, 336
Rearrangement, 2-oxonia-[3.3]-sigmatropic 68, 478
–, [3.3]-sigmatropic
–, 2-ethylenephosphorylamines via – **68**, 185
Reformatsky synthesis
– with ketones **38**, 624s68
Reformatsky-type synthesis
– of β-hydroxyketones **1**, 677s68
Reissert reaction, asym., catalyzed
– with pyridine-3-carboxylic acid derivs. **68**, 269
Replacement
– of acoxy groups by hydrogen **68**, 41
– of bromine by hydrogen **68**, 10
– of carbonyl sulfur by oxygen **68**, 113
– of halogen by hydrogen **53**, 9s68
– of hydroxyl groups by hydrogen **68**, 10
– of sulfhydryl groups by hydrogen **68**, 425
Resolution (optical) (s.a. Res section, and under Stereoisomers in Vol. **1-50**)
– by non-conventional methods, review **27**, 57s68
– by supercritical fluid chromatography, overview **27**, 57s68
Resolution, kinetic
–, Haller-Bauer reaction with – **68**, 149
–, of
alcohols, sec. by asym. aerobic oxidation, review **27**, 57s68
2-ethylenecarbonic acid esters **68**, 124
lactams by hydrolytic ring opening **68**, 64
–, dynamic
–, α-acylaminocarboxylic acid esters from Δ²-5-oxazolones **68**, 60

– on asym. homogeneous hydrogenation **67**, 22s68
–, sulfinic acid esters from acid chlorides **68**, 53
–, –, enzymatic
– with lipases, review **27**, 57s68
–, –, non-enzymatic
–, review **27**, 57s68
Resolving agents
–, design by crystal engineering, review **27**, 57s68
Retro-Michael addition, Ir-catalyzed 68, 50
Rhenium complexes
bis(tetraphenylphosphonium) hexakis(thiocyanato)rhenium(IV) **47**, 111s68
[hydridotris(3,5-dimethylpyrazolyl)-borato]rhenium(VII) oxide **68**, 486
pentacarbonylrhenium(I) bromide **68**, 72
Rhenium oxides
methylrhenium oxide
–, reactions with –, review **27**, 851s68
methylrhenium oxide, micro-encapsulated **68**, 57
Rhodacyclopropanones
– as intermediates **68**, 462
Rhodium(II) acetate 68, 144, 380, 388
Rhodium(III) acetoacetonate 31, 719s68
–(III) 2-aminoalcohol complexes, chiral **46**, 42s68
–(II) caprolactamate **68**, 91
–(II) carboxylates, chiral
– α-imidocarboxylates, chiral **47**, 955s68; **64**, 183s68
– tetrakis[(S)-N-(1,8-naphthoyl)-*tert*-leucinate] **23**, 819s68
–(III) chloride **68**, 462
– complexes
acetoacetonato(dicarbonyl)rhodium(I) **62**, 306s68; **68**, 321, 322
bis(acetonitrile)(cyclooctadiene)-rhodium(I) fluoroborate **58**, 447s68
bis(cyclooctadiene)rhodium(I) fluoroborate **68**, 35
– triflate **68**, 320
bis(norbornadiene)rhodium(I) fluoroborate **68**, 119
– hexafluoroantimonate **68**, 36
carbonyl(chloro)[1,3-bis(diphenyl-phosphino)propane]rhodium(I) dimer **55**, 296s68
carbonyl(chloro)bis(tri-2-furyl-phosphine)rhodium(I) **68**, 408
carbonyl(hydrido)tris(triphenyl-phosphine)rhodium(I) **68**, 453
chlorobis(ethylene)rhodium(I) dimer **68**, 457, 458, 459
chloro(cyclooctadiene)rhodium(I) dimer **43**, 725s68; **59**, 221s68; **61**, 446s68; **68**, 38, 219, 324, 460, 461
chlorotris(triphenylphosphine)-rhodium(I) **68**, 63, 326, 374, 472, 481
(1,5-cyclooctadiene)(hydroxy)-rhodium(I) dimer **56**, 646s68; **68**, 455
(1,5-cyclooctadiene)(methoxy)-rhodium(I) dimer **68**, 77
(1,5-cyclooctadiene)(η⁶-naphthalene)-rhodium(I) hexafluoroantimonate **68**, 353, 456

dicarbonyl(chloro)rhodium(I) dimer **68**, 323
dichloro(pentamethylcyclopenta-dienyl)rhodium(III) dimer **68**, 198
– –, chiral
aquo(diacetato)[2,6-bis(4(S)-isopropyl-Δ²-oxazolin-2-yl)phenyl]-rhodium(III) **68**, 33
dirhodium(II) tetrakis((R,R)-1,3-di-phenyl-4-triflyl-2-imidazolidonate) **47**, 770s68
– tetrakis[3(S)-(2,3-naphthalene-dicarboximido)-2-piperidonate] **68**, 454
[(2S,4S)-2,4-bis(diphenylphosphino)-pentane]rhodium(I) hexafluoro-antimonate **60**, 307s68
– complexes, polymeric, chiral
poly[bis(1,1′-binaphthyl-2,2′-diyl N,N-dimethylphosphoramidite)-(cyclooctadiene)rhodium(I) fluoroborate] complexes **68**, 37
–(I) phosphabarrelene complexes **4**, 667s68
–(I) phosphine-cyclic phosphoramidite complexes, chiral **68**, 34
–(I) phosphine-phosphite complexes, cyclic, polymer-based, chiral **49**, 683s68
–(II) pivalate **43**, 943s68
– vinylidene complexes
–, review **27**, 851s68
Ring-closing ene-yne metathesis
– in ionic liquids **56**, 325s68
Ring-closing metathesis (s.a. Methylenation-ring closing metathesis, Cyclopropanation, intramolecular-ring closing metathesis, and under Interchange, intramolecular in Vol. **1-50**)
–, update **56**, 495s68
– –, aromatizing **56**, 495s68
Ring closure, carbonylative, Pd-catalyzed
–, α-(benzofuran-2-yl)carboxylic acid esters via – **68**, 484
– –, dehydrogenative, aerobic, asym., Pt-catalyzed
–, review **27**, 57s68
Ring expansion, carbonylative, Rh-catalyzed, regiospecific 68, 219
Ring-opening metathesis-cross metathesis
– with desymmetrization **68**, 319
Rubidium fluoride 61, 340s68
Ruthenate s. Tetrapropyl perruthenate
Ruthenium/carbon/zeolite 68, 48
Ruthenium π-allyl complexes
– as intermediates **68**, 489
Ruthenium carbene complexes
carbonyl(chloro)bis(tricyclohexyl-phosphine)(3,3-dimethylprop-2-enylidene)ruthenium(II) fluoroborate **65**, 298s68
dichloro(tricyclohexylphosphine)-[*o*-isopropoxy(nitro)benzylidene]-ruthenium(II) complexes **59**, 467s68
Grubbs′ complex **68**, 352
–, scavenging **49**, 985s68
– – –, N-heterocyclic
alkylidene(dichloro)ruthenium imidazolidin-2-ylidene complex **68**, 339, 480, 481

dichloro(2-isopropoxy-3-methoxy-
benzylidene)ruthenium(II)
imidazolidin-2-ylidene complex
64, 497s68
– – –, –, chiral
chloro(2-isopropoxy-3-phenyl-
benzylidene)[1-(2'-oxy-1,1'-bi-
naphthyl-2-yl)-3-mesityl-
imidazolidin-2-ylidene]-
ruthenium(II), chiral 68, 319
– carbonyls
dodecacarbonyltriruthenium
56, 152s68; 62, 306s68; 68, 243, 489
– complexes
acetonitrile(cyclopentadienyl)bis[2-
(diphenylphosphino)-6-tert-butyl-
pyridine]ruthenium(II) hexafluorophosphate 68, 118
(η⁶-benzene)dichlororuthenium(II)
dimer 68, 23
bis(acetonitrile)(cyclopentadienyl)-
(triphenylphosphine)ruthenium(II)
hexafluorophosphate 68, 276
bis(acetonitrile)[hydridotris(pyrazolyl)borato](triphenylphosphine)-
ruthenium(II) hexafluorophosphate
68, 152, 338, 347, 497
carbonyl(chloro)(hydrido)bis(tricyclohexylphosphine)ruthenium(II)
68, 249
carbonyl(dihydrido)tris(triphenylphosphine)ruthenium(II) 68, 32
carbonyl(η³-2-methallyl)[1,1'-bis-
(diphenylphosphino)ferrocene]-
ruthenium(II) hexafluoroantimonate
65, 97s68
carbonylruthenium(II) porphyrin
complexes 23, 819s68
carbonyl(5,10,15,20-tetraaryl-
porphyrinato)ruthenium(II)
complexes 43, 943s68
chloro(pentamethylcyclopentadienyl)-
ruthenium(II) 3, 758s68
dicarbonyl(chloro)ruthenium dimer
64, 302s68
dichloro(p-cymene)ruthenium(II)
dimer 23, 819s68; 29, 787s68;
64, 52s68
dichloro(norbornadiene)bis(triphenylphosphine)ruthenium(II) 45, 416s68
dichloro(pentamethylcyclopentadienyl)ruthenium(III) dimer 68, 74
dichloro[5,10,15,20-tetrakis(2,6-di-
chlorophenyl)porphyrinato]-
ruthenium(IV) 68, 75
dichloro(5,10,15,20-tetramesityl-
porphyrinato)ruthenium(IV) 68, 65
dichlorotris(triphenylphosphine)-
ruthenium(II) 68, 196
diruthenium complexes, thiolate-
bridged 64, 338s68; 68, 175, 244, 490
tris(acetonitrile)(cyclopentadienyl)-
ruthenium(II) hexafluorophosphate
64, 12s68; 68, 82
tris(acetonitrile)(pentamethylcyclopentadienyl)ruthenium(II) –
62, 230s68
Ruthenium complexes, chiral
bis[4-aryl-4,5-dihydro-3H-dinaphtho-
[2,1-c;1',2'-e]phosphepine]dibromo-
ruthenium(II), chiral 68, 26

(S)-[4,4'-bis(diphenylphosphino)-
2,2',5,5'-tetramethyl-3,3'-bithienyl]-
ruthenium(II) bis(trifluoroacetate)
46, 67s68
(2,6-dicarboxylatopyridine)-
ruthenium(II) 2,2'-(pyridine-2,6-di-
yl)bis(5,6-dihydro-4H-1,3-oxazine)
complexes, chiral 68, 73
dichloro[2,2'-bis(diarylphosphino)-1,1'-
dicyclopentane]ruthenium(II)
complexes, chiral 68, 25
– complexes, chiral, supported
dibromo[2,2'-bis(diphenylphosphino)-
1,1'-binaphthyl]ruthenium(II),
mesoporous silica-supported, chiral
61, 29s68
–(II) complexes, water-soluble,
supramolecular, chiral 68, 23
– cyclopropylcarbenes, bicyclic
– as intermediates 68, 498
– (Z)-α,β-ethylenecarbene complexes
– as intermediates 68, 480
Ruthenium(IV)-grafted hydrotalcite
68, 373
– hydride complexes/silica gel 65, 128s68
Ruthenium hydroxide/γ-alumina
56, 274s68
– π-ketene complexes
– as intermediates 68, 347
– trichloride 63, 55s68, 304s68; 68, 76,
99, 121, 361
– –/hydrotalcite 62, 355s68
– vinylidene complexes
–, review 27, 851s68

Saccharin N-sodio deriv.
– as reagent 21, 358s68
Samarium 13, 838s68; 23, 628s68;
53, 230s68
Samarium complexes
(η⁸-cyclooctatetraene)(tetrahydrofuran)samarium(I) iodide 49, 41s68
Samarium diiodide 23, 793s68; 28, 28s68;
61, 13s68; 68, 165, 270, 271
–(III) nitrate 1, 591s68
–(III) triflate 8, 367
Scandium complexes
methyl[2,2,6,6-tetramethyl-3,5-N,N-
bis(2,6-diisopropylphenyl)-3,5-di-
iminatoheptane]scandium methyl-
tris(pentafluorophenyl)borate
46, 287s68
Scandium –, supported
o-(propylaminomethyl)phenoxy-
scandium(III) bis(triflate), silica-
supported 43, 573s68
–(III) perfluorooctanesulfonamide
66, 77s68
–(III) sulfate bis(triflate), polymer-
based 57, 421s68
–(III) triflate 4, 729s68; 8, 165s68;
58, 238s68; 61, 431s68; 65, 334s68;
68, 45, 58, 94, 148, 220, 299, 350, 567
Selenides (s.a. Oxyselenation)
– special s.
eneselenides

ketoselenides
–, ar. (s.a. Arylseleno…)
– from
halides, ar. 53, 230s68
Selenium
– as reactant 68, 235
– as reagent 32, 345s68; 68, 182
Selenocarbonic acid esters (s.a. Monoselenoiminocarbonic acid esters)
Selenoglycosides
– special s.
2-deoxyselenoglycosides
Selenolic acid aryl esters
– from
1-acetylene-1-selenides, ar. 2, 818s68
Selenonium salts
– special s.
acetyleneselenonium salts
Selenothiolic acid esters
–, synthesis and reactions, review
44, 533s68
α-Selenylation, organocatalyzed
– of aldehydes 68, 245
Semicarbazides
– special s.
cyanosemicarbazides
Semicarbazones
– startg. m. f.
oxo compds. 12, 252s68; 34, 172s68;
47, 146s68; 52, 96s68
1,2-Silaboration, regiospecific, Pd-
catalyzed 68, 466
1,2-Silaboration, regiostereospecific
– of allenes 68, 241
Silanes (s.a. Hydrosilylation)
– special s.
acylsilanes
alkoxysilanes
allenesilanes
arylsilanes
carbamylsilanes
cyclopropylsilanes
di(silanes)
enesilanes
enoxysilanes
ethylenesilanes
halogenosilanes
tetrasilanes
Silica 68, 80
–, immobilization of catalysts in ionic
liquids within pores of – 68, 409
Silica, mesoporous
–, catalytic significance of immobilization
of organometallics on –, review
65, 447s68
Silica-phosphoric acid/silica/sodium
nitrate 4, 274s68
Silica-sulfonic acid, functionalized
28, 141s68
Silica-sulfuric acid (s.a. Sodium bromate/
silica-sulfuric acid) 28, 141s68; 68, 222
Silica chloride 59, 57s68
Silicon, hypervalent
– as reactive site, review 42, 887s68
Silicon hydrides, organo-
– special s.
diethoxymethylsilane
diphenylsilane
ethyldimethylsilane
phenylsilane
polymethylhydrosiloxane
triethoxysilane

(Silicon hydrides, organo-
– special s.)
triethylsilane
tris(trimethylsilyl)silane
Silicon tetrabromide/silica gel 52, 96s68
1-Siloxyacetylenes
– special s.
4-aryl-1-siloxyacetylenes
6-siloxy-1,5-enynes
– startg. m. f.
cyclobut-2-enecarbonyl compds., 2-
siloxy- **68**, 289
β-Siloxyaldehydes, chiral 68, 346
1-Siloxy-1,3-dienes
– special s.
1-siloxy-1-siloxylamino-1,3-dienes
2-Siloxy-1,3-dienes
– special s.
1-alkoxy-3-siloxy-1,3-dienes
2-α-Siloxy-1,4-dienes 67, 397s68
6-Siloxy-1,5-enynes
– startg. m. f.
1,4-cyclohexadienes, 1-siloxy- **68**, 344
2-cyclohexenones **68**, 496
1-Siloxylamino-1,3-dienes
– special s.
1-siloxy-1-siloxylamino-1,3-dienes
α-Siloxynitriles
– from
ketones, asym. induction **65**, 253s68
**1-Siloxy-1-siloxylamino-1,3-dienes,
N-protected**
– startg. m. f.
(E)-α,β-ethylenecarboxylic acid
amides, N-protected, γ-subst.,
synthesis **68**, 445
Silver acetate 6, 880s68; **68**, 288
Silver(I) acetylides
– as reactant **68**, 254
Silver carbonate 68, 412
– **complexes**
[1-(2-oxy-1,1'-binaphthyl-2-yl)-3-
mesitylimidazolidin-2-ylidene]-
silver(I) dimer, chiral **68**, 363
– **fluoroborate 55**, 296s68
– **nitrate 39**, 759s68; **60**, 74s68
– **phosphotungstate 65**, 334s68
– **triflate 44**, 154s68; **68**, 74, 194, 254, 278, 345, 437
– **triflimide 68**, 289
Silylacetylenes
– special s.
4-hydroxy-1-silylacetylenes
ω-silyl-2,(ω-1)-diyn-1-ols
silylethynyl...
trimethylsilylacetylene
O-Silyl O-alkyl keteneacetals s.a. under
Aldol-type... and O-Silyl O-aryl
keteneacetals
O-Silyl O-aryl keteneacetals
– startg. m. f.
2-pyrones, 3,4-dihydro- **68**, 434
Silylation, benzylic, chelation-controlled
– of hydrazones, o-subst. **68**, 243
C-Silylation, regiospecific
– with vinylsilanes **68**, 249
α-Silylboronic acid esters
– special s
ethylene-α-silylboronic acid esters
β-Silylboronic acid esters
– special s.
ethylene-β-silylboronic acid esters

N-Silylcarboxylic acid amides
– special s.
N-silyldicarboxylic acid amide silyl
esters
Silyldiazo compds.
– special s.
diazomethyltrimethylsilane
**N-Silyldicarboxylic acid amide silyl
esters**
– from
dicarboxylic acid anhydrides **68**, 140
2-Silyl-1(Z),4-dienes
– from
β,γ-ethylenehalides **66**, 318s68
ω-Silyl-2,(ω-1)-diyn-1-ols
– startg. m. f.
pyran ring, 2-silyl-, condensed **68**, 82
2-Silylenestannanes
– special s.
2'-hydroxy-2-silylenestannanes
Silyl enol ethers s. Enoxysilanes
2-Silyl-1(Z),3-enynes
– from
α,β-acetyleneiodides **66**, 318s68
Silyl ethers s.a. Alkoxysilanes, O-
Desilylation, Siloxy..., O-Silylation
Silylethynylarenes
– startg. m. f.
indenes **42**, 915s68
o-Silylethynylation, catalyzed
– of N-benzylanilines **64**, 378s68
N-Silylhydrazines
– special s.
1,2-bis(*tert*-butyldimethylsilyl)-
hydrazine
N-Silylhydrazones
– as intermediates **68**, 45
Silyllithium compds.
– as reactants **68**, 237
Silylmercury compds.
– in synthesis, review **32**, 604s68
Silylphosphines
–, hydrophosphination, regiospecific
with – **68**, 239
γ-Silylsulfones
– special s.
β,γ-ethylene-γ-silylsulfones
Silyl triflates
– special s.
triethylsilyl triflate
trimethylsilyl triflate
o-Silyltriflates
– startg. m. f.
carbazoles **68**, 464
(E)-β-Silylvinylation 66, 311s68
2-Silylvinylzincates
– as intermediates **68**, 237
**Simmons-Smith-type cyclopropanation,
In-mediated 68**, 404
Sodium/ammonia, liq. 68, 246
Sodium alkoxides
– methoxide/magnesium oxide
33, 851s68
– **amides**
– bis(trimethylsilyl)amide **68**, 431, 432
– as reactant **68**, 149
– **ascorbate**
– as reagent **68**, 184
– **azide 68**, 184
– **bromate/silica-sulfuric acid 29**, 233s68
– **bromide 68**, 125
– **chlorite**

– as re-oxidant **68**, 79
– **compds., organo-**
– special s.
arylsodium compds.
– **dihydridobis(2-methoxyethoxo)-
aluminate 68**, 296
– **formate**
– as reactant **2**, 642s68
– as reagent **68**, 23
– D-**gluconate**
– as reagent **65**, 253s68
– **hydridotriacetoxoborate 46**, 317s68
– **hydrogen carbonate**
– as co-catalyst **68**, 70
– – **sulfate/silica gel 66**, 178s68; **62**, 195s68
– – **sulfite 68**, 125, 166
– **hydroxide/bentonite 41**, 199s68
– **hypochlorite 52**, 108s68; **68**, 90
– **iodate 47**, 431s68
– **iodide 48**, 346s68; **65**, 237s68; **68**, 210, 212, 391
– **lauryl sulfate**
– as surfactant **33**, 830s68
– **nitrite** (s.a. under Silica-phosphoric
acid) **66**, 100s68
– **octadecyl sulfate**
– as surfactant **68**, 325
– **periodate 68**, 121
– **tetrachloroaurate 11**, 770s68; **59**, 137s68
– **tetrahydridoborate 36**, 45s68; **68**, 44, 121, 170, 228, 285, 343
–, reduction with – in aprotic media **68**, 21
– –/**boric acid 18**, 467s68
– –/**Dowex 50X8-100 30**, 17s68
– –/**indium(III) chloride 29**, 968s68
Solid-phase reactions s. Polymer-based
...
Solid-state reactions
–, acylals from aldehydes **56**, 63s68
–, acylthioureas from carboxylic acid
chlorides **22**, 470s68
–, [2+2]-cycloaddition with diaryl ketones
19, 764s68
–, disulfides from mercaptans **4**, 274s68
–, Knoevenagel condensation **46**, 713s68
–, oxo compds. from oximes **40**, 107s68
–, N-tosylation **2**, 312s68
**Sonogashira acylation-Michael addition-
Pictet-Spengler cyclization 68**, 420
Sonogashira coupling
– at low catalyst loading **27**, 851s68; **68**, 416
– in aq. ammonia **27**, 851s68
– in water **27**, 851s68
– under continuous flow **27**, 851s68
– –, Cu-free
– in ionic liquids **63**, 411s68
– –, heterogeneous **63**, 411s68
– –, Cu-, ligand- and amine-free **63**, 411s68
– –, Pd- and ligand-free **66**, 384s68
– –, polymer-based
– in water **27**, 851s68
**Sonogashira coupling-intramolecular
Diels-Alder reaction** (s.a.
Carbopalladation, intramolecular-
Sonogashira coupling-intramolecular
Diels-Alder reaction) **40**, 669s68
(–)-Sparteine
– as reagent **33**, 786s68

381 Spi – Sul

2-Spiroaziridines, 3-sulfinyl-
– startg. m. f.
  α-aminoaldehydes, cyclic **68**, 136
**2λ⁵-2,2′-Spirobi(1,3,2-benzodioxa-
phosphole)**
– as reagent **68**, 54
**1,1′-Spirobiindane, (S)-7,7′-bis[bis(3,5-
dimethyl-4-methoxyphenyl)-
phosphino]-**
– as reagent **27**, 57s68
2-Spirofurans, tetrahydro- **64**, 353s68
**2-Spiroimidazolidines, 4,5-diphenyl-,
chiral**
– as reagent **23**, 819s68
**3-Spiroindolenines, 2-arylthio-
46**, 983s68
Spiroketals
– from
  α,β-acetylene-ω-benzyloxy-ω′-
  hydroxyketones **68**, 138
Spiroorthocarboxylic acid esters
– from
  1-(arylthio)enolethers, cyclic and diols
  68, 112
3-Spirooxindoles, chiral 48, 952s68
Spiropyrrolidines
– special s.
  dispiropyrrolidines
Spiroquinolines
–, chemistry, review **42**, 853s68
**3-Spiro-1,2,4-trioxanes, 6-α-arylthio-
68**, 224
Stannanes (s.a. Hydrostannylation)
– special s.
  acetylenestannanes
  allenestannanes
  arylstannanes
  distannanes
  enestannanes
  epoxystannanes
  ethylenestannanes
  halogenostannanes
  hydroxystannanes
  silylstannanes
Stannylation s.a. Germylstannylation
2-Stannyl-1,3-dienes 52, 419s68
2-Stannyl-1,4,6-dienynes
–, 3-component synthesis, regiostereospecific **68**, 318
1,2-Stannyl group migration
–, hydrogenation, homogeneous with –
  68, 32
1,1-Stannylthioethers
– startg. m. f.
  2-aminothioethers **58**, 447s68
**Staudinger ligation, intramolecular
68**, 180
Steroids, polyoxy-
– via oxidation, transition metal-
  catalyzed, review **27**, 851s68
Stetter reaction
– in ionic liquids **28**, 648s68
– –, intramolecular, asym., catalytic
  68, 335
Stilbene oxides
– special s.
  o-acetylenestilbene oxides
Stilbenes
–, synthesis, catalytic, review **42**, 970s68
Styrenes
–, hydrogenation, heterogeneous in water
  68, 39

– special s.
  o-acetylenestyrenes
  vinylaryl...
(E)-β-Styryl halides
– from
  arylzinc bromides, synthesis **68**, 294
Styryl triflates
– special s.
  o-halogeno-β-styryl triflates
Substitution, ar., electrophilic
–, regiocontrol, review **66**, 356s68
Succinic acids, chiral 37, 657s68
Succinimides
– special s.
  N-halogenosuccinimides
Sugars s. Carbohydrates
Sulfamic acid
– as reagent **1**, 591s68; **68**, 62
Sulfamides
–, N-arylation **59**, 173s68
Sulfenamides
– special s.
  S-glycosylsulfenamides
α-Sulfenylation, asym., organocatalyzed
– of oxo compds. **68**, 228
Sulfido compds. s. Thiiranes from Vol. 51
Sulfinic acid amides (s.a. Sulfinyl-
amin...)
– startg. m. f.
  β,γ-ethylenesulfoxides **68**, 227
– – esters
– from
  sulfinic acid chlorides, dynamic kinetic
  resolution **68**, 53
Sulfinic acids
– startg. m. f.
  sulfones, ar. **68**, 232
Sulfinylamines
– special s.
  ethylenesulfinylamines
  2-(hydroxylamino)sulfinylamines
**β-(Sulfinylamino)ketones, cyclic
60**, 245s68
N-Sulfinylimines
– startg. m. f.
  2-(hydroxylamino)sulfinylamines,
  asym. induction **68**, 271
1-(Sulfinyl)thioenolethers
– from
  dithiocarboxylic acid esters **68**, 231
Sulfonamidopeptides
–, synthesis, review **19**, 33s68
Sulfonation, ar. 68, 222
Sulfones
– from
  thioethers **25**, 80s68
– special s.
  ethylenesulfones
  hydroxysulfones
  polysulfones
  silylsulfones
Sulfones, ar.
– from
  arylboronic acids and sulfinic acids
  68, 232
– special s.
  diaryl sulfones
Sulfonic acid amides (s.a. Sulfonyl-
amin...)
–, N-alkylation **56**, 159s68
–, amination, intramolecular, asym. with –
  64, 183s68

–, N-dealkylation, oxidative **68**, 18
– special s.
  N-acylsulfonic acid amides
  halogenosulfonic acid amides
Sulfonic acid azides
– special s.
  3-pyridylsulfonyl azide
– – derivs.
– special s.
  ketosulfonic acid derivs.
– – esters (s.a. Sulfonyloxy...)
– special s.
  aminosulfonic acid esters
  enol sulfonates
– – halides
– startg. m. f.
  β-hydroxysulfones **68**, 221
Sulfonic acids
– special s.
  camphorsulfonic acid
  2,4-dinitrobenzenesulfonic acid
  4-dodecylbenzenesulfonic acid
  p-toluenesulfonic acid
Sulfonium salts
– special s.
  halogenosulfonium salts
– triflates
– special s.
  arylbis[2-(carbomethoxy)ethyl]-
  sulfonium triflates
N′-Sulfonylamidines
– from
  acetylene derivs., terminal, azides and
  amines **68**, 181
Sulfonylamines (s.a. Sulfonic acid
amides)
– special s.
  acetylenesulfonylamines
  di(sulfonylamines)
  ethylenesulfonylamines
  halogenosulfonylamines
  N-sulfonylbenzylamines
  N-sulfonyl-1,2-diamines
  N-sulfonyldiarylmethylamines
– startg. m. f.
  N-sulfonylureas **68**, 197
–, ar.
– startg. m. f.
  N-sulfonyldiarylmethylamines, asym.
  conversion **68**, 458
**2-(Sulfonylamino)alcohols, N-protected,
chiral**
– as intermediates **68**, 142
**β-(Sulfonylamino)carboxylic acid
amides**
– special s.
  diazo-β-(sulfonylamino)carboxylic
  acid amides
α-(Sulfonylamino)carboxylic acid esters
– special s.
  α-aryl-α-(sulfonylamino)carboxylic
  acid esters
  β-halogeno-α-(sulfonylamino)-
  carboxylic – –
Sulfonylamino group migration
– special s.
  tosylamino group migration
α-(Sulfonylamino)ketones
– special s.
  β-hydroxy-α-(sulfonylamino)ketones

γ-(Sulfonylamino)sulfoxides
– special s.
  halogeno-γ-(sulfonylamino)sulfoxides
  hydroxy-γ-(sulfonylamino)sulfoxides
N-Sulfonylation
– special s.
  N-tosylation
N-Sulfonylbenzylamines
– from
  arylsilanes 58, 447s68
N-Sulfonyl-1,2-diamines
– special s.
  pyrrolidines, 2-(arenesulfonylamino-methyl)-
–, chiral
– as reagent 68, 24
–, PEG-based, chiral
– as reagent 68, 24
–, polymer-based, chiral
– as reagent 51, 26s68; 68, 24
N-Sulfonyldiarylmethylamines
– from
  sulfonylamines, ar. and aryl-boroxines, asym. conversion 68, 458
N-Sulfonylhydrazines
– special s.
  diethyl 4-(hydrazinosulfonyl)benzylphosphonate
Sulfonylhydrazones
–, cycloaddition, 1,3-dipolar, intramolecular, dehydrogenative with – 34, 909s68
– special s.
  tosylhydrazones
N-Sulfonylimines
– special s.
  N-tosylimines
– startg. m. f.
  α-diazo-β-(sulfonylamino)carboxylic acid amides, asym. induction with 2 extra C-atoms 68, 265
o-Sulfonyloxyarylmagnesium chloride
– startg. m. f.
  arynes, functionalized 68, 402
(Sulfonyloxyaryl)phosphines
– startg. m. f.
  (aminoaryl)phosphine oxides 68, 180
Sulfonyloxyhalides
– special s.
  triflyloxyhalides
N-Sulfonylsulfilimines
– special s.
  γ,δ-ethylene-N-tosylsulfilimines
N-Sulfonylureas
– from
  sulfonylamines and imidodicarbonates 68, 197
N-Sulfonylurethans
– special s.
  N-carbo-tert-butoxy-2-(trimethylsilyl)-ethanesulfonamide
1,1-Sulfonylurethans
– startg. m. f.
  α-(carbalkoxyamino)nitriles 60, 408s68
Sulfoxides (s.a. Sulfinyl...)
– from
  thioethers 29, 233s68
–, asym. oxidation 68, 52
–, – – –, review 27, 57s68
–, oxidation with H_2O_2, review 37, 120s68
– special s.

α-arylsulfoxides
ethylenesulfoxides
halogenosulfoxides
sulfonylaminosulfoxides
Sulfoximines
–, N-arylation 62, 171s68; 65, 178s68
– special s.
  N-[2-(2,4,6-triisopropylbenzylamino)-phenyl]-S-methyl-S-phenyl-sulfoximine
Sulfoxonium salts
– special s.
  trimethylsulfoxonium iodide
Sulfur
– as reactant 68, 218
Sulfuric acid
– as oxidant 47, 431s68
Sulfurous acid esters, cyclic
– special s.
  glycol sulfites, cyclic
Sulfur trioxide
– as reactant 68, 222
Sulfuryl chloride 4, 274s68
Sultams
–, N-alk-1-ynylation 65, 172s68
Suzuki coupling
– in aq. medium, review 27, 851s68
– in water under microwaves, review 27, 851s68
Suzuki diaryl coupling
– at low catalyst loading 37, 902s68
– in aq. media 37, 902s68
– under aerobic conditions 37, 902s68
– under microwaves in water 37, 902s68
– using palladium(II) imidazol-2-ylidene complexes 37, 902s68
– using 2-(1-pyrazolyl)benzaldimine, N-aryl- (as ligand) 68, 467
– with ar. chlorides, hindered 37, 902s68
– – –, environmentally friendly
–, review 27, 851s68
– – –, ligand-less 37, 902s68
– – –, polymer-based 37, 902s68
Synthesis, asym. (s.a. Catalysis, asym., Desymmetrization, Resolution)
–, enzymatic
–, review 27, 57s68
–, total
–, cross-coupling, Pd-catalyzed in –, review 27, 851s68
– via metathesis, review 27, 851s68

Tandem catalysis
–, indoles from o-bromo-β-styryl triflates under – 68, 192
–, methylene compds. from alcohols via oxo compds. under – 68, 472
Tantalum pentachloride/silica gel 50, 151s68
Tartaric acid and derivs.
–, synthesis, review 30, 321s68
Tellurides
– special s.
  enetellurides
Telluronium salts, oligo(ethylene glycol)-based

– as reagent 62, 378s68
Telluroxides
– special s.
  bis(2,4,6-triisopropylphenyl) telluroxide
2.2′:6′,2′′-Terpyridyl tri-N-oxides, chiral
– as reagent 55, 433s68
Tetraalkylammonium bromide
– as reagent 29, 233s68
– hypophosphites
– as reagent 64, 478s68
Tetra-n-butoxysilane
– as reagent 38, 584s68
Tetra-n-butylammonium acetate
– as reagent 68, 472
– bromide
– as ionic liquid 12, 288s68
– as reagent 35, 607s68; 68, 164
– cyanide
– as reagent 65, 253s68
– dichromate
– as reagent 34, 172s68
– difluorotriphenylsilicate
– as reagent 58, 406s68
– fluoride
– as reagent 34, 610s68; 45, 35s68; 48, 194s68; 66, 34s68; 68, 239, 432, 470
– halides
– as reagent 67, 207s68
– hydrogen sulfate
– as reagent 68, 368
– iodide 9, 507s68; 68, 199
– nitrite
– as reagent 68, 51
– persulfate 44, 420s68
– phenoxide
– as reagent 68, 434
– phosphomolybdate 25, 80s68
– tribromide 46, 162s68
Tetra-n-butylphosphonium bromide
– as reagent 41, 325s68; 59, 219s68
Tetraethoxysilane
– as reagent 9, 720s68
Tetraethylammonium carbonate
– as reagent 52, 137s68
– hydroxide
– as reagent 68, 1
Tetraformylhydrazine
–, formylation, ar. with – 68, 355
Tetrahydridoborate, ion exchanger-supported
– as reagent 28, 288s68
–, polymer-based
– as reagent 40, 19s68
Tetrakis(dimethylamino)ethylene
– as reagent 34, 825s68
all-cis-Tetrakis(diphenylphosphino-methyl)cyclopentane
– as reagent 27, 851s68
Tetrakis(trimethylsilyl)methane
– as reagent 68, 118
Tetralins, 1-aryl-3-hydroxymethyl-2-vinyl-
– by ring contraction 68, 443
Tetralols, chiral 51, 26s68
1,1,3,3-Tetramethylbutyl isocyanide
– as reagent 41, 564s68; 67, 255s68
N,N,N′,N′-Tetramethylfluoro-formamidinium hexafluorophosphate
– as reagent 39, 162s68
1,1,3,3-Tetramethylguanidine

– as reagent **10**, 263s**68**; **62**, 274s**68**;
66, 424s**68**; **68**, 304
**N,N,N′,N′-Tetramethylpropylene-
diamine**
– as reagent **39**, 593s**68**
Tetraphenylphosphonium iodide
– as reagent **68**, 205
Tetraphenylporphyrin
– as sensitizer **68**, 55
Tetra-*n*-propylammonium bromate
37, 323s**68**
– perruthenate
– as reagent **61**, 71s**68**
Tetrasilanes
– special s.
tetrakis(trimethylsilyl)methane
Tetrazole, (S)-5-(pyrrolidin-2-yl)-
– as reagent **62**, 282s**68**
1,2,4,5-Tetroxanes
– from
1,1-di(hydroperoxides) and acetals
66, 52s**68**
Thianaphthene… s. Benzo[*b*]thiophen…
**4*H*-1,3-Thiazines, 5,6-dihydro-
25**, 458s**68**
–, –, 6-iodomethyl- **48**, 434s**68**
2*H*-1,3-Thiazin-2-ones, tetrahydro-
– from
isothiazolidines **68**, 219
**1,3-Thiazin-4-ones, tetrahydro-
9**, 672s**68**
**Thiazole-4-carboxylic acid esters,
2-α-acylamino-**
–, 4-component synthesis **68**, 403
Thiazoles, 2,4,5-trisubst. 68, 403
Thiazolidine-2-thiones, 3-acyl-
–, aldol condensation, asym. with –
45, 383s**68**
4-Thiazolidones, 2-imino-
– from
2,2,2-trichloroalcohols **38**, 523s**68**
Δ²-Thiazolines
– special s.
bis(Δ²-thiazolines)
**Thiazolium chloride, 3-benzyl-5-
(2-hydroxyethyl)-4-methyl-**
– as reagent **28**, 648s**68**
***anhydro*-Thiazolium hydroxides,
4-hydroxy-**
–, chemistry, review **42**, 853s**68**
Thiazolium iodides, polymer-based
– as reagent **28**, 648s**68**
– salts
– special s.
dipeptidylthiazolium salts
Thiazolo[4,5-*c*]carbazoles 8, 688s**68**
Thienothiophenes
–, chemistry, review **42**, 853s**68**
Thiiranes
– from
epoxides **68**, 61
Thioacetals s. Mercaptals
Thioaurones
–, synthesis, review **42**, 853s**68**
Thiocarbonyl compds. s.a. under
Replacement of carbonyl sulfur
Thiochroman-4-ones 6, 854s**68**
Thioenolethers
– from
α,β-ethyleneiodides and mercaptans
68, 230
– special s.

sulfinylthioenolethers
Thioethers (s.a. Alkylthio…,
Organothio…, Sulfenylation)
– special s.
aminothioethers
benzyl thioethers
ethylenethioethers
hydroxythioethers
ketothioethers
stannylthioethers
thioenolethers
– startg. m. f.
sulfones **25**, 80s**68**
sulfoxides **29**, 233s**68**
–, asym. oxidation **68**, 52
–, – –, review **27**, 57s**68**
–, oxidation with H_2O_2, review **37**, 120
Thioethers, ar. (s.a. Arylthio…)
– from
aryl tosylates **53**, 230s**68**
halides, ar. **68**, 229
– special s.
diaryl sulfides
m-hydroxythioethers
6-Thioglycitols 30, 17s**68**
Thioglycosides
–, use in sequential glycosidation, review
41, 173s**68**
Thioimidoyl radicals
– as intermediates **68**, 425
Thiolic acid aryl esters
– from
carboxylic acid halides **53**, 230s**68**
Thiolic acid esters
– from
carboxylic acids **39**, 162s**68**
oxazolidine-2-thiones, 3-acyl-
46, 494s**68**
– special s.
halogenothiolic acid esters
hydroxythiolic acid esters
ketothiolic acid esters
thiolic acid aryl esters
Thioketones
– from
ketones **34**, 525s**68**
**Thionophosphoromonoamidates
22**, 594s**68**
Thionyl chloride 25, 396s**68**; **47**, 710s**68**
**Thiophene-3-carboxylic acid esters, 2,3-
dihydro-, 4-acyl-5-alkylthio- 68**, 310
Thiophenes
– from
α,β-dihalogenoketones **68**, 395
γ-diketones **67**, 159s**68**
–, 2-amino- s.a. under Gewald
–, cyano- **29**, 845s**68**
–, 2,3,4,5-tetrahydro-, 3,4-fused
34, 954s**68**
Thiophenols s. Mercaptans, ar.
Thiophosphoric… s.a. Monothiol-
phosphoric…
O-Thiophosphorylation s. O-Monothiol-
phosphorylation, O-Dithiophosphorylation
**Thiophosphoryl dichlorides, amino-
22**, 594s**68**
4*H*-Thiopyrones, tetrahydro-
–, aldol condensation, asym. with –
58, 245s**68**
Thiosemicarbazides
– special s.

acylthiosemicarbazides
Thioureas
–, N-alkylation, reductive **46**, 317s**68**
– from
benzotriazoles, N-amidinyl- **68**, 225
– special s.
acylthioureas
aminothioureas
N-[3,5-bis(trifluoromethyl)phenyl]-N′-
[2-(dimethylamino)cyclohexyl]-
thiourea
N-carbalkoxythioureas
halogenothioureas
Thorium complexes
bis(η^5-pentamethylcyclopentadienyl)-
dimethylthorium(IV) **68**, 279
Tin(IV) alkoxides, organo-
dibutyltin dimethoxide
Tin(II) chloride 18, 48s**68**; **24**, 525s**68**;
40, 567s**68**; **43**, 725s**68**; **55**, 337s**68**
Tin(IV) chloride 19, 787s**68**; **68**, 116
Tin complexes
5,10,15,20-tetraphenylporphyrinato-
tin(IV) bis(triflate) **55**, 205s**68**;
68, 61
Tin dioxide 31, 719s**68**
– –, sulfated/zeolite 63, 90s**68**
Tin(IV) enolates, organo- s.a. Enoxystannanes
Tin halides, organo-
– special s.
tributyltin chloride
– hydrides, organo-
– special s.
tributyltin hydride
Tin(IV) hydroxides, triorgano-
– special s.
trimethyltin hydroxide
**Tin(IV) perfluorooctanesulfonimide
61**, 85s**68**
Tishchenko reaction s.a. Aldol-
Tishchenko reaction
Titanacyclopenta-2,3,4-trienes
–, review **27**, 851s**68**
Titanacyclopentenes
– as intermediates **68**, 255
Titanation s.a. Propargyltitanation
Titanium(IV) alkoxides
– tetraisopropoxide **49**, 898s**68**;
62, 423s**68**; **66**, 275s**68**
– –/(R)-1,1′-bi-2-naphthol **48**, 440s**68**
– –/3-butenylmagnesium chloride
68, 255
– –/ethylmagnesium bromide
39, 418s**68**
– –/isopropylmagnesium chloride
68, 305
**Titanium(IV) bis(1,1′-bi-2-naphthoxide)
complexes, polymeric, self-
assembled, chiral 56**, 242s**68**
**– bis(Δ²-oxazoline) complexes, chiral
50**, 15s**68**
Titanium complexes
bis(indenyl)dimethyltitanium(IV)
58, 126s**68**
dicyclopentadienyl(phenyl)-
titanium(III) **43**, 571s**68**
dimethyltitanocene **35**, 622s**68**
[2-(pyrrol-2-yl)-2-(η^5-pyrrolyl)-
propane-N,N′-diyl][bis(dimethylamino)]titanium(IV) **68**, 151
titanocene dichloride/manganese
68, 260, 495

titanocene dichloride/zinc **40**, 567s68
Titanium dioxide 55, 205s68
–(IV) salen complexes, polymeric, chiral 63, 253s68
– tetrachloride 11, 51s68; **64**, 432s68; **68**, 308, 426
– –/indium 54, 475s68
– –/magnesium 56, 393s68
– –/manganese 66, 280s68
– –/samarium 32, 610s68; **47**, 940s68
– –/tetra-n-butylammonium iodide 56, 253s68
– –/zinc 11, 452s68
– trichloride/aluminum 30, 561s68
Titanocene... s. under Titanium complexes
***p*-Toluenesulfonamide**
– as reagent **68**, 167
***p*-Toluenesulfonic acid**
– as reagent **2**, 818s68; **16**, 201s68; **55**, 337s68; **68**, 117, 172, 221, 224, 372
– –/montmorillonite 8, 688s68
***p*-Toluenesulfonyl chloride**
– as reagent **38**, 239s68
1,4-S→C-Tosylamino group migration
– with inversion of S-chirality **68**, 206
N-Tosylation, solid-state 2, 312s68
Tosylhydrazone salts
– as alternatives to diazo compds., review **65**, 369s68
Tosylimines
– from
aldehydes **68**, 196
aziridines, N-tosyl- **68**, 154
– startg. m. f.
3-ethylenetosylamines, stereospecific synthesis **68**, 442
Total synthesis s. Synthesis, total
Transesterification (s.a. OC||C)
– in a fluorous 2-phase medium **61**, 85s68
–, Pd-catalyzed **68**, 122
–, polymer-based
– of N''-(carbo-9-fluorenylmethoxy)-guanidines **54**, 100s68
Transfer-hydrogenation, asym.
– of
aryl ketones in water **68**, 24
α-arylketones **46**, 42s68
ketones in aq. medium **68**, 23
–, –, organocatalyzed
– of α,β-ethylenealdehydes **68**, 28
–, heterogeneous
– of aldehydes **17**, 65s68
Transition metal alkylidene and alkylidyne complexes, higher-valent
–, review **27**, 851s68
Transition metal alkyls
– as reagent, review **27**, 851s68
Triallylborane
– as reactant **68**, 446
Triarylbismuth dichlorides
–, C-α-arylation with – **68**, 449
Triarylbismuthines
–, 1,4-addition, asym. with – **55**, 452s68
Triarylboranes
– startg. m. f.
benzylalcohols, sec., asym. synthesis **68**, 438
Triarylphosphines, polymeric
– as reagent **68**, 169
–, water-soluble

– as reagent **56**, 464s68
Triaryl(vinyl)bismuthonium salts
–, α-vinylation with – **66**, 424s68
1,5,7-Triazabicyclo[4.4.0]dec-5-ene
– as reagent **62**, 39s68
1,2,4-Triazine ring, 3-amino- 16, 505s68
1,2,4-Triazines
– startg. m. f.
azocines, 4,5-dihydro-, 3-amino- **68**, 378
1,3,5-Triazine
– in synthesis, review **42**, 853s68
1,3,5-Triazines, sym.
– from
nitriles **31**, 296s68
1,2,3-Triazole
– as reagent **39**, 593s68
1,2,3-Triazoles
– from
acetylene derivs., terminal and halides **68**, 184
–, 1,4-disubst. **68**, 184
1,2,4-Triazole
– as reagent **39**, 593s68
1,2,4-Triazoles, 1-alkylthio-
–, α-sulfenylation, asym. with – **68**, 228
4H-1,2,4-Triazoles
– from
thioiminoesters **28**, 404s68
Δ²-1,2,4-Triazolines
– from
N¹-formylsemicarbazides **20**, 320s68
1,2,4-Triazol-5-ylidenes, N-condensed, chiral 68, 335
Tribromide ion s. 4-Aza-1-azoniabicyclo[2.2.2]octane tribromide, 1-benzyl-, Imidazolium –, Pyridinium hydrobromide perbromide
Tri-n-butylethylphosphonium tosylate
– as reagent **68**, 252
Tri-n-butyl phosphate
– as reagent **18**, 776s68
Tri-n-butylphosphine
– as reagent **68**, 32, 449
Tri-tert-butylphosphine
– as reagent **29**, 845s68; **47**, 839s68; **48**, 694s68; **59**, 173s68; **68**, 459, 463
Tri-tert-butylphosphonium fluoroborate
– as reagent **68**, 461
Tri-n-butyltin chloride
– as reagent **29**, 845s68
Tri-n-butyltin hydride
– as reagent **68**, 492
Trichloroacetylamines
– startg. m. f.
carbobenzoxyamines **68**, 15
carbo-*tert*-butoxyamines **68**, 15
Trichloroisocyanuric acid
– as reagent **4**, 810s68; **42**, 463s68; **68**, 69, 139, 202
Trichloromethyl β-alkoxy-α,β-ethyleneketones
– startg. m. f.
heterocyclics, review **42**, 853s68
– chloroformate
– as reagent, review **67**, 224s68
3,3,3-Trichloropropyl(triphenyl)-phosphonium chloride
– as reactant **68**, 431
Tricyclohexylphosphine
– as reagent **41**, 564s68; **68**, 290, 464
Trienes, cross-conjugated, cyclic

65, 314s68
–, macrocyclic, 15-membered
–, review of Pd-catalyzed syntheses **27**, 851s68
1,2,7-Trienes
– special s.
halogeno-1,2,7-trienes
(E)-1,3,5-Trien-3-olates
– as intermediates **68**, 333
1,3,n-Trien-m-ynes, silyl-tethered
–, [4+2+2]-cycloaddition, intramolecular, Rh-catalyzed, regiostereospecific **68**, 353
Triethanolamine N-oxide
– as reagent **65**, 253s68
Triethoxy(methyl)silane 9, 720s68
Triethoxysilane
– as reagent **50**, 15s68
Triethylborane
– as reagent **68**, 63, 295
Triethylenediamine
– as reagent **12**, 288s68; **37**, 902s68; **68**, 491
Triethyl phosphite
– as reagent **68**, 292
Triethylsilane
– as reagent **11**, 51s68; **39**, 33s68
O-Triethylsilylation 68, 9
Triethylsilyl triflate
– as reagent **68**, 9
Triflimide
– as reagent **51**, 339s68
1,1,1-Trifluorides
– from
halides **44**, 577s68
Trifluoroacetaldehyde ethyl hemiacetal
– startg. m. f.
trifluoromethyl derivs., review **16**, 180s68
Trifluoroacetaldimines
–, chemistry, review **16**, 180s68
Trifluoroacetaldehyde acetals
–, review **16**, 180s68
Trifluoroacetic anhydride
– as reagent **4**, 729s68; **7**, 798s68
Trifluoromethanesulfonic acid
– as reagent **57**, 207s68; **63**, 282s68
– – esters
– special s.
aryl triflates
enol –
– anhydride
– as reagent **31**, 296s68; **46**, 983s68
(E)-2-(Trifluoromethyl)enolethers 68, 115
Trifluoromethyl derivs. (s.a. Peptides, trifluoromethylated)
– from
trifluoroacetaldehyde ethyl hemiacetal, review **16**, 180s68
Trifluoroperoxyacetic acid
– as reagent **68**, 120
Triflyloxyhalides
– startg. m. f.
diynes **68**, 391
Tri-2-furylgermane
– as reagent, review **65**, 461s68
Tri-2-furylphosphine
– as reagent **68**, 294, 410, 469
1,1,1-Trihalides
– special s.
ethylene-1,1,1-trihalides

2,2,2-Trihalogenalcohols
– special s.
  acetylene-2,2,2-trihalogenalcohols
(S)-N-[2-[(2,4,6-Triisopropylbenzyl-
  amino)phenyl]-S-methyl-S-phenyl-
  sulfoximine
– as reagent 56, 422s68
Triisopropyl borate
– as reagent 15, 151s68
Tri(o-methoxyphenyl)phosphine
– as reagent 62, 306s68
Trimethyl(N,N-dimethylcarbamyl)-
  silane
– as reactant 68, 428
Trimethylphosphine
– as reagent 68, 316, 328
– –/di-2-pyridyl diselenide 39, 172s68
Trimethyl phosphite
– as reactant 68, 248, 374
Trimethylsilylacetylene
– as reactant 68, 435
Trimethylsilyl azide
– as reagent 64, 141s68
Trimethylsilyl chloride
– as reagent 16, 395s68; 42, 829s68;
  55, 337s68; 61, 441s68; 68, 216, 227,
  260, 284, 329, 441
– cyanide
– as reactant 68, 256, 269
– nitrate, in situ-generated
– as reagent 68, 195
– triflate
– as reagent 52, 310s68; 55, 337s68;
  63, 63s68; 68, 451
– vinyl ether
– as reagent 68, 339
Trimethylsulfonium iodide
– as reactant 68, 422
Trimethyltin hydroxide
– as reagent 68, 7
1,2,4-Trioxanes
– special s.
  3-spiro-1,2,4-trioxanes
–, 6-α-arylthio-
– from
  2-ethylenealcohols, ketones and
  arylmercaptans 68, 224
2,4,8-Trioxa-6-phosphaadamantane,
  1,3,5,7-tetramethyl-6-(2,4-di-
  methoxyphenyl)-
– as reagent 62, 451s68
–, 1,3,5,7-tetramethyl-6-phenyl-
– as reagent 37, 902s68; 51, 171s68
1,2,4-Trioxepanes, acid-stable
–, protection of carbonyl groups as –
  68, 117
Triphenylgermane
– as reagent, review 65, 461s68
Triphenylphosphine
– as reagent 33, 851s68; 68, 310, 336,
  426, 450
–, polymer-based
– as reagent 29, 845s68
Triphenylphosphine/carbon tetrachloride
– as reagent 66, 169s68; 68, 213
–/2,3-dichloro-5,6-dicyanoquinone
– as reagent 68, 51
–/diethyl azodicarboxylate
– as reagent 32, 333s68
–/diisopropyl –
– as reagent 54, 100s68

–/iodine
– as reagent 27, 941s68
Triphenylphosphine dihalides
– as reagent 68, 214
Triphenylphosphine oxide
– as reagent 34, 209s68; 68, 256
Triphenylphosphine N-tosylimine
– as reactant 68, 196
Triphenyl phosphite
– as reagent 68, 17
Triphenylphosphonium perchlorate
– as reagent 53, 301s68
Tri(phosphines)
– special s.
  ferrocenyltri(phosphines)
Tris(4-fluorophenyl)phosphine
– as reagent 53, 61s68
1,1,3-Tris(indol-3-yl)alkanes 5, 549s68
Tris(Δ²-oxazolines), chiral
– in asym. synthesis, review 27, 57s68
Tris(pentafluorophenyl)borane
– as reagent 41, 176s68; 67, 82s68;
  68, 439
Tris(m-sulfophenyl)phosphine trisodium
  salt
– as reagent 68, 325
Tris[4-(trifluoromethyl)phenyl]-
  phosphine
– as reagent 68, 83
Tris(2,4,6-trimethoxyphenyl)phosphine
– as reagent 40, 619s68
Tris(trimethylsilyl) phosphite
– as reagent 29, 593s68
Tris(trimethylsilyl)silane
– as reagent 65, 107s68
Tritiation, ar. 39, 555s68
Tri-o-tolylphosphine
– as reagent 51, 190s68; 68, 412, 494
Triton X-100
– as reagent 40, 475s68
Trityl alcohols
– startg. m. f.
  carbonic acid aryl esters 68, 120
Trivinylindium compds.
– as intermediates 68, 294
Tropone-5-carboxylic acid esters,
  2-acylamino-
–, synthesis, polymer-based 40, 521s68
Tungstate (s.a. Imidazolium decatungstate, 1-butyl-3-methyl-)
Tungsten complexes
  carbonylbis(nitrosyl)[tris(2-pyridyl)-
    phosphine oxide]tungsten
    bis(fluoroborate) 68, 312
  pentacarbonyl(THF)tungsten 68, 337
– hexachloride 68, 215

Ugi condensation (s.a. Aza-Wittig
  synthesis-Ugi condensation)
–, update 17, 809s68
– –, fluorous 17, 809s68
– –, intramolecular 17, 809s68
Ugi condensation-intramolecular
  Michael addition 68, 403
Ugi condensation-Knoevenagel
  condensation 68, 357

Ullmann diaryl ether synthesis,
  polymer-based 54, 90s68
Ultrasonication
–, review 41, 644s68
Uracil ring
– from
  urethans 40, 225s68
Urea-hydrogen peroxide 25, 80s68;
  44, 117s68; 62, 80s68
Ureas
–, N-acylation 52, 146s68
– special s.
  aminoureas
  glycosylureas
  peptidylureas
  sulfonylureas
Ureas, sym.
– from
  amines 66, 169s68
Urethans (s.a. Carbalkoxyamin…,
  N-Decarbalkoxylation)
–, Michael addition, asym., Lewis acid-
  catalyzed with – 68, 150
– special s.
  eneurethans
  enol carbamates
  sulfonylurethans
– startg. m. f.
  uracil ring 40, 225s68
Urethans, N-subst.
– from
  alcohols and prim. amines 68, 158
Uronium salts
– special s.
  2-(1H-benzotriazol-1-yl)-1,1,3,3-tetra-
    methyluronium hexafluorophosphate

Vilsmeier formylation
– under microwaves 9, 871s68
Vinyl… s.a. En…, α,β-Ethylene…
Vinyl acetate
– as reactant 68, 122
2-Vinylalcohols, cyclic 68, 489
α-(o-Vinylaryl)ketones 68, 407
Vinylation (s.a. Friedel-Crafts vinylation,
  Heck –, Hydrovinylation)
α-Vinylation
– with triaryl(vinyl)bismuthonium salts
  66, 424s68
N-Vinylation, Pd-catalyzed
– with vinyl ethers 68, 176
O-Vinylation
– of phenols 61, 100s68
(E)-2-Vinylcyclopropanecarboxylic acid
  esters 42, 829s68
Vinylcyclopropanes, aldehydo-
– startg. m. f.
  (E)-3-ethylene-1,6-halogenhydrins,
    cyclic 68, 309
–, tricyclic
– from
  dienynes 68, 498
Vinyl ethers (s.a. Enolethers)
–, N-vinylation, Pd-catalyzed with –
  68, 176
Vinyl halides s. α,β-Ethylenehalides

Vinyl-N-heterocyclics, N-condensed, bicyclic 59, 496s68
Vinyl ketones s. α,β-Ethyleneketones
Vinyloxy-2-acetylenes
–, Claisen rearrangement, Au(I)-catalyzed with asym. induction **68,** 343
–, pyrroles via – **68,** 360
Vinylsilanes (s.a. Enesilanes)
–, C-silylation, regiospecific with – **68,** 249
Vinylstannanes s. Enestannanes
–, α-subst.
– from acetylenestannanes **68,** 32
(E)-Vinylpalladium complexes
– as intermediates **68,** 419

Water
– as medium, overview **47,** 48s68
–, C-C synthesis (in aq. medium), review **47,** 48s68
Water equivalent
–, o-hydroxyoximes as – **68,** 68
Willgerodt-Kindler reaction
–, review **2,** 180s68
Williamson ether synthesis, Zn-catalyzed
– under microwaves **68,** 108
Wittig synthesis (s.a. Aza-Wittig synthesis, Carbopalladation, intramolecular-Wittig synthesis)
– under microwaves **39,** 854s68
Wittig synthesis-epoxidation 68, 444
Wolff-Kishner reduction, Sc(III)-catalyzed 68, 45

Xanthenes
– special s.
4,5-bis(diarylphosphino)xanthenes
4,5-bis(diphenylphosphino)xanthene, 9,9-dimethyl-
(S)-N-(3,5-Xylyl)-2-(N-methyl-

formamido)-3-methylbutyramide
– as reagent **36,** 670s68

Yeast
– as reagent **68,** 12
N-Ylids s. Ammonium ylids, Azomethinium ylids
P-Ylids s. Alkylidenephosphoranes
Ytterbium(III) chloride 68, 483
Ytterbium(III) triflate 21, 416s68; **46,** 321s68; **49,** 766s68, 843s68; **53,** 198s68; **54,** 413s68; **59,** 333s68; **60,** 236s68; **63,** 63s68; **66,** 242s68; **68,** 227, 367

Zeolites (s.a. Chromium trioxide/zeolite) **68,** 222
Zinc 1, 537s68; **13,** 539s68; **19,** 561s68; **26,** 564s68; **68,** 101, 161
Zinc/ammonium chloride 35, 609s68; **68,** 42
Zinc/copper 25, 59s68
Zinc/hydrazinium monoformate 29, 324s68
–/**iodine 23,** 863s68
–/**iron 13,** 27s68
–/**N-methylimidazole 24,** 9s68
– acetylides
–, Michael addition with –, asym. induction **65,** 266s68
Zincates
– special s.
2-silylvinylzincates
Zinc bis(Δ²-oxazoline) complexes, chiral 54, 296s68
– **bromide 16,** 201s68
– **chloride 23,** 139s68; **68,** 238, 284
– –/silica **68,** 293
– **compds., dialkyl-**
diethylzinc as reagent **68,** 438
– as reactants **68,** 363
– **dichromate 52,** 108s68
– **enolates**

–, 1,4-addition-intramolecular-electrophile trapping via – **68,** 292
– **fluoride 49,** 591s68
– **fluoroborate 60,** 194s68
– **halides, alkyl-**
–, preparation from dialkylzincs **29,** 853s68
– **halides, organo-**
– special s.
arylzinc bromides
bis(iodozincio)methane
– startg. m. f.
γ-diketones **68,** 329
– **iodide 3,** 689s68; **11,** 59s68
– **oxide 68,** 401
– **perchlorate 68,** 168
– L-**prolinate/alumina 50,** 471s68
– **triflate 35,** 476s68; **65,** 266s68
Zirconacyclics
– special s.
azazirconacyclopentenes
1,2-Zirconacyclobut-3-enes, 1,1-bis(η⁵-cyclopentadienyl)-1,3,4-triaryl-
– as reagent **68,** 307
Zirconacyclopentanes, 2-methyl-
– startg. m. f.
1,7-dienes **54,** 444s68
Zirconacyclopenta-2,3,4-trienes
–, review **27,** 851s68
Zirconate complexes
– in chemistry, review **27,** 851s68
Zirconia, persulfated 28, 141s68
Zirconium(IV) alkoxides
– tetra-*tert*-butoxide **61,** 434s68
– tetra-*n*-propoxide **68,** 306
Zirconium complexes
di-*n*-butylzirconocene **68,** 407
dimethylzirconocene **68,** 200
zirconocene dichloride **68,** 250, 254
Zirconium complexes, organo-
–, coupling with ethylene derivs., heterosubst., review **67,** 413s68
– special s.
2-ethylenezirconocene complexes
Zirconium dioxide 31, 719s68
– **tetrachloride 1,** 591s68; **19,** 563s68; **23,** 182s68; **41,** 457s68; **48,** 216s68; **68,** 168, 212, 217
–(IV) **triflate 5,** 549s68; **68,** 167
Zirconocene... s.a. under Zirconium complexes
Zirconocene η²-olefin complexes
–, reactions with enolethers, cyclic **68,** 250
Zirconyl chloride 68, 110

Supplementary References in Volume 68

No.	Suppl. Ref. Vol. Page
Volume 1	
13	68, 6
374	68, 114
391	68, 96
522	68, 244
537	68, 216 (2)
542	68, 230
569	68, 302
591	68, 229
677	68, 160
Volume 2	
103	68, 28
108	68, 321
288	68, 75
312	68, 82
532	68, 136
621	68, 216
642	68, 232
818	68, 45
Volume 3	
46	68, 6, 24
62	68, 29
322	68, 97
341	68, 101
560	68, 160
632	68, 224
654	68, 221
661	68, 221
689	68, 249
758	68, 314

No.	Suppl. Ref. Vol. Page
Volume 4	
214	68, 59
274	68, 135
316	68, 110
457	68, 122
486	68, 127
513	68, 134
552	68, 139
667	68, 202, 203
729	68, 233
737	68, 234
756	68, 93
810	68, 306
Volume 5	
32	68, 9
247	68, 87
341	68, 96
346	68, 117
518	68, 211
549	68, 228
666	68, 319, 320
Volume 6	
135	68, 231
170	68, 37
461	68, 114
854	68, 307
880	68, 314
898	68, 249
Volume 7	
246	68, 59
764	68, 231

No.	Suppl. Ref. Vol. Page
777	68, 223
782	68, 224
798	68, 231
Volume 8	
22	68, 6
87	68, 19
165	68, 40
563	68, 112
602	68, 130
688	68, 147
823	68, 228
899	68, 307
917	68, 318
927	68, 97
Volume 9	
254	68, 53
507	68, 111
512	68, 111
672	68, 140
710	68, 148
720	68, 154
741	68, 160
770	68, 184
871	68, 241
947	68, 307
Volume 10	
3	68, 1
50	68, 13
79	68, 319
125	68, 36
225	68, 305
258	68, 83

Supplementary References

No.	Suppl. Vol.	Ref. Page

Volume 10 continued

No.	Suppl. Vol.	Ref. Page
263	68,	84
296	68,	110
394	68,	123
520	68,	160
617	68,	248
639	68,	305

Volume 11

No.	Suppl. Vol.	Ref. Page
51	68,	14
59	68,	13
87	68,	45
424	68,	97
452	68,	232
573	68,	124
770	68,	184
821	68,	221
829	68,	227

Volume 12

No.	Suppl. Vol.	Ref. Page
42	68,	8
119	68,	24
252	68,	62
288	68,	66
376	68,	83
455	68,	321
497	68,	108
510	68,	11
686	68,	145
689	68,	147
867	68,	256
931	68,	212

Volume 13

No.	Suppl. Vol.	Ref. Page
27	68,	7
80	68,	18
102	68,	27
103	68,	11
236	68,	57
361	68,	84
365	68,	87
441	68,	104
442	68,	98
487	68,	110
526	68,	121, 229
539	68,	123
561	68,	125
730	68,	222
786	68,	241
837	68,	321
838	68,	301
896	68,	140

Volume 14

No.	Suppl. Vol.	Ref. Page
366	68,	82
666	68,	139
806	68,	223
836	68,	302
852	68,	244

Volume 15

No.	Suppl. Vol.	Ref. Page
151	68,	36
168	68,	306

Volume 16

No.	Suppl. Vol.	Ref. Page
180	68,	321
201	68,	3
395	68,	88
505	68,	117
652	68,	139
733	68,	179
735	68,	179
820	68,	321
827	68,	233
888	68,	179

Volume 17

No.	Suppl. Vol.	Ref. Page
32	68,	8
65	68,	17
165	68,	145
169	68,	35, 321
451	68,	102
490	68,	111
784	68,	102
809	68,	221
880	68,	184, 188
884	68,	253
942	68,	314

Volume 18

No.	Suppl. Vol.	Ref. Page
48	68,	11
180	68,	306
193	68,	45
354	68,	83
416	68,	110
467	68,	18
638	68,	136
647	68,	137
699	68,	321
762	68,	208
776	68,	197
881	68,	300

Volume 19

No.	Suppl. Vol.	Ref. Page
33	68,	321
190	68,	44
356	68,	81
378	68,	137
471	68,	10
554	68,	120
561	68,	122
563	68,	78
630	68,	132
674	68,	140
764	68,	179
787	68,	210
972	68,	310

Volume 20

No.	Suppl. Vol.	Ref. Page
71	68,	318
320	68,	122

No.	Suppl. Ref.					
	Vol.	Page				

Volume 20 continued

No.	Vol.	Page
458	68,	144
501	68,	161, 322
533	68,	211
542	68,	211

Volume 21

270	68,	72
358	68,	88
416	68,	100
439	68,	86
445	68,	234
543	68,	122
719	68,	173
744	68,	209
805	68,	30
879	68,	300
988	68,	318

Volume 22

268	68,	80
470	68,	111
493	68,	120
528	68,	124
565	68,	129
588	68,	135
594	68,	135
705	68,	179
730	68,	209
826	68,	241
877	68,	178, 300

Volume 23

85	68,	13
139	68,	37, 38
182	68,	51
348	68,	84

479	68,	119
543	68,	311
628	68,	146
656	68,	30
693	68,	185
700	68,	181
739	68,	322
793	68,	229
819	68,	239, 242, 243, 244
863	68,	251

Volume 24

9	68,	3
85	68,	29
118	68,	322
149	68,	44
408	68,	101
491	68,	119
525	68,	122
555	68,	125
582	68,	125
601	68,	87
625	68,	7
709	68,	198
711	68,	198
839	68,	251
955	68,	111
983	68,	3

Volume 25

59	68,	29
80	68,	33
117	68,	50
182	68,	75
185	68,	76
396	68,	133
458	68,	147
466	68,	148 (2)
483	68,	157
527	68,	211
649	68,	120
701	68,	318

Volume 26

55	68,	18
70	68,	29
398	68,	110
471	68,	122
564	68,	135
592	68,	139
827	68,	236
852	68,	244
884	68,	171

Volume 27

24	68,	3
57	68,	21, 322
65	68,	27
113	68,	35
198	68,	228
361	68,	96
435	68,	87
724	68,	208
729	68,	323
738	68,	213
761	68,	221
782	68,	233
785	68,	224
835	68,	246
843	68,	245
851	68,	257, 263, 276, 323
871	68,	258
899	68,	325
941	68,	307

Volume 28

13	68,	325
28	68,	11
118	68,	2
141	68,	59
258	68,	83
288	68,	40
404	68,	117
418	68,	119

Supplementary References

No.	Suppl. Vol.	Ref. Page

Volume 28 continued

521	68,	212
584	68,	148
610	68,	158
641	68,	188
648	68,	191
795	68,	245
856	68,	271
889	68,	305

Volume 29

180	68,	154
186	68,	57
233	68,	55, 77, 135
262	68,	157
324	68,	8
476	68,	124
593	68,	148
668	68,	181
746	68,	325
752	68,	91
787	68,	243
821	68,	250
845	68,	259
853	68,	267
872	68,	272
910	68,	221, 306
912	68,	313
932	68,	283
968	68,	310
973	68,	313
992	68,	318

Volume 30

4	68,	1
5	68,	2
17	68,	13
154	68,	73
217	68,	87
243	68,	95
297	68,	111
321	68,	325
463	68,	102
467	68,	302
561	68,	166
691	68,	314
701	68,	319

Volume 31

5	68,	2
49	68,	27
101	68,	325
123	68,	57
135	68,	51
185	68,	63
296	68,	88
395	68,	95
452	68,	121
522	68,	136, 144
622	68,	178
719	68,	221
812	68,	247
847	68,	257
920	68,	307

Volume 32

11	68,	6, 325
64	68,	29
148	68,	60
279	68,	325
333	68,	103
345	68,	105
604	68,	325
610	68,	63
617	68,	227
764	68,	229

Volume 33

43	68,	12
71	68,	29
76	68,	30
145	68,	49
370	68,	325
412	68,	111
477	68,	129
491	68,	132
593	68,	153
627	68,	180
658	68,	198
694	68,	307
753	68,	239
768	68,	240
786	68,	154, 246, 325
830	68,	264
851	68,	255
874	68,	274
879	68,	284
962	68,	313

Volume 34

165	68,	57
172	68,	64
187	68,	67
209	68,	72
371	68,	132
525	68,	141
610	68,	159, 162
626	68,	178
693	68,	325
706	68,	229
790	68,	7
825	68,	262
832	68,	259
909	68,	305
954	68,	309

Volume 35

39	68,	20
87	68,	51
141	68,	325
348	68,	99
454	68,	178
474	68,	189
476	68,	186
549	68,	244
592	68,	214
607	68,	272

No.	Suppl. Vol.	Ref. Page

Volume 35 continued

609	68,	8
622	68,	270
655	68,	306
661	68,	325

Volume 36

45	68,	20
148	68,	50
266	68,	109
561	68,	142, 145, 155
652	68,	181
670	68,	18
674	68,	188
677	68,	194
715	68,	218
798	68,	158
864	68,	277
877	68,	273
879	68,	279
884	68,	279
885	68,	270
957	68,	312 (2)

Volume 37

49	68,	30
80	68,	34
86	68,	75
120	68,	325
128	68,	45
265	68,	80
270	68,	81
316	68,	96
319	68,	306
323	68,	32
369	68,	114
446	68,	125
626	68,	325

657	68,	184
674	68,	197
806	68,	239
833	68,	269
834	68,	313
902	68,	291, 292
933	68,	325

Volume 38

1	68,	326
100	68,	38
211	68,	72
239	68,	80
523	68,	144
557	68,	148
584	68,	145, 155
624	68,	162
668	68,	181 (2)
669	68,	130 (2)
723	68,	326
756	68,	231
759	68,	284
772	68,	237
802	68,	246
813	68,	266
836	68,	252
861	68,	269

Volume 39

14	68,	7
33	68,	14
74	68,	30
124	68,	46
157	68,	57
162	68,	59
171	68,	64
172	68,	63
214	68,	72
223	68,	74
231	68,	64
363	68,	326
418	68,	63

480	68,	135
555	68,	153
578	68,	179
593	68,	158 (2)
759	68,	249
844	68,	270
854	68,	273 (2)

Volume 40

19	68,	13
57	68,	37
99	68,	58
107	68,	64 (2)
176	68,	84
225	68,	97
254	68,	109
315	68,	123
458	68,	177
475	68,	197
493	68,	218
521	68,	236
540	68,	245
567	68,	161
568	68,	251
576	68,	254
592	68,	241
619	68,	284
669	68,	265

Volume 41

48	68,	326
134	68,	326
173	68,	326
176	68,	69
199	68,	65
240	68,	76
261	68,	80
325	68,	56, 103
339	68,	101
457	68,	125
564	68,	151
644	68,	326

Supplementary References

No.	Suppl. Vol.	Ref. Page

Volume 41 continued

696	68, 326
744	68, 239
942	68, 309
946	68, 310

Volume 42

45	68, 21, 326
58	68, 28
115	68, 43
127	68, 42
146	68, 53
164	68, 60
235	68, 76, 135
241	68, 78
416	68, 122
420	68, 123
463	68, 129
676	68, 208, 326
695	68, 218
725	68, 326
829	68, 256
853	68, 326
887	68, 328
915	68, 283
970	68, 328

Volume 43

40	68, 328
69	68, 30
162	68, 61
187	68, 69
264	68, 91
316	68, 100
404	68, 72
421	68, 131
431	68, 130
456	68, 126
520	68, 328
531	68, 154

563	68, 163
564	68, 161
571	68, 164
573	68, 164
576	68, 165
625	68, 127
725	68, 235
765	68, 224, 230
806	68, 261
847	68, 274
897	68, 299
943	68, 244, 309
957	68, 311
962	68, 312
980	68, 328

Volume 44

117	68, 44
129	68, 48
149	68, 55
154	68, 126
214	68, 72
301	68, 76, 103
414	68, 127
420	68, 130
460	68, 142 (2)
496	68, 328
533	68, 329
568	68, 159
577	68, 273
602	68, 329
621	68, 266
622	68, 194
776	68, 247
889	68, 299
942	68, 306

Volume 45

10	68, 5
22	68, 20
35	68, 30
70	68, 44
88	68, 72
95	68, 62

100	68, 66
116	68, 72
120	68, 53, 75
122	68, 77
150	68, 83
171	68, 91
290	68, 149
383	68, 166
397	68, 199
416	68, 201
417	68, 188
436	68, 215
459	68, 239
486	68, 329
542	68, 273
555	68, 294, 299

Volume 46

40	68, 14
42	68, 17 (2)
45	68, 18
47	68, 18
67	68, 28
106	68, 46 (2)
162	68, 141
186	68, 66
192	68, 65
194	68, 67
267	68, 84
287	68, 94
317	68, 98
321	68, 99
335	68, 107
346	68, 247
432	68, 126
451	68, 190
494	68, 143
592	68, 163
662	68, 182
713	68, 223, 226
738	68, 236
906	68, 299
954	68, 309
968	68, 311
983	68, 313

No.	Suppl. Vol.	Ref. Page

Volume 47

34	68,	20
48	68,	329
106	68,	138
111	68,	46
146	68,	61
147	68,	62
337	68,	113
431	68,	130 (3)
468	68,	135
488	68,	137
576	68,	156
584	68,	158
622	68,	247
640	68,	253
698	68,	213
710	68,	233
727	68,	230
770	68,	244
773	68,	244
786	68,	248
793	68,	231
829	68,	304
839	68,	259
940	68,	307
955	68,	309

Volume 48

68	68,	28
108	68,	38
129	68,	41, 44
164	68,	58
194	68,	70
216	68,	72
346	68,	109
367	68,	117
434	68,	127
440	68,	129
447	68,	131
625	68,	329
626	68,	161

640	68,	329
686	68,	202
687	68,	201
691	68,	208
694	68,	199
771	68,	237
892	68,	280
893	68,	280
952	68,	309

Volume 49

8	68,	5
41	68,	14
127	68,	42
254	68,	84
343	68,	117
398	68,	125
518	68,	152
530	68,	154
591	68,	167
610	68,	170
611	68,	171
638	68,	29
675	68,	197
683	68,	204
718	68,	218
762	68,	234
763	68,	229, 233
766	68,	229
781	68,	258
829	68,	258
836	68,	208 (2)
843	68,	267
898	68,	282
932	68,	302
936	68,	221
953	68,	310
985	68,	316

Volume 50

15	68,	14
61	68,	43
146	68,	84
151	68,	88

182	68,	101
185	68,	103
187	68,	105
305	68,	138
335	68,	146
343	68,	149
379	68,	170
382	68,	310
387	68,	244
443	68,	219
471	68,	229
495	68,	223
555	68,	329

Volume 51

3	68,	1
18	68,	11
26	68,	15, 16
46	68,	33
55	68,	5, 38
76	68,	53
131	68,	92
132	68,	92
133	68,	96
146	68,	101
163	68,	8
171	68,	116, 117
188	68,	123
190	68,	124
226	68,	140, 141
292	68,	171
315	68,	194
339	68,	211
345	68,	215
355	68,	218
416	68,	258
424	68,	268

Volume 52

4	68,	5
10	68,	4
68	68,	42
96	68,	63
108	68,	68

Supplementary References

No.	Suppl. Vol.	Ref. Page
Volume 52	continued	
137	68,	90
146	68,	99
171	68,	116
273	68,	168
297	68,	185
310	68,	193
363	68,	232
398	68,	249
419	68,	207, 208
459	68,	284
467	68,	299
485	68,	310
491	68,	313
495	68,	318
497	68,	320
Volume 53		
9	68,	8
22	68,	14
61	68,	43
79	68,	61
198	68,	66
199	68,	208
213	68,	138
230	68,	145, 146
240	68,	149
301	68,	195
302	68,	189
318	68,	197
435	68,	266
453	68,	285
473	68,	264
496	68,	311
500	68,	77, 319
Volume 54		
10	68,	3
63	68,	37
79	68,	57, 106
83	68,	59
90	68,	66
100	68,	72
108	68,	135
109	68,	77
138	68,	93
153	68,	105
157	68,	96
244	68,	155
266	68,	329
296	68,	186
299	68,	277
307	68,	189
338	68,	211
357	68,	230
367	68,	229
388	68,	242
394	68,	245
395	68,	248
413	68,	145, 255
414	68,	256
444	68,	274
459	68,	279
465	68,	279
475	68,	302
484	68,	309
Volume 55		
3	68,	4
26	68,	15
79	68,	55
81	68,	60
113	68,	77
146	68,	99
159	68,	112, 113, 329
166	68,	118
175	68,	124
182	68,	127
205	68,	136, 140, 141
239	68,	162
249	68,	168
296	68,	204
337	68,	225
361	68,	238
391	68,	253
433	68,	274
434	68,	274
451	68,	285
452	68,	287
454	68,	293
497	68,	314
Volume 56		
9	68,	5
39	68,	25
61	68,	52
63	68,	3, 5, 38
73	68,	42
129	68,	91
137	68,	95
152	68,	106
154	68,	108
159	68,	111
211	68,	141
223	68,	146
242	68,	159
253	68,	166
274	68,	306
294	68,	198
313	68,	214
326	68,	219
347	68,	233
393	68,	255
422	68,	274
445	68,	292
454	68,	300
464	68,	287
466	68,	306
495	68,	315
Volume 57		
27	68,	17
80	68,	56
120	68,	81
145	68,	105
207	68,	145
230	68,	329
243	68,	166
310	68,	228

No.	Suppl. Vol.	Ref. Page
Volume 57	continued	
315	68,	234
316	68,	222
363	68,	253
376	68,	258
377	68,	264
418	68,	329
421	68,	279
438	68,	294
442	68,	271
Volume 58		
7	68,	3
32	68,	19
51	68,	144
58	68,	38
69	68,	49
78	68,	57, 59
126	68,	90
129	68,	94
194	68,	138 (2)
233	68,	158, 159
236	68,	162
238	68,	279
245	68,	164
314	68,	220
315	68,	221
353	68,	245
406	68,	282
432	68,	279
447	68,	274, 288
462	68,	297
482	68,	311
Volume 59		
20	68,	10
40	68,	2
41	68,	302
57	68,	34
76	68,	60

No.	Suppl. Vol.	Ref. Page
137	68,	94
164	68,	111
173	68,	116
203	68,	136
219	68,	136
221	68,	151
234	68,	156
279	68,	177
293	68,	189
304	68,	197
311	68,	208
333	68,	220
411	68,	270
431	68,	282
447	68,	298
467	68,	303
496	68,	315
498	68,	317
Volume 60		
34	68,	22
36	68,	22
49	68,	34
55	68,	36
67	68,	45
74	68,	50
147	68,	108
153	68,	329
169	68,	50
180	68,	132
182	68,	133
186	68,	134
194	68,	140
236	68,	163
245	68,	170
247	68,	171
249	68,	172
252	68,	232
267	68,	182
288	68,	201
300	68,	207
307	68,	212
341	68,	233
376	68,	250
379	68,	253

No.	Suppl. Vol.	Ref. Page
408	68,	267
412	68,	267
427	68,	273
455	68,	254
498	68,	316
500	68,	319
Volume 61		
13	68,	7
29	68,	17
30	68,	17
42	68,	31
71	68,	46
74	68,	50, 329
75	68,	50
85	68,	59
100	68,	69
132	68,	84
143	68,	92
209	68,	138
312	68,	213
340	68,	223
343	68,	153
344	68,	202
375	68,	252
382	68,	301
427	68,	284
431	68,	279
434	68,	282
441	68,	285
446	68,	291 (2)
463	68,	292
Volume 62		
18	68,	12
20	68,	13
39	68,	238
42	68,	27
80	68,	48
102	68,	63
117	68,	68
159	68,	95
171	68,	113
194	68,	132

Supplementary References

No.	Suppl. Vol.	Ref. Page

Volume 62 continued

195	68,	131
196	68,	133
203	68,	134
230	68,	151
264	68,	302
271	68,	175
274	68,	174
282	68,	182
300	68,	195
306	68,	201
318	68,	213
355	68,	235
378	68,	248
379	68,	246
381	68,	253
403	68,	258, 264
423	68,	282
429	68,	278
449	68,	290
451	68,	294
452	68,	299
468	68,	247
482	68,	304

Volume 63

55	68,	32
63	68,	38
80	68,	42
86	68,	50
88	68,	50
90	68,	53
129	68,	80
140	68,	83
142	68,	104
147	68,	91
167	68,	108
195	68,	157
219	68,	146
248	68,	162
253	68,	165

266	68,	170
277	68,	224
281	68,	185
282	68,	186
304	68,	198
326	68,	211
356	68,	224
359	68,	231
364	68,	222
406	68,	298
411	68,	257
424	68,	273
427	68,	274
430	68,	277
449	68,	285

Volume 64

12	68,	6
34	68,	311
52	68,	35
81	68,	49 (2)
85	68,	50
86	68,	54
120	68,	72
141	68,	90
143	68,	90
151	68,	100
175	68,	117
183	68,	120
210	68,	151
211	68,	152
239	68,	165
240	68,	165
244	68,	167
260	68,	182 (2)
302	68,	212
338	68,	235
353	68,	243
355	68,	248
365	68,	250
378	68,	254
383	68,	268
406	68,	269
432	68,	283
448	68,	292

449	68,	299
453	68,	293, 294
478	68,	28
497	68,	303, 316

Volume 65

6	68,	5
17	68,	115
88	68,	329
93	68,	59
97	68,	60
107	68,	67
126	68,	306
128	68,	77
169	68,	102
171	68,	112
172	68,	113
197	68,	129
223	68,	149
237	68,	156
253	68,	158
266	68,	186
298	68,	201
314	68,	212
316	68,	309
334	68,	233
369	68,	329
372	68,	344
377	68,	329
399	68,	254
404	68,	256
434	68,	276
447	68,	329
450	68,	268
461	68,	329
465	68,	286
477	68,	300
489	68,	311

Volume 66

16	68,	9
28	68,	17
34	68,	19
42	68,	25

No.	Suppl. Vol.	Ref. Page
Volume 66 continued		
52	68,	32
61	68,	36
70	68,	41
77	68,	43
97	68,	65
100	68,	52
119	68,	118
128	68,	14
135	68,	330
155	68,	89
160	68,	91
165	68,	95
169	68,	96
178	68,	101
181	68,	97
204	68,	111, 330
214	68,	120
225	68,	127
240	68,	146
242	68,	140
272	68,	161
275	68,	162
280	68,	166
287	68,	330
290	68,	172
292	68,	173
311	68,	189
314	68,	186
318	68,	194
356	68,	330
365	68,	106
366	68,	236
367	68,	237
384	68,	251
399	68,	253
406	68,	256
413	68,	260
424	68,	280
442	68,	284, 330
451	68,	284
495	68,	330
Volume 67		
22	68,	16
30	68,	25
69	68,	330
82	68,	98
119	68,	78
146	68,	91
149	68,	92
159	68,	103
187	68,	117
188	68,	330
189	68,	330
207	68,	125
212	68,	129
213	68,	129
215	68,	131
222	68,	330
224	68,	330
225	68,	294
231	68,	141
245	68,	148
255	68,	155
275	68,	170
276	68,	165
330	68,	204
335	68,	207
342	68,	4
365	68,	330
371	68,	330
386	68,	330
397	68,	249
413	68,	330
439	68,	279
448	68,	293
461	68,	292
449	68,	316
Volume 68		
95	68,	72
202	68,	82
226	68,	330
290	68,	219
351	68,	184, 213